ANNUAL REVIEW OF PHYSIOLOGY

ANNUAL REVIEW OF PHYSIOLOGY

VICTOR E. HALL, *Editor*
University of California, Los Angeles

ARTHUR C. GIESE, *Associate Editor*
Stanford University

RALPH R. SONNENSCHEIN, *Associate Editor*
University of California, Los Angeles

VOLUME 31

1969

ANNUAL REVIEWS, INC.
4139 EL CAMINO WAY
PALO ALTO, CALIFORNIA, U.S.A.

ANNUAL REVIEW, INC.
PALO ALTO, CALIFORNIA, U.S.A.

Standard Book Number 8243-0331-8
Library of Congress Catalogue Card Number 39–15404

FOREIGN AGENCY

Maruzen Company, Limited
6 Tori-Nichome, Nihonbashi
Tokyo

PRINTED AND BOUND IN THE UNITED STATES OF AMERICA
BY GEORGE BANTA COMPANY, INC.

PREFACE

This volume of the *Annual Review of Physiology* makes its appearance in the world of scientific literature at a time pregnant with change. The inexorable growth of the literature, it is now generally accepted, can be coped with only with the assistance of automated mechanisms. Thus the handling of the primary documents of science, the original papers, is coming under better control through governmental and private automated systems, large and small.

What can we anticipate relative to the second great function of the literature, the summarization and evaluation of the newer findings and their relating to the existing structure of scientific knowledge? Can computers help here?

The present structure of this part of the literature of physiology comprises a very large number of reviewing journals (such as *Physiological Reviews, Ergebnisse der Physiologie*), monographs, handbooks (notably those being published by the American Physiological Society), and advanced textbooks. While the general quality of these works is high, they suffer from two principal defects. First, they are out-of-date by the time they are published and undergo rapid obsolescence, and second the discussion of a given topic is so scattered among this complex (rarely accessible in one place) that its location and availability for consultation are very difficult. Where can one find an answer to the question: what is the best available review on, for example, cerebellar function?

It would appear that the most elementary mechanisms to help in this matter would be a computerized constantly updated and thoroughly indexed inventory of reviews, which could be queried by telephone or airmail. No computer could compile such a work, but it could make the work of qualified scientists universally and rapidly available.

While not as far-reaching as just proposed, a beginning is being made in this direction in that writers for the *Annual Review* are more and more frequently devoting the first paragraphs to a critical mention of recently published reviews in their fields. This is a tendency definitely to be encouraged.

Again it is time to thank the midwives of the Review, who bring into the world the gestated products of our authors: Joann Huddleston, our multi-purpose all-competent Assistant Editor, and the Banta Press who materialize it all.

V. E. H.
A. C. G.
R. R. S.

v

CONTENTS

A WORD ABOUT REPRINTS

The reader may be puzzled by the conspicuous number (1017 to 1036) aligned in the margin with the title of each review in this volume; it is a key for use in the ordering of reprints. These are priced uniformly at $0.95 each, postpaid. Payment must accompany the order if the purchase totals less than $10.00. All payments are to be made to Annual Reviews, Inc. in U.S. dollars. California orders are subject to 5 per cent sales tax. Delivery in the U.S.A. will require approximately two to six weeks.

Reprints, also at $0.95 each, are available from the *Annual Review of Biochemistry* and the *Annual Review of Psychology* (since 1961 in both cases) and from the *Annual Review of Microbiology* starting with Volume 22 (1968).

The sale of reprints of articles published in the *Reviews* was initiated with Volume 30 in the belief that reprints in individual copies, in sets covering stated topics, and in quantity for classroom use will have a special appeal to students and to teachers.

A HALF CENTURY IN SCIENCE AND SOCIETY

By Maurice B. Visscher

Department of Physiology, University of Minnesota Medical School
Minneapolis, Minnesota

Writing for one's colleagues, young and old, about a half-century of experiences in science and society is an opportunity which challenges one to be pertinent and constructive in what one chooses to treat. Anyone who has worked in large institutions for a lifetime and lived through the societal explosions and turmoil of the twentieth century has seen enough to provide material for volumes of anecdote and commentary. In this brief account my intention is to recount a few of my own experiences as a scientist and as a citizen.

It may not be inappropriate to start out by saying that I was born into a Calvinist Dutch family, a grandson of immigrants who left the Netherlands in the eighteen-forties to escape the then-current wave of religious intolerance and to seek their better economic fortunes in the New World. These immigrants began building a college before their own houses were completed. Their motive was to provide clergymen and teachers. My father and his three brothers and two sisters graduated from that college, as did I. My own tendency to participate in the actualities of academic, social, and political life of our times has at least a partial explanation in the intellectual milieu in which I was raised. Despite the authoritarian nature of Calvinist doctrine, more than lip service was paid to devotion to evidence and logic. Hope College, which the pioneers established, very early appointed professionally trained scientists to its staff and encouraged serious study of the sciences. So successful was it, in fact, that in an analysis of the origins of Doctors of Philosophy in the natural sciences in the United States, Hope College was found to be among the first ten institutions in the country as to the fraction of its baccalaureates obtaining such degrees in the first half of this century. The college did also, however, provide a very large number of clergymen and teachers. Its "success" in the sciences was not what its founders envisioned as its mission, and I know that some of its recent governing board members have not been happy with the fact that, as in my own case, many of its graduates have strayed away from Calvinist theology.

There is a certain irony in the fact that the very rigidity of the Calvinist position promotes a sense of urgency in those individuals who for logical reasons have had to reject its theology, to be candid about their rejection of it, and even to be more "evangelistic" about their newfound intellectual outlook than they would probably have been if they had not had such strict upbringing. I doubt that if I had been raised in a humanistic Unitarian fam-

1

ily, I would have been as active in the promotion of humanistic religious organizations as I have been. My father took a relaxed view of religious matters. He had prepared himself for teaching and did teach in elementary and high schools for part of his life, turning to part-time and full-time farming later.

In the latter connection, I should like to mention that my own experiences in participation in the hard work of a family earning a living from the soil have made me very skeptical about the idea that there is some soul-saving grace in youngsters being obligated to spend much of their out-of-school hours in gainful occupation. For me, at least, it consumed so much time and energy that only a fortunate set of genes allowed me to get a reasonably good education in spite of the necessity to participate in earning a living. Perhaps I am wrong, but I think that my father's interest in intellectual matters and in nature study had much more to do with my interest in scholarly things and in my energetic pursuit of them than did the long out-of-school work hours imposed on me by the economic status of my immediate family. There may be poison in economic affluence, but it probably stems from the perversion of family interest from pursuit of knowledge to pursuit of pleasure in some wealthy families, rather than from the lack of necessity for gainful occupation on the part of the children.

My boyhood, adolescent, and college years were undoubtedly fortunate for me because they opened my eyes to the great range of opportunities which were open to reasonably intelligent and diligent persons. Before I graduated from college, I had literally no fixed idea as to what I wanted to do with my life. I saw so many attractive things to do that it was hard for me to make a choice. Two exceptionally stimulating biology teachers piqued my interest in the biological sciences. One was Miss Lydya Rogers in my high school, and the other, Dr. Frank N. Paterson, in my college years. I took courses in college in botany, zoology, embryology, bacteriology, physiology, comparative anatomy, and genetics, as well as inorganic, qualitative and quantitative analytical and physiological chemistry. My physiology was a skimpy one-year, and my mathematical background in college was also inadequate. But I enjoyed literature, history, political science, philosophy and psychology, and some Greek and Latin which have been valuable to me in vocabulary and language structure.

My family circle included a number of lawyers, several ministers and missionaries, one physician, several teachers, farmers and businessmen. One of my older brothers was earning his doctorate in zoology at Johns Hopkins while I was a college student. My physician uncle was actually my favorite. He had reduced fractures of my arm twice as well as having sewed up a partly severed finger, and his gentle, confident way of giving professional help impressed me with the usefulness of his calling. He was such a kindly person that even when he left my blood aunt for another woman, I couldn't but think that my aunt was in large measure at fault. A divorce in a Calvinist family is not a conventional or approved procedure, and I kept my counsel pretty largely to myself on this matter.

Family attitudes undoubtedly have great impact on the career choices of young people, and in my case it was a virtual certainty that I would enter some so-called learned profession. Even my father, who had abandoned teaching himself, appeared to take it for granted that I would.

I ended up deciding to go into some medical science. I applied for scholarships for study in medicine and any one of the three sciences, bacteriology, biochemistry, or physiology. Bacteriology was on the list because I had registered for a "Problems" elective in my senior year, and had made a rather serious study of the colon bacillus count, the organic matter, and other chemical characteristics of the water in the river and lake system into which the city of Holland, Michigan, in which Hope College is situated, dumped its raw sewage at that time. In connection with that study, I read what I could about sanitary engineering and found it to be interesting.

At this point came the decisive turn toward the medical research field, and almost accidentally it happened that the dean of the Medical School of the University of Minnesota, Elias Potter Lyon, had come from Hillsdale College, another of the small private colleges in Michigan, and made it a practice to look into small liberal arts colleges for likely candidates for graduate and medical education at Minnesota. He had sent announcements of scholarship opportunities at Minnesota to my biology professor, who in turn advised me to apply. Dean Lyon offered me a modest stipend as a Teaching Fellow to study at Minnesota. I accepted gladly. It was the circumstance of the scholarship offer in a physiology department that undoubtedly decided for me that my career would be in physiology rather than biochemistry or microbiology.

The fate that brought me to the University of Minnesota for my graduate and medical education was a fortunate one for my subsequent career for many reasons. I put first among the advantages the fact that my graduate advisor, the late professor Frederick Hughes Scott, encouraged me to use the field of physical chemistry as the minor field for my Ph.D. program. The background of physical chemistry permitted me to approach the problems of material transport and other basic problems in ways that would have been impossible without it.

Another advantage that accrued from my acceptance as a student at Minnesota derived from the very permissive attitude of the faculty of the Medical School with regard to curriculum choices for medical students. The faculty had set up an "honors program" for specially selected students which eliminated entirely the lock-step curriculum for such students. It permitted satisfying the requirements of any department by private study and comprehensive examination, in lieu of registration for its regular courses. It resulted in my being able to satisfy the requirements for both the Ph.D. and the M.D. degrees in four calendar years of registration in the University but with considerable independent study. I spent one summer delivering babies and another in a substitute internship in internal medicine under the supervision of a superb clinical teacher, Dr. George E. Fahr, during which time I learned enough about the problems of diagnosis and treatment of disease in patients to give me a healthy respect for the clinical investigator and for the competent physician as well.

The fact that virtually all fixed formalities, aside from examinations and a modest amount of clinical experience, were eliminated from the M.D. requirements at Minnesota for honors students permitted and encouraged me to gain a broader and more useful background for both teaching and research than I would otherwise have obtained. It may be pertinent to note that at the present time, when reform in medical education is in the air and the emphasis is being placed in many institutions upon integrating, streamlining, and shortening the so-called core curriculum, one is actually making the process even more rigidly lock-step than it was before. The elaborately planned "integration" of material, supposedly for easier comprehension by the student, contributes to the rigidity. It is to be questioned whether serious students need such spoon-feeding, and furthermore it is doubtful that medicine as a learned profession will be improved by the imposition of greater rigidities in the core curriculum. I regret the fact that students at Minnesota will in the immediate future have less freedom of action than I myself had forty-seven years ago. It seems to me to be odd that in this age of emphasis upon flexibility in education, medical schools should be moving in the direction of discouraging independence of action.

Major factors in my own education as a scientist were my experiences as a postdoctoral National Research Council fellow in two great centers of physiological research, University College, London, and the University of Chicago. Working at the laboratory bench and the operating table with the late Ernest Starling, and discussing problems with A. V. Hill, E. B. Verney, and a dozen other staff members and students at University College, and doing the same with Anton J. Carlson, Arno B. Luckhardt, George E. Burget, and others at the University of Chicago, were priceless opportunities to broaden my knowledge and sharpen my scientific wits. At the University of Chicago I also met A. Baird Hastings and imbibed from him the points of view of the Van Slyke school. In fact Baird Hastings taught me practicable micromethods for measuring the $[H^+]$ in blood, which allowed George Burget and me to discover the pH dependence of epinephrine in its action on blood vessels, a phenomenon which has been found to be a general one for most catecholamine actions upon receptors.

I consider that my most creative work has been done in the field of transport of materials. It may be of interest that my work in this whole field began with a request in 1930 from a post-doctoral student, Dr. W. R. Pendleton, that I help him investigate the possibility of using the entire intact intestine as a dialyzing mechanism in acute renal failure. I suggested that the first thing to do would be to study the transport of urea and other crystalloids across the intestinal mucosa at various levels of the gut. So began a dozen years of work because I became intrigued with the complexities of the processes involved. Univalent ion impoverishment by the gut proved to occur against electrochemical gradients, and water moved at rates not proportional to water activity ratios. At about this time I had the good fortune to move to an institution where my colleagues in physics were making radio isotopes with a van de Graaf machine and the late Professor John H. Williams provided me with isotopes of chloride and sodium, permitting me to study directly the bidirectional movements of those ions. Professor A. O. C. Nier had just perfected his mass spectrometer, and his generous cooperation allowed us to study mass isotopes of various elements as well.

The point I am trying to make is that I owe to students and colleagues the greatest of debts. A University—a community of scholars—from the beginner in the search for knowledge to the most sophisticated scholar, is an environment in which creativity can and does flourish. Our society has not produced any other mechanism which is as generally successful in the advancement of basic knowledge. It is certainly true that many basic discoveries have been made in research institutes, divorced from educational activities, but historically until the present most basic discoveries have come from the universities and other similar teaching institutions.

There are voices today suggesting that this era is passing, because teaching must be the primary function of educational institutions and for them additions to knowledge are secondary goals. However, I would point out that graduate education is impossible except in the context of creative scholarship. Insofar as an educational institution even pretends to carry on graduate instruction it must of necessity support research as a major function. Unless it does, its graduate programs are a fraud, both upon its students and upon society at large. The proportionate emphasis upon teaching and research activities that may be optimal may be arguable, but again let it be noted well that graduate schools are the training grounds for almost all investigators. An environment in which mediocre research is done is not optimal for the training of superior investigators. Thus, if only to have superior investigators to work in industrial and other nonteaching research institutes, one must support universities liberally enough to provide them with adequate quotas of the most competent researchers. To do otherwise would be to kill the goose that lays the golden egg.

SCIENTIFIC COMMUNICATION

The last half-century has seen the most rapid changes in the support of the scientific enterprise that have ever occurred. Over that time the annual budget of the Medical School with which I am asssociated has increased by more than two orders of magnitude. When I began work as a graduate student I could have read all of the pages published in every physiological journal in the world and still have had much time for laboratory research and teaching. Today it has been calculated that to read or rather to scan the physiological periodical literature appearing in a single year, allowing one minute per page, would require the full time of a scholar for more than three years.

We in scientific work must recognize that the very success of science in transforming society in ways agreeable to its populations has brought about a demand for further advances and a willingness to spend, even an insistence upon providing, the additional funds to multiply the magnitude of the enterprise in one lifetime. In the biological sciences practical exploitation of knowledge of genetics, pest control, and plant and animal nutrition has greatly affected all of agriculture and animal husbandry. In the biomedical field we have seen the virtual disappearance in many countries of numerous diseases, and the therapeutic control of many others. Virus attenuation for vaccination, the chemotherapeutic and antibiotic agents, advances in diagnoses and management of surgical diseases, and many other developments based upon scientific discoveries have so pleased the public at large that it has come to believe that all that is necessary to solve other health problems is to direct the allocation of money to employ people to solve them. There is a real danger, first, that uninformed persons in positions of influence and power may waste vast sums in attempting to achieve practical results and, second, that after failing to get the desired practical results, they may bring disillusionment to a public that has come to expect the impossible, with consequent loss of support for the scientific enterprise. The public at large does not realize that, although creativity and originality can be encouraged by appropriate incentives, fresh ideas cannot simply be ordered and produced. Furthermore, successful practical solutions of particular problems require that basic background knowledge be available. Open-heart surgery, for example, could not have been achieved without a great deal of background knowledge of myocardial metabolism and other aspects of cardiac physiology, as well as of respiration, blood coagulation, and other physiologic phenomena. Practical solutions to organ transplantation problems will not be achieved until the mechanisms of the immune response are better understood. Approaches to prevention of arteriosclerosis and hypertension are very unlikely to succeed until facts now unknown are discovered.

The huge expansion of the scientific effort has brought severe problems in the field of scientist-to-scientist communication. As I have already noted, it has become impossible for any scientist even to scan the literature in any broad field. The research scientist now must rely upon others to bring information to his attention. He must even rely upon the judgment of others as to what is important for him to know. As yet we have very imperfect tools to classify, store, and retrieve information. The explosion of knowledge is itself the major cause of our distress in this regard.

My own activities in attempting to help solve this problem have been directed toward improving the effectiveness of abstracting and indexing and of critical compendiums and reviews. In the first category I undertook, as President of the Board of Directors of Biological Abstracts, Inc., to obtain financial subsidy from federal sources to allow it to continue its operations, after it had incurred large deficits which had prevented publication of indexes for a number of years. *Biological Abstracts* was put back on its financial feet and has since become an important element in the field of information source identification and retrieval.

In the second category I served on the Board of Publication Trustees of the American Physiological Society, part of the time as its Chairman, and had to do with the initiation and the first ten years of production of the *Handbook of Physiology* series as Chairman of its Editorial Committee. In this series, of which thirteen volumes have appeared, we have attempted to have summarized by the most competent experts the present state of knowledge in large fields of physiology. The entire field has not yet been covered, but already a second treatment has been begun for the first section, neurophysiology, which was published ten years ago. This effort is pointed at providing a solid base for graduate students and teachers, as well as investigators, to start from in beginning serious study of any problem about which they may have little first-hand knowledge of the primary literature.

As to the third category, my main interest has been in helping, as a member of its Board, in the development of the program of *Annual Reviews*. Annual Reviews, Inc. now publishes critical review volumes yearly in each of fourteen major areas of science. It is expanding into other fields. It aims to bring new knowledge into focus. It also provides a fairly convenient and very inexpensive indexing mechanism for searches by scientists in their private libraries. As a nonprofit organization it is able, largely because of the generous unpaid service of all of its distinguished invited authors and the token payments to its Editors and Editorial Committees, to provide these services at a fraction of the cost of comparable volumes published commercially.

My interests in these activities are related to my belief that scientists must concern themselves with the control of the information exchange process, if the element of usefulness is to be given first priority. I am also concerned that the costs of information retrieval mechanisms be held to a minimum.

The mechanisms we are now using for secondary publication are certainly not optimal for all aspects of information storage and retrieval. They are fragmentary in their coverage of the huge volume of primary publication and they are time consuming for exhaustive searches. However, there is no substitute for expert judgment in any critical review and I venture to predict that such periodic reviews will be useful for a very long time to come. Machine methods may soon lighten the loads of the review authors, by locating for them all the pertinent papers in a limited field which they should see. Criticism, integration, and interpretation will, I expect, remain the job of the scientific scholar.

SCIENTIST AS CITIZEN

Two women whom I wish I had never encountered have played roles in my life as a citizen. The first was Irene Castle McLaughlin, a famous dancer of the World War I period, and the second was Christine Gesell Stevens, a very prominent New York and Washington socialite. The former was the leader of the antivivisectionist movement in Chicago in the thirties and the latter is the most influential proponent of regulatory and restrictive legislation to control animal experimentation today on the Washington scene. Both of them are quite obviously more interested in protecting pets than people. Irene Castle McLaughlin operated the Orphans of the Storm, a pet refuge near Chicago. Christine Gesell Stevens operates the Animal Welfare Society in New York, which provides a forum for her views.

Irene Castle McLaughlin had much to do with inducing William Randolph Hearst to order the editors of his chain of newspapers to initiate and maintain a barrage of scurrilous and fraudulent attacks on animal experimentation in the thirties. It will be remembered that the Great Depression was causing newspapers to disappear in those years. One of my friends, Llewellyn Jones, had been the Literary Editor of a major Chicago daily, which went bankrupt, and was pounding the pavements looking for a job. He was approaching the absolute end of his financial rope before he took a feature-writing job with the Hearst papers in Chicago as a last resort to feed his family. His first assignment was to assemble more material on the "brutality" and "futility" of animal experimentation. His first call was to my office in the Department of Physiology of the University of Illinois. He told me what his predicament was and asked whether I would help him write a constructive story on the great service that animals, especially unwanted pound animals, were making to human welfare through research. He also intended to point out how additional financial support could improve the housing and care of such animals. It turned out that his hope that his editor would accept a reasoned factual account and a constructive proposal was a vain one, and his writings were rejected. A month later he came back to visit me saying, "I have just received my certificate of sanity. I have been fired by the Hearst people!"

The scientific community at first believed that the orders given by W. R. Hearst, Sr. to his editors to attack "vivisection" might have been based on genuine misinformation and that he might be amenable to persuasion. A large group of Chicago biologists, headed by the then President of the National Academy of Sciences, Frank R. Lillie, and including of course Anton J. Carlson, addressed a long telegram to Mr. Hearst at his San Simeon ranch, detailing the reasons for supporting rather than attacking the use of animals in scientific study. Our naiveté was apparent to us a few days later when we learned that Irene Castle McLaughlin herself was at that very time a house guest at his ranch. No change in the Hearst policy occurred until a number of important drug and cosmetic advertisers in the Hearst magazine chain withdrew their accounts because of the attacks. The reaction then was quite prompt.

Mrs. McLaughlin attempted in 1934 to get the Council of the City of Chicago to rescind an ordinance which authorized the poundmaster to release to approved scientific institutions unclaimed impounded animals which would otherwise be put to death. She appeared before the Aldermen in public hearings and attempted to gain the support of various civic groups. In one of her appearances before the City Council she was asked somewhat facetiously by an Alderman as to why she was so much interested in dogs. Her reply was, "In my lifetime a lot of men have, but no dog has ever let me down." In her zeal to stop animal experimentation she challenged scientists to debate the justification for "vivisection" with her before women's groups, thinking she would have sympathetic audiences. She had exhausted the patience of such hardy debaters in Chicago as Anton Carlson and Andrew Ivy who then headed the Departments of Physiology at the University of Chicago and Northwestern University. Since I was their very junior colleague as Head of the Department of Physiology at the Chicago branches of the University of Illinois, they insisted that it would be my turn to meet the lady in her challenge to debate before a thousand or so of the members of the Chicago Women's City Club in the huge ballroom of the Michigan Boulevard Blackstone Hotel, and also later before a little smaller group in the Oak Park Arms hostelry in the swank west suburban area of Chicago. I was forewarned that Mrs. McLaughlin made it a practice in such debates to be the second speaker and always to time her arrival so as to be able to make an entrance interrupting the first, dressed in arresting attire and leading a couple of beautiful dogs on leash to the platform. So, anticipating such behavior, I arranged that the wife of a colleague would sit in the front row with a four-year-old son who would, on the proper signal, come up to the platform and sit on my lap if "Irene" came in with her canine stage props. I also arranged to speak entirely from lantern slides, with the ballroom entirely darkened, and spent much of my allotted time on the benefits that "vivisection" had brought to child health and welfare.

Mrs. McLaughlin behaved according to prediction and made an entrance to the stage—in pitch darkness—with two sleek white Russian wolfhounds on leash. She was sitting quietly when I asked for the lights as I finished. After she was "introduced", I waited a decent amount of time to let her get well into her tirade against the sadistic scientists before I motioned for my own stage stealer to cross the platform. When he did and climbed on my knees, a loud titter went over the audience of women. Mrs. McLaughlin faltered, flustered, turned to me and said, "If I had known that you would use such unfair tactics, I would have brought a half-a-dozen children my-self." Which, as a matter of fact, she did two weeks later at the Oak Park Arms Hotel. A "vivisectionist" certainly could hardly be expected to give undue quarter to a superannuated misanthropic danseuse who put pets be-fore people. It would be simpler if the 1968–1969 version of opponents of animal experimentation were as naive as Irene Castle McLaughlin, but some of them are not.

Irene Castle McLaughlin was a straightforward antivivisectionist and was recognized by the saner sections of the public as a crank. She never suc-ceeded in putting her ideas across. Christine Gesell Stevens is a person of much greater plausibility and asks, not for abolition, but rather for rigid regulation and restriction of the use of animals in research. I have labeled her and her ilk as the neoantivivisectionists, since they maintain that they are not opposed to all use of animals in scientific study, but only oppose what are in their opinions unnecessary and improper uses.

Mrs. Stevens is the daughter of the late Dr. Robert Gesell who was Pro-fessor of Physiology at the University of Michigan. A few years before his death Robert Gesell shocked his physiological colleagues by beginning a crusade for the regulation and restriction of the use of living animals in scien-tific study. He appeared before a business meeting of the American Physio-logical Society and proposed a resolution which would have placed that So-ciety in the position of requesting the Congress of the United States to enact legislation similar to the British Cruelty to Animals Act of 1876. He charged that cruelties were being perpetrated upon animals in many research labora-tories and that millions of animals were sacrificed annually in useless and painful experiments. He asserted that tissue cultures could be substituted for whole animals in large segments of medical research, as for example in testing anticancer and other drugs. As might be anticipated, his ideas did not receive a very warm reception from his scientific colleagues. His motion was referred to a committee of three past-presidents of the Society, of which I happened to be one, who met for several hours with him to try to ascertain what precisely was in his mind. We attempted to learn what specific incidents Gesell could describe, but he persisted in generalizations such as, "you know as well as I do that many investigators are careless" and "millions of mice are uselessly made to suffer in cancer therapy studies."

After his death his daughter, who had married Mr. Roger Stevens, a very wealthy and powerful behind-the-scenes politician, has carried on the ven-detta her father began in his dotage against former colleagues.

The drive on the part of the antivivisectionists of various shades to put major impediments in the way of animal experimentation made it necessary for the medical and related biological science community to organize an edu-cational arm, the National Society for Medical Research, to counteract the propaganda for special legal measures to regulate and harass scientists and scientific institutions in their employment of animals. The late Professor

Anton Carlson persuaded the Association of American Medical Colleges to spearhead the organization of a hundred or more scientific and professional societies to carry on this work. He himself was the President of the NSMR until shortly before his death and was followed by Dr. Lester Dragstedt, Dr. Hiram Essex, and four years ago by myself. I had been a Board member since the inception of NSMR and its Vice President for a number of years, and became convinced of the pressing need to expand the educational work of the NSMR when important political figures on the national scene were enlisted by Mrs. Stevens on the side of the neoantivivisectionists.

The former legal counsel for the Stevens' financial empire, now Associate Justice of the U.S. Supreme Court, Mr. Abe Fortas, wrote for her the draft of a bill which is the U.S. counterpart of the British Cruelty to Animals Act of 1876. On account of her husband's position of political influence, having been Chairman of the Finance Committee of the Democrats and a friend of Presidents and of many Senators and Congressmen, she was able to induce a dozen top leaders in the Congress to sponsor her proposed legislation. Many of her one-time supporters have since backed away from her camp, but in this era in which Federal regulation of industry, business and trade is regularly accepted practice, it does not seem improper to some Congressmen to extend regulation into the scientific enterprise, especially since the Federal government is the major supporter of such work. The idea that general anti-cruelty laws and professional self-regulation might constitute superior control mechanisms does not seem to appeal to those members of Congress who have listened to Mrs. Stevens as a personal friend and a political power by matrimony.

The biological science community is not finished with the problems of legislation in the animal welfare field. Further regulatory legislation threatens at the present time and the animal welfarists have access to mass circulation magazines with inflammatory and misleading, even false statements about the use of animals in scientific research. The general public is still inadequately informed about the realities of the situation and it is my personal view that it would condone legislation which would be harmful to its own interests. Furthermore, many scientists, fortunately not a majority, are so frightened by the "little old ladies of both sexes" in the antivivisectionist camp that they advocate accepting bad legislation in order to avoid something worse, as Darwin and Huxley did in Britain in 1876.

LOYALTY-SECURITY PROBLEMS AND SCIENCE

The key role of science in modern military matters has made scientists the objects of suspicion and distrust as well as the instruments of innovation in weaponry and defense. The discoveries that led to the development of atomic fission and fusion bombs were obviously not entirely fortunate for scientists or for society. The atomic bomb has made life insecure for the human race as a whole, and the drive for secrecy about its science and technology spread the poison of suspicion as to the loyalty and reliability of scientists over the whole community, not simply in the military establishment. The fear that scientists might reveal the "secret" of the bomb to Russians, Chinese, or even Frenchmen, set the stage for the Oppenheimer and Condon persecutions and provided the atmosphere in which the then President Truman felt obliged to issue the government-wide Executive Order in 1947 requiring loyalty-security clearance for every Federal employee in all categories. That Executive Order in turn provided the base upon which the Joe McCarthy communists-in-government scare was built. Truman undoubtedly thought he was inaugurating a controllable system of clearance procedures but as it turned out, he began the McCarthy-Nixon-HUAC era.

This era had major implications for science. Instead of encouraging loyal service for government agencies it discouraged any service at all by many scientists who saw in the system the beginnings of a police-state with "thought-control", comparable in many respects to the practices of the authoritarian regimes that World War II was fought to eliminate as threats to individual freedom. As the representative of the American Association of Scientific Workers, I introduced a resolution into the Council of the American Association for the Advancement of Science calling for a committee study of the effects of the loyalty-security order on science and scientists. The resolution was adopted and I was asked to chair a Special Committee on Civil Liberties of Scientists for the AAAS. It was fortunate that one Committee member from the field of political science was already engaged in a Foundation-supported study of the entire loyalty-security problem and therefore highly competent legal and other staff talent was available for the study. We made a detailed documented report to the Executive Committee of the AAAS and submitted a digest of it for publication in *Science*. It was eventually published there, but only after a battle lasting several months with some timid souls, and also, it must be admitted, a few apparent supporters of Joseph McCarthy, on the governing body of the AAAS.

My own loyalty-security reliability was brought up for questioning after this activity on my part. I was a member of the first Study Section of the National Heart Institute and my dossier was not automatically cleared by the Agencies Loyalty-Security Board. I was presented with an interrogatory document which asked me not only to provide precise information about my travels abroad with dates of visits to each city, about all of my organizational connections, about persons I had met or known or corresponded with in my contacts at home and abroad, but also asked me what I knew about the opinions and organizational affiliations of a score or more of particular named persons, several of whom I had never met. I debated whether to comply with the demand for such information, but I decided that I would go ahead in order to be able to speak freely as a "cleared" person in the future rather than be impeded by a cloud of suspicion. I resolved, however, to resign my appointment to the Study Section of the NIH once I had fought

the thing through. Actually I knew nothing about any possibly "communist-
or communist-front" connections of any of the people they named and I
myself had done nothing much worse from the loyalty board's viewpoint
than support Norman Thomas' Democratic Socialist Party a few times and
Franklin D. Roosevelt's campaigns a few more times, aside from having been
an officer of the American Association of Scientific Workers and having been
instrumental in developing organized efforts to publicize the menace of the
entire loyalty-security system to the future of civil liberties, especially in the
scientific and academic communities.

In due time, but only after I was informed by the chief security officer at
the University of Minnesota that my telephone was being tapped and that
he was under orders to open private office files in loyalty-security investigation cases, my clearance came through. A person with slightly more paranoid
tendencies might have broken under such strain, but I confined myself to
carrying out my previous resolve to have nothing to do in the future with
any government work which required the filing of documents detailing under
oath anything more than my affirmation of loyalty to my country. This has
resulted in declinations on my part to serve in several capacities, the most
recent one being as a Special Consultant to the World Health Organization.
The United States and the USSR as well as a few other countries refuse to
allow their nationals to serve the United Nations Specialized Agencies without full and fresh security-loyalty clearance. I have continued to serve in
capacities where such clearance is not required.

An amusing, if it were not so tragic, incident in this connection occurred
in relation to service as an official U.S. Delegate to the General Assembly of
the International Union of Physiological Sciences in 1956. The U.S. was
entitled to five Delegates. The five were elected by the U.S. National Committee for the IUPS and their names forwarded to the Department of State
five months before the Assembly meeting for official designation, a practice
since discontinued, in part because of this episode. The Department cleared
two of the delegates very promptly, and two more after a short delay. The
fifth person was never cleared, despite the fact that he was at the time a high
official in another Federal agency and had within the immediately preceding
six months been "cleared" by that agency after a full investigation. I refrain from mentioning names because the Joe McCarthy spirit is still alive
in the land, albeit somewhat discredited but not muted, as the existence of
the John Birch Society attests.

INTERNATIONAL COOPERATION IN THE SCIENTIFIC ENTERPRISE

Physiologists have pioneered in the development of scientist-to-scientist
communication. Except for periods of world war, International Congresses
have been held triennially since 1889. Initially the Congresses were small
gatherings, because physiologists were few. Arrangements were relatively
simple and a Permanent Committee for the International Physiological

Congresses, with one representative from each major country from which participants came, constituted the only continuing body to provide contacts between the groups of scientists in various parts of the world. The Secretary of that Committee was the agent of continuity. After World War II it became apparent to many persons that occasional large international meetings, although useful, could not serve as the sole mechanism of international direct communication and cooperation in physiology. In several other fields of science international unions had been developed, and were cooperating through the International Council of Scientific Unions (ICSU) in promoting both international and interdisciplinary projects. When the United Nations Educational, Scientific, and Cultural Organization (UNESCO) was established it undertook to assist the work of ICSU by substantial subventions which supported substantive projects rather than the organizational expenses of the Unions.

Since UNESCO is supported as an intergovernmental agency, its programs and budgets are controlled by governmental representatives. Initially the "S" in UNESCO was quite liberally supported, but it began to lose its place of relative importance, particularly because the United States Department of State became more interested in developing the general communications field. This was not out of harmony with the stated purposes of UNESCO which stress the importance of building "the defenses of peace in the minds of men", but combined with the reluctance of governments to spend adequate sums of money on the U.N. Specialized Agencies, it has put a crimp in the programs of international cooperation in science.

At the 1950 Physiological Congress in Copenhagen the decision was made by the Permanent Committee to explore the possibility of setting up an International Union of Physiological Sciences to become an adhering part of ICSU. The question was to be considered further and the organizing meeting for the Union was planned to occur in 1953 in conjunction with the next International Congress in Montreal. As the representative of the United States and the Secretary of the Committee I had major responsibility in the matter. The IUPS was organized in its present form at that time. There was much skepticism as to whether an International Union would actually provide the physiologists of the world with much additional opportunity to carry on cooperative projects.

The events of the intervening years have justified the Union concept but it must be admitted that the IUPS has not yet accomplished as much as its more enthusiastic promoters, among whom I was one, had hoped. As one of its officers, its General Secretary for the first six years of its operation, I can hardly criticize too freely. We set up a number of Travelling Lecture-Conference Teams which were supported by special grants. A Newsletter was established by IUPS and opportunities for special smaller symposia were provided. The organization automatically provided for a more acceptable and more democratic method of control of all international activities in matters physiological. The IUPS failed, however, in one of its initial objectives, namely to provide an umbrella organization for related groups such as biophysics, nutrition, biochemisty, and pharmacology. Although the latter group was initially a part of the Union, and became a Sub-Union, it has now split off completely. The others never were part of the IUPS.

The IUPS also joined the organization now known as the Council of International Organizations of Medical Sciences (CIOMS), supported in part then by UNESCO and the World Health Organization (WHO) by regular subventions, but now supported regularly only by WHO and dues from its members. CIOMS has assisted in providing travel grants for younger investigators attending scientific meetings and in providing modest funds to assist in publications related to Congresses and Conferences. It has organized Conferences and Symposia of importance to the progress of physiology. CIOMS has taken the lead, among international nongovernmental organizations (NGOs), in considering the problems of ethics and legality in the use of human subjects in scientific study. In sum the CIOMS has performed useful services.

None of the NGOs has been as useful in solving problems of international cooperation in science until now as one might have hoped they would be. But international tensions, jealousies, and suspicions, not to mention financial niggardliness, have been the main inhibiting factors. At the scientist-to-scientist level accomplishments have been real. I do not doubt that, if human society survives its present state of international anarchy on the military side, the scientific community will be partly responsible for having built bridges of understanding and cooperation in ventures of human importance.

As an American of great loyalty to my country—I mean its people rather than any particular party in power that may misrepresent them—I cannot refrain from mentioning another episode which disturbed me greatly in the area of international relations in science. As I noted before, I was the General Secretary of the IUPS from 1953–1959. In that capacity I received the applications of physiological societies in various parts of the world for memberships in the IUPS. About a month before the meeting of the General Assembly of the IUPS in Buenos Aires in 1959, I received an application from the Secretary of the Physiological Society group in Taipai, Taiwan for its admission as the "Chinese Physiological Society". It was a regulation of the IUPS that the statutes of adhering organizations be provided for evaluation as to their consistency with IUPS principles, and that information be given as to the geographic area within which resided the physiologists who were members of the organization applying for membership. Neither had been supplied and I wrote asking for them. I suspected that a political problem was being thrown at the IUPS but I did not realize how hot the problem would turn out to be. No action was possible before the Council met in Buenos Aires.

I arrived in Buenos Aires by air at about 3:00 a.m. on the morning before the Council was to meet and reached my hotel at 4:30 to go to bed for some sleep. At 8:00 a.m. I was awakened by a telephone call from the American Embassy asking me to call on an official there about some unspecified urgent matter before the Council meeeting. I was not left in doubt long about the nature of the urgent matter because I had no sooner turned over to get another wink of sleep than another call from the Embassy of the Republic of China aroused me again. The Ambassador very much wanted to see me that day to reinforce the application for membership of the Chinese Physiological Society in IUPS. I invited him to have tea or sherry with me at my hotel that afternoon. By that time I surmised that the application from Taipai was not simply one from a group of scientists but I still did not realize how much importance was attached to it by the U. S. Department of State.

When I called later in the morning at the United States Embassy office, housed in the upper floors of a building in downtown Buenos Aires whose lower floors were occupied by a major private American bank, the first Secretary informed me that the Department of State was greatly interested in having the Republic of China recognized as the spokesman for Chinese in "cultural" affairs and read to me a long cablegram from Washington outlining particularly the importance attached to having the Republic of China become the Chinese participant in the Olympic Games Committee and he indicated that the same interest applied to international scientific organizations. I told him quite candidly that the Council of the IUPS was not likely to approve of the application in its present form and that the U.S. delegation to the Assembly had discussed the matter and was not disposed to vote for approval of the application in the form submitted, because the Nationalist Chinese on Taiwan did not in fact represent the major Chinese physiological community.

At this juncture the Embassy official asked me whether the American Physiological Society did not receive and use Federal funds, and whether it might not be embarrassed if such funds were to be withheld. I replied that it did carry on some work under Federal subsidy but that it did so only to serve the national interest and that I doubted that the U.S. National Committee for the IUPS would be willing to subordinate scientific organizational principles to international power politics.

I brought the substance of this message from the U.S. Embassy to the Delegates from the U.S. to the General Assembly and there was unanimous agreement that, although we would welcome the Taiwanese physiologists into the IUPS, we would not admit their organization under false pretenses as to the geographic area and population group that it represented.

The Ambassador from the Republic of China proved to be a very charming and intelligent person. I explained what I thought would be the difficulty in accepting the request for admission to the IUPS of the Taiwanese as the "Chinese Physiological Society" and suggested that with some more accurate limitation of its scope the group would be very welcome as a member organization. At our first meeting he was not averse to some kind of alteration in the name of the organization. Later, however, he apparently received instructions from Taipai to press for the name implying representation for the whole Chinese community, and changed his stand on this score.

The Council of the IUPS objected, as I thought it would, to the proposal to admit the Taiwanese physiologists under the guise of representing all Chinese physiologists. The General Assembly accepted the decision of the Council. We thought the matter would rest at that point, at least for three years, but we were wrong. A few days after the actions of the Council and Assembly were made known to the U.S. Embassy, we were called to the Embassy to be told that the Department of State wanted us to request an extraordinary meeting of the General Assembly to reconsider the matter. The five members of the U.S. delegation to the Assembly decided reluctantly to make a pro forma request to the President of IUPS to consider calling such a meeting, making it clear to him that we ourselves were not changing our position. Professor C. Heymans, the President, declined to call an extraordinary meeting. The tragedy was that we were forced to make known to our foreign colleagues that the United States Department of State was attempting to intrude its power and influence into international scientific union business. With the change in the administration in Washington the next year, this policy of the Department of State was abandoned and attempts at coercion upon scientific unions have ceased, hopefully permanently.

It would not leave a correct impression to refer only to troubles that physiologists have had with the Department of State. Actually in all matters in which major "cold war" policies were not involved, the Department has been helpful. In connection with arrangements for the 1968 International Congress it has made every effort to avoid problems in obtaining visas for foreign participants. It is unquestionably aware of the valuable role that international communication and cooperation can play in the progress of science and its utilization.

A Postlude

I have purposely dealt primarily with the nontechnical aspects of my experiences because I hope they may illuminate some of the social and political problems with which scientists have had to deal in the last half-century. Physiologists are going to be confronted with attempts to restrict and regulate the use of animals for many years to come. The era of almost unquestioned acceptance of the virtue and the value of scientific progress is already at an end. The United States Congress is moving into a phase of interest in early practical results, rather than continuing to have confidence that scientists themselves will take advantage of new basic knowledge to make practical advances. Without doubt larger fractions of the scientific enterprise will be devoted to planned and organized attacks on specific applied problems in the near future than was true in the past. What effect this will have on long-term progress, even in applied science, is by no means certain. It could result in stultification of the enterprise if it brings about discouragement to basic scientists. It has yet to be shown that basic science progress can be a byproduct of applied research. The opposite we know frequently happens.

The growth in magnitude of the scientific enterprise in the twentieth century forces scientists themselves to take an active interest in the social and political forces that actually control their lives and their work. The best hope that we can have is that the public spokesmen for science may have good judgment and that they may be successful in influencing the public and the political leaders in society to adopt policies that will not in the end be self-defeating. In a democratic society one must be optimistic about the ultimate power of reason.

GROWTH AND DIFFERENTIATION[1]   1018

with special emphasis on the central nervous system

BY STEN SKOGLUND

Department of Anatomy, Karolinska Institute, Stockholm, Sweden

The title of this chapter invites a broad survey of the development of nervous functions, but in view of the wealth of work in the field and the multidisciplinary approach used, this would be altogether unrealistic. My intention is to integrate morphology and physiology with some comments on seemingly interesting biochemical aspects. No comprehensive review of this topic has been presented, at any rate during the past ten years. Although a complete review of all the experimental work in the field in recent years cannot be made in the limited space available, references will be made to earlier works, in order to integrate recent achievements with earlier results. The review will deal mainly with the development in mammals. This does not imply that I consider results about growth and differentiation in submammalian species as less important. On the contrary, most basic knowledge has been achieved in fairly simple organisms, but the developmental physiology—at least with respect to the central nervous system—is less well known in these species.

Trying to review the field even with the limitations given above, one still encounters difficulties. Many kinds of mammalian species have been used in developmental work, and one is apt to inquire into the rationale of such an approach. The appearance of various electrophysiological phenomena seems to follow the same general sequence on different time scales in different species. Consequently, one cannot disregard the feeling that the only reason underlying some papers is the somewhat unsatisfactory explanation that the work has never been done in that particular species before. Thus for several reasons, certain papers will be intentionally omitted, others because their wider application might be concealed for the author of this review. Others will be missing on account of pure ignorance, either with respect to their importance, or to simple unawareness of their existence. Although the review with these faults, excusable or not, will mainly mirror my personal interests, it is my hope that it will promote discussion in the field and encourage others to give their points of view.

For a long time, developmental investigations were primarily studies of behavior. These works, dealing mainly with the development of motor functions and the appearance of different afferent inputs, have been largely summarized (23, 24, 112). Several of the fundamental rules were given, such

[1] The survey of literature for this review was concluded in June 1968.

19

as craniocaudal and proximodistal development, and the first appearance
of somesthesis as against audition and vision. On the efferent side, it could
be established that the muscles first respond to electrical stimulation directly, and then later to stimulation of their nerves. The great progress in
electrophysiology from the early 1930s, however, promoted studies of fundamental neurophysiological processes involved in development. Progress was
nevertheless slow, and it was not until the beginning of the 1950s that such
studies appeared (58, 63, 86). These works did mark the application of
modern electrophysiological techniques to the study of developmental processes. In the following, the spinal cord will, for obvious reasons, be considered separately from supraspinal structures. In each section, morphology
and physiology will be correlated. This will be followed by an attempt to
relate some of the changing properties common to immature neurons with
biochemical and homeostatic changes during development; experimentally
changed development will then be considered. Finally, application of the
developmental approach to neurobiology in the light of current ideas in the
field will be considered and an appreciation endeavored.

Spinal Cord

Malcolm (63, 64) demonstrated the presence of a monosynaptic pathway, and the absence of inhibition in the spinal cord of the newborn kitten.
These observations were confirmed (94, 96) and it was further shown that
while there is no early inhibition between antagonists, a strong inhibition
develops later from flexors to extensors. In addition, there is a long-lasting
homosynaptic depression. Not until some time after birth can posttetanic
potentiation of the monosynaptic potential be demonstrated (39, 42, 97, 111).

Several of these observations were confirmed in the sheep (117) and in
the cat (111) by Wilson, who also demonstrated strong heterosynaptic actions between synergic motoneuron pools. Eccles and collaborators (37)
stated, on the basis of intracellular experiments, that the motoneurons of
three-week-old kittens have properties and connections largely similar to
those of motoneurons in adult cats. Furthermore, they showed (38) that the
long-lasting inhibition of extensors from flexors was most likely due to both
presynaptic inhibition and homosynaptic depression. In a later publication
(39), the monosynaptic EPSP in motoneurons of kittens ten days of age or
more were shown to be larger than in adult animals, which was explained in
terms of a greater transmitter mobilization than in adult animals. It was
further claimed that the number of motoneurons in the subliminal fringe is
extremely small or absent in very young kittens. However, since only
kittens ten days of age or more were studied, the early postnatal period—
when most of the changes occur—was not included. Moreover, the experimental evidence for the small subliminal fringe, as already pointed out (98),
is not satisfactory.

Naka (74, 75), using intracellular techniques, studied kitten motoneurons
both pre- and postnatally. His results, as he himself pointed out, were in good

accordance with those of Skoglund and Wilson, apart from the existence of early facilitation. In the presence of a strong heterosynaptic action between synergists (111), facilitation appears as an inhibition of the monosynaptic potential as a whole, and could also explain the depression of the mono-synaptic test-reflex when conditioned at low repetition rate on the synergist (101). This would also be part of the explanation of the missing subliminal fringe, and the finding of larger responses than in the antidromic control (39, 101). In repeating these experiments under proper control conditions, a fairly small subliminal fringe was found in the newborn stage (101); it decreased up to some ten days of age, and then increased again. The possibility of estimating the size of the subliminal fringe is greatly limited on the following grounds. There might exist a large subliminal fringe in terms of number of small motoneurons which, because of their thin axons, will contribute little to the monosynaptic potential as a whole. On the other hand, the antidromic potential used as control will, at least in the early stages—in view of the small differentiation in the fiber spectrum—include fibers which will subsequently become separated into the gamma range. Both these factors tend to reduce the difference between the monosynaptic potential and the antidromic response, and thus the size of the virtual subliminal fringe. The size of the potential difference, moreover, never tells the size of the subliminal fringe in terms of number of motoneurons.

Thus, these studies of development of the spinal reflex pathways show that maturational changes must occur in the afferent connections, although changes in the postsynaptic excitability cannot be ruled out as the explanation of the changes observed. On the other hand, the homosynaptic depression and the reactions to tetanic stimulation of the afferents found in the newborn kitten show that maturational changes in the properties of the afferent fibers must also occur. This and the observations on development of the tonic stretch reflex (93) point to changes in the afferents as the main cause of the attaining of adult reflex patterns.

In a series of investigations (93–97), the present author studied the postnatal development of the locomotor system, correlating neurophysiological findings with behavior regarding stance and locomotion. Some of these findings will be briefly recalled.

Demonstration of the presence of alpha-rigidity, but not of classical intercollicular decerebrate rigidity (gamma-rigidity), in the hindlimbs of the kitten—which, at birth, does not stand or walk—could be correlated to the lack of tonic stretch reflexes in hindlimb muscles (93). The muscle spindles were found to exhibit only short-lasting, low-frequency responses, and gamma-driving was absent (95). The later appearance of tonic stretch reflexes and gamma-rigidity could be correlated to the sequential appearance of tonic discharges from muscle spindles and gamma innervation. The subsequent appearance of the latter has been nicely shown by Zelena in the rat (114). The appearance of several phenomena in the monosynaptic pathway could be correlated to the postnatal functional changes in the peripheral nerve fibers (95, 97). Thus the appearance of tonic discharges from muscle spindles, posttetanic potentiation, and facilitation between synergists could be correlated to the attainment of a conduction velocity of 20 m/sec, when the absolute refractory period reaches adult values. Wilson (111) confirmed the view that a change in the properties of the afferent fibers is the most probable explanation of the postnatal changes, although changes in their connections must also be taken into account (96).

On the basis of extensive measurements of diameters of peripheral nerve fibers and spinal roots, the conclusion was reached (102) that a correlation exists between the appearance of tonic stretch reflexes and decerebrate rigidity in different parts of the peripheral system with the attaining of a fiber diameter of three to four microns.

To obtain a more direct morphological correlation to the change in function of peripheral nerve fibers than fiber size, ultrastructural and histochemical studies were made (11–14). It was shown that a great change takes place in the morphology of the node-paranode region in fibers from the newborn to the adult stage. This change starts before the fibers reach four microns and is qualitatively finished around six microns. First, there is a change in the paranodal region of a nerve fiber which involves a certain process of myelin disintegration (13, 14), leading to the formation of furrows and the trefoil-like appearance of the large adult myelinated fiber in cross section (62). At this stage, around four microns large aggregations of mitochondria appear in the aforementioned furrows, and the concentration per unit Schwann cell cytoplasm increases rapidly up to the stage corresponding to six to seven microns for the largest myelinated fibers (12). Concomitantly with the changes in the paranodal region, the nodal region undergoes great changes, with the appearance of a node gap and the microvilli-like Schwann cell protrusions (11). The whole process has been denoted as nodalization (11), and is suggested to be the third and final step in the maturation of a myelinated nerve fiber, the first two being separation and myelination.

Apart from being an interesting developmental phenomenon in itself—about which little seems to be known so far—the disintegration of the myelin is also interesting from the functional viewpoint, since certain short internodes appear to become completely demyelinated. Whether or not this process is a part of branching has not hitherto been possible to determine, but it is not present after the first postnatal month. Since Schwann cells are eliminated, a reduction in the number of nodes is a consequence. This could, in addition to functional changes in the fiber, signaled by a shortening of the refractory period, be part of the explanation of the shortening of conduction time in the reflex pathway (41, 94). Furthermore, these observations, summarized above, invalidate the statements of Masurovsky et al. (66), who claimed that their tissue-cultured four-micron fibers were fully differentiated. As pointed out (98), the correlation between fiber size and function appears to be but a relative one, and differs in different peripheral systems. As shown (91) when the $NADH_2$-tetrazolium reductase activity is used as a measure of the stage of nodalization, the largest fibers in the vagi, being about two microns and of equal size to those in the sural nerve, are mature but not the sural fibers. The vagal fibers also showed functionally mature characteristics. Nodalization therefore appears to be a better measure of maturity than fiber size (11).

The great effectiveness of skin stimulation in eliciting responses observed by many earlier authors could be due to an earlier development of cutaneous as compared to muscular receptors. Alternatively, the greater effectiveness of these receptors could be ascribed to the existing central organization and excitability in the neonatal period. In view of the later development of the cutaneous afferents with regard to fiber size as compared to the muscular ones (102), the first alternative would seriously invalidate the concept of a correlation between fiber size and function in the spinal somatic system. It could also be argued that the development of the fibers is one process independent of the function of the receptors, differing in different afferent systems.

The aforementioned problems were studied by Ekholm (41), who could show that the cutaneous receptors develop more slowly than the muscular ones—fully in accordance with the development of their nerve fibers—and, furthermore, that a good correspondence exists between the appearance of tonic discharges and the attaining of a conduction velocity of 20 m/sec. Simultaneously, there is an increase in firing frequency up to a conduction velocity of 40 m/sec, when the adult range is reached. The former corresponds to a fiber diameter of four microns and the latter would correspond roughly to a fiber size of six to seven microns, when the fibers appear to be qualitatively mature (12).

As a consequence of the findings with respect to the development of the cutaneous afferents, the explanations of their great effectiveness in eliciting reflex responses must be sought in the central nervous system. The concealed reflexes in the Sherringtonian sense were found to be dominant in the early postnatal period (41). The subsequent changes in the cutaneous reflex patterns can obviously be due partly to a change in the cutaneous innervation pattern itself and its central connections. Several observations nevertheless indicate a change in the central excitability brought about by the appearance of tonic discharges from muscle spindles as an essential part of the explanation of the appearance of an adult reflex pattern (41).

Interesting in this context are the correlations that have been made between the fiber spectrum in newborn man (77) and the presence of posttetanic potentiation in the monosynaptic pathway (16). The similarities between the development in man and in the cat with regard to peripheral nerve fibers is (54) further strengthened by the observation on the ultrastructural level.

To sum up, a rapid and sequential change occurs postnatally in the afferent inflow from different afferent systems mainly following a craniocaudal and proximodistal course which can be correlated to changes in the afferent neurons attaining qualitatively mature morphological characteristics simultaneously with functional ones (11–14). Partly at least as a consequence thereof, spinal reflex pattern undergo a change. The immature peripheral neuron is characterized by its slow frequency discharge and its tendency to become hyperpolarized (41, 95, 97). No studies of immature neurons in the spinal cord like those made in the neocortex (80) have been published, but as evidenced by the slow fusion frequency of immature muscles, the motoneurons as well would have low firing frequencies (41). Moreover a considerable postnatal development occurs in the efferent pathway and the neuromuscular transmission too (see 76).

Changes in the synaptology of afferents as the underlying cause for the developmental reflex changes have so far not been studied to any great extent in the spinal cord. The view is expressed that, despite our increasing knowledge of the physiology of the spinal cord, little has actually been added to our morphological knowledge since the days of Cajal. The overt effects of the activity of spinal motoneurons, muscle contractions, might have appeared too conspicuous and prevented a further penetration into the minute connectivity of spinal reflex systems. In the brain, on the other hand—where the electrical activity is unintelligible in terms of actual functions, other than signs of connections and neuronal activity—there has been a greater need than in the spinal cord to correlate specific electrical events with different morphological structures. If we consider the spinal cord from the same point of view, we do actually know at least as much, and even more, about its morphology than about that of the brain. In view of the functional meaning of the enormous amounts of synaptic boutons on, for instance, a motoneuron, which either fires the muscle fibers in its motor unit or not, our actual knowledge might appear scantier than that about supraspinal structures.

Some studies of the spinal cord development in mammals were published earlier (see 67). The postnatal growth of the spinal cord in the kitten was studied with respect to macroscopic growth of various regions, the increase in the cell volume of motoneurons, and the change in cell/grey coefficient (67). It was concluded, from gross measurements of length and surface changes, that the cervical cord volume develops first, followed by the lumbar region, whereas the thoracic region develops last, which seems to conform with physiological data (93). In studying the growth of motoneurons, the proximal first hundred neurons in lamina IX in both C7 and L7 were chosen (67). This means that more or less the same neurons were studied during development. A continuous increase in the size of the largest neurons from birth on was found, whereas mean growth changes were very slight during the first fortnight. A change in growth rate during the second half of the first month was a general finding. These observations are in good agreement with the change in the cell/grey coefficient.

In a similar study of the postnatal spinal cord development in the rat (45), the lumbar segment used was not specified. However, a very elegant method of weighing 400 dried motoneurons from various developmental stages was used. The results are generally compatible with the aforementioned and with earlier studies on rats.

Correlations between the ultrastructural features of the neuropile and the reflex activity in monkey fetuses have been published (17). However, little qualitative information is reported, and that given could equally well have been obtained by light microscopy, apart from the observation regarding the boutons. In the early developmental stages, they are shown to be located mainly on the dendrites of the motoneurons, and have few vesicles. This finding is, as pointed out, in accordance with the concept of excitatory synapses being located on dendrites, whereas inhibitory ones are axosomatic. The later appearance of the inhibitory connections on motoneurons correlates well with the aforementioned later development of inhibitory mechanisms (96).

By both light- and electron microscopy, the ventral horn cells appear with great uniformity in the newborn kitten (see 101). The ventral horn appears practically devoid of myelin during the first fortnight. The very rapid changes in neuronal size during the first postnatal month (67) might imply great changes in the localization of the boutons, which have established functional contact at birth. Although such changes might play an important role in the developmental changes in the spinal reflex pattern, this cannot be the sole reason for the great changes taking place during the first fortnight, when the mean neuron size seems to change very little (67). One is apt to ascribe the early functional changes chiefly to the functional changes in the afferents, but further work is needed to evaluate the relative importance of various changes in the spinal reflex systems (101).

A technically different approach to these problems, in which the simplicity of early developmental stages and the potential complexity of the growing mammalian nervous system can be studied, is the elegant tissue culture technique used by Crain and his collaborators. Most of their hitherto published work has been presented in summaries (27–29), which would mainly be consulted for references. In these, the development of organotypic bioelectrical activities in central nervous tissues during maturation in culture is described, and correlated with the results of morphological studies on these cultures (20–22). It is stated (27–29) that embryonic spinal cord explants can form organized synaptic networks *in vitro*, and that dorsal root ganglia attached to these cord sections can develop functional connections with cord neurons. This also applies to the nervous connections with growing skeletal muscle tissue, which becomes functional.

The development of the bioelectrical activity in these explants occurs in close association with the development of synaptic junctions, but the simultaneous changes in the neurons themselves have so far attracted little attention. No doubt this tissue culture technique would offer splendid opportunities for the analysis in single neurons of chemical changes contributing to the developing complexity of the bioelectrical activity.

Supraspinal Centers

A great deal of work has been done on the maturation of supraspinal structures, and much of the basic information is collected in books from several symposia (9, 69, 78) but no comprehensive review has been written. Consequently it is necessary to summarize some of the essential results of these earlier studies, to serve as a background for the evaluation of work in progress and recent achievements.

First, it must be pointed out that numerous rediscoveries are made in this field when new species are used. Possibly because of the lack of a comprehensive review and a less satisfactory knowledge of the literature, earlier well-known facts are often presented as new. This emphasizes the need of better integration in the field, and a realization of where new information is most likely to be obtained. The above might appear too critical, but it can certainly be claimed that the use in developmental studies of, for instance, the cat—whose neurophysiology and neuromorphology are well known in the adult stage—could, for several reasons, be expected to give more valuable information for comparison than the use of other less well-known species. Sometimes the use of a particular species gives special opportunities for studying a certain system but, on the other hand, this advantage is often counterbalanced by the enormous work involved in bringing knowledge about such a new preparation to a level with others not providing these special opportunities. This applies particularly to knowledge of the morphological substrate.

Most of the early work on maturation of the brain was concerned chiefly with the development of electrical activity in various species. These studies were followed by attempts to correlate cortical morphology and functions in both the newborn rabbit (34, 58, 61, 65) and the newborn cat (43, 65, 83, 84, 86). Of the earlier studies, the extensive and penetrating work of Purpura and his collaborators (79) is of special interest.

The observations of the presence of axodendritic synapses on apical dendrites of pyramidal neurons in the newborn kitten, and the virtual absence of axosomatic ones—which appear during the first weeks, with a further elaboration of axodendritic synapses on apical and basilar dendrites during the second and third week—were correlated to electrical activity evoked by cortical, subcortical, and peripheral nerve stimulation (79). The response to all these stimulations in the newborn kitten was a surface negativity, which was correlated to the relatively well-developed axodendritic pathways, whereas initial surface positivity appearing during the first weeks was correlated to the later appearance of axosomatic and basilar axodendritic synapses. These correlations are further strengthened by the observation in the cerebellar cortex of a lack of initial surface negativity in the newborn stage, when the apical dendrites of Purkinje cells are poorly developed. It is concluded that development of the synaptic organization in the depths of the cerebellar cortex precedes the organization of superficial axodendritic synaptic pathways, this being the reverse of development in the cerebral cortex.

An important step for further analyses of this kind was undoubtedly taken by Bernhard and his group in introducing the fetal sheep in this type of experimental work (7, 40). This preparation allows a study of more immature developmental stages than in the newborn kitten, and a first correlation of this development to morphological changes has also been made (8).

On the basis of extensive Golgi and Nissl staining studies in the fetal sheep (116), the conclusion is reached that the developmental stage of the somesthethic area, reached in the middle of the sheep's fetal life, corresponds to that in the same area of the newborn cat, in which axodendritic synapses are present. Prior to this stage (65 days), the sheep's cortex is electrically inexcitable. From 58–65 days, important changes take place in the pyramidal cells. There is thus a close correlation between the significant steps in functional development in terms of electrical cortical activity and synaptic activation on the one hand, and histological changes on the other (8).

Some results seemingly different from those in the kitten, as mentioned above, have been obtained in the sheep (70). Thus, during the first period of complete electrical quiescence in response to direct electrical stimulation of the cortex, a surface-positive response is obtained on tactile stimulation of the nose. This is followed, at a later stage, by a surface-negative response, which increases while the first positive one decreases, to increase again in the later stages of gestation, when the adult pattern of an initially and predominantly positive biphasic response is established. A correlation of these changes to the developing morphology of the sheep brain indicates (70) that the early surface-positive response should be correlated to the appearance of presumably afferent fibers (116), and that this potential reflects the summation of postsynaptic events in stellate cells and basal dendrites. Later development would then reflect a migration of this active zone towards the surface. Alternatively, it has been proposed that this surface-positive wave could be generated by the synchronous depolarization of presynaptic afferent terminals (8) and would then reflect only a more immature stage of development. Further work is evidently needed to settle this controversial point.

The results of the earlier studies in the sheep have recently been extended and integrated with those from a study of the development of the corpus callosum (68), in which it was shown that, concomitantly with the appearance of a direct cortical response, a transcallosal response is obtained within a limited frontoparietal region corresponding to the suprasylvian gyrus, and then spreading over the surface of the cortex. Interhemispheric delayed responses, mediated by extracallosal pathways, were found to develop later. The spontaneous cortical activity appearing from about sixty days seems to be relatively independent of transcallosal activity, and to remain fairly bi-

laterally synchronous after callosal transection. The subsequent development of the transcallosal response is also correlated with the appearance of
myelin in the corpus callosum, signaled by a rapid increase in conduction
velocity at the end of the gestation period. A further study of the morphological development of callosal fibers in the sheep, of the type made in the
rat (44), and further to ascertain the development of their mode of termination and the distribution of their boutons on the neurons of the contralateral
side would be of great interest.

   Additional morphological studies of the brain are certainly needed to dis-
close the intimate relations between physiological events and morphology
with respect to the afferent systems. Degeneration studies seem to be required to trace the origin of afferent fibers to the cortex, which—in view of
the less numerous boutons present during early developmental stages
—might allow determination of the localization on the cortical neurons of
different afferent systems. Studies such as the stereotaxic atlas of the di- and
mesencephalon in the rabbit during the first postnatal week (107) form a
highly important and necessary basis for such investigations, apart from
being a prerequisite for further electrophysiological experiments of thalamocortical projections.

   Another important technique in studying developmental cortical processes, the use of chronically implanted electrodes (46, 47, 60, 90), allows a
study of the successive stages of development in one and the same animal.
Still another technical procedure, which can also be used in combination
with the aforementioned, is application of the transcortical recording introduced by Verley (104) into developmental studies.

   As in the spinal cord, explants of the cerebral cortex of mice have provided excellent opportunities to study the development of electrical activity
and synaptology (27–29). From the early existence of spike responses to the
appearance of long-lasting evoked potentials and oscillatory afterdischarges,
the presence of a laminar structure, and the subsequent development within
these layers of glial and neuronal populations, it is concluded that the super-
ficial-negative and deep-positive slow waves represent a summation of postsynaptic potentials. Just as in the spinal cord, this excellent technique might
provide the best-controlled situation for both morphological and physiological studies of neuronal maturation. Especially, the intracellular technique
might provide the necessary tool for evaluating the relative importance of
synaptological changes versus maturational variations in neuronal properties. A correlation of the latter to single-cell analyses of biochemical changes
would be highly desirable.

   In an attempt to distinguish between the relative roles of synaptological
arrangements and of neuronal properties in the characteristic features of
immature cortical activity, Purpura et al. performed a highly important
intracellular study on immature neocortical neurons (80). One interesting
finding was the long-latency EPSPs on stimulation of specific thalamocortical projections, usually succeeded by lengthy IPSPs. Prolonged EPSPs un-

accompanied by IPSPs had a slow rise time and relatively large amplitude, and they elicited single discharges. Injection of hyperpolarizing current, inverting the early phases of IPSPs, did not alter the time course or effectiveness of residual phases of IPSPs in depressing the direct excitability of immature neurons. Cells in which thalamic stimulation induced EPSP-IPSP sequences had summation of EPSPs during repetitive stimulation, and exhibited postactivation facilitation. Cells with prolonged IPSPs usually showed summation thereof in response to repetitive stimulation. In addition the spike potentials of immature neurons showed great changes during both spontaneous activity and repetitive stimulation.

Of great interest in this context is, of course, the prominent hyperpolarization following activity, which is compatible with the signs of hyperpolarization observed in the spinal afferents (41, 97). The slow rise time of EPSPs led the authors to suggest that they are correlated to an axodendritic localization of synaptic engagement, whereas the rapid increase in the rise time would signal an increasing number of axosomatic synapses. The inhibitory activity, on the other hand, is inferred to depend on axosomatic connections, in view of the finding that IPSPs might be inverted to depolarizing potentials by transmembrane hyperpolarization. Another interesting observation of spikes during IPSP summation indicates the localization of boutons elsewhere than on the soma, i.e. on the axon; this requires the operation of axo-axonal synapses, which according to the authors have never been described.

Another important feature observed (80) was the lack of repetitive discharges, which is suggested to depend on sustained release of transmitter substance, but could merely reflect a prolonged absolute refractory period, just as in peripheral neurons. The so-called fatigability during repetitive stimulation of peripheral and central pathways is, according to these authors, probably attributable to the prolonged and powerful hyperpolarization following the initial EPSP. In their opinion this seems likely, in view of the ability of these neurons to show postactivation potentiation, which indicates the presence of fairly mature afferents compared to those in the spinal cord. On the other hand, fatigability could be but an expression of a postactivation hyperpolarization in both afferents and postsynaptic neurons. In view of the functional properties of immature spinal afferent neurons, slow conduction velocity and a tendency to hyperpolarization, this does not appear unlikely.

Purpura and collaborators studied the corticospinal tract in the kitten (79), and found that the conduction velocity remains fairly constant during the first fortnight postnatally. This is succeeded by a very rapid increase, which would correspond roughly to the myelination and subsequent increase in size of the axons. Although no morphological studies have been made in the kitten, the growth of the corticospinal tract has been studied in rats. Thus, it was shown that the corticospinal tract grows from four weeks postnatally to at least nine months (10). In an interesting study (32), it was demonstrated that the corticospinal tract has reached the crus cerebri at

17.5 days half way through the pons at 20.5 days, and decussates at 22 days gestation. Surgical destruction of various regions adjacent to the cortico-spinal tract did not interfere with its growth. The corticospinal tract obviously underlies the afferent systems in development, and one might question its functional significance. A systematic study of central pathways is, however, needed to further elucidate the sequence of events taking place centrally. So far, only the sequential myelination of central tracts has been studied (103). This should provide a satisfactory basis for studies on the ultrastructural level. Evidently, the nerve fibers of the central nervous system undergo similar but hitherto less well-known functional changes, which accounts for the change in conduction velocity, and probably also for the ability to mediate high frequencies, as in peripheral nerve fibers. The conduction time reaching adult values far earlier than conduction velocity (85, 105) is a developmental feature whose morphological correlate remains to be elucidated.

CHARACTERISTICS OF IMMATURE NEURONS AND THEIR DEPENDENCE ON HOMEOSTASIS

So far, the synaptology underlying the development of neuronal activity has mainly been considered, but changes in enzymatic processes subserving the manufacture of transmitter and functional changes within the neurons themselves with increase, for instance, of metabolic activity have also been discussed (79, 80), especially with regard to spinal afferents (100). An evaluation of the central nervous system is far beyond the scope of this review. Most of the earlier achievements in this field have been summarized in several reviews. The characteristics of immature neurons with, e.g., low firing frequency (41, 59, 95), tendency to hyperpolarization (41, 97), and slow conduction velocity might be a product of both intracellular and extracellular factors, and in this context biochemical observations are of interest.

Himwich and co-workers (1–3, 35, 55, 56) studied the relation between neurophysiological and behavioral maturation on the one hand, and the amino acid content of various brain regions on the other. It is scarcely necessary to stress the general objection that these estimates of the alterations in the free amino acid concentration refer to the whole brain or parts of it. Consequently, the correlation of such changes to behavioral ones during development appears somewhat bold. In the dog, glutamic acid increases by more than 50 per cent even on the wet weight basis, which implies that a real change must have taken place, since the change in water content is only one of 10 per cent, and the same seems to apply on the dry weight basis. Glutamine falls after birth, whereas aspartic acid and GABA show a slight increase. The main change in all these substances occurs during the first thirty to forty days, which coincides with the period of the fastest development. Similar results have been reported earlier (5). But Berl & Purpura (6) stated that, in most instances, developmental curves of amino acids cannot be correlated with the appearance of glutamic acid compartmentation.

There is, however, a good correlation between compartmental development and morphological development of neurons, and this development perhaps reflects cellular fine structure differentiation.

It is obviously necessary to establish all kinds of developmental biochemical changes, but to give them direct functional correlations seems to require studies on the single-cell level. The collected data nevertheless invite speculation about the possible significance of the changes in concentration of glutamic acid, which is the major source of the intracellular anions. A relative shortage of this ion in the early stages might be part of the explanation of the tendency of immature neurons to become hyperpolarized.

The developmental change in the excitability of neurons, as well as the change in the electrical properties of the peripheral nerve fibers, could—at least partly—be due to postnatal changes in the extracellular concentration of ions (100). However, since the change in the properties of peripheral nerve fibers seems to be correlated to the nodalization process (11), appearing at different times in different systems, a combination of extra- and intracellular factors must be responsible for the overall changes in excitability (100). Several investigations of the extracellular concentration of sodium, calcium, and potassium show that the concentration of the last-mentioned ion is higher in the fetus than the adult, both during the later part of the gestation period and during the first postnatal period (100, 108). Various reasons for the increased extracellular potassium concentration have been inferred. But regardless of its origin, it is obvious, as pointed out (108), that immature animals seem to flourish with a very high serum concentration of potassium which, in an adult animal, would cause severe signs of hyperkalemia. Although the functional implications of a change in the oxidative metabolism and the cation concentration invite speculations (99, 100), further studies are needed to elucidate the relative importance of such changes, in combination with modifications in the individual neurons themselves, for the maturation of various nervous activities. Alterations in other homeostatic conditions during development should not be disregarded.

Hitherto, purely neurophysiological and neuromorphological changes during maturation have been considered, and little attention has been paid to the role of changes in homeostatic conditions other than extracellular concentrations of ions for the development of different reflex patterns. The development of respiration has only lately been studied, and that of circulatory regulation is even less known. In my opinion, such factors have, to a great extent, been overlooked in the study of the development of nervous functions, and call for much more attention in the future. I also believe that the multidisciplinary approach to the study of development should even be broadened, to cover all the changes that take place during development and that, to a large extent, interact with each other in exerting their influence on the developing functions of the central nervous system. In other words, it is a too often neglected fact in the study of development that several factors influencing a reflex might change simultaneously with the specific changes in the reflex pathway itself. Such extraneural changes might be important additional reasons for the functional changes observed.

Although such fields as respiration and circulation cannot be reviewed here in detail, it does appear necessary to refer to some recent achievements, in order to further emphasize the role of changing homeostatic regulations for the study of the developing central nervous system. At the same time, our knowledge of the maturation of some important nervous regulatory mechanisms will be summarized.

The existence of the Hering-Breuer reflex in the newborn stage has been reported in several works (see 91). As recently shown, the intercostal regulation of breathing, on the other hand, is not present in the newborn kitten (91). The response to oxygen lack, as shown in several species (15, 30, 91), seems to be well developed. Until recently, few data have been presented on the function of the central chemoreceptor system during development (see 91).

Acid-base balance has also been studied, with the general finding that there is compensated respiratory alkalosis during the first 24 postnatal hours (4, 81). As demonstrated by Schwieler (91), the central chemoreceptors are functioning in the newborn kitten, but the response is often biphasic—especially with exposure to high concentrations of carbon dioxide—with an initial augmentation and a later depression of breathing. Furthermore, a paradoxical response to injection of base was often seen, with an initial increase in respiration in response to a first injection, whereas a second one produced the usual adult response, a diminution. This general tendency to augmentation in response to all kinds of stimuli might be part of the general feature of increased excitation found in the central nervous system during development, as well as of the lack of inhibition encountered in most systems studied. The apnoeic periods often seen in the neonate might also be reflections of the inability of immature neurons to mediate high frequencies of activity over long periods. It has thus been demonstrated that despite a continuous afferent inflow from the peripheral chemoreceptors in response to oxygen lack, the animal stops breathing (91). However, other afferent stimulations will cause respiration to start again. Further experimentation is needed here to elucidate the mechanisms underlying these respiratory reflex responses.

In addition to the respiratory regulation in the newborn differing from that in the adult animal, a greater sensitivity to changes in acid-base balance was also encountered (91). The concomitant and ensuing pH shifts might be of great importance for the functions in other systems in the central nervous system, but—as demonstrated (91)—such changes also influence the input from vagal receptors. The possible influence of pH variations on both central and peripheral systems other than the respiratory one remains to be studied.

Unfortunately, little or nothing is known about potential changes in the circulation of the central nervous system concomitant with respiratory ones, which might be part of the mechanism underlying some of the phenomena observed. As known, the immature organism has low blood pressure (see 31). However, since the distance the blood travels along major arteries is shorter, it has been claimed by Mott (see 31) that the mean velocity of the blood flow is less than that in the adult, although the circulation time is the same. Resistance to blood flow is also less in some tissues (25). The problem of a sufficient supply of oxygen—since the metabolic rate is higher in the developing organism than in the adult—is, although arterial pressure is lowered, solved by the shorter distance and a greater vascularity in some organs, and in certain species by a higher hemoglobin concentration, and at least in some by a larger blood volume per kilogram of body weight (71).

Although the sinus receptors seem to function in immature animals (72), their contribution to cardiovascular control has not yet been systematically studied. This also applies to the effects of hypoxia, which is difficult to interpret, in view of its direct action on the central nervous system, as well as on the heart and the peripheral vessels. Dawes (31) claimed that there is little doubt that peripheral vasodilatation caused by increasing metabolic activity is induced by local mechanisms, for instance in the heart and the brain, during hypoxia and hypercapnia. However, since arterial blood pressure remains fairly stable despite lengthy respiratory arrest (91), a redistribution of blood must, under such circumstances, take place. This implies the ability to reduce blood flow to areas which metabolize less and are less essential for survival. As suggested by Dawes (31), a small fall in arterial pressure might cause a comparatively large reduction of blood flow in areas not actively vasodilated: small arteries closing, and limiting blood flow, as a consequence of a small blood pressure fall. This would imply a strictly local mechanism and, as pointed out (31), an immature spinal animal can maintain its blood pressure for hours, which indicates that central regulatory mechanisms are less developed and important. The peripheral active mechanisms for regulating blood pressure might be developed earlier than the local ones. Acceleration of the heart by stellate ganglion stimulation has been demonstrated in the lamb at seventy days gestation, but release of catecholamines from the adrenals in response to splanchnic stimulation has not been demonstrated until after birth in this species (26). Hypoxia evidently releases the catecholamines before nervous regulation is established in the lamb (31, p. 184), and this is also the case in the newborn rabbit (18).

Although much indirect information thus indicates the existence of regulatory mechanisms in circulation that would ensure an appropriate blood supply to the central nervous system by local mechanisms during a small fall in arterial pressure under hypoxic conditions, the direct effects of hypoxia on the central nervous system must also be taken into account. The well-known neonatal tolerance to anoxia has been the subject of many investigations of cortical activity. As a rule, an increased sensitivity to anoxia with increasing age is encountered and is, of course, nothing but a reflection of the increase in number of mitochondria in brain tissue (82), and the resulting increasing importance of oxidative metabolism. As pointed out (106), the relatively fast recuperation of cortical activity in the immature animal, even after long periods of anoxia, is noteworthy.

Comparatively little clinical experimental work has been done on postnatal development of the regulatory mechanisms of respiration and circulation. The importance of the results of animal experiments for clinical medicine is obvious. With respect to developmental clinical neurology considerable progress has been made, and quite a few papers have been published in the field (87–89), but it would lead too far to review them here.

EXPERIMENTALLY CHANGED DEVELOPMENT

So far, mainly studies of normal development have been discussed. Development does, however, offer excellent possibilities of disclosing the influence of peripheral receptors on the development of central pathways. Moreover, as pointed out in the aforegoing, there is a need for studies of degeneration to elucidate the localization of boutons of neurons in various synaptic connections.

One type of study in this context deals with peripheral receptors (113–115), but so far the changes in the muscle receptors induced by tenotomy lack physiological correlations with respect to the development of spinal reflexes. Another type of investigation is that of Buller & Lewis (19), who showed that the histochemical differentiation of muscle does not take place if the afferent supply to a spinal cord segment is severed. However, the difficulty in all these investigations is that the experimentally induced changes also cause direct trophic changes.

Another interesting approach to elucidation of the effect of external stimuli on the development of nervous structures—which does not include any direct experimentally induced trophic changes—is the work by Gyllensten and co-workers on the visual pathway (48–53). This work showed that the visual cortex is retarded in growth in mice reared in darkness or with inherited retinal dystrophy (48, 49, 51). Both neural and vascular changes are described in the optic pathways and the visual cortex (50, 52) of mice reared in darkness. Highly interesting is the demonstration of hypertrophy in the auditory cortex of both growing and adult mice kept in darkness (53). Nevertheless, effects on motor functions in these animals might produce measurable morphological changes in other cortical areas as well, which have not been investigated.

In this connection, the work of Wiesel & Hubel on the visual cortex is obviously of interest (57, 109, 110). They showed that in kittens with one eye closed by suture from birth, very few cells could be driven in the visual cortex from the deprived eye. This also applies to the cells of the visual cortex in animals with both monocular and binocular deprivation. These authors further concluded that the effect of closure of one eye on the visual cortex depends on whether the other eye is closed. In animals with an artificial squint, little effect on the visual cortex was noted. Monocular or binocular deprivation by lid closure during the first three months led to virtual

blindness, as well as to marked morphological changes in the lateral geniculate body, and severe deterioration of innate cortical connections. Although
reopening of the eyes led to some recovery, the animals remained severely
handicapped. The authors concluded that the animals' ability to recover
from the effects of early monocular or binocular visual deprivation—whether
measured behaviorally, morphologically, or in terms of single-cortical-cell
physiology—is severely limited even for recovery periods over one year.

An additional group of studies in this context should be briefly mentioned, namely those on the effects of various kinds of malnutrition during
development (33, 36, 73, 92). Obviously, further investigations along these
lines, including morphological, neurophysiological, biochemical, and behavioral studies, are of great importance for elucidating the effects of specific
nutrients on the development of nervous functions. In the light of the severe
starvation existing in many parts of the world, clarification of the nutrients
essential during various developmental stages for normal maturation of, in
the first place, the mental activities, might be the absolute prerequisite for
creating the necessary intellectual capabilities for achieving the measures
intended to correct overpopulation, the fundamental cause of the current
situation.

There is a legitimate need in clinical medicine for knowledge of various
nervous functions, such as respiration, circulation, and reflexology, at various developmental stages. It is, however, also obvious from the foregoing
that a study of nervous development might have wider applications for the
study of fundamental and important nervous actions.

General Considerations

From time to time, it is claimed that the main results in different fields
of research have been achieved. Subsequent advances usually reveal the
prematurity of such statements. As far as the central nervous system is concerned, such probably unrealistic opinions have not been put forward to any
great extent. The reason is probably not so much a more modest attitude of
the research workers in the field, but simply the too conspicuous lack of real
knowledge about the multitude and the—to say the least—intriguing diversity of nervous actions thought to be involved in, for instance, advanced
mental processes. With the seemingly immense difficulty of finding a solution of the relevant problems, it is perhaps not surprising that attempts have
been made to apply an intellectual reasoning, similar to the concept of the
genetic code, one of the great biological achievements of our time, to the
nervous system to explain some of its functions.

The idea proposed that since there is a genetic memory in DNA there is
a neurological one in RNA is based on the assumption that the RNA molecule present in all cells should fulfill a specific function in nerve cells. Although it is irresistible to inquire into the meaning of the word "memory"
in the context of the genetic code and its neurological meaning, this would
most likely terminate in a sad statement about the weakness of the analyz-

ing machine, the brain, whose function is to be disclosed. The high rate and specificity of the protein synthesis of neurons, mainly limited to the soma, might be the prerequisite for the maintenance of the axon and the dendrites which are a considerable fraction of the total cell volume. Thus the protein synthesis is but an expression of the genetic "memory" underlying the shaping of the morphological characteristics of a neuron. Compared to the various neurological theories of memory the foregoing proposed lacks glamor but it is relatively compatible with the concept of the genetic code.

Unwilling to participate consciously either in the optimistic claims of the great achievements of our time, or in deceptive pessimistic conceptions of the improbabilities of further progress, I must ask why, despite our efforts, actual knowledge about the central nervous system seems to lag behind that in many other fields of research. The importance of an increasing knowledge in the field of molecular biology for the understanding of the function of all kinds of cells, including neurons, should not be denied. Nevertheless, the nervous system in itself contains a specificity, in addition to that shared by all living cells. A realization of this undeniable fact might prevent the seeking of solutions outside the nervous system itself, and give rise to more purposeful efforts. Both neuroanatomists and neurophysiologists are highly aware of one of the specificities of neurons, their enormous connectivity. Faced with the situation in a spinal motoneuron, for instance, which to the best of our knowledge will either fire its muscle fibers in a motor unit or not, this same neuron is equipped with some 10,000 boutons. The question inevitably arises whether this is not an essential part of the ingenuity of the nervous system. It is obvious that the existing situation poses problems which, with the experimental methods available today, appear difficult to solve. Despite knowledge of the morphology of nervous connections, we still lack a comprehensive and meaningful picture of the interconnections of a neuron in a specific system and, consequently, of the origin of boutons with different localizations on that neuron.

In an attempt to simplify the experimental situation, the use of nervous systems in lower organisms has been proposed. It is presumed not only that such simple systems will furnish an easier experimental situation, but also that—with a thorough knowledge of both the connectivity in and the function of such a system—the fundamental process in nervous action would be more easily disclosed. In restricting the analyses of fundamental processes to lower organisms, it must nevertheless be remembered that they will never present the complexity of systems of the higher-order animals. In recalling the general statement from evolution that higher nervous activities do not start until a certain evolutionary stage is reached, it might be questioned whether such functions can ever be studied in lower forms, unless it is assumed that the higher nervous functions are achieved by nothing more than the arithmetic summation of simple ones. The idea that mental functions are but the sum of simple reflex mechanisms might certainly be a useful one, but in the achievement of such functions the complexity might still be the key.

Let us assume that progress in the understanding of the function of the nervous system is, in fact, to be achieved by an increased knowledge of the specific chemistry of single neurons, as well as of the specific connections and their localization on the neurons in various functional systems. The use of an organism in either normal or experimentally changed development might then present several unique possibilities which do not exist in any adult organism. Thus, the successive acquiring of more complex connections initially gives the advantages of the simple system in association with the possibility of studying the acquiring of the characteristics of the neuron itself, and their dependence on the connections, and intra- and extracellular factors.

LITERATURE CITED

1. Agrawal, H. C., Davis, J. M., Himwich, W. A. Postnatal changes in free amino acid pool of rat brain. *J. Neurochem.*, **13**, 607–15 (1966)

2. Agrawal, H. C., Davis, J. M., Himwich, W. A. Water content of developing kitten brain. *Ibid.*, **14**, 179–81 (1967)

3. Agrawal, H. C., Fox, M. W., Himwich, W. A. Neurochemical and behavioral effects of isolation-rearing in the dog. *Life Sci.*, **6**, 71–78 (1967)

4. Albert, M. S., Winters, R. W. Acid-base equilibrium of blood in normal infants. *Pediatrics*, **37**, 728–32 (1966)

5. Berl, S. Postnatal changes in amino acid metabolism of kitten brain. In *The Developing Brain*, **9**, 178–86 (Himwich, W. A., Himwich, H. E., Eds., *Progr. Brain Res.*, Elsevier, Amsterdam-New York, 1964)

6. Berl, S., Purpura, D. P. Regional development of glutamic acid compartmentation in immature brain. brain. *J. Neurochem.*, **13**, 293–304 (1966)

7. Bernhard, C. G., Kaiser, I. H., Kolmodin, G. M. On the development of cortical activity in fetal sheep. *Acta Physiol. Scand.*, **47**, 333–49 (1959)

8. Bernhard, C. G., Kolmodin, G. M., Meyerson, B. A. On the prenatal development of function and structure in the somesthetic cortex of the sheep (See Ref. 9), 60–77

9. Bernhard, C. G., Schadé, J. P., Eds. *Developmental Neurology*, **26** (*Progr. Brain Res.*, Elsevier, Amsterdam /London/New York, 1967)

10. Bernstein, J. J. Relationship of cortico-spinal tract growth to age and body weight in the rat. *J. Comp. Neurol.*, **127**, 207–18 (1966)

11. Berthold, C.-H. Ultrastructure of postnatally developing peripheral nodes of Ranvier. *Acta Soc. Med. Upsalien.*, **73**, 145–68 (1968)

12. Berthold, C.-H., Skoglund, S. Histochemical and ultrastructural demonstration of mitochondria in the paranodal region of developing feline spinal roots and nerves. *Acta Soc. Med. Upsalien.*, **72**, 37–70 (1967)

13. Berthold, C.-H., Skoglund, S. Postnatal development of feline paranodal myelin-sheath segments. I. Light-microscopy. *Ibid.*, **73**, 113–26 (1968)

14. Berthold, C.-H., Skoglund, S. Postnatal development of feline paranodal myelin-sheath segments. II. Electronmicroscopy. *Ibid.*, 127–44

15. Biscoe, T. J., Purves, M. J. Carotid body chemoreceptor activity in the new-born lamb. *J. Physiol. (London)*, **190**, 443–54 (1967)

16. Blom, S., Hagbarth, K.-E., Skoglund, S. Post-tetanic potentiation of H-reflexes in human infants. *Exptl. Neurol.*, **9**, 198–211 (1964)

17. Bodian, D. Development of fine structure of spinal cord in monkey fetuses. I. The motoneuron neuropil at the time of onset of reflex activity. *Bull. Johns Hopkins Hosp.*, **119**, 129–49 (1966)

18. Brundin, T. Studies of the preaortal paraganglia of newborn rabbits. *Acta Physiol. Scand.*, **70**, *Suppl. 290* (1966)

19. Buller, A. J., Lewis, D. M. Further observations on the differentiation of skeletal muscles in the kitten hind limb. *J. Physiol. (London)*, **175**, 133–370 (1965)

20. Bunge, R. P., Bunge, M. B., Peterson, E. R. An electron microscope study of cultured rat spinal cord. *J. Cell Biol.*, **24**, 163–91 (1965)

21. Bunge, M. B., Bunge, R. P., Peterson, E. R. The onset of synapse formation in spinal cord cultures as studied by electron microscopy. *Brain Res.*, **6**, 728–49 (1967)

22. Bunge, M. B., Bunge, R. P., Peterson, E. R., Murray, M. R. A light electron microscope study of long-term organized cultures of rat dorsal root ganglia. *J. Cell Biol.*, **32**, 439–66 (1967)

23. Carmichael, L. Ontogenetic development. In *Handbook of Experimental Psychology*, 281–303 (Stevens, S. S., Ed., Wiley, New York, 1951)

24. Carmichael, L. The onset and early development of behavior. In *Manual of Child Psychology*, 60–185 (Carmichael, L., Ed., Wiley, New York, 1954)

25. Celander, O. Studies of the peripheral circulation. In *The Heart and Circulation in the Newborn and Infant*, 98–110 (Cassels, D. E., Ed., Grune & Stratton, New York, 1966)

26. Comline, R. S., Silver, M. Development of activity in the adrenal medulla of the foetus and newborn

animal. *Brit. Med. Bull.*, **22**, 16–20 (1966)

27. Crain, S. M. Development of "organo-typic" bioelectric activities in central nervous tissues during maturation in culture. *Intern. Rev. Neurobiol.*, **9**, 1–43 (1966)

28. Crain, S. M. Bioelectric interactions between neurons in brain tissue cultures. *20th Ann. Conf. Eng. Med. and Biol.*, November 1967 (Boston, Mass., USA)

29. Crain, S. M., Peterson, E. R. Onset and development of functional interneuronal connections in explants of rat spinal cord-ganglia during maturation in culture. *Brain Res.* **6** 750–62 (1967)

30. Cross, K. W., Malcolm, J. L. Evidence of carotid body and sinus activity in foetal and newborn animals. *J. Physiol. (London)*, **118**, 10P (1952)

31. Dawes, G. S. Control of the circulation and breathing in the newborn. In *Foetal and Neonatal Physiology*, 177–90 (Year Book Med. Publ., Chicago, 1968)

32. DeMyer, W. Ontogenesis of the rat corticospinal tract. Normal events and effects of intra-uterine neurosurgical lesions. *Arch. Neurol.*, **16**, 203–11 (1967)

33. Dobbing, J. The influence of early nutrition on the development and myelination of brain. *Proc. Roy. Soc. B*, **159**, 503–12 (1964)

34. Do Carmo, R. J. Direct cortical and recruiting responses in postnatal rabbit. *J. Neurophysiol.*, **23**, 496–504 (1960)

35. Dravid, A. R., Himwich, W. A., Davis, J. M. Some free amino acids in dog brain during development. *J. Neurochem.*, **12**, 901–6 (1965)

36. Eayrs, J. T., Horn, G. The development of cerebral cortex in hypothyroid and starved rats. *Anat. Record*, **121**, 53–61 (1955)

37. Eccles, R. M., Shealy, C. N., Willis, W. D. Patterns of innervation of kitten motoneurones. *J. Physiol. (London)*, **165**, 392–402 (1963)

38. Eccles, R. M., Willis, W. D. Presynaptic inhibition of the monosynaptic reflex pathway in kittens. *J. Physiol. (London)*, **165**, 403–20 (1963)

39. Eccles, R. M., Willis, W. D. The effect of repetitive stimulation upon monosynaptic transmission in kittens. *Ibid.*, **176**, 311–21 (1965)

40. Eidelberg, E., Kolmodin, G. M., Mey-erson, B. A. Ontogenesis of steady potential and direct cortical response in fetal sheep brain. *Exptl. Neurol.*, **12**, 198–214 (1965)

41. Ekholm J. Postnatal changes in cutaneous reflexes and in the discharge pattern of cutaneous and articular sense organs. *Acta Physiol. Scand.*, *Suppl. 297* (1967)

42. Ekholm, J., Skoglund, S. Possible factors influencing the demonstration of post-tetanic potentiation of the H-reflex as studied in the cat. *Exptl. Neurol.*, **9**, 183–97 (1964)

43. Ellingson, R. J., Wilcott, R. C. Development of evoked responses in visual and auditory cortices of kittens. *J. Neurophysiol.*, **23**, 363–75 (1960)

44. Fleischhauer, K., Wartenberg, H. Elektronenmikroskopische Untersuchungen über das Wachstum der Nervenfasern und über des Auftreten von Markscheiden im Corpus callosum der Katze. *Z. Zellforsch.*, **83**, 568–81 (1967)

45. Ford, D. H., Cohan, G. Changes in weight and volume of the motor neurons of the rat spinal cord ventral horn with increasing age. *Acta Anat.*, **69**, 1, 2 (1968)

46. Garma, L., Verley, R. Générateurs corticaux étudiés par électrodes implantées chez le lapin noveau-né. *J. Physiol.*, **57**, 811–18 (1965)

47. Garma, L., Verley, R. Activités cellulaires corticales étudiées par électrodes implantée chez le lapin nouveau-né. *Ibid.*, **59**, No. 5, 357–76 (1967)

48. Gyllensten, L. Postnatal development of the visual cortex in darkness (mice). *Acta Morphol. Neerl.-Scand.*, **2**, 331–45 (1959)

49. Gyllensten, L. Development of the visual cortex in mice with inherited retinal dystrophy. *J. Comp. Neurol.*, **122**, 79–89 (1964)

50. Gyllensten, L., Malmfors, T. Myelinization of the optic nerve and its dependence on visual function. A quantitative investigation in mice. *J. Embryol. Exptl. Morphol.*, **11**, Part 1, 255–66 (1963)

51. Gyllensten, L., Malmfors, T., Norrlin, M.-L. Effect of visual deprivation on the optic centers of growing and adult mice. *J. Comp. Neurol.*, **124**, No. 2, 149–60 (1965)

52. Gyllensten, L., Malmfors, T., Norrlin-Grettve, M.-L. Developmental and

functional alterations in the fiber
composition of the optic nerve in
visually deprived mice. *Ibid.*, **128,**
413–18 (1966)

53. Gyllensten, L., Malmfors, T., Norrlin,
M.-L. Growth alteration in the
auditory cortex of visually deprived
mice. *Ibid.*, **126,** 463–69

54. Hildebrand, C., Skoglund, S. Ultrastructural features of the nodal region in lumbar spinal roots of newborn man. *Acta Soc. Med. Upsalien.*,
72, 71–75 (1967)

55. Himwich, W. A., Davis, J. M., Agrawal, H. C. Biochemical substrates
for the development of the ma-
tured evoked potential. *Recent Advan. Biol. Psychol.*, **9,** 271–79 (1967)

56. Himwich, W. A., Dravid, A. R. Amino
acid content of various brain parts
as related to neurophysiological and
behavioural maturation (See Ref.
68), 257–68

57. Hubel, D. H., Wiesel, T. N. Binocular
interaction in striate cortex of kittens reared with artificial squint. *J.
Neurophysiol.*, **28,** 1041–59 (1964)

58. Hunt, W. E., Goldring, S. Maturation
of evoked response of the visual
cortex in the postnatal rabbit.
*Electroencephalog. Clin. Neurophys-
iol.*, **3,** 465–71 (1951)

59. Hyvärinen, J. Analysis of spontaneous
spike potential activity in developing rabbit diencephalon. *Acta
Physiol. Scand.*, **68,** *Suppl. 278*
(1966)

60. Klingberg, F., Schwartze, P. Über
photisch ausgelöste Nachentladun-
gen im visuellen Cortex der Ratte
während der Ontogenese. *Pflügers
Arch.*, **292,** 90–99 (1966)

61. Laget, P., Delhaye, N. Étude de développement néonatal de diverses
activités électriques corticales chez
le lapin. *Actualités Neurophysiol.*,
4, 259–84 (1962)

62. Landon, D. N., Williams, P. L., Ultrastructure of the node of Ranvier.
Nature, **199,** 575–77 (1963)

63. Malcolm, J. L. The development of re-
flex activity in the newborn kitten.
Abstr. 19th Intern. Physiol. Congr.,
Montreal, 1953, 586

64. Malcolm, J. L. The appearance of inhibition in the developing spinal
cord of kittens. In *Biochemistry of
the Developing Nervous System*, 104–
7 (Waelsca, H., Ed., Academic
Press, New York, 1955)

65. Marty, R. Développement post-natal

des réponses sensorielles du cortex
cérébral chez le chat et le lapin.
*Arch. Anat. Microscop. Morphol.
Exptl.*, 131–264 (1962)

66. Masurovsky, E. B., Bunge, M. B.,
Bunge, R. P. Cytological studies of
organotypic cultures of rat dorsal
root ganglia following X-irradiation
in vitro. II. Changes in Schwann
cells, myelin sheaths and nerve
fibres. *J. Cell Biol.*, **32,** 497–518
(1967)

67. Mellström, A., Skoglund S. Quantitative morphological changes in some
spinal cord segments during postnatal development. *Acta Physiol.
Scand.*, *Suppl.* (1968)

68. Meyerson, B. A. Ontogeny of interhemispheric functions. An electrophysiological study in pre- and
postnatal sheep. *Acta Physiol.
Scand.*, *Suppl. 312* (1968)

69. Minkowski, A., Ed., *Regional Development of the Brain in Early Life*
(Blackwell, Oxford and Edinburgh,
1967)

70. Molliver, M. E. An ontogenetic study
of evoked somesthetic cortical responses in the sheep (See Ref. 9),
78–91

71. Mott, J. C. Haemorrhage as a test of
the cardiovascular system in rabbits of different ages. *J. Physiol.*,
181, 728–52 (1965)

72. Mott, J. C. Cardiovascular function
in newborn mammals. *Brit. Med.
Bull.*, **22,** 66–69 (1966)

73. Mourek, J., Himwich, W. A., Myslive-
cek, J., Callison, D. A. The role of
nutrition in the development of
evoked cortical responses in rat.
Brain Res., **6,** 241–51 (1967)

74. Naka, K.-I. Electrophysiology of the
fetal spinal cord. I. Action potentials of the motoneuron. *J. Gen.
Physiol.*, **47,** 1003–22 (1964)

75. Naka, K.-I. Electrophysiology of the
fetal spinal cord. II. Interaction
among peripheral inputs and recurrent inhibition. *Ibid.*, 1023–38

76. Nyström, B. Postnatal structural and
functional development in the efferent neuromuscular system of the
cat (Thesis, Brogenhardt Tryckeri,
Stockholm, 1968)

77. Nyström, B., Skoglund, S. Calibre
spectra of spinal nerves and roots in
newborn man. *Acta Morphol. Neerl.-
Scand.*, **6,** 115–27 (1965)

78. Purpura, D. P., Schadé, J. P., Eds.,
Growth and Maturation of the Brain,

4 (*Progr. Brain Res.*, Elsevier, Amsterdam/London/New York, 1964)

79. Purpura, D. P., Shofer, R. J., Noback, C. R. Comparative ontogenesis of structure-function relations in cerebral and cerebellar cortex (See Ref. 78), 187–221

80. Purpura, D. P., Shofer, R. J., Scarff, T. Properties of synaptic activities and spike potentials of neurons in immature neocortex. *J. Neurophysiol.*, 28, 925–42 (1965)

81. Purves, M. J. The respiratory response of the newborn lamb to inhaled CO_2 with and without accompanying hypoxia. *J. Physiol. (London)*, 185, 78–94 (1966)

82. Samson, F. E., Balfour, W. M., Jacobs, R. J. Mitochondrial changes in developing rat brain. *Am. J. Physiol.*, 199, 693–96 (1960)

83. Scheibel, A. B. Neural correlates of psychophysiological developments in the young organism. *Recent Advan. Biol. Psychiat.*, 4, 313–27 (1962)

84. Scheibel, M. E., Scheibel, A. B. Some structuro-functional correlates of development in young cats. *Electroencephalog. Clin. Neurophysiol.*, *Suppl. 24*, 235–46 (1963)

85. Scherrer, J. Electrophysiological aspects of cortical development. In *Brain Reflexes*, 22, 480–89 (Asratyan, E. A., Ed., *Progr. Brain Res.*, Elsevier, Amsterdam/London/New York, 1967)

86. Scherrer, J., Oeconomos, D. Réponses évoquées corticales somesthétiques des mammifères adultes et noveaunés. *Les Grandes Activités du Lobe Temporal*, 249–68 (Masson, Paris, 1955)

87. Schulte, F. J. Reflex activation and inhibition of spinal motoneurones of the newborn. *Acta Paediat. Latina*, 17, 784–95 (1964)

88. Schulte, F. J., Michaelis, R., Filipp, E. Neurologie des Neugeborenen. I. Ursachen und klinische Symptomatologie von Funktionsstörungen des Nervensystems bei Neugeborenen. *Z. Kinderheilk.*, 93, 242–63 (1965)

89. Schulte, F. J., Schwenzel, W. Motor control and muscle tone in the newborn period. Electromyographic studies. *Biol. Neonatorum*, 8, 198–215 (1965)

90. Schwartze, P., Klingberg, F. Beitrag

zur Technik der Elektrogrammableitung im chronischen Versuch während der postnatalen Entwicklung kleiner Laboratoriumstiere. *Z. Med. Labortech.*, 8, 170–75 (1967)

91. Schwieler, G. Respiratory regulation during postnatal development in cats and rabbits and some of its morphological substrate. *Acta Physiol. Scand.*, *Suppl. 304* (1968)

92. Sereni, F., Principi, N., Perletti, L., Sereni, P. Undernutrition and the developing rat brain. I. Influence on acetylcholinesterase and succinic acid dehydrogenase activities and on norepinephrine and 5-OH-tryptamine tissue concentrations. *Biol. Neonatorum*, 10, 254–65 (1966)

93. Skoglund, S. On the postnatal development of postural mechanisms as revealed by electromyography and myography in decerebrate kittens. *Acta Physiol. Scand.*, 49, 299–317 (1960)

94. Skoglund, S. The spinal transmission of proprioceptive reflexes and the postnatal development of conduction velocity in different hindlimb nerves in the kitten. *Ibid.*, 318–29

95. Skoglund, S. The activity of muscle receptors in the kitten. *Ibid.*, 50, 203–21

96. Skoglund, S. Central connections and functions of muscle nerves in the kitten. *Ibid.*, 222–37

97. Skoglund, S. The reaction to tetanic stimulation of the two-neuron arc in the kitten. *Ibid.*, 238–53

98. Skoglund, S. Nobel symposium 1. In *Muscular Afferents and Motor Control*, 245–59 (Almqvist & Wiksell, Stockholm; Wiley, New York, London, Sydney, 1965)

99. Skoglund, S. Postnatal changes of NAD-diaphorase and succinic dehydrogenase in the spinal cord of the cat. *Acta Soc. Med. Upsalien.*, 72, 30–36 (1967)

100. Skoglund, S. Plasma ion concentration as a basis for an hypothesis regarding neuronal excitability changes during development. *Acta Soc. Med. Upsalien.*, 72, 76–84 (1967)

101. Skoglund, S. Maturation of reflex activity in *Neural Interactions. The Interneuron*. UCLA forum in Medical Sciences (Symp. held Sept. 1967 in Los Angeles, 1968)

102. Skoglund, S., Romero, C. Postnatal growth of spinal nerves and roots (a morphological study in the cat

with physiological correlations). *Acta Physiol. Scand.*, **66**, 1–50 (1965)

103. Tilney, F., Casamajor, L. Myelinogeny as applied to the study of behavior. *Arch. Neurol. Psychiat.*, **12**, 1–66 (1924)

104. Verley, R. Recherches sur le développement des activités électro-corticales avec des électrodes cortical radiaires. *J. Physiol.*, **57**, No. 3, 407–36 (1965)

105. Verley, R. Étude comparée de l'évolution des vitresses de conduction contrales et périphériques au cours de l'ontogénèse. *J. Physiol.*, **59**, No. 1, 306–7 (1967)

106. Verley, R., Mourek, J. Tolerance a l'anoxie de système nerveux néonatal (chez le lapin et le chat). *Physiol. Bohemoslov.*, **15**, 122–29 (1966)

107. Verley, R., Siou, G. Relations spatiales de quelques structures diencéphaliques et mésencéphaliques chez le lapin noveau-né. *J. Physiol.*, **59**, No. 4, 257–79 (1967)

108. Widdowson, E. M., McCance, R. A. The effect of development on the composition of the serum and extracellular fluids. *Clin. Sci.*, **15**, 361–65 (1956)

109. Wiesel, T. N., Hubel, D. H. Comparison of the effects of unilateral and bilateral eye closure on cortical unit responses in kittens. *J. Neurophysiol.*, **28**, 1029–40 (1965)

110. Wiesel, T. N., Hubel, D. H. Extent of recovery from the effects of visual deprivation in kittens. *Ibid.*, No. 6, 1060–72

111. Wilson, V. J. Reflex transmission in the kitten. *J. Neurophysiol.*, **25**, 263–75 (1962)

112. Windle, W. F. *Physiology of the Fetus*: Origin and extent of function of prenatal life (Saunders, Philadelphia, 1940)

113. Zelena, J. Development of muscle receptors after tenotomy. *Physiol. Bohemoslov.*, **12**, 30–36 (1963)

114. Zelena, J. Development, degeneration and regeneration of receptor organs. In *Mechanisms of Neural Regeneration*, **13**, 175–213 (Singer, M., Schadé, J. P., Eds., *Progr. Brain Res.*, Elsevier, Amsterdam/London/New York, 1964)

115. Zelena, J., Hnik, P. Motor and receptor units in the soleus muscle after nerve regeneration in very young rats. *Physiol. Bohemoslov.*, **12**, 277–90 (1963)

116. Åström, K.-E. On the early development of the isocortex in fetal sheep (See Ref. 9), 1–59

117. Änggård, L., Bergström, R., Bernhard, C. G. Analysis of prenatal spinal reflex activity in sheep. *Acta Physiol. Scand.*, **53**, 128–36 (1961)

COMPARATIVE ASPECTS OF MUSCLE[1,2,3,4]　　　　**1019**

By Graham Hoyle
Department of Biology, University of Oregon
Eugene, Oregon

INTRODUCTION

Comparative aspects of muscle were last reviewed by myself in 1961 (1), molluscan muscle (specifically) in 1963 (2), and insect muscle in 1964 (3). Two more recent papers considered diversity of fiber structure and function (4, 5). The present review takes up where these left off. The period covered most intensively is 1966–1967, the most productive year yet for relevant publications. The first symposium devoted exclusively to the topic was held in Washington, D. C., December 1966, and its papers have been published in *American Zoologist* (vol. 7, pp. 433–669). The contributions ranged from descriptions of unpublished work to general reviews [Atwood (6)—crustacean and Usherwood (7)—insect]. Excellent comprehensive reviews of comparative aspects of membrane excitability and responsiveness, much of it related to muscle, have been given by Grundfest (8, 9). Some material of interest to comparative physiologists is contained in the accounts of two general muscle symposia (10, 10a).

A consideration of invertebrate muscle independent of either membrane or neuromuscular physiology, such as can be done for vertebrate muscle,

---

[1] The survey of literature for this chapter was concluded in June 1967.

[2] Abbreviations used in this review: E system (general term for invaginating tubules connected to the surface membrane); T system (special term for the same tubules when they are radially oriented); SL (sarcomere length); SR (sarcoplasmic reticulum); EGTA (ethylene glycol bis-β-aminoethyl ether-N,N′-tetraacetate), calcium chelating agent; EPSP (excitatory postsynaptic potential—at neuromuscular junction); IPSP (inhibitory postsynaptic potential—at neuromuscular junction); JP (junctional potential—general term).

[3] Prepared during the tenure of a Guggenheim Foundation Fellowship while on sabbatical leave, at the Department of Physiology, University College, London.

[4] *Special note.* The literature of comparative nerve and muscle physiology is scattered through over 100 journals and it is becoming increasingly difficult to keep track of more than a fraction. I apologize to all whose papers have been overlooked or removed in the 4:1 condensation by elimination. In our laboratory in Eugene, we have built up a library of reprints of papers in the comparative muscle field which is freely available to all students and visitors. It would be greatly appreciated if you would contribute copies of your papers to this collection. We also have a growing library of electron micrographs of diverse muscles and neuromuscular junctions to which several distinguished electron microscopists have kindly contributed. Additional papers will be gratefully received. Don't bury yours!

is not yet profitable. In the lower phyla a separation is not technically feasible, as it is in arthropods. But even where it is possible, interest for comparative physiologists still lies to a large extent in the subtlety, complexity, and biological meaning of the overall neuromuscular phenomena, reflecting synaptic as well as muscular events.

The modern position of comparative physiology in relation to muscle studies is becoming increasingly difficult to define, and in preparing this review I found myself hopping backwards and forwards among several different roles. At one extreme the subject is concerned with the descriptive physiology of invertebrate and lower vertebrate animals for its own sake, as part of Zoology, on two levels: *understanding* the evolutionary process; and *assuming* certain evolutionary aspects in order to illuminate basic physiological understanding. At the latter level it merges with the abstraction, 'general' physiology. We cannot expect a physician concerned with the many terrifying muscular diseases to be overly concerned with crabs, yet at another level comparative physiologists are exploring also the fundamental processes, molecular architecture, and contractile machinery with which he is very much concerned. Evolutionary diversification (= adaptive radiation) has provided a number of preparations from among invertebrates which are uniquely suited technically to exploitation by chemical and physical methods, as the example of the remarkably useful squid giant axon has so clearly established. But these examples are a byproduct, not the *raison d'être*, of comparative physiology.

Muscle studies went through a long 'dead' period from the comparative point of view, from about 1910 to 1950, in which many important pieces of knowledge, such as the transverse tubular system and sarcoplasmic reticulum, were completely forgotten, as well as features of graded contraction, of I-band length changes and of myosin location [see comments by A. F. Huxley (11)]. Fortunately, the study of muscle has now returned to a broader approach, and progress during the last five years has been dramatic, though the forces which led to the earlier suppression of 'difficult' knowledge are still in evidence. It is highly significant, however, that Lee Peachey, in his 1968 review (12), has been extremely liberal in his literature survey. No fewer than 67 references—almost one third of the total—are to papers concerned with invertebrates and the flavor is as much comparative as 'general'. Most of these are concerned with ultrastructure, which has proved to be of extraordinarily rich variety in invertebrates. Biochemical and thermodynamic studies are still done very largely on one amphibian muscle which was favored by Hill. Yet it would be wrong, also, simply to equate comparative physiology with invertebrate physiology. The comparative physiologist is also concerned with the broad spectrum of vertebrate animals. It is the 'general' physiologist who makes the restrictions, to facilitate a focusing of attention on a restricted problem. But with muscle, this is more than usually difficult.

The present review will cover briefly the recent contributions from invertebrates and some vertebrates to aspects of both structure and function, except where these have already been fully covered by Peachey. For the benefit of zoologists, a phylum-by-phylum review is included.

GENERAL ASPECTS

FIBER CONTENT OF A MUSCLE

Until relatively recently a homogeneity of fiber composition of a muscle was taken for granted, but the discovery of the slow fibers of frog and inconsistencies in crustacean muscle have led to a critical examination of the fiber composition of several arthropod muscles, where the large size of the fibers renders a fiber-by-fiber examination possible. In the abdominal flexors of the crayfish a simple division exists, with a thin superficial layer being composed of slow fibers forming a tonic system (13), while the thicker, deeper bundle are fast fibers forming a phasic system (14). The abdominal extensors of crayfish and rocklobster are also divided into phasic and tonic subsystems (15). In extreme contrast, the flexor of the dactylopodite of the *Cancer magister* walking leg contains slow, fast, and various intermediate forms of fiber intermingled apparently at random (16). In the fan-shaped accessory flexor of the carpopodite of the same species, slow fibers occur to the outer margin, fast ones to the inner, with intermediates centrally located (17). Slow fibers occur in both a distal and a proximal deep bundle in the claw closer of *Randallia* (18). A beautiful example of an orderly distribution of fiber types occurs in the anterior rotator of the paddle of the Hawaiian swimming crab *Portunus sanguinolentus* (19). Here, a distinct coloration facilitates recognition. Fast fibers are transparent/white, slow ones pink/brown and intermediates light pink/grey. They are collected together into three distinct bundles and are attached to the internal skeleton in such a way that the fast fibers are 2.5× longer than the slow ones. Sarcomere lengths are inversely related to speed of contraction and relaxation, fast fibers being 2.4 μ, slow ones longer than 6μ, and intermediates about 4μ. Electric responsiveness is also related; the fast fibers give propagated, overshooting action potentials, the slow ones are inexcitable or give small graded responses, while intermediates give larger graded electrogenesis. There is a nice functional differentiation associated with a separate innervation of the bundles. The slow fibers are used only in tonic raising of the paddle, the intermediates in all ordinary maneuvering and swimming movements, and the fast ones only in a rapid, powerful escape thrust. But separate innervation is not general. The three kinds of fiber in the accessory flexor receive branches from the same single excitatory axon (17). Spikes do not occur in these fast fibers, only graded responses evoked by large JPs showing little facilitation.

A very subtle division of fiber types is present in the eyestalk levator of *Podophthalmus vigil* (20, 21). Here the fibers are all of long-sarcomere type, but an inner bundle contains pinkish fibers of small diameter and 13 μ SL, while an outer bundle has white, larger fibers with 9 μ SL. Some white fibers are quite fast while some pink ones are very slow. A few pink fibers in each muscle develop appreciable resting tension in the absence of EPSPs, which is rapidly relaxed by polarizing current (22). These studies were done on single fibers and comparable studies do not yet seem feasible in insects, but a number of pointers to similar kinds of complexity have appeared, including pink color of some fibers and electron microscopic differences (8, 23).

Sufficient information has accumulated from physiological, pharmacological, histochemical, and electron microscopic sources to indicate that fiber types may be diverse in all phyla. Peachey (12) comments extensively on fiber differences in vertebrates and I include below some further examples. A theoretical and computer analysis of the effect of admixture of fast and slow elements in determining the form of a combined twitch, though with particular reference to cat intercostals, has been made (24).

Fiber Architecture

The simple notion of a muscle fiber as a collection of parallel-aligned contractile filaments wrapped up in sausage-skin envelope of sarcolemmal complex must give way in view of improved understanding of a variety of fine structures. The period covered by the review has seen the introduction of cannulated fibers of giant size, all from crustaceans, including the large spider crabs *Maia squinado* (25) and the Alaskan king crab *Paralithoides kamchatka*, and of the large barnacles *Balanus nubilus* (26) and *B. aquilia*. The largest of these fibers exceed 3 mm in diameter and 6 cm in length. The barnacle fibers have individual tendons, 4–5 mm long. Sarcolemmas of the latter are tough enough to permit force measurement after cannulation (26a). Conduction into the centers of such fibers provides, in principle, a great problem, but it has been simply solved by the development of a series of clefts invaginated from the surface membrane, which penetrate throughout the sarcoplasm after much branching. From the clefts, T tubules have only some 2μ to travel to reach the most distant points of contact with the SR. The ultimate tubular conduction distance is much less than in a vertebrate fiber 1/20 as thick (27). Nerve terminals are not exclusively—or even mainly—located at the perimeter, but are found deep inside the clefts (28). Excitation travels from the inside outwards as much as from the outside in.

Unlike giant nerve fibers, which achieve the functional advantage of a high velocity of conduction, giant size in a muscle fiber seems to be no advantage. The size may merely be an indirect consequence of general growth in a system which has a fairly fixed number of fibers, for the numbers are only very slightly larger in a large adult than in a juvenile.

In the majority of fibers, mitochondria occur both peripherally and between myofilament clusters. In striated fibers of squid mantle, by contrast, they only occur in the center of the fiber and the majority of the fiber volume is occupied by this central core of giant mitochondria, with a thin peripheral ring of contractile filaments (29).

The most peculiar cytoarchitecture of any muscle is that in the large muscular cells of nematodes, where the cell bodies are extended into the nervous system to make contacts with each other and with central nerve cells. The latter are, in fact, the neuromuscular junctions, centrally, not peripherally located (30, 31). Perhaps even more surprising, is that similar neuromuscular junctions, formed by inwards projections from the muscle fiber, terminating on spinal cord fibers, have also been found in an animal of high evolutionary status, *Amphioxus* (32).

Ultrastructure

Within the review period it has become clear that the detailed macro-molecular architecture of striated muscle is extremely varied. The differences relate to function rather than to species characteristics and are of profound significance for comparative physiology. The general framework of thin filaments interdigitating with thick ones and running parallel to the long axis is the only universal one. Lengths of thick filaments currently known range from only 0.5μ in the squid mantle to over 10μ in slow fibers from crab leg or eyestalk levator muscle. The corresponding thin-filament lengths are 0.3 and 6.0μ. Regulatory devices for determining filament lengths must have a muscle-fiber-type-specific molecular mechanism. They are fairly constant for a given fiber type, but fibers with a 4:1 ratio of filament lengths can exist side by side in a small muscle (5).

The different lengths are related to contraction speed. Where fibers could be compared, in the extensor of the carpopodite of *Ocypode ceratophthalma* (4), a linear relation was found between contraction time and the logarithm of sarcomere length.

No corresponding differences in SL of fibers have yet been found in verte-brate muscles, which are rather homogeneous in this respect, with lengths in the narrow range $1.8–2.8 \mu$. Differences in speed in vertebrate muscles seem to be related to differences in the extent of development of longitudinal SR and to enzymatic differences. Differences in the extent to which a fiber is invaded by SR also play a role in invertebrate fibers. Fast fibers have a more extensive SR in some crustacean (33, 34) and some insect (29) muscle fibers.

The SR is commonly a perforated double sheet, but triple sheets occur (21), and the thicknesses and complexities of the sheets are a source of varia-tion.

Unusual forms of the SR have been found, for example in an ostracod muscle (35), and more should be expected. In the latter, it takes the form of rosettes, as seen in transverse section (TS), with a core element. The latter is a longitudinally running invagination from the plasma membrane. To this and other kinds of tubule serving the probable function of inwards transmis-sion of excitation and elicitation of release of activator from SR, I have pro-posed the general term E tubule (36). Thus these elements form a major source of structural variation. They may be entirely transverse (T tubules), entering the fiber at regularly arranged sites, corresponding to the average location of Z regions, as occurs in fish muscle (37), or they may be extremely sparse in some slow reptilian fibers (38). Hess (39) denied their existence in the latter, but a counter-claim has been entered for the same material (38). Since they are so rare, they must branch internally and run longitudinally in order to make contact with the sparse SR.

The locations of E (or T) tubules is thus a major source of variation. The E system provides a large capacitance, with resistive element, effectively in parallel with that of the surface membrane, and increases the effective capacitance of the latter by up to severalfold. The nature of the system will greatly influence the endplate or JP, and therefore the characteristics of excitation. Biophysical aspects are discussed by Falk & Fatt (40) for frog and crayfish fibers, and for crab fibers by Eisenberg (41) and Peachey (42). Some idea of the complexities this can lead to, even within one muscle, as a result of variations in detail, may be obtained by considering the various forms of endplate potential obtained in a drug-treated sartorius of frog (43). Some of the variation in crustacean JP shapes (cf. 40) may be due to variations in detail of the local cleft and E system. In a comparison of the E systems of frog and toad (44), branching increased the quantity of the system by ~30 per cent, but with more frequent branching in the toad.

Z region.—The detailed nature of the Z band of vertebrate fibers (45–49) and insect flight muscle have been studied (50). The former studies do not agree as to detailed structure and it is clear that the region is not yet understood. It is clearly mainly a zone where I filaments of contiguous sarcomeres interconnect. In fast fibers of fish myotomes the filaments terminate short of the Z region, whereas in slow fibers of reptiles they overlap (5). The extent of overlap is related to the speed of contraction (49). Overlap also occurs in the *Lethocerus* flight muscle studied by Ashurst (50). Differences in the extent of overlap probably account for the marked differences which occur in Z-band widths. There must be differences in the ways in which the I filaments crosslink in different kinds of Z region. In fast vertebrate fibers they enter the region in a square array, but in frog slow fibers this cannot be discerned (51). In insect flight muscle and in copepod fast fibers the hexagonal array persists into the Z region (52, 53).

Numbers of thin filaments.—A major source of variation in invertebrates, and between them and vertebrates, relates to the numbers of thin filaments. Vertebrate fibers all have a 2:1 ratio of thin to thick, resulting in the familiar hexagonal array in the trigonal positions of the hexagonal thick-filament lattice, except in the embryonic state, when they have (chick) a 7:1 ratio (54). This array has yet to be established for any invertebrate muscle. A 2:1 ratio, when it exists, is associated with a loose, nonorderly array, but most invertebrate fibers appear to have ratios exceeding 2:1 (5; see reviews in 54a, b). Fast copepod fibers and insect flight muscle fibers, except lepidopterans, have a highly ordered 3:1 ratio and the thin filaments are situated in between thick ones along their lattice lines, so there are also six thin filaments round each thick one. Auber (55, 56) has recently shown that the number is increased to from 7–10 in a butterfly (*Vanessa*) which has a low rate of flapping in flight and Reger & Cooper (57) found this also in *Achalarus*. Several insect skeletal muscles have been shown to have orbits of 10 (4:1 ratio), or 12 which may be due either to a 5:1 ratio or to a 6:1 ratio, depending on the locations of thin filaments (54a). The latter number is also found in abdominal muscles (58), which in insects are also striated. In crustacea, similar high ratios have been encountered, and one kind of slow fiber present in a crab has a 7:1 ratio (21). Within one muscle the slow fibers always have the higher ratio (29). Orbits are generally irregular when the ratio exceeds 5:1. For some interesting comparative pictures see also (59).

The arrangement of the contact points between T or E systems and SR varies considerably (60): there is a major difference within the vertebrates as one passes up the evolutionary scale. Fish and frog fibers have a regularly spaced T system which eventually forms partial collars around the Z regions of myofilament clusters. An interesting but rare exception has been found by Kilarski (61) in a teleost extrinsic eye muscle fiber which was also small and red, where triads occurred at the A-I junctional level. Elements of SR abut on the T system from each sarcomere, resulting in a 'triad' when seen in longitudinal section (LS). In reptiles, birds, and mammals the contact points are located over the A band just inside the A-I junctions and they may be diadic or pentadic as well as triadic. In some slow fibers the tubules run longitudinally, giving a triadic appearance when seen in TS (38). The functional significance of these differences is obscure, but releasing calcium at the A-I junctions may be expected to be more efficient than releasing it close to the Z region, from which it would have to diffuse along the I band to the sites of action (62). Triads are occasionally found in invertebrate muscles but they are never of the fish type. The contact points are mainly 'diadic', formed where the transversely, obliquely, or longitudinally running tubules come into contact with SR. The tubules are not round, but markedly flattened, in section. Contact points do not occur near the Z band, but at the A-I junction. However, several other such contact points may occur along the A band, forming a line of diads. The contact points of the SR (cysternae) with the E tubules are characterized by an absence of perforations, the presence of densely staining granules, and a complex structure in the 120 Å space (63, 64). The latter may be shaped like waffle ribs, for it always leads to the appearance of regularly spaced cross-connections in sections which show the membranes clearly, and to a grid when seen in face view.

Triads in fetal rat gastrocnemius lie parallel to the fiber axis, but come to take up a transverse orientation during development (64).

A-filament substructure.—The molecular architecture of rabbit psoas muscle myosin was treated in an intensive fine structural and speculative study by Pepe (65). That of *Lethocerus* flight muscle may be deduced comparatively from the data presented by Reedy (66, 67). The significant point is that the two clearly cannot be identical in the way the myosin molecules pack together. Thus we may expect significant differences at this level. These will be even more marked in the case of thick filaments such as are found in some copepod (68) and crab (21) muscles, in which there are two M bands lying on either side of the center, which is thick (200–260 Å) and dense, leading into thinner, apparently hollow, tapering regions. Baccetti (69) has used optical rotation methods to study the packing of subunits in polychaete (*Perinereis*), fly (*Musca*), and human abdominal fibers and found in all three types a hollow core containing two units, surrounded by a peripheral ring of 9 units. We have found a similar arrangement in some insect and crab fibers but not in others. In *Carcinus* leg fibers Gilev (70) found either 13–15 or 18 units, but the filaments were quite large (220–250 Å in these cases). The subunits then occur in two rings, with 10–12 in the outer ring and 4–6 in the inner one. According to Reger (57), lepidopteran flight muscle fiber A filaments are resolvable into subunits 15–25 Å in diameter, with 3–4 occurring at mid-sarcomere level and 6–8 elsewhere.

In rabbit psoas in the model of Pepe (65), the thick filaments contain 12 subunits, but they are closely packed, not in rings. A hollow center may nevertheless be seen in transverse sections of fish muscle, at least in the M region. The dorsal longitudinal muscles of the polychaete *Syllis* undergo a de-differentiation and a re-differentiation during stolonization in which the thick filaments of a single fiber break up and reform. In the new and final one they are thinner (280 Å) than originally (350 Å) (71).

Other Structural Elements

Z tubules.—A special feature of a number of arthropod fibers, first reported by Peachey (72) and confirmed by Selverston (28) for barnacle giant fibers and by Hoyle & McNeill for crab and some insect fibers, is the existence of wide transverse tubules encircling, or making close contact with, the Z regions. The points of contact are thickened and desmosome-like. Peachey proposed the term Z tubule for them. They may play a structural role, or they may play a special role in exciting the Z regions of supercontracting fibers to open up, as tentatively proposed by Hoyle et al. (73).

Mitochondria.—Very little special attention has yet been paid to the mitochondria, but there is no doubt that these are widely varied between muscle fibers of different types, especially in size, which varies over a thousandfold range, and in shape. There may be significant differences within the same fiber. Hagopian (74) has recognized three different shapes in femoral fibers of the cockroach *Leucophaea*.

M region.—Many invertebrate fibers, especially those with a long sarcomere length, resemble frog slow fibers (51) in not having conspicuous M bands [e.g. Hagopian (74)—cockroach, Hoyle (5)—locust, barnacle etc.]. There are bridges between the thick filaments, but they appear to occur along the whole length of the A band. Double M bands occur in some copepod fibers (53) and some crab fibers (21).

Auber (75) and Reger (76) have independently found that in moth flight muscle fibers (but not in leg muscles), there is a well-defined transverse tubular collar in the center of the sarcomere in the M region.

Ultrathin filaments.—The earlier structural models of striated muscle compatible with constancy of length of A and I bands placed a hypothetical elastic (S) filament between the inner ends of the I filaments across the H zone. Another possible elastic filament was indicated, connecting I filaments to Z band (77). These have both been dropped unnecessarily. Physical evidence for a very thin filament in a variety of invertebrate and vertebrate fibers has recently been presented (78) for intact muscle, and for the ghosts from which myosin and actin have been removed (79, 80). These filaments run from Z band to M band in parallel with the other filaments. The evidence does not satisfy Peachey (12), but bearing in mind the difficulty in resolving a 20–25 Å filament the reader should consider the evidence, judge for himself and await further developments.

Apparent anomalous contractions.—Light microscope studies on invertebrate muscle fibers have frequently been invoked as indicating that the simple sliding-filament hypothesis may not be universally applicable. This has usually taken the form of demonstrating shortening of the A band of glycerinated fibrils contracting in the presence of ATP [e.g. De Villafranca & Marshhaus (81)—*Limulus*; Hehn & Schlote (82)—*Carausius*; Gilmour & Robinson (83)—grasshopper; Baskin & Wiese (84)—giant barnacle]. Only in the barnacle fibers has the phenomenon been critically examined in the only way possible, by electron microscopy: it was shown (84a) that although the A band does appear to shrink, the thick filaments remain at constant length. The appearance is caused by individual filaments moving separately towards one or other of the Z regions so that there is a shrinking dense zone of overlap in the center of the sarcomere. Galey (85), however, found shrinking and thickening of A bands of frog muscle fibers (semitendinosus) in a study using high-resolution electron microscopy. It is most important to resolve these issues. Other as yet unexplained phenomena are tension development at lengths exceeding overlap of thick and thin filaments (86) and shortening of I bands of glycerinated muscle on adding ATP (87). Most muscle physiologists and electron microscopists imply in conversation that this work is without value, but are unwilling to criticize it formally in print.

Insect flight muscle is notoriously unable to shorten to any great extent, and this is almost equally true after glycerination, in contractions induced by ATP (down to 80 per cent rest length). But in the presence of ITP (inosine triphosphate) the contraction is down to 30 per cent of rest length. The latter is in supercontraction range, but it is not accomplished by interdigitation of thick filaments across the Z region (see below). Instead, the thick filaments definitely shorten and become thicker (up to 30 per cent) (88).

Reversible supercontraction is now recognized in barnacle giant fibers and larval insect fibers. The mechanism has been explored by electron microscopy and found to be the same in both (73, 89). Perforations occur in the Z bands and through these perforations the thick filaments are able to pass, and interdigitate with those from the contiguous sarcomere.

ENZYME DIFFERENCES

To the various biophysical and ultrastructural differences which have together formed a basis for remarkable evolutionary divergence, biochemical differences must be added. The extent of these can hardly be imagined at the present time. Some significant comparisons have been made by Bárány (99) in regard to the ATPase activity of various myosins extracted under comparable conditions. Muscles from cat, sloth, squid, *Limulus*, *Thyone*, and dogfish were compared, and data on frog and barnacle are also available. The contraction times of these muscles range from 27 msec for cat flexor hallucis longus, to 15,000 msec for dogfish mesenteric retractor, though this is a smooth muscle. Myosin ATPase was highest in the former and lowest in the latter, with a 200-fold difference. The others ranged roughly between them, in proportion to speed. The sloth muscles were 4–5× slower than the cat. Differences in such enzymes as succinic dehydrogenase, phosphorylase, lipase in relation to speed are well known.

EXCITATION-CONTRACTION COUPLING

Several investigators have studied various aspects of membrane potential /tension relationships and the influence of ions and drugs upon them, with a view to throwing some light on the coupling mechanism. A variety of single fibers from both vertebrates and invertebrates have been used. Work in this field which utilizes whole muscle should be considered with extreme caution in view of inhomogeneities. Even the ubiquitous frog's sartorius was shown over 50 years ago (100) to suffer from this.

Of greatest interest in this field is the introduction of cannulated giant crustacean fibers into which various solutions can be injected and the effect on contraction studied. Caldwell (101, 102) used fibers from the leg of the spider crab *Maia squinado* and showed that Ca^{++}, Sr^{++}, or Ba^{++} all give contraction when injected and that either injected Ca^{++} or caffeine gives contraction when the fiber has previously been depolarized and allowed to relax. Caffeine releases internally bound calcium, probably from cysternal sacs of the SR. In the same preparation, ion injection showed that contraction starts at a free Ca^{++} of about $10^{-7}M$ and reaches a maximum at about $10^{-6}M$. Since the total Ca content is about $10^{-3}M$/kg wet weight, most of the cellular calcium is bound, with a release occurring during excitation. No precise meaning can be assigned to the molar concentration value in relation to contraction, since it is the quantity of ions injected which is really significant.

The *Maia* fibers are unfortunately fragile, obliquely attached to the skeleton, and unsuited to force registration. Giant fibers of remarkable experimental convenience and tough enough for force registration after cannulation, each one having an individual tendon, were discovered in 1962 (103). Ashley (104) has compared the amounts of the calcium-binding agent EGTA required to suppress contraction in *Maia* and *Balanus* fibers. In the former it was about equal to the estimated level of fiber calcium, but in the latter it was much higher when potassium was used to depolarize the fiber. This difference may be due to significant amounts of calcium ions entering from the external medium. Hagiwara et al. (105) have demonstrated that the membrane has a low sodium conductance even when depolarized, and a high Ca^{++} conductance. The graded electrogenic (spike) response is due to a conductance increase for a divalent cation, normally calcium. The height of the spike is proportional to the ratio of external to internal potassium (106).

The amount of calcium ions entering per impulse for a large spike is about 50 μmole/cm^2 fiber perimeter. This amount is equivalent to an internal concentration of about $10^{-4}M$, significant enough though not sufficient by itself to saturate the troponin-actomyosin, especially in view of binding by SR and outwards movement of the same ion. Direct entry of calcium is important in heart muscle (107) and smooth muscle (108) of vertebrates, though not in skeletal muscle (109). Suppression of contraction below 5 per cent could not be achieved by EGTA injection on *Balanus* fibers. Since the EGTA should easily suppress entering calcium and most internally released calcium, this suggests a very high concentration indeed at small sites in the fiber, presumably the SR cysternae. Hagiwara (106) concluded that at the level of internal calcium permitting all-or-none spikes there was no tension, but Ashley obtained a condition in which small amounts of tension, summating and also facilitating, accompanied all-or-none spikes. All these results strongly support the theory that coupling results principally from a release of bound calcium from sites inside the fiber, with a small contribution from directly entering calcium.

A direct test of the hypothesis was first devised by Jöbsis & O'Connor (110), who caused toad sartorius to take up the purple dye murexide in the presence of dimethylsulfoxide. The dye changes color in the presence of calcium in the presumed coupling concentration range and this was followed spectrophotometrically. The color change took place very rapidly and briefly and reached its peak well in advance of peak tension. This delightful experiment is unfortunately fraught with technical difficulties, not the least of which is the opacity change accompanying contraction. An extraordinarily pretty biological method has been devised to follow calcium release directly, by Ridgway (111, 112). This takes advantage of the fact that the bioluminescent protein aequorin, produced by the medusa *Aequorea aequorea* (113), is caused to emit a bright blue-green light by calcium ions (it does not require ATP) in the $10^{-8}-10^{-6}M$ concentration range. Only strontium ions, which are not present in the fiber, can duplicate this action.

The protein is prepared in a highly purified state and injected into the fibers along their length. Such fibers emit light when stimulated, up to several hundred flashes per injection. The light output affords a direct and approximately quantitative measure of the time course and characteristics of the calcium release. Light starts to be emitted within 1 msec of depolarization past the threshold, and tension starts after 2–6 msec. The light output ceases to rise within 1 msec of cessation of stimulation, and declines exponentially.

It has virtually ceased by the time tension reaches its peak. The rate of rise of force is proportional to the calcium concentration and the amount of force is related to the product of $[Ca^{++}] \times$ time. Light is not further emitted during relaxation, which shows that the return of calcium to SR occurs either gradually or via a bound intermediate. Data on the rate of removal of Ca^{++} come from studies on isolated vesicles [*B. nubilus*—Hasselbach, quoted by Hagiwara & Nakajima (106)] and indirect buffer-injection studies all suggest a rate of about 0.5 μmole/g/min at 25° C.

The active-state development is very different from that in frog twitch fibers (114). Any degree of intensity from zero to twice that in a tetanus may be obtained, depending on the intensity and duration of stimulation and the ionic content of the bathing medium. The active state is directly related to the calcium released. Direct measurements of this are not available for frog's sartorius, but it may be deduced that a sufficiently large release occurs in a single twitch to cause actual or almost complete saturation of the troponin-actomyosin binding sites, which explains very simply the basic difference between these two kinds of fibers. About 80 msec of intensive depolarization is needed at 20° C in *Balanus* fibers to attain maximum active state. As a part of the Hill dogma it was thought that the action potential was a simple switch device concerned to turn on active state. The latter would decline at a characteristic rate. From the new understanding of the coupling process, it must be expected that the rising and falling phases of the action potential will influence the time courses of onset and decline of active state, and also the intensity. The influence will be more conspicuous in fibers where saturation of the contractile machinery does not occur following an action potential. Evidence for this has been obtained by Sandow (115) for frog muscle and by Hoyle (116) for crustacean muscle.

Controversy continues to rage as to whether certain potentiating effects of repetition of stimulation are due to increases in intensity of active state or merely to its prolongation [e.g. Desmedt & Hainaut (117) criticized by Rosenfalck (118)]. It is a vital part of the Hill dogma that the conversion to the active state must be complete when it occurs. In view of present knowledge about the complexities of the process—inwards transmission, excitation of the SR, release of activator, diffusion of activator, continuous binding of activator by SR—it would be very surprising indeed if 100 per cent saturation of activation of the contractile system of fibers could occur in each activation, and it must be regarded as probable that variations in the intensity of development of the active state play a significant role. This will be especially true of slow fibers.

Sandow (119) has obtained evidence that potentiators may have an independent action on the velocity of contraction, so that the fiber does not necessarily shorten at the maximum velocity consistent with the load (another Hill dogma). The velocity may be enhanced.

The mode of spread of activation to release sites is the subject of controversy. One view arising from observations of Huxley & Taylor (120) is that a spread of potential occurs electrotonically down the T or E tubules. The rate of inwards transmission of excitation has been measured for isolated frog fibers by first making them shorter so that the fibrils are wavy, and then filming the progressive straightening. This is said to occur from the outside inwards, but supporting photographs are not to be seen (121, 122). The rate is stated to be 8 cm/sec at 20° C. The alternative is the suggestion of Girardier et al. (123) that the tubules serve as pathways for the flow of current, which passes directly across the walls of the tubule principally in the regions of contact with SR, which probably have a high conductance to chloride ions, in crustacean muscle, and thence across the myoplasm and surface membrane. It is not easy to see exactly how the hypotheses may be distinguished experimentally. Each gives an identical time course, dependent on the dimensions and properties of the tubular walls and lumen. Reuben et al. (124) list three features of their 'channeled current' hypothesis: tension is a continuous function of membrane depolarization and could occur without, or even during, hyperpolarization; membrane current will determine coupling; Cl ions directly participate in coupling. None of these points is totally incompatible with an electronic spread of activation. They *are* incompatible with a simple threshold potential trigger system such has been tacitly assumed, though not explicity stated, by a number of investigators. Variations in the apparent threshold have been shown to be related to immediate history in terms of stimulation [(16)—crab fibers] and to external [Ca^{++}] [(125)—frog fibers.] When an agent influences apparent threshold, it affects also the threshold for latency relaxation—in vertebrate fibers—in the same direction (126). A notable difference between invertebrate muscles and the few vertebrate ones tested is that the former do not show latency relaxation. The longer time required to develop maximum active state in the invertebrate fibers may result from progressive recruitment of contractile elements, so that there is a lack of synchrony in the molecular events, which prevents the rather weak latency relaxation effect from showing up, or it may be absent in them. The central problem has now become the kinetics of release from a single coupling site, and this is not at present technically feasible.

The importance of the E tubules is emphasized by experiments in which they are disrupted by osmotic shock. The twitch fibers of the frog continue to produce propagated action potentials, but fail to contract (127). However, this does not apply to "slow" fibers after a similar treatment (128).

Some interesting experiments reported by Sugi & Ochi (129) must represent the spread of excitation in the tubular network. By local stimulation of the surface of an isolated crayfish fiber they obtained an inwards spread of contraction proportional to the intensity and duration of excitation. But with a larger pipette the excitation spreads transversely also, and in this, successive brief depolarizations were more effective than a single prolonged one. A very strong current through the larger pipette caused the whole perimeter of the fiber to give a ring contraction, with neither longitudinal spread along the fiber nor transverse spread into its center. Similar responses were obtained in frog fibers (130).

Crayfish fibers depolarized by calcium-free, isosmotic potassium propionate do not contract in response to ionic challenges, but caffeine (10–80 mM), ethanol (1–3 per cent), or acetone (1–3 per cent) gives tension which is blocked by procaine. When the fibers are skinned, reversible contraction occurs in response to a small pH change, or monovalent anions in the lyophilic series $SCN > I > Br > NO_3 > Cl$ (131).

In an ingenious, simple experiment Gillis (132) used *Carcinus* fibers with a long SL to show that iontophoretic application of calcium is most effective when applied at the A-I junctional region. Several indirect studies supported the calcium hypothesis; for example Aidley (133) on locust leg muscle and Zacharova & Zachar (134) on isolated crayfish fibers. Sudden withdrawal of calcium from the external medium leads to an exponential decline in peak tension, with a time constant of several tens of seconds. Different rates of binding of calcium by SR may be expected to influence the rate of relaxation of a fiber. In vertebrate muscle, speed increases during development. This is nicely correlated with speed of uptake of calcium by isolated reticulum (microsomal fraction) and there is a corresponding increase in ATPase activity (135).

The possibility that the coupling sites of vertebrate muscle (triads) are the target for the powerful paralyzing agent tetanus toxin has been raised by the finding that poisoned muscle, incubated with antitoxin labeled with peroxidase and stained for the latter, shows an electron-opaque reaction product in these regions (136).

MECHANISM OF CONTRACTION

The comparative approach has not yet played a major role in developing and testing theories of contraction, with one notable exception: studies on insect flight muscle. These have an extremely regular array of myofilaments and the thin filaments maintain a hexagonal lattice throughout, instead of changing to a square one near the Z region. The arrangement is especially regular in relation to cross bridges in a state of rigor. This has enabled Reedy (67) to produce the most exact data yet available for the ultrastructure of any muscle, and a theory of contraction based upon a pushing action by cross bridges. But as a general model for muscle there are some serious peculiarities of flight fibers. Maximum force is pathetically weak (0.3 kg/cm^2) compared with $\sim$5 kg/cm^2 in crab fibers of comparable SL, and the extent of shortening is a mere 1–2 per cent compared with up to 86 per cent in supercontracting arthropod fibers. However, another advantage is offered by flight muscles, for they can be made to undergo effectively normal contractions after isolation and glycerinization.

It is only necessary for glycerinated fibers to be connected to a suitable elastic load and to be supplied with ATP and calcium above $10^{-7}M$ for oscillatory contractions to occur. Even a single fiber may be used (137).

Under comparable conditions an ordinary skeletal fiber simply develops force and shortens and so does the flight fiber if the load is stiff. The ATPase activity is proportional to log $[Ca^{++}]$ between 10^{-8} and $10^{-6} M$. But if the lever system has a natural period of oscillation at a frequency up to ~100 cps oscillatory tension is developed. The contractile activity is switched off by a little shortening and switched on again by stretch. Forcible elongation increases tension and ATPase activity (138, 139). Both stretch and release influence tension after a small delay, so that in a normal cycle the increased power initiated by stretch is developed during the shortening. Thus positive oscillatory work is done in each cycle. Extra ATPase activity is associated with the stretch, provided the free calcium level is sufficiently high and Mg ions are present to reduce the total activation below the maximum possible. If the oscillations are not spontaneous but driven, the extra ATPase activity is greater than during isometric contraction by an amount proportional to the rate of doing work (140).

The most favored current hypotheses concerning the final molecular event suppose that heavy meromyosin portions of the myosin molecule, which project from the thick filaments, are responsible, by shortening or rotating, pulling or pushing. These bridges are seen particularly clearly in the flight muscle fixed in rigor, and are turned inwards (141). X-ray studies show that the diffraction pattern of rabbit psoas fibers, which is probably a result of the regular array of cross bridges, does change during contraction (142), although repeat periods of major structural elements do not. These results can only be explained by a rotation or pushing action of cross bridges if these develop the force. Other theories depend upon cross-bridge shortening (143), electrostatic forces (144), colloidal system long-range forces (145), and the invocation of a contractile ultrathin filament in parallel with the ordinary ones (146).

SYNAPTIC TRANSMISSION

Detailed studies on the events associated with release of transmitter substance from frog fast junctions (147–149) have led to a 'calcium hypothesis' (150). Spread of the nerve action potential into the terminals is considered to lead to an entry of calcium ions which initiate an electrosecretion process. In addition, they start a process of activation in the terminal which prepares more transmitters for release and this can result in facilitation. In a fast-type junction this occurs within the time of a single action potential. What happens in a slow one showing facilitation is not known, but it is possible to speculate on a possible mechanism of gradually increasing amounts of available transmitter. The comparative study of the processes involved will be bound to be of great interest for comparative neurophysiology for in many systems synaptic facilitation is of vital functional significance.

A feature of the recent comparative literature on transmission has been the growing evidence of the possible direct role of L-glutamic acid as a neuromuscular excitatory transmitter substance, and of γ-aminobutyric acid (GABA) as its inhibitory counterpart. This is now strong for crustaceans

(151–153) and substantial for insects (154, 155). Similar excitatory and inhibitory actions of these substances have also been found in a preparation of the snail pharyngeal retractor (156). A summary has been given by Kerkut (153). Florey (157) has also examined the data, but has not been able to accept a complete identity of the substances with the naturally occurring ones. However, their ability to activate the relevant subsynaptic membranes is no longer in question. Local iontophoretic applications to crayfish muscle (158, 159) give results so closely resembling those to be expected from natural agents that most physiologists are convinced. There are, however, problems in accepting the data unreservedly. If glutamic acid is a transmitter it must be destroyed by glutamic carboxylase—which is present in the tissues —and a product of the reaction is GABA!

Glutamate appears in the perfusate of a cockroach leg following stimulation of the nerve (152) and it leads to increased height of miniature JPs at $10^{-6}M$ as well as a contracture. Usherwood (154) has provided convincing evidence that GABA mimics the inhibitory-conditioning axon transmitter in locusts and that glutamate mimics the excitatory action. At variance is a claim that acetylcholine, long known to be ineffective at insect neuromuscular junctions, can cause depolarization of blowfly flight muscle fibers when injected into the hemolymph (160).

The substance extracted from crayfish muscle by Van der Kloot (161) which enhances contraction in low concentration and is called by him Factor S has still not been fully identified. It has recently been extracted also from cockroach muscle and found to potentiate the contraction of the extensor trochanteris (162). It has some catechol-4 properties, but also is an amine of unknown kind.

Uchizono (163) has claimed that vesicles from inhibitory synapses are ovoid rather than spherical, as are excitatory ones. Some of the evidence regarding this possibility has been positive (164), some negative (165).

Of interest in relation to transmission is the resting membrane and the changes brought about by transmitter action. Increasing evidence points to a wide variety of resting conductance in insect fibers. Although most behave conventionally, as potassium electrodes (2, 8), others do not (166–168) and may be multielectrode systems in which active transport also plays a significant role (167). Inhibitory activity is always associated with an activation of the chloride conductance (10), and excitatory activity with a general conductance increase (10, 11). Electrical activity generated in nonsynaptic membrane varies widely. Some reactions to depolarizing current probably involve specific sodium conductance increase, with a nondelayed potassium conductance increase, as well, which renders the action potential abortive and proportional to the stimulus. Other membranes are impermeant, or relatively so, to sodium, and depolarizing activation is associated with a rise in conductance to divalent ions. Magnesium, which is present in high concentration in the hemolymph of phytophagous insects, probably carries the major part of the current (cf. 159).

All the evidence points to excitation being determined, as in other systems, by conductance increases. For any given membrane response this is easily checked, so the suggestion recently made by Wareham et al. (170) that the excitatory response is due to a conductance *decrease* is irresponsible. They gave no direct evidence for it. The recent knowledge of internal systems of clefts and tubules has revealed the need for extreme caution in time to achieve a new equilibrium when studying the influence of ionic changes in the bathing medium (cf. 171, 172).

In addition to the quick-acting transmitter actions, nerves probably release a number of other substances which influence muscle. When the nerve to the retractor unguis of a locust is cut, there is an extremely quick atrophy of the muscle (173), which must depend upon a trophic agent released from the nerve. Osborne (174) has found a peculiar nerve ending on segmental muscles of blowfly larvae, which occurs in addition to normal neuromuscular junctions. It appears to extrude a vesicular material and could have a trophic function. The direct transport of substances from nerve cells to muscles has been dramatically demonstrated for a snail preparation (175) and for a rabbit preparation (hypoglossal nucleus-nerve-tongue) (176).

SPECIFIC ASPECTS

COELENTERATES

Two important advances have been made in the experimental study of coelenterate nerve-muscle physiology, one methodological, the other an original finding. The former is the development of a simple method for recording electrical activity of the muscle sheets, due to Josephson (177). He has illuminated a mystery over thirty years old that is related to Pantin's classical work on the remarkable facilitation, attributed to the neuromuscular junction, which occurs in the withdrawal response of *Calliactis* (178). The trick was the use of suction electrodes at the surface. By connecting the suction tube to a mechanical recorder the mechanical response may also be recorded. An electrical potential in the muscle was found to precede contraction by 12 msec. There was only a single response to each signal (there might have been a burst) and this showed virtually infinite facilitation from the first to the second (as predicted). The responses clearly resemble arthropod externally recorded JPs, and an arthropod-like facilitating system seems implicated.

The other development is the long-suspected discovery (179) that transmission of nerve-impulse-like activity can occur in nonnervous layers. Both G. H. Parker and Pantin believed that this might exist and referred to it as 'neuroid transmission'. It does take an electrical form, and it propagates along epidermal sheets of the hydromedusa *Sarsia*, passing inwards and exciting the nerve net, which in turn can cause contraction. The nature of the electrical activity remains to be determined.

A preparation of an anthozoan column has been developed and force-velocity curves determined (180). The response characteristics were markedly different, depending on whether the strip was pre- or afterloaded. This could reflect local reflex influences, but similar phenomena do occur in isolated arthropod fibers, for example.

There is little new ultrastructural work, but electron microscopy of subumbrellar surfaces (181, 182) has confirmed the presence of true cross-striated muscle fibers. The sarcomere length is very short (0.8–1.5 μ), but both Z and M bands are evident and there is a well-defined H zone. Filament numbers and arrangements were unfortunately not determined.

PLATYHELMINTHS

The platyhelminths continue to be the most underinvestigated major phylum, but that great sympathizer for the neglected group, Jakes Ewer, has given them some attention. The polyclad *Planocera* has longitudinal muscles consisting of a large number of units which individually do not show facilitation (183). Ewer (184) hypothesizes a similar controlling machinery in the spontaneously acting nerve networks of both platyhelminths and echinoderms.

In *Dugesia* and *Notoplana*, electron microscopy by Macrae (185) revealed 200 Å diam. thick filaments and 50 Å thin filaments. The general arrangement of filaments suggested the oblique striation in annelid, molluscan, and other pseudostriated fibers. This was reinforced by finding dense bodies associated with the sarcolemma, to which thin filaments are attached. The surface membrane touches cysternae of the SR, presumably making the functional equivalent of diads. There is apparently no T or E system. Fibers in the *Dugesia* head are spindle-shaped, with Z columns almost perpendicular to the long axis. Up to twelve thin filaments surround each thick one (186).

NEMATODA

Excellent progress has been made at both the physiological and the ultrastructural level in exploring the extraordinary large muscle fibers of nematodes. The former effort is due to del Castillo and associates (187–189). The cells have a low resting potential (about 30 mV) and spontaneously depolarize rhythmically every 140–650 msec. A slow wave initiates a spike which overshoots by up to 10 mV. Directly excitable electrogenesis is graded. The spontaneous potentials originate at the points of contact of arms from the muscle cells with axons running in the nerve cord. These arms are interconnected to form a functional syncitium. The resting potential at first increases with increasing external K^+ (replacing Na^+ at constant Cl^-), then decreases with a 23 mV/10×K_o slope. Both sodium and chloride conductances at rest are lower, but the resting potential decreases with raised external chloride with a 59 mV for 10×Cl_o^- slope. Substitution of SO_3^{--} for Cl^- leads to a depolarization, while NO_3^- Br^-, or I^- causes hyperpolarization. The action potential has an enormous undershoot, almost as large as the depolarizing phase, so appears diphasic. It may be compared with that obtained in *Tenebrio* larva (190), which it resembles. The undershoot is probably due to a large, late increase in potassium conductance (191). The esophageal cells of *Ascaris* also contract, with radially arranged myofibrils. A 40 mV resting potential is associated with extracellular organic anions, and Cl_0^- causes a depolarization. Action potentials overshooting by 18 mV initiate contraction. The action potential is prolonged, with associated contraction, normally, but if a brief hyperpolarizing pulse is given during the plateau a regenerative, fast, upside-down (hyperpolarizing) action potential, probably due to potassium conductance increase, is produced. This causes a rapid, synchronous relaxation. A cell fully depolarized by Cl^- can still give the large potassium spike.

Rosenbluth (192–194) and Reger (195) have studied the ultrastructure. The fibers *are* striated, though with an oblique orientation of the filaments. Columns of Z material are arranged around a sarcoplasmic core crammed with mitochondria. Thin filaments form orbits of 10–12 around 230 Å thick filaments which have nondense cores in their central regions. Invaginations from the plasma membrane form an E system and contact cysternal elements of SR to form either diads or triads. Contraction occurs by sliding, but there is an additional mechanism of length change, shearing, in which the angle of obliquity decreases and the Z bands become nearly perpendicular to the fiber axis. The extreme obliquity permits, in principle, sarcomeres to act either in series or individually. The sarcomeres are virtually longitudinal in orientation and almost coextensive with the muscle fiber, so a single sacromere can develop tension effectively between widely separated points on the surface. Such an arrangement is efficient for the development of isometric tension, though such efficiency can seldom be of direct value to the worm.

ANNELIDA

Annelids share with platyhelminths the lowest scoring in physiological interest, but they have scored some ultrastructural hits. The uninucleate, axial-cored fibers of the leech, with their radially arranged, flat, ribbonlike divisions of fibrillar material, have been examined electron microscopically by Pucci & Afzelius (196) and Röhlich (197). There is a regular alternation of dense lines, which correspond to lines of Z bodies, with SR tubular elements. Comparable features are apparent in a polychaete fiber examined by Bouligand (198). Large numbers of thin filaments, at least ten per orbit, surround thick filaments which lie in fairly regular hexagonal array, though with wide separation of the thick filaments so that they do not share thin ones. It is difficult to see how, if force must be developed by waggling of bridges, such a structure does not collapse completely upon excitation. The obliquity is marked. Even in heart muscle of annelids (199) this stagger of filaments is to be found. There is, however, an absence of E-system elements continuous with the plasma membrane, but large vesicles of the SR do contact the membrane and are probably equivalent to diads. Since the fibers are not very thick and contraction times are not required to be very brief, diffusion from these peripheral elements is probably adequate.

Rosenbluth (200) studied muscle fibers of the fast polychaete *Glycera* and was particularly interested in comparing them with *Ascaris* fibers. This exercise is of little value, but *Glycera* muscles are of interest for their own sake. They have linear rather than planar Z bands, and these are not of the 'dense body' kind so familiar in invertebrates. Of special interest in view of the growing knowledge that multiple fiber types are widespread, was his demonstration of perhaps the most primitive occurrence of the phenomenon, for he found at least two types in *Glycera* muscle. One, which formed the majority, with thick filaments about 3 μ long, had a well-developed SR. A second set had longer and thicker thick filaments and contained conspicuously less SR.

ECHIUROIDEA

The burrowing echiuroid worm *Urechis* has been studied by Lawry (201) from a functional point of view. An outcome of interest to comparative physiologists was his proof that the so-called neural canal is, in fact, a giant axon mediating the startle response.

ECHINODERMATA

That extraordinary product of the fortunes of evolution known as Aristotle's lantern, which Barbellian poetically referred to: "after aeons of evolution it never smells musty of age," has at last received the attention it deserved (202, 203) and further work should follow. The muscle cells are unfortunately tiny (8–12 μ diam.), but up to 2 cm long, and should not be beyond the limits for microelectrode recording. Neuromuscular junctions on the uninucleate cells are very simple (203). Cobb (204) has also studied the innervation of the *Astropecten* tube foot and shown that the neuromuscular relations bear an extraordinary resemblance to those of nematodes. A fine, conductile muscle process extends down from the ampulla, in which the muscle fiber is located, towards the radial nerve. There it forms a proximal neuromuscular synapse. Although primarily concerned with conduction, the process does contain a small core of fibrils, demonstrating its muscular identity.

A study of the lantern retractor muscle of *Parechinus* by Boltt & Ewer (205) provided further evidence for its cholinergicity (and connection to the chordate stem?). A useful review of the scant data by Takahashi (206) also contains original work which throws doubt on the identity of von Uexküll's well-known *Spermuskulatur* of the sea urchin spine, that is, the inner layer of muscle. Undoubtedly, the outer ring is muscular and the inner layer can dramatically change in stiffness. It is even caused to shorten by epinephrine, and a wash suffices to counter this action and produce lengthening. But the fine structure of the layer in no way resembles muscle. Thus we have here a material that is certainly functional and probably under nervous control, which has some of the properties of muscle but is not muscle in the ordinary sense. Further studies will be awaited with interest. The outer material contains dense bodies, indicating Z material, and thick and thin filaments in the outer ring of muscle (207).

In the wall of the foot, protoplasmic connections between muscle cells have been found (208). A study has been made of the calcareous beamlets of *Asterias*, to which smooth fibers containing only thin filaments are attached (209).

MOLLUSCA

Without doubt one of the more outstanding personal achievements, rewarding more than ten years of often frustrated effort, was the penetration by Dr. Betty Twarog (210, 211) of single muscle fibers in the *Mytilus* anterior byssal retractor muscle (ABRM). These 8 μ fibers, embedded in tough connective tissue, have resisted many attempts. Now we know that they have a surprisingly high resting potential (55–72 mV, av 65 mV) and that they are electrically excitable. Junctional potentials are up to 22 mV, with a remarkably slow rate of decay ($\frac{1}{2}$ time of about $\frac{1}{2}$ sec). The action potentials do not overshoot the zero, but may almost do so, having maximum heights of 50 mV fired from a membrane potential of 35–40 mV.

Contractions were elicited in a number of ways, but of greatest interest was her finding that in those evoked by neural stimulation, JPs alone did not give rise to tension. This surprising observation places molluscan muscle in sharp contrast to arthropod muscle in this respect, but allies it with some vertebrate fibers. The threshold for *e–c* coupling coincided, approximately, with the spike generation threshold, so tension was associated with spikes. One drug which blocks cholinergic synapses, methantheline, reduced and prevented JP formation. However, the evidence does not definitely support the already well-established cholinergicity of the ABRM because the drug could have been acting presynaptically. There is also the grave danger in analyses based on sampling electrical activity in only a few—or even many—fibers, while studying tension in the whole muscle, of being seriously misled owing to inhomogeneity of the fiber population. This type of analysis has already been shown to lead to pitfalls in crustacean muscle (18).

The normal and also catch contractions can be elicited by acetycholine and this response was studied in relation to the innervation. The amount of normal tension was not affected by severing the connective to the ganglion, but catch tension was greatly influenced. Slight and hard to elicit in the presence of the ganglion, it became progressively greater and more certainly elicited as the connection was progressively severed (212). Raising the temperature in the preparation connected to the ganglion also reduced catch until it was missing at 30° C. The catch prevention or reduction is apparently due to release of an agent from relaxing nerves which permeates the fibers and acts directly. The range over which 5-HT quantitatively reduced catch tension elicited by acetylcholine was $10^{-8} - 10^{-6} M$.

Twarog also studied the length-tension curve of ganglion-free muscle bundles and the relation of catch tension to ordinary tension. The two are simply proportionally related. External calcium exerted no selective action on the catch, affecting normal tension and catch tension to equal extents. Agents which reduce catch tension at the same time increase excitability, leading to repetitive spike responses. This is presumably due to a reduced free intracellular calcium and suggests that as in barnacle fibers, the action potential is mediated by calcium conductance increase.

Thus catch may be due to a persistence of free calcium, as Twarog (213, 214), and also Leenders (215), have suggested. These results lend weight to the hypothesis that contraction in catch muscles is by a normal actin-myosin-tropomyosin interaction (216) and that a slow rate of breakage of crosslinks accounts for catch tone. But catch is not equivalent to active state, and the presence of calcium in other muscles would be associated with the capacity to shorten. The hypothesis also leaves unresolved the role of paramyosin whose presence in large quantities is a characteristic of the muscles. Millman (217) has considered the load borne by the very long (30 μ) thick (600 Å) filaments of the ABRM. The force must be much greater at the center than is the case in vertebrate filaments. The paramyosin could perhaps be a structural prop helping to bear the load. Elliot (218) examined the opaque adductor muscle of the oyster electron microscopically and found paramyosin in the form of stacks of longitudinal lamellae.

Chemical studies on catch have been hampered after glycerination because they cannot be made to show the phenomenon. The opaque part of the oyster adductor has been shown to possess catch features similar to those of the ABRM (219). Normal actin and myosin periodicities can be seen in X-ray diffraction images of the ABRM, permitting a study of the changes associated with contraction. The periodicities do not change (220), which shows that contraction is by a relative sliding.

A welcome study on the ABRM from a famous biochemical laboratory (221) showed that when ABRM suddenly relaxes from the catch state, phosphate, arginine, and calcium are all released. This finding is consistent with the possibility of a special set of myosin-actin-tropomyosin (and/or paramyosin) links associated with catch. These authors suggest the possibility of a direct complexing of calcium with 5-HT. In contrast to the theory that a normal actomyosin system is involved in the catch was the demonstration that catch can be obtained in preparations poisoned by thiourea [Rüegg (222)]. The latter substance prevents actomyosin ATPase from splitting ATP and inhibits contraction of actomyosin. After it has been added to the ABRM it also prevents acetylcholine-evoked, and other contractions. These treatments do not give contractions in normal muscle treated by thiourea, which simply prevents relaxation (223). The unfortunate conclusion from the above is that in spite of continued high-level attention and significant new findings, we are still far from having a satisfactory picture of the catch mechanism.

There has been a smattering of new contributions concerned with molluscan preparations other than the ABRM. The radula protractor of *Busycon* yields a preparation permitting studies of length-tension relations (224). Stretch from 30 to 60 mm leads to a marked rise in tetanus, but not twitch, tension; passive tension only increases markedly at great extents of stretch. The radula muscle of *Buccinum* has been further examined by Mattisson & Arvidsson (225). They found relaxation by succinate and contraction by glutamate, and compared the ultrastructure in the relaxed state and after continuous stimulation for 4–12 hr. Stimulated muscles were found to be more regular in organization, with filaments more parallel and Z regions more in line. Other investigators (not published) are known to have found that thin filaments are not in orbit around thick ones in the relaxed muscle, but must move into orbits upon stimulation.

An old molluscan preparation, the snail retractor pharynx, has been reinvestigated by Ozeki (226). The response to a single shock, whether directly or indirectly stimulated, is always small. The response to the second of a pair of similar shocks is, by contrast, always very large, and the difference could not be attributed entirely to neuromuscular facilitation. This phenomenon is being studied more directly in arthropod fibers, where it can also occur and is attributable to a summation of released calcium, the first 'package' being too small to activate much of the actomyosin. Ozeki (227) also studied the effects of calcium and sodium ions on potassium contractures in the preparation; it gives a maximum tension at 13.1 mM Ca^{++}, equal to 2.5 kg/cm², and thereafter declines with further increases in calcium.

The very interesting muscles operating the squid chromatophore have been studied by Kinosita (228) and found to be spirally striated. A nice preparation of the *Loligo* chromatophore has been developed by Florey (228a), in which the nerve was stimulated via a suction electrode and the resulting chromatophore response recorded by an optical method. Membrane responses were recorded from individual muscle fibers, which form a ring round the pigment cell, with intracellular electrodes. A single stimulus gives a junction potential and a twitch. A stepwise expansion of dorsal skin chromatophores occurs through successive tetanic contractions in an increasing number of fibers, in the intact animal. Spontaneous contractions preceded by generator potentials leading to spikes occur especially in aging preparations; they spread among the other fibers, so that contraction is synchronous. Contraction is evoked by acetylcholine and antagonized by 5-HT. An excellent study of the ultrastructure of the organ, muscles, and neuromuscular junctions has been presented by Cloney & Florey (228b). Adjacent muscle fibers may be coupled through close junctions. The first electron micrographs of neuromuscular junctions—of cephalopod and snail—have been published (229, 230). The junctions on snail muscle consist of simple bands filled with characteristic vesicles and a close apposition of the smooth surface membranes of nerve and muscle. More complex claws, some of which receive branches of two nerve fibers, occur in the *Octopus* sucker.

CRUSTACEA

The ease of separation of single axons, coupled with the large size of many of the muscle fibers, including some up to 5 mm diam. (more than 20× larger than any others), and with universal availability, has maintained the position of crustaceans as the group receiving most attention outside the vertebrates. Insects run them a close second, but there is still an interesting reversal of attention compared with other aspects of physiology, in which the insect literature greatly exceeds that on crustacea. Convenience of experimental manipulation thus overrides other aspects and there is a complete merging with 'general' physiology.

Continuing a trend which was just apparent at the time of the earlier review (1), great emphasis has been placed upon differences between fibers, which came as something of a surprise to physiologists. From several laboratories (Grundfest, Zachar, Hoyle, Atwood) papers are coming, in which not only physiological, but also correlated ultrastructural data are being obtained from single muscle fibers. Differences between muscles which are very fast acting and entirely phasic and others which are entirely tonic are no greater then differences between fibers in one muscle, but marked nonetheless. Dorai-Raj (17) showed that the thin, fan-shaped distal head of the *Cancer* accessory flexor is composed of three distinct groups of fibers, each with distinctive histology, synaptic physiology, and membrane excitability, in spite of the fact that they share a common axon. One margin contains only 'fast' fibers with phasic responses, short SL, and large active response. The other margin contains only 'slow' fibers which are electrically inexcitable, have long sarcomeres, are slow to contract and relax, and can sustain prolonged contractions. The middle group has properties intermediate between the extremes, but is not homogeneous. Starting in 1962 our laboratory made a fiber-by-fiber analysis of crab muscles with a triple innervation. These studies again revealed histologically and physiologically different fibers. Fibers are more-or-less randomly mixed in the extensor, but are grouped in others; for instance slow fibers usually occur in a proximal bundle [Atwood (6)]. Slow and fast fibers of the abdominal flexor of crayfish are grouped into separately innervated, discrete muscles: a deep, thick set comprising entirely fast fibers which cannot sustain a long contraction, and a thin superficial layer of slow fibers (13, 14). Both gross innervation of the muscle and that of individual fibers are more complex than in leg muscles. Ten large motor axons supply the phasic muscle and six the tonic one. The former are relatively conventional in supply, each receiving a single fast axon, one of several slow ones and the common inhibitor. The inhibitor has but a small effect on the excitatory responses of the other fibers. The ultimate complexity seen in a slow fiber was as many as five tension steps per fiber. The antagonist muscle has a complex fiber population (15). Medial fibers are fast, with 30–50 msec twitches reaching half-peak tetanic force, a spike (possibly Ca^{++}-mediated), and short SL (only $2\,\mu$). Lateral fibers, though still of relatively short SL (some crab fibers have 15 μ long sarcomers) at 4.5 μ, behave quite differently. They may give no depolarizing responses and they contract slowly, maintaining the contraction for long periods.

Differences in fiber properties within one muscle probably account for the earlier mystery known as the 'paradox'. An intensive search of muscles showing the phenomenon by Atwood & Hoyle (18) eventually revealed a small cluster of slow fibers deep within the muscle, which gave large JPs to single impulses. These fibers give tension at low frequencies of stimulation while contributing little to the externally recorded action potentials.

There are now known exceptions to every earlier generalization. Fast phasic fibers were considered either not to receive an inhibitory innervation or not to be prevented from responding mechanically in a near-maximal way. But fast fibers of *Pachygrapsus* claw closer and of *Procambarus* deep abdominal flexors are greatly attenuated by inhibition (231).

Unfortunately, the extraordinary subtlety and complexity of such muscles, unsuspected until recently, renders inevitable the tedious, fiber-by-fiber analysis of any muscle which is to be fully understood. It has now become ridiculous to refer to "the crab muscle fiber" in a general way. The differences run the whole gamut of specialized knowledge, gross innervation, ultrastructural, biochemical, biophysical, and pharmacological. On the basis of membrane excitability in relation to contractile response, Atwood et al. (16) recognized seven different kinds of fiber in the adductor of the dactyl of *C. magister*, but there was a continuum rather than discrete categories. In the carpopodite extensor of *Ocypode ceratophthalma*, SLs of 2.4, 5, 6.7, and 10 μ were found (4) and twitch times were logarithmically related to these, a range of speeds which is over a hundredfold. A comparison of relaxation times for fibers having different times of relaxation drawn from different muscles of different species (i.e. not single fibers) showed 30 msec for the (av. 2.3 μ) crayfish deep abdominal extensor, 40 msec for the (av. 4.5 μ) *Carcinus* extensor, 2000 for the (av. 9 μ) crayfish contractor epimeralis, 2000–5000 for the (10–12 μ) crab accessory flexor and 6000–10,000 for the 8–14 μ superficial abdominal extensor of crayfish. These are necessarily crude comparisons, being made on whole muscles and even comparing fresh with saltwater forms, but they show the same relationship ($t = k\log$ SL).

A valuable comparative study of the zinc concentrations of fast and slow muscles, which presumably means a dominant proportion of fast to slow fibers, was made for six lobster muscles. A generalization was made regarding average sarcomere width, which is certainly correlated with speed. The results (232) showed a five times greater zinc content in the slower muscles. Lactic and glutamic dehydrogenase, as well as carbonic anhydrase, are zinc metalloenzymes.

We may ask to what extent differences in fiber structure and properties are genetically determined directly and to what extent they are related to innervation, functional activities, and needs? Denervation and cross-innervation experiments might help to solve these questions, but it seems that many crustacean motor nerves do not degenerate following section, so this may not be a valid method. There is, however, a notable correlation between the fiber properties and the neuromuscular properties in some muscles. Atwood (233) has produced a very interesting generalization based on his studies on crab muscles. If there is a basic triple innervation (fast, slow, and inhibitor), there is a continuum from fibers having a dense fast-axon innervation, to fibers having almost none. The slow-axon innervation is the converse, being least in those with the densest fast and vice versa. Inhibitory innervation parallels slow axon innervation, except to fibers with a dense fast-axon supply, in which it is suppressed. Muscle fiber type is associated with the innervation so that fast muscle fibers—associated with large electrogenesis, short striations, well-developed SR, etc., are those with the least slow-axon innervation, and slow fibers, with weak electrogenesis, wide striations, less well-developed SR, etc., are the converse. While this scheme is adequate to explain the apparently random distribution of fiber types occurring in some *Cancer* muscles, exceptions with grouped fibers are also common. In both crustaceans and insect the shortest fibers in a given muscle tend also to be the slowest. They have the longest sarcomeres, and so undergo the greatest per cent length change per sarcomere.

An important addition to the technical repertoire was that of focal extracellular recording which permits examining the local current flow (234); this has been used to study synaptic facilitation (235). There are wide differences in the extents of facilitation at different synapses (from zero to infinity) even for different junctions of the same muscle, and these differences had no explanation. The focal currents were small at facilitating synapses and local failures frequent. By contrast, currents were great at nonfacilitating sites and there were no failures.

Those fibers which receive no inhibitory innervation are often fast, and they are insensitive to γ-aminobutyric acid, which mimics the action of the inhibitory transmitter substance.

A mystery of long standing has been the time constant of decay of the slow-EPSP, which, in some fibers, can be markedly different from that of the fast axon innervating the same fiber, even when the heights of the two appear identical. Falk & Fatt (40) have proposed by way of explanation that the time courses of transmitter release and action may differ. Considering the combined membrane capacitance (C_m) and that of the E system (C_e), if transmitter action is very brief there will be insufficient time for the voltage across C_e to develop to the same level as across C_m. There will then be an early rapid component of potential drop across the effective resistance of the E tubules (R_e). An actual model was built, and proved to work as predicted. However, the situation may, in part, arise from different locations of the nerve terminals, which may lie deep within clefts of these fibers.

Several studies have been carried out on isolated single crayfish fibers, and none of the authors has suggested that there is a mixture of slow and fast fibers in them. Twenty-four fibers studied by Henček & Zachar (237) had a radius in the range 96–299 μ; $R_i = 203 \pm 43$ cm; $R_m = 9.86r$; $\lambda = 0.0156r$ mm; $R_0 = 50.39 \times 10^5 r$ (Ω); $r_i = 6.46 \times 10^8/r^2$ (Ω/mm); $C_m = 22.9 \pm 6.6$ μ F/cm^2. The resting potential was 77 mV in van Harreveld's crayfish solution containing 5.4 mM KCl and it behaved as a potassium electrode. There is, however, a high Cl$^-$ conductance, for a sudden change in Cl$_0$ caused a transient decrease in potential. Probably both K$^+$ and Cl$^-$ contribute about equally to the total conductance (238). Potassium content, determined by neutron activation analysis, was 167 ± 20 mM/kg fiber water (239). Tension develops at about the same membrane potential (-50 mV) at which graded electrogenesis starts (240). Even supramaximal stimuli did not push the tetanus: twitch ratio beyond 4.5:1.

It has long been known that crayfish give different physiological responses at different times of year. One cause of the variations has become clear with studies on the protein, Na, K, Ca, Mg, Cl, PO$_4$, Cu, lactate, sugar, and blood cell content over a fourteen-month period (241). There is a rise of at least 10 per cent in all these in winter, with a sharp decline in the spring which reverses before the June/July molt and then declines 30 per cent at molt.

ARACHNIDA

A welcome addition to the extremely scanty literature on arachnid muscles is the publication by Rathmeyer (242) of a paper on neuromuscular transmission in a tarantulid spider *Europelma hentzi*, and more papers are to follow, including electron microscopy of the muscles. He gives the composition of an artificial saline and describes results of intracellular stimulation and recording, for the flexor metatarsi (there is no extensor). The fibers have potassium electrode properties and each receives branches from three motor axons, leading to three sizes of JP, all small (2–3 mV), which both facilitate and summate. When the JPs reach about 30 mV depolarization, graded responses occur. Occasionally a large, overshooting response arises. One axon gives large facilitation and fast contraction, while another also gives a large facilitation but a slow contraction. The third axon gives little facilitation but a fast contraction. These findings suggest that further work will reveal an irregular distribution of nerve fibers, and an inhomogeneous population of muscle fibers.

Three excitatory axons have also been claimed for *Limulus* (there may be still more) and the possibility raised that *Limulus* leg muscles may receive an inhibitory axon (4).

INSECTA

Pringle (244) has extensively reviewed insect flight muscle, and not only have several recent reviews been specially devoted to skeletal muscles of insects [Hoyle (2), Aidley (245), Usherwood (7)], but Peachey (12) had a section on them in his general review. They have therefore been largely omitted from consideration here, but there is one recent finding of significance, namely that of Bergman & Pearson (246) who have discovered a common inhibitor axon in the cockroach. While examining the metathoracic anterior coxal levator (182C & 182D of Carbonell), they found hyperpolarizing potentials of up to -10 mV in 50 per cent of the fibers of 182C and in 80 per cent of 182D. These could be evoked by stimulating nerve trunk 4r2 (of Pipa & Cook) and the impulses followed in 6Br4, which supplies the muscle. A marked fall in tension occurred. As many as 3 EJP sizes occurred, proportional to the size of nerve impulses extracellularly recorded. If these are not due to two excitatory axons separately plus the two firing together, that would be the first example of an insect muscle fiber receiving more than two excitatory axons. The important observation was that as the inhibitory axon fired, correlated impulses occurred at the same time, in all the major ipsilateral nerve trunks except trunk 2. This would bring the sternal and tergal remotors (172 & 174) and the coxal depressor (177E) into a state of synchronous inhibition with the coxal levator. This is proof that the axon is a common inhibitor, the first to be discovered in an insect. The functional role of common inhibitors in crustacea is still not understood, the most likely theory being that they accelerate relaxation. A similar function may be expected in the cockroach.

CHORDATA

Regrettably, very little attention has been paid to the evolutionally significant protochordates. A good deal of new interest has been shown in various fish muscles, especially on the most primitive type, the hagfish *Myxine* (247). A comparison of the elasmobranch dogfish *Scyliorhinus* with a teleost, *Torpedo*, has been presented (248) and a valuable general review of innervation prepared by Barker (249). A large number of detailed histochemical studies have appeared, especially of mammalian muscle, but few achieve the desirable objective of coordinated physiological, histological, and electron microscopic studies on the same muscle. An exception is the useful study by Lännergren & Smith (250) on toad muscle. Resting and action potentials of fast twitch fibers of elasmobranch fish with teleosts have been compared (251). The resting potential of the teleost is determined by the potassium conductance, but that of elasmobranchs appears, surprisingly, to be dominated by the chloride ion conductance. The action potentials of both are due to sodium conductance increase and are blocked by tetrodotoxin, but although that of the elasmobranchs overshoots, that of the teleosts examined did not.

One outstanding general feature of the results is that vertebrate, like invertebrate, muscles contain several different kinds of fiber. No satisfactory system of classification seems possible, or even worth attempting, except where fibers are obviously either 'slow' or 'fast'.

In *Myxine* (252, 253), slow fibers have a low resting potential (46 ± 0.5 mV) and a twitch time exceeding 500 msec while 'fast' fibers have a more normal resting potential (74.6 ± 0.3 mV) and a twitch time of only 150 msec.

Focal EPSPs occur in the latter, giving rise to propagated action potentials, while in 'slow' fiber there are distributed JPs and graded responses. The slow fibers have a very high specific resistance, probably associated with relatively low potassium ion conductance, but a high sodium conductance, which would explain the low resting potential. A similar pattern may be widespread in fish. Fast fibers are white, at least in white fish; slow fibers are dark. The color seems to be mainly associated with a greater density of mitochondria which are grey-pink, but the blood supply is also richer to slow fibers. Electron microscope studies of the two kinds of fiber have been made by Nishihara (254).

Pennycuick [quoted by Bone (255)] found that when the fish is swimming there is no electrical activity in its white fibers although these form the bulk of the muscle. This seems to be the case also for salmon and for tuna [Rayner & Keenan (256)]. Lännergren & Smith (257) found three types of fiber in toad muscle, recognizing an intermediate between slow and fast. The latter are larger (100–150 μ), with moderate lipid and enzyme (succinic dehydrogenase and DON-diaphorase) content. Endplates on these fibers are essentially *en plaque* and have a high cholinesterase activity. In location they surround smaller fibers which in turn form two groups. The smaller were 35–70 μ, clear, lacking lipid, and low in enzyme content. They contracted slowly. The second type of small fiber, perhaps with a further subdivision 40–70 and 55–110 μ, was more typical of slow fibers, having a high lipid and enzyme content and being slow to fatigue. Nerve endings on these fibers were *en grappe*.

The mechanical responses to depolarization by K^+ and acetylcholine were examined in single-fiber preparations of the slow *Xenopus* fibers. Surprisingly, the curve relating tension to membrane potential is extremely steep, and possibly not S-shaped. It is not yet possible to correlate this finding with ultrastructural features, but it suggests that the calcium release sites must be activated simultaneously, rather than successively (as the depolarization spreads inwards) as in fast fibers.

A large comparative study on muscle fibers of birds, with a strong histochemical emphasis, has been published in monographic form (259); it demonstrates the presence of functionally related fiber types in different bird muscles, classified on the basis of carbohydrate (fast) and lipid (slow) content and related enzymes. Fibers of the chicken anterior lattissimus dorsi, which is 7 × slower at 20° C than the posterior partner, differed only in the density of the E system, that of the slow fibers being less well developed, with fewer contacts, largely at the I-band level, and many tubules running longitudinally (260).

Differentiation of fiber types must be of primitive origin in both invertebrates and vertebrates. Already in *Amphioxus* three kinds of muscle lamellae can be distinguished (261). One kind have narrow, irregularly shaped fibrils, numerous mitochondria, and glycogen granules. At the other extreme are wide lamellae with few mitochondria and little glycogen. Others have intermediate characteristics. It is immediately clear from comparative relationships that the former are probably physiologically slow and the latter fast. Bear in mind that among vertebrates the speed differences are not associated with sarcomere spacing or myofilament ratio differences, but with SR development and different enzyme activities. However, the speed range is very small compared with enormous ranges in invertebrate muscle.

Mammals remain the group in which a diversity of fiber types remains least generally accepted—except among histochemists. The eye muscles have been most intensively studied, not without rather violent controversy. Rhesus monkey extrinsic eye muscles have been convincingly shown to have a highly complex fiber substructure (262) equaling that of crab muscles. Two distinct groups of fiber occur, which are clearly characteristic of fast and slow as discussed above. But there are also many intermediates, so that although slow movements are probably produced by one set and fast ones by another, either extreme may be backed up by an intermediate. Hess (263) has maintained on the basis of ultrastructural studies on cat eye muscle fibers and their innervation that there are slow and fast components, and Pilar (264) obtained physiological evidence for an inner layer of fast fibers surrounded by an outer layer of slow ones, but while Bach-y-Rita & Ito (265) agree that there are two kinds of fiber, they believe that all are excited by propagated action potentials, whereas Hess & Pilar (263) claimed JP activation of a majority of the slow fibers. The matter has been discussed by Peachey (12), who pointed out that the conditions were more normal in the Hess & Pilar experiments; but when equivalent conditions were obtained in more recent experiments by Pilar (264), he was still able to obtain convincing evidence for independently innervated slow fibers giving only JPs in cat superior oblique eye muscles.

There is nothing sacred, however, as some writers imply, about propagated action potentials. It should not come as a surprise to find a multiterminally innervated fiber having slow contraction characteristics and activated by JPs, in any muscle of any animal. The conversion of a nonpropagating to a propagating membrane is likewise readily achieved ionically by small shifts in ionic content of extracellular composition alone. There may be fibers which change during the course of a day, perhaps in synchrony with feeding and other activity cycles.

The partial interconvertibility of mammalian fast and slow fiber characteristics has been further established by several investigators. Dubowitz (266) cross-innervated slow soleus and fast flexor hallucis longus of newborn kittens and rabbits and adult cats and found a dramatic series of changes in the histochemical patterns, though somewhat surprisingly the ATPases were not affected. The histological conversion of fast to slow type is complete, but the converse is only partial.

Histochemists generally recognize three fiber types, categorized as A, B, C, but a continuum is more probable. Romanul (267) and independently Yellin (268) detected as many as eight different kinds in rat calf muscle, gastrocnemius, plantaris, and soleus. The three major distinct kinds, probably corresponding to slow, fast, and intermediate, may be associated with distinct motor units at least in the flexor digitorum of the cat (269) and hindlimb muscles of the toad *Xenopus laevis* (270). It thus becomes possible to envisage special motor pathways for quick contractions, others for long-maintained ones, even though a common set of muscles is utilized, by selective innervation of groups of fibers having different contractile characteristics. This trend is seen also in invertebrate fibers as has been noted above. Thus, a high mitochondrial and enzyme content is characteristic of slow muscle fibers which are more-or-less continually active in postural and slow locomotory activity. But it reappears as a phenomenon in some phasic muscles which are specialized to produce the fastest possible speed. This is accomplished at the expense of space, so force is presumably reduced. An extreme example has been found in the stapedius, which has very few myofilament clusters but abundant mitochondria (271). The muscle contracts frequently, and rapidly, but is not required to develop much force.

Mouse gastrocnemius and soleus both contain at least two types of fiber (272). Thicker (fast) fibers contain few mitochondria and no fat and are the predominant ones of the gastrocnemius. Thinner fibers (slow) with many mitochondria and a high triglyceride content predominate in the soleus. Rat diaphragm also contains slow and fast fibers (273). Speed of contraction of rabbit laryngeal muscles is proportional to succinate dehydrogenase activity (274).

It should be expected that slow red fibers, with their high mitochondrial and enzyme content, should contain more zinc than fast white fibers, since zinc is likely to be associated with these enzymes. Pig muscles of the predominant color types were examined 47 days after intracutaneous injection of ^{65}Zn (275) and a 3–4 × greater concentration of the isotope found in the red fibers.

Some strange but interesting "myoid" cells in the thymus gland of reptiles and birds have been examined electron microscopically (276). They are striated, but with weakly defined Z regions; some consisted mainly of thin filaments, while some had only thin filaments.

CONCLUSIONS

We have witnessed an astonishing acceleration of interest in all aspects of muscle in the last two years, especially in the comparative field. The latter has revitalized the core, which had become stilted in its persistent following of a rather narrow track. It is clear that we can now look forward to a period of greatly increased understanding of the nature of muscle, its function, and its evolution.

BIBLIOGRAPHY

1. Hoyle, G. Neuromuscular physiology. *Advan. Comp. Physiol. Biochem.*, 1, 177–216 (1962)
2. Hoyle, G. Muscle and neuromuscular physiology. *The Physiology of Mollusca*, 2, 313–51 (Wilbur, K., Youge, C. M., Eds., Academic Press, New York, 392 pp., 1964)
3. Hoyle, G. Neural control of skeletal muscle. In *The Physiology of Insecta*, 2, 407–49 and 859–61 (Rockstein, M., Ed., Academic Press, New York, 905 pp., 1965)
4. Hoyle, G. Specificity of muscle. In *Invertebrate Nervous Systems*, 151–67 (Wiersma, C. A. G., Ed., Chicago Univ. Press, Chicago, 1967)
5. Hoyle, G. Diversity of striated muscle. *Am. Zool.*, 7, 435–49 (1967)
6. Atwood, H. L. Crustacean neuromuscular mechanisms. *Am. Zool.*, 7, 527–51 (1967a)
7. Usherwood, P. N. R. Insect neuromuscular mechanisms. *Am. Zool.*, 7, 553–82 (1967)
8. Grundfest, H. Comparative electrobiology of excitable membranes. *Advan. Comp. Physiol. Biochem.*, 2, 1–116 (1966)
9. Grundfest, H. Some comparative aspects of membrane permeability control. *Fed. Proc.*, 26, 1613–26 (1967)
10. *Symposium on Muscle* (Ernst, E., Straub, F. B., Eds., Akad. Kiadó, Budapest, 259 pp., 1968)
10a. *The contractile process. J. Gen. Physiol.*, 50, No. 6, Part 2, 292 pp.
11. Huxley, A. F. Muscle structure and theories of contraction. *Progr. Biophys.*, 7, 257–318 (1957)
12. Peachey, L. D., Muscle. *Ann. Rev. Physiol.*, 30, 401–40 (1968)
13. Kennedy, D., Takeda, K. Reflex control of abdominal flexor muscles in the crayfish. II. The tonic system. *J. Exptl. Biol.*, 43, 229–46 (1965)
14. Kennedy, D., Takeda, K. Reflex control of abdominal flexor muscles in the crayfish. I. The twitch system. *Ibid.*, 211–27
15. Parnas, I., Atwood, H. L. Phasic and tonic neuromuscular systems in the abdominal extensor muscles of the crayfish and rock lobster. *Comp. Biochem. Physiol.*, 18, 701–23 (1966)
16. Atwood, H. L., Hoyle, G., Smyth, T., Jr. Mechanical and electrical responses of single innervated crab-muscle fibres. *J. Physiol.*, 180, 449–82 (1965)
17. Dorai-Raj, B. S. Diversity of crab muscle fibres innervated by a single motor axon. *J. Cellular Comp. Physiol.*, 64, 41–54 (1964)
18. Atwood, H. L., Hoyle, G. A further study of the paradox phenomenon of crustacean muscle. *J. Physiol.*, 181, 225–34 (1965)
19. Hoyle, G. Correlated physiological and ultrastructural studies on specialized muscles. 2a. Neuromuscular physiology of the anterior rotator of the paddle of *Portunus sanguinolentus* (In preparation)
20. Hoyle, G. Correlated physiological and ultrastructural studies on specialized muscle fibers. 1a. Neuromuscular physiology of the levator of the eyestalk of *Podophthalmus vigil* (Weber). *J. Exptl. Zool.*, 167, 471–86 (1968)
21. Hoyle, G., McNeill, P. A. Correlated physiological and ultrastructural studies on specialized muscle fibers. 1b. Ultrastructure of the levator of the eyestalk of *Podophthalmus vigil* (Weber). *J. Exptl. Zool.*, 167, 487–522 (1968)
22. Hoyle, G. Resting tension and break contraction in crustacean muscle fibers. *J. Exptl. Zool.*, 167, 551–66 (1968)
23. Smit, W. A., Becht, G., Beenakkers, A. M. T. Structure, fatigue, and enzyme activities in 'fast' insect muscles. *J. Insect Physiol.*, 13, 1857–68 (1967)
24. Biscoe, T. J., Taylor, A. The effect of admixture of fast and slow muscle in determining the form of the muscle twitch. *Med. Biol. Eng.*, 5, 437–79 (1967)
25. Caldwell, P. C., Walster, G. Studies on the micro-injection of various substances into crab muscle fibers. *J. Physiol.*, 169, 353–72 (1963)
26. Hagiwara, S., Naka, K. The initiation of spike portntial in barnacle muscle fibers under low intracellular Ca^{++}. *J. Gen. Physiol.*, 48, 141–62 (1964)
26a. Hagiwara, S., Takahashi, K., Junge, D. Excitation-contraction coupling in a barnacle muscle fiber as examined with voltage clamp tech-

nique. *J. Gen. Physiol.*, **51**, 157–76 (1968)

27. Selverston, A. Structure and function of the transverse tubular system in crustacean muscle fibers. *Am. Zool.*, **7**, 515–25 (1967)

28. Selverston, A. *Structure and function of the tubular system in crustacean muscle fibers* (Ph.D. thesis, Univ. Oregon, Eugene, 1967)

29. Hoyle, G. (Unpublished data)

30. DeBell, J. T., Castillo, J. del, Sanchez, V. Electrophysiology of the somatic muscle cells of *Ascaris lumbricoides*. *J. Cellular Comp. Physiol.*, **62**, 159–78 (1963)

31. Castillo, J. del, Mello, W. C. de, Morales, T. The initiation of action potentials in the somatic musculature of *Ascaris lumbricoides*. *J. Exptl. Biol.*, **46**, 263–79 (1967)

32. Flood, P. R. A peculiar mode of innervation in *Amphioxus*. Light and electron microscopic study of the so-called ventral roots. *J. Comp. Neurol.*, **126**, 181–217 (1966)

33. Fahrenbach, W. H. The fine structure of fast and slow crustacean muscles. *J. Cell Biol.*, **35**, 69–79 (1967)

34. Cohen, M. J., Hess, A. Fine structural differences in "fast" and "slow" muscle fibers of the crab. *Am. J. Anat.*, **121**, 285–304 (1967)

35. Fahrenbach, W. H. A new configuration of the sarcoplasmic reticulum. *J. Cell Biol.*, **22**, 477–81 (1964)

36. Hoyle, G. Nature of the excitatory sarcoplasmic reticular junction. *Science*, **149**, 70–72 (1965)

37. Franzini-Armstrong, C., Porter, K. R. Sarcolemmal invaginations constituting the T system in fish muscle fibers. *J. Cell Biol.*, **22**, 675–96 (1964)

38. Hoyle, G., McNeill, P. A., Walcott, B. Nature of invaginating tubules in *Felderstruktur* muscle fibers of the garter snake. *J. Cell Biol.*, **30**, 197–201 (1966)

39. Hess, A. The sarcoplasmic reticulum, the T system, and the motor terminals of slow and twitch muscle fibers in the garter snake. *J. Cell Biol.*, **26**, 467–76 (1965)

40. Falk, G., Fatt, P. Electrical impedance of striated muscle and its relation to contraction. In *Studies in Physiology*, 64–70 (Springer-Verlag, Berlin, 1965)

41. Eisenberg, R. S. The equivalent circuit of single crab muscle fibers as determined by impedance measurements with intracellular electrodes. *J. Gen. Physiol.*, **50**, 1785–1806 (1967)

42. Peachey, L. D. Transverse tubules in excitation-contraction coupling. *Fed. Proc.*, **24**, 1124–34 (1965)

43. Steinbach, A. B. Unusual endplate potentials which reflect the complexity of muscle structure. *Nature*, **216**, 1331–33 (1967)

44. Peachey, L. D., Schild, R. F. The distribution of the T system along the sarcomeres of frog and toad sartorius muscles. *J. Physiol.*, **194**, 249–58 (1968)

45. Knappeis, G. G., Carlsen, F. The ultrastructure of the Z disc in skeletal muscle. *J. Cell Biol.*, **13**, 323–35 (1962)

46. Reedy, M. K. See discussion pp. 458–60, *Proc. Roy. Soc. B*, **160** (1964)

47. Franzini-Amstrong, C., Porter, K. R. The Z disc of striated muslce fibrils. *Z. Zellforsch.*, **61**, 661–72 (1964)

48. Kelly, D. E. Models of Z band fine structure based on a looping filament configuration. *J. Cell Biol.*, **34**, 827–40 (1967)

49. Hoyle, G. Fine structure of the Z band of striated muscle (In preparation)

50. Ashurst, D. A. Z-line of the flight muscle of belostomatid water bugs. *J. Mol. Biol.*, **27**, 385–89 (1967)

51. Page, S. G. A comparison of the fine structures of frog slow and twitch muscle fibres. *J. Cell Biol.*, **26** 477–97 (1965)

52. Garamvölgyi, N. The arrangement of the myofilaments in the insect flight muscle. *J. Ultrastruct. Res.*, **13**, 409–24 (1965)

53. Bouligand, Y. Les ultrastructures du muscle strié et de ses attachés au squelette chez les Cyclops (Crustacés Copépodes). *J. Microscopie*, **1**, 377–94 (1962)

54. Fischman, D. A. An electron microscope study of myofibril formation in embryonic chick skeletal muscle. *J. Cell Biol.*, **32**, 557–75 (1967)

54a. Toselli, P. A., Pepe, F. A. The fine structure of the ventral intersegmental abdominal muscles of the insect *Rhodnius prolixus* during the molting cycle. 1. Muscle structure at molting. *J. Cell Biol.*, **37**, 445–61 (1968)

54b. Hagopian, M., Spiro, D. The filament lattice of cockroach thoracic muscle. *J. Cell Biol.*, **36**, 433–42 (1968)

55. Auber, J. Particularités ultrastructurales des myofibrilles des muscles du vol chez des Lepidoptères. *Compt. Rend. Acad. Sci.*, **264**, 621–24 (1967)

56. Auber, J. Distribution of the two kinds of myofilaments in insect muscle. *Am. Zool.*, **7**, 451–56 (1967)

57. Reger, J. F., Cooper, D. P. A comparative study on the fine structure of the basalar muscle of the wing and the tibial extensor muscle of the leg of the lepidopteran *Achalarus lyciades*. *J. Cell Biol.*, **33**, 531–42 (1967)

58. Smith, D. S., Gupta, B. L., Smith, U. The organization and myofilament array of insect visceral muscles. *J. Cell Sci.*, **1**, 49–57 (1966)

59. Slautterback, D. B. The ultrastructure of cardiac and skeletal muscle. In *The Physiology and Biochemistry of Muscle as a Food*, 39–68 (Briskey, E. J., Cassens, R. G., Trautman, J. C., Eds., Univ. Wisconsin Press, Madison, 1966)

60. Smith, D. S. The organization and function of the sarcoplasmic reticulum and T-system of muscle cells. *Progr. Biophys.*, **16**, 107–42 (1966)

61. Kilarski, W. The fine structure of striated muscles in teleosts. *Z. Zellforsch.*, **79**, 562–80 (1967)

62. Podolsky, R. J. Excitation-contraction coupling in striated muscle. *Fed. Proc.*, **24**, 1112–15 (1965)

63. Hoyle, G. Nature of the excitatory sarcoplasmic reticular junction. *Science*, **149**, 70–72 (1965)

64. Walker, S. M., Schrodt, G. R. Triads in foetal muscle. *Nature*, **216**, 985–88 (1967)

65. Pepe, F. A. The myosin filament. 1. Structural organization from antibody staining observed in electron microscopy. *J. Mol. Biol.*, **27**, 203–25 (1967)

66. Reedy, M. K. Cross-bridges and periods in insect flight muscle. *Am. Zool.*, **7**, 465–81 (1967)

67. Reedy, M. K. Ultrastructure of insect flight muscle. 1. Screw sense and structural grouping in the rigor cross-bridge lattice. *J. Mol. Biol.*, **31**, 155–76 (1968)

68. Bouligand, Y. Les ultrastructures musculaires des Copépodes. III. Nature de la bande de contraction C_m des sarcomeres. *J. Microscopie*, **3**, 699–710 (1964)

69. Baccetti, B. Nouvelles observations sur l'ultrastructure du myofilament. *J. Ultrastruct. Res.*, **13**, 245–56 (1965)

70. Gilëv, V. P. Ultrastructure of thick filaments of muscle fiber. *Proc. 6th Intern. Conf. Electron Microscopy*, **11**, 689–90 (1966)

71. Wissocq, J. C. Étude ultrastructurale de l'évolution des muscles longitudinaux lors de la stolonisation expérimentale de *Syllis amica* (Quatrefages) (Annelide Polychète). *Z. Zellforsch.*, **83**, 449–67 (1967)

72. Peachey, L. Transverse tubules in crab muscle. *J. Cell Biol.*, **23**, 70A (1964)

73. Hoyle, G., McAlear, J. H., Selverston, A. Mechanism of supercontraction in a striated muscle. *J. Cell Biol.*, **26**, 621–40 (1965)

74. Hagopian, M. The myofilament arrangement in the femoral muscles of the cockroach, *Leucophaea maderae* Fabricius. *J. Cell Biol.*, **28**, 545–62 (1966)

75. Auber, J. Remarques sur la structure des fibrilles des muscles du vol d'insectes au niveau de la strie M. *Compt. Rend. Acad. Sci.*, **264**, 2916–18 (1967)

76. Reger, J. F. The organization of sarcoplasmic reticulum in direct flight muscle of the lepidopteran *Achalarus lyciades*. *J. Ultrastruct. Res.*, **18**, 595–99 (1967)

77. Hanson, J., Huxley, H. E. The structural basis of contraction in striated muscle. *Symp. Soc. Exptl. Biol.*, **9**, 228–64 (1965)

78. McNeill, P. A., Hoyle, G. Evidence for superthin filaments. *Am. Zool.*, **7**, 483–98 (1967)

79. Walcott, B., Ridgway, E. B. The ultrastructure of myosin-extracted striated muscle fibers. *Am. Zool.*, **7**, 499–504 (1967)

80. Garamvölgyi, N., Kerner, J. The ultrastructure of the insect flight muscle fibril ghost. *Acta Biochim. Biophys. Hung.*, **1**, 81–88 (1966)

81. DeVillafranca, G. W., Marshhaus, C. E. Contraction of the A band. *J. Ultrastruct. Res.*, **9**, 156–65 (1963)

82. Hehn, G., Schlote, F. Inkonstanz der

A-zone und Fehlen einer H-zone beim quergestreiften Eileitermuskel von *Carausius morosus*. *Z. Zellforsch.*, **63**, 459–77 (1964)

83. Gilmour, D., Robinson, P. M. Contraction in glycerinated myofibrils of an insect (orthoptera, acrididae). *J. Cell Biol.*, **21**, 385–96 (1964)

84. Baskin, R. J., Wiese, G. M., Contraction band formation in barnacle myofibrils. *Science*, **143**, 134–36 (1964)

84a. McAlear, J., Hoyle, G., Selverston, A. The phenomenon of A band contraction, an artifact of preparation. *J. Cell Biol.*, **23** 57A (1964)

85. Galey, F. R. Local contraction patterns of striated muscle. *J. Ultrastruct. Res.*, **11**, 389–400 (1964)

86. Carlsen, F., Fuchs, F., Knappeis, G. G. Contractility and ultrastructure in glycerol-extracted muscle fibers. II. Ultrastructure in resting and shortened fibers. *J. Cell Biol.*, **27**, 35–46 (1965)

87. Sjöstrand, F. S., Jagendorf-Elfvin, M. Ultrastructure studies of the contraction-relaxation cycle of glycerinated rabbit muscle. 1. The ultrastructure of glycerinated fibers contracted by treatment with ATP. *J. Ultrastruct. Res.*, **17**, 348–78 (1967)

88. Zebe, E., Meinrenken, W., Rüegg, J. C. Superkontraktion glycerinextrahierter synchroner Insektenmuskeln in Gegenwart von ITP. *Z. Zellforsch.*, **87**, 603–21 (1968)

89. Osborne, M. P. Supercontraction in the muscles of the blowfly larva: an ultrastructural study. *J. Insect Physiol.*, **13**, 1471–82 (1967)

90. Huxley, H. E. The mechanism of muscle contraction. *Sci. Am.*, **213**, 18–27 (1965)

91. Robertson, J. D. Design principles of the unit membrane. In *Principles of Biomolecular Organization*, 357–417 (Wolstenholme, G. E. W., O'Connor, M., Eds., Churchill, London, 491 pp., 1966)

92. Hiramoto, Y. Physical state of muscle protoplasm. *Annotationes Zool. Japonica*, **29** 63–69 (1956)

93. Huxley, A. F., Taylor R. E. *J. Physiol.* (*London*), **144** 426–41 (1958)

94. Aronson, J. Observations on the variations in size of the A region of arthropod muscle. *J. Cell Biol.*, **19**, 359–67 (1963)

95. Bowden, J. The structure and innervation of lamellibranch muscle. *Intern. Rev. Cytol.*, **7**, 295–335 (1958)

96. Hanson, J., Lowy, J. The structure of F-actin and of actin filaments isolated from muscle. *J. Mol. Biol.*, **6**, 46–60 (1963)

97. Peterson, R. P. A note on the structure of crayfish myofilaments. *J. Cell Biol.*, **18**, 213–18 (1963)

98. Ebashi, S. Structural proteins and their interactions. *Symp. Biol. Hung.*, **8**, 77–87 (1967)

99. Bárány, M. ATPase activity of myosin correlated with speed of muscle shortening. *J. Gen. Physiol.*, **50**, 197–218 (1967)

100. Basler, A. Über den Einfluss der Reizstärke und der Belastung auf die Muskelkurve. *Pflügers Arch.*, **102**, 254 (1094)

101. Caldwell, P. C., Walster, G. Studies on the microinjection of various substances into crab muscle fibers. *J. Physiol.*, **169** 353–72 (1963)

102. Portzehl, H., Caldwell, P. C., Ruegg, J. C. The dependence of contraction and relaxation of muscle fibres from the crab *Maia squinado* on the internal concentration of free calcium ions. *Biochim. Biophys. Acta*, **79** 581–91 (1964)

103. Hoyle, G., Smyth, T., Jr. Giant muscle fibers in a barnacle, *Balanus nubilus* Darwin. *Science*, **139**, 49–50 (1963)

104. Ashley, C. C. The role of cell calcium ion in the contraction of single cannulated muscle fibers. *Am. Zool.*, **7**, 647–59 (1967)

105. Hagiwara, S., Chichibu, S., Naka, K. The effects of various ions on resting and spike potentials of barnacle muscle fibers. *J. Gen. Physiol.*, **48**, 163–79 (1964)

106. Hagiwara, S., Nakajima, S. Effects of the intracellular Ca ion concentration upon the excitability of the muscle fiber membrane of a barnacle. *J. Gen. Physiol.*, **49**, 807–18 (1966)

107. Niedergerke, R. Movements of Ca in beating ventricles of the frog heart. *J. Physiol.*, **167**, 551–80 (1963)

108. Hurwitz, L., von Hagen, S., Joiner, P. D. Acetylcholine and calcium on membrane permeability and

contraction of intestinal smooth muscle. *J. Gen. Physiol.*, **50**, 1157–72 (1967)

109. Sandow, A. Excitation-contraction coupling in skeletal muscle. *Pharmacol. Rev.*, **17**, 265–320 (1965)

110. Jöbsis, F. F., O'Connor, M. J. Calcium release and reabsorption in the sartorius muscle of the toad. *Biochem. Biophys. Res. Commun.*, **25**, 246–52 (1966)

111. Ridgway, E. B., Ashley, C. C. Calcium transients in single muscle fibers. *Biochem. Biophys. Res. Commun.*, **29**, 229–34 (1967)

112. Ridgway, E. B., Ashley, C. C., Hoyle, G. Calcium mediated light emission from single muscle fibers. *Fed. Proc.*, **27**, 375 (1968)

113. Johnson, F. H., Shimomura, O. The chemistry of luminescence in coelenterates. In *Chemical Zoology*, **11**, 233–61 (Florkin, M., Scheer, B. T., Eds., Academic Press, New York & London, 639 pp., 1968)

114. Hoyle, G., Abbott, B. C. Dynamic properties of giant muscle fibers of the barnacle. *Am. Zool.*, **7**, 611–14 (1967)

115. Sandow, A., Taylor, S. R., Preiser, H. Role of the action potential in excitation-contraction coupling. *Fed. Proc.*, **24**, 1116–23 (1965)

116. Hoyle, G. Resting tension "negative" contraction and "break" contraction in specialised crustacean muscle fibers. *J. Exptl. Zool.*, **167**, (1968)

117. Desmedt, J. E., Hainaut, K. Kinetics of myofilament activation in potentiated contraction: staircase phenomenon in human skeletal muscle. *Nature*, **217**, 529–32 (1968)

118. Rosenfalck, P. Staircase phenomenon of human muscle: relation to the active state. *Nature*, **218**, 958–59 (1968)

119. Sandow, A., Seaman, T. Muscle shortening velocity in normal and potentiated contractions. *Life Sci.*, **3**, 91–96 (1964)

120. Huxley, A. F., Taylor, R. E. Local activation of striated muscle fibers. *J. Physiol.*, **144**, 426–41 (1958)

121. Gonzalez-Serratos, H. Inward spread of contraction during a twitch. *J. Physiol.*, **185**, 21P (1966)

122. Gonzalez-Serratos, H. *Studies on the inwards spread of activation in isolated muscle fibers* (Ph.D. thesis, Univ. London, 188 pp., 1967)

123. Girardier, L., Reuben, J. P., Brandt, P. W., Grundfest, H. Evidence for anion permselective membrane in crayfish muscle fibers and its possible role in excitation-contraction coupling. *J. Gen. Physiol.*, **47**, 189–214 (1963)

124. Reuben, J. P., Brandt, P. W., Garcia, H., Grundfest, H. Excitation-contraction coupling in crayfish. *Am. Zool.*, **7**, 623–45 (1967)

125. Constantin, L. L. Some effects of alterations in external calcium conconcetration on frog skeletal muscle. *J. Physiol.*, **191**, 102P (1967)

126. Lorkovic, H., Edwards, C. Threshold for contracture and delayed rectification in muscle. *Life Sci.*, **7**, 367–80 (1968)

127. Gage, P. W., Eisenberg, R. S. Action potentials without contraction in frog skeletal muscle fibers with disrupted transverse tubules. *Science*, **158**, 1702–3 (1967)

128. Stefani, E., Steinbach, A. Persistence of excitation contraction coupling in "slow" muscle fibers after a treatment that destroys transverse tubules in "twitch" fibres. *Nature*, **218**, 681–82 (1968)

129. Sugi, H., Ochi, R. The mode of transverse spread of contraction initiated by local activation in single crayfish muscle fibers. *J. Gen. Physiol.*, **50**, 2145–66 (1967)

130. Sugi, H., Ochi, R. The mode of transverse spread of contraction initiated by local activation in single frog muscle fibers. *Ibid.*, 2167–76

131. Chiarandini, D. J., Brandt, P. W., Reuben, J. P. Drug-evoked contractions and caffeine-induced action potentials in isolated crayfish muscle fibers. *J. Gen. Physiol.*, **50**, 2501 (1967)

132. Gillis, J. M. Contraction of isolated crab myofibrils by local application of calcium ions. *J. Physiol.*, **191**, 103–4P (1967)

133. Aidley, D. J. The effect of calcium ions on potassium contracture in a locust leg muscle. *J. Physiol.*, **177**, 94–102 (1965)

134. Zacharova, D., Zachar, J. The effect of external calcium ions on the excitation-contraction coupling in single muscle fibres of the crayfish. *Physiol. Bohemoslov.*, **16**, 191–207 (1967)

135. Fanburg, B. L., Drachman, D. B., Moll, D., Roth, S. I. Calcium trans-

port in isolated sarcoplasmic reticulum during muscle maturation. *Nature*, **218**, 962–64 (1968)

136. Zacks, S. I., Sheff, M. F. Tetanus toxin: fine structure localization of binding sites in striated muscle. *Science*, **159**, 643–44 (1968)

137. Jewell, B. R., Rüegg, J. C. Oscillatory contraction of insect fibrillar flight muscle. *Proc. Roy. Soc. B*, **164**, 428–59 (1966)

138. Rüegg, J. C., Tregear, R. T. Mechanical factors affecting the ARPase activity of glycerol-extracted insect fibrillar flight muscle. *Proc. Roy. Soc. B*, **165**, 497–512 (1966)

139. Chaplain, R. A. The effect of Ca^{++} and fibre elongation on the activation of the contractile mechanism of insect fibrillar flight muscle. *Biochim. Biophys. Acta*, **131**, 385–92 (1967)

140. Rüegg, J. C. ATP-driven oscillation of glycerol-extracted insect fibrillar muscle: mechano-chemical coupling. *Am. Zool.*, **7**, 457–64 (1967)

141. Reedy, M. K., Holmes, K. C., Tregear, R. T. Induced changes in orientation of the cross-bridges of glycerinated insect flight muscle. *Nature*, **207**, 1276–80 (1965)

142. Huxley, H. E., Brown, W. The low-angle X-ray diagram of vertebrate striated muscle and its behaviour during contraction and rigor. *J. Mol. Biol.*, **30**, 383–434 (1968)

143. Davies, R. E. A molecular theory of muscle contraction: calcium-dependent contractions with hydrogen bond formation plus ATP-dependent extensions of part of the myosin-actin cross-bridges. *Nature*, **199**, 1068–74 (1963)

144. Ingels, N. P., Thompson, L. N. P. Electrokinematic theory of muscle contraction. *Nature*, **211**, 1032–35 (1966)

145. Elliott, G. F. Variations of the contractile apparatus in smooth and striated muscles. *J. Gen. Physiol.*, **50**, 171–84 (1967)

146. Hoyle, G. Comments in relation to mechanism of contraction on muscle ultrastructure. In *Symposium on Muscle* (Ernst, E., Straub, F. B., Eds., Akad. Kiadó, Budapest., 259 pp., 1968)

147. Katz, B., Miledi, R. The timing of calcium action during neuromuscular transmission. *J. Physiol.*, **189**, 535–44 (1967)

148. Katz, B., Miledi, R. A study of synaptic transmission in the absence of nerve impulses. *Ibid.*, **192**, 407–36 (1967)

149. Katz, B. The release of acetylcholine from nerve endings by graded electric pulses. *Proc. Roy. Soc. B.*, **167**, 23–38 (1967)

150. Katz, B., Miledi, R. The role of calcium in neuromuscular facilitation. *J. Physiol.*, **195**, 481–92 (1968)

151. Kravitz, E. A., Potter, D. D. A further study of the distribution of aminobutyric acid between excitatory and inhibitory axons of the lobster. *J. Neurochem.*, **12**, 323–28 (1965)

151a. Iversen, L. L., Kravitz, E. A., Otsuka, M. Release of gamma-aminobutyric acid (GABA) from lobster inhibitory neurones. *J. Physiol.*, **188**, 21P (1966)

152. Kerkut, G. A., Leake, L. D., Shapira, A., Cowan, S., Walker, R. J. The presence of glutamate in nerve-muscle perfusates of *Helix, Carcinus* and *Periplaneta*. *Comp. Biochem. Physiol.*, **15**, 485–502 (1965)

153. Kerkut, G. A. Biochemical aspects of invertebrate nerve cells in *Invertebrate Nervous Systems*, 5–37 (Wiersma, C. A. G., Ed., Univ. Chicago Press, Chicago, 1967)

154. Usherwood, P. N. R., Grundfest, H. Peripheral inhibition in skeletal muscle of insects. *J. Neurophysiol.*, **28**, 497–518 (1956)

155. Kerkut, G. A., Walker, R. J. The effect of L-glutamate, acetylcholine and gamma-aminobutyric acid on the miniature end-plate potentials and contractures of the coxal muscles of the cockroach, *Periplaneta americana*. *Comp. Biochem. Physiol.*, **17**, 435–54 (1966)

156. Kerkut, G. A., Leake, L. D. The effects of drugs on the snail pharyngeal retractor muscle. *Comp. Biochem. Physiol.*, **17**, 623–33 (1966)

157. Florey, E. Comparative pharmacology: neurotropic and myotropic compounds. *Ann. Rev. Pharmacol.*, **5**, 357–82 (1965)

158. Takeuchi, A., Takeuchi, N. Localized action of gamma-aminobutyric acid on the crayfish muscle. *J. Physiol.*, **177**, 225–38 (1965)

159. Takeuchi, A., Takeuchi, N. Electrophysiological studies of the action of GABA on the synaptic membrane. *Fed. Proc.*, **26**, 1633–38 (1967)

160. McCann, F. V., Reece, R. W. Neuromuscular transmission in insects:
effects of injected chemical agents.
Comp. Biochem. Physiol., **21**, 115–
24 (1967)

161. Van der Kloot, W. G. Factor S—a
substance which excites crustacean
muscle. *J. Neurochem.*, **5**, 245–52
(1960)

162. Cook, B. J. An investigation of factor
S, a neuromuscular excitatory sub-
stance from insects and crustacea.
Biol. Bull., **133**, 526–38 (1967)

163. Uchizono, K. Morphological background of excitation and inhibition at synapses. *J. Electronmicroscopy (Tokyo)*, **17**, 55–66 (1968)

164. Atwood, H. L., Jones, A. Presynaptic
inhibition in crustacean muscle:
axo-axonal synapse. *Experientia*, **23**,
1036 (1967)

165. Hoyle, G., McNeill, P. A. Correlated
physiological and ultrastructural
studies on specialized muscle fibers.
1c. Neuromuscular junctions of the
eyestalk levator of *Podophthalmus
vigil* (Weber). *J. Exptl. Zool.*, **167**,
523–50 (1968)

166. Huddart, H. The effect of potassium
ions on resting and action potentials in lepidopteran muscle. *Comp.
Biochem. Physiol.*, **18**, 131–40
(1966)

167. Huddart, H., Wood, D. W. The effect of DNP on the resting potential and ionic content of some insect
skeletal muscle fibres. *Comp. Biochem. Physiol.*, **18**, 681–88 (1966)

168. Huddart, H. Generation of membrane
potentials in lepidopteran muscle.
1. Analysis of a mixed electrode
system in the skeletal muscle fibers
of *Sphinx ligustri* (L). *Arch. Intern. Physiol. Biochem.*, **75**, 245–60
(1967)

169. Weevers, R. de G. A lepidopteran
saline: effects of inorganic cation
concentrations on sensory, reflex
and motor responses in a herbivorous insect. *J. Exptl. Biol.*, **44**,
163–75 (1966)

170. Wareham, A. C., Duncan, C. J.,
Bowler, K. Permeability and excitation of insect muscle. *Nature*,
217, 907–71 (1967)

171. Usherwood, P. N. R. Permeability of
insect muscle fibers to potassium
and chloride ions. *J. Physiol.*,
191, 29–30P (1967)

172. Cochrane, D. G., Elder, H. Y. Morphological changes in insect muscle

during influx and efflux of potassium ions, chloride ions and water.
J. Physiol., **191**, 30–31P (1967)

173. Usherwood, P. N. R. Changes in
structural, physiological and pharmacological properties of insect excitatory nerve-muscle synapses
after motor nerve section. *Nature*,
218, 589–91 (1968)

174. Osborne, M. P. The fine structure of
neuromuscular junctions in the
segmental muscles of the blowfly
larva. *J. Insect Physiol.*, **13**, 827–33
(1967)

175. Kerkut, G. A., Shapira, A., Walker,
R. J. The transport of ^{14}C-labelled
material from CNS$\rightleftharpoons$ anode along
a nerve trunk. *Comp. Biochem.
Physiol.*, **23** 729–48 (1968)

176. Korr, I. M., Wilkinson, P. N., Chor-
nock, F. W. Axonal delivery of
neuroplasmic components to mus-
cle cells. *Science*, **155**, 342–45 (1967)

177. Josephson, R. K. Neuromuscular
transmission in a sea anemone. *J.
Exptl. Biol.*, **45**, 305–19 (1966)

178. Pantin, C. F. A. The nerve net of the
Actinozoa. 1. Facilitation. *J. Exptl.
Biol.*, **12**, 119–38 (1935)

179. Mackie, G. O., Passano, L. M.,
Pavans de Ceccatty, M. Physiologie
du comportement de l'hydromeduse
Sarsia tubulosa Sars. Les systèmes
à conduction aneurale. *Compt.
Rend. Acad. Sci.*, **264** 366–69 (1967)

180. Arai, M. N. Contractile properties of
a preparation of the column of
Pachycerianthus torreyi (Anthozoa).
Comp. Biochem. Physiol., **14**, 323–
37 (1965)

181. Chapman, D. M., Pantin, C. F. A.,
Robson, E. A. Muscle in coelenterates. *Rev. Can. Biol.*, **21**, 267–77
(1962)

182. Kawaguti, S., Hamakoshi, T. Electron
microscopic studies on the striated
and smooth muscles of an antho-
medusa, *Spirocodon saltatrix*. *Biol.
J. Okayama Univ.*, **9**, 127–39 (1963)

183. Gruber, S. A., Ewer, D. W. Observations on the myo-neural physiology
of the polyclad, *Planocera gilchristi*.
J. Exptl. Biol., **39**, 459–77 (1962)

184. Ewer, D. W. Networks and spontaneous activity in echinoderms
and platyhelminthes. *Am. Zool.*, **5**,
563–72 (1965)

185. MacRae, E. K. The fine structure of
muscle in a marine turbellarian. *Z.
Zellforsch.*, **68**, 348–62 (1965)

186. Morita, M. Electron microscopic

studies on planaria. 1. Fine structure of muscle fiber in the head of the planarian *Dugesia dorotocephala*. *J. Ultrastruct. Res.*, **13**, 383–95 (1965)

187. DeBell, J. T., Castillo, J. del, Sánchez, V. Electrophysiology of the somatic muscle cells of *Ascaris lumbricoides*. *J. Cellular Comp. Physiol.*, **62**, 159–78 (1963)

188. Castillo, J. del, Mello, W. C. de, Morales, T. Influence of some ions in the membrane potential of *Ascaris* muscle. *J. Gen. Physiol.*, **48**, 129–40 (1964)

189. Castillo, J. del, Morales, T. The electrical and mechanical activity of the esophageal cell of *Ascaris lumbricoides*. *J. Gen. Physiol.*, **50**, 603–29 (1967)

190. Belten, P., Grundfest, H. Potassium activation and K spikes in muscle fibers of the mealwork larva (*Tenebrio molitor*). *Am. J. Physiol.*, **203**, 488–94 (1962)

191. Grundfest, H. The anomalous spikes of *Ascaris* esophageal cells. *J. Gen. Physiol.*, **50**, 1955–59 (1967)

192. Rosenbluth, J. Ultrastructural organization of obliquely striated muscle fibers in *Ascaris lumbricoides*. *J. Cell Biol.*, **25**, 495–515 (1959)

193. Rosenbluth, J. Ultrastructure of somatic muscle cells in *Ascaris lumbricoides*. II. Intermuscular junctions and glycogen stores. *Ibid.*, **26**, 579–91 (1965)

194. Rosenbluth, J. Obliquely striated muscle. III. Contraction mechanism of Ascaris body muscle. *Ibid.*, **34**, 15–33 (1967)

195. Reger, J. F. The fine structure of the fibrillar network and sarcoplasmic reticulum in smooth muscle cells of *Ascaris lumbricoides* (var. suum). *J. ultrastruct. Res.*, **10**, 48–57 (1964)

196. Pucci, I., Afzelius, B. A. An electron microscope study of sarcotumbules and related structures in the leech muscle. *J. Ultrastruct. Res.*, **7**, 210–24 (1962)

107. Röhlich, P. The fine structure of the muscle fiber of the leech. *J. Ultrastruct. Res.*, **7**, 399–408 (1962)

198. Bouligand, Y. La disposition des myofilaments chez une annelide polychete. *J. Microscopie*, **5**, 305–22 (1966)

199. Heumann, H. G., Zebe, E. Über Feinbau und Funktionsweise der Fasern aus dem Hautmuskelschlauch des Regenwurms, *Lumbricus terrestris* L. *Z. Zellforsch.*, **78**, 131–50 (1967)

200. Rosenbluth, J. Obliquely striated muscle. IV. Sarcoplasmic reticulum, contractile apparatus, and ondomysium of the body muscle of a polychaete, *Glycera*, in relation to its speed. *J. Cell Biol.*, **36**, 245–59 (1968)

201. Lawry, J. V., Jr. Neuromuscular mechanisms of burrow irrigation in the echiuroid worm *Urechis caupo* fisher & macginitie. 2. Neuromuscular activity of dissected preparations. *J. Exptl. Biol.*, **45**, 357–68 (1966)

202. Cobb, J. L. S., Laverack, M. S. The lantern of *Echinus esculentus* (L). 1. Gross anatomy and physiology. *Proc. Roy. Soc. B*, **164**, 624–40 (1966)

203. Cobb, J. L. S., Laverack, M. S. The fine structure of the lantern retractor muscle and its innervation. *Ibid.*, 651–58

204. Cobb, J. L. S. The innervation of the ampulla of the tube foot in the starfish *Astropecten irregularis*. *Ibid.*, **168**, 91–99 (1967)

205. Boltt, R. E., Ewer, D. W. Studies on the myoneural physiology of echinodermata. V. The lantern retractor muscle of *Parechinus*: responses to drugs. *J. Exptl. Biol.*, **40**, 727–33 (1963)

206. Takahashi, K. Muscle physiology. In *Physiology of Echinodermata* (Boolootian, R. A., Ed., Wiley, New York)

207. Kawaguti, S., Kamashima, Y. Electron microscopy on the spine muscle of the echinoid. *Biol. J. Okayama Univ.*, **11**, 31–40 (1965)

208. Kawaguti, S. Electron microscope structure of the podial wall of an echinoid with special reference to the nerve plexus and the muscle. *Biol. J. Okayama Univ.*, **10**, 1–12 (1964)

209. Uhlmann, K. Über die Verbindung der Muskulatur mit dem Skelett bei dem Echinodermen *Asterias rubens* L. *Z. Zellforsch.*, **87**, 210–17 (1968)

210. Twarog, B. M. Factors influencing contraction and catch in *Mytilus* smooth muscle. *J. Physiol.*, **192**, 847–56 (1967)

211. Twarog, B. M. Excitation of *Mytilus* smooth muscle. *Ibid.*, 857–68

212. Hidaka, T., Osa, T., Twarog, B. M. The action of 5-hydroxytryptamine on *Mytilus* smooth muscle. *J. Physiol.*, **192**, 869–77 (1967)

213. Twarog, B. M. Catch and the mechanism of action of 5-hydroxytryptamine on molluscan muscle: a speculation. *Life Sci.*, **5**, 1201–13 (1966)

214. Twarog, B. M. The regulation of catch in molluscan muscle. *J. Gen. Physiol.*, **50**, 157–69 (1967)

215. Leenders, H. J. Ca-coupling in the anterior byssal retractor muscle of *Mytilus edulis* L. *J. Physiol.*, **192**, 681–93 (1967)

216. Lowy, J., Millman, B. M. The contractile mechanism of the anterior byssus retractor muscle of *Mytilus edulis*. *Phil. Trans. B*, **246**, 105–48 (1963)

217. Millman, B. Mechanism of contraction in molluscan muscle. *Am. Zool.*, **7**, 583–91 (1967)

218. Elliott, G. F. Electron microscope studies of the structure of the filaments in the opaque adductor muscle of the oyster *Crassostrea angulata*. *J. Mol. Biol.*, **10**, 89–104 (1964)

219. Millman, B. M. Contraction in the opaque part of the adductor muscle of the oyster (*Crassostrea angulata*). *J. Physiol.*, **173**, 238–62 (1964)

220. Millman, B. M. Elliott, G. F. X-ray diffraction from contracting molluscan muscle. *Nature*, **206**, 824–25 (1965)

221. Minihan, K., Davies, R. E. Energy requirements for relaxation from tonic contractions ('catch') in an invertebrate muscle. *Nature*, **208**, 1327–29 (1965)

222. Rüegg, J. C. Actomyosin inactivation by thiourea and the nature of viscous tone in a molluscan smooth muscle. *Proc. Roy. Soc. B*, **158**, 177–95 (1963)

223. Rüegg, J. C., Straub, R. W., Twarog, B. M. Inhibition of contraction in a molluscan smooth muscle by thiourea, an inhibitor of the actomyosin contractile mechanism. *Proc. Roy. Soc. B*, **158**, 156–76 (1963)

224. Hill, R. B., Marantz, E., Beattie, B. A., Lockart, J. M. Mechanical properties of the radula protractor of *Busycon canaliculatum*. *Experientia*, **24**, 91–92 (1968)

225. Mattisson, A. G. M., Arvidsson, J. A. Some effects of electrical stimulation and exogenous metabolites on the contractile activity and the ultrastructure of the radula muscle of *Buccinum undatum*. *Z. Zellforsch.*, **73**, 37–55 (1966)

226. Ozeki, M. Electrical and mechanical activities of the retractor pharynx muscle of a snail. *Japan. J. Physiol.*, **12**, 293–311 (1962)

227. Ozeki, M. Effects of calcium and sodium ions on potassium induced contracture and twitch tension development of the retractor pharynx muscle of a snail. *Ibid.*, **14**, 155–64 (1964)

228. Kinosita, H., Ueda, K., Takahashi, K., Murakami, A. Contraction of squid chromatophore muscle. *J. Fac. Sci. Univ. Tokyo*, **10**, 409–19 (1965)

228a. Florey, E. Nervous control and spontaneous activity of the chromatophores of a cephalopod, *Loligo opalescens*. *Comp. Biochem. Physiol.*, **18**, 305–24 (1966)

228b. Cloney, R. A., Florey, E. Ultrastructure of cephalopod chromatophore organs. *Z. Zellforsch.*, **89**, 250–80 (1968)

229. Graziadei, P. The ultrastructure of the motor nerve endings in the muscles of cephalopods. *J. Ultrastruct. Res.*, **15**, 1–13 (1966)

230. Kerkut, G. A., Woodhouse, M., Newman, G. R. Nerve-muscle junction in the snail *Helix aspersa*. *Comp. Biochem. Physiol.*, **19**, 309–11 (1966)

231. Atwood, H. L., Parnas, I., Wiersma, C. A. G. Inhibition in crustacean phasic neuromuscular systems. *Comp. Biochem. Physiol.*, **20**, 163–77 (1967)

232. Bryan, G. W. Zinc concentrations of fast and slow contracting muscles in the lobster. *Nature*, **213**, 1043–44 (1967)

233. Atwood, H. L. Selective actions of inhibitory axons on different crustacean muscle fibers. In *Invertebrate nervous systems*, 169–73 (Wiersma, C. A. G., Ed., Chicago Univ. Press, Chicago, 1967)

234. Dudel, J. The mechanism of presynaptic inhibition at the crayfish neuromuscular junction. *Pflügers Arch.*, **284**, 66–80 (1965)

235. Atwood, H. L. Variations in physiological properties of crustacean

motor synapses. *Nature*, **215**, 57–58 (1967)

237. Henček, M., Zachar, J. The electrical constants of single muscle fibres of the crayfish (*Astacus fluviatilis*). *Physiol. Bohemoslov.*, **14**, 297–311 (1965)

238. Zachar, J., Zacharova, D., Henček, M. Membrane potential of the isolated muscle fibre of the crayfish (*Astacus fluviatilis*). *Physiol. Bohemoslov.*, **13**, 117–28 (1964)

239. Zachar, J., Ájter, V. The sodium and potassium content of single muscle fibres of the crayfish. *Physiol. Bohemoslov.*, **14**, 113–25 (1965)

240. Zacharova, D., Zachar, J. Contractions in single muscle fibres with graded electrogenesis. *Physiol. Bohemoslov.*, **14**, 401–11 (1965)

241. Andrews, P. Über den Blutchenisms des Fusskrebses *Orconectes limosus*. *Z. Vergleich. Physiol.*, **57**, 7–43 (1967)

242. Rathmeyer, W. Neuromuscular transmission in a spider and the effect of calcium. *Comp. Biochem, Physiol.*, **14**, 763–87 (1965)

243. Parnas, I., Abbott, B. C., Shapiro, B., Lang, E. Machanical and electrical studies of leg closer muscle of *Limulus*. *J. Gen. Physiol.*, **50**, 2500 (1967)

244. Pringle, J. W. S. The contractile mechanism of insect fibrillar muscle. *Progr. Biophys. Mol. Biol.*, **17**, 1–60 (1967)

245. Aidley, D. J. The excitation of insect skeletal muscles. *Advan. Insect Physiol.*, **4**, 1–31 (1967)

246. Bergman, S. J., Pearson, K. G. Inhibition in cockroach muscle. *J. Physiol.*, **22–23P** (1968)

247. Jansen, J. K. S., Andersen, P. Anatomy and physiology of skeletal muscles. In *The Biology of Myxine* 161–94 (Brodal, A., Fange, R., Eds., Universitatsforlaget, Oslo, 1963)

248. Bone, Q. Patterns of muscular innervation in the lower chordates. *Intern. Rev. Neurobiol.*, **6**, 99–149 (1964)

249. Barker, D. Innervation of vertebrate muscle (in preparation, 1968)

250. Lännergren, J., Smith, R. S. Types of muscle fibres in toad skeletal muscle. *Acta Physiol. Scand.*, **68**, 263–74 (1966)

251. Hagiwara, S., Takahashi, K. Resting and spike potentials of skeletal muscle fibres of salt-water elasmo-branchs and teleost fish. *J. Physiol.*, **190**, 499–518 (1967)

252. Andersen, P., Jansen, J. K. S., Løyning, Y. Slow and fast muscle fibres in the Atlantic hagfish (*Myxine glutinosa*). *Acta Physiol. Scand.*, **57**, 167–79 (1963)

253. Alnaes, E., Jansen, J. K. S., Rudjord, T. Spontaneous junctional activity of slow and fast parietal muscle fibres of the hagfish. *Acta Physiol. Scand.*, **60**, 240–55 (1964)

254. Nishihara, H. Studies on the fine structure of red and white fin muscles of the fish (*Carrassius auratus*). *Arch. Histol. Japon.*, **28**, 425–47 (1967)

255. Bone, Q. On the function of the two types of myotomal muscle fibre in elasmobranch fish. *J. Marine Biol. Assoc.*, **46**, 321–49 (1966)

256. Rayner, M. D., Keenan, M. J. Role of red and white muscle in the swimming of the skipjack tuna. *Nature*, **214**, 392–93 (1967)

257. Lännergren, J., Smith, R. S. Types of muscle fibres in toad skeletal muscle. *Acta Physiol. Scand.*, **68**, 263–74 (1966)

258. Lännergren, J. Contractures of single slow muscle fibres of *Xenopus laevis* elicited by potassium, acetylcholine or choline. *Acta Physiol. Scand.*, **69**, 362–72 (1967)

259. George, J. C., Berger, A. J. *Avian Myology* (Academic Press, New York, 500 pp., 1966)

260. Page, S., Slater, C. R. Observations on fine structure and rate of contraction of some muscles from the chicken. *J. Physiol.*, **179**, 58–59P (1965)

261. Flood, P. R. Structure of the segmental trunk muscle in *Amphioxus*. *Z. Zellforsch.*, **84**, 389–416 (1968)

262. Miller, J. E. Cellular organization of rhesus extraocular muscle. *Invest. Opthalmol.*, **6**, 18–39 (1967)

263. Hess, A., Pilar, G. Slow fibres in the extraocular muscles of the cat. *J. Physiol.*, **169**, 780–98 (1963)

264. Pilar, G. Further study of the electrical and mechanical responses of slow fibres in cat extraocular muscles. *J. Gen. Physiol.*, **50**, 2289–2300 (1967)

265. Bach-y-Rita, P., Ito, F. In vivo studies on fast and slow muscle fibers in cat extraocular muscles. *J. Gen. Physiol.*, **49**, 1177–98 (1966)

266. Dubowitz, V. Cross-innervated mam-

malian skeletal muscle: histological, physiological and biochemical observations. *J. Physiol.*, **193**, 481–96 (1967)

267. Romanul, F. C. A. Enzymes in muscle. *Arch. Neurol.*, **11**, 355–68 (1964)

268. Yellin, H. Neural regulation of enzymes in muscle fibers of red and white muscles. *Exptl. Neurol.*, **19**, 92–103 (1967)

269. Olson, C. B., Swett, C. P. A functional and histochemical characterization of motor units in a heterogeneous muscle (flexor digitorum longus) of the cat. *J. Comp. Neurol.*, **128**, 475–98 (1966)

270. Smith, R. S., Lännergren, J. Types of motor units in the skeletal muscle of *Xenopus laevis*. *Nature*, **217**, 281–83 (1968)

271. David, H., Gerhardt, H. J., Uerlings, I. Die submikroskopische Struktur des Muskulus Stapedius des Meerschweinchens. *Z. Zellforsch.*, **70**, 334–46 (1956)

272. Schmalbruch, H. Fasertypen in der Unterschenkelmuskulatur der Maus. *Z. Zellforsch.*, **79** 64–75 (1967)

273. Bubenezer, H. J. Die dünnen und die dicken Muskelfasern des Zwerchfells der Ratte. *Z. Zellforsch.*, **69**, 520–50 (1966)

274. Hall-Craggs, E. C. B. The contraction times and enzyme activity of two rabbit laryngeal muscles. *J. Anat.*, **102**, 241–55 (1968)

275. Cassens, R. G., Hoekstra, W. G., Faltin, E. C., Briskey, E. J. Zinc content and subcellular distribution in red versus white porcine skeletal muscle. *Am. J. Physiol.*, **212**, 688–92 (1967)

276. Raviola, E., Raviola, G. Striated muscle cells in the thymus of reptiles and birds: an electron microscopic study. *Am. J. Anat.*, **121**, 623- 46 (1967)

EXERCISE[1]

Including Weightlessness

BY LARS-GÖRAN EKELUND

Department of Clinical Physiology, Karolinska Institute, Stockholm, Sweden

INTRODUCTION

The importance of studying the reaction of the human body during exercise is in general accepted. Estimations performed at rest, so-called basal values, have no great significance because the normal situation for an individual is not rest but some form of exercise, even if of a very low degree. Measures made during exercise are also much more reproducible than those during rest, as the resting condition is not so well defined as an exercise condition. Exercise is also needed to evaluate the whole capacity of many systems.

BOOKS, REVIEWS, SYMPOSIA

A good summary of the knowledge of the physiology of physical exercise will be found in the proceedings of a symposium held in Dallas (1). In a book on clinical physiology edited by Sjöstrand (2) two chapters deal with exercise, one with accommodation to physical work under normal and pathological conditions, and one with exercise tests. The concept of physical working capacity and its testing were the subject of a symposium held in Stockholm (3). The related concept of fitness is discussed by Shephard (4). A comprehensive review of the regulation of the circulation during exercise in man is given by Bevegård & Shepherd (5). Both the circulatory and the respiratory adaptations to work are dealt with by Dempsey & Rankin (6), who discuss the adaptation of the gas transport system during exercise in health and disease. A new edition of Morehouse & Miller's monograph on the physiology of exercise (10) was published in 1967. Karvonen & Barry (8) have edited the results of a symposium dealing with physical activity and the heart. Chapter two in the excellent book by Marshall & Shephard (7) deals with cardiac dynamics during exercise. Nutrition and physical activity were the topics of a symposium (12).

Circulatory problems during weightlessness are the subject of a chapter in a book (9) on physiology of inactivity and weightlessness. Some related problems are handled in proceedings of the second international symposium on basic environmental problems of man in space (11).

---

[1] The survey of literature was concluded in June 1968 and deals mainly with normal subjects. Some papers concerning pathological conditions are cited in the literature list but are not mentioned in the text.

EXERCISE TESTING

To test the functional capacity of the circulatory system one needs a reproducible tool to produce a measurable load. One of the most widespread instruments is the mechanical or electrically braked bicycle ergometer, on which one can set a known load measured in watts or kilopondmeters per minute. But in spite of a known constant mechanical work load, which with an electrically braked cycle can also be held constant at different pedaling frequencies, physiological loads differ, depending on several factors, especially the pedaling rate. Eckermann & Millahn (14) tested in detail this earlier-known influence of pedaling rate on the physiological load. They measured oxygen uptake and heart rate at two loads and four pedaling speeds. There were highly significant differences between 30 and 40 rpm and between 40 and 90 rpm, in both heart frequency and oxygen uptake; the mean oxygen uptake differed by 24–37 per cent between 40 and 90 rpm. The optimal pedaling frequency for these 12 young untrained men was about 45 rpm. In another report (15) in which an electrically braked cycle was used, there were also significant differences in heart and respiratory rates at different pedaling rates, with a constant load. In a further study (16) a mechanically braked cycle was used at various speeds with different power outputs. From the measured oxygen uptakes and the different work loads, regression lines were calculated for the different pedaling rates. A decline in working efficiency with increasing pedaling rate was very marked at the high speeds: 360 kpm/min, performed at a pedaling rate of 120 rpm, was equivalent physiologically to 1000 kpm/min at 50, 60, or 70 rpm. From earlier investigations and the last-mentioned study it is clear that pedaling rate must be standardized even with an electrically braked cycle. The rotational energy of the cycle may also influence the physiological work. At the 16th International Congress of Sports Medicine held in Hanover in June 1966, the research committee on standardization of ergometry of the International Council of Sports and Physical Education proposed several criteria, one of which was the dimension of the revolving masses. When arm work was used (17) to test the influence of different values of rotational energy, the biological effort measured as heart rate decreased with the increase in rotational energy.

All the above factors, and others such as the radius of the pedal, should be standardized and kept constant during an investigation. These factors must also be considered when comparing investigations with different types of cycle (18–24, 177). Even if the biological stress is measured as oxygen uptake or the equivalent, the results may differ, depending on the force and speed developed by different muscle groups with, for instance, a difference in pressure reaction during exercise (149). The same factors may have an influence if a treadmill is used, because the same load can be attained with the different combinations of speed and force.

EFFECT OF TRAINING

Normal subjects.—As reported in earlier studies, both in young and elderly subjects training decreases the heart rate response to a given submaximal work load. Cumming et al. (25) studied 6 boys and 6 girls between 13–15 years of age with a 6-day period of training and found a decline in submaximal pulse rate by 6 beats/min for a constant load, but no change in measured maximal oxygen uptake. O'Donnell et al. (29) described a 20-week jogging program of 32 middle-aged and 32 60-year-old men. The heart rate during a standard stepping test decreased after 4 weeks of training by over 8 beats/min and after 8 weeks by an additional 6 beats/min, with no further decrease at 20 weeks. No estimate was made of maximal oxygen uptake. In this group, there was a very limited decrease in weight and in subcutaneous fat, but no significant change in arterial pressure or in serum cholesterol or triglyceride levels. Williams et al. (28) studied 13 Bantu males before and after prolonged daily exercise (4 hr) at aerobic levels of work followed by exhaustive bouts of maximal effort, lasting from 4 to 16 weeks. This strange regime influenced both the maximal oxygen uptake, which increased between 1 and 20 per cent (average 7 per cent), and the level of oxygen intake at which excess lactate appeared in the blood. This level was raised by between 4 and 33 per cent (average 16 per cent).

Eight male students were studied during submaximal and maximal exercise before and after 16 weeks of hard physical training (173). The maximal oxygen uptake increased by 16.2 per cent from 3.15 to 3.68 liters/min, partly because of an increased arteriovenous oxygen difference and partly because of increased cardiac output (dye dilution), caused by an increase in stroke volume. After training, the heart rate, cardiac output, and blood lactate concentration were lower, the stroke volume unchanged, and the arteriovenous oxygen difference higher at comparable oxygen uptakes. The maximal heart rate was unchanged. The mechanical efficiency increased about 6 per cent at 900 kpm/min, but the pedaling rate was not given. The regression equation for cardiac output on oxygen uptake lay on a 2.3 liters/min lower level after training, but had the same slope. There were no signs of curvilinearity.

Before training   cardiac output (l/min) $= 6.15 + 5.30 \cdot$ oxygen uptake (l/min)
After training   cardiac output (l/min) $= 3.86 + 5.96 \cdot$ oxygen uptake (l/min)

The level before training was about 1 liter/min lower than values obtained by the Fick method (55) but with the same slope. In another investigation on the effect of training on the oxygen transport system in man (30) the oxygen uptake was studied at maximal work intensity in treadmill exercise. At 82–90 per cent of the maximal speed of the treadmill, oxygen uptake was about the same as at the maximal speed, whereas heart rate was lower; this indicates that at the maximal speed either stroke volume or arteriovenous oxygen difference decreased. One may conclude that an adequate training of the oxygen transport system can be maintained at a somewhat smaller than maximal load, which will also increase the blood volume. A study with radioiodinated albumin (179) confirmed that after 16 weeks of training total blood volume increased by 6 per cent solely because of an increase in plasma volume. The maximal oxygen uptake increased by 18 per cent.

The ability of middle-aged individuals to increase their cardiovascular capacity by training has been discussed. In 9 male subjects between 40–60 years of age who were trained for 1 hr 3 times a week for 6 months, there was an increase of 15 per cent in maximal oxygen uptake per kilogram body weight compared to 1.7 per cent increase for 6 sedentary controls (38). After an 8-week period of physical conditioning, 10 previously sedentary males, aged 36–56 years, showed increased working capacity, and reduced heart rate at a constant work load (26). Pulmonary diffusing capacity at rest increased and was significantly related to the reduction in heart rate at a given work load, while residual volume, forced or timed vital capacity, tidal volume during exercise, and body weight were unaltered by training.

In another study 10 young students trained for 6 to 8 weeks, while 3 of the men played water-polo for ~3 months (27). In the latter group there was a significant increase in resting diffusing capacity and a decrease in heart rate during a standard step test exercise. The increase in resting diffusing capacity seems related to the known increase in the ratio of stroke volume to total-body hemoglobin with training. In a group of men who underwent rigorous physical training for 5 months, the training resulted in a slower heart rate during exercise but no effect on the total blood volume, or on diffusing capacity or pulmonary capillary blood volume at rest or during exercise (107).

Patients.—Knowledge of the effect of training has been applied not only to normal individuals but also to patients with different diseases. Its effect has been studied by testing the functional capacity in a submaximal exercise test or, in greater detail, by heart catheterization. A group of 8 patients with emphysema (31), aged 49–69 years, all of whom were hypoxemic and unable to walk slowly for more than 3 min without unbearable dyspnea, were trained for 21 days with a treadmill in five daily sessions of 10 min each. The work intensity was increased according to each patient's tolerance. As a result of the training the patients' ability to walk improved, with a relatively slower pulse and lengthening of stride. Circulatory measurements showed an increase in arteriovenous oxygen difference and a significant decrease in cardiac output at the same load. Lactate production and oxygen debt were unaffected. The red cell mass increased in those trained while breathing air and decreased in those trained while breathing oxygen. The effect of training is thus most pronounced in the specific exercise for which subjects are trained and is related to a better coordination and economy of movement. On the other hand, the training of the circulatory system was not so marked because the training could only be performed at a relatively low level.

That a cardiac disability of either coronary or valvular etiology nearly always results in a hypokinetic circulation is quite clear from several investigations (63, 64), some of which will be referred to later on. From training experiments in dogs it is established that physical conditioning can be achieved in the presence of acute myocardial infarction (84) and that the exercise program is not harmful. The experiment was performed in two groups of dogs which had their coronary arteries ligated so as to produce infarction of ∼15–30 per cent of the left ventricle. All animals were then examined during exercise between the 3rd and 6th day after the ligation. Thereafter the animals were divided randomly into a trained and a control group. The trained group was exercised on a treadmill for 30 min twice daily 6 days a week for a period of 5 weeks after the coronary occlusion. After training, these dogs had a slower heart rate both at rest and during exercise and also a lower cardiac output. The control dogs showed significantly greater rises in lactate and plasma catecholamines during exercise than the trained animals. No harmful effects of training developed. All animals showed collateral channels and there was no difference in this or in other pathological findings between the trained and control dogs.

The coronary artery area, the number of extracoronary collateral arteries, and the capillary-fiber ratio were increased in rats, who swam for 1 hr daily for 10 weeks (168). Rats exercised intermittently for 1 hr twice weekly for 10 weeks showed an increase only in extracoronary collateral arteries and capillary-fiber ratio. After cessation of exercise, ventricular weights regressed rapidly but the extracoronary collateral arteries and capillary-fiber ratio remained significantly greater than in the controls in the first group at 42 days after exercise.

A training program for patients with hypokinetic circulation has been tried with good results in patients with healed infarctions (113–116). Training for 24 weeks, two evenings a week, with increasing intensity produced very favorable changes in mood and increased muscular endurance (115). Another group trained three periods weekly for 1 to 2 months on a bicycle ergometer at a load which produced a heart rate of over 100 beats/min, ending with a short period up to a level which induced chest pain or a heart rate of ∼150 beats/min (113). The training resulted in a reduction of exercise heart rate and tension-time index, and enhancement of stroke volume. The left ventricular function was improved and the exercise tolerance increased. Evidently patients with a myocardial infarction derive great benefit from increase in physical activity, but the optimal level and the time for start of training have not yet been established.

Even if it seems quite clear that training will have a beneficial effect in patients who have been satisfactorily operated upon for a valvular disease, no studies appear to have been published. Five patients of mean age 43 years with slight or moderate mitral stenosis, all of whom had undergone only medical treatment and were in sinus rhythm, trained for 4 weeks with a 5-min training period 5 times weekly in the supine position at the maximal tolerable load (32). The patients had a higher pulse rate increase for a given oxygen consumption than did normal subjects of the same age. After the 4-week training period all patients reported marked subjective improvements, and a 13 per cent mean decrease in heart rate at a given oxygen consumption was observed. The diffusing capacity during exercise was not affected by the training. Even if it seems unsuitable to train patients with valvular disease before attempts have been made to restore their valvular function, these results show that the training can have a positive effect. The marked subjective improvement may result mainly from a more economical performance of the exercise. The improvement in pulse rate response indicates a greater availability of oxygen per heart beat after training, which, as can be deduced from other training studies, might be mostly an effect of a more economical peripheral utilization, with an increase in arteriovenous difference of oxygen.

The effect of exercise on both the myocardial and the skeletal muscle has also been studied. Forced swimming provides a convenient method of exercising small animals in a relatively controlled environment. Crews & Aldinger (33) exercised 15 albino rats 6 hr a day, 6 days a week, up to 118 hr. The first animal was then operated upon; the last animal, after a total swimming time of 250 hr. Before the direct exercise period there was an initial acclimatization period with a successive increase in exercise time. A group of 15 control rats were studied at the same time as each exercised animal. In the exercise group the resting heart rate was 21 per cent lower than in the control group, but there was no significant difference in arterial pressure. A significant increase in isometric systolic tension at three levels of end diastolic tension indicated an increase of the potential myocardial contraction. The heart volume increased by 33 per cent, and the heart weight by 34 per cent. The wall thicknesses of the right and left ventricles increased between 36–39 per cent. The liver also increased in weight, but not the adrenals. The response to a standardized dose of epinephrine was much greater in the controls than in the exercise group, which indicates that the myocardium may have become relatively refractory to the catecholamines as a result of the adrenal medullary activity that accompanies the stresses produced by swimming. A histochemical analysis of the hypertrophied heart was performed by Kunze & Citoler (34), who trained rats for 10–30 days by forcing them to swim with increased intensity. The nuclei of the myocardial cells diminished in number per unit area, reflecting an increase in the mean cell volume. Heart weight increased by ~20 per cent. By giving the rats ^{3}H-thymidine and then performing autoradiography, they found a significant increase in the concentration of deoxyribonucleic acid per unit amount of muscle nucleus.

Acute exercise, swimming for 60–120 min, induced a significant increase in the whole mitochondrial mass of heart muscles in rats, which swam for 60–120 min (165). Whether this corresponds to an increase in the metabolic function is not yet known. The increase in skeletal muscle occurs during normal development as a growth process and also as a result of a work-induced growth. To test whether the work-induced growth of skeletal muscles depends on the pituitary growth hormone, Goldberg (35) compared two groups of rats, one of which was hypophysectomized. He induced compensatory hypertrophy in one limb by cutting the tendons of the synergistic muscle. The increase in muscle weight was rapid, with histological evidence of increased diameters of the muscle cells, and was maximal after ∼5 days and similar in both groups. Thus the pituitary growth hormone was not essential for skeletal muscle hypertrophy. By prolonged treadmill training of rats the skeletal muscle myoglobin content increased almost twofold compared with the control group, with no significant change in muscle weight (36). The animals exercised 5 days per week and the program was made progressively more vigorous, ending with an all-out exercise test in which they ran to exhaustion. The same program had been found to result in a large increase in exercise capacity with an increase in running time from a mean of 29 to 192 min. The increase in myoglobin was limited to those muscles directly involved in the activity of running. There is indirect evidence that myoglobin acts as an oxygen store and helps to support aerobic metabolism by releasing oxygen to cytochrome oxidase when a lack of oxygen becomes the limiting factor during muscle contraction. This, however, can play only a small part in the adaptation of the capacity for prolonged aerobic exercise, which depends rather on the adaptation of local metabolites in the muscles, as will be discussed later on.

That physical training has a beneficial effect not only on the central circulatory adaptation but also on the circulation in the legs has been demonstrated in patients with arteriosclerosis obliterans in the legs (37, 194). Five men, aged 52–72 years, walked for 1 hr on a treadmill at a level of 75 per cent of the maximal walking time; this was repeated 30 times over a period of 3–8 months. After the training program there were increases in resting systolic pressure at the ankle, in time of onset of claudication pain, and in maximal walking time of all subjects. The data signified a significant increase in collateral circulation at rest and during and after the exercise.

METABOLISM DURING EXERCISE

Metabolism during short-time exercise and especially during prolonged exercise offers an important field for study. The quantitative role of protein, fats, and carbohydrate in the energy yield during muscular activity for long periods has been known from indirect estimations (respiratory quotients) performed between 1910 and 1930. The main focus in the last few years has been on fatty acid metabolism, partly as a result of the interest in hyperlipemia and arteriosclerosis. Most recently, however, carbohydrate metabolism has been further evaluated, partly because of the development of methods for local study of the carbohydrate depots.

Carbohydrates.—These problems have been studied by Hultman (68) and some of his findings will be mentioned further on in detail. That the glycogen content in working muscles is one of the most important factors for prolonged exercise is quite clear. The rate of decrease in glycogen is dependent on the relative work load, as shown by Hermansen, Hultman & Saltin (48), who give values for the decrease in muscle glycogen in 8 physically fit students who performed three 1-hr exercise periods at weekly intervals, at varying work levels. Decreases in muscle glycogen were 0.31, 0.83, and 1.56 g per 100 g muscle per hour at levels of 25, 54, and 78 per cent of the maximal oxygen uptake, respectively. It is not only the relative work level, but also the absolute work level, which determines the rate of glycogen utilization, as is obvious from the values in the two papers by Ahlborg et al. (46, 47), derived from different work levels and a wide scatter of absolute work loads in contrast to the rather selected materials used by Hermansen, Hultman & Saltin (48). In 31 subjects the partial correlation coefficients between utilized muscle glycogen and absolute and relative load were, respectively, 0.477 with constant relative load and 0.388 with constant absolute load.

The rate of utilization of glycogen with time appears to be exponential rather than linear, as indicated in the values obtained from several biopsies during prolonged exercise (48, 181). This may fit in with the well-known fact that the respiratory quotient decreases during prolonged continuous exercise, so that a greater part of the energy will derive from combustion of fat. Hermansen, Hultman & Saltin (48) found no decrease in respiratory quotient, but the exercise was intermittent, with 20 min of work and 15 min of rest. They present in a diagram the mean values for the decrease in glycogen against time in two groups of 4 subjects performing either the above-mentioned intermittent exercise or continuous exercise. They interpret the results as if there were no essential difference between the two types of exercise, but the diagram indicates a much more rapid decrease after the first 20-min period of the intermittent exercise. This may be explained by a short initial anaerobic period at the beginning of each work period, which seems to be quite clear from the blood lactate values. These generally decrease with time, as reported earlier (46, 69), but increase periodically in the first half of each 20-min work cycle.

The alinearity in the rate of utilization of glycogen is well illustrated by the results for 1-hr work at the three levels (48). Thus with a linear decrease, the value for a work level of 28 per cent of the maximal oxygen uptake gives a work time of ∼3 hr, and the 54 per cent work level gives a work time of ∼2 hr, which is quite different from the actual findings. In reality, at a relative work level of ∼25 per cent the exercise can continue for an almost unlimited time and at a level of ∼50 per cent for 1–3 hr. Thus, even at a very low exercise level there must be a nonlinear rate of glycogen utilization. At only 40–60 per cent of the maximal oxygen uptake the muscle glycogen concentration is one of the main determinants of the capacity for prolonged continuous exercise (46, 47). There is a close correlation between performance time and decrease in muscle glycogen and also between energy developed and decrease in muscle glycogen (46, 47). After prolonged exercise, there was a significant decrease in the potassium content and a probably significant increase in the chloride space and chloride and sodium contents in muscle (46), but all these changes were too slight to have been the limiting factor for the physical working capacity in these experiments.

The above studies were performed in a fasting state without any nutrition during the exercise period. In practice, for instance in athletics and heavy daily exercise, some type of nutrition, rich in carbohydrate content, is always taken during the exercise. Then the question arises whether there can be any utilization of the glucose content in blood to diminish the utilization of the muscle glycogen. Ahlborg et al., in a study of 9 subjects (46), repeated the test after 6 months with a continuous intravenous infusion of 20 per cent glucose solution to 2 subjects. This procedure produced no difference in performance time or utilization of glycogen. A further study was performed by Bergström & Hultman (181) on 10 subjects working for 1 hr with one leg at a time, first without glucose infusion and then, with the other leg, with glucose infusion. The utilization of muscle glycogen was significantly lower when glucose was infused, but the absolute difference was small. The experimental conditions used gave rise to several problems, however, one of which is the difficulty of knowing the actual load for each individual, because 2 subjects cycled on each side of a bicycle ergometer at the same time with one leg and no check was made of individual oxygen uptakes or heart rates. Moreover, the subjects did not work until exhaustion; the work time was fixed, and therefore the estimated difference in muscle glycogen utilization with and without glucose infusion might imply a difference only in the first part of the utilization curve.

With the correlation between performance time and muscle glycogen content in mind, the possibility of increasing the glycogen content is of great interest. In connection with the influence of different diets on muscle glycogen synthesis, Hultman & Bergström (180) observed that a carbohydrate-rich diet, after the muscle glycogen depots had been emptied by previous exercise, greatly enhanced the synthesis of muscle glycogen to a supernormal level. To evaluate this finding further, Ahlborg et al. (47) investigated the effect of different diets in connection with continuous leg exercise at a level of about 71 per cent of the subjects' maximal oxygen uptake. Glycogen content was estimated before and after the men exercised until exhaustion. The subjects were randomly divided into three groups, the first group being fed with a more than 90 per cent carbohydrate diet directly after the initial exercise. The second group had a fat-protein diet with less than 1 per cent of the calories in the form of carbohydrate for 1 day, after which a new test was performed to exhaustion, followed by a period of carbohydrate diet. The third group had a fat-protein diet for 3 days and then, after a new test to exhaustion, a carbohydrate diet. After the initial decrease in muscle glycogen there was only minor restitution during the following 1 or 3 days on a fat-protein diet. During the periods of carbohydrate-rich diet the muscle glycogen was restored to supernormal values. The restitution was quicker and lasted longer in the subjects who had been on a fat-protein diet than in those whose carbohydrate period started directly after the first prolonged exercise. There was also a tendency to a longer lasting and higher increase in the third group with fat-protein diet for 3 days. Twelve of the subjects carried out three prolonged exercise tests at three levels of muscle glycogen and there was a close correlation between the work time and initial muscle glycogen content.

Immediately after the exercise period the isometric strength at the knee decreased but then was quickly restored, in contradistinction to the muscle glycogen, so that there was no correlation between isometric strength and muscle glycogen. The investigation was repeated by Bergström et al. (182) who, after initial prolonged intermittent exercise at a load of ~75 per cent of the maximal oxygen uptake, gave 6 individuals fat and protein for 3 days and then a carbohydrate-rich diet for a further 3 days, with exercise periods until exhaustion and muscle biopsies before and after the different periods. The results were identical with these reported earlier, apart from the findings in 3 individuals who had the carbohydrate-rich diet during the first 3 days after the initial exercise. The muscle glycogen in no case decreased to less than half its initial value, but increased to supernormal values after the 3 days on protein and fat. This pattern of change is quite different from other reports, but the reason is unclear.

It is well established that adenosine triphosphate (ATP) constitutes the initial source of energy for muscle contraction. ATP can be regenerated in several ways, one of which is by transphosphorylation of phosphorylcreatine (PC). Hultman, Bergström & McLennan Anderson (183) therefore studied the concentrations of PC and ATP together with that of glycogen in leg muscle biopsies in connection with different types of exercise. The PC concentration decreased rapidly during the first 2 min of continuous work, then remained relatively constant. The very rapid resynthesis of PC after work was complete within a few minutes. The work load was inversely related to the PC concentration during work, and directly correlated with the glycogen store, so that the PC level at a certain work load is lower if the glycogen store is decreased. The ATP concentration decreases during the first minutes of work but then returns to the basal level during continuous, moderate work. At heavy work levels with pronounced decreases of PC, the ATP concentration also remains decreased. Thus the contents of both PC and ATP seem to vary in parallel with the relative work load and, via enzyme activation and inhibition respectively, may regulate the rate of glycolysis. Apparently, local enzymatic changes regulate the relation between those components of the energy derived from fatty acid or carbohydrate combustion. From earlier investigations with respiratory quotient measurements it is quite clear that, for a given level of work, the organism adapts to a higher degree of fat utilization after a period of fat- and protein-rich diet and that this adaptation is mediated through local enzymatic changes. Such changes also explain the differences between people who are physically fit and those who are not. Local factors in the muscles are also decisive for the enhancement of glycogen synthesis after exercise during a carbohydrate period, as shown in Bergström & Hultman's investigation with one-leg work (180).

A knowledge of these local factors can give us ways of influencing the capacity for prolonged exercise by changing the local metabolism. One such influence is the above-mentioned diet-induced increase in muscle glycogen. In a study by Ahlborg, Ekelund & Nilsson (45) a chemical preparation was found to increase the capacity for prolonged exercise under standardized conditions by ~50 per cent. Six normal young men were exercised until exhaustion on 4 consecutive days under standardized conditions. Starting 18 hr before the first exercise test they were given 5 tablets every 6th hr. Placebos were given before the tests on days 1, 2, and 4, and before day 3 the active substance, 1.75 g of potassium-magnesium-aspartate, was given. The placebo and active tablets were identical in form and the leader of the tests and the subjects were unaware of the contents. On the days of placebo medication there were no significant differences between work times to exhaustion but on day 3, after the active substance, the mean work time was 128 min compared to 85 min on the day before, a highly significant difference. The mechanism behind this interesting observation is not clear and will be investigated by biopsy studies of the muscles. One possibility is an accelerated resynthesis of glycogen in the muscles under the influence of potassium-magnesium-aspartate. Another mechanism may be the supplying of a greater part of the energy during work from fat, mediated through an influence of the aspartate on the local enzymatic systems.

Lactate.—The concept of oxygen debt in relation to the metabolism of lactic acid (174) has been under debate for many years, no clear solution having been reached. The role of the myoglobin-bound oxygen has been discussed, but earlier calculations on myoglobin content had indicated that it could store only about half the oxygen needed. The above-mentioned increase in muscle myoglobin (36) after training may change this figure, so that it will be adequate for the oxygen requirement. As pointed out by Hultman, Bergström & Andersson (183), the alactic oxygen debt can be adequately explained by breakdown of the amount of PC and ATP found in muscles in connection with exercise. The common way of calculating lactate production and metabolism is to assume a given distribution volume of an order of magnitude of the body water, and the lactate homogeneously distributed within that volume. Hultman's thesis (68) indicates values of local lactic acid concentration in the working muscles of the order of 20–30 meq/liter muscle water. There is thus a marked gradient between the muscle and the blood during heavy exercise, and a large quantity of lactate may remain in exercising muscles. Identical values for muscle tissue lactate after maximal exercise in men were later published by Diamant, Karlsson & Saltin (184). Thus one has to be critical of the information obtained from calculation of excess lactate. Keul, Keppler & Doll (42) estimated the lactate-pyruvate ratio and its relation to oxygen pressure in arterial coronary venous and femoral venous blood. They conclude that the lactate-pyruvate ratio corresponds to the excess lactate, whose determination yields the same information, and that the lactic acid output from working skeletal muscle is not the result solely of an oxygen deficiency. Problems encountered in the production of lactate are further discussed in several publications (40, 41, 43, 44).

In connection with the discussion of factors limiting prolonged exercise it was mentioned that glucose infusion decreased the rate of glycogen utilization only to a very minor degree and did not clearly increase the performance time. The study of glucose uptake in muscle and other tissues, mostly with estimation of the arteriovenous glucose difference in relation to the flow (39, 43, 51), is hazardous and has given conflicting results. For a better evaluation some type of isotope kinetics is needed and Young et al. (50) made a study of prolonged exercise with administration of ^{14}C-labeled glucose. They used a rather extreme variant of prolonged exercise, having 30 male individuals work for 9 hr on a treadmill, after which they were assumed to be in a steady state with respect to blood sugar and free fatty acid levels in the blood. Thereafter uniformly labeled glucose-^{14}C was injected as a single dose and measurements were made of glucose specific activity in blood and the $^{14}CO_2$ content of expired air. The incorporation of various metabolites into glucose was also studied. The observations were made during an additional 4.5-hr period of exercise. The individuals worked at a load of $\sim$33 per cent of the maximal work capacity and each period of exercise consisted of 1 hr and 20 min of walking, followed by 10 min of rest. The glucose pool was calculated to be 26.2 g; the glucose oxidation rate was 79.0 mg/kg/hr at rest and 175 mg/kg/hr during exercise. There were also indications of an increased rate of production of blood glucose during exercise; the production rate was 206 mg/kg/hr, which maintained the blood glucose at a stable level, so simultaneously providing fuel for oxidative metabolism. The factors which tend to increase glucose oxidation were not analyzed.

Lipids.—Issekutz, Paul & Miller (49) studied glucose and fatty acid metabolism in normal and pancreatectomized dogs during steady-state exercise lasting 4 hr. They used radioactively labeled albumin palmitate and glucose and found in the normal dogs an increased utilization of glucose during work; but the part of the energy derived from glucose was small, amounting to $\sim$12 per cent both at rest and during exercise. The corresponding figures for free fatty acids were 31 per cent at rest, 40 per cent at the beginning of exercise, and 71 per cent at the end of exercise. In the pancreatectomized dogs the level of glucose at rest was high and of the same level as in normal working dogs, but the per cent energy derived from glucose was small, 7.5 at rest and 6.3 during exercise. In these dogs, however, the contribution of free fatty acid to the overall energy expenditure was much higher than in normal dogs with 60.5 per cent at rest and 85.3 per cent during exercise. During continuous infusion of glucose the free fatty acid contribution at rest was 19.5 per cent and during work 47.9 and 65.1 per cent at the beginning and end of exercise. With the same type of prolonged exercise, i.e. 9 + 4.5 hr of exercise, Young et al. (118) also studied fatty acid metabolism in man with a single injection of labeled palmitate-^{14}C. They found that $\sim$37 per cent of CO_2 was derived from free fatty acids at rest and $\sim$50 per cent during exercise. The figures for exercise compare well with earlier published values, but the figure at rest is almost double the earlier values, which may be due to a more prolonged resting period.

The calculations in such studies are highly dependent on the compartment model used, and Havel, Ekelund & Holmgren (117) performed a kinetic analysis of the oxidation of palmitate-1-^{14}C in man during prolonged heavy muscular exercise. Their results indicate that under these working conditions almost half of the free fatty acids leaving the blood are oxidized directly (i.e., are transferred to mitochondrial oxidative sites through small intermediate compartments). The remainder enter larger compartments apart from the direct pathway. Most of these fractions reenter the direct oxidative pathway within 30 min. These observations suggest that the esterified fatty acids contained in working muscle cells are rapidly renewed. From local studies of the uptake and release of free fatty acids and other metabolites in the legs of exercising men, Havel, Pernow & Jones (172) found that about half of the fatty acids and more than half of the glucose oxidized in the leg derived from local stores of lipid and carbohydrate. To further evaluate the importance of the local stores of lipids, studies must be made with muscle biopsies and preliminary reports have been presented by Carlson, Ekelund & Fröberg (187) who studied the lipid content in muscle biopsy before and after prolonged exercise in men.

Hagenfeldt & Wahren (185) studied the free fatty acid metabolism in the human forearm during exercise, recording the uptake, release, and oxidation of individual free fatty acids and glycerol during a 60-min exercise period. Radioactively labeled fatty acids and glycerol were infused together with a dye infusion for the determination of blood flow. Muscular uptake of free fatty acid rose with the arterial concentration and the muscle showed a slight preference for linoleic and oleic acid compared to palmitic acid. The forearm respiratory quotient indicated a constant fat oxidation during the period of exercise. The uptake of free fatty acid covered ~50 per cent of the fat oxidation. Glycerol was also oxidized by the exercising muscle with 23 and 31 per cent of CO_2 derived from infused labeled glycerol. From the $^{14}CO_2$-production curves the size of a small pool of esterified fatty acids could be calculated at ~0.6 μmole fatty acid per g muscle, corresponding to the smaller pool calculated by Havel, Ekelund & Holmgren (117). From gas-chromatographic analysis of the water-soluble metabolites they found that β-hydroxybutyrate left the muscle labeled with radioactivity, and they discussed the possibility that part of the fatty acid oxidation of exercising muscle proceeds via acetoacetate and β-hydroxybutyrate formation (67). They therefore studied (186) the uptake, release, and oxidation of β-hydroxybutyrate. They found at rest a significant net muscular uptake of both β-hydroxybutyrate and acetoacetate amounting to ~50 per cent. During the 60-min exercise period the net arteriovenous difference of both substances declined continuously. During the latter half of the period acetoacetate was produced by the muscle. With a labeled $D(-)$-β-hydroxybutyrate as tracer it was shown that ~25 per cent of the arterial β-hydroxybutyrate was taken up by the muscle during exercise in two experiments, despite the presence of a net β-hydroxybutyrate release. In humans under normal conditions β-hydroxybutyrate and acetoacetate could not be major substrates for the energy production because of their low blood concentration, but the situation may be quite different, for instance, during fasting or different diseases.

Carlström (66) studied the fatty acid metabolism in male, newly diagnosed diabetic patients without insulin treatment. Even at rest the diabetics, compared with controls of the same age, showed elevated levels of plasma free fatty acids, and exercise produced a more pronounced increase of lipid mobilization manifested through a greater increase of both the plasma free fatty acid and the plasma glycerol concentration during and after exercise. The exercise-induced lipid mobilization seemed to be most pronounced in the diabetics with early onset of the disease. From analysis of the individual fatty acids in the plasma fraction, which revealed a higher percentage of oleic acid and a lower percentage of myristic acid, in combination with the concomitant increase in fatty acids and glycerol, the author concludes that a greater mobilization from adipose tissue may occur in the diabetics compared with normal individuals. With norepinephrine infusions he found no evidence of an increased sensitivity to circulating catecholamines, but whether the cause was an increased sympathetic activity or some other lipolytic agent was not determined.

The role of insulin in regulating the mobilization of free fatty acids during exercise has been discussed, but no values have earlier been reported for plasma insulin during exercise. Hunter & Sukkar (166), using a radio-immunoassay method, studied the plasma insulin level during 2 hr treadmill exercise in 6 subjects in the postabsorptive state. The plasma insulin level decreased significantly in 5 of the 6 subjects after the 1st hr, then increased slowly after the exercise. Plasma glucose, insulin, and free fatty acids have been studied during 1 hr exercise in connection with an oral glucose tolerance test (188).

The clinical interest in fasting and exercise as treatment for obesity and as a possible therapeutic approach to atherosclerotic diseases has stimulated studies of metabolic changes during such conditions. A study performed under extreme conditions was that of Carlson & Fröberg (52) on 12 men who walked 50 km each day for 10 days with a daily caloric intake of ~200 cal. Blood glucose decreased slightly during the first 6 days of the study and then increased. The concentrations of free fatty acids and glycerol in plasma increased during the first 6 days, then decreased somewhat. The plasma concentrations of cholesterol, phospholipids, and triglycerides decreased markedly during the study; the decreases in all components were confined mainly to the low-density fractions. Similar findings, but of a much smaller magnitude, were reported by Hoffman, Nelson & Goss (53) when they investigated 355 male officers, aged 40–55 years, who were placed into two groups according to the amount of exercise they performed. The 229 individuals who had taken part in some exercise program for at least a year exhibited lower levels of total lipid, cholesterol, β-lipoprotein, and triglycerides, and there were indications of lower values for the very low-density lipoproteins.

Relatively little is known about the effects of exercise on the metabolism of exogenous plasma triglycerides, but a decrease in the turbidity of alimentary lipemia after exercise was reported earlier. Carlson et al. (169) therefore studied the removal of exogenous triglycerides from blood by injecting a fat emulsion before, during, and after exercise. They found only very small changes, which cannot explain the reduction of alimentary lipemia after exercise. On the other hand Jones & Havel (170), with radioactively labeled chylomicrons injected in rats at rest and during exercise, found a somewhat greater rate of removal of chylomicrons from the blood during exercise, but still on a minor scale. When dealing with alimentary lipemia another important factor has to be considered, the transport of lipids from the alimentary channel to the blood stream, and Carlson et al. (187) have found evidence of a slower absorption of an ingested fat emulsion during exercise.

Fordtran & Saltin (171) found that 1 hr exercise of $\sim$71 per cent of maximum oxygen uptake did not affect gastric emptying of a solution containing 13.3 per cent glucose and 0.3 per cent NaCl. Intestinal absorption of glucose, water, sodium, chloride, potassium or bicarbonate was not influenced by the exercise.

CENTRAL CIRCULATION

Normal subjects.—Concerning the central circulatory adaptation during short-time exercise a considerable amount of knowledge is now available (62, 85, 86). For references see especially the review by Bevegård & Shepherd (5) and the symposium *Physiology of Muscular Exercise* (1). One missing point is the adaptation of the central circulation in the 46 to 65 year age-group. This group is important because it includes many patients who come for further evaluation of their central circulation. For younger men and women and older men, we know their central hemodynamics during exercise rather well (55).

Emirgil et al. (54) compared the pulmonary pressure and flow in two groups of patients, one averaging 39 years of age and one averaging 66 years. Measurements were made with the subjects in the supine position at rest and during light exercise (about twofold increase of the cardiac output over the resting state). To further exaggerate the expected differences between the groups, unilateral pulmonary artery occlusion was performed during rest and exercise with the aid of a balloon-catheter. Arteriovenous oxygen difference and cardiac output were within the limits of normal for all subjects in both groups, and did not differ significantly between the groups. Right ventricular end diastolic pressures were within normal limits in all subjects, both at rest and during exercise. The pulmonary capillary pressure increased up to 12 mm Hg in some subjects in both groups, a finding which in respect to the older ages differs somewhat from earlier investigations. The older group showed a steeper increase of pulmonary artery mean pressure in relation to the increase in cardiac output than did the younger group. Thus, obvious differences exist between the pulmonary vascular beds of the older and younger subjects. These differences are consistent with the microscopic changes observed in the lung with increasing age; intimal fibrosis of the pulmonary arteries has been noted under the age of 40.

Two papers have dealt with the influence of age on the hemodynamic response to bicycle (89) or treadmill (90) exercise at varying work loads. The two reports show rather consistent findings which, for the younger age-group, correspond well with those of Ekelund & Holmgren (55). The oldest groups, 50–69 and 40–48 years, differed from the younger in circulatory response both as to flow and as to arterial pressure. With bicycle exercise the cardiac output-oxygen uptake relation had the same slope as in younger individuals, but the line lay on a lower level, about 1 liter/min, as in earlier reports on older age-groups. The arteriovenous oxygen difference increased by an amount corresponding to the decline in cardiac output. In the treadmill study the slopes of the cardiac output-oxygen uptake relations differed in old and young age-groups, so that at low loads the cardiac output was higher and at high loads lower than in the younger age-groups. This may be an effect of the form of exercise—most other studies have been performed with bicycle exercise—but also of the intermittent work, used to avoid variations in results secondary to prolonged work periods (56, 69). However, the effect of a prolonged work period is marked when the load is constant, but with successively increased loads during rather short periods the influence will be less than if the subjects rest in the sitting position, which may cause a rather marked blood volume displacement. In both studies brachial arterial pressure, especially systolic pressure, clearly deviated in the old age-group. At an oxygen uptake of 1 liter/min the mean systolic pressure in the 18–34 age-group was 150 mm Hg and for the 50–69 group 181 mm Hg. Mean pressure differed significantly but differences in diastolic pressure were not so clear. The increase in systolic arterial pressure and total peripheral resistance seemed to be linear over the age-groups studied. In one study (89) no difference in respiratory parameters was found between age-groups and in the other (90) the oldest age-group developed larger minute volumes of ventilation for a given load compared to the younger groups.

Short-time exercise up to 10 min is commonly used to test the circulatory reaction. For metabolic studies, however, as mentioned above, one has to use exercise lasting from 30 min up to several hours, sometimes with work levels which bring the individual to exhaustion.

Ahlborg (70) found that the capacity for prolonged exercise (100 min) is influenced by factors other than those involved in brief exercise (6 min), such as oxygen transport capacity. In another study of this difference (178) he showed that an ordinary circulatory training did not influence the capacity for prolonged exercise significantly. In prolonged exercise the metabolic factors are important, and also other circulatory factors such as the ability to maintain a circulatory steady state.

The circulatory and respiratory adaptation during prolonged exercise has been analyzed (69, 175, 176) in young healthy men during continuous exercise of up to 1 hr on a bicycle ergometer in the sitting and supine position. Cardiac output remained constant in the different body positions and at different relative working intensities. Heart rate increased steadily, with a corresponding decrease in stroke volume which was most marked at the highest relative working intensity, but there were no differences in the effects of exercise in the supine and the sitting positions at the same relative intensity. During the exercise, pressure in both the systemic and the pulmonary circulation decreased. The decrease in the systemic pressure was related to the relative working intensity and was caused by a lowering of the peripheral resistance. The decrease of mean pulmonary pressure was more marked during supine than during sitting exercise. The findings implied a less effective filling of the heart due to changes in the available filling energy, probably as a result of a lowering in the vasomotor tone. There were also indications of a change in the mechanical properties of the myocardium (176).

Sowton & Burkart (57) later studied hemodynamic changes in 7 patients during 30-min continuous sitting exercise at a low load, 300 kpm/min. The same mechanism as during prolonged continuous exercise may also come into play during repeated exercise. For instance, Burkart, Barold & Sowton (56) studied normal individuals and some patients during sitting bicycle work at three work levels, repeated after a rest period of 30 min. There were changes similar to those during continuous exercise (69), with a lower pulmonary artery pressure and lower aortic pressure during the second exercise period. The effect of previous exercise might be one explanation for the conflicting results reported by Marx et al. (58) concerning the maintenance of aortic pressure during exercise. They reported that the proximal aortic pressure in 6 healthy men remained almost constant during four grades of treadmill exercise requiring from 43 to 87 per cent of maximal oxygen intake. At room temperature of 43.3° C the aortic pressure was always slightly lower than at 25.6° C. Exercise to exhaustion in the heat was not associated with peripheral circulatory collapse and hypotension. The experimental procedure with 15–20 min rest periods in the sitting position between the different work loads might be another important factor in explaining the unusual finding of an unchanged aortic pressure during increasing loads. With well-defined and calibrated catheter systems we have always found in our laboratory a progressive increase of aortic mean and systolic pressure with increase of load either in sitting or in supine position (55).

The neural explanation of cardiac adaptation during exercise has interested several researchers over a long period. In the last 15 years, studies have been performed on dogs which have been denervated in different ways. Goldstone & Wyndham (59) studied 8 dogs after cardiac denervation by complete thoracic sympathectomy and selective removal of all thoracic cardiac vagal branches. Exercised on the treadmill, the dogs still possessed some residual ability to increase their cardiac output, though much less than normal dogs. Cardiac output increased by only 30 per cent at 3 mph (compared with 73 per cent in the normal dogs) and did not increase further at 5 mph. The increase was almost entirely due to a rise in heart rate. Some dogs developed a greater arteriovenous oxygen difference and others an anaerobic metabolism with an increase of lactic acid in the blood. The conclusion from further investigations on vagotomized and sympathectomized dogs (189) is that, in spite of the well-known role of the central nervous system in adapting the heart to exercise, the heart possesses a residual intrinsic ability to increase its output during exercise.

In the discussion of the regulation of circulation and ventilation during exercise, different peripheral control systems have been described. The two main opinions are that chemoreceptors are located in the muscles which are stimulated by metabolic factors, or that muscular mechanoreceptors control the ventilation and heart rate when different loads are applied. To evaluate the influence of mechanical receptors, Heinrich, Ulmer & Stegemann (190) let 5 subjects exercise on a bicycle with varying load and pedaling frequencies. Ventilation and heart rate were related only to oxygen consumption and were independent of mechanical factors. These results exclude the effect of muscular mechanoreceptors on the control circuits for ventilation and heart rate under the condition described, i.e. exercise in steady-state with rather large muscle groups.

In lightly anesthetized dogs Flandrois et al. (122) found that a neurogenic ventilatory stimulus originated from muscle spindles and articular receptors. However, in humans Stegemann & Böning (123) found evidence of chemoreceptors in the muscles which stimulated the ventilation and, to a lesser degree, the circulation.

Hypertensive patients.—One condition in which study during exercise is of real importance is arterial hypertension, as the arterial pressure increases more during exercise in hypertensive than in normal subjects. Borderline cases can therefore be classified much more easily. Other essential points are that measuring the intra-arterial pressure excludes the sometimes markedly different pressures obtained by the indirect method and that measuring during exercise excludes the pure psychogenic hypertension.

Levy, Tabakin & Hanson (60) studied 20 young, untreated, labile hypertensive subjects and their age-matched normal controls during exercise. A similar investigation was performed by Amery et al. (61) but on patients of a wider age range (61 patients from 19–68 years of age) and with a more definite and stable increase in blood pressure. In the first study only 10 subjects exhibited a diastolic pressure of more than 90 mm Hg at rest; during exercise an additional 6 subjects showed diastolic hypertension. During exercise the normal and hypertensive groups demonstrated almost parallel pressure deviations; both at rest and during exercise there were highly significant differences between the two groups in pressure but not in heart rate, cardiac output, or stroke volume. Only 3 in the hypertensive group could be categorized as high output, low resistance, labile hypertensive patients. Ejection time, ejection time index, or maximal upstroke velocity of the pressure pulse did not differ significantly, but 3 of the hypertensive subjects had a prolonged and 3 a short ejection time index. Thus the 3 with the short ejection time were able to compensate for their hypertension and produce a normal tension time index in contrast to the other subjects. The data do not indicate clearly whether the so-called hypertensive subjects really are hypertensive or constitute an extreme variant of normal subjects.

In contrast, the second study (61) deals with clear-cut cases of hypertension with a mean diastolic pressure in the three age-groups of 129–135 mm Hg. In the middle-aged (35–49 years) and older subjects (50–60 years) the systolic pressure showed a greater increase with exercise than in normals of their age. This did not apply to subjects aged 19–34 years. The cardiac output in relation to oxygen uptake was normal during exercise in the middle-aged and elderly group, but the oldest group showed a reduced maximal cardiac output. In the youngest age-group cardiac output was normal at rest but considerably below normal values at all levels of exercise. The total peripheral resistance decreased during exercise but was significantly higher in all groups than in normal subjects. The subjects with the most severe hypertension had lower maximal oxygen uptake, cardiac output, and stroke volume. Lund-Johansen (191) has published a careful study of the hemodynamics, with flow and pressure measurements at rest and during exercise, in early essential hypertension. Comparing 93 hypertensive men aged 17–66 years with 48 normotensive men, he found higher total peripheral resistance during exercise in the hypertensives at all ages. The cardiac output lay on a lower level in relation to oxygen uptake in the hypertensives at all ages. Only at rest were there some young subjects with a high cardiac output.

The value of exercise in detecting early changes in the vascular system is evident from Carlström & Karlefors' (65) report on 11 male patients with newly diagnosed diabetes of the juvenile type who were compared with 8 healthy men of comparable age. Insulin treatment was discontinued for at least 2 days prior to the investigation. There were no significant differences between the diabetic and the control groups in heart rate, cardiac output, stroke volume, or arterial pressures at rest. Neither ketoacidosis nor dehydration was evident in the diabetics. During exercise at 600 kpm/min oxygen uptake, cardiac output, and stroke volume were not significantly different, but systolic, diastolic, and mean arterial pressures were significantly higher in the diabetic group. The cause of the higher pressure was not a higher cardiac output but a higher vascular resistance.

RENAL FUNCTION DURING EXERCISE

Castenfors (91–98) has investigated renal function during exercise with the special aim of studying the physiological mechanism of exercise proteinuria. During cross-country skiing for 85 km (91), and also supine exercise for 45 min (93), first at a low level, then after 1 hr rest at a high level of intensity, urinary protein excretion markedly increased, possibly as a result of renal vasoconstriction and an increase in glomerular permeability. There was also evidence of an individual constitutional factor in the glomerular membrane as an important element in the mechanism of exercise proteinuria. The protein excretion during exercise was not correlated with the plasma renin content. As reported earlier, the clearance of p-aminohippuric acid decreased during exercise with a negative correlation to the work intensity (94, 95). Inulin clearance decreased during light exercise but showed no further decrease during heavy exercise, and the effect of exercise was influenced by the degree of hydration. The clearance of water and the urine flow indicated a release of antidiuretic hormone.

Electrolytes in plasma were also studied by Castenfors (95) and Aurell et al. (99) during supine exercise for 45 min at different loads. During severe exercise urinary sodium excretion decreased markedly, while the excretion varied in milder exercise. Potassium excretion showed a much less marked decrease than sodium during severe exercise, with wide individual variations, and increased in most subjects during milder exercise. The predominant factor was considered to be increased tubular reabsorption of sodium during exercise, perhaps secondary to a change in medullary blood flow or an aldosterone effect. Plasma sodium increased at the beginning of exercise but then gradually decreased. Potassium and phosphate increased markedly, which is consistent with other reports (46). The increased potassium level seems to result from a release of potassium from working muscles in connection with a glycogenolysis, and the increased plasma phosphate concentration could then be due to liberation of phosphate from high energy phosphate compounds in active muscles.

Exercise, ganglionic blocking agents, and changes in sodium load were used to evaluate the stimulus for renin release (96–98). The results suggest that acute changes in renin release from the juxtaglomerular apparatus are mediated through the sympathetic renal nerves, but other mechanisms may also participate.

Respiratory Adaptation During Exercise

The improved techniques for measuring blood gas tensions have made possible more reliable determinations of, for instance, the alveolar arterial oxygen tension difference and the physiological dead space. Several communications give values for these variables during exercise in normal subjects (100–102). During exercise the difference between old and young people diminishes and the upper limit for the alveolar arterial oxygen tension difference amounts to about 17 mm Hg in contrast to the resting condition, in which it is dependent on age. The main factor in the difference seems to be the distribution and, to a lesser extent, a real anatomical shunt. Also in respect to dead space there is no difference during exercise between young and aged, with a value of 0.18 for the ratio between dead space and tidal volume during exercise.

In normal individuals the oxygen cost of breathing is not a limiting factor during exercise, because even at a level of exercise which gives a ventilation of about 70 liters/min, only 10–15 per cent of the oxygen consumed was utilized by the respiratory muscles (103). In patients with chronic obstructive pulmonary disease, however, the oxygen cost of ventilation is much higher for a given load, so that the respiratory muscles account for 35–40 per cent of the total oxygen consumption even at low levels of exercise, for which reason the oxygen cost of breathing seems to be an important limiting factor on exercise performance in such patients. Estimation of the maximal level of exercise from the values of a maximal voluntary ventilation test is uncertain because the fraction of the maximal voluntary ventilation which can be sustained during exercise is rather variable (104).

Patients with pulmonary fibrosis and with hypoxemia at rest behave in different ways during exercise, depending on whether the fibrosis is of

idiopathic type or caused by silicosis (105). The arterial oxygen tension difference was unchanged. In the group with idiopathic pulmonary fibrosis the
arterial oxygen tension decreased during exercise and seemed to be caused by
the perfusion of hypoventilated areas. Exercise induces significant bronchospasm in asthmatic patients, but the mechanism is as yet unknown. The
autonomic nervous system seems not to be the main factor, as β-adrenergic,
α-adrenergic, or cholinergic blockade did not affect the decrease in peak
expiratory flow rates induced by exercise in a group of 15 children (106).

PERIPHERAL CIRCULATION

A good estimation of peripheral circulation, especially during exercise, is a
still unsolved problem. Several papers deal with the comparison between the
isotope clearance method and simultaneously performed occlusion plethysmography (109–111). The flow can only be measured after exercise and the
plethysmography has a higher degree of reproducibility, with a coefficient
of variation of 13 per cent against 21 per cent for ^{133}Xe clearance. With repeated determinations the ^{133}Xe clearance decreases progressively, which was
interpreted as due to the existence of a multicompartment system. The
thermodilution method seems to be reliable, but the weak point is that the
determination has to be performed in a big vessel such as the femoral artery
(108). Dye dilution can also be used (193), but the method may not be sensitive enough in some cases to demonstrate local disturbances. With the
[133]Xe clearance technique it is possible to quantitate the degree of arterial insufficiency in patients with intermittent claudication, even with the method's
high coefficient of variation. The ^{133}Xe clearance flows correlated well with
the walking distance measured on a treadmill, while the postexercise blood
flow measured by plethysmography was not correlated with that distance
(82). A measure of the maximal diffusion capacity for sodium can be obtained
(112) with simultaneous estimations of the clearance of several isotopes,
such as ^{133}Xe and [24]Na. This value in forearm muscles increased successively
with rising work load and was considered to reflect an increase in capillary
surface area and perhaps variations in a nonuniform capillary circulation.

The effectiveness of the circulation to the arms and legs during exercise
can be studied by following arteriovenous lactate differences of the working
region (147–150). Working with small muscle groups produces high lactate
levels in the blood, as revealed, for instance, by comparison with leg exercise
(149). Another situation which increases the lactate production is an insufficient oxygen supply due to, for instance, occlusion of the arteries to the
muscles. During prolonged exercise the lactate concentration in plasma
declines with time and the same situation is found in human forearm muscle
during a 60-min exercise period (150). This change, interpreted as an
adaptational reaction resulting in improved muscle cell oxygenation, is also
found when one combines arm and leg exercise (149). The arterial lactate
concentration during standardized exercise could be used as a simple guide
for the functional assessment of the appropriate stimulation rate in patients
with artificial pacemakers (146). An optimal stimulation rate improved the

ability to sustain bicycle exercise by increasing the leg blood flow. At the same time the lactate concentration in blood was decreased.

The local regulation of the peripheral circulation is related to changes in the metabolic state of the tissues and in the vascular transmural pressure acting through adrenergic nerve activity. By application of subatmospheric pressure to the lower part of the body one can increase the sympathetic vasoconstrictor action. Forearm blood flow was studied during such increased sympathetic activity and during normal conditions at different work levels by Strandell & Shepherd (119). The muscle blood flow was reduced at low levels but the effect lessened as the exercise increased in severity, so that with maximal activity no effect of significance was observed. The sympathetic adrenergic nerves thus modulate the local dilator mechanism in active muscles. The metabolic factors seem to be more important than transmural pressure in determining the tone of the resistance vessels, while the reverse is true of precapillary sphincters (120). Myogenic autoregulation of filtration exchange via alteration of precapillary sphincter tone may be important. The problem of postexercise hyperemia in local regulation has been studied by Brandon et al. (121). They found no vasoactive substances in venous blood from exercising muscles using cross-transfusing technique, but they found an altered response of the superfused guinea pig ileum to venous blood drained from human skeletal muscle after exercise. The substance was not identified. There were also findings implying a role of acetylcholine in the postexercise hyperemia.

Not much is known about the cerebral blood flow during exercise. An earlier study, using the nitrous oxide method, showed a slight decrease in cerebral blood flow, but later Russek & Beaton (124) reported a rather marked increase in cerebral blood flow measured with an impedance rheograph. The exercise consisted of a step test, which gave an increase in heart rate between 42 and 61 beats/min, so that the exercise was harder than in the earlier report.

EXERCISE AT HIGH ALTITUDES

The Olympic Games in Mexico City have stimulated an interest in exercise at high altitudes. Numerous papers have been published (13, 125–138, 145, 151, 152, 167, 195, 196). The maximal performance measured as maximal oxygen uptake falls by ∼3–3.5 per cent for every 1000 feet above 5000 feet, and at 4000 m the reduction in maximal oxygen uptake is 26 per cent (125). The reduction was somewhat more marked on the 3rd day than on the 48th day. Ventilation increased markedly even at maximal exercise. The maximal heart rate was unchanged but showed larger individual variations. Training at high altitudes may increase the oxygen uptake to almost the same amount as at sea level and concomitantly there is an increase in hemoglobin and hematocrit (126).

Some investigators have not found a complete compensation for the decrease of performance with altitude and this has been explained as an effect of the previous training level, in which case athletes with very high aerobic capacity and at their maximum training level would be more affected by altitude than others. There are also reports of a potentiating effect of low oxygen tension during training on the subsequent cardiovascular performance (127). Such an effect might be due to a shift in the upper limit of the arteriovenous oxygen difference or to activation of a nonoxidative, nonglycolytic exergonic metabolism. The low oxygen tension has certain effects, such as diminishing the maximal heart rate, which is evident at a very high altitude. The circulatory changes corresponding to the changes in work performance are an increase in cardiac output at corresponding intensity of exercise compared with sea level, a slight elevation in arterial pressure, and a fall in total peripheral resistance (128). The enhanced cardiac output is due primarily to an increased heart rate during submaximal exercise, but at maximal exercise the heart rate is often somewhat less than at sea level.

When studying the effect of altitude, one often uses simulated situations with different oxygen mixtures at sea level, and it does not seem as if the altitude itself has any special effect (133). There are also reports of a decrease in cardiac output during exercise at high altitudes (129), which is in contrast to other reports and may be due to a difference in body position, supine or sitting, during the exercise.

During work under hypoxia there is an earlier change to an anaerobic metabolism with an increase in lactate in arterial blood (135). The free fatty acid level is also higher in blood, both at rest and during work, as a result of an increased adrenergic activity. But in spite of the higher free fatty acid level, oxidation of free fatty acids in the heart muscle seems to be diminished during work. Blood levels of amino acids and ammonia are also higher, which may be an energy conservation process. Exercise during hypoxia causes a greater decrease of oxygen tension in arterial blood than at rest, the degree depending on the partial pressure of oxygen (136). This is interpreted as a result of an insufficient oxygen diffusion in the lungs. The decrease in oxygen saturation is more marked, as a result of the marked decrease of pH in arterial blood during exercise (137).

Hypoxia certainly introduces changes at the cellular level, as reflected in the increased activity of such oxidative enzymes as GOT, GPT, LDH during and after exercise (153). This increase is enhanced by exercise during hypoxia (138). The enzyme and tissue changes were less in trained than in untrained rats both at sea level and at high altitudes, which corresponds well with findings after prolonged exercise in well-trained human subjects (139, 197).

Weightlessness

Little on the influence of weightlessness is available in the general literature, because most results are in proceedings from symposia or are given in special technical reports from local research centers. A short communication has been presented on human circulation times during weightlessness produced by parabolic flight (154). There were insignificant changes in arm-to-lung circulation and arm-to-tongue circulation, so that the method of injecting macroaggregated human albumin can be used to study regional pulmonary blood flow during weightlessness. Changes in blood volume and red blood cell mass should be an important factor during weightlessness as indicated by simulated studies with bed rest and water immersion and by weightlessness during space-flight (198). One study has been published (155) on astronauts before and after Gemini orbital flights. The red blood cell mass decreased in all three flights, which were of different length; the plasma volume decreased only in the two shorter flights, ~97 and 121 hr, but increased in the third flight of 330 hr. Of 4 astronauts studied, 3 showed a significant shortening of the erythrocyte lifespan during the flights. Probably as a result not only of weightlessness but also of an increased gravitational force, the excretion of catecholamines and catecholamine metabolites increased in several pilots (156).

At the opposite end of the scale, the influence of increased gravitational stress on the adaptation of cardiovascular and pulmonary function to exercise has been studied by Rosenhamer (157–159). The stroke volume was only ~25 per cent lower at 3 G than at 1 G during exercise, so exercise prevented the circulatory collapse induced by increased gravitational force. The ventilatory response was changed, with a greater total respiratory minute volume in relation to oxygen uptake at 3 G than at 1 G during exercise. The venous admixture in per cent of cardiac output was increased during exercise at 3 G.

THERMOREGULATION

A comprehensive review of the regulation of internal body temperature during different conditions has been given by Hammel (200) and several articles dealing with thermoregulation and sweat rate during exercise have been published (201–205). The thermoregulatory reactions do not seem to be influenced by the neuromuscular events during exercise (201).

LITERATURE CITED

1. Chapman, C. B., Ed., *Physiology of Muscular Exercise. Proc. Symp. Feb. 7-9, 1966, Dallas, Texas. Circ. Res. Suppl. 1*, 20 and 21 (1967)
2. Sjöstrand, T. *Clinical Physiology. Pathophysiological basis and practical application* (Svenska Bokförlaget, Stockholm, 1967)
3. *Physical Working Capacity and Its Testing. Proc. Symp. May 5-6, 1966, Stockholm. Försvarsmedicin, 3*, 137–221 (1967)
4. Shephard, R. J. Physiological determinants of cardiorespiratory fitness. *J. Sports Med. Phys. Fitness, 7*, 111–34 (1967)
5. Bevegård, B. S., Shepherd, J. T. Regulation of the circulation during exercise in man. *Physiol. Rev., 47*, 178–213 (1967)
6. Dempsey, J. A., Rankin, J. Physiologic adaptations of gas transport systems to muscular work in health and disease. *Am. J. Phys. Med., 46*, 582–647 (1967)
7. Marshall, R. J., Shepherd, J. T. Cardiac dynamics during exercise. *Cardiac Function in Health and Disease*, 31–65 (Saunders, Philadelphia, 1968)
8. Karvonen, M. J., Barry, A. J. *Physical Activity and the Heart. Proc. Symp. Aug. 22-29, 1964, Helsinki* (Thomas, Springfield, Ill., 1967)
9. McCally, M. *Hypodynamics and Hypogravics: The Physiology of Inactivity and Weightlessness* (Academic Press, New York/London, 1968)
10. Morehouse, L. E., Miller, A. T. *Physiology of Exercise*, 5th ed. (Mosby, St. Louis, 1967)

11. *Proc. 2nd Intern. Symp. Man in Space, Paris, 1965* (Springer-Verlag, Wien, 1967)

12. *Nutrition and Physical Activity. Symp. Swedish Nutr. Found. V, Uppsala, 1966* (Almqvist & Wiksell, Uppsala, 1967)

13. Margaria, R., Ed., *Exercise at Altitude (Excerpta Med. Monogr.,* Amsterdam, 1967)

14. Eckermann, P., Millahn, H. P. Der Einfluss der Drehzahl auf die Herzfrequenz und die Sauerstoffaufnahme bei konstanter Leistung am Fahrradergometer. *Intern. Z. Angew. Physiol.,* 23, 340–44 (1967)

15. Carroll, P. J. Heart rate response to bicycle ergometer exercise as a function of physical fitness. *Univ. Alberta Res. Unit Rept. 6-M, 1967*

16. Banister, E. W., Jackson, R. C. The effect of speed and load changes on oxygen intake for equivalent power outputs during bicycle ergometry. *Intern. Z. Angew. Physiol.,* 24, 284–90 (1967)

17. von Maidorn, K., Stoboy, H., Wagner, A. Die Abhängigkeit der Leistungspulssumme von der Rotationsenergie der Schwungmassen eines Ergometers. *Z. Kreislaufforsch.,* 56, 597–603 (1967)

18. Cumming, G. R., Friesen, W. Bicycle ergometer measurement of maximal oxygen uptake in children. *Can. J. Physiol. Pharmacol.,* 45, 937–46 (1967)

19. Magel, J. R., Faulkner, J. A. Maximum oxygen uptakes of college swimmers. *J. Appl. Physiol.,* 22, 929–38 (1967)

20. Hyde, R. C. The Åstrand-Ryhming nomogram as a predictor of aerobic capacity for secondary school students. *Univ. Alberta Res. Unit Rept. 3-F, 1967*

21. von Döbeln, W., Åstrand, Irma, Bergström, A. An analysis of age and other factors related to maximal oxygen uptake. *J. Appl. Physiol.,* 22, 934–38 (1967)

22. Eichhorn, J., Brüner, H., Klein, K. E., Wegmann, H. M. Fehleinschätzungen der maximalen Sauerstoffaufnahme bei ihrer Bestimmung mit indirekten Methoden. *Intern. Z. Angew. Physiol.,* 24, 275–83 (1967)

23. Shephard, R. J. The prediction of maximum oxygen intake from postexercise pulse readings. *Intern. Z. Angew. Physiol.,* 24, 31–38 (1967)

24. Saltin, B., Åstrand, P.-O. Maximal oxygen uptake in athletes. *J. Appl. Physiol.,* 23, 253–58 (1967)

25. Cumming, G. R., Goodwin, A., Baggley, G., Antel, J. Repeated measurements of aerobic capacity during a week of intensive training at a youths' track camp. *Can. J. Physiol. Pharmacol.,* 45, 805–11 (1967)

26. Swenson, E. W., Zauner, C. W. Effects of physical conditioning on pulmonary function and working capacity in middle-aged men. *Scand. J. Resp. Dis.,* 48, 378–83 (1967)

27. Rosenberg, Edith. Effect of physical training on single breath diffusing capacity measured at rest. *Intern. Z. Angew. Physiol.,* 24, 246–53 (1967)

28. Williams, C. G., Wyndham, C. H., Kok, R., von Rahden, M. J. E. Effect of training on maximum oxygen intake and on anaerobic metabolism in man. *Intern. Z. Angew. Physiol.,* 24, 18–23 (1967)

29. O'Donnell, T. V., Nye, E. R., Heslop, J. H., Hunter, J. D. Middle-aged men on a twenty-week jogging programme. *New Zealand Med. J.,* 67, 284–87 (1967)

30. Karlsson, J., Åstrand, P.-O., Ekblom, B. Training of the oxygen transport system in man. *J. Appl. Physiol.,* 22, 1061–65 (1967)

31. Paez, P. N., Phillipson, E. A., Masangkay, M., Sproule, B. J. The physiologic basis of training patients with emphysema. *Am. Rev. Resp. Dis.,* 95, 944–53 (1967)

32. Anderson, A. D., Zohman, L. R. Exercise training in the supine position in patients with mitral stenosis. *Am. J. Med. Sci.,* 254, 464–76 (1967)

33. Crews, J., Aldinger, E. E. Effect of chronic exercise on myocardial function. *Am. Heart J.,* 74, 536–42 (1967)

34. Kunze, W.-P., Citoler, P. Zunahme DNS-synthetisierender Herzmuskelkerne durch Training. *Naturwissenschaften,* 20, 540–41 (1967)

35. Goldberg, A. L. Work-induced growth of skeletal muscle in normal and hypophysectomized rats. *Am. J. Physiol.,* 213, 1193–98 (1967)

36. Pattengale, P. K., Holloszy, J. O. Augmentation of skeletal muscle myoglobin by a program of treadmill running. *Am. J. Physiol.,* 213, 783–85 (1967)

37. Skinner, J. S., Strandness, D. E. Exer-

cise and intermittent claudication.
II. Effect of Physical Training.
Circulation, **36**, 23–29 (1967)

38. Kasch, F. W., Carter, J. E., Phillips,
W. H., Ross, D. W., Boyer, J. L.
A training program for middle-
aged males. *J. Assoc. Phys.
Mental Rehab.*, **21**, 102–4 (1967)

39. Whichelow, M. J., Butterfield, W. J.
H., Abrams, M. E., Sterky, G.,
Garratt, C. J. The effect of mild
exercise on glucose uptake in human forearm tissues in the fasting state and after oral glucose administration. *Metabolism*, **17**, 84–96
(1968)

40. Davies, C. T. M., Knibbs, A. V.,
Musgrove, J. The effect of recovery
exercise on the removal of lactic
acid from the blood. *J. Physiol.
(London)*, **196**, 61P–62P (1968)

41. Saiki, H., Margaria, R., Cuttica, F.
Lactic acid production in submaxi-
mal work. *Intern. Z. Angew.
Physiol.*, **24**, 57–61 (1967)

42. Keul, J., Keppler, D., Doll, E. Lactate-pyruvate ratio and its relation
to oxygen pressure in arterial
coronarvenous and femoralvenous
blood. *Arch. Intern. Physiol. Biochim.*, **75**, 573–78 (1967)

43. Keul, J., Doll, E., Keppler, D. The
substrate supply of the human
skeletal muscle at rest, during and
after work. *Experientia*, **23**, 1–6
(1967)

44. Keul, J., Doll, E., Keppler, D., Reindell, H. Zur Bedeutung der Lak-
tatbildung bei Intervallarbeit. *Z.
Kreislaufforsch.*, **56**, 823–30 (1967)

45. Ahlborg, B., Ekelund, L.-G., Nilsson,
G. Effect of potassium-magnesium
aspartate on the capacity for prolonged exercise in man. *Acta Physiol. Scand.*, 238–45 (1968)

46. Ahlborg, B., Bergström, J., Ekelund,
L.-G., Hultman, E. Muscle glycogen and muscle electrolytes during prolonged physical exercise.
Acta Physiol. Scand., **70**, 129–42
(1967)

47. Ahlborg, B., Bergström, J., Brohult,
J., Ekelund, L.-G., Hultman, E.,
Maschio, G. Human muscle glycogen content and capacity for
prolonged exercise after different
diets. *Försvarsmedicin*, **3**, 85–100
(1967)

48. Hermansen, L., Hultman, E., Saltin,
B. Muscle glycogen during pro-
longed severe exercise. *Acta Physiol.
Scand.*, **71**, 129–39 (1967)

49. Issekutz, B., Paul, P., Miller, H. I.
Metabolism in normal and pancreatectomized dogs during steady-
state exercise. *Am. J. Physiol.*, **213**,
857–62 (1967)

50. Young, C. R., Pelligra, R., Shapira,
J., Adachi, R. R., Skrettingland,
K. Glucose oxidation and replacement during prolonged exercise in
man. *J. Appl. Physiol.*, **23**, 734–41
(1967)

51. Baker, P. G., Mottram, R. F. The
metabolism of exercising human
muscle. *J. Physiol. (London)*, **194**,
64P–65P (1968)

52. Carlson, L. A., Fröberg, S. O. Blood
lipid and glucose levels during a
ten-day period of low-calorie intake
and exercise in man. *Metabolism*,
16, 624–34 (1967)

53. Hoffman, A. A., Nelson, W. R., Goss,
F. A. Effects of an exercise program on plasma lipids of senior air
force officers. *Am. J. Cardiol.*, **20**,
516–24 (1967)

54. Emirgil, C., Sobol, B. J., Campodonico,
S., Herbert, W. H., Mechkati, R.
Pulmonary circulation in the aged.
J. Appl. Physiol., **23**, 631–40 (1967)

55. Ekelund, L.-G., Holmgren, A. Central
hemodynamics during exercise. *Circ.
Res.*, **20** and **21**, *Suppl. 1*, 1–33—1–
43 (1967)

56. Burkart, F., Barold, S., Sowton, E.,
Hemodynamic effects of repeated
exercise. *Am. J. Cardiol.*, **20**, 509–15
(1967)

57. Sowton, E., Burkart, F. Haemodynamic changes during continuous
exercise. *Brit. Heart J.*, **29**, 770–74
(1967)

58. Marx, H. J., Rowell, L. B., Conn,
R. D., Bruce, R. A., Kusumi, F.,
Maintenance of aortic pressure and
total peripheral resistance during
exercise in heat. *J, Appl. Physiol.*,
22, 519–25 (1967)

59. Goldstone, B. W., Wyndham, C. H.
Cardiac adaptation to exercise.
Pflügers Arch., **295**, 15–29 (1967)

60. Levy, A. M., Tabakin, B. S., Hanson,
J. S. Hemodynamic responses to
graded treadmill exercise in young
untreated labile hypertensive patients. *Circulation*, **35**, 1063–72
(1967)

61. Amery, A., Julius, S., Whitlock, L. S.,
Conway, J. Influence of hypertension on the hemodynamic response
to exercise. *Circulation*, **36**, 231–37
(1967)

62. Binak, K., Harmanci, N., Sirmaci, N.,

Ataman, N., Ogan, H. Oxygen extraction rate of the myocardium at rest and on exercise in various conditions. *Brit. Heart J.*, **29**, 422–27 (1967)

63. Jonsson, B., Lee, S. J. K. Haemodynamic effects of exercise in isolated pulmonary stenosis before and after surgery. *Brit. Heart J.*, **30**, 60–66 (1968)

64. Kasalicky, J., Hurych, J., Widimsky, J., Dejdar, R., Metys, R., Stanek, V. Left heart haemodynamics at rest and during exercise in patients with mitral stenosis. *Brit. Heart J.*, **30**, 188–95 (1968)

65. Carlström, S., Karlefors, T. Hemodynamic studies during exercise in newly diagnosed, juvenile diabetics. *Acta Med. Scand.*, **181**, 759–67 (1967)

66. Carlström, S. Studies on fatty acid metabolism in male diabetic patients during exercise. *Acta Univ. Lundensis*, Sect. 11, No 20 (1967)

67. Hagenfeldt, L. *Muscle metabolism of individual free fatty acids and ketone bodies* (Doctoral thesis, Univ. of Stockholm, 1968)

68. Hultman, E. Studies on muscle metabolism of glycogen and active phosphate in man with special reference to exercise and diet. *Scand. J. Clin. Lab. Invest.*, **19**, *Suppl. 94* (1967)

69. Ekelund, L.-G. Circulatory and respiratory adaptation during prolonged exercise. *Acta Physiol. Scand.*, **70**, *Suppl. 292* (1967)

70. Ahlborg, B. Capacity for prolonged exercise in man. *Försvarsmedicin*, **3**, *Suppl. 1* (1967)

71. Najmi, M., Griggs, D. M., Jr., Kasparian, H., Novack, P. Effects of nitroglycerin on hemodynamics during rest and exercise in patients with coronary insufficiency. *Circulation*, **35**, 46–54 (1967)

72. Parker, J. O., West, R. O., Di Giorgi, S. The hemodynamic response to exercise in patients with healed myocardial infarction without angina. *Circulation*, **36**, 734–51 (1967)

73. Parker, J. O., West, R. O., Di Giorgi, S. Hemodynamic effects of Propranolol in coronary heart disease. *Am. J. Cardiol.*, **21**, 11–19 (1968)

74. Furberg, C. Adrenergic beta-blockade and physical working capacity. *Acta Med. Scand.*, **182**, 119–27 (1967)

75. Cumming, G. R., Carr, W. Hemody-

namic response to exercise after beta-adrenergic and parasympathetic blockade. *Can. J. Physiol. Pharmacol.*, **45**, 813–19 (1967)

76. Fleming, J., Hamer, J. Effects of beta-adrenergic blockade during exercise in hypertensive and ischaemic heart-disease. *Lancet*, **ii**, 1217–29 (1967)

77. Grandjean, T., Rivier, J. L. Cardiocirculatory effects of beta-adrenergic blockade in organic heart disease. *Brit. Heart J.*, **30**, 50–59 (1968)

78. Åström, H. Haemodynamic effects of beta-adrenergic blockade. *Brit. Heart J.*, **30**, 44–49 (1968)

79. Nordenfelt, I., Westling, H. A note on the haemodynamic effects of nitroglycerine and related substances in normal subjects. *Acta Med. Scand. Suppl. 472*, 81–87 (1967)

80. Arborelius, M., Jr., Lecerof, H., Malm, A., Malmborg, R. O. Acute effect of nitroglycerin on haemodynamics of angina pectoris. *Brit. Heart J.*, **30**, 407–11 (1968)

81. Robinson, B. F. Mode of action of nitroglycerin in angina pectoris. *Brit. Heart J.*, **30**, 295–302 (1968)

82. Tønnesen, K. H. Muscle blood flow during exercise in intermittent claudication. *Circulation*, **37**, 402–10 (1968)

83. Hornsten, T. R., Bruce, R. A. Effects of atrial fibrillation on exercise performance in patients with cardiac disease. *Circulation*, **37**, 543–48 (1968)

84. Kaplinsky, E., Hodd, W. B., Jr., McCarthy, B., McCombs, H. L., Lown, B., Effects of physical training in dogs with coronary artery ligation. *Circulation*, **37**, 556–65 (1968)

85. Harris, P., Segel, N., Bishop, J. M. The relation between pressure and flow in the pulmonary circulation in normal subjects and in patients with chronic bronchitis and mitral stenosis. *Cardiov. Res.*, **2**, 73–83 (1968)

86. Yu, P. N., Murphy, G. W., Schreiner, B. F., Jr., James, D. H. Distensibility characteristics of the human pulmonary vascular bed. *Circulation*, **35**, 710–23 (1967)

87. Segel, N., Bishop, J. M. Circulatory studies in polycythaemia vera at rest and during exercise. *Clin. Sci.*, **32**, 527–49 (1967)

88. Massey, D. G., Becklake, M. R.,

McKenzie, J. M., Bates, D. V. Circulatory and ventilatory response to exercise in thyrotoxicosis. *New Engl. J. Med.*, **276**, 1104–12 (1967)

89. Julius, S., Amery, A., Whitlock, L. S., Conway, J. Influence of age on the hemodynamic response to exercise. *Circulation*, **36**, 222–30 (1967)

90. Hanson, J. S., Tabakin, B. S., Levy, A. M. Comparative exercise-cardiorespiratory performance of normal men in the third, fourth, and fifth decades of life. *Circulation*, **37**, 345–60 (1968)

91. Castenfors, J., Mossfeldt, F., Piscator, M. Effect of prolonged heavy exercise on renal function and urinary protein excretion. *Acta Physiol. Scand.*, **70**, 194–206 (1967)

92. Castenfors, J. Renal function during exercise. With special reference to exercise proteinuria and the renin release. *Acta Physiol. Scand.*, **70**, *Suppl. 293* (1967)

93. Bozovic, L., Castenfors, J., Piscator, M. Effect of prolonged, heavy exercise on urinary protein excretion and plasma renin activity. *Acta Physiol. Scand.*, **70**, 143–46 (1967)

94. Castenfors, J., Piscator, M. Renal haemodynamics, urine flow and urinary protein excretion during exercise in supine position at different loads. *Acta Med. Scand. Suppl. 472*, 231–44 (1967)

95. Castenfors, J. Renal clearances and urinary sodium and potassium excretion during supine exercise in normal subjects. *Acta Physiol. Scand.*, **70**, 207–14 (1967)

96. Bozovic, L., Castenfors, J. Effect of dihydralazine on plasma renin activity and renal function during supine exercise in normal subjects. *Acta Physiol. Scand.*, **70**, 281–89 (1967)

97. Castenfors, J. Effect of ethacrynic acid on plasma renin activity during supine exercise in normal subjects. *Acta Physiol. Scand.*, **70**, 215–20 (1967)

98. Bozovic, L., Castenfors, J. Effect of ganglionic blocking on plasma renin activity in exercising and pain-stressed rats. *Acta Physiol. Scand.*, **70**, 290–92 (1967)

99. Aurell, M., Carlsson, M., Grimby, G. Hood, B. Plasma concentration and urinary excretion of certain electrolytes during supine work. *J. Appl. Physiol.*, **22**, 633–38 (1967)

100. Vale, J. R. Pulmonary gas exchange in normal subjects at rest and during moderate exercise. *Scand. J. Resp. Dis.*, **48**, 394–406 (1967)

101. Scherrer, M., Birchler, A. Altersabhängigkeit des alveoloarteriellen O₂-Partialdruckgradienten bei Schwerarbeit in Normoxie, Hypoxie und Hyperoxie. *Med. Thorac.*, **24**, 99–117 (1967)

102. Hertle, F. H., Meerkamm, F., Strunk, E. Das Verhalten des alveoloarteriellen Sauerstoff-Druckgradienten bei submaximaler Ergometerbelastung. *Verhandl. Deut. Ges. Inn. Med.*, **73**. Kongress (1967)

103. Levinson, H., Cherniack, R. M. Ventilatory cost of exercise in chronic obstructive pulmonary disease, *J. Appl. Physiol.*, **25**, 21–27 (1968)

104. Shephard, R. J. The maximum sustained voluntary ventilation in exercise. *Clin. Sci.*, **32**, 167–76 (1967)

105. Stanek, V., Widimsky, J., Kasalicky, J., Navratil, M., Daum, S., Levinsky, L. The pulmonary gas exchange during exercise in patients with pulmonary fibrosis. *Scand. J. Resp. Dis.*, **48**, 11–22 (1967)

106. Sly, R. M., Heimlich, E. M., Busser, R. J., Strick, L. Exercise-induced bronchospasm: Effect of adrenergic or cholinergic blockade. *J. Allergy*, **40**, 93–99 (1967)

107. Reuschlein, P. S., Reddan, W. G., Burpee, J., Gee, J. B. L., Rankin, J. Effect of physical training on the pulmonary diffusion capacity during submaximal work. *J. Appl. Physiol.*, **24**, 152–58 (1968)

108. Hlavova, A., Linhart, J., Přerovsky, I., Ganz, V., Fronek, A. Measurement of blood flow in the femoral artery in man at rest and during exericse by local thermodilution. *Scand. J. Clin. Lab. Invest.*, **19**, *Suppl. 99*, 86–89 (1967)

109. Siggaard-Andersen, J., Bonde Petersen, F. Venous occlusion plethysmography and ¹³³Xe muscle clearance measured simultaneously on the calf in normal subjects. *Scand. J. Clin. Lab. Invest.*, **19**, *Suppl. 99*, 106–12 (1967)

110. Bonde Petersen, F., Siggaard-Andersen, J. Blood flow in skin and muscle, evaluated by simultaneous venous occlusion plethysmography and ¹³³Xe clearance. *Ibid.*, 113–19

111. Bonde Petersen, F., Siggaard-Andersen, J. Simultaneous venous oc-

clusion plethysmography and Xe[133] clearance measurements on the calf of the leg after repeated exercise. *Acta Chir. Scand.*, **133**, 273–76 (1967)

112. Strandell, T., Shepherd, J. T. The effect in humans of exercise on relationship between simultaneously measured ^{133}Xe and [24]Na clearances. *Scand. J. Clin. Lab. Invest.*, **21**, 99–107 (1968)

113. Frick, M. H., Katila, M. Hemodynamic consequences of physical training after myocardial infarction. *Circulation*, **37**, 192–202 (1968)

114. Rechnitzer, P. A., Yuhasz, M. S., Paivio, A. U., Lefcoe, N., Picard, H. A. The acute effects of exercise on serum lipids of patients with previous myocardial infarction. *J. Sports Med. Phys. Fitness*, **7**, 177–81 (1967)

115. Rechnitzer, P. A., Yuhasz, M. S., Paivio, A., Picard, H. A., Lefcoe, N. Effects of a 24-week exercise programme on normal adults and patients with previous myocardial infarction. *Brit. Med J.*, **1**, 734–35 (1967)

116. McPherson, B. D., Paivio, A., Yuhasz, M. S., Rechnitzer, P. A., Picard, H. A., Lefcoe, N. Psychological effects of an exercise program for post-infarct and normal adult men. *J Sports. Med. Phys. Fitness*, **7**, 95–102 (1967)

117. Havel, R. J., Ekelund, L.-G., Holmgren, A. Kinetic analysis of the oxidation of palmitate-1-^{14}C in man during prolonged heavy muscular exercise. *J. Lipid Res.*, **8**, 366–73 (1967)

118. Young, D. R., Shapira, J., Forrest, R., Adachi, R. R., Lim, R., Pelligra, R. Model for evaluation of fatty acid metabolism for man during prolonged exercise. *J. Appl. Physiol.*, **23**, 716–25 (1967)

119. Strandell, T., Shepherd, J. T. The effect in humans of increased sympathetic acitivity on the blood flow to active muscles. *Acta Med. Scand. Suppl. 472*, 146–67 (1967)

120. Lundvall, J., Mellander, S., Sparks, H. Myogenic response of resistance vessels and precapillary sphincters in skeletal muscle during exercise. *Acta Physiol. Scand.*, **70**, 257–68 (1967)

121. Brandon, K. W., Cooper, C. J., Fewings, J. D., Walsh, J. A., Whelan, R. F. Some aspects of post-exercise

hyperaemia in man. *Australian J. Exptl. Biol. Med. Sci.*, **44**, 379–92 (1966)

122. Flandrois, R., Lacour, J. R., Islas-Maroquin, J., Charlot, J. Limbs mechanoreceptors inducing the reflex hypernea of exercise. *Resp. Physiol.*, **2**, 335–43 (1967)

123. Stegemann, J., Böning, D. Die Wirkung erhöhter Metabolitkonzentrationen im Muskel auf die Ventilation. *Pflügers Arch.*, **294**, 217–22 (1967)

124. Russek, M., Beaton, J. R. Effect of acute exercise on cerebral blood flow in man. *Proc. Soc. Exptl. Biol. Med.*, **125**, 738–41 (1967)

125. Buskirk, E. R., Kollias, J., Akers, R. F., Prokop, E. K., Reategui, E. P. Maximal performance at altitude and on return from altitude in conditioned runners. *J. Appl. Physiol.*, **23**, 259–66 (1967)

126. Faulkner, J. A., Daniels, J. T., Balke, B. Effects of training at moderate altitude on physical performance capacity. *J. Appl. Physiol.*, **23**, 85–89 (1967)

127. Banister, E. W., Jackson, R. C., Cartmel, J. The potentiating effect of low oxygen tension exposure during training on subsequent cardiovascular performance (British Columbia, Canada, 1967). *Intern. Z. Angew. Physiol.*, **26**, 164–79 (1968)

128. Vogel, J. A., Hansen, J. E., Harris, C. W. Cardiovascular responses in man during exhaustive work at sea level and high altitude. *J. Appl. Physiol.*, **23**, 531–39 (1967)

129. Hartley, L. H., Alexander. J. K., Modelski, M., Grover, R. F. Subnormal cardiac output at rest and during exercise in residents at 3100 m altitude. *J. Appl. Physiol.*, **23**, 839–48 (1967)

130. Faulkner, J. A., Kollias, J., Favour, C. B., Buskirk, E. R., Balke, B. Maximum aerobic capacity and running performance at altitude. *J. Appl. Physiol.*, **24**, 685–91 (1968)

131. West, J. B. Exercise limitations at increased altitudes. *Med. Thorac.*, **24**, 333–37 (1967)

132. Dill, D. B., Myhre, L. G., Brown, D. K., Burrus, K., Gehlsen, G. Work capacity in chronic exposures to altitude. *J. Appl. Physiol.*, **23**, 555–60 (1967)

133. Robertson, W. G., Quigley, D., McRae, G. L. Effect of exercise on

oxygen consumption at decreased pressure. *Aerospace Med.*, **38**, 617–19 (1967)

134. Alexander, J. K., Hartley, L. H., Modelski, M., Grover, R. F. Decrease in cardiac output during exercise in sea level residents following ascent to 3100 m altitude. *J. Appl. Physiol.*, **23**, 849–58 (1967)

135. Keul, J., Doll, E., Erichsen, H., Reindell, H. Die arteriellen Substratspiegel bei Verminderung der Sauerstoffkonzentration in der Inspirationsluft während körperlicher Arbeit. *Intern. Z. Angew. Physiol.*, **25**, 89–103 (1968)

136. Doll, E., Keul, J., Brechtel, A., Reindell, H. Die arteriellen Blutgase bei Verminderung der Sauerstoffkonzentration in der Inspirationsluft während körperlicher Arbeit. *Intern. Z. Angew. Physiol.*, **25**, 46–59 (1968)

137. Wyndham, C. H., Williams, C. G., von Rahden, M. J. E., Kok, R., Strydom, N. B. The effect on the partial pressure of oxygen in arterial blood of exercise up to the individual's maximum at medium altitude. *Life Sci.*, **6**, 919–24 (1967)

138. Altland, P. D., Highman, B., Nelson, B. D. Serum enzyme and tissue changes in rats exercised repeatedly at altitude: effects of training. *Am. J. Physiol.*, **214**, 28–32 (1968)

139. Ahlborg, B., Brohult, J. Immediate and delayed metabolic reactions in well-trained subjects after prolonged physical exercise. *Acta Med. Scand.*, **182**, 41–53 (1967)

140. Bellet, S., Roman, L. R., Nichols, G. J., Muller, O. F. Detection of coronary-prone subjects in a normal population by radioelectrocardiographic exercise test. *Am. J. Cardiol.*, **19**, 783–87 (1967)

141. Bellet, S., Roman, L. The exercise test in diabetic patients as studied by radioelectrocardiography. *Circulation*, **36**, 245–54 (1967)

142. Lester, M., Sheffield, L. T., Reeves, T. J. Electrocardiographic changes in clinically normal older men following near maximal and maximal exercise. *Circulation*, **36**, 5–14 (1967)

143. Robb, G. P., Marks, H. H. Postexercise electrocardiogram in arteriosclerotic heart disease. *J. Am. Med. Assoc.*, **200**, 918–26 (1967)

144. Rosner, S. W., Leinbach, R. C., Presto, A. J., Jackson, L. K., Weihrer, A. L., Caceres, C. A.

Computer analysis of the exercise electrocardiogram. *Am. J. Cardiol.*, **20**, 356–62 (1967)

145. Grover, R. F., Reeves, J. T. Pulmonary ventilation during exercise at altitude. Repr. from *Excerpta Med. Monogr.*, *Intern. Symp.*, *Milan*, *Sept. 29–Oct. 2, 1966*

146. Edhag, O., Zetterquist, S. Peripheral circulatory adaptation to exercise in restricted cardiac output. *Scand. J. Clin. Lab. Invest.*, **21**, 123–35 (1968)

147. Hlavova, A., Linhart, J., Přovsky, I., Ganz, V. Lactate and pyruvate changes in the leg during and after exercise in normal subjects and in patients with femoral artery occlusion. *Clin. Sci.*, **34**, 397–409 (1968)

148. Hlavova, A., Linhart, J., Přovsky, I., Ganz, V. Circulatory and metabolic changes in the leg in man during and after exercise. *Proc. Symp. Circ. Skeletal Muscle, Smolenice, Czechoslovakia, 1966* (Pergamon, Oxford) (In press)

149. Freyschuss, U., Strandell, T. Limb circulation during arm and leg exercise in supine position. *J. Appl. Physiol.*, **23**, 163–70 (1967)

150. Wahren, J., Hagenfeldt, L. Human forearm muscle metabolism during exercise. I. *Scand. J. Clin. Lab. Invest.*, **21**, 257–62 (1968)

151. Clode, M., Edwards, R. H. T., Goodwin, T., Hughes, R. L., Jones, N. L. The effects of hypoxia on graded exercise in man. *J. Physiol. (London)*, **192**, 32P–33P (1967)

152. Åstrand, P.-O. Circulatory and respiratory response to acute and prolonged hypoxia during heavy exercise. *Med. Thorac.*, **24**, 118–28 (1967)

153. Papadopoulos, N. M., Leon, A. S., Bloor, C. M. Effects of exercise on plasma and tissue levels of lactate dehydrogenase and isoenzymes in rats. *Proc. Soc. Exptl. Biol. Med.*, **125**, 999–1002 (1967)

154. Warren, B. H. Human circulation times during weightlessness produced by parabolic flight. *Aerospace Med.*, **38**, 1019–20 (1967)

155. Fischer, C. L., Johnson, P. C., Berry, C. A. Red blood cell mass and plasma volume changes in manned space flight. *J. Am. Med. Assoc.*, **200**, 579–83 (1967)

156. Weil-Malherbe, H., Smith, E. R. B., Bowles, G. R. Excretion of catecholamines and catecholamine

metabolites in project mercury pilots. *J. Appl. Physiol.*, **24**, 146–51 (1968)

157. Linnarsson, D., Rosenhamer, G. Exercise and arterial pressure during simulated increase of gravity. *Acta Physiol. Scand.*, **74** 50–57 (1968)

158. Rosenhamer, G. Antigravity effects of leg exercise. *Acta Physiol. Scand.*, **72**, 72–80 (1968)

159. Rosenhamer, G. Influence of increased gravitational stress on the adaptation of cardiovascular and pulmonary function to exercise. *Acta Physiol. Scand.*, **68**, *Suppl. 276* (1967)

160. Bruce, R. A., Lind. A. R., Franklin, D., Muir, A. L., MacDonald, H. R., McNicol, G. W., Donald, K. W. The effects of digoxin on fatiguing static and dynamic exercise in man. *Clin. Sci.*, **34**, 29–42 (1968)

161. V. Falkenhahn, A., Hollmann, W., Kenter, H., Wenrath, H., Bouchard C. Der Einfluss von Digitalis auf die Leistungsfähigkeit gesunder Ratten im Schwimmversuch. *Arzneimittel-Forsch.*, **17**, 551–53 (1967)

162. Friesen, W. J., Cumming, G. R. Effects of digoxin on the oxygen debt and the exercise electrocardiogram in normal subjects. *Can. Med. Assoc. J.*, **97**, 960–64 (1967)

163. Beiser, G. C., Epstein, S. E., Stampfer, M., Robinson, B., Braunwald, E. Studies on digitalis. XVII. Effects of ouabain on the hemodynamic response to exercise in patients with mitral stenosis in normal sinus rhythm. *New Engl. J. Med.*, **278**, 131–37 (1968)

164. Furberg, C. Effects of beta-adrenergic blockade on ECG, physical working capacity and central circulation with special reference to autonomic imbalance. *Acta Med. Scand. Suppl. 488* (1968)

165. Laguens, R. P., Gomez-Dumm, C. L. A. Fine structure of myocardial mitochondria in rats after exercise for one-half to two hours. *Circ. Res.*, **11**, 271–79 (1967)

166. Hunter, W. M., Sukkar, M. Y. Changes in plasma insulin levels during muscular exercise. *J. Physiol. (London)*, **196**, 110P–112P (1968)

167. Hansen, J. E., Stelter, G. P., Vogel, J. A. Arterial pyruvate, lactate, pH, and P_{CO_2} during work at sea level and high altitude. *J. Appl. Physiol.*, **23**, 523–30 (1967)

168. Leon, A. S., Bloor, C. M. Effects of exercise and its cessation on the heart and its blood supply. *J. Appl. Physiol.*, **24**, 485–90 (1968)

169. Carlson, L. A., Ekelund, L.-G., Fröberg, S. O., Hallberg, D. Effect of exercise on the elimination of exogenous triglycerides from blood in man. *Acta Med. Scand. Suppl. 472*, 245–52 (1967)

170. Jones, N. L., Havel, R. J. Metabolism of free fatty acids and chylomicron triglycerides during exercise in rats. *Am. J. Physiol.*, **213**, 824–28 (1967)

171. Fordtran, J. S., Saltin, B. Gastric emptying and intestinal absorption during prolonged severe exercise. *J. Appl. Physiol.*, **23**, 331–35 (1967)

172. Havel, R. J., Pernow, B., Jones, N. L. Uptake and release of free fatty acids and other metabolites in the legs of exercising men. *J. Appl. Physiol.*, **23**, 90–99 (1967)

173. Ekblom, B., Åstrand, P.-O., Saltin B., Wallström, B. Effect of training on circulatory response to exercise. *J. Appl. Physiol.*, **24**, 518–28 (1968)

174. Margaria, R. Aerobic and anaerobic energy sources in muscular exercise (See Ref. 13)

175. Ekelund, L.-G. Circulatory and respiratory adaptation during prolonged exercise of moderate intensity in the sitting position. *Acta Physiol. Scand.*, **69**, 327–40 (1967)

176. Ekelund, L.-G., Holmgren, A., Ovenfors, C. O. Heart volume during prolonged exercise in the supine and sitting position. *Acta Physiol. Scand.*, **70**, 88–98 (1967)

177. Davies, C. T. M. Limitations to the prediction of maximum oxygen intake from cardiac frequency measurements. *J. Appl. Physiol.*, **24**, 700–6 (1968)

178. Ahlborg, B. Effect of circulatory training on capacity for prolonged exercise in man (To be published)

179. Oscai, L. B., Williams, B. T., Hertig, B. A. Effect of exercise on blood volume. *J. Appl. Physiol.*, **24**, 622–24 (1968)

180. Hultman, E., Bergström, J. Muscle glycogen synthesis in relation to diet studied in normal subjects. *Acta Med. Scand.*, **182**, 109–17 (1967)

181. Bergström, J., Hultman, E. A study of the glycogen metabolism during exercise in man. *Scand. J. Clin. Lab. Invest.*, **19**, 218–28 (1967)

182. Bergström, J., Hermansen, L., Hultman, E., Saltin, B. Diet, muscle gly-

cogen and physical performance. *Acta Physiol. Scand.*, **71**, 140–50 (1967)

183. Hultman, E., Bergström, J., McLennan Anderson, N. Breakdown and resynthesis of phosphorylcreatine and adenosine triphosphate in connection with muscular work in man. *Scand. J. Clin. Lab. Invest.*, **19**, 56–66 (1967)

184. Diamant, B., Karlsson, J., Saltin, B. Muscle tissue lactate after maximal exercise in man. *Acta Physiol. Scand.*, **72**, 383–84 (1968)

185. Hagenfeldt, L., Wahren, J. Human forearm muscle metabolism during exercise. II. *Scand. J. Clin. Lab. Invest.*, **21**, 263–76 (1968)

186. Hagenfeldt, L., Wahren, J. Human forearm muscle metabolism during exercise. III. *Scand. J. Clin. Lab. Invest.*, **21**, 314–20 (1968)

187. *Intern. Symp. Exercise Biochem.*, Brussels, June 6-8, 1968

188. Reinheimer, W., Davidson, P. C., Albrink, M. J. Effect of moderate exercise on plasma glucose, insulin, and free fatty acids during oral glucose tolerance tests. *J. Lab. Clin. Med.*, **71**, 429–37 (1968)

189. Ashkar, E., Stevens, J. J., Houssay, B. A. Role of the sympathico-adrenal system in the hemodynamic response to exercise in dogs. *Am. J. Physiol.*, **214**, 22–27 (1968)

190. Heinrich, K. W., Ulmer, H.-V., Stegemann, J. Sauerstoffaufnahme, Pulsfrequenz und Ventilation bei Variation von Tretgeschwindigkeit und Tretkraft bei aerober Ergometerarbeit. *Plügers Arch.*, **298**, 191–99 (1968)

191. Lund-Johansen, P. *Hemodynamics in early essential hypertension* (Doctoral thesis, Univ. Bergen, Norway, 1967)

192. Horsefield, K., Segel, N., Bishop, J. M. The pulmonary circulation in chronic bronchitis at rest, and during exercise breathing air and 80 percent oxygen. *Clin. Sci.*, **43**, 473–83 (1968)

193. Wahren, J. A dye dilution method for the determination of brachial artery blood flow during rhythmic exercise. *Scand. J. Clin. Lab. Invest.*, **19**, Suppl. 99, 70–71 (1967)

194. Larsen, O. A., Lassen, N. A. Effect of daily muscular exercise in patients with intermittent claudication. *Scand. J. Clin. Lab. Invest.*, **19**, Suppl. 99, 168–71 (1967)

195. Hughes, R. L., Clode, M., Edwards, R. H. T., Goodwin, T. J., Jones, N. L. Effect of inspired O2 on cardiopulmonary and metabolic responses to exercise in man. *J. Appl. Physiol.*, **24**, 336–47 (1968)

196. Lahiri, S., Milledge, J. S., Chattopadhyay, H. P., Bhattacharyya, A. K., Sinha, A. K. Respiration and heart rate of Sherpa highlanders during exercise. *J. Appl. Physiol.*, **23**, 545–54 (1967)

197. Ahlborg, B., Brohult, J. Liver reaction as manifested in increased activity of ornithine carbamoyl transferase in serum after short heavy exercise and prolonged exercise in man. *Försvarsmedicin*, **4**, 133–40 (1968)

198. Webb, P. Weight loss in men in space. *Science*, **155**, 558–60 (1967)

199. Lockhart, A., Tsareva, M., Schrijen F. Haemodynamic effects of pharmacological denervation of the heart at rest and during exercise in patients with chronic lung disease. *Cardiov. Res.*, **2**, 100–7 (1968)

200. Hammel, H. T. Regulation of interna body temperature. *Ann. Rev. Physiol.*, **30**, 641–710 (1968)

201. Nielsen, B. Thermoregulatory responses to arm work, leg work and intermittent leg work. *Acta Physiol. Scand.*, **72**, 25–32 (1968)

202. Melchior, H., Hildebrandt, G. Die Hautdurchblutung verschiedener Körperregionen bei Arbeit. *Intern. Z. Angew. Physiol.*, **24**, 68–80 (1967)

203. Pugh, L. G. C. E. Cold stress and muscular exercise with special reference to accidental hypothermia. *Brit. Med. J.*, **2**, 333–37 (1967)

204. Dill, D. B., Horvath, S. M., van Beaumont, W., Gehlsen, G., Burrus, K. Sweat electrolytes in desert walks. *J. Appl. Physiol.*, **23**, 746–51 (1967)

205. Pugh, L. G. C. E., Corbett, J. L., Johnson, R. H. Rectal temperatures, weight losses, and sweat rates in marathon running. *J. Appl. Physiol.*, **23**, 347–52 (1967)

KIDNEY, WATER, AND ELECTROLYTES[1,2] 1021

By E. E. Windhager[3]

Department of Physiology, Cornell University Medical College, New York City

Introduction

Several excellent monographs, review articles, and symposia published during the period covered by the present survey have been concerned with renal physiology (1–7), membrane transport (4, 8, 9), microdissection studies of the developing mammalian kidney (10), humoral and enzyme activity of the kidney (11–13), and clinical disturbances of fluid and electrolyte metabolism and renal function (14–16).

Morphology

The glomerular ultrastructure of human (17), and rhesus monkey (18) kidneys has been studied recently. Zamboni et al. (19) claim that the mesangial cells of the renal glomerulus are continuous with smooth muscle of the afferent arterioles and might participate in the regulation of glomerular pressure. Dietrich (20) studied the ultrastructure of bundles of vasa recta in the inner stripe of rat renal medulla after perfusion with glutaraldehyde. The arterial vasa recta were covered with pericytes and lined with an interrupted endothelium. Venous vasa recta were characterized by fenestrated endothelium. An electronmicroscopic study of the renal papilla of the rabbit has been published (21). Suzuki & Mostofi (22) noted intramitochondrial bodies in the thick limb of Henle of rat kidneys whose function is presently unknown. The occurrence of "intercalated cells" in distal convoluted tubles of rat kidneys has been demonstrated and their ultrastructure described (23).

McKenna & Angelakos (24) examined the adrenergic innervation of the dog kidney, using fluorescence histochemical methods in conjunction with chemical assays for catecholamine. Adrenergic innervation could be demonstrated along the arterial blood vessels and vasa recta but not in efferent arterioles or along tubule cells.

Schmidt-Nielsen & Davis (25) found fluid movement across renal tubules of reptiles to be correlated with the width of tubular intercellular spaces, which suggests that the compartment located between cell membranes and epithelial basement membrane is part of the pathway of fluid transfer from

---

[1] The survey of literature was concluded in June 1968.

[2] Among the abbreviations used in this chapter are: ADH (antidiuretic hormone); DOCA (deoxycorticosterone acetate); E_{PAH} (extraction ratio of PAH); GFR (glomerular filtration rate); PAH (*p*-aminohippurate); RPF (renal plasma flow).

[3] Career Scientist of the New York Health Research Council, I-405.

lumen to peritubular fluid space. A similar conclusion had been reached in studies on perfused collecting tubules of rabbit kidneys (26). Thoenes (27) described in detail the interspaces in proximal and distal tubular epithelium of rat kidneys. He made the potentially important suggestion that these spaces contain an organic intercellular substance. Entry of ferritin molecules into the interspaces between neighboring cells was observed only when the hydrostatic pressure in peritubular capillaries had been elevated during fixation. Revel & Karnovsky (28) report that lanthanum (20 Å or smaller) does not penetrate tight junctions of proximal or distal tubular cells of mouse kidneys. It is evident that electronmicroscopic techniques are not so advanced that pathways of strong electrolytes can be detected or evaluated directly.

Rouffignac & Morel (29) analyzed the anatomical distributions of nephrons by careful microdissection of kidneys of rat, Meriones, Psammomys, golden hamster, and mouse. About 60 per cent of the nephrons of these animals reach the surface of the renal cortex and are thus accessible to micropuncture. The proximal tubules of these "surface nephrons" are shorter than the remaining nephrons. The absolute length of proximal tubules in "surface nephrons" averaged 6.5 mm in the mouse, 8.6 mm in the hamster, 4.1 mm in Psammomys, 7.8 mm in Meriones, and 8.9 mm in the rat.

GLOMERULAR FUNCTION

The mechanism by which glomerular filtration rate is increased during expansion of the plasma volume has been examined in the toad by Uranga (30). The hydrostatic pressure within the occluded ureter was taken as an index of glomerular capillary pressure, an assumption supported by results of her previous micropuncture study on toads (31). During plasma volume expansion produced by the infusion of 4 per cent dextran, a rise in ureteral stop-flow pressure was observed. A similar increase in ureteral pressure was found in isolated toad kidneys perfused by blood of a donor toad, whose renal arteries and veins had been ligated and whose plasma volume had been expanded. These results imply that the circulating level of a glomerular pressure substance is increased during expansion of the plasma volume. The glomerular pressure response could only be abolished by the excision of the liver, which suggests that the substance might originate in this organ.

Hardwicke et al. (32) investigated the sieving characteristics of the glomerular membrane using Sephadex G-200 for analyzing the constituent molecular sizes of polydisperse radioactively labeled dextran and polyvinylpyrollidon in serum and urine of rabbits. A sigmoid curve relationship between the logarithm of molecular size and absolute permeability suggested a normal distribution of "apparent pore size" in the glomerular membrane. Dextran and polyvinylpyrollidon of a molecular radius of < 24 Å crossed the membrane as readily as creatinine and thus may be used for measuring glomerular filtration rate. With increasing molecular size the renal clearance decreased rapidly until molecules > 60 Å were virtually excluded from the filtrate. In a similar study of glomerular permeability in humans (33) the permeability profile was essentially identical to that described in rabbits. Mogensen (34) reports that in man, the renal clearance of dextran of molecular weight higher than 55,000 approaches zero, while it averaged 95 ml/min at a molecular weight of 15,000. Cohen & Walker (35) suggested that clearances of amylase and glutamic pyruvic transaminase can be used to assess renal glomerular permeability. Elevation of the renal venous pressure, a condition known to cause proteinuria, led to a disproportionately high increase in the clearance of amylase (low molecular weight enzyme) with relatively little change in the clearance of transaminase (high molecular weight enzyme). The authors consider dilatation of pores of approximately the same size as amylase to be characteristic of the increase in glomerular permeability in this condition.

Zender & Falbriard (36) and Favre et al. (37) continued to study polyfructosan as a test substance for measuring glomerular filtration rate by analyzing the plasma decay after a single injection. They claim that the reproducibility of calculated polyfructosan clearance values is equal to or better than that of clearances of inulin or creatinine during continuous infusion and collection of urine samples. A small fraction of inulin infused may be retained by renal tissue (38).

In male albino rats, Goldman (39) measured the endogenous creatinine clearance which averaged 0.709 ml/min per 100 g body weight. Correlations of calculated creatinine clearance with body weight, kidney weight, and surface area were approximately the same. Therefore, in the weight range used (200–450 g), it seems most practical to use body weight as the unit of relating values of glomerular filtration rate in rats.

Spiro (40) studied the disaccharide unit of the glomerular basement membrane in regard to its detailed chemical structure and its linkage to the peptide portion. Thoenes (41) concluded from enzymatic studies that nephrotoxic antigen is mainly contained in the polysaccharide fraction of the basement membrane.

RENAL BLOOD FLOW

Ladefoged et al. (42) compared renal blood flow values in isolated dog kidneys derived from washout curves of inert gases with measurements obtained from electromagnetic flowmeters and found good agreement between flowmeter values and those obtained with ^{133}Xe and ^{85}Kr washout techniques. Recirculation and resorption of indicator in fat tissue surrounding the kidney apparently explain why previous measurements on kidneys *in situ* have yielded low perfusion values. Extrapolation of the final slope to calculate the area under the washout curve may be a major source of error in estimating blood flow.

The intrarenal distribution of total blood flow to the kidney continues to receive attention. Aukland & Wolgast (43) have studied the effect of hemorrhage on intrarenal distribution of blood flow in dogs. Medullary blood flow was estimated from the local clearance of H gas in the outer medulla measured polarographically with needle-shaped platinum electrodes, from the clearance of ^{85}Kr, and from the mean transit time of ^{32}P-labeled erythrocytes measured by a small semiconductor detector inserted into the outer medulla. Cortical blood flow was calculated from cortical red cell transit time and from total renal blood flow measured by an electromagnetic flowmeter. Hemorrhagic hypotension (50–60 mm Hg mean arterial pressure) led to a progressive and fairly uniform rise in renal vascular resistance, with no selective hemodynamic response in the juxtamedullary circulation. These conclusions differ from those of Carriere et al. (44) and Truninger et al. (45), who used ^{85}Kr and ^{133}Xe (external recording) in similar studies and found reduced cortical, but unchanged medullary blood flow during hemorrhagic hypotension. It should be realized that insertion of detector probes into renal tissue (43) constitutes a considerable trauma which can lead to renal shutdown and thus alter the kinetics of washout of inert gases. Also, transit time of erythrocytes may give erroneous estimates of the absolute magnitude of blood flow since local intrarenal hematocrit values are not identical with that of peripheral blood (46).

Using the ^{133}Xe washout technique, Rosen et al. (47) examined the effect of denervation and tissue rejection on the intrarenal distribution of blood flow in transplanted dog kidneys. Control studies demonstrated that kidneys redistribute their blood flow after laparotomy and mobilization of the kidney: the fraction of blood perfusing the fastest (cortical) compartment diminished. Homo- and autotransplanted kidneys showed no alterations in blood flow distribution. Cortical blood flow seemed reduced by immunological processes during rejection of transplanted kidneys and this effect may contribute to renal failure under these circumstances. The same methods of measuring distribution of blood flow in human kidneys (48) gave results essentially similar to those in the dog. Four exponential components of the washout curve are thought to correspond to cortical, outer medullary, inner medullary, and renal fat perfusion rates. In homotransplanted kidneys a correlation was observed between creatinine clearance and the percentage of renal blood flow supplying the fastest component. Complete anuria was associated with either the absence of, or a marked reduction in the percentage of, blood flow to this compartment. These results support the notion that the fastest component of the Xe washout curve represents the blood flow to the renal cortex in man.

Moffat (49) extended his studies of intrarenal red cell distribution to the condition of hydropenia. After intravenous injection of a suspension of erythrocytes labeled with the fluorescent dye Thioflavin S, the number of fluorescent cells present per unit volume of glomerular tissue was counted. In hydropenic, in contrast to nondehydrated rats (50), the number of fluorescent cells was significantly less in the juxtamedullary than in the cortical glomeruli. This was interpreted as indicating a diminished blood flow through the juxtamedullary glomeruli under conditions of dehydration.

However, as previously discussed by Thurau et al. (46), clamping of the renal pedicle must lead to blood flow from arteries to the renal veins until pressure in all vessels is equalized. Hence, red cell distribution after these events may not truly reflect prior *in vivo* conditions. On the other hand, a reduction in medullary blood flow during antidiuresis agrees with current concepts of urinary concentration. Reduced medullary blood flow would help to conserve the steep osmotic gradient in the medulla.

Most methods of estimating medullary blood flow require a functional separation of cortical and medullary circulation. This is particularly relevant with the use of the extraction ratio for PAH (E_{PAH}) or for Diodrast (iodopyracet) ($E_{Diodrast}$). Since both substances are secreted into the tubular lumen by proximal tubular epithelium, a series arrangement of cortical and medullary blood vessels would lead to different tracer concentrations in blood entering the two vascular beds. Proximal tubular transport would be reflected in blood traversing the medulla. On the other hand, an anatomical arrangment of a parallel circuit between cortical and medullary blood supply requires that blood entering the juxtamedullary vessels contains tracers such as PAH at the same concentration as in the renal artery and is not influenced by proximal tubular transfer. Slotkoff et al. (51) examined this problem in dogs by comparing the concentration ratio of Diodrast to that of an intravascular tag (colloidal ^{198}Au) in renal tissue to the ratio of these substances in blood entering the kidney. Stop flow was used to reduce the delivery of proximal tubular fluid into distal portions of the nephron. Diodrast-^{131}I and ^{198}Au were infused for 1 min into the root of the aorta. Kidneys were removed at 30 and 60 sec and radioactivity estimated in sections of cortex, outer medulla, and papilla. The Diodrast-to-gold ratio in the cortex was much higher than in renal arterial blood, which implies accumulation of Diodrast by cortical nephrons. A mean ratio higher than 1.0 in the outer medulla was thought to be due to passive diffusion of Diodrast from cortex to papilla. In the papilla the ratio was nearly identical to that in arterial blood. These results are taken to indicate that the cortical and medullary circulations are functionally independent since extraction of Diodrast from juxtamedullary blood by cortical nephrons prior to the blood entering the vasa recta would have resulted in a ratio much less than unity. Slotkoff et al. (51) point out, however, that E_{PAH} and $E_{Diodrast}$ will be influenced by the amount of PAH or Diodrast diffusing out of the collecting ducts. Hence, low extraction ratios do not necessarily prove augmentation of medullary blood flow since the results will also be influenced by such factors as water permeability, urine flow rate, and tracer concentration in collecting duct urine.

Nashat & Portal (52) have proposed that the flow resistance of efferent arterioles may be largely determined by blood viscosity which in turn depends upon the hematocrit. Changes in hematocrit would thus modify the filtration fraction. Total-body hematocrit was altered acutely in anesthetized dogs by rapid infusion of packed red cells, dextran solution, or hypertonic mannitol. A reduction of hematocrit resulted in a decrease in filtration fraction and a rise of hematocrit in an increase in filtration fraction.

The effect of ureteral occlusion on the renal circulation of dogs undergoing osmotic diuresis has been studied by Hársing et al. (53). Renal blood flow was measured directly (venous outflow) and indirectly from ^{86}Rb uptake. They also investigated the intrarenal distribution of blood flow on the basis of ^{86}Rb content of cortex, outer medulla, and inner medulla. Directly and indirectly measured total blood flow showed good agreement under free-flow conditions. During ureteral occlusion, directly measured values of renal blood flow were significantly higher than the control values, whereas Ru-uptake data indicated a decrease in indirectly estimated renal blood flow. The ratio of cortical to total blood flow decreased from 0.78 to 0.48, the extraction ratio of PAH (E_{PAH}) from 0.75 to 0.52. The difference between values obtained by direct and indirect measurements of renal blood flow was ascribed to the opening of arteriovenous shunts, i.e., diminution of renal capillary perfusion despite unchanged or even increased total renal blood flow. It is tempting to speculate that transverse shunts between descending and ascending vasa recta might be involved.

Disagreement continues with respect to the intrarenal hemodynamic response to osmotic diuresis. Baldwin et al. (54) observed significant reductions in GFR in normotensive human subjects undergoing strong osmotic diuresis induced by mannitol infusion. The extraction ratio of PAH (E_{PAH}) was unchanged and the maximal reduction in effective renal blood flow was <10 per cent. The results make it unlikely that a redistribution of blood flow from cortex to medulla took place; however, they are at variance with previous reports by other authors (55–57) who observed significant reductions in E_{PAH} during osmotic diuresis. Furthermore, Thurau et al. (58), analyzing dye dilution curves recorded at the surface of the renal cortex and in the inner medulla, concluded that medullary blood flow is increased during osmotic diuresis.

Attempting to define the mechanism of renal autoregulation of blood flow, Basar et al. (59) examined the dynamics of pressure-induced changes in flow resistance in isolated, artificially perfused rat kidneys. Applying defined changes in pressure, they analyzed the resulting flow pattern for changes in shape, amplitude, and phase, concluding that the reactive increase of flow-resistance in the autoregulated kidney is due to at least two mechanisms. A short-lasting, rate-sensitive reactive component which appears can be distinguished from a second, long-lasting, rate-independent component which has a delay of 5–10 sec. At least the rapid component appears to be due to a direct myogenic response to changes in transmural pressure gradients. Using the same perfused kidney preparation, Baumgarten et al. (60) concluded that catecholamines do not act as transmitter substances in autoregulation.

The action of ATP, 3,5-AMP, adenosine, and dipyridamol on isolated strips of renal arteries was studied by Walter & Bassenge (61): all caused relaxation. However, the relaxing effect of the nucleotides on renal vascular smooth muscle is at variance with the renal vasoconstrictive response *in vivo* observed by several investigators (62–64).

Bálint & Châtel (65) have re-examined the effect of epinephrine and of norepinephrine on renal blood flow and glomerular filtration rate. Small doses did not change GFR significantly but always reduced renal blood flow. Filtration fraction was increased; therefore, constriction of the efferent arterioles must have occurred. Larger doses caused preglomerular vasoconstriction, resulting in simultaneous reductions of GFR and renal blood flow. Köver et al. (66) reported that bradykinin infusion into one renal artery of anesthetized dogs results in renal vasodilatation and simultaneous decreases in the extraction ratio of PAH. The clearances of creatinine and PAH were not significantly changed, but urinary osmolality declined. The authors suggest that the hormone causes preferential vasodilatation of renal medullary vessels and hence reduces medullary osmolality.

Lockett (67) used perfused cat kidneys to evaluate the effect of changes in Po_2, Pco_2, and pH on renal hemodynamics independent of all reflex or extrarenal hormonal responses which might occur in the intact animal. High levels of Po_2 (>220 mm Hg) led to irreversible increases in vascular resistance, thought to be due to platelet clumping (68). In contrast to the response in intact animals, hypoxia ($Po_2 < 80$ mm Hg) did not cause renal vasoconstriction. Denervation may explain this result. Only slight changes in renal vascular resistance resulted from changes in pH. However, large, reversible alterations in flow resistance occurred in response to changes in arterial Pco_2. Elevation of the partial pressure of CO_2 decreased, vascular resistance and lowering had the opposite effect. In isolated kidneys, CO_2 apparently acts as a vasodilator.

A greater contribution of left than of right renal lymph flow to thoracic duct lymph flow has been described (69).

The juxtaglomerular apparatus.—The role of the juxtaglomerular apparatus has been thoroughly reviewed by Vander (70) and Brown et al. (71) and has been the topic of a recent symposium (72).

Vander (70) in his excellent appraisal of current concepts emphasized that the control of renin release consists of extra- and intrarenal mechanisms which generally are synergistic in their action. The extrarenal control involves the sympathetic nervous system and circulating angiotensin which exerts a negative feedback control. Two types of intrarenal mechanisms, a baroreceptor and a "macula densa" control, must still be postulated to explain all available experimental evidence. Vander proposed that, by some mechanism, the Na load delivered to the macula densa is detected and that an inverse relationship exists between Na load and the release of renin. He considered concomitant changes in intracellular Na concentration of macula densa cells as a potential link in the chain of events connecting Na load and renin secretion. Recent micropuncture studies agree with this hypothesis. In a microperfusion study of single short loops of Henle in rat kidneys, Schnermann (73) observed that the Na concentration of the total loop reabsorbate varies directly as a function of the rate of inflow of isotonic Ringer's solution into the pars recta of the proximal tubule. Furthermore, Landwehr et al. (74) [reported in more detail by Windhager (75)] have shown that reduction of GFR in the rat by means of a renal arterial clamp caused decreased Na delivery to the distal tubule and diminished concentration in the loop reabsorbate. Since virtually all measurements during acute reduction of renal arterial pressure have demonstrated enhanced renin release, these results lend strong support to Vander's hypothesis.

Thurau (62, 76–78) has postulated the opposite effect—that an increase in Na load stimulates renin release. According to this view, the juxtaglomerular apparatus plays an important role in the mechanism of autoregulation. His conclusions were partly based upon the observation that proximal tubular lumina collapsed in response to increasing the Na concentration of fluid at the macula densa site. The apparent discrepancy might be resolved if techniques are applied by which the function of a single glomerulus and its corresponding juxtaglomerular apparatus can be assessed simultaneously. It seems desirable to evaluate the different enzymatic steps of the renin-angiotensin system within the single juxtaglomerular apparatus. How changes in enzyme activities in the juxtaglomerular apparatus itself are related to renal venous renin output remains to be demonstrated.

Evidence against mediation of renal autoregulation by angiotensin has been presented by Belleau & Earley (79). These authors measured changes in renal vascular resistance during reduced aortic pressure in normal and renin-depleted dogs in the absence and presence of exogenous renin or angiotensin. Changes in renal vascular resistance due to small changes in the intrarenal production of angiotensin should have been minimized or abolished by the vasoconstrictive effect of the infused compounds. Autoregulation in the presence of exogenous renin or angiotensin was as complete as in the control observations.

Assaykeen et al. (80) have studied the time course of disappearance of exogenous dog renin from the plasma of nephrectomized dogs. The disappearance curve consisted of two exponential components, a rapid component with an average half-time of 6 ± 1 min, and a slower one with a mean half-time of 79 ± 7 min. Circulating angiotensin levels had no effect on either half-time value and the presence of adequate substrate was demonstrated. After nephrectomy, circulating renin levels declined at a rate consistent with the kinetics of the disappearance of exogenous renin. Heacox et al. (81) found significant arterial-hepatic venous differences in renin activity in dogs under control conditions, after stimulation of endogenous renin secretion (acute salt depletion) and after infusion of exogenous renin. No significant arterial-portal venous renin differences were observed. They concluded that the liver is the major site of renin inactivation.

In dogs, Otsuka et al. (82) detected a continued increase in circulating renin levels after hemorrhage, at a time when blood pressure was returning toward normal. This suggests that factors other than simple stretch of the juxtaglomerular cells are involved in this particular response, most likely the Na load to the distal tubules. Dogs on low-Na diet showed the highest values of renin after hemorrhage, whereas nephrectomy suppressed the rise in renin secretion after blood loss.

Studies on acute salt depletion have shown that the plasma activity level of renin increases, but the pressor response to infused renin and angiotensin is simultaneously diminished (83). Miller et al. (84) demonstrated that in dogs, the renin-angiotensin system is quantitatively responsible for the increased aldosterone secretion of salt depletion. In unanesthetized animals in which plasma renin activities had been increased within the physiological range either by infusion of hog renin or by acute salt depletion, secretion of aldosterone was always enhanced. The dose responses to exogenous renin infusion and acute salt depletion were quantitatively similar. Plasma Na, plasma K, and Porter-Silber chromagen were unchanged, which indicates that certain other factors known to alter aldosterone secretion were not changed by the salt depletion.

Failure to "escape" from mineralocorticoids is not always associated with high levels of plasma renin (85). When dogs with a small arteriovenous fistula were given daily injections of DOCA, the renal Na "escape" occurred. However, plasma renin levels were reduced during DOCA administration, both during the initial Na retention and after "escape". Administration of DOCA to dogs with a larger arteriovenous fistula but without evidence of congestive failure led to Na retention and subsequent development of congestive heart failure; plasma renin levels were low, despite the failure to "escape" from mineralocorticoids. Renin substrate was unaltered in these experimental situations. Plasma renin activity was enhanced in dogs with low-output right heart failure due to tricuspid insufficiency and pulonic stenosis. Thus, in experimental heart failure the renin-angiotensin system was activated, but in congestive heart failure produced by DOCA ("no escape") the plasma renin level was suppressed.

Carretero & Gross (86) examined the relationship between renin and angiotensinogen during saline loading and other experimental conditions in rats. Angiotensinogen (renin substrate) concentration was measured indirectly as the yield of angiotensin II after incubation of excess amounts of renin with plasma samples. Angiotensinase activity was inhibited by EDTA. After bilateral nephrectomy, which entails decreased renin levels, plasma substrate concentration increased and reached a maximum within 8 hr. After bilateral adrenalectomy, renin production is increased but plasma substrate is gradually reduced. In these two conditions, a simple negative correlation between enzyme and substrate seemed to exist. However, in other situations a more complex pattern was found. Thus, rats treated with overdoses of DOCA and a high Na load showed only a slight increase in substrate despite a marked reduction in plasma renin. Unilateral clamping of the renal artery leads to increased renin levels and simultaneously to slight elevations in substrate concentration. Renin concentration was unchanged after unilateral nephrectomy, but substrate levels were slightly increased. Carretero & Gross suggest that factors other than renin and angiotensinogen participate in the enzyme-substrate reaction and stress the need for studies on the effect of changes in Na balance on the production and release of renin substrate.

Rapp (87) estimated the juxtaglomerular index (JGI) in unilaterally nephrectomized rats on normal salt intake, on dietary Na loading, and after treatment with antimineralocorticoid. He concluded that juxtaglomerular granularity can be markedly increased or decreased independently of systemic blood pressure or pulse pressure. The results support the view that the JGI is a function of renal Na metabolism rather than blood pressure per se. The relative cell volume of distal tubule cells, measured in formalin-fixed sections of rat kidney cortex, was increased by DOCA, but decreased by aldactone. These observations suggest that cell volume and rate of Na transport are related, as proposed by Ussing (88). Wågermark et al. (89), using a histochemical fluorescence method for biogenic monoamines combined with staining of juxtaglomerular cell granules, demonstrated sympathetic nerve terminals in rat kidneys in portions of walls of juxtaglomerular arterioles containing granulated cells. This finding provides a morphological basis for a direct influence of sympathetic nervous activity on the release of renin.

Arakawa et al. (90) isolated and then determined the amino acid composition of human angiotensin I; the composition resembles that of horse angiotensin I. Ostrovsky et al. (91) developed a method for quantitative measurements of a precursor of a lysophospholipid renin inhibitor. The physiological importance of preinhibitor remains to be studied. Dahlheim et al. (92) described a method of achieving renin substrate (angiotensinogen) concentrations of ∼1000 times that found with previous techniques. According to Oken & Biber (93) biologically effective immunization against angiotensin can be produced in rats, using angiotensin complexed to rat albumin with carbodiimide. The arterial pressure response to synthetic and native rat angiotensin was greatly diminished.

Comparative physiological studies in marine teleosts and Cetacea (94) and in the American opossum (95) are consistent with the existence of a functional renin-angiotensin system in these species.

Capelli et al. (96) report that parallel changes in renal activity of glucose-6-phosphate dehydrogenase and of renin occur in response to alterations in Na balance. The functional relationship of the dehydrogenase to Na metabolism and to the renin-angiotensin system remains unknown.

TUBULAR ELECTROPHYSIOLOGY

Giebisch (97) has summarized recent developments in this field. The most significant findings are concerned with permeability properties of individual cell boundaries in amphibian nephrons and in distal tubular epithelium of rat kidneys.

Boulpaep (98) has reconfirmed a transepithelial potential difference of some 15 to 20 mV (lumen negative) in proximal tubules of Necturus kidney. From an analysis of transient changes in electrical potential difference across peritubular or luminal membrane induced by sudden alterations in the ionic composition of the fluid environment, the partial conductances of K and Cl were measured. The calculated transport numbers for K and Cl were 0.54 (T_K) and 0.20 (T_{Cl}). The peritubular membrane potential must be considered predominantly a K and Cl diffusion potential. This conclusion was confirmed by input resistance measurements of the same preparation by means of a DC bridge circuit. These studies also provided evidence for anomalous rectification across the peritubular cell membrane. However, K and Cl diffusion potentials do not fully account for the total peritubular potential difference. The most important findings concerning the luminal cell border are: 1. Variation of luminal K and Cl concentrations at constant product was almost ineffective in changing the potential across the luminal cell membrane. The combined contribution of K and Cl ions to the membrane current was about 17 per cent. 2. Perfusion of the lumen with choline chloride containing solutions resulted in hyperpolarization of the luminal membrane, indicating a significant degree of Na permeability of this cell barrier. 3. The magnitude of the luminal membrane potential cannot be explained in terms of a K or Cl electrode but depends upon the magnitude of the peritubular membrane potential. A significant parallel pathway exists in addition to the cellular pathway across the proximal tubular epithelium. The luminal potential difference is driven, to a significant extent, by the peritubular voltage generator via an extracellular shunt path.

Sullivan (99) measured electrical potential differences across peritubular and luminal cell membranes of distal tubules of Amphiuma. This amphibian is particularly well suited for studies of distal tubular function, inasmuch as the ventral surface of its kidney, accessible for micropuncture, is composed almost exclusively of convolutions of distal tubules. The transtubular potential is of magnitude and direction similar to that in rat distal tubules (peritubular membrane potential 70 mV, cell negative; transepithelial potential 45 mV, lumen negative). The peritubular membrane potential is highly selective in its permeability to K ions, but the luminal membrane is about equally permeable to Na and K ions. Distal tubular epithelium of Amphiuma possesses essentially the same electrophysiological characteristics as the distal tubule of rat kidneys.

Results on voltage attenuation along proximal tubules of the Japanese newt, previously reported in a preliminary form (100), have led Hoshi & Sakai (101) to conclude that extracellular shunts exist between lumen and peritubular fluid.

Tubular Transport of Strong Electrolytes

A number of concepts of ion and water transport, conceivably applicable to the renal tubule, have evolved from studies in other epithelial tissues. Diamond & Bossert (102) have published the complete analytical treatment of their theory of "standing osmotic gradients" as developed for the gall bladder. In studies of isolated frog skins, Nutbourne (103) observed marked effects of small hydrostatic pressure gradients (<5 mm H_2O) on short-circuit current: it increased when pressure was higher on the outside of the skin, and decreased when pressure was higher on the inside. Nutbourne proposed a model for Na transport in which changes in hydrostatic pressure on one side of the epithelium alter the geometry of intercellular channels and thus influence transport. Either a change in bulk flow through such channels or a direct effect of pressure on the activity of the Na pump is considered. Funder, Ussing & Wieth (104) examined the effect of CO_2 and H ions on Na transport in frog skins. Their results indicate that active transport of Na is facilitated by conditions lowering the intracellular pH of the transporting cells. Rotunno et al. (105) confirmed previous reports that a large fraction of intracellular Na is present in a complexed state. This finding, in conjunction with results of measurements of Na content and fluxes, led Cereijido et al. (106) to propose a new model for Na transport across frog skin epithelium. Its essential feature is the existence of two separate Na-containing compartments. Only the smaller one is thought to participate in active transport of Na.

Coupling of solute fluxes has been described in the frog skin by several investigators (107–109). The possible existence of this phenomenon must be recognized in attempts to categorize the mode of transport of solutes.

Baumann, Fromter & Ullrich (110) have summarized their studies of passive permeability properties of proximal tubules of rat kidneys. The reflection coefficient of NaCl was about 0.69; that of various nonelectrolytes varied with the molecular radius. In a similar study on proximal tubules of Necturus kidneys, Bentzel et al. (111) obtained the same value of 0.69 for the mean apparent reflection coefficient of plasma electrolytes, i.e., primarily NaCl. A number of lipid-insoluble nonelectrolytes of widely varying molecular size had apparent reflection coefficients of $\sim$0.5. The authors were careful to consider their data representative primarily for the permeability properties of the barrier closest to the tubular lumen.

Estimates of the electrochemical driving forces and of net fluxes of Na and K in cortical slices of guinea pig kidneys led Whittembury (112, 113) to propose the existence of two types of Na pumps, both located at the peritubular cell barrier. The first type was refractory to ouabain but sensitive to ethacrynic acid. The net efflux of Na produced by this pump was accompanied mainly by Cl efflux. He suggests that this mode of Na extrusion produces the large net NaCl efflux out of the proximal tubule. The second type was characterized by the simultaneous uptake of K into the cell. The mechanism of this coupling effect could be via the pump or through a passive channel. It was refractory to ethacrynic acid but sensitive to ouabain. Presumably, this pump does not produce net solute transfer across the cell membrane and is responsible for maintaining the normal intracellular ionic composition. Both modes were sensitive to anoxia, and inhibition of either pump lowers respiration. Studies on kidney slices (114) incubated in low-ion media suggest that the water content of the tissue may determine oxygen consumption and K accumulation. Willis (115) found the cation transport in nonhibernating rodents to be more sensitive to temperature than the supporting respiration.

Strong evidence that Na-K-activated ATPase is involved in renal Na transport has been presented by Katz & Epstein (116, 117). Adaptive changes in enzyme activity occurred in response to chronically increased or decreased Na reabsorption. Enhanced reabsorption was induced by contra-lateral uninephrectomy which was paralleled by an increase in Na-K-ATPase per milligram of protein in a microsomal fraction of kidney cortex. Significantly, no change in other microsomal enzymes such as Mg^{++}-dependent ATPase, glucose-6-phosphatase, succinic dehydrogenase, or glutaminase was observed. Similar increases in Na-K-ATPase activity occurred when Na reabsorption was increased by feeding the rats a high-protein diet or after injection of methylpredisnolone, but Na-K-ATPase activity was reduced when renal Na transport was diminished after bilateral adrenalectomy. In a subsequent study [Manitius et al. (118)], glucocorticoids increased Na-K-ATPase activity in the kidney by increasing the quantity of plasma membrane per cell, rather than by increasing the activity of enzyme per unit of plasma membrane. Jørgensen (119) found that the reduction in enzyme activity during developing adrenal insufficiency corresponded to the rate of change in concentrations of Na and K in plasma. A high Na intake could postpone and partly prevent the reduction in enzyme activity during developing adrenal insufficiency. Jørgensen suggests that Na-K-ATPase is not primarily under the control of the adrenals, but is at least in part influenced by the concentration of Na in plasma.

Arcila et al. (120) have continued their studies on the energy coupling of renal tubular Na transport. In dogs, hypoxia had no demonstrable effect on renal function, but enhanced the ability of cyanide to produce natriuresis. This is cited as indirect evidence that cyanide blocks Na reabsorption by its action on renal metabolism. *In vitro* studies on tissue of dog kidneys with evidence of cortical ischemia (121) suggest that mitochondrial enzyme activity is reduced in this condition. Cortical blanching was associated with decreased capacities for complete oxidation of substrates in cortical and medullary homogenates.

An extensive micropuncture study of the transfer pattern of water, Na, and K in proximal and distal tubules of the dog nephron has been reported by Bennett et al. (122). In antidiuretic dogs, slightly less than half the filtered Na, K, and water was reabsorbed in the surface convolutions of the proximal tubule, corresponding to ∼50 to 60 per cent of its total length. Fluid reabsorption was isosmotic, and both Na and K concentrations of proximal fluid samples were not different from those in plasma. Fluid reabsorption in the loops of Henle was 25 per cent, in distal tubules 10 per cent, and in collecting ducts 20 per cent of the filtered water. Distal fluid was always hypo-osmotic to plasma, in contrast to the results obtained in rats. A limiting concentration gradient of Na occurred throughout the distal tubule and net reabsorption was negligible. Reabsorption of K in proximal tubules and loops of Henle was similar despite widely varying rates of excretion induced by K depletion or K loading. During low rates of K excretion the collecting ducts were found to be the site of net K reabsorption, whereas during high excretion rates net addition of K occurred in the distal tubule. The authors propose a passive mode of K transfer in the proximal tubules. In single tubules of the rhesus monkey Bennett et al. (123) found results essentially similar to those in the dog. Distal fluid samples were always hypo-osmotic to plasma. Fursemide blocked Na reabsorption and inhibited K reabsorption in the water impermeable segment of the nephron rather than in proximal tubules. Acetazolamide blocked proximal tubular reabsorption of bicarbonate.

Effect of changes in glomerular load.—The mechanism responsible for the well-known proportionality of glomerular filtration rate and proximal tubular reabsorption of Na has recently inspired three hypothetical explanations. According to one, a hormonal feedback loop is involved in the adjustment of reabsorption to load. The second assumes that the absolute rate of reabsorption varies in direct proportion to the proximal luminal cross-sectional area. Finally, an essential role has been assigned to peritubular capillary absorption by its ability to alter either the Na concentration or the hydrostatic pressure in the spaces that probably exist between neighboring tubular cells and basement membrane.

Wiederholt et al. (124), working on rat kidneys *in vivo*, measured fluid reabsorption in pump-perfused single proximal tubules as a function of perfusion rate and tubular diameter. Transtubular fluid movement was estimated from the relative inulin concentration in collected perfusate and known rates of inflow of perfusion fluid into perfused segments. Luminal diameters were estimated photomicrographically. Fractional fluid reabsorption remained unchanged over a range from 10 to 24 nl/min. Tubular diameters increased with elevation of the perfusion rate. At the highest rate of perfusion (44 nl/min) no further increase in luminal diameter was observed and fractional fluid reabsorption was depressed. However, the fraction of perfusate reabsorbed could be elevated into the range observed at lower perfusion rates when tubules were further dilated by ureteral clamping. The results were consistent with the view, previously expressed by Gertz (1965), that the absolute rate of proximal fluid reabsorption is proportional to the tubular luminal cross-sectional area. The theoretical implications of this relationship for the control of proximal Na reabsorption have been analyzed by Bossert & Schwartz (125).

In contrast, Brenner et al. (126) concluded that at least under conditions of aortic or ureteral clamping, reabsorptive rate is governed by some factors other than tubular luminal geometry. Using a recollection technique on single tubules of rat kidney, they measured the immediate and late changes in reabsorptive rate after an acute alteration in filtration rate produced by aortic constriction and release of constriction. Fractional fluid reabsorption, as measured by the inulin tubule fluid-to-plasma (TF/P) ratio, increased after aortic constriction and decreased after release; but in most instances, absolute rates of reabsorption changed in parallel to glomerular filtration. The change was similar whether collections were made less than 1 or more than 5 min after the change in aortic pressure. The rapid time course of this adjustment in transport rate was taken as evidence against an extrarenal humoral feedback mechanism. However, it is not immediately apparent why an intrarenal hormone release phenomenon should require a measurable period of delay between initating event and completion of the regulation via the feedback loop. Brenner and co-workers (126) also measured TF/P inulin ratio, transit time of lissamine green, and flow rate of fluid in single proxima tubules before and during aortic constriction or release of constriction. Changes in calculated reabsorptive rate and the simultaneous change in calculated cross-sectional area of the tubular lumen were rarely proportional. In other experiments, these same measurements were made before and during partial ureteral clamping. Despite large increments in calculated cross-sectional area, the absolute rate of reabsorption remained relatively unchanged or fell in proportion to the change in GFR. These findings are in contrast to previously published results (127). Brenner et al. (126) point out that inadvertent contamination of proximal samples by distal fluid during elevation of intratubular pressure constitutes a serious hazard in micropuncture. Timed, quantitative fluid collection to calculate GFR of the punctured tubule provides a convenient criterion for the exclusion of unsatisfactory proximal fluid samples under these conditions.

Steinhausen (128) studied the effects of changes in luminal diameter, produced by elevation of the ureteral pressure, on fluid reabsorption in proximal tubules. The half-time of reabsorption of fluid from injected drops of 0.9 per cent saline was not significantly different from that observed under control conditions. In contrast, the tubular occlusion time, the time interval between acute occlusion of the renal artery and complete collapse of the proximal tubular lumen, was markedly prolonged during ureteral clamping. This is taken to indicate inhibition of proximal reabsorption. Proximal tubular lumina were significantly dilated during elevation of the ureteral pressure. These results lend no support to the view that luminal cross-sectional area determines rate of reabsorption. However, it is still uncertain whether the occlusion time is solely a reflection of reabsorptive rate in proximal tubules. Wahl et al. (129) analyzed this method quantitatively, to test its reliability as an index of transport; they found occlusion time constant over a GFR range from 0.3–3.2 ml/min g kidney weight and concluded that fluid reabsorption during arterial occlusion is directly pro-proportional to the free-flow luminal diameter prior to clamping. Fluid reabsorption remained constant during the shrinkage in luminal diameter which occurred during clamping of the artery and was approximately twice as high as values calculated from micropuncture, split-drop, and cinematographic experiments.

Observing that transient intermittent renal vein occlusion in dogs, as well as an increase in perfusion pressure or a decrease in hematocrit in perfused kidneys, leads to Na diuresis, Mills (130) inferred that pressure-sensitive areas exist in the kidney. These areas are thought to be located distal to the afferent arterioles, possibly in the juxtaglomerular cells, and to act upon tubular Na transport via an unknown humoral agent.

The renal vein was partially occluded to test the effect of reduced peritubular capillary absorption on tubular transport (131). During control periods, proximal tubular reabsorptive capacity, measured in split-drop experiments, was linearly related to filtration fraction. Absolute fluid reabsorption during free flow varied directly with the square of the tubular luminal radius and GFR. During partial renal venous occlusion, tubular reabsorptive capacity decreased as a function of reductions in renal plasma flow. The relationship between absolute reabsorption and luminal cross-sectional area was lost but proportionality between absolute reabsorption and GFR was sustained. It was suggested that capillary absorption partly determines the rate of epithelial transport either by altering active Na transport across the cell membrane or by varying the backflux of solute and water through the epithelium. The Na concentration or the hydrostatic pressure in spaces between tubular cells and basement membrane is considered as of primary importance in regulating transepithelial reabsorption and may be influenced by capillary absorption as well as luminal diameter changes.

Martino & Earley (132, 133) proposed that physical factors such as renal vascular resistance, arterial pressure, and oncotic pressure of plasma in peritubular capillaries determine the natriuretic response to expansion of the extracellular fluid volume. The depression of renal Na reabsorption caused by saline infusion could be reversed by infusing hyperoncotic protein solution, which suggests that augmented uptake of interstitial fluid by the capillaries facilitates tubular reabsorption.

The view that capillary absorption may influence transport rests in part upon assumptions concerning the hydraulic permeability of peritubular capillaries. Unfortunately, little is known about this aspect of tubular function and only two relevant papers have been published over the past several years. The first one is that of LeBrie (134) who examined the permeability of renal peritubular capillaries of dogs in terms of the volume of plasma which gives up its test molecule to the interstitial fluid per unit time (Renkin's "transcapillary transport coefficient"). Test substances were dextran fractions with mean molecular weights ranging from 51,000 to 255,000 and radioactive iodinated serum albumin (RISA) with a mean molecular weight of 69,000. Renal lymph-to-plasma ratios of these test molecules were obtained and compared to those reported for hepatic, intestinal, cervical, and leg capillaries. LeBrie concluded that renal capillaries, like capillaries from other areas, have a relatively isoporous small-pore system and another larger-pore system through which bulk filtration or unrestricted diffusion occurs. Comparison of Renkin's coefficient in control conditions and during saline infusion indicated a significant increase in renal capillary permeability or surface area to albumin during saline infusion. Similar studies by Gärtner et al. (135) on rat kidneys indicate that the total permeability of postglomerular capillaries is several times larger than that of glomerular capillaries. Thus, relatively small changes in oncotic or hydrostatic pressure might lead to large alterations in capillary absorption.

Bricker (136), Cort (137), and Pearce (138) have summarized observations supporting the view that a natriuretic hormone, sometimes called "third factor", exists. Reports that plasma or plasma dialysate obtained from volume-expanded donor rats prolongs the half-time of reabsorption in split-drop experiments (139) could not be substantiated in a reinvestigation (personal communication: F. C. Rector, Jr., and D. W. Seldin). Presently available methods have not directly demonstrated the existence of a humoral agent capable of inhibiting Na reabsorption by primary inhibition of transport at the epithelial level.

The adaptive reabsorptive response in the remaining kidney of rats after unilateral nephrectomy has been studied by Katz & Epstein (140). An increase in kidney size occurred during the first 24 hr after surgery, before there was any increase in glomerular filtration rate. After 3 days, the rise in filtration rate exceeded the increase in weight. The results do not support the view that increased glomerular load per gram kidney tissue is the initial stimulus for the early changes in renal hypertrophy. Hayslett et al. (141) found the filtration rate nearly doubled in the remaining kidney of rats, 2 to 4 weeks after uninephrectomy. Fractional fluid reabsorption in proximal and distal tubules remained the same as in controls. The half-time of fluid reabsorption in split-drop experiments was unchanged in proximal tubules, but was significantly shortened in distal tubules. Tubular volume increased in both portions of the nephron, but the volume increase in proximal segments was twice that in distal tubules. In proximal convolutions the increase in reabsorptive rate occurred in approximate proportion to the increase in tubular volume. In contrast, a disproportionate increase in reabsorptive rate occurred in distal tubules. The authors infer that a rise in activity of Na-K-activated ATPase during hypertrophy explains the augmented rate of tubular transport. A biphasic pattern of stimulation of protein synthesis in remaining kidneys after uninephrectomy was observed by Coe & Korty (142).

Salt loading and salt depletion.—The effect of rapid expansion of extracellular fluid volume on proximal and distal tubular fluid reabsorption has been investigated in rats by Hayslett et al. (143). In split-drop experiments on single nephron segments, proximal fluid reabsorption was significantly inhibited. The degree of inhibition was nearly identical in rats previously loaded with or deprived of salt. Since renal stores of renin are low after chronic salt loading and depleted in salt deficiency, the observed similarity in tubular response to saline infusion seemed to be independent of the renin-angiotensin system. Distal tubular reabsorption, also measured by the split-drop method, was increased during acute saline loading. This result should be compared with the apparent inhibition of fluid reabsorption and unchanged magnitude of absolute Na transport in distal tubules of saline-expanded rats, in the free-flow micropuncture experiments of Landwehr et al. (144). Snap-frozen histological sections of kidneys removed during saline diuresis revealed expansion of both tubular and interstitial volume of the renal cortex (143).

Stein et al. (145) proposed on the basis of clearance experiments on dogs that hypotonic saline loading progressively inhibits proximal tubular Na reabsorption. Initially, the distal tubule reabsorbs a large fraction of the proximal rejectate but eventually, during continued loading, distal tubular transport reaches a maximum. This transport limit, induced by hypotonic saline loading, could not be characterized by classical Tm kinetics and was not caused by the high rate of volume flow, since it failed to appear in mannitol diuresis. The major increment in Na excretion developed during saline loading only after saline had altered the capacity of the distal tubule to transport Na.

Eknoyan et al. (146) again stressed the hazards involved in using $T_{H_2O}^c$ as an index of Na reabsorption in the ascending limb of Henle's loop during solute diuresis. This is a consequence of the fact that in dogs distal fluid is always hypo-osmotic to plasma [Clapp & Robinson (1966)]. As solute diuresis progresses, the delivery of hypoosmotic fluid to the collecting ducts in the medulla results in values of $T_{H_2O}^c$ that are falsely low and do not reflect the full extent of water reabsorption. C_{H_2O} is a better index of Na reabsorption in the ascending limb since the low water permeability of the distal tubule helps to preserve the effect of salt transport out of the lumen of the diluting segment. C_{H_2O} depends mainly on the load of Na delivered to the diluting segment. The validity of interpreting changes in C_{H_2O} and urinary volume flow rate V as a relative measure of Na reabsorption and delivery was strengthened by tissue studies which showed a rise in papillary osmolality with rising urine flow rates during hypotonic saline diuresis. During expansion of the extracellular volume (acutely or chronically by DOCA) prior to infusion of hypotonic saline, Na excretion was greater and C_{H_2O} less, at any given V, than in the absence of prior loading. The diminished C_{H_2O} indicates that expansion on the extracellular volume inhibits Na reabsorption in the ascending limb of Henle's loop.

Potter (147) reported that sheep infused with hypertonic saline excrete more salt and reabsorb more free water when pretreated with high Na intake. In stop-flow experiments on dogs undergoing saline diuresis, Bercovitch & Levitt (148) observed elevations of distal Na/creatinine clearance ratios and decreases in creatinine clearances. They concluded that fractional Na and water reabsorption in distal nephron segments is inhibited during saline diuresis. The same conclusion was reached in a micropuncture study in the rat (144).

The well-known diuretic effect of left atrial stretch has given rise to the speculation that cardiac afferent fibers contribute to the control of renal salt and water metabolism. To evaluate this possibility Knox et al. (149) studied the effect of chronic cardiac denervation on the renal response to saline infusion. Natriuresis resulted in controls as well as in "denervated" dogs, which suggests that extrinsic cardiac nerves play only a minor role in regulating Na excretion by the kidneys.

Schrier et al. (150) examined the renal response to acute expansion of the extracellular fluid volume in dogs before and after catecholamine depletion with reserpine. Mean arterial pressure and thus renal perfusion pressure were depressed after reserpine, but filtered loads of Na were comparable before and after administration of the drug. In the absence of reserpine, Na excretion was increased during volume expansion but this effect was abolished by reserpine. It seems that the natriuretic response to acute volume expansion can be influenced by changes in renal perfusion pressure which are mediated by the adrenergic nervous system.

Efforts continue, to define the trigger mechanism for the natriuretic action of acute expansion of the extra cellular fluid volume. Thus, Schrier et al. (151) have studied the effect of infusions of dextran-saline or dextran-glucose solutions of different oncotic pressure and total solute concentration on the volume of body fluid compartments and renal function in dogs. The results suggest that the stimulus to natriuresis was an increase of total extracellular fluid volume, including interstitial space, rather than of volume. This thesis is supported by the work of Kessler et al. (152) who observed a greater natriuretic response to isotonic rather than to equal volumes of isoncotic albumin in saline. Nizet (153) observed a decrease in Na excretion after addition of serum albumin or of dextran in isolated perfused dog kidneys submitted to a saline load. The isolated kidney is able to reject excess plasma Na without extrarenal hemodynamic or hormonal interference (154). Changes in the interstitial volume of the kidney may be of primary importance in eliciting natriuresis.

A hepatic role in the control of Na excretion has been proposed by Daly et al. (155). Infusion of 5 per cent saline into the portal vein of dogs led to a greater natriuretic response than infusion into the femoral vein. In 9 out of 16 experiments, the clearance of inulin was significantly reduced but Na excretion was markedly increased, which indicates a tubular action. The authors infer that a humoral, natriuretic factor may be involved in the regulation of Na excretion and that a possible site for its production is the liver. Production may be stimulated by increased Na concentrations of portal blood.

Behrenbeck et al. (156) have performed electrolyte balance studies during acute salt depletion in dogs. They concluded that loss of Na and entry of water are responsible for the decline in intracellular Na concentration in this condition. On the other hand, hypernatremia leads to cellular dehydration and net entry of Na into the cells (157). Acute salt depletion sensitizes the adrenal's response to stimuli normally provoking aldosterone secretion (158).

POTASSIUM

Giebisch et al. (159) have reviewed their extensive studies of renal tubular K transport in rats. Alterations in the K excretion rate must be interpreted in terms of functional changes in distal tubules and collecting ducts. Recent evidence indicates that this also holds true for modifications in tubular K transport due to acid-base imbalances (160). One of the most important factors determining distal transtubular net movement of K is the electrical potential difference across distal tubular epithelium. Net movement of K into distal tubules consists of passive transfer from cell to lumen and of carrier-mediated, active uptake from lumen into cells. Na-K ion exchange does not occur on a one-to-one basis. On the peritubular side of distal cells an active transport process for Na out of the cell and for K in the opposite direction must still be postulated, but the question of Na-K coupling at this site remains open. Luminal permeabilities of Na and K are approximately equal in magnitude.

Bennett et al. (122, 123) detected no difference in K concentration between proximal tubular fluid and plasma of dogs (122) and rhesus monkeys (123). This observation, in conjunction with Frömter & Hegel's (1966) finding no electrical gradient across rat proximal tubules, led the authors to conclude that K reabsorption in proximal tubules is passive; this argument rests primarily on their confidence in their ultramicroanalytical method of measuring K concentrations.

Alexander & Levinsky (161) have shown that the well-known adaptation to high K intake which manifests itself in the tolerance of acute loads of K that are lethal to rats on normal diet depends largely on extrarenal factors. Increased kaliuresis occurs but is not the major mechanism responsible for increased K tolerance. Despite nephrectomy, rats previously fed a high-K diet maintained lower plasma K concentrations for at least 2 hr after an acute K load than did rats on a regular diet. Chronic adrenal insufficiency abolished adaptation but subsequent administration of DCA restored it. Acute adrenalectomy just before K loading did not abolish adaptation. The results indicate that increased tolerance depends on a chronic increase in mineralocorticoid secretion. The excess K removed from the extracellular fluid by adapted rats was not lost into the gastrointestinal tract. The authors suggest that the more rapid lowering of plasma K after acute loading in adapted rats is due to increased uptake by one or more tissues stimulated by chronic aldosteronism. It seems logical to extend this argument by assigning an essential role to increased cellular K concentrations as a driving force for distal tubular K secretion during adaptation.

According to Goldman et al. (162), ^{42}K exchange in dog kidneys *in vivo* after intrarenal arterial injection of the isotope has a half-time of <2.5 min. This exchange rate is more rapid than that in isolated tissue preparations. The light microscopic and ultrastructural changes produced by high-K media in isolated flounder tubules have been described by Trump et al. (163), for example cell swelling, occlusion of tubular lumina, widening of endoplasmic reticulum, and mitochondrial swelling.

The natriuretic effect of acute K loading is probably due to diminished net ionic reabsorption in the distal tubule (164). Dewhurst et al. (165) observed that maximum K excretion did not usually coincide with peak natriuresis and point out that no adequately tested explanation of the natriuretic effect of K salts has been offered.

Working with rat kidney slices, Bowman & Landon (166) concluded that the mercurial diuretic meralluride lowered intercellular K concentrations, depressed membrane ATPase activity, and reduced tissue respiration.

CHLORIDE

Further evidence that Cl distribution and transport in renal tissue are not necessarily passive has been obtained by Abramow et al. (167), who studied the distribution and exchange rate of Cl in suspensions of renal tubules as well as in single fragments of proximal tubules under different conditions. In normal medium the average steady state concentration of Cl in tissue of separated tubules was about 50 meq/liter tissue water. Addition of ouabain resulted in a rise in Cl concentration. Neither the concentration of Cl in tissue nor the exchange rate of ^{36}Cl was altered when the concentration of K in the bathing medium was varied over a wide range. Chloride in tissue water was kinetically heterogenous and exchanged at at least two different rates. Ouabain had no significant effect on the rate of Cl exchange, in contrast to the previously reported reduction in exchange rates of Na and K. The transcellular flux of Cl was much less than that of Na under similar conditions, which indicates that this Na flux is not representative for transepithelial transport of NaCl. Chloride is not distributed in proximal tubules, in accord with a Donnan relationship. However, no direct evidence for an energy-consuming, active transport process for Cl in proximal tubules has been provided.

Active transport of Cl has been observed in the isolated toad bladder after removal of all K on both sides of the tissue (168) and in the skin of the South American frog *Leptodactylus ocellatus* (169).

MULTIVALENT IONS

Massry et al. (170) have confirmed that the excretion of Ca and Mg may increase during saline diuresis despite a marked fall in its filtered load. The clearances of Ca and Na were linearly related during normal and reduced GFR without significant difference between their regression slopes. In contrast, a difference in the corresponding slopes was found for Mg and

Na. Increments in clearance of Mg were less at reduced filtration rates. The data are compatible with competition for a common reabsorptive site for Na, Ca, and Mg in the nephron. The absolute rate of reabsorption of these ions is simultaneously depressed during expansion of the extracellular fluid volume induced by saline infusion. Duarte & Watson (171) have shown in micropuncture studies on dogs that the calciuretic effect of saline loading is at least in part due to proximal tubular inhibition of Ca reabsorption.

Reduction in extracellular Ca concentration produced by EDTA infusion leads to antidiuresis (172), whereas the parenteral infusion of Ca leads to natriuresis (173). Fülgraff & Heidenreich (174) found the half-time of fluid reabsorption in split-drop experiments prolonged when Ca was used to partly substitute for Na in the perfusion fluid, which suggests inhibition of Na transport. However, Ca may have acted as a poorly reabsorbable solute rather than exerting a direct effect on tubular cells. The possible action of Ca ions on intrarenal distribution of blood flow or on alterations in peritubular capillary permeability with secondary effects on epithelial reabsorption has not been considered.

Working with kidney slices, Kleinzeller et al. (175) showed that removal of Ca from the bathing medium results in an increase in Na and a decrease in K content of the cells. Enhanced leakiness of the cell membrane to Na and K were considered as probable explanations but the possibility that lack of Ca ions interferes also with the activity of the Na-K pump could not be excluded.

Lowering of the Na concentrations to 20 mM/liter in aortal and portal perfusion fluid of doubly perfused frog kidneys caused a marked reduction in Ca reabsorption (176). Vogel & Stoeckert interpreted this as evidence for coupling of Na and Ca transport.

In frogs (*Rana temporaria*), blood is normally saturated with calcium carbonate and in equilibrium with the deposits in the endolymphatic sacs (177). Hodgkinson et al. (178) detected no significant amounts of nonexchangeable calcium in urine of humans.

Walser's (179) comprehensive review of Mg metabolism is of particular interest. Clark (180) observed that supplemental but nontoxic amounts of orally administered Mg ions decreased urinary P excretion. According to Gitelman et al. (181), intact parathyroid glands are essential for the development of hypercalcemia and hypophosphatemia in Mg deficiency. However, Ginn & Shanbour (182) found that the increased rate of excretion of inorganic phosphate in Mg-deficient rats is not due solely to hyperparathyroidism. The responsible mechanism remains elusive.

Phosphaturia subsequent to administration of bicarbonate or acetazolamide probably results from alkalinization of tubular urine or tubular cells (183). Grose & Sciver (184) studied the parathyroid-dependent phosphaturia and aminoaciduria which develops in vitamin D-deficient rats. Phosphaturia preceded aminoaciduria by 2 to 4 weeks; both occurred only at plasma Ca levels below 6.5 mg/100 ml and could be suppressed promptly by parathy-

roidectomy. Koloušek (185) observed increased urinary excretion and reduced plasma concentrations of inorganic phosphate after single injections of
lysine vasopressin but the nature of this response remains unknown. Ginsburg (186) examined the effect of metabolic alkalosis and acidosis on renal
transport of arsenic in dogs. Arsenate reabsorption was less sensitive to the
depressant effect on $NaHCO_3$ infusion than was phosphate reabsorption.
HCl and NaCl infusions depressed arsenate reabsorption but had little effect
on phosphate reabsorption.

TUBULAR TRANSPORT OF ORGANIC COMPOUNDS

Passow (187) has derived an equation which describes the steady state
diffusion of nonelectrolytes in the absence of net water flow across epithelial
brush borders. This theoretical treatment is an attempt to resolve the
apparent incongruity of currently used compartmental analyses and morphological facts, as known from electronmicroscopy of renal tubular epithelium.

Glucose.— Additional evidence indicates that glucose transport depends
upon intratubular Na concentration. Ruedas & Weiss (188) showed that
reducing Na concentration in perfusion fluid to less than 50 mM/liter leads
to a gradual decline in net glucose reabsorption by perfused isolated rat
kidneys. However, even in virtually Na-free media about 25 per cent of the
tubular glucose load was still reabsorbed. Ouabain addition ($7 \times 10^{-4}M$/liter)
to the perfusion fluid resulted in a 40 per cent decrease in net Na transport
and a concomitant decrease of net glucose reabsorption of ∼30 per cent. The
authors suggest that a Na-K-activated, ouabain-sensitive ATPase is responsible for the liberation of energy for the active transport of Na as well as
for active transport of glucose.

Robson et al. (189) have reported that during expansion of the extracellular fluid volume caused by saline infusion, the maximal rate of glucose
transport (Tm) decreased while glomerular filtration increased. They offer
one possible interpretation, that a natriuretic factor may influence a rate-
limiting step in glucose transport.

Infusion of L-glucose results in tubular secretion of this compound (190).
Increased loading with D-glucose augmented the tubular secretion of L-
glucose; phlorizin, but not probenecid, inhibited secretion. Stop-flow analysis
indicated the site of secretion of L-glucose to be in the proximal tubule
and possibly even in distal tubules. Huang & Woosley implicate counter-
transport in D-glucose reabsorption and L-glucose secretion.

Results of Keller's (191) clearance and stop-flow experiments on humans
and dogs suggest that the rate of glucose excretion, though normally very
small, varies directly with proximal tubular flow rate and may be determined
by the transepithelial glucose concentration gradient. Deetjen & Boylan
(192) concluded that proximal tubular reabsorption of glucose rises with
increasing rates of proximal tubular volume flow. Single tubular segments
were perfused with ^{14}C-labeled glucose and reabsorption evaluated on the

basis of isotope concentration ratios of collected perfusate/injected perfusion fluid. The authors assumed absence of ^{14}C backflux because only insignificant amounts of label were detected in collected perfusate after intravenous injection of ^{14}C-glucose. However, active, reabsorptive movement was not stopped. Hence, backflux of label might have been masked by reabsorption.

Studies on kidney cortex slices (193) indicate that D-glucose, D-galactose, α-methyl-D-glucoside, and D-xylose share a common active transport system. Kleinzeller et al. (194) concluded that glucose and galactose are transported across the luminal membrane by an active Na^+-dependent, phlorizin-sensitive mechanism and traverse the basal cell membrane along their concentration gradient by a Na^+-independent, phlorizin-sensitive process of facilitated diffusion.

Urea.—Rabinowitz & Baines (195) used a microinjection method to evaluate renal tubular permeability to methylurea, acetamide, and urea in the rat. Their results suggest that: (*a*) the permeability of the distal and collecting tubule to all three compounds is the same; (*b*) the permeability of the proximal tubule and loop of Henle, taken together, is in the order: acetamide > methylurea > urea; (*c*) proximal tubules and loop of Henle are the sites where the major portion of reabsorption of acetamide and methylurea occurs; (*d*) the injected compounds were distributed in a greater volume than the tubular lumen, which indicates transient entry into cells and interstitial fluid with subsequent re-entry into the tubular lumen.

Carlisky et al. (196) studied the excretion of urea by toad kidneys (*B. arenarum*). The clearance of urea was always lower than that of inulin, which indicates reabsorption. Reabsorption was passive and the levels of arginase were low. This is in contrast to frog kidneys (*R. catesbiana*) in which urea is secreted into the tubular lumen and arginase activity is high. The findings strengthen the view that renal arginase is related to active transport of urea. In rats, Carrasquer et al. (197) found high urea concentrations in distal fluid samples collected during stop-flow conditions. This supports the general notion that urea is less permeable than water in this nephron segment. However, contamination of distal fluid by collecting duct urine is a possible source of error in such experiments (126).

Urate.—Skeith & Healey (198) demonstrated that the New World monkey *Cebus albifrons* (ring-tailed monkey) may be a suitable laboratory model for renal handling of urate in the human. The serum uric acid level ranged between 1.5–3.0 mg/100 ml, which suggests a lack of uricase. There was extensive reabsorption, which could partially be blocked by probenecid, sulfinpyrazone, and chlorothiazide. Reabsorption was increased by pyrazinoic acid, lactate, and β-hydroxybutyrate infusions. Increased rates of bidirectional urate transport with enhanced urate supply to the kidney have been described in normal man (199).

Renal transport of uric acid in guinea pigs was examined by Mudge et al. (200) using stop-flow analysis. Uric acid was normally either reabsorbed, or secreted, or both. The stop-flow pattern revealed no significant distal permeability to urate. Probenecid strongly inhibited proximal urate secretion, making proximal reabsorption apparent. Pyrazinoic acid slightly inhibited secretion. The uptake of urate by kidney slices was essentially the same for the guinea pig as for the rabbit. As in other laboratory mammals, there is bidirectional transport of urate in the proximal segment of guinea pig kidneys.

Ferris & Gorden (201) observed that angiotensin and norepinephrine, given intravenously to normal humans in amounts sufficient to raise the diastolic pressure 20 mm Hg, causes depression of tubular urate secretion. The effect was not due to a reduction in filtration rate or osmolar clearance and appeared to be related to a decrease in effective renal blood flow, which suggests an indirect effect on tubular transport.

Other organic acids and bases.—Baines et al. (202) have used the microinjection method, devised in Gottschalk's laboratory, to study PAH excretion by rat kidneys. The volume of distribution of PAH injected into the proximal tubular lumen was greater than that of simultaneously injected inulin or mannitol, but its urinary excretion was complete except when plasma PAH levels exceeded 10 mg/100 ml. The results demonstrate a transtubular efflux of PAH in the cortex and medulla. Raising plasma PAH concentration increased the loss of microinjected PAH, presumably by competitively inhibiting influx back into the tubular lumen.

Tanner (203) used micropuncture techniques to study PAH and Diodrast transport in Necturus kidneys. The previously demonstrated reabsorption and secretion of Diodrast were localized in proximal tubules. Net PAH reabsorption also occurs at this site. PAH in microinjected solutions inhibited Diodrast reabsorption. Octanoate inhibited net PAH reabsorption in the proximal convolution. Using a new freeze-dry autoradiographic technique, Wedeen & Jernow (204) obtained evidence for active cellular uptake of hippurate at the peritubular border of rat kidney cells. "Uremic" serum, collected from bilaterally nephrectomized rats, specifically inhibits the *in vitro* uptake of PAH by rat renal cortical slices (205).

A detailed study [Møller (206, 207)] of the relationship between transport of urate and PAH in the rabbit kidney supports the generally held view that these two compounds have a common transport system.

Renal tubular transport of α-ketoglutarate (α-KG) has been studied by Balagura & Stone (208). Using clearance and extraction procedures, experiments were performed on dogs during intravenous infusions of citrate, α-KG, or both, in normal acid-base balance and in acute respiratory and metabolic alkalosis. Administration of citrate, or acute alkalosis, depressed the normally observed net reabsorption and uptake of α-KG, or converted them to net secretion and production. Under these conditions, renal cortical concentrations of α-KG were elevated. The mechanisms whereby alterations in acid-base balance alter the excretion pattern of α-KG involve, at least in part, variations in the rate of operation of the tricarboxylic acid cycle in the tubular epithelium.

Active secretion of 1, 2-dihydroxybenzene (catechol) by tubular cells of the chicken has been demonstrated (209). This transport occurs apparently by a pathway which is separable from organic anion and cation transport systems. Catechol selectively inhibits epinephrine transport, which suggests a common pathway for catecholamines and catechol. Cathechol is conjugated during its passage from portal perfusion fluid to urine, which indicates a tubular conjugation step. Galvin et al. (210) studied the urinary excretion of β-hydroxybutyrate and acetoacetate during experimental ketosis in humans. Probenecid binding (30 per cent) by renal cortical slices and homogenates has been reported (211).

Amino acids and protein.—Wilson & Scriver (212) have confirmed the interaction in transport of proline, hydroxyproline, and glycine in rat kidneys *in vivo*. Cortical slices showed several systems available for the uptake of amino acids and glycine, rather than a single common transport. Similarly, the basic amino acids were transported separately from cystine by multiple mediations rather than by a single common system. Hence, transport of neutral and basic amino acids is characterized by both individual and group specificities.

Weiss et al. (213) used isolated, perfused rat kidneys to study the effect of alterations in urinary pH on the excretion of various amino acid esters. The clearance of methylglycine, ethylglycine, ethylalanine, and methylvaline decreased with increasing urine pH. In contrast, the clearance of the corresponding nonesterified amino acids increased with increasing pH of the urine. These results support the thesis that nonionic diffusion, i.e., pH-dependent back diffusion, plays a significant role in the renal excretion of amino acid esters.

Thier (214) studied the relationship of amino acid accumulation to transepithelial Na transport in the toad bladder. The mucosal surface was impermeable to amino acid movement in either direction. Uptake against concentration gradients occurred at the serosal cell surface. The accumulation of the neutral amino acid α-aminoisobutyric acid was Na dependent, ouabain sensitive, and unaffected by anaerobiosis. Thier considers the active uptake of amino acids to be independent of transepithelial Na transport, though the energy-requiring steps for both processes are probably located in the serosal surface of the cells. With respect to the cationic amino acid L-lysine, a different mode of uptake was postulated. Accumulation was not inhibited by the lack of either Na or O_2 or by the presence of ouabain. The results on α-aminoisobutyric acid resembled those obtained in kidney slices (215).

Developmental aspects of amino acid accumulation have been studied by Webber & Cairns (216).

Wilde et al. (217) have provided morphological evidence that albumin, tagged as albumin-Evans blue, migrates through the proximal tubular wall of rat kidneys not in the form of free molecules in cytoplasm, but by enclosure within single membrane vesicles.

REGULATION OF ACID-BASE

"Hydrogen ion exchange mechanism" has been the subject of a recent symposium (218). There are two opposing views, based upon different technical approaches, on the H ion distribution across cell membranes. Carter et al. (219, 220) concluded from measurements with pH-sensitive glass microelectrodes that H ions in the aqueous phase of intracellular fluid are in electrochemical equilibrium with those of extracellular fluid. This suggests that the main determinants of intracellular pH are the membrane potential difference and the pH of extracellular fluid. In contrast is the conclusion reached from estimates of intracellular pH as measured by the distribution of CO_2 and DMO (5,5-dimethyl-2 4-oxazolidinedione). Butler et al. (221) summarized their, and other, work on the use of weak electrolytes as indicators of intracellular pH. They have countered the claim of active transport of DMO, of its binding, and of permeability of cell membranes to the ionized form of DMO. Butler et al. (222) also advanced further evidence that calculation of intracellular pH of muscle from the total acid-labile CO_2 and the pCO_2 on the assumption of impermeability of the membrane to bicarbonate is probably valid. The intracellular pH of skeletal muscle as calculated from the distribution of CO_2 and DMO is much higher than the value of 6.0 reported by Carter et al. (220). Besides the possibility of unrecognized technical errors, the two techniques may reflect a different aspect of intracellular acidity. Thus, microelectrodes may indicate the pH of the bulk phase of cytoplasmatic water, whereas DMO because of its diffusibility might also reflect the pH of various other intracellular compartments. The crucial question as to the H ion activity in the immediate vicinity of cell membranes cannot be approached directly with currently available techniques.

Struyvenberg et al. (223) used separated canine renal tubules to calculate pH from the distribution of DMO-^{14}C, using inulin as a measurement of extracellular water. At normal P_{CO_2} and extracellular bicarbonate concentration, renal cells were more alkaline (mean pH 7.32) than most other mammalian cells. Cell acidity varied as a direct linear function of extracellular acidity when the latter was changed by variations of either P_{CO_2} or extracellular HCO_3^- concentration, but CO_2 had a greater effect. Inhibition of carbonic anhydrase by addition of $10^{-5} M$ acetazolamide increased intracellular pH. Surprisingly, neither acute K depletion nor rapid repletion significantly affected cell pH. However, recent results obtained in muscle indicate that the *in vivo* buffer capacity of low-K skeletal muscle is significantly less than the buffer capacity of control skeletal muscle (224).

According to Steinmetz (225), acidification by turtle bladder epithelium depends upon production and enzymatic hydration of metabolic carbon dioxide. Hydrogen ion secretion into the mucosal medium is associated with appearance of alkali on the serosal side of the bladder. The transepithelial potential difference has no major influence on the rate of acidification. Active

H ion and active Na ion transport in the turtle bladder are independent of each other (226). Using the same tissue, Brodsky & Schilb (227) proposed active transport of bicarbonate in its ionized form. This view depends critically on the observation that the CO_2 tension of the mucosal fluid declines during acidification.

Vieira & Malnic (228) have presented further evidence that reabsorption of HCO_3^- in proximal and distal tubules is mediated by active transport of H ions from cell interior into the tubular lumen. In a micropuncture study, they used antimony microelectrodes for the *in situ* measurement of pH of tubular fluid. In proximal tubules of rats under control conditions and during $NaHCO_3$ diuresis the intraluminal pH *in vivo* was found identical to the equilibrium pH calculated from plasma P_{CO_2} and luminal (HCO_3^-). However, during intravenous infusion of acetazolamide, intraluminal pH was 0.41 unit lower than the calculated equilibrium pH. In the distal tubule a "disequilibrium pH" of 0.54 pH units was observed without inhibition of carbonic anhydrase. Although qualitatively in agreement with *in situ* measurements obtained with glass microelectrodes (229), the absolute magnitude of the disequilibrium pH in proximal tubules during acetazolamide infusion and in distal tubules was significantly smaller. A different degree of carbonic anyhdrase inhibition obtained in the two studies might account for the differences. Quantitative considerations of the electrochemical driving forces indicate that H ions are actively secreted into the tubular lumen of proximal and distal tubules.

Bernstein & Clapp (230) have studied the effect of metabolic acidosis and alkalosis and of acetazolamide on bicarbonate reabsorption by the dog nephron. Bicarbonate concentrations in tubule fluid were estimated by means of the quinhydrone-microelectrode method. Under control conditions of normal acid-base balance, late proximal fluid samples contained bicarbonate at about the same concentration as in arterial blood, in contrast to the decline found in rats. A significant drop in HCO_3^- level was observed in distal tubule fluid. During ammonium chloride acidosis, proximal and distal bicarbonate concentrations were reduced to values of 5.3 and 4.4 meq/liter, at arterial bicarbonate concentrations of 13.3 meq/liter. A further decline in bicarbonate concentration occurred along the collecting ducts. During metabolic alkalosis induced by bicarbonate infusions, HCO_3^- concentration was markedly higher in late proximal tubule fluid than in blood. Acetazolamide increased proximal tubular bicarbonate concentrations.

Using micropuncture techniques, Weinstein (231) has investigated the effect of acetazolamide on tubular reabsorption of bicarbonate and Cl in rat kidneys. Acetazolamide did not alter the absolute magnitude of proximal tubular fluid reabsorption since a decrease in inulin clearance was compensated by an equivalent increase in proximal fractional fluid reabsorption. The tubular fluid/plasma (TF/P) Cl concentration ratio averaged 1.15 in the middle third of the proximal tubule under control conditions but was only 0.92 in rats infused with acetazolamide. TF/P for bicarbonate, calculated from the Cl data and plasma electrolytes, increased to 1.5 to 2.0 at the proximal convolution. Thirty to 50 per cent of filtered bicarbonate was excreted in bladder urine of acetazolamide-infused rats. In these animals the urine was virtually free of Cl ions. Weinstein proposed that in proximal tubules of acetazolamide-treated rats, active Na transport continued with increased Cl reabsorption compensating for a decreased rate of H ion secretion.

In dogs during acute metabolic alkalosis, Ullmann (232) observed that partial occlusion of the ureter of one kidney increased the bicarbonate threshold beyond that of the other unobstructed kidney. This effect could not be explained by changes in P_{CO_2} of renal blood. Since larger bicarbonate concentration differences between plasma and urine occurred when ureteral occlusion was prolonged, the author considered transit time an important factor in regulating tubular bicarbonate reabsorption. However, increased renal blood flow during ureteral occlusion could play a role in the increase in reabsorption of bicarbonate.

Studies in dogs on a low-salt diet have helped to define the factors which determine whether infusion of the Na salt of an anion will induce metabolic alkalosis (233). Berkman and his associates found that only sodium nitrate, but not sodium chloride (more reabsorbable than nitrate) or sodium sulfate (less reabsorbable than nitrate), induced metabolic alkalosis. To produce metabolic alkalosis, an anion must be sufficiently reabsorbable to compete with Cl for reabsorption and to replace it in urine. Also, the anion must be sufficiently less reabsorbable than Cl so as not to be conserved as efficiently and thereby to leak from the body and create a deficit of reabsorbable anion.

The correction of metabolic alkalosis by the kidney after infusion of fluid containing electrolytes at concentrations equal to their preinfusion levels in plasma has been studied (234). Cohen concludes that it is the amount of Cl, reaching the distal nephron, rather than the concentration itself, which leads to preferential reabsorption of Cl in hypochloremia.

Kunau et al. (235) re-examined the effect of K deficiency on proximal bicarbonate reabsorption by using an experimental model which excluded any possible alteration in bicarbonate reabsorption due to differences in extracellular fluid volume (236). Bicarbonate concentrations in proximal tubule fluid of K-deficient rats were much lower than in normal rats, although systemic alkalosis and expansion of extracellular fluid volume (ECFV) were the same. Massive expansion of ECFV in K-deficient rats increased proximal tubular HCO_3 concentration slightly, but to levels always lower than in control animals. The results indicate that K deficiency enhanced proximal tubular HCO_3 reabsorption. This effect can be augmented in ECFV and partially, but not completely, canceled by expansion of ECFV. It should be realized that the effect varies among species. For example in the dog, but not in rats, expansion of ECFV will completely correct metabolic alkalosis despite persistence of hypokalemia.

Human subjects recovering from metabolic acidosis retain more Na than subjects repleted with K (237). Lennon & Lemann suggest that Na retention in K depletion is due to increased fractional reabsorption of proximal tubular fluid.

Intracellular alkalosis develops more rapidly after infusion of $NaHCO_3$ than of lactate (238). Lactate is probably first metabolized in the liver and heart, thus acting as a delayed $NaHCO_3$ infusion. Engel et al. (239) have made an extremely well-controlled study of the quantitative displacement of acid-base relationships during chronic respiratory acidosis in humans. Lemann et al. (240) observed diminished tubular reabsorption of Ca during metabolic acidosis. The impaired ability of patients with renal tubular acidosis to conserve Na and K is probably caused by a primary limitation of distal tubules to establish transepithelial H ion gradients (241). Diminished transfer of H^+ from cell to lumen might then result in increased distal potential differences (lumen more negative to peritubular fluid) and thus in higher rates of passive K secretion. Passive Na entry into cells might be hindered in a similar fashion or by reduced carrier-mediated exchange of Na and H in the luminal cell membrane. Morris (242) reported that administration of fructose in patients with hereditary fructose intolerance can induce a reversible tubular dysfunction with the characteristics of renal tubular acidosis. It also includes impaired reabsorption of α-amino N and phosphate. The causal enzymatic defect, the virtual absence of fructose-1-phosphate aldolase, occurs in the kidney as well as in the liver. Adverse effects can result if patients with fructose intolerance receive inulin infusions.

Edelmann et al. (243) suggest that the low plasma bicarbonate concentration of normal infants is caused by a renal threshold for HCO_3 lower than that normally found in adults, functional and morphological heterogeneity of nephrons of the infant being considered partly responsible.

Conclusive evidence has been presented by Stone, Balagura & Pitts (244) that the free base NH_3 attains diffusion equilibrium in all renal phases: blood, interstitial fluid, proximal and distal cells, and proximal and distal tubular fluid. In the dog kidney ammonia exists as a single, well-mixed pool. About one third of urinary ammonia was derived from performed arterial ammonia and according to previous studies in the same laboratory, 75 per cent of urinary ammonia is derived from deamidation and/or deamination of plasma glutamine, alanine, glycine, and glutamate. The authors could account for all of the ammonia which leaves the kidney in renal blood and in urine. Micropuncture studies by Oelert et al. (245) have shown that equilibrium of P_{NH_3} between proximal and distal tubule fluid and renal venous blood is reached in rat kidneys. Microperfusion experiments in single tubules indicate that the permeability of all cortical nephrons is at least 1×10^{-2} cm/sec.

The enzymatic pathways of ammonia production by the dog kidney *in vivo* have been studied by Stone & Pitts (246). They concluded that preformed ammonia and ammonia derived from the amide nitrogen of plasma glutamine are added directly to urine without significant incorpora-tion into amino acid intermediates. Hence, neither reductive amination of α-KG to form glutamate nor transfer of the amide-N of glutamine to the corresponding keto acids to form glutamate, aspartate, alanine, or glycine occurs to an appreciable extent. "Glutaminase II" may participate signifi-cantly in forming ammonia, possibly by forming aspartate and alanine by direct transamination of oxalacetate and pyruvate and liberating the amide N as ammonia. Transfer of the N of alanine to α-KG and subsequent oxida-tive deamination of the resulting glutamate can account for the ammonia formed from alanine. Glycine is not an important intermediate in renal N metabolism.

Kamm et al. (247) continued their studies of renal glucose production under conditions of acid-base alterations. Glucose production was increased in cortical slices from rats with respiratory acidosis. Thus, respiratory acidosis has an effect similar to that of metabolic acidosis. Glucose produc-tion by kidney slices was increased in media made acidic by reducing HCO_3, and decreased in media made alkaline by raising HCO_3. Gluconeogenesis was also increased in media made acidic by elevation of the CO_2 tension and decreased in media made alkaline by reducing Pco_2. The authors sug-gest that both *in vivo* and *in vitro* pH, rather than CO_2 tension or bicarbonate concentration, is the most important acid-base variable affecting renal gluconeogenesis. They further suggest that acidosis augments renal glu-coneogenesis through direct stimulation of one of the rate-limiting reactions involved in the conversion of oxalacetate to glucose. The resultant increase in the rate of removal of glutamate, a precursor of oxalacetate and inhibitor of the glutaminase reaction, may be an important step in the mechanism by which acidosis increases renal ammonia production. Recent studies (248) of the concentration of metabolites in rat kidneys support this hypothesis.

On the other hand, Pitts (249) has considered that in the dog, acidosis may lead to the accumulation of keto acids by inhibition of the condensing reaction of the Krebs cycle, which would then lead to a stimulation of NH_3 production via the reaction sequence catalyzed by glutamine-keto acid aminotranferase and ω-amidase. Goorno et al. (250) found the conversion of acetate-2-^{14}C to $^{14}CO_2$ unimpaired in kidney slices obtained from rats in metabolic acidosis, interpreting this as evidence against inhibition of the Krebs cycle. However, CO_2 is reincorporated in Krebs cycle intermediates and measurements of $^{14}CO_2$ alone cannot exclude the condensing enzyme hypothesis. Goldstein (251) concluded that in the rat, glutaminases (phos-phate dependent and independent), but not the aminotransferase, play a significant role in glutamine deamination and NH_3 production. Metabolic acidosis produced a fall in keto acids, a finding which Goldstein considered inconsistent with inhibition of the condensing enzyme reaction. He proposes that acidosis stimulates incorporation of α-KG into gluconeogenic pathways and thus tends to increase the rate of glutamate deamination. This argu-ment fails to take into account that increased rates of utilization of Krebs cycle intermediates for gluconeogenesis may decrease, in acidosis, the concentrations of keto acids despite reduced activity of the condensing enzyme.

CONCENTRATING AND DILUTING MECHANISM

A most important recent finding concerning the renal countercurrent mechanism has been published only in abstract form (252). Jamison concluded from micropuncture studies in the rat that Na reabsorption out of the lumen and low water permeability characterize the wall of the thin ascending limb of Henle's loop. Hence, the thin loop functions as a countercurrent multiplier.

The permeability properties of collecting ducts have been examined by Morgan et al. (253) in perfusion studies on collecting tubules of the isolated rat papilla. The permeability coefficient of medullary collecting ducts was 53 $cm \cdot sec^{-1} \cdot 10^{-5}$ and increased to 95 $cm \cdot sec^{-1} \cdot 10^{-5}$ when ADH was added. The corresponding values for urea were 13.8 and 20.2, respectively. Hyperosmolality of the bathing medium resulted in net reabsorption of water from the lumen. ADH increased the rate of fluid absorption from 4.1 nl $cm^{-2} min^{-1} mosmol^{-1}$ to 21.0. Urea and NaCl did not remove as much water as an equal osmolal concentration of mannitol. When a reflection coefficient of 1.0 for mannitol was assumed, reflection coefficients for NaCl and urea were 0.9 and 0.4. Fluid withdrawn from collecting ducts never had osmolality significantly higher than that of the surrounding medium. When medium and perfusion fluid had the same initial osmolality, the collected perfusate retained its original osmolality. The results lend no support to the lineal multiplication hypothesis (254).

In order to characterize the functional response of Henle's loop to alterations in load entering the pars recta of proximal tubules, Schnermann (73) performed microperfusion experiments on single short loops of Henle in rat kidneys. Fractional and absolute reabsorption rates of Na, K, and water between the end of proximal convolutions and a site ~20 per cent of distal tubule length were studied as a function of perfusion rate. In 56 per cent of the control perfusions, net Na and K reabsorption increased in proportion to the increase in perfusion rate. In this group of experiments, early distal tubular Na concentration remained constant or decreased at higher perfusion rates. Essentially similar results obtained during mannitol and saline diuresis and in dehydrated rats indicate that changes in Na concentration in interstitial fluid of the medulla do not significantly influence net reabsorption of Na. Resistance to flow declined and the tubular diameter of the resistance segment, most likely the thin segment of the loop, increased when higher rates of perfusion were used. In 44 per cent of the experiments, the early distal tubular Na concentration rose with elevations of the perfusion rate. The author considers this latter group of perfusion experiments as not representative of normal function of the loop of Henle. The implications of this study for concepts of autoregulation of glomerular filtration have been discussed in the section on the juxtaglomerular apparatus.

Consonant with Schnermann's (73) finding of relative constancy of fractional Na reabsorption in loops of Henle is the observation of Heller & Vostal (255) that the Na concentration in the renal papilla rises as a function of the Na level in plasma. The mechanism by which the tubular epithelium of Henle's loop increases its Na transport in response to augmented loads is still unkown. Any direct analysis of this question will have to separate the functions of the pars recta from that of the ascending limb.

Further evidence that oxidative metabolism is of importance for the functional integrity of the renal medulla has been advanced by Heller & Tata (256). No significant changes occurred in corticomedullary Na and urea gradients of rat kidneys after infusion of monoiodoacetate. After intravenous administration of KCN and malonate, however, the gradients were smaller or disappeared. The authors conclude that the establishment of corticomedullary gradients in the rat depends in part on aerobic metabolism.

Anaerobic glycolysis may, however, be an important energy-yielding pathway in the inner medulla of the kidney (257). This conclusion rests on the studies of Dell & Winters who observed increased corticomedullary lactate gradients in dog kidneys during solute diuresis. The results do not prove, but are consistent with the hypothesis that increased medullary transport of Na is energized by glycolysis. The lactate formed would then be trapped by countercurrent diffusion.

Solomon (258) has reported that Li, but not Ru or Cs, is accumulated in the renal medulla.

By microspectrophotometry Wilde & Vorburger (259) examined the distribution of Evans blue (T-1824, taken as an index of albumin) in capillary cross sections of frozen-dried hamster kidneys. The authors confirmed the previously reported increase in albumin. Interstitial accumulation of Evans blue was observed in the inner zone of the medulla and may represent an extravascular pool of albumin. T-1824 concentration increased within descending vasa recta in that region of the outer medulla where vasa recta occur in isolated bundles. At the border between outer and inner medulla, the concentration was twice that in tissues other than the kidney. A further increase in dye concentration occurred within the inner medulla where the vasa recta fan out and are no longer arranged in bundles. Only in the inner zone was interstitial accumulation of Evans blue observed. The authors conclude that the increase in albumin concentration in descending vasa recta is caused by the lateral shunt of water from descending into ascending limbs of the vascular loop. The possible role of the vasa recta as a countercurrent multiplier system for salt, activated by a gradient of hydrostatic pressure, seems unlikely. Quantitative considerations indicate that the hydrostatic pressure drop along descending vasa recta could at best account for only 18 per cent of the osmotic work. Further studies are needed to evaluate the role of protein in the medulla under conditions of marked alterations in distribution of renal blood flow.

Pinter (260) has confirmed that the quantity of plasma albumin in the renal medulla is larger than can reasonably be attributed to intravascular plasma. He found a statistically significant correlation between osmotic U/P ratios and the quantities of extravascular albumin in the medulla. This finding is consonant with enhanced shunting of water between the limbs of vasa recta during an increase in concentrating ability of the kidney. Albumin-bound urea cannot sustain a significant difference in urea concentrations between interstitial fluid and collecting duct urine in the renal medulla (261).

Rabinowitz (262) studied the effect of acute administration of methylurea, acetamide, and urea on the concentrating ability of vasopressin-infused rats. The observed increase in urinary osmolality was always exceeded by a rise in the concentration of the infused compounds in tissue water of the renal papilla, and this was in turn exceeded by the rise in their concentration in the urine. Enhancement of the renal concentrating ability by methylurea and acetamide is apparently brought about by the accumulation of these compounds in the interstitial fluid of the papilla in high concentrations secondary to passive reabsorption from the collecting ducts. Carrasquer & Diana (263) presented data on renal medullary tissue analysis, obtained in stop-flow experiments and after release of ureteral occlusion, which support the generally held view that the permeability of the loop of Henle and of distal tubules to urea is restricted. In clinical studies, Klahr et al. (264) found evidence that the renal defect of malnutrition may be due to a reduction in urea concentration in the renal medulla.

The countercurrent system of uricotelic birds apparently functions with the Na pump in the ascending limb of Henle's loop as a "single effect," and no other solutes contribute significantly to the osmotic gradient in the medullary cone (265). Selkurt & Wathen (266) have studied the renal concentrating mechanism of the squirrel monkey (*Saimiri sciureus*). The kidney of this animal differs from that of the dog in that, although $T^c_{H_2O}$ may decrease at high rates of solute excreretion, it does not typically develop a positive free-water clearance. This suggests that, in contrast to conditions in the dog and rhesus monkey (123), distal tubular fluid may achieve osmotic equilibrium with plasma, but micropuncture experiments are needed to verify this.

A mathematical model of the concentrating mechanism has been developed without inclusion of active Na transport in thin ascending loops of Henle (267). The need for such a complicating assumption has recently been obviated by the direct studies of Jamison (252).

ANTIDIURETIC HORMONES

Forsling et al. (268) have suggested that the frequent reports of enhanced sensitivity of the rat to vasopressin may have been due to fortuitous use of a particularly sensitive batch of rats, or to a high endogenous secretion of vasopressin due to operative trauma. They proposed that assays commenced shortly after surgery on Wistar rats, weighing only 100–150 g and infused intravenously with vasopressin (0.5–3 μu/min), allow the detection of as little as 0.5 μu of plasma arginine vasopressin. Diabetes insipidus rats may be more satisfactory than normal rats in the bioassay of ADH (269).

Gauer & Tata (270) have extended their quantitative analysis of the antidiuretic effect of vasopressin in rats. After single intravenous injections of 20 μu the antidiuretic response was not significantly different from that which was induced by 1 μu Tonephrin or 6 μu Pitressin. The amount of antidiuretic activity recovered in the urine was not measurably less than that injected. This suggests that very little antidiuretic activity is quickly bound at the tubular receptor sites where it induces near-maximal antidiuresis. The vasopressin water-equivalent was 4 ml per μu ADH during the antidiuretic period which lasted 50 min. Assuming $2.5 \cdot 10^{-6}$ μ moles arginine vasopressin per mu Pitressin, the vasopressin water-equivalent would be 1 mole arginine vasopressin for 10^8 moles of water. If these considerations are applied to the human kidney, the requirement to saturate the receptors is 200–500 μu vasopressin. On this basis it can be predicted that the human kidney in the complete absence of vasopressin may lose 26 liters water per day. This prediction agrees with observations in diabetes insipidus patients and supports the validity of extrapolating concepts developed in rats to other organsisms.

A new concept concerning the mechanism of vasopressin action has been proposed by Hays (271). Studies on complex synthetic membranes show that osmotic flow can be limited by one (thin, dense) barrier, and the diffusion rate of isotope water by a second (thick, porous) barrier in series with the first. Conventional calculations of pore radius in membranes are based on the ratio of osmotic to diffusional flow, assuming both flows to be rate-limited by the same barrier in the membrane. Calculation of a pore radius in the presence of two barriers in series, as found in artificial membranes, is meaningless, greatly overestimating the size of the pores determining osmotic flow. Hays postulated that vasopressin acts by markedly increasing the rate of diffusion of water across an outer barrier of the membrane, with little or no accompanying increase in pore size. This study raises serious doubts about the validity of some previous investigations on complex epithelial membranes in which pore radii have been calculated.

Civan & Frazier (272) used microelectrodes to demonstrate that about 98 per cent of the total electrical resistance change following vasopressin occurs at the mucosal permeability barrier of the transporting cells of the toad bladder. This finding agrees with similar studies on other tissues.

Evidence that the lateral interspaces between neighboring epithelial cells may be part of the pathway of osmotically induced water flow has been presented by Ganote et al. (26). Isolated cortical collecting tubules of rabbit kidneys were examined for changes in ultrastructure under conditions of alterations in transtubular net flux of water. Vasopressin-induced osmotic water movement led to marked dilatation of lateral interspaces, bulging of apical cell membranes into the tubular lumen, and formation of intracellular vacuoles. The authors conclude that the ultrastructural changes were caused by transepithelial bulk movement of water and that vasopressin induces osmotic flow by increasing water permeability of the luminal cell membrane.

Studies on the effect of Ca and Mg ions on the toad bladder response to cyclic AMP, theophylline, and ADH analogues lend support to the hypothesis of Petersen & Edelman (1964) that there are separate types of sites of ADH-induced cyclic AMP production (273). Calcium at high concentration inhibits the effect on osmotic water flow of Pitressin and arginine vasopressin, and inhibits the response to theophylline but not that of lysine vasopressin, oxytocin, arginine vasotocin, and cyclic AMP. The effect of Ca on osmotic water flow was paralleled by a similar effect on the diffusional flux of urea. In contrast to Ca, Mg inhibited the effect of all analogues of vasopressin tested except cyclic AMP. These results are consistent with the existence of a Ca-sensitive site of hormone-induced cyclic AMP production, affecting osmotic and solute permeability at the mucosal barrier, and a Ca-insensitive site affecting Na transport at the serosal surface of the cell.

Senft et al. (274) observed that dehydration of rats leads to a doubling of renal 3',5'-AMP concentration. Renal 3',5'-AMP phosphodiesterase was not influenced by vasopressin, which indicates that the increase in cyclic AMP in dehydrated rats is not due to inhibition of the enzyme catalyzing the breakdown of AMP. The results strengthen the thesis that stimulation of adenyl cyclase is responsible for the observed increase in AMP during antidiuresis. Administration of 3',5'-AMP in man results in antidiuresis with the maximal effect occurring during the initial 30 min after injection (275).

Adenyl cyclase is stimulated not only by vasopressin but also by parathyroid hormone (276). However, parathyroid-sensitive adenyl cyclase is located mainly in the renal cortex whereas the vasopressin-sensitive adenyl cyclase predominates in the renal medulla. The enzyme may be a mediator of the phosphaturic effect of parathyroid hormone.

Davis et al. (277) used the micropuncture-recollection technique to reinvestigate the effect of vasopressin on proximal tubular reabsorption of Na in dog kidneys. In contrast to earlier reports (278), neither infusion of vasopressin nor water diuresis had any detectable influence on proximal salt and water reabsorption.

Harrington & Valtin (279) examined the renal tissue composition of rats with hereditary hypothalamic diabetes insipidus after acute and prolonged administration of vasopressin. The concentrating defect in these animals was still evident when osmotic equilibration between urine and the renal papilla had been achieved. Full correction of the defect was associated with a rise in papillary osmolality. The authors conclude that subnormal osmolality of the renal papilla, which can be corrected only gradually by administration of vasopressin, accounts for the initial concentrating defect and the long time required for its correction. They further propose that reduction in water content and increase of urea content are primarily responsible for restoration of papillary osmolality to normal; the mechanism remains unknown.

The effect of prolonged water diuresis on electrolyte and H ion excretion was studied by Massry et al. (280) in permanent residents of a hot climate, accustomed to drink large amounts of fluids in excess of their thirst. Water diuresis induced a marked increase in ammonia excretion and a decrease in K output in the urine. There was a significant inverse relationship between H and K ion excretion. Thus, prolonged water diuresis in acclimatized persons did not appreciably alter electrolyte excretion except for a significant fall in K excretion. Dilution of intracellular K concentration, dilutional acidosis, or suppressed aldosterone secretion may be causal factors for these phenomenon.

Kuhn & Peeters (281, 282) observed increased kaliuresis in sheep and goats after administration of arginine vasopressin but not after lysine vasopressin (283) and suggested that the kaliuresis is related to the high K content of a herbivorous diet. However, Macfarlane et al. (284) found increased rates of urinary K excretion in camels and Merino sheep even when the animals had been artificially depleted of K. The mechanism of ADH-induced kaliuresis remains unknown.

Inhibition of vasopressin-induced antidiuresis by norepinephrine in water-loaded normal humans has been described by Fisher (285). He considers that catecholamine may block the cellular mechanisms of vasopressin-induced antidiuresis and presents suggestive evidence that such inhibition might be competitive. However, a direct effect of norepinephrine on the distribution of renal blood flow cannot be ruled out. Enhanced perfusion of vasa recta might lead to a decrease in medullary osmolality and thus reduce vasopressin-induced antidiuresis. Perlmutt (286) reports that occlusion of renal artery of anesthetized dogs during mild water diuresis results in an increase in the free-water clearance of the contralateral kidney, possibly due to decreased activity of ADH. Vagotomy abolished this effect and actually led to a decrease in free-water clearance. As alternative, one might consider that messages can be carried via nervous reflex routes from one kidney to the other which may lead to changes in medullary blood flow and thus alter the renal concentrating ability.

Thorn & Willumsen (287) made the interesting observation that the inactivation of antidiuretic hormone by slices and homogenates from the inner medulla of rat kidneys is inhibited by urea in concentration higher than 0.5 M. Provided a similar effect occurs *in vivo*, urea must be considered as a potentiating factor for ADH under conditions of dehydration. Park et al. (288) concluded that the action of ADH is less effective in hypothermia than in euthermia. The direction of the vector of acceleration has been related with urine flow rate and ADH secretion (289). Henry et al. (290) reported that loss of no more than 10–20 per cent of the estimated blood volume leads to a sharp drop in atrial stretch receptor firing. Simultaneously, ADH levels in blood were often increased to significant levels.

Studies of the *in vitro* release mechanism of vasopressin (291) lend support to the hypothesis that the first precursor of vasopressin is mainly synthesized in the supraoptic nucleus and that the neurosecretory granules go through a "maturation" process during their passage to the nerve endings in the neurohypophysis.

RENAL ACTION OF ADRENAL STEROIDS

Mineralocorticoids.—Fimognari, Fanestil & Edelman (292) continued their studies of the role of messenger RNA and protein synthesis in the response to aldosterone in adrenalectomized rats. The conditions under which reproducible responses to aldosterone in unanesthetized, uncatheterized rats were obtained were defined. There was a latent period of an hour in antinatriuresis and kaliuresis, and a progressive response to maximum levels 3 hr after injection of aldosterone. Actinomycin D inhibited the antinatriuretic response to aldosterone, but had no effect on the kaliuretic response; this confirmed the previous report by Williamson (1963). These results imply that the kaliuretic response is not coupled to the antinatriuretic effect and is not mediated by induction of RNA and protein synthesis. Aldosterone-induced uptake of orotate-^{3}H into RNA eliminates the possibility that aldosterone exerts its effect solely by changes in blood supply to the kidney or the transport of the labeled precursor of RNA across the renal cell membrane.

Kirsten et al. (293) used toad bladders *in vitro* to study the activity of various enzymes involved in the tricarboxylic acid cycle in response to aldosterone. The activities of the following enzymes had increased 2 hr after addition of 10^{-7} aldosterone to the serosal bathing medium: condensing enzyme, isocitrate dehydrogenase, glutamate dehydrogenase, glutamate-oxaloacetate transaminase, and malate dehydrogenase. There was no change in activity of lactate dehydrogenase, aldolase, and pyruvate kinase. The changes in enzyme activity had about the same time course as the stimulation of Na transport. There was a significant positive relationship between relative increments in Na transport and condensing enzyme activity per milligram of mucosal protein. The effects of aldosterone on both Na transport and enzyme activity enhancement were abolished by actinomycin D and puromycin. The increase in enzyme activity was not dependent on the presence of Na in the mucosal bathing medium and was independent of any possible effect of transepithelial Na transport on enzyme activity. The authors conclude that the stimulation in enzyme activity contributing to the supply of aerobic energy for the enhanced Na transport induced by aldosterone is complementary to an independent action of the hormone to facilitate entry of Na into the transport process.

In the toad bladder, aldosterone reduces CO_2 liberation from glucose-1-^{14}C even in the absence of any Na in the surrounding fluid (294). This finding suggests that aldosterone shuts down the hexose monophosphate shunt pathway for glucose oxidation. How such an effect can be related to the action of aldosterone on Na transport is presently not understood.

In studies of renal enzyme activities of the aldosterone effect in normal and adrenalectomized rats, Kinne & Kirsten (295) observed changes in condensing enzyme activity to be by far the most pronounced enzyme alterations.

A suggestion that a reduction in proximal tubular fluid reabsorption is the consequence of decreased secretion of mineralocorticoids (296) is based upon the decrease in reabsorptive capacity of proximal tubules (split-drop experiments) in rats under conditions of chronic salt loading and the reversal of this effect to normal 90–120 min after aldosterone administration. The authors note that other investigators (143), also working with rats, have detected no changes in proximal tubular reabsorption either during chronic salt loading or subsequent to aldosterone administration. The discrepancy between the results of these two groups remains unresolved.

Kassirer et al. (297) investigated the role of aldosterone in metabolic alkalosis produced in humans by selective depletion of HCl. In this condition, aldosterone secretion was diminished, probably because of loss of K. Hence, contrary to a commonly held opinion, the high bicarbonate concentration in plasma, characteristic for metabolic alkalosis, could not have been caused by increased aldosterone production. In alkalotic subjects receiving DOCA the administration of saline led to decreased bicarbonate reabsorption and suppressed acid excretion ("saline resistant" alkalosis). The "saline resistant" alkalosis is not caused by aldosterone excess or K depletion or a combination of these factors. The authors emphasize the need for a reappraisal of the way in which aldosterone excess contributes to the genesis and maintenance of alkalosis in primary aldosteronism.

Sodium depletion in dogs stimulates aldosterone production in the adrenal gland by accelerating the conversion of corticosterone into aldosterone and probably of cholesterol to pregnenolone (298). In rats, only accelerated conversion of corticosterone to aldosterone has been demonstrated (299).

Massry et al. (300), working with dogs, concluded that the interrelationship between Na, Ca, and Mg excretion could be masked during increased delivery of these ions to the distal tubule.

Aldosterone may facilitate entry of Na into cells of rat diaphragm *in vitro* (301).

The mechanism of the well-known inhibition of water diuresis in adrenal insufficiency has been examined for the first time by direct methods of perfusing single tubules in rat kidneys. Stolte et al. (302) calculated hydraulic conductivities of the tubular wall from the per cent osmotic equilibration of a hypo-osmotic perfusate. With the use of cryoscopic measurements which yield maximum values, and inulin concentration ratios which provide minimum estimates, the hydraulic conductivity of distal tubules increased after adrenalectomy. Hormone substitution with either cortisone 2.5 mg/100 g b.w. per day, i.m., or dexamethasone 0.05 mg/100 g b.w. per day, i.m., re-established towards normal water permeability after 3 days of treatment. There was no evidence for any significant change in water permeability of the proximal tubules. The authors consider their results to be compatible with the view that glucocorticoids decrease the water permeability of distal tubules directly. This conclusion is supported by Marumo's studies (303) on toad bladder epithelium *in vitro*. Osmotic and diffusional water permeability had decreased 90 min after addition of cortisol to the serosal bathing fluid of steroid-depleted tissue. There was no measurable alteration in the ADH-induced increase in water permeability of the toad bladder.

Humoral agents released from heart and lungs, with Na-retaining action in perfused, isolated kidneys, have been found by Lockett (304, 305).

SOME FACTORS CHANGING TUBULAR FUNCTION

Bonjour et al. (306) have reported that in rats, subpressor doses 0.25 μg/kg·min of angiotensin II enhance the natriuretic and diuretic response to expansion of the extracellular fluid space. The magnitude of the diuretic response varied as a function of the degree of expansion and depended upon the rate of Na excretion during the control period preceding the angiotensin infusion. There was no diuretic or natriuretic effect of angiotensin when the same dose was given without expansion of extracellular volume. This study should be consulted whenever previous reports about the action of angiotensin on tubular function in rats are considered. Recent studies (307) from the same laboratory have shown that in unanesthetized water-loaded rats in a state of water diuresis, angiotensin elicits a diuretic and natriuretic effect comparable in every respect to that observed in rats during isotonic saline diuresis.

Malvin & Vander (308) concluded that there are no species differences between rat and dog as regards the effects of angiotensin on renal function. Low doses 20 ng/min kg decreased Na excretion and GFR. At higher doses 80-1000 ng/min kg, Na excretion was elevated despite diminished GFR. Potassium excretion, in all rats at all dose levels, was decreased. The decrement in K excretion was not related to Na excretion, but did correlate well with both GFR and renal plasma flow reductions.

Systemic or renal intra-arterial infusion of angiotensin into dogs with partial obstruction of the inferior caval vein and ascites resulted in more pronounced natriuresis than that in equally infused control dogs (309). The mechanism of the enhanced natriuresis in caval dogs is unknown. In this context, it is pertinent to recall the earlier demonstration of increased Na reabsorption in proximal tubules of dogs with obstruction of the thoracic caval vein (310). Berkowitz et al. (311) have discussed the possible relationship between alterations in the renin-angiotensin system and deterioration of function of isolated, perfused dog kidneys. Yamamoto et al. (312) observed angiotensin production and subsequent vasoconstriction in perfused kidneys of dogs.

Several recent studies have demonstrated that prostaglandins exert significant effects on the excretory function of the kidney. Thus, Johnston et al. (313) observed an increase in urine volume, urinary Na excretion, free-water clearance, and renal plasma flow after infusion of prostaglandin E_1 into the renal artery of dogs. Prostaglandin E_1 may have a direct tubular action, in particular an inhibitory effect on ADH-induced water transfer.

Vander (314) infused prostaglandin E_1 or E_2, 10–5000 ng/min into the right renal artery of anesthetized antidiuretic dogs. Only in the experimental kidney was there an increase in urine flow, solute excretion, and total renal plasma flow. The extraction ratio of PAH was significantly reduced; filtration rate did not change. The increase in Na excretion did not correlate with changes in renal plasma flow. There was no demonstrable effect on blood pressure, plasma Na, or renin release. Vander therefore suggests that the natriuretic effect of prostaglandin is of tubular origin.

Direct evidence for interference of prostaglandin E_1 with vasopressin-induced osmotic water flow has been obtained in perfusion experiments on isolated collecting tubules of rabbit kidneys (315). Grantham & Orloff suggest that prostaglandin E_1 interferes with the action of cyclic AMP by competing with it at a site which influences the generation of cyclic AMP. They further propose that in intact animals, prostaglandin may serve as an important modulator of the action of vasopressin.

Although there is little doubt that some direct action of prostaglandins on tubular function exists, the possibility should be considered that some of the observed effects of the hormone are secondary to intrarenal alterations in vascular perfusion pressure. Cameron et al. (316) found that helical strips from small renal arteries, partially contracted by catecholamines, plasma contracting factor, or KCl, are relaxed by prostaglandin in low concentration and are contracted further by high concentrations of the hormone. Thus, at least under certain conditions, prostaglandin may act as a vasodilator in the peritubular capillary network.

Lee et al. (317) have reported the identification of prostaglandins E_2, $F_{2\,alpha}$, and A_2 from the medulla of rabbit kidneys. Nissen (318) found that changes in salt balance influence the number of lipid droplets in renal interstitial cells. This is taken as suggestive evidence that the lipid droplets contain prostaglandins.

Park et al. (319) concluded from their studies on anesthetized dogs that 5-hydroxytryptamine in small doses has a specific ability to promote Na reabsorption. They consider it likely that this effect is mediated by the adrenal gland since antinatriuresis could not be elicited in adrenalectomized animals. However, a subtle vascular effect cannot be excluded. Parathyroid extracts induced renal vasodilatation and increased excretion of Na, Ca, and inorganic phosphate in dogs (320). Renal arterial infusion of several cholinomimetic agents enhanced the urinary output of Na, Cl, K, total solutes, and increased urine volume flow (321).

Blake & Jurf (322) presented evidence suggesting that the natriur sis found in rabbits after acute renal denervation is due either to a direct effect on tubular transport or to a redistribution of filtration to nephrons of lesser reabsorptive capacity, i.e., cortical rather than juxtamedullary nephrons. Lesions in the area of the dorsomedial nucleus of the hypothalamus caused natriuresis, whereas increased reabsorption of Na and water was observed after electrical stimulation of the posterior hypothalamus (323).

The effect of arterial infusions of ouabain on the electrolyte excretion of rat kidneys has been studied by Ramsay & Sachs (324). Ouabain produced a threefold increase in K excretion and more than doubling of the urinary H$^+$ concentration. Only about half the animals responded with an increase in urinary Na excretion. A definite species difference exists in the response of the kidney of rats and that of chicken and dogs.

LITERATURE CITED

1. Pitts, R. F. *Physiology of the kidney and body fluids*, 2nd ed. (Year Book Publ. Inc., Chicago, 1968)
2. Ullrich, K. J., Hierholzer, K. In *Nierenkrankheiten*, 1–50 (Sarre, H., Ed., Georg Thieme, Stuttgart, 1967)
3. Ullrich, K. J. In *Kurzgefasstes Lehrbuch der Physiologie*, 227–52 (Keidel, W. D., Ed., Georg Thieme, Stuttgart, 1967)
4. Mach, R. S., Ed. Symposion sur eau, electrolytes et perméabilité des membranes. *Bull. Schweiz. Akad. Med. Wiss.*, **23**, 195–385 (1967)
5. Cort, J. H., Thomson, A. E., Eds. Symposium on the regulation of body fluid volume. *Can. J. Physiol. Pharmacol.*, **46**, 287–354 (1968)
6. Robinson, J. R., Ed. Second Kanematsu Conference on the kidney. *Med. J. Australia*, **54**, 277–318 (1967)
7. Steinmetz, P. R. Excretion of acid by the kidney—functional organization and cellular aspects of acidification. *New Engl. J. Med.*, **278**, 1102–9 (1968)
8. Porter, K. R., Ed. Symposium on biophysics and physiology of biological transport. *Protoplasma*, **63**, 1–336 (1967)
9. Northcote, D. H., Ed. Structure and Function of Membranes. *Brit. Med. Bull.*, **24**, 99–184 (1968)
10. Oliver, J. *Nephrons and Kidneys* (Hoeber Med. Div., Harper and Row, New York, Evanston, and London, 117 pp., 1967)
11. Warten, J., Ed. Symposium on hormone and enzyme activity of the kidney. *Pathol. Biol.*, **15**, 609–86 (1967)
12. Maren, T. H., Carbonic anhydrase: chemistry, physiology, and inhibition. *Physiol. Rev.*, **47**, 595–781 (1967)
13. *Renal Hypertension* (Page, I. H., McCubbin, J. W., Eds., Year Book Med. Publ., Chicago, 321 pp., 1968)
14. *Renal Failure* (Brest, A. N., Moyer, J. R., Eds., Lippincott, Philadelphia and Toronto, 295, 1967)
15. Welt, L. G., Ed. Symposium on Uremia. *Am. J. Med.*, **44**, 653–802 (1968)
16. Herms, W. Die Auswirkungen von Störungen des Elektrolythaushaltes auf Struktur und Funktion der Niere. *Klin. Wochschr.*, **45**, 1169–80 (1967)
17. Jørgensen, F., Bentzon, M. W. The ultrastructure of the normal human glomerulus. Thickness of glomerular basement membrane. *Lab. Invest.*, **18**, 42–8 (1968)
18. Rosen, S., Tisher, C. C. Observations on the Rhesus monkey glomerulus and juxtaglomerulus apparatus. *Lab. Invest.*, **18**, 240–48 (1968)
19. Zamboni, L., Martino, C. A re-evaluation of the mesangial cells of the renal glomerulus. *Histochemie*, **86**, 364–83 (1968)
20. Dietrich, H. J. Die Ultrastruktur der Gefässbündel im Mark der Rattenniere. *Histochemie*, **84**, 350–71 (1968)
21. Johnson, F. R., Darnton, S. J. Ultrastructural observations on the renal papilla of the rabbit. *Histochemie*, **81**, 390–406 (1967)
22. Suzuki, T., Mostofi, F. K. Intramitochondrial bodies in the thick limb of Henle of the rat kidney. *J. Cell Biol.*, **33**, 605–24 (1967)
23. Griffith, L. D., Bulger, R. E., Trump, B. F. Fine structure and staining of mucosubstances on "intercalated cells" from the rat distal convoluted tubule and collecting duct. *Anat. Record*, **160**, 643–62 (1968)
24. McKenna, O. C., Angelakos, E. T. Adrenergic innervation of the canine kidney. *Circ. Res.*, **22**, 345–54 (1968)
25. Schmidt-Nielsen, B., Davis, L. E. Fluid transport and tubular intercellular spaces in reptilian kidneys. *Science*, **159**, 1105–8 (1968)
26. Ganote, C. E., Grantham, J. J., Moses, H. L., Burg, M. B., Orloff, J. Ultrastructural studies of vasopressin effect on isolated perfused renal collecting tubules of the rabbit. *J. Cell Biol.*, **36**, 355–67 (1968)
27. Thoenes, W. Neue Befunde zur Beschaffenheit des basalen Labyrinthes im Nierentubulus. *Histochemie*, **86**, 351–63 (1968)
28. Revel, J. P., Karnovksy, M. J. Hexagonal array of subunits in intercell. junction of the mouse heart and liver. *J. Cell Biol.*, **33**, C7 (1967)

29. Rouffignac, C. de, Morel, F. Étude par microdissection de la distribution et de la longueur des tubules proximaux dans le rein de cinq espèces de rongeurs. *Arch. Anat. Microscop. Morphol. Exptl.*, **56**, 123–32 (1967)

30. Uranga, J. Influence of the liver on regulation of glomerular pressure in the toad. *Am. J. Physiol.*, **213**, 1244–48 (1967)

31. Uranga, J. The pressure in Bowman's capsule and the occluded ureter of the toad. *Acta Physiol. Latinoam.*, **15**, 77–85 (1965)

32. Hardwicke, J., Hulme, B., Jones, J. H., Ricketts, C. R. The measurement of glomerular permeability to polydisperse radioactively-labelled macromolecules in normal rabbits. *Clin. Sci.*, **34**, 505–14 (1968)

33. Hulme, B., Hardwicke, J. Human glomerular permeability to macromolecules in health and disease. *Clin. Sci.*, **34**, 515–29 (1968)

34. Mogensen, C. E. The glomerular permeability determined by dextran clearance using sephadex gel filtration. *Scand. J. Clin. Lab. Invest.*, **21**, 77–82 (1968)

35. Cohen, A. M., Walker, W. G. The use of renal clearances of enzymes as an indicator of selective permeability of the renal glomerulus. *J. Lab. Clin. Med.*, **70**, 571–80 (1967)

36. Zender, R., Falbriard, A. Reproductibilité de la "clearance glomerulaire relative" mesurée par le Polyfructosan-S l'inulin sans collection d'urine. *Helv. Physiol. Pharmacol. Acta*, **25**, 62–77 (1967)

37. Favre, H., Zender, R., Falbriand, A. Decroissance plasmatique du Polyfructosan-S chez l'homme après injection unique. *Helv. Physiol. Pharmacol. Acta*, **26**, 79–86 (1968)

38. Falbriard, A., Busser, R., Zender, R. Rétention intrarénale d'une faible fraction d'inulin. *Helv. Physiol. Phamacol. Acta*, **25**, 123–33 (1967)

39. Goldman, R. Endogenous creatinine clearance by rats. *Proc. Soc. Exptl. Biol. Med.*, **125**, 1021–24 (1967)

40. Spiro, R. G. The structure of the disaccharide unit of the renal glomerular basement membrane. *J. Biol. Chem.*, **242**, 4813–23 (1967)

41. Thoenes, G. H. Enzymatische Untersuchungen an glomerulären Basalmembranen. *Naturwissenschaften*, **54**, 285 (1967)

42. Ladefoged, J., Pedersen, F., Bassenge, E., Rohde, R., Doutheil, U. Renal blood flow in isolated kidneys measured with an electromagnetic flowmeter and by Xenon-133 and Krypton-85 wash-out techniques. *Pflügers Arch.*, **299**, 30–37 (1968)

43. Aukland, K., Wolgast, M. Effect of hemorrhage and retransfusion on intrarenal distribution of blood flow in dogs. *J. Clin. Invest.*, **47**, 488–501 (1968)

44. Carriere, S., Thorburn, G. D., O'Morchoe, C. C. C., Barger, A. C. Intrarenal distribution of blood flow in dogs during hemorrhagic hypotension. *Circ. Res.*, **19**, 167–79 (1966)

45. Truninger, B. P., Rosen, S. M., Oken, D. E. Renale Hämodynamik, und hämorrhagische Hypotension. *Klin. Wochschr.*, **44**, 875–62 (1966)

46. Thurau, K., Valtin, H., Schnermann, J. Kidney. *Ann. Rev. Physiol.*, **30**, 441–524 (1968)

47. Rosen, S. M., Truninger, B. P., Kriek, H. R., Murray, J. E., Merrill, J. P. Intrarenal distribution of blood flow in the transplanted dog kidney: effect of denervation and rejection. *J. Clin. Invest.*, **46**, 1239–53 (1967)

48. Rosen, S. M., Hollenberg, N. K., Dealy, J. B., Jr., Merrill, J. P. Measurement of the distribution of blood flow in the human kidney using the intra-arterial injection of [133]Xe. Relationship to function in the normal and transplanted kidney. *Clin. Sci.*, **34**, 287–302 (1968)

49. Moffat, D. B. Medullary blood flow during hydropenia. *Nephron*, **5**, 1–6 (1968)

50. Moffat, D. B. The distribution of red blood cells in the renal cortex. *Clin. Sci.*, **28**, 125–30 (1965)

51. Slotkoff, L. M., Eisner, G. M., Lilienfield, L. S. Functional separation of renal cortical-medullary circulation: significance of Diodrast extraction. *Am. J. Physiol.*, **214**, 935–41 (1968)

52. Nashat, F. S., Portal, R. W. The effects of changes in hematocrit on renal function. *J. Physiol.*, **193**, 513–22 (1967)

53. Hársing, L., Szánto, G., Bartha, J.

Renal circulation during stop flow in the dog. *Am. J. Physiol.*, 213, 935-38 (1967)

54. Baldwin, D. S., Löwenstein, S., Chasis, H. Renal hemodynamic response to osmotic diuresis in man. *Proc. Soc. Exptl. Biol. Med.*, 125, 1259-64 (1967)

55. Braun, W. E., Lilienfield, L. S. Renal hemodynamic effect of hypertonic mannitol infusions. *Proc. Soc. Exptl. Biol. Med.*, 114, 1-6 (1963)

56. Pilkington, L. A., Binder, R., de Haas, J. C. M., Pitts, R. F. Intrarenal distribution of blood flow. *Am. J. Physiol.*, 208, 1107-13 (1965)

57. Hársing, L., Bartha, J. Renal blood flow and p-aminohippurate extraction in osmotic diuresis. *Acta Physiol. Acad. Sci. Hung.*, 30, 225-32 (1966)

58. Thurau, K., Deetjen, P., Kramer, K. Hämodynamik des Nierenmarkes. II. Wechselbeziehung zwischen vaskulärem und tubulärem Gegenstromsystem bei arteriellen Drucksteigerungen Wasserdiurese und osmotischer Diurese. *Pflügers Arch.*, 270, 270-80 (1960)

59. Basar, E., Tischner, H., Weiss, Ch. Untersuchungen zur Dynamik druckinduzierter Änderungen des Strömungswiderstandes der autoregulierenden, isolierten Rattenniere. *Pflügers Arch.*, 299, 191-213 (1968)

60. Baumgarten, H. G., Leichtweiss, H. P., Weiss, Ch. Untersuchungen über die Bedeutung sympathischer Überträgerstoffe bei der Autoregulation des Perfusionsvolumenstromes der Rattenniere. *Pflügers Arch.*, 299, 214-25 (1968)

61. Walter, P., Bassenge, E. Wirkung von ATP, A-3,5-MP, Adenosin und Dipyridamol an Streifenpräparaten der A. coronaria, A. renalis und der V. portae. *Pflügers Arch.*, 299, 52-65 (1968)

62. Thurau, K. Renal hemodynamics. *Am. J. Med.*, 36, 698-719 (1964)

63. Hashimoto, K., Kumakura, S. The pharmacological features of the coronary, renal, mesenteric, and femoral arteries. *Japan. J. Physiol.*, 15, 540-51 (1965)

64. Ono, H., Ingaki, K., Hashimoto, K. A pharmacological approach to the nature of the autoregulation of the renal blood flow. *Japan. J. Physiol.*, 16, 625-34 (1966)

65. Bálint, P., Châtel, R. Die Wirkung von Adrenalin und von Noradrenalin auf die Nierenhämodynamik beim Hund. *Arch. Exptl. Pathol. Pharmakol.*, 258, 24-36 (1967)

66. Köver, G., Szöcs, E., Temler, E. Effect of bradykinin on renal function. *Acta Physiol. Acad. Sci. Hung.*, 33, 11-18 (1968)

67. Lockett, M. F. Effects of changes in P_{O_2}, P_{CO_2}, and pH on the total vascular resistance of perfused cat kidneys. *J. Physiol.*, 193, 671-78 (1967)

68. O'Brien, J. R. The mechanism and the prevention of platelet adhesions and aggregation considered in relation to arterial thrombosis. *Blood*, 24, 309-12 (1964)

69. O'Morchoe, C. C. C., O'Morchoe, P. J. Renal contribution to thoracic duct lymph in dogs. *J. Physiol.*, 194, 305-15 (1968)

70. Vander, A. J. Control of renin release. *Physiol. Rev.*, 47, 359-82 (1967)

71. Brown, J. J., Lever, A. F., Robertson, J. I. S. Renin and angiotensin in health and disease. *Schweiz. Med. Wochschr.*, 97, 1635-38, 1679-86 (1967)

72. Wood, J. E., Guest Ed. Renin mechanisms and hypertension. *Circ. Res.*, 21, *Suppl. II*, 1-226 (1967)

73. Schnermann, J. Microperfusion study of single short loops of Henle in rat kidney. *Pflügers Arch.*, 300, 255-82 (1968)

74. Landwehr, D., Schnermann, J., Klose, R. M., Giebisch, G. The effect of acute reduction in glomerular filtration rate on renal tubular sodium and water reabsorption. *Fed. Proc.*, 26, 547 (1967)

75. Windhager, E. E. Glomerulo-tubular balance of salt and water. *Physiologist*, 11, 103-14 (1968)

76. Thurau, K., Schnermann, J. Die Natriumkonzentration an den Makula densa-Zellen als regulierender Faktor für das Glomerulumfiltrat. *Klin. Wochschr.*, 43, 410-13 (1965)

77. Thurau, K. Intrarenal regulation of sodium balance. *Bull. Schweiz. Akad. Med. Wiss.*, 23, 363-69 (1967)

78. Thurau, K., Schnermann, J., Nagel, W., Horster, M., Wahl, M. Com-

position of tubular fluid in the macula densa segment as a factor regulating the function of the juxtaglomerular apparatus. *Circ. Res. Suppl. II*, 20, 21, 79–90 (1967)

79. Belleau, L. J., Earley, L. E. Autoregulation of renal blood flow in the presence of angiotensin infusion. *Am. J. Physiol.*, 213, 1590–95 (1967)

80. Assaykeen, T. A., Otsuka, K., Ganong, W. F. Rate of disappearance of exogenous dog renin from the plasma of nephrectomized dogs. *Proc. Soc. Exptl. Biol. Med.*, 127, 306–10 (1968)

81. Heacox, R., Harcey, A. M., Vander, A. J. Hepatic inactivation of renin. *Circ. Res.*, 21, 149–52 (1967)

82. Otsuka, K., Assaykeen, T. A., Ganong, W. F. Effect of nephrectomy and a low sodium diet on the increase in plasma renin levels produced by hemorrhage. *Proc. Soc. Exptl. Biol. Med.*, 127, 704–7 (1968)

83. Bianchi, G., Brown, J. J., Lever, A. F. Robertson, J. I. S., Roth, N. Changes of plasma renin concentration during pressor infusions of renin in the conscious dog: the influence of dietary sodium intake. *Clin. Sci.*, 34, 303–14 (1968)

84. Miller, R. E., Vander, A. J., Kowalczyk, R. S., Geelhoed, G. W. Aldosterone secretion and plasma renin during renin infusion and acute salt depletion. *Am. J. Physiol.*, 214, 228–31 (1968)

85. Johnston, C. I., Davis, J. O., Robb, C. A., Mackenzie, J. W. Plasma renin in chronic experimental heart failure and during renal sodium "escape" from mineralocorticoids. *Circ. Res.*, 22, 113–25 (1968)

86. Carretero, O., Gross, F. Renin substrate in plasma under various experimental conditions in the rat. *Am. J. Physiol.*, 213, 695–700 (1967)

87. Rapp, J. P. Dissociation of JG granularity and blood pressure in adrenal regeneration. *Am. J. Physiol.*, 213, 947–53 (1967)

88. Ussing, H. H. Relationship between osmotic reaction and active sodium transport in the frog skin epithelium. *Acta Physiol. Scand.*, 63, 141–55 (1965)

89. Wågermark, J., Ungerstedt, U., Ljungqvist, A. Sympathetic innervation of the juxtaglomerular cells of the kidney. *Circ. Res.*, 22, 149–53 (1968)

90. Arakawa, K., Nakatani, M., Minohara, A., Nakamura, M. Isolation and amino acid composition of human angiotensin I. *Biochem. J.*, 104, 900–6 (1968)

91. Ostrovsky, D., Sen, S., Smeby, R. R., Bumpus, F. M. Chemical assay of phospholipid renin preinhibitor in canine and human blood. *Circ. Res.*, 21, 497–505 (1967)

92. Dahlheim, H., Weber, P., Herold, I., Thurau, K. Untersuchungen über präparative Anreicherungsmöglichkeiten des Reninsubstrats (Angiotensinogen). *Pflügers Arch.*, 298, 131–40 (1967)

93. Oken, D. E., Biber, T. U. L. Biologically effective immunization against angiotensin. *Am. J. Physiol.*, 214, 791–95 (1968)

94. Malvin, R. L., Vander, A. J. Plasma renin activity in marine teleost and Cetacea. *Am. J. Physiol.*, 213, 1582–84 (1968)

95. Johnston, C. I., Davis, J. O., Hartcroft, P. M. Renin-angiotensin system, adrenal steroid and sodium depletion in a primitive mammal, the American Opossum. *Endocrinology*, 81, 633–42 (1967)

96. Capelli, J. P., Wesson, L. G., Aponte, G. E. The effect of sodium on renal renin and on glucose-6-phosphate dehydrogenase in the kidneys, salivary glands and adrenal glands. *Nephron*, 5, 106–23 (1968)

97. Giebisch, G. Some electrical properties of single renal tubule cells. *J. Gen. Physiol.*, 51, 315s–25s (1968)

98. Boulpaep, E. L. Ion permeability of the peritubular and luminal membrane of the renal tubular cell. In *Transport und Funktion intracellulärer Elektrolyte*, 98–105 (Krück, F., Ed., Urban & Schwarzenberg, München, Berlin, Wien, 1967)

99. Sullivan, W. J. Electrical potential differences across distal renal tubules of Amphiuma. *Am. J. Physiol.*, 214, 1096–1103 (1968)

100. Hoshi, T., Sakai, F., Haga, M. Electrical properties of renal tubules of the newt. *J. Physiol. Soc. Japan*, 24, 378 (1962)

101. Hoshi, T., Sakai, F. A comparison of the electrical resistance of the sur-

face cell membrane and cellular wall in the proximal tubule of the newt kidney. *Japan. J. Physiol.*, **17**, 627–37 (1967)

102. Diamond, J. M., Bossert, W. H. Standing gradient osmotic flow. A mechanism for coupling of water and solute transport in epithelia. *J. Gen. Physiol.*, **50**, 2061–83 (1967)

103. Nutbourne, D. M. The effect of small hydrostatic pressure gradients on the rate of active sodium transport across isolated living frog-skin membranes. *J. Physiol.*, **195**, 1–18 (1968)

104. Funder, J., Ussing, H. H., Wieth, J. O. The effects of CO_2 and hydrogen ions on active Na transport in the isolated frog skin. *Acta Physiol. Scand.*, **71**, 65–76 (1967)

105. Rotunno, C. A., Pauchan, M. I., Cereijido, M. Location of mechanism of active transport of sodium across the frog skin. *Nature*, **210**, 597–99 (1966)

106. Cereijido, M., Reisin, I., Rotunno, C. A. The effect of sodium concentration on the content and distribution of sodium in the frog skin. *J. Physiol.*, **196**, 237–53 (1968)

107. Ussing, H. H. Active sodium transport across the frog skin epithelium and its relation to epithelial structure. *Ber.Bunsenges.Physik.Chem.*, **71**, 807–13 (1967)

108. Biber, T. U. L., Curran, P. F. Coupled solute fluxes in toad skin. *J. Gen. Physiol.*, **51**, 606–20 (1968)

109. Franz, T. J., Galey, W. R., Van Bruggen, J. T. Further observations on asymmetrical solute movement across membranes. *J. Gen. Physiol.*, **51**, 1–12 (1968)

110. Baumann, K., Fromter, E., Ullrich, K. J. Passiver Stofftransport durch Epithelzellschicht von Harnkanalchen. *Ber. Bunsenges. Physik. Chem.*, **71**, 834–38 (1967)

111. Bentzel, C. J., Davies, M., Scott, W. N., Zatzman, M., Solomon, A. K. Osmotic volume flow in the tubule of Necturus kidney. *J. Gen. Physiol.*, **51**, 517–33 (1968)

112. Whittembury, G. Sodium and water transport in kidney proximal tubular cells. *J. Gen. Physiol.*, **51**, 303s–14s (1968)

113. Whittembury, G. Sobre los mecanismos de absorcion en el tubo proxi-

mal del rinon. *Acta Cient. Venezolana Suppl.* **3**, 71–83 (1967)

114. Little, J. R., Robinson, J. R. The effect of water content upon the respiration and the cations of kidney slices. *J. Physiol.*, **191**, 91–106 (1967)

115. Willis, J. S. Cold resistance of kidney cells of mammalian hibernators: cation transport vs. respiration. *Am. J. Physiol.*, **114**, 923–28 (1968)

116. Katz, A. I., Epstein, F. H. The role of sodium-potassium activated adenosine triphosphatase in the reabsorption of sodium by the kidney. *J. Clin. Invest.*, **46**, 1999–2011 (1967)

117. Katz, A. I., Epstein, F. H. Physiological role of sodium-potassium activated adenosine triphosphatase in the transport of cations across biological membranes. *New Engl. J. Med.*, **278**, 253–61 (1968)

118. Manitius, A., Bensch, K., Epstein, F. H. (Na^+-K^+)-activated ATPase in kidney cell membranes of normal and methylprednisolonetreated rats. *Biochim. Biophys. Acta*, **150**, 563–71 (1968)

119. Jørgensen, P. L. Regulation of the (Na^+-K^+)-activated ATP hydrolyzing enzyme system in rat kidney. I. The effect of adrenalectomy and of the supply of sodium on the enzyme system. *Biochim. Biophys. Acta*, **151**, 212–24 (1968)

120. Arcila, H., Saimyoji, H., Kessler, R. H. Accentuation of cyanide natriuresis by hypoxia. *Am. J. Physiol.*, **214**, 1063–67 (1968)

121. Randall, H. M., Jr., Cohen, J. J. Effect of renal ischemia on anaerobic CO_2 production by dog kidney *in vitro. Proc. Soc. Exptl. Biol. Med.*, **125**, 947–53 (1967)

122. Bennett, C. M., Clapp, J. R., Berliner, R. W. Micropuncture study of the proximal and distal tubule in the dog. *Am. J. Physiol.*, **213**, 1254–62 (1967)

123. Bennett, C. M., Brenner, B. M., Berliner, R. W. Micropuncture study of nephron function in the Rhesus monkey. *J. Clin. Invest.*, **47**, 203–16 (1968)

124. Wiederholt, M., Hierholzer, K., Windhager, E. E., Giebisch, G. Microperfusion study of fluid reabsorption in proximal tubules of rat kidneys. *Am. J. Physiol.*, **213**, 809–18 (1967)

125. Bossert, W. H., Schwartz, W. B. Relation of pressure and flow to control of sodium reabsorption in the proximal tubule. *Am. J. Physiol.*, **213,** 793–802 (1967)

126. Brenner, B. M., Bennett, C. M., Berliner, R. W. The relationship between glomerular filtration rate and sodium reabsorption by the proximal tubule of the rat nephron. *J. Clin. Invest.*, **47,** 1358–74 (1968)

127. Rector, F. C., Jr., Brunner, F. P., Seldin, D. W. Mechanism of glomerotubular balance. I. Effect of aortic constriction and elevated ureteropelvic pressure on glomerular filtration rate, fractional reabsorption, transit time, and tubular size in the proximal tubule of the rat. *J. Clin. Invest.*, **45,** 590–602 (1966)

128. Steinhausen, M. Messungen des tubulären Harnstromes und der tubulären Reabsorption unter erhöhtem Ureterdruck. Intravitalmikroskopische Untersuchungen an der Nierenrinde von Ratten. *Pflügers Arch.*, **298,** 105–30 (1967)

129. Wahl, M., Nagel, W., Fischbach, H., Thurau, K. On the application of the occlusion time method for measurements of lateral net fluxes in the proximal convolution of the rat kidney. *Pflügers Arch.*, **298,** 141–53 (1968)

130. Mills, I. H. The cardiovascular system and renal control of sodium excretion. *Can. J. Physiol. Pharmacol.*, **46,** 297–303 (1968)

131. Lewy, J. E., Windhager, E. E. Peritubular control of proximal tubular fluid reabsorption in the rat kidney. *Am. J. Physiol.*, **214,** 943–54 (1968)

132. Martino, J. A., Earley, L. E. Demonstration of a role of physical factors as determinants of the natriuretic response to volume expansion. *J. Clin. Invest.*, **46,** 1963–78 (1967)

133. Martino, J. A., Earley, L. E. The effects of infusion of water on renal hemodynamics and the tubular reabsorption of sodium. *Ibid.*,1229–38

134. LeBrie, S. J. Renal peritubular capillary permeability to macromolecules. *Am. J. Physiol.*, **213,** 1225–32 (1967)

135. Gärtner, K., Vogel, G., Ulbrich, M. Untersuchungen zur Penetration von Makromolekülen (Polyvinylpyrrolidon) durch glomeruläre und postglomeruläre Capillaren in den Harn und die Nierenlymphe und zur Grösse der extravasalen Umwälzung von ^{131}I-Albumin im Interstitium der Niere. *Pflügers Arch.*, **298,** 305–21 (1968)

136. Bricker, N. S. The control of sodium excretion with normal and reduced nephron populations. The preeminence of third factor. *Am. J. Med.*, **43,** 313–21 (1967)

137. Cort, J. H. The source and chemical nature of the natriuretic activity of plasma evoked by saluretic "Volume reflexes". *Can. J. Physiol. Pharmacol.*, **46,** 325–33 (1968)

138. Pearce, J. W. The renal response to volume expansion. *Can. J. Physiol. Pharmacol.*, **46,** 305–13 (1968)

139. Rector, F. C., Jr., Martinez-Maldonado, M., Kurtzman, N. A., Sellman, J. C., Oerther, F., Seldin, D. W. Demonstration of a hormonal inhibitor of proximal tubular reabsorption during expansion of extracellular volume with isotonic saline. *J. Clin. Invest.*, **47,** 761–73 (1968)

140. Katz, A. I., Epstein, F. H. Relation of glomerular filtration rate and sodium reabsorption to kidney size in compensatory renal hypertrophy. *Yale J. Biol. Med.*, **40,** 222–30 (1967)

141. Hayslett, J. P., Kashgarian, M., Epstein, F. H. Functional correlates of compensatory renal hypertrophy. *J. Clin. Invest.*, **47,** 774–82 (1968)

142. Coe, F. L., Korty, P. R. Protein synthesis during compensatory renal hypertrophy. *Am. J. Physiol.*, **213,** 1585–89 (1967)

143. Hayslett, J. P., Kashgarian, M., Epstein, F. H. Changes in proximal and distal tubular reabsorption produced by rapid expansion of extracellular fluid. *J. Clin. Invest.*, **46,** 1254–63 (1967)

144. Landwehr, D. M., Klose, R. M., Giebisch, G. Renal tubular sodium and water reabsorption in the isotonic sodium chloride-loaded rat. *Am. J. Physiol.*, **212,** 1327–33 (1967)

145. Stein, R. M., Abramson, R. G., Kahn, T., Levitt, M. F. Effects of hypotonic saline loading in hy-

drated dog: evidence for a saline-induced limit on distal tubular sodium transport. *J. Clin. Invest.*, **46**, 1205–14 (1967)

146. Eknoyan, G., Suki, W. N., Rector, F. C., Jr., Seldin, D. W. Functional characteristics of the diluting segment of the dog nephron and the effect of extracellular volume expansion on its reabsorptive capacity. *J. Clin. Invest.*, **46**, 1178–88 (1968)

147. Potter, B. J. The influence of previous salt ingestion on the renal function of sheep subjected to intravenous hypertonic saline. *J. Physiol.*, **194**, 435–55 (1968)

148. Bercovitch, D. D., Levitt, M. F. Effects of saline loading on distal tubular sodium and water reabsorption. *Proc. Soc. Exptl. Biol. Med.*, **125**, 552–56 (1967)

149. Knox, G. F., Daves, B. B., Berliner, R. W. Effect of chronic cardiac denervation on renal response to saline infusion. *Am. J. Physiol.*, **213**, 174–78 (1967)

150. Schrier, R. W., McDonald, K. M., Jagger, P. I., Lauler, D. P. The role of the adrenergic nervous system in the renal response to acute extracellular fluid volume expansion. *Proc. Soc. Exptl. Biol. Med.*, **125**, 1157–62 (1967)

151. Schrier, R. W., McDonald, K. M., Marshall, R. A., Lauler, D. P. Absence of natriuretic response to acute hypotonic intravascular volume expansion in dogs. *Clin. Sci.*, **34**, 57–72 (1968)

152. Kessler, E., Hughes, R. C., Orlando, C., Shamlou, G. Comparative effects of saline and isoncotic albumin in saline on sodium excretion. *Proc. Soc. Exptl. Biol. Med.*, **125**, 543–48 (1967)

153. Nizet, A. Influence of serum albumin and dextran on sodium and water excretion by the isolated dog kidney. *Pflügers Arch.*, **301**, 7–15 (1968)

154. Nizet, A., Godon, J. P., Mahieu, P. Comparative excretion of isotonic and hypertonic sodium chloride by isolated dog kidney. *Arch. Intern. Physiol. Biochim.*, **76**, 311–18 (1968)

155. Daly, J. J., Roe, J. W., Horrocks, P. A comparison of sodium excretion following the infusion of saline into systemic and portal veins in the dog: evidence for a hepatic role in the control of sodium excretion. *Clin. Sci.*, **33**, 481–87 (1967)

156. Behrenbeck, D. W., Dorge, A., Reinhardt, H. W. Untersuchungen am wachen Hund über die Einstellung der Natriumbilanz. III. Elektrolytbilanzen und Natriumrejektion nach akutem Natriumentzug durch Peritonealdialyse oder wiederholter Mannitolinfusion. *Pflügers Arch.*, **300**, 226–43 (1968)

157. Groh, J., Zdansky, P., Sistek, J., Kvasnickova, E. Volumregulation der Zelle bei der experimenteller Hypernatriämie. *Pflügers Arch.*, **298**, 154–58 (1967)

158. Espiner, E. A., Tucci, J. R., Jagger, P. I., Pauk, G. I., Lauler, D. P. The effect of acute diuretic induced extracellular volume depletion of aldosterone secretion in normal man. *Clin. Sci.*, **33**, 125–34 (1967)

159. Giebisch, G., Klose, R. M., Malnic, G. Renal tubular potassium transport. *Bull. Schweiz. Akad. Med. Wiss.*, **23**, 287–312 (1967)

160. Giebisch, G., Mello-Aires, M., Malnic, G. Micropuncture study of renal potassium excretion during acute acid-base disturbances in the rat. *Fed. Proc.*, **27**, 695 (1968)

161. Alexander, E. A., Levinsky, N. G. An extrarenal mechanism of potassium adaptation. *J. Clin. Invest.*, **47**, 740–48 (1968)

162. Goldman, A. G., Yalow, A. A., Garelick, H., Patrick, C., Levitt, J. I., Wolfman, M. Rapidity of ^{42}K exchange in the functioning canine kidney. *Clin. Sci.*, **33**, 285–99 (1967)

163. Trump, B. F., Ginn, F. L. Studies of cellular injury in isolated flounder tubules. II. Cellular swelling in high potassium media. *Lab. Invest.*, **17**, 341–51 (1968)

164. Kahn, M., Bohrer, N. K. Effect of potassium-induced diuresis on renal concentration and dilution. *Am. J. Physiol.*, **212**, 1365–75 (1967)

165. Dewhurst, J. K., Harrison, F. A., Keynes, R. D. Renal excretion of potassium in the sheep. *J. Physiol.*, **195**, 609–21 (1968)

166. Bowman, F. J., Landon, E. J. Organic mercurials and net movements of potassium in rat kidney slices. *Am. J. Physiol.*, **213**, 1209–17 (1967)

167. Abramow, M., Burg, M. B., Orloff, J. Chloride flux in rabbit kidney

tubules *in vitro. Am. J. Physiol.*, **213**, 1249–53 (1967)

168. Finn, A. L., Handler, J. S., Orloff, J. Active transport in the isolated toad bladder. *Am. J. Physiol.*, **213**, 179–84 (1967)

169. Fischbarg, J., Zadunaisky, J. A., De Fisch, F. W. Dependence of sodium and chloride transports on chloride concentration in isolated frog skin. *Am. J. Physiol.*, **213**, 963–69 (1967)

170. Massry, S. G., Coburn, J. W., Chapman, L. W., Kleeman, C. R. Effect of NaCl infusion on urinary Ca^{++} and Mg^{++} during reduction in their filtered loads. *Am. J. Physiol.*, **213**, 1218–24 (1967)

171. Duarte, C. G., Watson, J. F. Calcium reabsorption in proximal tubule of the dog nephron. *Am. J. Physiol.*, **212**, 1355–60 (1967)

172. Schuck, O., Cort, J. H. On the interaction of calcium, sodium, and water transport in the diuresing kidney. *Can. J. Physiol. Pharmacol.*, **46**, 275–80 (1968)

173. Fülgraff, G., Heline, H. J., Sparwald, E., Heidenreich, O. Die Wirkung von Calciumionen auf die glomeruläre Filtrationrate und die Electrolyt und Wasserausscheidung von intakten und isoliert perfundierten Rattennieren. *Arch. Intern. Pharmacodyn.*, **172**, 49–61 (1968)

174. Fülgraff, G., Heidenreich, O. Mikropunktionsuntersuchungen über die Wirkung von Calciumionen auf die Resorptionskapazität und auf die prozentuale Resorption im proximalen Konvolut von Ratten. *Arch. Exptl. Pharmakol. Pathol.*, **258**, 440–51 (1967)

175. Kleinzeller, A., Knotkova, A., Nedvikova, J. The effect of calcium ions on the steady-state ionic distribution in kidney cortex cells. *J. Gen. Physiol.*, **51**, 326s–34s (1968)

176. Vogel, G., Stoeckert, J. Die Bedeutung des Natriums für den renaltubulären Calcium Transport bei Rana ridibunda. *Pflügers Arch.*, **298**, 23–30 (1967)

177. Simkiss, K. Calcium and carbonate metabolism in the frog (Rana temporiara) during respiratory acidosis. *Am. J. Physiol.*, **214**, 627–34 (1968)

178. Hodgkinson, A., Zarembski, P. M.,

Nordin, B. E. C. Non-exchangeable calcium in human urine. *Nature*, **214**, 1045 (1967)

179. Walser, M. Magnesium Metabolism. *Ergebn. Physiol.*, **59**, 185–296 (1967)

180. Clark, I. Effects of magnesium ions on calcium and phosphorus metabolism. *Am. J. Physiol.*, **214**, 348–56 (1968)

181. Gitelman, H. J., Kukolz, S., Welt, L. G. The influence of the parathyroid glands on the hypercalcemia of experimental magnesium depletion in the rat. *J. Clin. Invest.*, **47**, 118–26 (1968)

182. Ginn, H. E., Shanbour, L. L. Phosphaturia in magnesium-deficient rats. *Am. J. Physiol.*, **212**, 1347–50 (1967)

183. Fulop, M., Brazeau, P. The phosphaturic effect of sodium bicarbonate and acetazolamide in dogs. *J. Clin. Invest.*, **47**, 983–91 (1968)

184. Grose, J. H., Scriver, C. R. Parathyroid-dependent phosphaturia and aminoaciduria in the vitamin D-deficient rat. *Am. J. Physiol.*, **214**, 370–77 (1968)

185. Kolousek, J. Urinary excretion of inorganic phosphates and free fatty acid levels in the rat sera after a single injection of lysine vasopressin. *Arch. Intern. Physiol. Biochim.*, **76**, 281–86 (1968)

186. Ginsburg, J. M. Effect of metabolic alkalosis and acidosis on renal transport of arsenic. *Am. I. Physiol.*, **212**, 1334–40 (1967)

187. Passow, H. Steady-state diffusion of non-electrolytes through epithelial brush borders. *J. Theoret. Biol.*, **16**, 383–98 (1967)

188. Ruedas, G., Weiss, Ch. Die Wirkung von Änderungen der Natriumkonzentration im Perfusionsmedium und von Strophanin auf die Glukoseresorption der isolierten Rattenniere. *Pflügers Arch.*, **298**, 12–22 (1967)

189. Robson, A. M., Srivastava, P. L., Bricker, N. S., The influence of saline loading on renal glucose reabsorption in the rat. *J. Clin. Invest.*, **47**, 329–35 (1968)

190. Huang, K. C., Woosley, R. L. Renal tubular secretion of L-glucose. *Am. J. Physiol.*, **214**, 342–47 (1968)

191. Keller, D. M. Glucose excretion in man and dog. *Nephron*, **5**, 43–66 (1968)

192. Deetjen, P., Boylan, J. W. Glucose reabsorption in the rat kidney. Microperfusion studies. *Pflügers Arch.*, **299**, 19–29 (1968)

193. Kleinzeller, A., Kolinská, K., Benes, I. Transport of monosaccharides in kidney-cortex cells. *Biochem. J.*, **104**, 852–60 (1967)

194. Kleinzeller, A., Kolinská, K., Benes, I. Transport of glucose and galactose in kidney-cortex cells. *Biochem. J.*, **104**, 843–52 (1967)

195. Rabinowitz, L., Baines, A. D. Microinjection studies of renal tubular permeability to methylurea and acetamide in the rat. *Am. J. Physiol.*, **214**, 745–48 (1968)

196. Carlisky, N. J., Botbol, V., Lew, V. L. Studies on excretion of urea by the toad kidney. *Proc. Soc. Exptl. Biol. Med.*, **125**, 687–92 (1968)

197. Carrasquer, G., Solomon, S., Sonnenberg, H. Evidence of restricted permeability to urea in rat distal tubule. *Proc. Soc. Exptl. Biol. Med.*, **125**, 828–34 (1967)

198. Skeith, M. D., Healey, L. A. Urate clearance in Cebus monkeys. *Am. J. Physiol.*, **214**, 582–84 (1968)

199. Steele, T. H., Rieselbach, R. E. The renal mechanism of urate homeostasis in normal man. *Am. J. Med.*, **43**, 868–75 (1967)

200. Mudge, G. H., McAlary, B., Berndt, W. O. Renal transport of uric acid in the guinea pig. *Am. J. Physiol.*, **214**, 875–79 (1968)

201. Ferris, T. F., Gorden, P. Effect of angiotensin and norepinephrine upon urate clearance in man. *Am. J. Med.*, **44**, 359–65 (1968)

202. Baines, A. D., Gottschalk, C. W., Lassiter, W. E. Microinjection study of *p*-aminohippurate excretion by rat kidneys. *Am. J. Physiol.*, **214**, 703–9 (1968)

203. Tanner, G. Micropuncture study of PAH and Diodrast transport in Necturus kidney. *Am. J. Physiol.*, **212**, 1341–46 (1967)

204. Wedeen, R. P., Jernow, H. I. Autoradiographic study of cellular transport of Hippuran-^{125}I in the rat nephron. *Am. J. Physiol.*, **214**, 776–85 (1968)

205. Hook, J. B., Munro, J. R. Specificity of the inhibitory effect of "uremic" serum on p-aminohippurate transport. *Proc. Soc. Exptl. Biol. Med.*, **127**, 289–92 (1968)

206. Møller, J. V. The relation between secretion of urate and p-aminohippurate in the rabbit kidney. *J. Physiol.*, **192**, 505–17 (1967)

207. Møller, J. V. The renal accumulation of urate and p-aminohippurate in the rabbit. *Ibid.*, 519–27

208. Balagura, S., Stone, W. J. Renal tubular secretion of alpha-ketoglutarate in dog. *Am. J. Physiol.*, **212**, 1319–26 (1967)

209. Quebbemann, A. J., Rennick, B. R. Catechol transport by the renal tubule in the chicken. *Am. J. Physiol.*, **214**, 1201–4 (1968)

210. Galvin, D., Harris, J. A., Johnson, R. E. Urinary excretion of betahydroxybutyrate and acetoacetate during experimental ketosis. *Quart. J. Exptl. Physiol.*, **53**, 181–93 (1968)

211. Berndt, W. O. Probenecid binding by renal cortical slices and homogenates. *Proc. Soc. Exptl. Biol. Med.*, **126**, 123–26 (1967)

212. Wilson, O. H., Scriver, C. R. Specificity of transport of neutral and basic amino acids in rat kidney. *Am. J. Physiol.*, **213**, 185–90 (1967)

213. Weiss, Ch., Braun, W., Zschaler, W. Über den Einfluss von Änderungen des Urin-pH auf die Ausscheidung einiger Aminosäureester an der perfundierten Rattenniere. *Arch. Pharmakol. Exptl. Pathol.*, **258**, 83–90 (1967)

214. Thier, S. O. Amino acid accumulation in the toad bladder. Relationship to transepithelial sodium transport. *Biochem. Biophys. Acta*, **150**, 253–62 (1968)

215. Fox, M., Thier, S., Rosenberg, L., Segal, S. Ionic requirements for amino acid transport in the rat kidney cortex slice. I. Influence of extracellular ions. *Biochim. Biophys. Acta*, **79**, 167–76 (1964)

216. Webber, W. A., Cairns, J. A. A comparison of the amino acid concentrating ability of the kidney cortex of newborn and mature rats. *Can. J. Physiol. Pharmacol.*, **46**, 165–69 (1968)

217. Wilde, W. S., Legan, S. J., Southwick, A. K. Reabsorption of albumin-Evans blue via membrane vesicles of proximal kidney tubule cells. *Proc. Soc. Exptl. Biol. Med.*, **127**, 776–81 (1968)

218. Physiology Symposium on "Hydrogen ion exchange mechanism in dif-

ferent organs and tissues". *Fed. Proc.*, **26**, 1303–31 (1967)

219. Carter, N. W., Rector, F. C., Jr., Campion, D. C., Seldin, D. W. Measurement of intracellular pH with glass microelectrodes. *Fed. Proc.*, **26**, 1322–26 (1967)

220. Carter, N. W., Rector, F. C., Jr., Campion, D. C., Seldin, D. W. Measurement of intracellular pH of skeletal muscle with pH-sensitive glass microelectrodes. *J. Clin. Invest.*, **46**, 920–33 (1967)

221. Butler, T. C., Wadell, W. J., Poole, D. T. Intracellular pH based on the distribution of weak electrolytes. *Fed. Proc.*, **26**, 1327–32 (1967)

222. Butler, T. C., Poole, D. T., Wadell, W. J. Acid-labile carbon dioxide in muscle: its nature and relationship to intracellular pH. *Proc. Soc. Exptl. Biol. Med.*, **125**, 972–74 (1967)

223. Struyvenberg, A., Morrison, R. B., Relman, A. S. Acid-base behavior of separated canine renal tubule cells. *Am. J. Physiol.*, **214**, 1155–62 (1968)

224. Sanslone, W. R., Muntwyler, E. Effect of altered plasma CO_2 on intracellular pH during potassium deficiency. *Proc. Soc. Exptl. Biol. Med.*, **126**, 750–54 (1967)

225. Steinmetz, P. R. Characteristics of hydrogen ion transport in urinary bladder of water turtle. *J. Clin. Invest.*, **46**, 1531–40 (1967)

226. Steinmetz, P. R., Ochami, R. S., Frazier, H. S. Independence of hydrogen ion secretion and transport of other electrolytes in turtle bladder. *J. Clin. Invest.*, **46**, 1541–48 (1967)

227. Brodsky, W. A., Schilb, T. P. Mechanism of acidification in turtle bladder. *Fed. Proc.*, **26**, 1314–21 (1967)

228. Vieira, F. L., Malnic, G. Hydrogen ion secretion by rat cortical tubules as studied by an antimony microelectrode. *Am. J. Physiol.*, **214**, 710–18 (1968)

229. Rector, F. C., Jr., Carter, N. W., Seldin, D. W. The mechanism of bicarbonate reabsorption in the proximal and distal tubules of the kidney. *J. Clin. Invest.*, **44**, 278–90 (1965)

230. Berstein, B. A., Clapp, J. R. Micropuncture study of bicarbonate reabsorption by the dog nephron.

Am. J. Physiol., **214**, 251–57 (1968)

231. Weinstein, S. W. Micropuncture studies of the effects of acetazolamide on the nephron function in the rat. *Am. J. Physiol.*, **214**, 222–27 (1968)

232. Ullmann, E. Factors modifying renal tubular bicarbonate reabsorption in the dog. *J. Physiol.*, **194**, 573–94 (1968)

233. Berkman, P. M., van Ypersele de Strihou, C., Neelle, M. A., Gulyassi, P. F., Schwartz, W. B. Factors which determine whether infusion of the sodium salt of an anion will induce metabolic alkalosis in dogs. *Clin. Sci.*, **33**, 517–25 (1967)

234. Cohen, J. J. Correction of metabolic alkalosis by the kidney after isometric expansion of extracellular fluid. *J. Clin. Invest.*, **47**, 1181–92 (1968)

235. Kunau, R. T., Jr., Frick, A., Rector, F. C., Jr., Seldin, D. W. Micropuncture study of the proximal tubular factors responsible for the maintenance of alkalosis during potassium deficiency in the rat. *Clin. Sci.*, **34**, 223–31 (1968)

236. Frick, A., Kunau, R. T., Jr., Rector, F. C., Jr., Seldin, D. W. Effect of volume expansion on the reabsorption of bicarbonate in the proximal convolution of the rat kidney. *Clin. Sci.*, **14**, 108–20 (1966)

237. Lennon, E. J., Lemann, J., Jr. The effect of a potassium-deficient diet on the pattern of recovery from experimental metabolic acidosis. *Clin. Sci.*, **34**, 365–78 (1968)

238. Cohen, R. D., Simpson, B. R., Goodwin, F. J., Strunin, L. The early effects of infusion of sodium bicarbonate and sodium lactate on intracellular hydrogen ion activity in dogs. *Clin. Sci.*, **33**, 233–47 (1967)

239. Engel, K., Dell, R. B., Rahill, W. J., Denning, C. R., Winters, R. W. Quantitative displacement of acid-base equilibrium in chronic respiratory acidosis. *J. Appl. Physiol.*, **24**, 288–95 (1968)

240. Lemann, J., Jr., Litzow, J. L., Lennon, E. J. Studies of the mechanism by which chronic metabolic acidosis augments urinary calcium excretion in man. *J. Clin. Invest.*, **46**, 1318–28 (1967)

241. Gill, J. R., Jr., Bell, H., Bartter, F. C.

Impaired conservation of sodium and potassium in renal tubular acidosis and its correction by buffer anions. *Clin. Sci.*, **33**, 577–92 (1967)

242. Morris, R. C., Jr. An experimental renal acidification defect in patients with hereditary fructose intolerance. I. Its resemblance to renal tubular acidosis. *J. Clin. Invest.*, **47**, 1389–98 (1968)

243. Edelmann, C. M., Jr., Soriano, J. R., Boichis, H., Gruskin, A. B., Acosta, M. I. Renal bicarbonate reabsorption and hydrogen ion excretion in normal infants. *J. Clin. Invest.*, **46**, 1309–17 (1967)

244. Stone, W. J., Balagura, S., Pitts, R. F. Diffusion equilibrium for ammonia in the kidney of the acidotic dog. *J. Clin. Invest.*, **46**, 1603–8 (1967)

245. Oelert, H., Uhlich, E., Hills, A. G. Messungen des Ammoniakdruckes in den corticalen Tubuli der Rattenniere. *Pflügers Arch.*, **300**, 35–48 (1968)

246. Stone, W. J., Pitts, R. F. Pathways of ammonia metabolism in the intact functioning kidney of the dog. *J. Clin. Invest.*, **46**, 1141–50 (1967)

247. Kamm, D. E., Fuisz, R. E., Goodman, D., Cahill, G. F., Jr. Acid-base alterations and renal gluconeogenesis: effect of pH, bicarbonate concentration, and P_{CO_2}. *J. Clin. Invest.*, **46**, 1172–77 (1967)

248. Alleye, G. A. Concentration of metabolic intermediates in kidneys of rats with metabolic acidosis. *Nature*, **217**, 847–48 (1968)

249. Pitts, R. F. The renal metabolism of ammonia. *Physiologist*, **9**, 97–109 (1966)

250. Goorno, W. E., Rector, F. C., Jr., Seldin, D. W., Relation of renal gluconeogenesis to ammonia production in the dog and rat. *Am. J. Physiol.*, **213**, 969–74 (1967)

251. Goldstein, L. Pathways of glutamine deamination and their control in the rat kidney. *Am. J. Physiol.*, **213**, 983–89 (1967)

252. Jamison, R. L. Micropuncture study of thin loop of Henle in the rat. (Abstr.) *Clin. Res.*, **16**, 386 (1968)

253. Morgan, T., Sakai, F., Berliner, R. W. *In vitro* permeability of medullary collecting ducts to water and urea. *Am. J. Physiol.*, **214**, 574–81 (1968)

254. Marsh, D. J. Hypo-osmotic reabsorption due to active salt transport in perfused collecting ducts of the rat renal medulla. *Nature*, **210**, 1179–80 (1966)

255. Heller, J., Vostál, J. The plasma sodium concentration: a factor influencing the osmolality of the fluid of the renal medullary tissue. *Physiol. Bohemoslov.*, **16**, 418–27 (1967)

256. Heller, J., Tata, P. S. Effect of some metabolic inhibitors on the electrolyte and urea concentration gradients in rat kidney. *Physiol. Bohemoslov.*, **16**, 428–40 (1967)

257. Dell, R. B., Winters, R. W. Lactate gradients in the kidney of the dog. *Am. J. Physiol.*, **213**, 301–7 (1967)

258. Solomon, S. Action of alkali metals on papillary-cortical sodium gradient of dog kidney. *Proc. Soc. Exptl. Biol. Med.*, **125**, 1183–86 (1967)

259. Wilde, W. S., Vorburger, C. Albumin multiplier in kidney vasa recta analyzed by microspectrophotometry of T-1824. *Am. J. Physiol.*, **213**, 1233–43 (1967)

260. Pinter, G. G. Distribution of chylomicrons and albumin in dog kidney. *J. Physiol.*, **192**, 761–72 (1967)

261. Pinter, G. G. Effects of pH and urea concentration on uptake of fluid and urea by solutions containing serum albumin. *Proc. Soc. Exptl. Biol. Med.*, **125**, 398–99 (1967)

262. Rabinowitz, L. Enhancement of renal concentrating ability in the rat by acetamide and methylurea. *Am. J. Physiol.*, **214**, 737–44 (1968)

263. Carrasquer, G., Diana, A. L. Effect of released urine flow on renal tissue creatinine, urea and Na in dogs. *Proc. Soc. Exptl. Biol. Med.*, **125**, 823–27 (1967)

264. Klahr, S., Tripathy, K., Garcia, F. T., Mayoral, L. G., Ghitis, J., Balaños, O. On the nature of the renal concentrating defect in malnutrition. *Am. J. Med.*, **43**, 84–96 (1967)

265. Skadhauge, E., Schmidt-Nielsen, B. Renal medullary electrolyte and urea gradient in chickens and turkeys. *Am. J. Physiol.*, **212**, 1313–18 (1967)

265. Skadhauge, E. Schmidt-Nielsen, B. Renal medullary electrolyte and urea gradient in chickens and turkeys. *Ibid.*, 1313–18

266. Selkurt, E. E., Wathen, R. L. Renal concentrating mechanism of the squirrel monkey. *Am. J. Physiol.*, **213**, 191–97 (1967)

267. Marumo, F., Yoshikawa, Y., Koshikawa, S. A study on the concentration mechanism of the renal medulla by mathematical model. *Japan. Circ. J.*, **31**, 1309–17 (1967)

268. Forsling, M. L., Jones, J. J., Lee, J. Factors influencing the sensitivity of the rat to vasopressin. *Am. J. Physiol.*, **196**, 495–505 (1968)

269. Kleeman, C. R., Vorherr, H., Houghoughi, M. Sensitivity of ADH of normal and diabetes insipidus rats. *Endocrinology*, **80**, 1168–69 (1967)

270. Gauer, O. H., Tata, P. S. Vasopressin studies in the rat. *Pflügers Arch.*, **298**, 241–57 (1968)

271. Hays, R. M. A new proposal for the action of vasopressin, based on studies of a complex synthetic membrane. *J. Gen. Physiol.*, **51**, 385–98 (1968)

272. Civan, M. M., Frazier, H. S. The site of the stimulatory action of vasopressin on sodium transport in toad bladder. *J. Gen. Physiol.*, **51**, 589–605 (1968)

273. Argy, W. P., Jr., Handler, J. S., Orloff, J. Ca^{++} and Mg^{++} effects on toad bladder response to cyclic AMP, theophylline, and ADH analogues. *Am. J. Physiol.*, **213**, 803–8 (1967)

274. Senft, G. M., Hoffmann, M., Munske, K., Schultz, G. Effects of hydration and dehydration on cyclic adenosine 3'5' monophosphate concentration in the rat kidney. *Pflügers Arch.*, **298**, 348–58 (1968)

275. Levine, R. A. Antidiuretic responses to exogenous adenosine 3',5'-monophosphate in man. *Clin. Sci.*, **34**, 253–60 (1968)

276. Chase, L. R., Aurbach, G. D. Renal adenyl cyclase: anatomically separate sites for parathyroid hormone and vasopressin. *Science*, **159**, 545–47 (1968)

277. Davis, B. B., Knox, F. G., Berliner, R. W. Effect of vasopressin on proximal tubule sodium reabsorption in the dog. *Am. J. Physiol.*, **212**, 1361–64 (1967)

278. Clapp, J. R., Watson, J. F., Berliner, R. W. Osmolality, bicarbonate concentration, and water reabsorption in the proximal tubule of the dog nephron. *Am. J. Physiol.*, **205**, 273–80 (1963)

279. Harrington, A. R., Valtin, H. Impaired urinary concentration after vasopressin and its gradual correction in hypothalamic diabetes insipidus. *J. Clin. Invest.*, **47**, 502–10 (1968)

280. Massry, S. G., Katz, A. I., Agmon, J., Toor, M. Effect of water diuresis on electrolyte and hydrogen ion excretion in hot climate. *Nephron*, **5**, 124–33 (1968)

281. Kuhn, E., Peeters, G. Influence de l'argenine-vasopressine sur l'excrétion, d'électrolytes chez la brebis. *Arch. Intern. Pharmacodyn.*, **168**, 14–27 (1967)

282. Kuhn, E., Peeters, G. Influence de la sécrétion réflectoire des hormones posthypophysaires sur l'excrétion du potassium chez la chèvre. *Ibid.*, **169**, 237–53

283. Kuhn, E. A comparison between the influence of arginine-vasopressin and lysine-vasopressin on water and electrolyte excretion in ewes. *Arch. Intern. Pharmacodyn.*, **168**, 417–25 (1967)

284. Macfarlane, W. V., Kinne, R., Walmsley, C. M., Siebert, B. D., Peter, D. Vasopressins and the increase of water and electrolyte excretion by sheep, cattle and camels. *Nature*, **214**, 979–81 (1967)

285. Fisher, D. A. Norepinephrine inhibition of vasopressin antidiuresis. *J. Clin. Invest.*, **47**, 540–47 (1968)

286. Perlmutt, J. H. Renal compensation during mild water diuresis and its inhibition by vagotomy. *Proc. Soc. Exptl. Biol. Med.*, **125**, 696–700 (1968)

287. Thorn, N. A., Willumsen, N. B. S. Effect of urea on the inactivation of antidiuretic hormone by the inner medulla of the rat kidney *in vitro*. *Acta Endocrinol.*, **56**, 132–38 (1967)

288. Park, C. S., Han, D. S., Kim, H. C., Hong, S. K. Medullary sodium and urea gradient of the dog kidney in hypothermia. *Proc. Soc. Exptl. Biol. Med.*, **127**, 1263–67 (1968)

289. Rogge, J. D., Moore, W. W., Segar, W. E., Fasola, A. F. Effect of +Gz and +Gx acceleration on peripheral venous ADH levels in humans. *J. Appl. Physiol.*, **23**, 870–74 (1967)

290. Henry, J. P., Gupta, P. D., Meehan, J. P., Sinclair, R., Share, L. The role of afferents from the low pressure system in the release of antidiuretic hormone during non-hypotensive hemorrhage. *Can. J.*

Physiol. Pharmacol., **46**, 287–98 (1968)

291. Bie, P., Thorn, N. A. *In vitro* studies of the release mechanism for vasopressin in rats. Studies of the possible release of hormone from hypothalamic tissue. *Acta Endocrinol.*, **56**, 139–45 (1967)

292. Fimognari, G. M., Fanestil, D. D., Edelman, I. S. Induction of RNA and protein synthesis in the action of aldosterone in the rat. *Am. J. Physiol.*, **213**, 954–62 (1967)

293. Kirsten, E., Kirsten, R., Leaf, A., Sharp, G. W. Increased activity of enzymes of the tricarboxylic acid cycle in response to aldosterone in the toad bladder. *Pflügers Arch.*, **300**, 213–25 (1968)

294. Sharp, G. W., Leaf, A. On the stimulation of sodium transport by aldosterone. *J. Gen. Physiol.*, **51**, 271s–79s (1968)

295. Kinne, R., Kirsten, R. Der Einfluss von Aldosteron auf die Aktivität mitochondrialer und cytoplasmatischer Encyme in der Rattenniere. *Pflügers Arch.*, **300**, 244–54 (1968)

296. Stumpe, K. O., Ochwadt, B. Wirkung von Aldosteron auf die Natrium und Wasserresorption in proximalen Tubulus bei chronischer Kochsalzbeladung. *Pflügers Arch.*, **300**, 148–60 (1968)

297. Kassirer, J. P., Appleton, F. M., Chazan, J. A., Schwartz, W. B. Aldosterone in metabolic alkalosis. *J. Clin. Invest.*, **46**, 1558–71 (1967)

298. Davis, W. W., Burwell, L. R., Casper, A. G. T., Bartter, F. C. Sites of action of sodium depletion on aldosterone biosynthesis in the dog. *J. Clin. Invest.*, **47**, 1425–34 (1968)

299. Marusic, E. T., Mulrow, P. J. Stimulation of aldosterone biosynthesis in adrenal mitochondria by sodium depletion. *J. Clin. Invest.*, **46**, 2101–8 (1967)

300. Massry, S. G., Coburn, J. W., Chapman, L. W., Kleeman, C. R. The acute effect of adrenal steroids on the interrelationship between the renal excretion of sodium, calcium and magnesium. *J. Lab. Clin. Med.*, **70**, 563–70 (1967)

301. Lim, V. S., Webster, G. D. The effect of aldosterone on water and electrolyte composition of incubated rat diaphragms. *Clin. Sci.*, **33**, 261–70 (1967)

302. Stolte, H., Brecht, J. P., Wiederholt, M., Hierholzer, K. Einfluss von Adrenalektomie und Glucocorticoiden auf die Wasserpermeabilität corticaler Nephronabschnitte der Rattenniere. *Pflügers Arch.*, **299**, 99–127 (1968)

303. Marumo, F. The effect of glucocorticoid on the water permeability of the toad bladder. *Pflügers Arch.*, **299**, 149–57 (1968)

304. Lockett, M. F. Hormonal actions of the heart and of lungs on the isolated kidney. *J. Physiol.*, **193**, 661–69 (1967)

305. Illett, K. F., Lockett, M. F. A renally active substance from heart muscle and from blood. *J. Physiol.*, **196**, 101–9 (1968)

306. Bonjour, J. P., Regoli, D., Roch-Ramel, F., Peters, G. Prerequisites for the natriuretic effect of val-5-angiotensin-2-amide in the rat. *Am. J. Physiol.*, **214**, 1133–38 (1968)

307. Bonjour, J. P., Peters, G., Chomety, F., Regoli, D. Renal effects of val-5-angiotensin-2-amide, vasopressin and diuretics in the rat, as influenced by water diuresis and by ethanol anesthesia. *Eur. J. Pharmacol.*, **2**, 88–105 (1967)

308. Malvin, R. L., Vander, A. J. Effects of angiotensin on renal function in the unanesthetized rat. *Am. J. Physiol.*, **213**, 1205–8 (1967)

309. Porush, J. G., Kaloyanides, G. J., Cacciaguida, R. J., Rosen, S. M. The effects of angiotensin II on renal water and electrolyte excretion in normal and caval dogs. *J. Clin. Invest.*, **46**, 2109–22 (1967)

310. Cirksena, W. J., Dirks, J. H., Berliner, R. W. Effect of thoracic vena cava obstruction on response of proximal tubule sodium reabsorption to saline infusion. *J. Clin. Invest.*, **45**, 179–88 (1966)

311. Berkowitz, H. D., Miller, L. D., Itskovitz, H. D. Renal function and the renin-angiotensin system in the isolated perfused kidney. *Am. J. Physiol.*, **213**, 928–34 (1967)

312. Yamamoto, K., Hasegawa, T., Ueda, J. Renin secretion in the perfused dog kidney. *Japan. J. Pharmacol.*, **18**, 1–8 (1968)

313. Johnston, H. H., Herzog, J. P., Lauler, D. P. Effect of prostaglandin E1 on renal hemodynamics, sodium and water excretion. *Am. J. Physiol.*, **213**, 939–46 (1967)

314. Vander, A. J. Direct effects of prostaglandin on renal function and renin release in anesthetized dog. *Am. J. Physiol.*, **214**, 218–21 (1968)

315. Grantham, J. J., Orloff, J. Effect of prostaglandin E₁ on the permeability response of the isolated collecting tubule to vasopressin, adenosin 3′5′-monophosphate, and theophylline. *J. Clin. Invest.*, **47**, 1154–61 (1968)

316. Strong, C. G., Bohr, D. F. Effects of prostaglandin E₁, E₂, A₁, and F₁ alpha on isolated vascular smooth muscle. *Am. J. Physiol.*, **213**, 725–33 (1967)

317. Lee, J. B., Crowshaw, K., Takman, B. H., Attrep, K. A., Gougoutas, J. Z. The identification of prostaglandins E₂, F₂ alpha and A₂ from rabbit kidney medulla. *Biochem. J.*, **105**, 1251–60 (1967)

318. Nissen, H. M. On lipid droplets in renal interstitial cells. II. A. Histological study on the number of droplets in salt depletion and acute depletion. *Histochemie*, **85**, 483–91 (1968)

319. Park, C. S., Chu, C. S., Park, Y. S., Hong, S. K. Effect of 5-hydroxytryptamine on renal function of the anesthetized dog. *Am. J. Physiol.*, **214**, 384–88 (1968)

320. Charbon, G. A., Brummer, F., Reneman, R. S. Diuretic and vascular action of parathyroid extracts in animals and man. *Arch. Intern. Pharmacodyn.*, **171**, 1–11 (1968)

321. Cohen, M. P., Carter, M. K. The effects of renal arterial infusion of cholinomimetic agents on renal function. *Arch. Intern. Pharmacodyn.*, **170**, 473–84 (1967)

322. Blake, W. D., Jurf, A. N. Renal sodium reabsorption after acute renal denervation in the rabbit. *J. Physiol.*, **196**, 65–73 (1968)

323. Natscheff, N., Piryova, B. Über die Wirkung des hinteren Hypothalamus auf die Nierenfunktion von Hunden im chronischen Experiment. *Pflügers Arch.*, **298**, 213–24 (1968)

324. Ramsay, A. G., Sachs, G. Effect of ouabain on Na⁺ and K⁺ excretion in the rat. *Proc. Soc. Exptl. Biol. Med.*, **126**, 294–98 (1967)

RESPIRATION[1]

By Norman C. Staub

Department of Physiology and Cardiovascular Research Institute, University of California Medical Center, San Francisco, California

With the availability of the National Library of Medicine's *Index Medicus* and MEDLARS literature retrieval system (1) it is no longer necessary, even if possible, to mention every paper that deals with respiration. After completing my outline for this review I requested a MEDLARS search covering the topics and dates I had chosen, to check up on my own bibliographic filing system. When the reference lists came back they included over 1000 citations. Of these about two thirds were not directly related to my chosen topics. Efficiency of retrieval is still the bane of indexing systems (2). The key words or other selection criteria are too broad, and the original indexing by author or abstractor is too uneven to permit exact requests. But I would rather have many extraneous references than miss a single important one. Finally, out of some 300 possibly relevant papers I have limited my bibliography to 108 papers.

I have followed the current trend of making a critical review and trying to fit the individual pieces together in a coherent picture. If, in doing so, I have misrepresented your views or otherwise disagreed with your concepts of how the lung functions I would be pleased to hear from you so that I may correct my information and thinking.

My review covers 1966–1968 literature because last year's analysis (3) dealt mainly with other problems. I have included a few prior references to bring points into perspective.

Pulmonary Circulation: Effects of Alveolar Hypoxia

To those physiologists who believe that the lung is a living organ capable of active adjustments of the distribution of ventilation and blood flow the last two years have been exceedingly fruitful. This is not to deny the importance of mechanistic factors so ably reviewed by Permutt (4), but it does take issue with one of his conclusions, " . . . all of these speculations deemphasize a direct vasoconstrictor effect of alveolar hypoxia." Since then almost every report I have seen indicates a direct, active vasomotor effect of acute or chronic alveolar hypoxia on the pulmonary circulation.

Why?—Let us look at the current literature in light of the following question: What is the genetic adaptive significance (survival of the fittest) of pulmonary vasoconstriction in response to decreased alveolar oxygen tension?

---

[1] The survey of literature for this review was concluded in May 1968.

The effects of acute and chronic whole animal hypoxia do not seem to show adaptive significance. Blount & Vogel (5) suggest that natives of high altitudes (Peru) over several generations may have less pulmonary hypertension than those who have lived at equally high altitude for only one or two generations (Leadville, Colorado). First and second generation natives, in turn, appear to have less pulmonary hypertension than do newcomers to high altitude. One might suggest that hypoxic pulmonary vasoconstriction reduces cardiac output and slows the transit of red cells through the pulmonary capillaries, thus allowing more time for completion of oxygen diffusion and chemical binding to hemoglobin. This does not appear to be the case. Cardiac output is not markedly altered at high altitude—either at rest or exercise (5). Besides, the average normal pulmonary capillary transit time is long enough so that levels of alveolar hypoxia compatible with long life would not lead to significant arterial desaturation on that basis (6).

Actually, the pulmonary hypertension developing at altitude is a bad thing for man (chronic mountain sickness), cattle (brisket disease) and, especially, pigs but not adult sheep (7).

Failing to find adaptive significance for whole-body hypoxia in the adult, we may next examine hypoxic pulmonary vasoconstriction in the fetus. Rudolph & Yuan (8) showed a potent dose-response relationship between pulmonary vascular resistance and Po_2 in newborn calves. Admittedly, the Po_2 measured was that of systemic arterial blood but they believe it is very close to pulmonary venous and alveolar Po_2 under their conditions. The level of response was influenced by the pH of the blood. Of great importance is the response threshold which is at alveolar Po_2 of 50–60 mm Hg at pH 7.1–7.3. This is to be compared to normal fetal pulmonary artery Po_2 and pH of about 20–30 mm Hg and 7.3, respectively (9).

Campbell and co-workers (10, 11) studied the effects of hypoxia and acidosis in perfused lung lobes of exteriorized lamb fetuses early and late in gestation. The physical situation of the fetal lung and circulation is different from the same animal after birth. Fetal alveolar spaces do not contain high Po_2 gas but rather contain fluid which reflects low tissue Po_2 and somewhat elevated Pco_2 (low pH). Most of the cardiac output does not go through the lungs (9, 12).

At 84–94 days gestation (10), perfusion of a lung lobe with hypoxic fetal blood following 2 to 3 min of cord clamping showed a marked shift in the lobar pressure-flow curve indicating a strong vasoconstrictor response. Perfusion with normally oxygenated fetal blood relieved the vasoconstriction within 15 sec. The response was completely localized within the lobe since pharmacological blockade of sympathetic reflexes had no influence. In a second paper (11) they studied lamb fetuses between 91 and 142 days gestation, looking for the development of reflex responses. In the younger fetuses hypoxia and acidosis induced by cord clamping invoked no vasoconstriction in a lung lobe perfused with normal fetal blood from a donor fetus. The same lobe perfused with hypoxic blood showed potent vasoconstriction. In the older fetuses cord clamping led to a small degree of vasoconstriction in the lobe perfused with well-oxygenated blood. Such constriction was abolished either by sympathectomy or by the administration of hexamethonium. Thus the main vasoconstrictor response is localized within the hypoxic lobe but in older fetuses there is a small added adrenergic constriction.

All these results point to the great local reactivity of the fetal and newborn pulmonary circulation and one is tempted to conclude that adult responses are merely residua of this fetal propensity. But there is a rather important negating factor. Pulmonary blood flow in the fetus is known to be low normally (9). New data of Rudolph & Heymann (12) using the distribution of radioactive-labeled microspheres show that in the nonexteriorized lamb fetus the total pulmonary flow averages only 4 per cent of total cardiac output. While this 4 per cent is very important to the lung (13), a further decrease would have no significance for right ventricular work or total blood flow to other organs. Therefore adaptive significance in the fetus would be meaningful only if the Po_2 and hydrogen ion concentration [H^+] in the normal fetal blood going to the lungs were causing chronic pulmonary vasoconstriction so that a large pulmonary blood fraction did not have to be pumped twice. To answer this we need to know the maximum possible blood flow through the lungs in a completely paralyzed fetal pulmonary vascular bed. Dawes (9) gives a partial answer in that the fetal pulmonary blood vessels can "vasodilate very greatly" in response to acetylcholine or histamine injections. But it is impossible for me to be certain from the data exactly where the normal flow level is. I gather from his various tables that the maximum flow is about two to three times the normal average. This would agree qualitatively with Rudolph & Heymann (12) whose maximum normal pulmonary blood flow in "undisturbed" fetuses was 9 per cent of total cardiac output, that is, about twice the average. However, Dawes' normal pulmonary flows are in the range of Rudolph's maximum flows. Without more evidence we cannot be certain about the adaptive significance of hypoxic pulomary vasoconstriction in the fetus.

An alternate interpretation of the fetal reactivity is that we are looking at the significance just backwards; that is, it is not the adult which shows persistence of the fetal reactivity—it is the fetal reactivity that is a harbinger of that in the adult. The explanation for the increased apparent fetal reactivity may be on two grounds: that the fetal pulmonary vasculature has relatively more muscle than the adult and that the levels of Po_2 are much lower and of [H^+] higher in fetal lung tissue because of the absence of a gas phase (14). One bit of evidence, however, doesn't fit. Grover (7) found no significant hypoxic pulmonary vascular reactivity in adult sheep whereas the fetal lamb shows an excellent effect.

A third possibility (and the one I favor) for adaptive significance of the hypoxic vasoconstrictor response lies in the adjustment of ventilation to perfusion ($\dot{V}/\dot{Q}$) within the lung. I do not necessarily mean by this the imbalance of $\dot{V}/\dot{Q}$ relative to gravity (15, 16). West (17) showed that in upright man the gravitational inequality in the lung does not significantly affect arterial P_{O_2}, pH, or P_{CO_2}. Of equal importance is the fact that many animals without significant hydrostatic $\dot{V}/\dot{Q}$ inequality show potent hypoxic vasoconstrictor responses. These include the rat (18) and the cat (14, 19). We should look for adaptive significance relative to regional ventilation and perfusion independently of the gravitational field of the earth. This, indeed, seems to be the trend of most of the current literature with many papers dealing with unilateral or unilobar hypoxia (10, 14, 20–24) or with the analysis of uneven $\dot{V}/\dot{Q}$ in human chronic bronchopulmonary disease (25–30).

Mechanism.—The mechanism by which alveolar hypoxia invokes an active pulmonary artery constriction at the level of the terminal respiratory unit (19) is still the subject of much confusion.

The threshold at which hypoxic pulmonary vasoconstriction begins in both newborn (8) and human adults (5, 23) is at relatively high alveolar oxygen tensions (50 to 70 mm Hg) but not high enough, according to West's calculations (17), to produce any increased lower zone vascular resistance in normal upright man. However, the levels of alveolar oxygen tension which provoke a strong vasoconstrictive reaction are within physiologically obtainable limits in lung units that are poorly ventilated relative to their perfusion. Considerable individual variability exists (7, 14, 29).

The threshold can be altered. In the newborn calf, alveolar oxygen tensions as high as 80 or 85 mm Hg may provoke a marked vasoconstrictor reaction if the pulmonary circulation is already modestly stressed (31) by ligating one pulmonary artery at sea level or at Denver, Colorado (altitude 5280 ft). Animals ligated at sea level developed insignificant pulmonary hypertension whereas those ligated at Denver developed rapidly progressive hypertension with most of the animals dying in right heart failure. One animal taken down to sea level not only survived but lost its pulmonary hypertension.

The relation of [H$^+$] to the hypoxic response is also relevant to mechanism. Rudolph & Yuan (8) showed a marked interdependence of [H$^+$] and P_{O_2} on the newborn calf's pulmonary circulation. Kato & Staub (19) found in anesthetized cats that self-perfused lobes ventilated with 10 per cent CO_2 in nitrogen (while the rest of the lung breathed 100 per cent O_2) showed somewhat greater narrowing of the small muscular pulmonary arteries and less shuntlike effect than lobes ventilated with 100 per cent nitrogen. They interpreted their evidence as supporting the interaction of increased hydrogen ion and reduced P_{O_2}.

Dugard & Naimark (15) studied the gravitational distribution of $\dot{V}/\dot{Q}$ using the Xe[133] scanning procedure in vertically suspended, anesthetized dogs. Acute alveolar hypoxia caused a more uniform distribution of pulmonary flow relative to lung volume and ventilation which they attributed to an increase in the mean pulmonary artery pressure due to generalized vasoconstriction rather than selective vasoconstriction in the lower zone. Of particular importance was their finding that in the presence of increased

[H$^+$], produced by the addition of 7–11 per cent CO_2 in the 9–11 per cent O_2 ventilating gas, there was a further redistribution of blood flow away from the lower zones of the lung. The authors conclude that there is both a qualitative and a quantitative difference between the response to hypoxia alone and the response to hypoxia plus hypercapnia. Haas & Bergofsky (16) come to a similar conclusion from a different series of observations. They found a smaller alveolar-arterial Po_2 difference in anesthetized, controlled-ventilation dogs during induced acidosis (metabolic and respiratory) or intravenous potassium or serotonin infusions. They concluded that generalized effects of these agents by increasing active vascular smooth muscle tension throughout the lung improved the gravity-dependent regional $\dot{V}/\dot{Q}$ distribution, thereby improving arterial Po_2.

I agree that gravity-dependent $\dot{V}/\dot{Q}$ unevenness is a convenient situation for demonstrating active pulmonary vasomotor effects to hypoxia and [H$^+$], but I do not agree that generalized vasoconstriction occurred. True, the added stimulus is nearly equal everywhere but the thresholds and sensitivities of the responding units are not. Some small muscular pulmonary arteries are closer to their active constrictor thresholds than others (32). West's (17) model lung shows apical and basal alveolar Po_2 and Pco_2. Clearly, the basal terminal respiratory unit arteries are much closer to their active vasoconstrictor thresholds. Returning to [H$^+$] effects, however, both groups clearly demonstrated that acidosis accentuates or triggers active pulmonary vasoconstriction.

In human studies, Harvey and associates (27) have confirmed in fifteen patients with chronic obstructive pulmonary disease their previous findings that increases in blood [H$^+$] accentuate the pulmonary vascular resistance increase found in the presence of arterial desaturation (alveolar hypoxia). They used the "Gomez formula" to satisfactorily predict pulmonary artery pressures from arterial pH and O_2 saturation levels. Stuart-Harris (33), reviewing the relation of cor pulmonale to chronic bronchitis and emphysema, showed that arterial desaturation and pH are good predictors of cor pulmonale.

Not all experiments on the action of [H$^+$] are confirmatory. Housley et al. (34) studied acute and chronic acidosis in patients with chronic bronchitis. Whether or not the patients were hypoxemic, they found a decrease in pulmonary vascular resistance with acidosis and concluded that acidosis does not cause pulmonary vasoconstriction. Lockhart and associates (30) studied patients with chronic pulmonary disease and found a poor relation between changes in arterial oxygen saturation and pH and pulmonary artery pressure.

To confuse the issue further, Barer, Howard & McCurrie (35) studied the effect of CO_2 and blood pH on unilobar pulmonary vascular resistance in anesthetized cats. With both the lobe and lung ventilated with high oxygen, they found that increases in alveolar CO_2 caused marked vasoconstriction comparable to equivalent blood pH changes by fixed acids. The reverse effect, a decrease in pulmonary vascular resistance, occurred when blood pH was increased. The response was dependent on the [H+] because infusions of bicarbonate or Tris buffer returned pulmonary vascular resistance to control levels in spite of continued high Pco_2 in the lungs and blood. Different results were obtained by Viles & Shepherd (36) using isolated, perfused cat lungs. At any given blood pH they found that increasing alveolar CO_2 decreased pulmonary vascular resistance. Their explanation is that [H+] does have a constrictor action on the pulmonary vascular smooth muscle but CO_2 molecules act directly to cause dilatation. Kato & Staub (19) showed that in the presence of normal alveolar oxygen tensions the addition of 10 per cent CO_2 to the inspired gas of a self-perfused lobe of the anesthetized cat had no effect on the dimensions of the small muscular pulmonary arteries in rapidly frozen lobes. In the same series of experiments these small vessels were actively narrowed by 10 per cent CO_2 in nitrogen. Thus, the role of CO_2 and [H+] on the pulmonary circulation is still not completely settled but most evidence indicates that in the presence of alveolar hypoxia, at least, acidosis has an additive and possibly a synergistic effect on pulmonary vascular resistance.

The time course of onset and cessation of the hypoxic vasoconstrictor response must be accounted for by any proposed mechanism. Fortunately, there is not much controversy over what happens. In the majority of animals examined the time course is rapid. In the cat Bergofsky & Holtzman (32) found that the response began within the first minute and was complete within 5 min. This coincides with the time period of 5–10 min used by Kato & Staub (19) in the cat lung which they rapidly froze to determine the dimensions of the small muscular pulmonary arteries. In the newborn calf, Silove & Grover (37) found a marked increase in pulmonary vascular resistance within the first minute of acute alveolar hypoxia. They also noted that the response continues to build for 2 to 3 min more. In fetal lamb Campbell (10) noted very rapid changes in pulmonary vascular resistance within 15 sec of changing perfusate oxygen tension and pH. Lopez-Majano (24) studied unilateral hypoxia in man and showed that within 2 min of the beginning of 100 per cent nitrogen ventilation to one lung, the hypoxic blood flow shift was 50 per cent of its final value which had previously been determined after 7 min of nitrogen ventilation. A similar result was obtained by Arborelius (20). In the isolated rat lung with constant pulsatile blood flow, Hauge (18) needed periods of only 2 min of hypoxic ventilation to evoke major changes in pulmonary vascular resistance. Indeed, his data showed continuous increases in pulmonary artery perfusion pressure throughout the 2 min test period. The return to room air ventilation was more rapid than the onset, which may be simply a manifestation of the higher pulmonary artery transmural pressure at the onset of recovery or may be significant in its own right.

Only in the rabbit does there appear to be a slow time course of the hypoxic vasoconstriction. Dale (22) studied the anesthetized rabbit, determining distribution of blood flow unilaterally by the Xe^{133} method while one lung rebreathed from a bag and the other lung breathed room air. The shift in blood flow away from the hypoxic, hypercapnic lung reached its maximum in approximately 20 min and was maintained for up to 3 hr.

It seems probable that we can rule out a prime role for the autonomic nervous system or circulating catecholamines as the mechanism of the acute hypoxic vasoconstriction. This does not mean that these factors are not important under some conditions, especially in the regulation of the volume distensibility of the central circulation. Campbell (10, 11) showed in the fetus that the pulmonary vasculature responds with vigorous, active constriction to hypoxia and acidemia even before the sympathetic nervous system becomes functionally active, but in mature fetuses that there is a small additional increase in resistance which is blocked by hexamethonium or cutting the sympathetic nerves. Silove & Grover (37) showed that neither α-adrenergic blockade (phenoxybenzamine) nor depletion of body stores of catecholamines by reserpine had any effect on the pulmonary vascular response to hypoxia in the newborn calf. Isoproterenol, a β-adrenergic stimulator, significantly decreased pulmonary vascular resistance during hypoxia.

Thilenius (38) found that α-blockade had no effect on the pulmonary arterial pressure rise or calculated pulmonary vascular resistance increase in response to inhalation of 10 per cent oxygen in unanesthetized dogs. With β-blockade (propranolol) the acute hypoxic rise in pulmonary artery pressure and calculated pulmonary vascular resistance was greater than before blockade. Hauge, Lunde & Waaler (39) examined the effects of catecholamines and adrenergic blocking agents on pulmonary blood volume and vascular resistance in isolated, blood-perfused cat and rabbit lungs. Epinephrine and norepinephrine decreased pulmonary blood volume as measured by continuous weighting of the specimens. This effect on the capacitance vessels was blocked by α-adrenergic blockade. Beta-adrenergic blockade did not affect pulmonary blood volume. Epinephrine usually decreased pulmonary vascular resistance whereas norepinephrine infusions normally increased it. The duration of the catecholamine response was about 30 min, which is incompatible with the time course of the hypoxic response in cats although it may be compatible in rabbits. Hauge (18) used the isolated, perfused rat lung and found in seven of ten experiments after α-adrenergic blockade that the pulmonary vasoconstrictor response to infused arterenol was abolished but the hypoxic vasoconstrictor response was not. In one of the three experiments that showed a reduction of the hypoxic response there was evidence that the blocking agent was acting nonspecifically to depress all forms of pulmonary vasoconstriction.

Only one major study supports an important role for catecholamines. Barer (14) investigated the reactivity of the pulmonary vasculature in the cat, both in collapsed and in ventilated lung lobes, in response to drugs and hypoxia. She found no effect of acute bilateral denervation of the lungs on the hypoxic response nor was there any definite change in pulmonary vascular resistance after adrenalectomy in four cats. However, after α-blockade the vasoconstrictor response during hypoxemia was completely abolished. In addition, after chronic catecholamine depletion (reserpine) in sixteen cats the response to acute alveolar hypoxia was diminished in a larger fraction than in forty control cats. Barer concluded that catecholamines might be involved in the hypoxic vasoconstrictor response although she admitted that this explanation entailed several problems. The blocking agents she used also reduced the pulmonary vasoconstrictor responses to other substances (5-hydroxytryptamine and histamine). Therefore, they were acting somewhat nonspecifically.

There is new evidence that low oxygen has a direct, specific action on the smooth muscle of the pulmonary arteries. Bergofsky & Holtzman (32) studied the effects of hypoxia on isolated specimens of pulmonary and systemic vascular smooth muscle. Hypoxia caused a reversible loss of potassium from the pulmonary artery specimens but there was no effect on pulmonary veins or systemic arteries. They calculated that the resting transmembrane potential of pulmonary artery smooth muscle cells decreased during hypoxia from 57 to 50 mV. They suggested that the decrease in transmembrane potential might sensitize the smooth muscle to other factors although it did not cause an increase in active tension by itself. They perfused isolated cat lungs with blood containing slight increases in potassium and showed that this increased the hypoxic vasoconstrictor response within a minute, which is well within the time course of the hypoxic response for cat lung. In a previous paper, Bergofsky (40) had studied the length-tension response of pulmonary artery strips from guinea pig and dog. When the nutrient bath was equilibrated with 3 per cent oxygen, the tension of the muscle strips was about 20 per cent greater at any given stretch compared to the same strip when the nutrient bath was equilibrated with 21 per cent oxygen. Neither pulmonary vein nor systemic arteries showed this effect of hypoxia. He admitted that the direct responses to hypoxia were small and suggested that in addition to the reversible potassium loss and lowering of transmembrane potential in hypoxia, there must be other factors in the hypoxic response in the intact lung.

These nice experiments of Bergofsky are clouded by the fact that Lloyd (41) did not confirm them. He found in isolated pulmonary artery strips from dogs and rabbits that nutrient bath anoxia or increase in [H+] depressed the tension in the muscle strips. He did find that increasing extracellular potassium ion increased the responsiveness of the strips to stimuli such as norepinephrine, but that anoxia and acidosis still depressed muscle tension.

I do not know the reason for the disagreement between the two investigators—they seem to have used similar technics. One difference is that Bergofsky used 3 per cent oxygen as his hypoxic P_{O_2} whereas Lloyd generally used 0 per cent oxygen. The more profound hypoxia used by Lloyd may have overwhelmed any increase in excitability by directly depressing cell metabolism related to the contractile mechanism. In Bergofsky's experiments, minimal oxygen was present for the maintenance of contractility but was decreased enough to affect the excitability of the cell. I am impressed by the selectivity that Bergofsky has found for the hypoxic potassium leakage and decrease in transmembrane potential in the pulmonary arteries. It is difficult to believe that it is not a real and important feature.

Another development is the implication of histamine in the hypoxic vasoconstrictor response. While studying the cardiopulmonary effect of tobacco on the dog lung, Aviado, Samanek & Folle (21) found in perfused dog lobes that ventilation with nitrogen increased the concentration of histamine in the lobar venous blood. The changes averaged more than 10 μg per liter of plasma. Barer (14) noted that histamine was a more potent vaso-constrictor in the cat lung than was norepinephrine. She tended to dismiss any physiologic role for histamine, however, because the antihistaminic drug mepyramine did not abolish the effect of hypoxia on pulmonary vessels although sometimes it diminished it. The problem with pharmacological agents is that they may have separate effects of their own. Altura & Zweifach (42) have shown that in the systemic circulation antihistamines may have a direct action of their own on the vascular smooth muscle. Thus, whether antihistaminic drugs affect hypoxic vascular resistance does not necessarily rule histamine in or out.

Barer & McCurrie (43) have modified Barer's (14) position because they now find that the histamine-releasing agent 48/80 markedly reduces or completely abolishes the hypoxic vasoconstrictor response in cat lung lobes for periods up to an hour.

Hauge (18) and Hauge & Melmon (44), using the isolated, blood-perfused rat lung, reported a strong correlation between factors that either activate or inhibit lung histamine and the vasoconstrictor response to hypoxia, while at the same time showing that other vasoactive agents (catecholamines, bradykinin, ATP, serotonin) were not well correlated to the response. Hauge showed that the histaminase-inhibiting compound semicarbazide potentiated hypoxic pressor responses and that 48/80, alone or with the histidine decarboxylase inhibitor NSD 1055, completely abolished the alveolar hypoxic pressor response when these agents reduced lung hista-mine by 90 per cent. The warning about overinterpreting pharmacological tests can be raised against Hauge's work; however, the arguments have less force here because he used several different types of agents and he always tested his preparations for responsiveness to other substances which should have revealed various nonspecific depressant effects.

If lung histamine is involved in the hypoxic response, this would be another physiological role for this ubiquitous compound. Kahlson & Rosen-gren (45) have recently reviewed the current thinking about histamine for-mation and its role in physiological regulation. Histamine is often present in tissues in a preformed state but it can also be produced as needed through enzyme induction by appropriate stimuli (histamine-forming capacity). In the case of the hypoxic response in the lung the time course is very rapid

for most animals, which is incompatible with induction of histamine synthesis. But it is well within the time course expected for release of stored
histamine. An unknown factor here is what aspect of the histamine metabolic
process would be sensitive to oxygen at the relatively high partial pressures
that evoke the vasoconstrictor response. Oxygen (18) is directly involved
only in the breakdown of histamine to an inactive form. Histamine release
from a storage site close to the small muscular pulmonary arteries or within
the muscle cells may be sensitive to the local tissue oxygen tension.

It is possible to make a hypothesis that relates histamine to the direct
effects of hypoxia on the pulmonary artery smooth muscle. The primary
hypoxic event in the lung may be the change in excitability of the smooth
muscle cells. It is not necessary for histamine to rise above its normal level
because the increased excitability of the smooth muscle would make the
normal histamine levels more effective. Thus histamine is the humoral factor
Bergofsky postulated (40) and it explains why tissue histamine levels are
correlated with the hypoxic response. It also removes the problem of the
high Po_2 threshold, at least as far as histamine release or metabolism is
concerned. The apparently negative findings of Lloyd in severe hypoxia (41)
are explained by the presence of histamine in the intact lung which together
with increased membrane excitability more than overcomes any direct
hypoxic depression of the contractile machinery's metabolism.

OXYGEN TOXICITY

Oxygen toxicity is reviewed in every symposium and book on hyperbaric oxygenation (46). The chief questions are: 1. Is there a basic difference
between the acute pulmonary toxicity in animals exposed to high oxygen
pressures and that which develops slowly without overt central nervous
system dysfunction when breathing oxygen at one atmosphere or less? 2. Is
there a threshold below which no life shortening or organ system pathology
occurs? 3. What are the principal oxygen-sensitive elements in the lung or
are the pulmonary manifestations secondary to systemic oxygen toxicity?

Haugaard (47) reviewed the cellular biochemical basis for oxygen
toxicity but with only scant reference to the lung. He did, however, discuss
the peroxidation of lipids, which is relevant to the controversy about the
effect of high oxygen partial pressure on alveolar surfactant. According to
current knowledge (48) the pulmonary surface-active material is phospholipid and contains many unsaturated double bonds in the fatty acid
chains.

Two groups provide evidence that surfactant in the lung is adversely
affected by high oxygen. Webb and co-workers (49) exposed adult guinea
pigs and rats to 4 atm of oxygen for 1 to 6 hr, killed the animals, and prepared
saline extracts from minced lung samples. There were no changes in maximum or minimum surface tension for 4 hr in rats and 2 hr in guinea pigs.
After these times there was a marked increase in minimum surface tension
and a slight increase in the maximum surface tension as well as a reduction

in the area of the hysteresis loop of the surface tension-area diagram. These results were correlated with progressive histologic lung changes consisting of capillary congestion, alveolar edema, and focal atelectasis. The authors concluded that there was a loss of surfactant and suggested that the oxygen directly attacks the unsaturated fatty acids in the phospholipid moiety of surfactant. This is possible, but in animals with pulmonary edema the surface tension of minced lung extracts can be interpreted in other ways. For example, there are substances in edema fluid capable of inhibiting surfactant. The correlation between changes in surface tension and lung pathology is important but correlation does not prove cause and effect. The authors do not mention whether any of their animals convulsed although the oxygen pressures and time of exposure are such that rats and guinea pigs should show severe central nervous system effects.

Lee and associates (50) followed anesthetized dogs breathing 100 per cent oxygen at 1 atm pressure for 24–30 hr. Compared to animals breathing air under similar conditions, the high oxygen-breathing dogs showed elevations in minimal surface tension of saline lung extracts. The authors took their lung samples from "hypostatic" areas of the lung, that is, areas which looked to be in the poorest condition. They concluded that an inhibition or absence of surfactant was probably an important element in the pulmonary damage of prolonged high oxygen therapy. One interesting aspect of their studies was that in a few dogs they ventilated only one lung with oxygen for 6 hr. They found that this lung had an increase in minimal surface tension relative to the air-breathing control lung. The importance of this experiment is that the arterial blood was at relatively normal Po_2 and therefore systemic hyperoxia was not contributing to the pulmonary derangement.

On the other hand, Fisher and co-workers (51) studied six young men breathing oxygen at 2 atm for 6 to 11 hr. All showed respiratory symptomatology (dry cough and substernal burning pains during inspiration). The symptoms increased with duration of oxygen exposure although chest X rays taken immediately after the experiment were interpreted as normal. Vital capacity decreased about 10 per cent and lung compliance decreased 16 per cent. There was a small increase in measured airway resistance. The authors felt the vital capacity decrease may have been a conscious or reflex restriction of inspiratory effort since FRC (functional residual capacity) and RV (residual volume) were not altered. They tried to relate the compliance changes to as many factors as they could think of, among these being changes in alveolar surfactant. Actually, the changes found were minimal and indicate no serious derangement of surfactant under the conditions specified.

If the problem of surfactant is still confused, then the problem of carbon monoxide pulmonary diffusing capacity, DL, and oxygen toxicity is chaotic. In strict time sequence, Caldwell and associates (52) studied four men breathing 98 per cent oxygen at 1 atm for periods of 30–74 hr. Single-breath DL was determined before and after the exposure, including the subdivisions DM (diffusing capacity of the alveolar-capillary membrane) and Vc (pulmonary capillary blood volume). Vital capacity decreased roughly proportional to the duration of the exposure. DL immediately after the exposure period was decreased compared to the precontrols and the recovery controls done later. Vc was not significantly altered but DM decreased. These effects were noticed after 40 hr exposure. In spite of negative chest X rays the authors implicated alveolar edema to explain the results. However, the ratio of DL/VA was relatively constant at all stages, that is, the depression of DL correlated well with the reduction in total lung capacity. Maybe the decrease in DM was due to less stretching of the alveolar capillary membrane at reduced volume.

Rosenberg & MacLean (53) observed eight men breathing oxygen at 1 or 3 atm for periods up to 3 hr. They measured single-breath DL 5 min after return to room air at normal pressure. One hundred per cent oxygen at 1 atm had no effect on any of the measurements whereas 100 per cent oxygen at 3 atm for 2 hr had no effect on overall DL but did increase DL/VA in two of six subjects. Using shorter periods of oxygen at 3 atm, they demonstrated an increase in DL/VA in all subjects. The authors interpret their evidence in terms of an increase in pulmonary capillary blood volume.

Puy and associates (54) investigated the same six male subjects breathing 100 per cent oxygen at 2 atm for 6 to 11 hr in whom pulmonary mechanics were measured (51). They measured DL, DM, and Vc as well as pulmonary blood flow, Q̇c, and pulmonary tissue volume, Vt. There was no consistent change in DL while the subjects were in the hyperbaric chamber, but it decreased 9 per cent after they left the chamber. Interestingly, there was a further drop in DL 12–20 hr later. A decrease in Vc accounted for the decreased DL. DM actually increased. They found no change in Q̇c and an insignificant decrease in Vt. These results give no support for pulmonary edema or capillary congestion. The authors agree that a redistribution of diffusing capacity with respect to lung volume is possible, but they believe that their findings are better explained by a direct toxic effect of oxygen on the pulmonary capillaries. The thing that intrigues me is the continued decline in diffusing capacity for up to 2 days following the high oxygen exposure. This is not discussed by the authors and is opposite to the findings of the other workers who showed that any changes, regardless of the direction, tended to recover shortly after leaving the exposure chamber.

There are new pathologic studies relevant to oxygen toxicity in lungs. Kistler, Caldwell & Weibel (55) exposed rats to 98.5 per cent oxygen at one atmosphere for 6–72 hr. After varying time intervals they examined the lungs grossly, microscopically, and by quantitative electron microscopy. Lung pathology was first seen at 48 hr. By 72 hr most of the animals showed severe lung damage with up to two thirds of all the alveoli filled with exudate. Microscopically, the alveolar septae were thickened, mainly by interstitial edema fluid. The alveolar epithelial cells and the granular pneumonocytes, appeared normal. It was the endothelial lining of the alveolar capillaries that showed severe damage. In many places the capillaries were obliterated by necrotic debris. At 72 hr the average air to blood pathlength was approximately twice that seen in normal control animals, almost entirely because of an increase in the interstitial barrier by edema fluid. The total number of capillaries was decreased approximately 50 per cent. The authors calculated that D_L was decreased by about 75 per cent after 72 hr, and concluded that oxygen is primarily toxic to the pulmonary vascular endothelium.

Similar experiments are reported by Schaffner, Felig & Trachtenberg (56) in rats exposed for 10 days to oxygen at nearly 1 atm. The alveolar septae were slightly thickened and hypercellular but the pulmonary capillaries well preserved, although occasionally endothelial cells were lifted slightly from the capillary basement membrane. The authors believe the main pathology is an edematous thickening of the alveolar-capillary membrane with a possible decrease in D_L because of the increased air to blood path. To account for the interstitial edema they concluded that the endothelial cells are more permeable than normal. Both types of alveolar epithelial cells are relatively insensitive to high oxygen.

There is considerable difference between Kistler's and Schaffner's studies. Kistler's rats were terminal after 3 days while Schaffner's animals were still active after 10 days. The lung damage reported by the former is far more advanced than that reported by the latter. Why? Is it reasonable to expect such variations between breeds of rats? Is there an additional factor in the environment of one group? Maybe the peak of lung damage occurs at 3 days and then there is recovery so that by 10 days the lung looks nearly normal.

Davis (57) cultured guinea pig lung slices for 14 days. The gross structure of the lungs was maintained for 6 to 7 days but subtle changes could be noted as early as 1 hr after explantation. Most interestingly, he saw the first signs of change in the endothelial lining of the pulmonary capillaries. Capillary structure began to break down after about 3 days. This sensitivity of the capillary endothelium in culture should be compared to the selective sensitivity of the same cells in the presence of high oxygen. In fact, it may be the high P_{O_2} in the culture chamber that caused the changes.

Brooksby and associates (58) studied rats maintained in enriched oxygen for 5 weeks and ten beagle dogs kept in 60 per cent oxygen at normal barometric pressure for 33 days. Every week some of the animals were killed and their lungs examined. During the first 2 weeks both groups of animals showed pulmonary edema and focal hemorrhages but in general the alveoli and bronchi appeared normal. The edema was in the perivascular spaces around the larger blood vessels. Beginning at about 3 weeks, the edema fluid became organized. There was rupture of alveolar septae with enlargement of the airspaces which contained considerable cellular debris. At 5 weeks the lungs showed large bullae. It was difficult to distinguish the pathology from emphysema. In the dogs, pulmonary angiograms during life revealed progressive enlargement of the pulmonary artery. The small pulmonary arteries did not fill, which correlated well with large increases in calculated vascular resistance. The authors believe the primary defect lies in the pulmonary vascular bed; the defect is characterized initially by hemorrhage and edema followed by disintegration of alveolar walls. Of special interest is that the dogs had only been breathing 60 per cent oxygen. The belief that inspired oxygen concentrations up to 0.6 atm are harmless (46) is not a safe conclusion.

Bean, Zee & Thom (59) made a strong case for the pulmonary oxygen damage being secondary to systemic, particularly central nervous system, effects. The lung pathology following exposure to convulsive agents is very similar to that seen in oxygen poisoning where the animals die in convulsions. Anesthetics, hypophysectomy, adrenalectomy, and sympathetic blockade gave protection to the lung. Their data suggest that high oxygen leads to excessive autonomic discharge and an overactive pituitary-adrenal stress response. The studies were done with short-term oxygen exposures at 3 or more atm total pressure. The authors feel, however, that the pulmonary damage from oxygen exposure at 1 atm is similar to that seen after exposures to high pressures.

Jamieson & Cass (60) do not agree that the pulmonary effects are secondary to those in the central nervous system. In young anesthetized rats exposed to 4 to 7 atm of oxygen with or without added CO_2, they followed EEG, diaphragmatic electromyogram (EMG), tracheal air flow, and heart rate. The animals died in ventilatory failure due to pulmonary consolidation. At the time of death, although the EEG was silent, the EMG continued to fire actively. They interpret their results as showing cerebral depression but with persistent brainstem function and claim that this proves a dissociation between central nervous system and pulmonary manifestations of oxygen toxicity. I do not see how they can draw such a conclusion, especially when the first change they noted was a depression of the EEG.

The only experiment that I would accept as showing whether high oxygen has a direct toxic effect on the lung would be if the lung could be made the sole hyperoxic organ. Earlier I mentioned an experiment along this line in which Lee and co-workers (50) used a tracheal divider in dogs and ventilated one lung with 100 per cent oxygen. They avoided systemic hyperoxia and still showed changes in minimal surface tension of saline extracts of the hyperoxic lung.

A more sophisticated investigation is that of Winter and associates (61) who made vena caval to arterial shunts in ten dogs so that about half of the cardiac output bypassed the lung. They compared these animals breathing 100 per cent oxygen at 2.5 atm with ten dogs that had no lung bypass. The dogs were awake and unmedicated at the time of exposure. The ten unoperated dogs convulsed at 5 to 7 hr and died after 12 hr. The ten operated dogs never convulsed but they all died in about 21 hr. A few additional dogs with venoarterial shunts were killed at 12 hr to compare with the unoperated dogs. At the time of spontaneous death both operated and unoperated dogs had similar lung pathology. The lungs were diffusely consolidated with focal hemorrhagic areas. The shunt dogs that were killed at 12 hr had normal-appearing lungs. The authors conclude that an important component of oxygen toxicity depends upon elevations in the arterial blood oxygen tension but that, in addition, there is a direct effect of oxygen in the lung. While this conclusion is certainly justified, there is still a small possibility that the oxygen toxicity may be via the blood passing through the pulmonary vascular bed rather than directly on the vascular endothelium itself.

PULMONARY STRUCTURE AND FUNCTION

Growth, development and aging of the lung.—Reid (62) briefly reviewed the embryology of the human lung and described three laws of development: 1. The bronchial tree is developed by the 16th week of gestation. 2. The alveolus, as it is commonly understood, is a postnatal development both in size and number. 3. The pulmonary vascular bed is extensively remodeled with postnatal lung growth.

There is little argument about the bronchial tree development; in fact, Boyden (63) adds further evidence that the distal bronchioles are converted into respiratory tissue with alveoli. The number of conducting airway generations decreases after birth. Emery & Wilcock (64) studied a uniform slice from the right middle lobe in humans ranging from newborn to 68 years and found some increase in airway growth in the last trimester of gestation, but agree that there is no increase in the number of conducting airways after birth.

The concept that alveolar growth is mainly a postnatal development apparently shocked some participants in the CIBA Symposium on Development of the Lung (65). Reid's explanation, however, was quite clear. The terminal airspaces at birth are large and, at most, show rudimentary alveolar partitions. It is an argument of terms whether these spaces should be called alveoli since there are so few of them relative to the adult (66). All workers agree that the number of alveoli increases dramatically from birth through childhood. Whether the total complement of adult alveoli is present at age 8 as Dunnill (66) determined or continues to increase through puberty (64, 67) is not completely settled.

The process of alveolar growth is extremely rapid shortly after birth (63, 68, 69) and the true alveoli stay relatively constant in size until puberty at which time alveolar size increases as the chest volume increases (64). Fuest, Haas & Schmitz (70) hold, however, that alveoli increase in size all during life. In 36 human lungs, fixed in the unopened thorax, they compared upper lobe alveoli with lower lobe alveoli. Up to 10 years of age the lower lobe alveoli were larger. Between the ages 20–40 the alveoli in both lobes were the same size. After 40 the upper lobe alveoli tended to be larger. It is difficult to know whether this is a real phenomenon or somehow related to the technical aspects of the method. It certainly does not agree with Glazier's (71) findings in dogs.

Most interest is centered on the problem of the mechanism of new alveolar formation. The terminal respiratory units grow, not by distal extension of the alveolar ducts and alveoli but by conversion of respiratory bronchioles into alveolar duct systems and terminal bronchioles into respiratory bronchioles (63). Boyden finds the single most rapid period of alveolar growth in the human is in the first 2 months of life.

Weibel (69) studied the growth of the rat lung from birth. He agrees with Reid that the newborn terminal air sacs are not proper alveoli. The partitions between sacs are thick, usually containing two capillary networks—one facing each sac. For the first 5 days lung volume and surface area increase proportionately, which indicates some formation of new air units. Very suddenly, between the 5th and 10th day, there is a tremendous increase in the number of alveoli. Weibel believes this rapid formation of new alveoli is by ingrowth of partitions containing capillaries into the primitive sacs. From the 10th day until adulthood, alveolar surface area increases nearly linearly with lung volume, which indicates a continued increase in the number and size of alveoli.

Weibel reports that the surface area of capillaries increases at about the same rate as the alveolar surface area in the rat but Fuest and co-workers (70) claim that during the period of increasing alveolar size (puberty and after) the capillary net does not increase but the meshwork becomes more separated. According to this concept the maximal pulmonary capillary volume is reached at the same time the number of alveoli stops increasing. Weibel, however, calculates that capillary volume continues to increase to adulthood and does not find the capillary mesh any wider in the adult than in the young rat.

The third developmental law is that of remodeling of the vasculature with lung growth. Reid comments on the growth of new capillaries which must occur as new alveoli are formed. She then uses the finding of "supernumerary" pulmonary artery branches (72) as further evidence of remodeling. This aspect of her work is not clear. I do not see how the postnatal growth of the terminal respiratory units would influence pulmonary artery development which occurs along with airway growth early in gestation (Reid's first law).

I am not completely convinced about the supernumerary vessels, partly because the published evidence is skimpy (72). I find it difficult to understand how the supernumerary arteries can contribute up to 45 per cent of the cross-sectional area of all pulmonary artery branches at a given level and yet show no evidence of filling on angiograms.

Sharply contrasted to the pulmonary vascular bed in early life is its almost total inertness in the adult. Except for brief reports by Pratt (73) and

Kleinerman (74), I am not aware of any substantial evidence that pulmonary vessels can grow or regenerate in the adult.

Plank (75) compared the fluid-filled fetal lung with the aerated lung of the newborn. In lungs of stillborn babies fixed in the thorax, the alveoli were not collapsed but were filled with fluid. The author states the walls were tortuous with many club-shaped projections on top of which there was always a blood-filled capillary. He regards this appearance as pathognomonic of liquid-filled alveoli. I agree that the alveoli look this way in liquid-filled alveoli (76), but this is not pathognomonic of the liquid-filled lung. It is also seen in the air-filled lung at low volume where the alveolar walls fold up (77, 78). Plank found the fluid-filled lung before birth to be uniformly inflated whereas in newborns that had breathed, most terminal air spaces were rounded and obviously well aerated but intermingled with these were atelectatic alveoli.

Nakamura, Takizawa & Morone (67) studied nine normal human lungs covering the period from birth to 68 years. The number of alveoli developed very rapidly in the infant but continued to increase until about 20 years of age. In adults about 60 per cent of the terminal air (alveolar volume) was in anatomical alveoli. The other 40 per cent was in the alveolar ducts. After age 40 the alveolar ducts get larger at the expense of the alveolar fraction.

Airways.—Beginning with the measurement of airway size in lungs fixed by uniform, modern methods (79), a number of workers have pointed out that most of the calculated airway resistance is not in the bronchioles but in the cartilagenous bronchi, that is, airways greater than 1 mm diameter in man (78, 80). Macklem & Mead (81) have now confirmed this by physiologic techniques in anesthetized dogs and cats and in isolated lungs from man, monkey, and dog. They used a tiny polyethylene catheter running peripherally through the lung parenchyma and wedged into 1.5–2.5 mm diameter airways with the open tip facing the bronchus proximal to it. They were able to apportion total lung resistance (RL) into a peripheral resistance (Rp) between the catheter and alveoli and a central resistance (Rc) between the catheter and the trachea. RL decreased as lung volume increased. Rp at minimal lung volume (10 per cent TLC) was only 15 per cent of RL, decreased steadily as lung volume increased, and became negligible at about 80 per cent TLC. Since Rp includes a small unknown component of lung tissue viscous resistance, the actual air flow resistance in the bronchioles is even less than reported. Thus the first several generations of cartilagenous bronchi account for most of the lung airway resistance and most of the lung anatomic deadspace. If we add to this the upper airway (mouth to carina) which accounts for about half of the total airway resistance and about half of the total anatomic deadspace, we find that the contribution of the small peripheral airways to total resistance is less than 10 per cent. This means that there can be marked changes in bronchiolar size without much change in measured airway resistance. Finally, since most of the airway resistance is in a common path, one would expect that the terminal respiratory units would be ventilated in proportion to their compliances and receive proportionate fractions of deadspace gas during inspiration.

Wilson (82) analyzed the design of the bronchial tree, using minimum entropy production as the fundamental biological design criterion. He derived a formula for the diameter of any given airway as a function of tracheal diameter and airway generation number. Plotting his equation for airway size and the measured airway size of Weibel & Gomez (79), he obtains an excellent fit for all airways from the trachea down to about 1 mm diameter, which includes the first ten generations of airways. This is an adequate fit, since by our discussion above most of R_L is in these cartilagenous bronchi. The equation is said to fit quite well over a wide range of breathing frequencies and ventilation rates, which suggests that the large airways do not change much in size during normal breathing.

Data by Hyatt & Flath (83) show similar results in that neither large nor small cartilagenous airways, whether within the lung or dissected free, show much change in diameter above 3 or 4 cm H_2O transairway pressure. Thus, if transpulmonary pressure is 3 to 5 cm H_2O at FRC, there will be little change in large airway size as lung volume increases and decreases above this level.

The Hyatt & Flath study indicates that transairway pressure in the intact lung is approximately the same as in the excised lung, that is, the pressure in the peribronchial space is not much different from pleural pressure. Earlier indirect evidence had suggested that pressure external to the large conducting blood vessels and presumably to the airways may be considerably more negative than pleural pressure in the closed chest. I hope that a direct determination of pressure in the perivascular and peribronchial interstitial spaces of the lung will soon be available to settle this issue.

Horsfield & Cumming (84, 85) have made a complete anatomical analysis of airway diameter, length, and branching in a resin cast of the lungs of a young man. This is a tedious chore, and the authors are to be congratulated on having completed it. They measured every airway branch from the trachea down to 700 μ maximum diameter. Beyond this point they resorted to a selective sampling technique. They make the novel suggestion that it is more meaningful to number airway generations from the terminal airway up to the trachea rather than the other way around. Under such a scheme airways of similar size and functional connotation have the same number. The reason is that the real lung is not formed by symmetrical dichotomy as was well known to anatomists (86) but has sometimes been lost sight of as a result of the simplified statistical lung described by Weibel & Gomez (79). A knowledge of the real lung's airways is important to the understanding of various forms of uneven ventilation (87, 88).

The 700 μ airways ranged from 8 to 22 generations from the trachea, average 14 to 15. The pathlength a gas molecule would have to follow from the trachea to this point varied from 7 to 21 cm; average 13 to 14 cm. The cumulative airway volume expressed as a transit time (ratio of the volume along a given airway to the volume of the lung distal to the final measured airway) shows less variation than the other two measurements (85). This is expected because most of the airway volume is in the larger common airways. In another paper Horsfield & Cumming (84) made a theoretical analysis of the airways on the basis of design for minimal work. Their result is identical to that of Wilson (82) in that there must be a compromise between airway size for low flow resistance and airway volume for low deadspace. On their airway cast, they measured the dimensional and branching angle relationships between parent and daughter airways and found that the real lung is quite close to the ideal pattern for minimal resistance and that the angle of airway branching is very close to that predicted for minimum volume and resistance. The relationship best fits airways greater than 1 mm diameter, which I take to be another confirmation of the findings of Macklem & Mead (81).

Finally, Olsen and his co-workers (89–91) made an elegant correlation of structure and function of the trachea and larger bronchi to test the hypothesis that reflex bronchoconstriction might stabilize airways under compressive and distensive forces. In anesthetized cats they showed (89) that reflex bronchoconstriction decreases the distensibility of the conducting airways and decreases anatomical deadspace in proportion to decreases in airway conductance $(1/R_L)$. In isolated trachea and bronchi they (90) showed that when the trachea and bronchi were constricted by adding acetylcholine to the organ bath they were much more rigid and maintained their patency better under compressive pressures. Finally, by rapid freezing of the isolated airways Olsen (91) demonstrated how the airways can become rigid. In the relaxed trachea the membraneous portion bulges out under distending pressures and folds in under compressive pressures obliterating most of the lumen. When the trachea constricts, however, the smooth muscle pulls the cartilage edges into an overlapping configuration, creating a solid circumference so the lumen of the trachea is maintained even under large compressive pressures. A similar event occurs in the cartilagenous bronchi, although there the cartilage plates are irregular and interconnected by fibrous tissue. The pictures of contracted and relaxed bronchi under compressive pressures show quite convincingly that the contracted ones maintain a larger lumen. The mechanism appears to be that the contraction of the endobronchial muscle pulls the cartilages into an overlapping, interdigitating position, effectively locking them together.

Alveoli: size, shape, and surface area.—The adage that the size of the package does not always determine the value of the goods certainly applies to the beautiful paper of Dunnill (92) in which he measured the volume fractions of alveoli, alveolar ducts, and calculated alveolar surface area as a function of the degree of lung inflation. This is the first really quantitative data relating these parameters during lung volume changes. He made the study on twelve lungs from six healthy greyhounds by fixing the lungs at different inflation pressures with formalin fumes. Total lung volume ranged from 350 to 1800 ml. The volume of alveoli and alveolar ducts ranged from 51–63 per cent and from 24 to 38 per cent of total lung volume, respectively. The remainder consisted of tissue and vascular elements. Of the total alveolar gas volume, V_A, about two thirds are in the anatomical alveoli and one third is in the alveolar ducts (76, 79, 92). The volume fraction of alveoli tended to increase with increasing lung volume at the expense of the alveolar ducts, but the data are scattered with only a few points at the extremes of lung volume. The alveolar surface area increases similarly with both total lung volume and alveolar volume. One would anticipate from the surface/volume relation for a segment of a sphere that surface area would increase as volume to the two-thirds power. The regression lines of Dunnill's work have somewhat steeper slopes, suggesting that alveolar shape is not a segment of a sphere. An alternate suggestion is that the alveoli may change shape during lung inflation. Unfortunately, he did not study alveolar shape. Dunnill concludes that the increase in alveolar surface area with lung volume is important for diffusion of oxygen across the alveolar-capillary membrane. This is true insofar as the membrane is thinned and the red cells are brought closer to the gas phase, but it is not true that the actual surface area for diffusion increases. With alveolar expansion the capillary mesh is stretched and becomes wider (70). Only alveolar surface closely related to red blood cells in capillaries is relevant to gaseous diffusion; the remainder is wasted.

Thurlbeck (93) measured the alveolar surface area of the normal human lung as a function of body size and age. He used the linear intercept method in 25 pairs of nonemphysematous lungs from patients between 25 and 79 years of age. The lungs were fixed, prepared, and measured in a standard fashion. The range of surface area when corrected to predicted TLC was 40–100 m². This correlated best with body length. Surface area decreased slightly with advancing age. In another paper Thurlbeck (94) compares all the published data of alveolar surface area at a standard volume with respect to age. Alveolar surface area increases from birth up to the age of about 20 and then decreases slowly at the rate of about 2.7 m² per 10 years thereafter. The decrease is less than 20 per cent over a span of 40–50 years.

Thurlbeck is mainly interested in emphysema, and in two papers (94, 95) he assesses the current methods used to quantify emphysema. The three classes of method are: visual measurements, the linear intercept method for surface area, and mechanical measurements. The main problem with the visual measurements is that they involve judgments by the observer that have not been sufficiently checked for intra- and interobserver repeatability. In the linear intercept method there is the problem of preparing the lung in a standard fashion and the fact that the sampling is small relative to the size of the lung. This is emphasized in the second paper (95) wherein some lungs with mild but obvious alveolar wall destruction were within the normal values for lung surface area. Thurlbeck concludes that the quantitative histological assessment of the lung is not completely foolproof and that observer judgment still plays an essential role. There is really no reason why the objective evaluation cannot be reliable. It should be possible with current technology to develop automated methods for large-scale measurement of lung internal surface area. One group (96) has attempted this and another group is evaluating a less specific but more rapid mechanical method (97).

To evaluate the effects of gravity on regional lung expansion, Glazier and co-workers (71) measured the size of alveoli by the linear intercept method in different parts of the lungs of greyhounds frozen slowly in different body positions. They confirmed the radioactive gas studies of Milic-Emili and associates (98) which indicate that in the normal lung at end expiration the apical alveoli are at a much higher volume than the basal alveoli. In vertically suspended dogs the apical alveoli were three to four times larger than those at the base. The major change in alveolar size occurred over the upper 10 cm of these 25–30 cm long lungs. In other experiments they showed that alveoli at any given hydrostatic level were the same size regardless of their location in the lung and that alveoli taken from the peripheral edge of the lung were no different from alveoli taken centrally. Any effects of body position or intrapulmonary location on alveolar size are not inherent within the anatomical structure but must be functional differences due to regional variations in transpulmonary pressure. The one unexpected finding was that in dogs frozen head-down, alveolar size was nearly the same at all levels.

The authors develop a theory to explain the differences in alveolar size both in the normal and in the inverted lung on the basis of the changing cross-sectional area of the lung from apex to base. Assuming that each horizontal cross section of the lung supports the weight of the lung below it, the smaller cross-sectional area of the upper lung must have a correspondingly greater expanding pressure (PTP). This appears to explain both the rapid change in alveolar size over the upper 10 cm of the normal vertical dog lung and the uniformity of alveolar size in the inverted dogs.

The authors' analysis of alveolus volume depends on whether the alveoli change shape over the range studied, since the linear intercept method assumes constant shape. They investigated this problem and found no evidence for a change in shape; an independent measure of lung alveolar shape suggests that over the range 25 to 100 per cent volume it may be considered as constant (77). One deficiency is in the proportion of alveolus to alveolar duct volume. Glazier states that the alveolar ducts make up about 9 to 12 per cent of the total alveolar volume both at the apex and the base, whereas Dunnill's (92) measurements in the same species show the average volume of alveolar ducts to be 33 per cent of the total alveolar volume. Apparently Glazier has included a large number of alveolar ducts in his alveolar volume fraction. This, however, is not too serious a problem if ducts and alveoli change volume proportionately. This is not quite true (92), but is close enough not to introduce a significant error.

Kuno & Staub (77) introduced a new technique for studying alveolar wall mechanics. Using fine tungsten microneedles, they made microholes 25 and

50 μ in diameter in alveolar walls of freshly excised air-inflated cat lungs. They studied the effects of lung volume upon the diameter of the holes by measuring their diameters in rapidly frozen lungs. Holes made during inflation and deflation at equal lung volumes were the same size. Holes made at increasing lung volume were somewhat larger than those made at lower lung volume. This is especially true at high transpulmonary pressures where the holes abruptly became quite large. Holes made at a fixed volume change size with lung volume. All of the holes closed up as the lung approached minimum volume, which in the cat is between 10 and 14 per cent of TLC. The resultant curves fit a cubic equation, as might be expected for a linear dimension against volume; not total volume but volume above minimum volume. Since the holes all close up, the authors interpret minimum volume as the point of zero tension in the alveolar walls and surface. Airway closure does not determine minimal volume under these conditions.

Calculating from the basic data, Kuno & Staub show that between about 25 and 100 per cent lung volume alveolar shape does not change significantly and alveolus volume is proportional to lung volume. At 10 per cent lung volume, alveolar surface area is 21 per cent of the maximum surface area. These data confirm the qualitative picture presented previously (78) that at low lung volume alveolar walls fold up with no further decrease in surface area and they also explain the tortuous alveolar walls seen in the fetus (75) and in pulmonary edema (76).

An interesting clinicopathologic correlation made both by Glazier (71) and by Kuno (77) is that injury to the alveolar walls, such as fenestrations, should be more serious events in the upper more expanded portion of the lung than in the lower zones. Greater expansion is not the only difference between the upper and lower lung, but it deserves to be emphasized because it has been generally overlooked.

Cavagna, Stemmler & DuBois (99) studied the mechanics of the lung at very low lung volumes. They showed in rabbits, cats, and dogs that the pressure-volume relation of the lung measured during oxygen absorption down to zero lung volume was very similar to that measured by very slow removal of air from the trachea with a syringe. The only possible explanation for the identity of the two curves is that the terminal airspaces of the lung are in direct continuity with the trachea, even with negative airway pressures. The finding of negative intrapulmonary pressures implies that the lungs resist collapse.

I see the process of deflation of the air-filled terminal respiratory units along their semistatic pressure-volume curve as follows. For most of the curve the alveoli and alveolar ducts maintain a nearly constant configuration and change volume proportionally (equal specific compliances). At or near FRC or RV some elastic recoil forces are relieved before others and the alveoli begin to change shape. The alveoli and ducts no longer have equal specific compliances. When the sum of all unit recoil forces equals zero (transterminal unit pressure equals zero), the unit is by definition at minimal volume.

There is no airway closure. If the terminal respiratory unit is to become still smaller, the alveolar walls can only fold up (like an accordion), thereby introducing distortion of elastic, collagen, and vascular networks and creating resistance to collapse. Major anatomical points still not completely determined are: the volume of onset and process of alveolus shape change, and the anatomical demonstration of the continuity of airways from trachea to alveolus at minimal volume.

The relevance of these considerations of minimal lung volume to normal upright man is that although lung FRC and RV are well above minimal volume, the gradient of lung size in the gravitational field (71, 98) implies that at these volumes the dependent terminal units may reach minimal volume. Under these conditions transpulmonary pressure at the base of the lungs would be zero. If the subject attempts to decrease lung volume further, transpulmonary pressure would go positive at the lung bases, causing airway collapse, gas trapping, and vascular compression. If there is any significant airway tone, there would be airway closure before minimal volume is reached. Milic-Emili and his associates (98) suggested that this may limit maximal expiration.

Leith & Mead (100), however, claimed that they could find no evidence of large or small airway closure at RV in either young or old normal subjects. In four of five men under 35 years they were able to obtain additional expired volume at RV by suddenly increasing pressure around the body to 40 cm H_2O, which indicates that the limitation of lung volume is more a matter of the balance of opposing forces in the chest wall than of airway closure. In five subjects over 40 years the maximal expiratory flow curves were considerably slower and in the majority little or no additional air could be forced out by suddenly increasing external pressure. They argued that the loss of lung elastic recoil with age reduced maximal expiratory flow rates and therefore it took longer to exhale through a given volume range. Thus, the older subjects never reached true residual volume but stopped expiring because of fatigue, lack of motivation, or limit of breath-holding ability.

I agree that the young and old subjects may have different mechanisms limiting overall lung RV, but the evidence does not rule out airway closure in the dependent portions of the lung. The critical experiment requires visualization of the regional airways during expiration to residual volume.

Ventilation/perfusion units.—There is now an adequate body of structural (71) and functional (17, 98) evidence to explain gross regional lung differences in ventilation and blood flow. The new problem is to quantify inhomogeneity of ventilation, perfusion, and ventilation/perfusion ratios within localized segments of the lung, that is, units distal to a given terminal conducting airway (for example, the terminal bronchiole).

Obviously, there must be a transition range between units that are far enough apart to be thought of as regionally separate and units that are so small and so close together that gas-phase diffusion from one unit to another may be thought of as complete within each breath (for example, two final-order alveolar ducts and their alveoli). Adjacent units that could not reach gas-phase diffusion equilibrium during a single breath would be responsible for local regional (parallel) inhomogeneity of ventilation.

During the review period a number of investigators have amassed considerable evidence that some of the local inhomogeneity is due to the fact that fresh air ventilation proceeds only into the proximal portion of the terminal air units [not to be confused with the terminal respiratory unit (78)] and there is not sufficient time for complete diffusion equilibrium to the deeper portions. The size of these terminal units is determined by the pattern of convective mixing of the fresh air ventilation during a single breath and would be responsible for local sequential (stratified) inhomogeneity of ventilation.

There is an analogous argument for parallel and stratified inhomogeneity of local blood flow and for ventilation/perfusion ratios.

Pulmonary blood flow reaches every portion of the available vascular bed by convective mixing. But during breathing, in addition to the airway deadspace, end-expiratory alveolar gas is present and the question is: Where does the fresh air go and to what extent does convective mixing occur in the terminal units? Muir (101), using aerosols which had essentially zero diffusivity, confirms earlier data in man that breaths of 0.5–2 liters from FRC over periods of 1–3 sec only mix with about 15 per cent of FRC convectively.

But what part of the FRC does that 15 per cent correspond to? We know from anatomical data (67, 79, 92) that alveolar duct volume constitutes about one third of alveolar volume. The maximal volumes inspired in Muir's experiments are just about sufficient to fill the alveolar duct fraction, which suggests that the anatomical alveoli get little or no fresh air mixed with them. If the volume of alveoli surrounding each alveolar duct is equal throughout the terminal unit, then fresh air ventilation is not stratified.

Read (102, 103) and Cumming (87, 104) take a different view. They suggest that the convective mixing occurs only in the proximal portion of the air unit (this requires both alveoli and ducts in that region to be convectively ventilated) and that gaseous diffusion is responsible for distal mixing. Both workers make extensive use of sequential expired gas analysis to support their theory and certainly their data are compatible with such a lung model.

This terminal air unit, however, must be represented anatomically in some way and it is in defining it that confusion has arisen. Gomez (105) calculated that a terminal bronchiole and all its distal respiratory bronchioles and alveolar duct systems constitute the functional unit of lung ventilation and perfusion (acinus). In man such units are ∼2–3 cm in length (104). Cumming and his associates (87, 104) claim that this unit is much too large not to have stratified ventilatory inhomogeneity within it. Read (102, 103) analyzes for stratified inhomogeneity in a unit consisting of a first-order respiratory bronchiole and all its distal subdivisions. It is about half the size of the acinus. Both Read and Cumming believe the functional unit is

conical, with its narrow end at the bronchiole and a wider base distally. I
believe such a model is incorrect. It is an unfortunate consequence of the use
of a statistical lung rather than a real lung. In my limited experience in this
field (78, 106) the terminal respiratory unit (TRU) based on Hayek's (86)
anatomical unit is the functionally significant unit. It consists of the last
order of respiratory bronchiole and all the alveolar duct systems distal to it.
The TRU is ~1/8 the size of Read's unit and 1/16 of Cumming's. Equally
important, it is not conical but spherical, with the respiratory bronchiole
actually opening near the center of the unit (78, 106). The upshot of this
argument is that there is undoubtedly local inhomogeneity in the lung. It is
partly a matter of terminology as to how much of the local inhomogeneity is
parallel and how much is stratified.

An additional factor of some importance for stratified inhomogeneity is
raised by Horsfield & Cumming (88) from their excellent quantitative
anatomical study of the airways (84, 85). Given several restrictive assumptions including (a) gas flows in a square front and (b) all units distal to corresponding airways are the same size and have the same compliance, the
authors show that in the time of a single breath the distal alveolar duct systems within the acinus have little time to receive fresh air and mix it by
diffusion, whereas those more proximal have much more time. On the other
hand, Kylstra, Paganelli & Rahn (107) have presented physiologic evidence
that in the fluid-filled lungs all alveolar duct systems receive a good basic
convective ventilation. I reported preliminary evidence that supports their
view (106).

The key problem is that we do not know the pattern of fresh air ventilation to the terminal air units. The work with fluid-filled lungs is interesting
but may not be relevant to the gas-filled lung.

Local ventilation inhomogeneity is, however, only part of the story.
Wagner, McRae & Read (108) have looked for inhomogeneity in the distribution of pulmonary blood flow within the terminal air units. In young
anesthetized male rats they injected I^{131}-MAA (macroaggregated albumin)
suspensions into the inferior vena cava and 5 min later killed the animals.
They removed and fixed the lungs inflated by filling them with 10 per cent
formalin. They cut a central slice from each lobe and from it made frozen
sections 100 μ thick, cut perpendicular to the pleural surfaces. The sections
were mounted on glass slides and prepared for autoradiography and then
counterstained for direct histologic examination. The MAA suspension had
been carefully prepared so as to contain no particles larger than 20 μ in
diameter. The emboli lodged in precapillary vessels or very small arterioles.

Wagner had previously studied the histology of the rat lung and concluded that the functional lobule as defined by Read (103) was a conical
structure 3 mm long, 2 mm wide at the pleural surface, and 0.4 mm at the
apex where the bronchiole entered. On this basis they divided the specimen
fields into four equal slices from the pleural surface to a depth of 3 mm and
counted radioactivity in each slice.

In six rats they analyzed a total of 25 different lobes and in every speci-men found that the slice under the pleural surface had about half as much radioactivity as the slice 3 mm deep. This suggested a decrease in blood flow from the apex of the lobule to the periphery. These basic results are impor-tant in their own right, but the authors go on to show that it is unlikely that the lobules are lined up neatly under the pleural surface. Calculating on a more graded alignment, they conclude that the proximal portion of the lobule receives four times as much blood flow per unit lung volume as does the peripheral portion.

Their explanation of the inhomogeneity of blood flow is that vascular resistance is greater distally in the lobule because of longer resistance vessels. An alternate possibility is that the capillary flow resistance may be less in the more proximal portion of the lobule if the capillary pathlengths are shorter in that region.

The study is well done but a few points remain to be settled. In the first place, they used the rat lung lobule which is a small unit relative to lobules in the human lung (103). The authors have not shown gradients of gas-phase tensions due to stratified inhomogeneity within these units in the rat lung. Whether they have demonstrated them in the human lung is another matter. Thus, their claim of having demonstrated a gradient of perfusion to match the gradient of ventilation within the lobule is incomplete. Secondly, the authors' explanation is satisfactory for zone 3 portions of lungs (17) but not for zone 2 portions. In the latter most of the vascular resistance is located at the downstream end of the collapsible vessels (presumably alveolar capil-laries or venules). The upstream resistances should have little effect on dis-tribution of blood flow within the lobule. Thirdly, there is a question about the origin of the alveolar capillary network. It is true that the capillaries form from the small vessels throughout their length, but many of the capillary networks may arise proximally in the lobule and extend over many alveoli distally. If this were true, there would be more embolization in the proximal lobule but it would not mean that the peripheral capillary nets did not re-ceive a fair share of the incoming blood. Fourthly, there is the problem of red cell transit times through the capillary bed. If the proximal capillary nets receive four times as much blood flow as the distal ones, this reduces the transit time through the capillaries sufficiently that one should be able to de-tect large alveolar-arterial Po_2 differences due to diffusion (6) by breathing suitable hypoxic mixtures. I am not aware that large, unexplained differences have been demonstrated.

LITERATURE CITED

1. Cummings, M. M. The biomedical communications problem. In *CIBA Foundation Symposium on Com-munication in Science: Documenta-tion and Automation*, 110–22 (de Reuck, A. V. S., Knight, J., Eds., Little, Brown, Boston, 274 pp., 1967)
2. Cleverdon, C. The efficiency of index languages (See Ref. 1), 84–93
3. Campbell, E. J. M. Respiration. *Ann. Rev. Physiol.*, **30**, 105–32 (1968)

4. Permutt, S. Respiration. *Ann. Rev. Physiol.*, **28**, 177–200 (1966)
5. Blount, S. G., Jr., Vogel, J. H. K. Altitude and the pulmonary circulation. *Advan. Internal Med.*, **13**, 11–31 (1967)
6. Staub, N. C. Alveolar-arterial tension gradient due to diffusion. *J. Appl. Physiol.*, **18**, 673–80 (1963)
7. Grover, R. F. Comparative physiology of hypoxic pulmonary hypertension. *International Symposium on the Cardiovascular and Respiratory Effects of Hypoxia, Kingston, Ontario, 1965. Proceedings*, 307–18 (Hatcher, J. D., Jennings, D. B., Eds., Hafner, New York, 406 pp., 1966)
8. Rudolph, A. M., Yuan, S. Response of the pulmonary vasculature to hypoxia and H^+ ion concentration changes. *J. Clin. Invest.* **45**, 399–411 (1966)
9. Dawes, G. S. The pulmonary circulation in the foetus and newborn. *Foetal and Neonatal Physiology*, 79–90 (Yearbook, Chicago, 247 pp., 1968)
10. Campbell, A. G. M., Dawes, G. S., Fishman, A. P., Hyman, A. I. Pulmonary vasoconstriction and changes in heart rate during asphyxia in immature foetal lambs. *J. Physiol. (London)*, **192**, 93–110 (1967)
11. Campbell, A. G. M., Cockburn, F., Dawes, G. S., Milligan, J. E. Pulmonary vasoconstriction in asphyxia during cross circulation between twin foetal lambs. *J. Physiol. (London)*, **192**, 111–22 (1967)
12. Rudolph, A. M., Heymann, M. A. The circulation of the fetus in utero: Methods for studying distribution of blood flow, cardiac output and organ blood flow. *Circ. Res.*, **21**, 163–84 (1967)
13. Chu, J., Clements, J. A., Cotton, E. K., Klaus, M. H., Sweet, A. Y., Tooley, W. H. Neonatal pulmonary ischemia. *Pediatrics.* **40**, 709–82 (1967)
14. Barer, G. R. Reactivity of the vessels of collapsed and ventilated lungs to drugs and hypoxia. *Circ. Res.*, **18**, 368–78 (1966)
15. Dugard, A., Naimark, A. Effect of hypoxia on distribution of pulmonary blood flow. *J. Appl. Physiol.*, **23**, 663–71 (1967)
16. Haas, F., Bergofsky, E. H. Effect of pulmonary vasoconstriction on balance between alveolar ventilation and perfusion. *J. Appl. Physiol.*, **24**, 491–97 (1968)
17. West, J. B. *Ventilation/Blood Flow and Gas Exchange* (Blackwell, Oxford, 117 pp., 1965)
18. Hauge, A. Role of histamine in hypoxic pulmonary hypertension in the rat. I. Blockade or potentiation of endogenous amines, kinins and ATP. *Circ. Res.*, **22**, 371–83 (1968)
19. Kato, M., Staub, N. C. Response of small pulmonary arteries to unilobar hypoxia or hypercapnia. *Circ. Res.*, **19**, 426–40 (1966)
20. Arborelius, M., Jr. *Respiratory Gases and Pulmonary Blood Flow. A Bronchospirometric Study* (Landby & Lundgrens, Malmö, Sweden, 80 pp., 1966)
21. Aviado, D. M., Samanék, M., Folle, L. E. Cardiopulmonary effects of tobacco and related substances. I. The release of histamine during inhalation of cigarette smoke and anoxemia in the heart-lung and intact dog preparation. *Arch. Environ. Health*, **12**, 705–11 (1966)
22. Dale, K. [133]Xenon-radiospirometry in rabbits with some observations on unilateral hypoxia. *Acta Physiol. Scand.*, **71**, 163–67 (1967)
23. Isawa, T., Shiraishi, K., Yasuda, T., Sasaki, H., Nagai, K., Haneda, Y., Oka, S. Effect of oxygen concentration in inspired gas upon pulmonary arterial blood flow. *Am. Rev. Respirat. Diseases*, **96**, 1199–1208 (1967)
24. Lopez-Majano, V., Wagner, H. N., Jr., Twining, R. H., Chernick, V. Time factor in the shifting of blood produced by unilateral hypoxia. *Am. Rev. Respirat. Diseases*, **96**, 1190–98 (1967)
25. Abraham, A. S., Hedworth-Whitty, R. B., Bishop, J. M. Effects of acute hypoxia and hypervolaemia singly and together, upon the pulmonary circulation in patients with chronic bronchitis. *Clin. Sci.*, **33**, 371–80 (1967)
26. Field, G. B. The effects of posture, oxygen, isoproterenol and atropine on ventilation-perfusion relationships in the lung in asthma. *Clin. Sci.*, **32**, 279–88 (1967)
27. Harvey, R. M., Enson, Y., Betti, R., Lewis, M. L., Rochester, D. F., Ferrer, M. I. Further observations on the effect of hydrogen ion on the

pulmonary circulation. *Circulation*, **35**, 1019–27 (1967)

28. Howard, P., Penman, R. W. B. The effect of breathing 30% oxygen on pulmonary ventilation-perfusion inequality in normal subjects and patients with chronic lung disease. *Clin. Sci.*, **32**, 127–37 (1967)

29. Lee, J., Read, J. Effect of oxygen breathing on distribution of pulmonary flow in chronic obstructive lung disease. *Am. Rev. Respirat. Diseases*, **96**, 1173–80 (1967)

30. Lockhart, A., Lissac, J., Salmon, D., Zappacosta, C., Benismail, M. Effects of isoproterenol on the pulmonary circulation in obstructive airways disease. *Clin. Sci.*, **32**, 117–87 (1967)

31. Vogel, J. H. K., McNamara, D. G., Hallman, G., Rosenberg, H., Jamieson, G., McCrady, J. D. Effects of mild chronic hypoxia on the pulmonary circulation in calves with reactive pulmonary hypertension. *Circ. Res.*, **21**, 661–69 (1967)

32. Bergofsky, E. H., Holtzman, S. A study of the mechanisms involved in the pulmonary arterial pressor response to hypoxia. *Circ. Res.*, **20**, 506–19 (1967)

33. Stuart-Harris, C. H. Pulmonary hypertension and chronic obstructive bronchitis. *Am. Rev. Respirat. Diseases*, **97**, 9–17 (1968)

34. Housley, E., Clarke, S. W., Hedworth-Whitty, R. B., Bishop, J. M. The effect of acidaemia on the pulmonary circulation in patients with chronic bronchitis. *Bull. Physio-Pathol. Resp.*, **3**, 563–66 (1967)

35. Barer G. R., Howard, P., McCurrie, J. R. The effect of carbon dioxide and changes in blood pH on pulmonary vascular resistance in cats. *Clin. Sci.*, **32**, 361–76 (1967)

36. Viles, P. H., Shepherd, J. T. Evidence for a dilator action of carbon dioxide on the pulmonary vessels of the cat. *Circ. Res.*, **22**, 325–32 (1968)

37. Silove, E. D., Grover, R. F. Effects of alpha adrenergic blockade and tissue catecholamine depletion on pulmonary vascular response to hypoxia. *J. Clin. Invest.*, **47**, 274–85 (1968)

38. Thilenius, O. G., Candiolo, B. M., Beug, J. L. Effect of adrenergic blockade on hypoxia-induced pulmonary vasoconstriction in awake dogs. *Am. J. Physiol.*, **213**, 990–98 (1967)

39. Hauge, A., Lunde, P. K. M., Waaler, B. A. Effects of catecholamines on pulmonary blood volume. *Acta Physiol. Scand.*, **70**, 323–33 (1967)

40. Bergofsky, E. H. A study of the mechanism whereby hypoxia regulates pulmonary perfusion: Relation between hypoxia and pulmonary arterial smooth muscle potentials. *Bull. Physio-Pathol. Resp.*, **2**, 297–309 (1966)

41. Lloyd, T. C., Jr. Influences of P_{O_2} and pH on resting and active tensions of pulmonary arterial strips. *J. Appl. Physiol.*, **22**, 1101–9 (1967)

42. Altura, B. M., Zweifach, B. W. Influence of reserpine and guanethidine on vascular reactivity and antihistamine constrictor action in the microcirculation. *Angiology*, **17**, 493–502 (1966)

43. Barer, G. R., McCurrie, J. R. Inhibition of the vasoconstrictor action of hypoxia on the pulmonary circulation by drugs. *J. Physiol. (London)*, **191**, 82P–83P (1967)

44. Hauge, A., Melmon, K. L. Role of histamine in hypoxic pulmonary hypertension in the rat. II. Depletion of histamine, serotonin, and catecholamines. *Circ. Res.*, **22**, 385–92 (1968)

45. Kahlson, G., Rosengren, E. New approaches to the physiology of histamine. *Physiol. Rev.*, **48**, 155–96 (1968)

46. Pittinger, C. B. Oxygen toxicity. *Hyperbaric Oxygenation*, 16–26 (Thomas, Springfield, Ill., 113 pp., 1966)

47. Haugaard, N. Cellular mechanisms of oxygen toxicity. *Physiol. Rev.*, **48**, 311–73 (1968)

48. Clements, J. A. The alveolar lining layer (See Ref. 65), 202–21

49. Webb, W. R., Lanius, J. W., Aslami, A., Reynolds, R. C. The effects of hyperbaric-oxygen tensions on pulmonary surfactant in guinea pigs and rats. *J. Am. Med. Assoc.*, **195**, 279–80 (1966)

50. Lee, C-J., Lyons, J. H., Konisberg, S., Morgan, F., Moore, F. D. Effects of spontaneous and positive-pressure breathing of ambient air and pure oxygen at one atmosphere pressure on pulmonary surface characteristics. *J. Thorac. Cardiov. Surg.*, **53**, 759–69 (1967)

51. Fisher, A. B., Hyde, R. W., Puy, R. J. M., Clark, J. M., Lambertsen, C. J. Effect of oxygen at 2 atmospheres on the pulmonary mechanics

of normal man. *J. Appl. Physiol.*, 24, 529–36 (1968)

52. Caldwell, P. R. B., Lee, W. L., Jr., Schildkraut, H. S., Archibald, E. R. Changes in lung volume, diffusing capacity, and blood gases in men breathing oxygen. *J. Appl. Physiol.*, 21, 1477–83 (1966)

53. Rosenberg, E., MacLean, L. D. Effect of high oxygen tensions on diffusing capacity for CO and Krogh's K. *J. Appl. Physiol.*, 23, 11–17 (1967)

54. Puy, R. J. M., Hyde, R. W., Fisher, A. B., Clark, J. M., Dickson, J., Lambertsen, C. J. Alterations in the pulmonary capillary bed during early O₂ toxicity in man. *J. Appl. Physiol.*, 24, 537–43 (1968)

55. Kistler, G. S., Caldwell, P. R. B., Weibel, E. R. Development of fine structural damage to alveolar and capillary lining cells in oxygen-poisoned rat lungs. *J. Cell Biol.*, 32, 605–28 (1967)

56. Schaffner, F., Felig, P., Trachtenberg, E. Structure of rat lung after protracted oxygen breathing. *Arch. Pathol.*, 83, 99–107 (1967)

57. Davis, J. M. G. The structure of guinea pig lung maintained in organ culture. *Brit. J. Exptl. Pathol.*, 48, 371–78 (1967)

58. Brooksby, G. A., Dennis, R. L., Datnow, B., Clark, D. Experimental emphysema: Histologic changes and alterations in pulmonary circulation. *California Med.*, 107, 391–95 (1967)

59. Bean, J. W., Zee, D., Thom, B. Pulmonary changes with convulsions induced by drugs and oxygen at high pressure. *J. Appl. Physiol.*, 21, 865–72 (1966)

60. Jamieson, D., Cass, N. CNS and pulmonary damage in anesthetized rats exposed to hyperbaric oxygen. *J. Appl. Physiol.*, 23, 235–42 (1967)

61. Winter, P. M., Gupta, R. K., Michalski, A. H., Lanphier, E. H. Modification of hyperbaric oxygen toxicity by experimental venous admixture. *J. Appl. Physiol.*, 23, 954–63 (1967)

62. Reid, L. The embryology of the lung (See Ref. 65), 109–24

63. Boyden, E. A. Notes on the development of the lung in infancy and early childhood. *Am. J. Anat.*, 121, 749–62 (1967)

64. Emery, J. L., Wilcock, P. F. The postnatal development of the lung. *Acta Anat.*, 65, 10–29 (1966)

65. *CIBA Foundation Symposium: Development of the Lung, London, 1965,* 127 (de Reuck, A. V. S., Porter, R., Eds., Little, Brown, Boston, 408 pp., 1967)

66. Dunnill, M. S. Postnatal growth of the lung. *Thorax*, 17, 329–33 (1962)

67. Nakamura, T., Takizawa, T., Morone, T. Anatomic changes in lung parenchyma due to aging process. *Diseases Chest*, 52, 518–24 (1967)

68. Balis, J. U., Delivoria, M., Conen, P. E. Maturation of postnatal human lung and the idiopathic respiratory distress syndrome. *Lab. Invest.*, 15, 530–46 (1966)

69. Weibel, E. R. Postnatal growth of the lung and pulmonary gas exchange capacity (See Ref. 65), 131–48

70. Fuest, H., Haas, J., Schmitz, G. A. Altersbedingte Veränderungen der Alveolen menschlicher Lungen. Zugleich ein Beitrag zum Problem von Form und Funktion. *Med. Welt*, 48, 2686–94 (1965)

71. Glazier, J. B., Hughes, J. M. B., Maloney, J. E., West, J. B. Vertical gradient of alveolar size in lungs of dogs frozen intact. *J. Appl. Physiol.*, 23, 694–705 (1967)

72. Elliott, F. M., Reid, L. Some new facts about the pulmonary artery and its branching pattern. *Clin. Radiol.*, 16, 193–98 (1965)

73. Pratt, P. C. The reaction of the human lung to enriched oxygen atmosphere. *Ann. N.Y. Acad. Sci.*, 121, 809–22 (1965)

74. Kleinerman, J. Reparative processes of the lung. In *Aging of the Lung*, 77–88 (Cander, L., Moyer, J. H., Eds., Grune & Stratton, New York, 371 pp., 1964)

75. Plank, J. A morphological contribution to the development of the human lung: Observations in the non-retracted lung (See Ref. 65), 156–65

76. Staub, N. C., Nagano, H., Pearce, M. L. Pulmonary edema in dogs, especially the sequence of fluid accumulation in lungs. *J. Appl. Physiol.*, 22, 227–40 (1967)

77. Kuno, K., Staub, N. C. Acute mechanical effects of lung volume changes on artificial microholes in alveolar walls. *J. Appl. Physiol.*, 24, 83–92 (1968)

78. Staub, N. C. The interdependence of pulmonary structure and function. *Anesthesiology*, 24, 831–54 (1963)

79. Weibel, E. R., Gomez, D. M. Ar-

chitecture of the human lung. *Science*, **137**, 577–85 (1962)

80. Green, M. How big are the bronchioles? *St. Thomas' Hosp. Gaz.*, **63**, 135–39 (1965–66)

81. Macklem, P. T., Mead, J. Resistance of central and peripheral airways measured by a retrograde catheter. *J. Appl. Physiol.*, **22**, 395–401 (1967)

82. Wilson, T. A. Design of the bronchial tree. *Nature*, **213**, 668–69 (1967)

83. Hyatt, R. E., Flath, R. E. Influence of lung parenchyma on pressure-diameter behavior of dog bronchi. *J. Appl. Physiol.*, **21**, 1448–52 (1966)

84. Horsfield, K., Cumming, G. Angles of branching and diameters of branches in the human bronchial tree. *Bull. Math. Biophys.*, **29**, 245–59 (1967)

85. Horsfield, K., Cumming, G. Morphology of the bronchial tree in man. *J. Appl. Physiol.*, **24**, 373–83 (1968)

86. Hayek, H. von. *Die Menschliche Lunge* (Springer, Berlin, 1953; Transl. by Krahl, V. E., Hafner, New York, 1960)

87. Cumming, G. Gas mixing efficiency in the human lung. *Resp. Physiol.*, **2**, 213–24 (1967)

88. Horsfield, K., Cumming, G. Functional consequences of airway morphology. *J. Appl. Physiol.*, **24**, 384–90 (1968)

89. Olsen, C. R., DeKock, M. A., Colebatch, H. J. H., Stability of airways during reflex bronchoconstriction. *J. Appl. Physiol.*, **23**, 23–26 (1967)

90. Olsen, C. R., Stevens, A. E., McIlroy, M. B. Rigidity of tracheae and bronchi during muscular constriction. *J. Appl. Physiol.*, **23**, 27–34 (1967)

91. Olsen, C. R, Stevens, A. E., Pride, N. B., Staub, N. C. Structural basis for decreased compressibility of constricted tracheae and bronchi. *J. Appl. Physiol.*, **23**, 35–39 (1967)

92. Dunnill, M. S. Effect of lung inflation on alveolar surface area in the dog. *Nature*, **214**, 1013–14 (1967)

93. Thurlbeck, W. H. The internal surface area of nonemphysematous lungs. *Am. Rev. Respirat. Diseases*, **95**, 765–73 (1967)

94. Thurlbeck, W. M. Internal surface area and other measurements in emphysema. *Thorax*, **22**, 483–96 (1967)

95. Thurlbeck, W. H. Measurement of pulmonary emphysema. *Am. Rev. Respirat. Diseases*, **95**, 752–64 (1967)

96. Duguid, J. B., Young, A., Cauna, D., Lambert, M. W. The internal surface area of the lung in emphysema. *J. Pathol. Bacteriol.*, **88**, 405–21 (1964)

97. Kory, C. R. Quantitative estimation of pulmonary emphysema in lung macrosections by photoelectric measurement of transmitted light. *Am. Rev. Respirat. Diseases*, **93**, 758–68 (1966)

98. Milic-Emili, J., Henderson, J. A. M., Dolovich, M. B., Trop, D., Kaneko, K. Regional distribution of inspired gas in the lung. *J. Appl. Physiol.*, **21**, 749–59 (1966)

99. Cavagna, G. A., Stemmler, E. J., DuBois, A. B. Alveolar resistance to atelectasis. *J. Appl. Physiol.*, **22**, 441–52 (1967)

100. Leith, D. E., Mead, J. Mechanisms determining residual volume of the lungs in normal subjects. *J. Appl. Physiol.*, **23**, 221–27 (1967)

101. Muir, D. C. F. Distribution of aerosol particles in exhaled air. *J. Appl. Physiol.*, **23**, 210–14 (1967)

102. Read, J. Alveolar populations contributing to expired gas tension plateaus. *J. Appl. Physiol.*, **21**, 1511–20 (1966)

103. Read, J. Stratification of ventilation and blood flow in the normal lung. *Ibid.*, 1521–31

104. Cumming, G., Horsfield, K., Jones, J. G., Muir, D. C. F. The influence of gaseous diffusion on the alveolar plateau at different lung volumes. *Resp. Physiol.*, **2**, 386–98 (1967)

105. Gomez, D. M. A physico-mathematical study of lung function in normal subjects and in patients with obstructive pulmonary diseases. *Med. Thorac.*, **22**, 275–94 (1965)

106. Staub, N. C. Time-dependent factors in pulmonary gas exchange. *Med. Thorac.*, **22**, 132–45 (1965)

107. Kylstra, J. A., Paganelli, C. V., Rahn, H. Some implications of the dynamics of gas transfer in water-breathing dogs (See Ref. 65), 34–58

108. Wagner, P., McRae, J., Read, J. Stratified distribution of blood flow in secondary lobule of the rat lung. *J. Appl. Physiol.*, **22**, 1115–23 (1967)

DIGESTION: MOTOR FUNCTION[1]

By E. E. Daniel

Department of Pharmacology, University of Alberta
Edmonton, Alberta, Canada

The authors for this volume have been invited to be selective and critical in dealing with their subjects. I have accepted this invitation and therefore must bear the responsibility for omissions which may be important and for inclusion of material which may be trivial or irrelevant. This article shows my prejudice in favour of articles which pose or attempt to answer the question, "How does it work?" It also reflects my ignorance of much of the background required to deal critically with the many studies of 'motility' in healthy or diseased humans; perhaps this will be mitigated by the availability at about the same time of Volume IV, on motility, of the *Handbook of Physiology, Alimentary Canal* and of a recent symposium on motility held in Belfast (1) and by other valuable reviews referred to throughout this article.

In considering how the gastrointestinal tract performs its motor functions, I will concentrate on examining control mechanisms: nervous, chemical other than by neurotransmitters, and myogenic electrical.

NERVOUS CONTROL OF ALIMENTARY TRACT MOTOR FUNCTION

Cholinergic.—Few seriously doubt that acetylcholine mediates nervous transmission in autonomic ganglia and between many postganglionic nerves, i.e., those termed cholinergic, and smooth muscle organs which they innervate, including the gastrointestinal tract. Two important questions as to its role in the gut have remained unsettled for some years. First, to what extent is acetylcholine produced within and released by the nervous structures of the intestine? Further, does some of the acetylcholine produced and released by nonnervous structures participate as a 'local hormone' in regulating gastrointestinal motility? Second, what factors, mechanical, nervous, chemical, electrical or other, control its synthesis and release?

Paton & Zar (2) have answered the question as to the origin of acetylcholine for longitudinal muscle of the guinea pig ileum, and have excellently summarized the contradictory data hitherto available, which will not therefore be repeated here. Paton (3) had shown by electron microscopy that Auerbach's plexus and its nervous ramifications formed a layer on the inner surface of the longitudinal muscle layer, appeared to send no nerve fibers into the longitudinal muscle layer and could be stripped off.

---

[1] The survey of literature for this review was concluded in May 1968.

In such 'denervated' preparations, the acetylcholine output (both resting and transmurally stimulated) dropped to undetectable levels as did the acetylcholine content. Furthermore, motor responses to eserine, nicotine, or DMPP (dimethylphenylpiperazinium iodide) and to transmural electrical stimulation were eliminated. These drugs are believed to act primarily or exclusively on nervous tissue. Denervation did not affect motor responses to acetylcholine, to other muscarinic stimulants, and to histamine, which therefore seem to act directly on longitudinal smooth muscle in the ileum. Denervated preparations gave lesser responses to angiotensin, barium ion, potassium ion, and serotonin (5-HT); hence, these substances apparently act partly on nervous structures in the innervated preparation.

Acetylcholine put out from the isolated whole ileum had the same properties as that from the innervated isolated strip, so that it was unnecessary to postulate another source of acetylcholine in the intact gut. Acetylcholine output was high at rest; at low rates of stimulation the volley output was high, while at high rates both volley and minute outputs were low; and the resting and low frequency outputs were sensitive to morphine. Paton & Zar suggest that these are characteristics of a relatively primitive transmission system and are linked with the absence of specialized neuroeffector systems.

The evidence for lack of such systems [long delay between nerve stimulation and postsynaptic potential (4–7), or absence of discrete postsynaptic potentials (8) in response to nerve stimulation] is consistent with a long diffusion path between nerve ending and muscle cell. Thus lack of penetration of postganglionic parasympathetic nerve fibers into the longitudinal muscle layer is consistent with other data. In addition to Paton's morphologic studies (3), earlier and subsequent studies have been made of the innervation of the intestine. All recent studies (see 9–11) agree on the absence of intimate, discrete contacts between nerve and smooth muscle cells (separation of 300 to 3000 Å having been reported) and on the presence of rather unspecialized series of terminals scattered along the nerve axons (endings *en passant*). Most authors (see 9–11) report the presence of some nerve fibers within the muscle layers. Their presence is implied by the size of the nerve-muscle gaps which have been reported. This subject was recently reviewed (9) and only recent studies (10–11) will be listed in the references.

Variations occur in the innervation of and the responses to a given mediator or drug by various intestinal segments in a single species as well as among different species. Hence we cannot extrapolate from the guinea pig ileum to other intestinal muscles.

Most studies of the circular muscle activity in peristalsis of the guinea pig ileum are consistent with acetylcholine being the mediator of nervous control: eserine enhances this response and that to transmural stimulation (see 12 for references); atropine, hyoscine, and related cholinergic blocking agents prevent it (see 12). Furthermore, increasing distention of the intestine which initiates peristaltic activity leads to increasing release of acetylcholine (13). Moreover, morphine, which inhibits release of acetylcholine from postganglionic intrinsic nerve fibers, also inhibited the increased release of acetylcholine by distention. This supports the idea that the origin of the acetylcholine released by distention is these fibers (see 12).

However, some evidence has been difficult to reconcile with acetylcholine mediation of circular muscle activity. Harry (14) showed that compared to longitudinal muscle strips, isolated strips of circular muscle were relatively insensitive to acetylcholine and other cholinergic agents and to agents indirectly acting such as DMPP unless the strips were pretreated with a potent anticholinesterase. Both direct and indirect cholinergic effects were prevented by hyoscine; indirect actions were prevented by hemicholinium. These results imply the existence of nervous structures which release acetylcholine when appropriately stimulated. Harry's hypothesis that the insensitivity of the circular muscle to drugs was a consequence of a very high concentration of acetylcholinesterase near receptors raises the question whether acetylcholine released from nerves is also subject to rapid hydrolysis.

Most recently Kottegoda (15) has directly challenged the notion that acetylcholine is the transmitter of nervous activity to the circular muscle of guinea pig ileum. He reported that when the ileum was stimulated coaxially with 0.1 msec pulses at a frequency of 1–10 per sec, the resultant contractions of the circular muscle were insensitive to hyoscine, morphine, hemicholinium, or Botulinum toxin. There was a reciprocal relaxation of longitudinal muscle. Contraction of circular muscle and relaxation of longitudinal were also produced by 5-HT and DMPP; these effects were abolished by tetrodotoxin. Details of this study will be awaited with interest.

The effects of substrates and ions on the synthesis and release of acetylcholine from the intestine appear to be similar to those at endings of motor nerves (see 1, 72 for references). The regulation of acetylcholine release as a control mechanism in motility does not seem to occur by changes in ion or substrate concentration. Rather, there is evidence that distention activates mechanoreceptors [whose identity is controversial, see (1, 72)] to set up nervous impulses [whose pathway is unknown, see (1, 72)] that finally impinge on postganglionic cholinergic nerves which leads to release of acetylcholine (see 13). In addition it now appears that sympathetic activity might affect motility by diminishing acetylcholine release as well as by a direct action on intestinal muscle.

Adrenergic.—Noradrenaline is well established as the transmitter of the inhibitory influence of sympathetic nerves on the intestine (16, 17). Studies of the distribution in the intestine of nervous tissue with the fluorescence characteristic of noradrenaline have raised some interesting questions. As expected, many axons, [but few or no nerve cells, are found in the plexuses containing noradrenaline (18–20), so most fibers appear to be postganglionic, originating in the sympathetic ganglia. The axons containing noradrenaline are characteristically associated with the myenteric plexus and not with the smooth muscle (18–20) in the stomach and small intestine.

Stimulation of perivascular nerves to various intestinal preparations was usually not effective in causing inhibition of motility until rates of stimulation >5/sec were used; discrete inhibitory postsynaptic potentials were not found, though gradual hyperpolarization after a delay was obtained (21, 22). Furthermore, noradrenaline can reduce acetylcholine output from the resting and transmurally stimulated intestine (23, 24). Also the actions of noradrenaline given intra-arterially in low doses *in vivo* on electrical and mechanical activity of the antrum and duodenum are often indistinguishable from those of atropine (25–27). Finally there is evidence that the α-adrenergic receptors are located in nervous tissue whereas β-adrenergic receptors are in muscle, since only the responses to α-receptor stimulants are depressed by cold storage (28). Alpha-receptor stimulants are also more effective against contractions from transmural stimulation than against contraction from added acetylcholine (24). Hence it has been postulated that sympathetic nerves may inhibit gastrointestinal motor function by interacting with myenteric nerves to inhibit acetylcholine release.

There is, however, convincing evidence that noradrenaline or adrenaline can also act directly on intestinal smooth muscles. In larger intra-arterial doses either drug suppresses slow waves and inhibits their propagation whereas atropine does not (25–27); this effect can be separated from a decrease in intestinal blood flow produced by noradrenaline (27). This inhibitory effect was decreased by β-adrenergic blocking agents. These results are consistent with the localization of β-receptors in intestinal smooth muscle already proposed (24) on the grounds that β-adrenergic agonists were as effective in inhibiting acetylcholine added to the bath as of acetylcholine released from nerves. Noradrenaline clearly can act through these receptors since it can inhibit responses to acetylcholine added to the bath and this response is prevented by β-blocking agents. Furthermore, a combination of β- with α-blocking agents was necessary to stop the inhibitory action of noradrenaline in responses to transmural nerve stimulation (24).

In the antrum of the dog (25, 26, 29, 30) similar results apply. Noradrenaline or adrenaline in larger doses slows the rhythm of the 5/min spikes, whether it is injected intra-arterially or intravenously (25, 26, 29) or released by an 'intestino-gastric' inhibitory reflex (31) or by strong stimulation of the vagus (29). There is thus no doubt that catecholamines have a direct inhibitory action on smooth muscle cells and the important question is, "Where does noradrenaline released from sympathetic nerves act?"

Gershon (32) has inferred that the effect of sympathetic nerve stimulation is mediated through direct action of released noradrenaline on smooth muscle. He showed that sympathetic nerve stimulation relaxed an isolated stomach, whereas tetrodotoxin (to inhibit all nervous activity) did not cause relaxation, nor did it affect the noradrenaline dose-response curve. However, the experiment was carried out in the presence of hyoscine to block any response to stimulation of cholinergic drugs. Thus it is obvious that there was no motor activity related to release of acetylcholine, so inhibition of activity from such release by sympathetic nerve stimulation was not to be expected. Hence these results do not eliminate the possibility that the sympathetics may act by inhibition of an acetylcholine release which is stimulating motor activity. The existence of β-receptors in smooth muscle which are excited by noradrenaline explains the above results.

Gershon also found that stimulation of perivascular sympathetic nerves at frequencies of 5/sec or greater was required to inhibit motor responses to transmural stimulation in his preparations. Similar rates of stimulation also caused partial inhibition of pendular movements (in the presence of hexamethonium), of a direct-acting stimulant (histamine, in the presence of hyoscine), and of acetylcholine either added to the bath or accumulated following eserine. However, his figure 2 suggests that direct-acting agents (histamine, acetylcholine) were only partially inhibited by perivascular nerve stimulation while responses to transmural stimulation were completely inhibited. No attempt was made to quantitate or equate the responses to various stimulants, nor to determine the optimal temporal relations between perivascular nerve stimulation and transmural stimulations required to obtain inhibition. So we are left with uncertainty whether perivascular nerve stimulation may have exerted part of its inhibitory action against transmural stimulation through inhibition of myenteric nerves.

Finally Gershon reported that perivascular nerve stimulation for a minute, at the same frequencies which inhibited responses to transmural stimulation, histamine, acetylcholine, or eserine, did not reduce the resting acetylcholine output. These experiments were carried out in the presence of sufficient eserine to preserve acetylcholine and cause contraction, and indicated to Gershon that reduction in acetylcholine output from nerves played no part in the relaxations he observed following stimulation of sympathetic nerves. However, the question may be raised whether efflux of acetylcholine through the serosal surface (the ends of the segments were tied) is an adequate measure of acetylcholine output from nerves during the same 1-min interval. More important, these results do not bear upon the question of the effect of sympathetic nerve stimulation on the increased acetylcholine output following transmural stimulation. Such experiments were not reported by Gershon, hence it seems that his results provide conclusive evidence that sympathetic nerve stimulation has direct inhibitory actions on smooth muscle, but do not preclude its having an indirect inhibitory as well, by reduction of the increased acetylcholine output associated with transmural stimulation and with peristaltic activity.

Before leaving the question of inhibition of intestinal motility, the bearing of the above results on Hirschsprung's disease should be noted. Bennett & Garrett (33) have shown that the distal aganglionic segment of the large bowel characteristic of this disease contains more than the normal quantity of postganglionic adrenergic fibers. The constriction of this segment and its failure to relax in response to nicotine, which relaxes normal colon *in vitro* apparently by noradrenaline release (34, 35), cannot be a result of absence of adrenergic nerves. Bennett & Garrett suggest that this failure of relaxation might be due to the absence of the myenteric plexus if sympathetic nerves normally bring about relaxation by inhibiting acetylcholine release from neurones in the plexus. In the absence of the myenteric plexus it is hard to believe that contraction in the distal segment is the result of release of acetylcholine. If noradrenaline acts directly on smooth muscle, it should be effective in relaxing the constricted segment in Hirschsprung's disease irrespective of the cause of contraction unless its release mechanism is impaired. Bennett & Garrett also point out that impaired relaxation of the colon in this disease may be a consequence of damage to the nonadrenergic inhibitory nerves.

Thought should be given to the possibility that impaired relaxation of gastrointestinal muscle is involved in other diseases such as 'pylorospasm', 'achalasia', and diverticular disease. As knowledge of inhibitory mechanisms in the gut increases and as the technology of study of human intestinal motility *in vivo* and *in vitro* develops, conclusive tests of such a possibility can be made.

Finally, adrenergic substances do not always inhibit the motility of the intestine. The excitatory effect of noradrenaline and other α-adrenergic stimulants on the terminal portion of the cat esophagus is discussed below (p. 219).

Nonadrenergic inhibitory.—Traditional views about the sympathetic inhibitory control of gastrointestinal motility have recently been shaken by the discovery of nonadrenergic inhibition of motility. The vagus has long been known to contain fibers whose stimulation inhibits gastric motility [see (36–39) for references]. Martinsson (38) proposed in 1965 that these were not adrenergic in the cat, although adrenergic inhibitory fibers also exist both in the sympathetic nerve supply of the coeliac axis (32, 40) and possibly in the vagus itself (40, 41). However, it was found by Martinsson in the cat stomach *in situ* (38, 39) and Campbell in the isolated guinea pig stomach (42) that neither α- nor β-adrenergic blocking agents nor both together could prevent vagal inhibition.

This was confirmed by Bülbring & Gershon (43) who showed *in vitro* that in doses capable of blocking inhibition of gastric motility by sympathetic nerve stimulation, adrenergic blocking agents did not prevent inhibition from vagal stimulation. These authors presented evidence that the vagal inhibitory transmitter was 5-HT. In the presence of hyoscine to block vagal cholinergic excitation, nicotinic agents and 5-HT were both inhibitory, but pentolinium blocked only the former effect. These two inhibitory actions could also be separated by desensitization of the receptors for 5-HT after large doses, a procedure which left nicotinic inhibition intact. As in the intestinal and in the superior cervical ganglia (44, 45), nicotine initially prevented both nicotinic and 5-HT inhibition of gastric motility (and vagal inhibition as well), but later 5-HT inhibition recovered, as did vagal inhibition partially. These findings (43) have been interpreted as a nonselective initial ganglionic blockade by nicotine, replaced later by a selective antagonism of nicotinic receptors. Further evidence that 5-HT receptors are distinct from nicotinic receptors was obtained (43) by showing that antagonists to the neural actions of 5-HT (biguanides and 5-hydroxy-2-methylindole) selectively prevented the inhibitory action of 5-HT and decreased vagal inhibition (see 46), but did not interfere with sympathetic inhibition. Tetrodotoxin or a combination of 5-HT desensitization with blockade of nicotinic receptors could prevent vagal inhibition. Tetrodotoxin also prevented gastric inhibition by 5-HT or nicotine. Bülbring & Gershon (43) suggested that 5-HT release from nerves plays a role in vagal inhibition since tetrodotoxin prevented its release from the mouse stomach under conditions which minimized its release from enterochromaffin cells (47) (asphyxiation of the mucosa and collection only of that 5-HT released into the serosal fluid). They postulate that vagal inhibitory ganglia receive both cholinergic and '5-hydroxytryptaminergic' preganglionic fibers which act synergistically in the same cell.

The action of 5-HT on gastric motility is not primarily inhibitory (47) since when injected intra-arterially, it usually increases antral motility in the dog, as it does in isolated stomachs (40). In both cases, excitatory actions of 5-HT were primarily indirect, by release of acetylcholine. Similar conclusions apply to the excitatory effects of 5-HT *in vitro* and *in vivo* on the intestine (see 72). Whether the excitatory action of 5-HT is pre- or postganglionic is uncertain, though most evidence favours a postganglionic site (see 72). In either case, the existence of primarily excitatory actions of 5-HT on stomach and intestine raises the question of how it functions as a mediator of nonadrenergic inhibition of motility. It must be kept in mind that hyoscine was used in the experiments of Bülbring & Gershon so that excitatory responses to 5-HT were suppressed. 5-HT can probably both excite and inhibit intrinsic cholinergic neurones in the gastrointestinal tract and the resultant effect on motility may depend upon factors such as the prior activity. There have been persistent reports that vagal stimulation initiates motor activity in the quiescent gut and inhibits motor activity in the active gut. Obviously, neuronal control of motility has a complexity hitherto unrecognized.

Nonadrenergic inhibition of motility has also been identified in the intestine, but at the time of writing, 5-HT mediation had not been associated with this inhibition. But 5-HT has been shown to inhibit motility in the human stomach and distal large bowel [see (72) for references], though it stimulates activity in the small bowel. Burnstock et al. (48), Holman & Hughes (49), and most recently Day & Warren (50) found that transmural stimulation of the taenia coli or intestine caused biphasic responses, of which the inhibitory response did not seem to be adrenergic since it was not abolished by doses of adrenergic blocking agents which interfered with sympathetic inhibition, It was, however, inhibited by reserpine so that the mediator must be depleted by reserpine as are noradrenaline and 5-HT [reserpine was not usually effective against the vagal inhibition of gastric motility and also did not deplete gastric 5-HT readily (51)].

Analysis of inhibition in the guinea pig taenia coli revealed a similar inhibitory response to transmural stimulation, distinct from sympathetic inhibition by stimulation of perivascular nerves (52-54). Not only was guanethidine, in amounts which prevented inhibition from perivascular nerves, ineffective against transmural stimulation, but also DMPP activated this response at a time when it blocked perivascular nerve stimulation. In addition, exclusion from the preparation of neurones from Auerbach's plexus prevented the response to transmural stimulation. A direct action of transmural stimulation on smooth muscle was excluded. Transmural stimulation of taenia coli was accompained by hyperpolarization of the cell membrane and inhibition of spike activity. Recovery from hyperpolarization had a time constant long enough to exclude passive discharge of membrane capacitance as an explanation. Hyperpolarization could be elicited by single transmural pulses in contrast to the repetitive stimulation required when perivascular nerves were stimulated.

The inhibitory hyperpolarizing response might be a consequence of increased conductance of the cell membrane to potassium (55). When the external potassium concentration was altered (and, therefore, the potassium equilibrium potential V_K), on transmural stimulation the membrane potential changed in the direction predicted if the hyperpolarization were caused by the membrane potential approaching V_K. Changes in chloride concentration had no such effects.

Bülbring & Tomita (56) recently reported that the inhibitory potential is abolished by tetrodotoxin (and therefore cannot be a direct muscle response as they earlier proposed). It was produced more readily (after a delay) by anodal currents which would hyperpolarize most cells in the current field. Anodal-break excitation was ruled out and it is difficult to understand the mechanism whereby nerve fibers are excited by such a hyperpolarizing current. They also report that the inhibitory potential decreases decrementally with distance from a single stimulating electrode, which they attribute to very short inhibitory nerve fibers. However, they were using a hypertonic Ringer solution to immobilize their preparation and thus may have affected the functional properties of this component tissue.

5-HT inhibits a number of gastrointestinal preparations (e.g., human colonic muscle, especially circular muscle, *in vitro* (see 112a). However, this relaxation was reported (112) to be prevented by methysergide whereas only antagonists to the neuronal actions of 5-HT had selective antagonistic effects in the studies of Bülbring & Gershon (43). Obviously, further study will be required to determine the nature of the nonadrenergic inhibitory substance transmitted in the intestine and whether it might be 5-HT.

CHEMICAL CONTROL OF MOTILITY

Naturally occurring chemicals other than acetylcholine, noradrenaline, and the nonadrenergic inhibitory substances affect gastrointestinal motility and may play physiological roles in its control.

Since the isolation of gastrin and the determination of its structure, it has been studied intensively. Already its effects on motility, in addition to those on secretion, have been established. In two recent studies (57, 58) the effects of the synthetic gastrin analog pentagastrin [ICI (50, 123)] were studied in man *in vivo* and on human intestine *in vitro*. Infusion of pentagastrin at rates yielding maximal acid secretion consistently increased the motility of the antrum, but not of the fundus, small intestine, or right or left colon. Misiewicz et al. (57) were unable to duplicate the stimulation of activity in the rectum and sigmoid colon observed by Logan & Connell (59) following single injections of pentagastrin. Bennett et al. (58) found that strips of human antrum (circular or longitudinal muscle) were stimulated by pentagastrin and by gastrins I or II. They also found occasional weak stimulation of longitudinal and circular muscle strips from the ascending or sigmoid colon. Little or no stimulation of strips from the intestine was observed. The motor effects of gastrin and pentagastrin on the antrum were directly on receptors in smooth muscle since they were not prevented by ganglionic blocking agents, local anesthetics, or hyoscine and were not potentiated by anticholinesterases.

Misiewicz and collaborators (57, 58) postulated that gastrin may play a direct role in controlling gastric motor activity. They reason that the amount of pentagastrin required to stimulate acid secretion maximally is near that present during a meal. If so, gastrin might be released in amounts able to affect gastric motility following eating. Stimulation of antral motility by pentagastrin was inhibited if gastric acid was allowed to reach the duodenum; the mechanism of this inhibition remains unsettled (57).

Caution in extrapolating results from studies with pentagastrin to gastrin itself is indicated since Neely (60) has shown that they had different effects when each was infused intravenously in the cat. Gastrin extract stimulated the small intestine and colon but pentagastrin did not. Pharmacological analysis suggested that the motility increase from gastrin was an indirect action; it was prevented by atropine. Unfortunately no evidence was presented that atropine was selective in its effects or effective against muscarinic cholinergic stimulation under the experimental conditions used. In other preparations *in vitro* (guinea pig ileum and rat colon), gastrin is known to have an indirect stimulating action via cholinergic neurones (61, 62). These results also emphasize species differences in the responses to gastrin. It must be emphasized that variations in actions *in vivo* or even *in vitro* are not necessarily a consequence of different cellular mechanims of action. This follows from differences in distribution and metabolism of a drug between species and in similar differences in the secondary responses induced by the various primary actions of the drug.

Prostaglandins are a group of unsaturated hydroxy- and hydroxyketo-long chain carboxylic acids. They are widely distributed in animal tissues [see (63) for references] and have a variety of effects in small doses on smooth muscles (see 63). Prostaglandins are released from a number of tissues including nervous tissue, muscle, adrenal tissue, and adipose tissue and the amounts are increased by nerve stimulation [see (64) for references].

Vogt (65, 66) has recently identified prostaglandin E_1 (PGE_1) and prostaglandin $F_{1\alpha}$ ($PGF_{1\alpha}$) with the biological activity released by frog stomach and intestine and previously called *Darmstoff*. This material causes intestinal contractions but its site of action is not settled (see 72). Coceani et al. (64) recently found that PGE_2, $PGF_{2\alpha}$, and small quantities of other prostaglandins were released from the rat stomach *in vitro*. This release was increased by vagal stimulation or by transmural stimulation and these increases were blocked by hyoscine. Hyoscine did not prevent spontaneous release of prostaglandins. Stimulation of periarterial sympathetic nerves did not affect prostaglandin release, though there was relaxation of the stomach. Elevation of intraluminal pressure also did not affect prostaglandin release. Aging of stomach at 2–4° C for 72 hr did not decrease spontaneous release of prostaglandins though nerves were damaged. The authors concluded that prostaglandins were released from smooth muscle. The release of prostaglandins from aged preparations was reduced 90 per cent by prior anoxia, presumably because of reduced synthesis of prostaglandins in smooth muscle. Facilitation of synthesis of prostaglandins may account for the increased release of prostaglandins by ascorbic acid. Other studies showed that transmural stimulation increased not only release of prostaglandins but also their synthesis. Bennett et al. (67) also found release of E-type prostaglandin from the rat stomach.

Coceani et al. (64) suggest that prostaglandins are formed and released spontaneously from smooth muscle cell membranes and that the process is speeded by contraction. In the spleen, where sympathetic stimulation leads to contraction, there was an increased release of prostaglandins. Coceani et al. (64) also speculate that prostaglandins may participate in excitation-contraction coupling in smooth muscle, possibly aiding the transmembrane transit or the release of calcium.

Bennett et al. (68) have found PGE_2 but no $PGF_{1\alpha}$ in the mucosa of human stomach. Similar quantities per gram were found in the mucosa of the body and of the pyloric region. Much less was in the submucosa and almost none in the smooth muscle portion of the wall. This raises the question whether Coceani et al. (64) may also have obtained prostaglandins from the mucosa of the rat stomach instead of from smooth muscle. None of their data appears to eliminate this possibility.

Prostaglandins have a direct action on rat fundal smooth muscle, unaffected by hyoscine or methysergide (69a), and on rat stomach (67). On longitudinal muscle strips from the body of human stomachs, PGE_2 caused contraction in very low doses (<2 mg/ml). Longitudinal muscle of antrum was much less sensitive or was even inhibited in some cases. The contractions were from a direct action on distinct prostaglandin receptors in smooth muscle, being largely unaffected by hexamethonium, hyoscine, cocaine, methysergide, or mepyramine. On circular muscle from the body or antrum of the stomach, PGE_2 was inhibitory in very small concentrations; it was more potent than adrenaline. The inhibition was not affected by cocaine or by combined α- and β-receptor blockage. Hence adrenergic receptors were not involved. Since both potassium- and acetylcholine-induced contractions were inhibited, nonselective antagonism was involved.

The gastrointestinal function of 5-HT has long been an enigma. Several recent reviews (69a–72) have considered its proposed role in peristalsis and the evidence need not be reviewed again. It has been envisaged to act as a sensitizer of mechanoreceptors in the mucosa, or as a transmitter of afferent nerve activity in Meissner's plexus to the myenteric plexus. The most recent proposal of a transmitter for nonadrenergic inhibitory nerves already discussed above, p. 208 et seq., is rather difficult to reconcile with evidence that 5-HT stimulates peristalsis.

No recent evidence clarifies the role of 5-HT in stimulating peristalsis. Burks & Long have reported a series of experiments demonstrating that 5-HT is released from intact and isolated dog intestine by a variety of agents (73–76). Acetylcholine, barium chloride, angiotensin, morphine, nicotine, DMPP, and catecholamines were all effective. All but catecholamines caused contraction and apparently no evidence clearly dissociates release from contraction in the remainder of cases. Release of 5-HT from enterochromaffin cells in isolated or in vivo intestine preparations from the guinea pig and other species by increased intraluminal pressure or mechanical deformation has already been demonstrated (69, 70, 77, 78) and this could be the mechanism in the experiments of Burks & Long. These authors also suggest that agents like nicotine may directly release 5-HT from storage granules, that there may be '5-hydroxytryptaminergic' neurones which are stimulated by various agents, or that catecholamine release may mediate 5-HT release.

The mechanisms whereby acid or other substances in the duodenum inhibit gastric fundal motility await clarification. No chemical agent has been definitely implicated. Pancreozymin possesses an inhibitory (78a, 78b) and an excitatory fraction (78b). Bile and micellar fat instilled in a Thiry loop of duodenum did not significantly diminish fundal or antral motility induced by feeding or by intravenous infusion of acetylcholine or of 5-hydroxytryptophan (78c).

ELECTRICAL CONTROL OF MOTILITY

The same unanswered question has persisted for many years: To what extent is the motility of the intestine a consequence of a myogenic origin and control of intestinal muscle contraction, operated through excitable membranes and modulated by nervous reflexes, and to what extent is nerve function an essential prerequisite for motility? The question has not been answered because there has been no method of denervating the intestine satisfactorily (i.e., completely and without damage to other structures), either acutely or chronically.

Paton & Zar (2), as described above, claim to have completely denervated the longitudinal muscle of the guinea pig ileum by mechanically stripping off the myenteric plexus. (Their paper should be consulted for references to earlier attempts.) In fact, the evidence presented suggests strongly that cholinergic nerves have been largely removed, but does not eliminate the presence of other types of nerves. Furthermore, this was an acute experiment which may not reveal the effect of any nervous influences which require longer to be manifest or to be eliminated (e.g., changes in number and distribution of receptors).

An alternative method of denervation was advocated by Hukuhara (79,80) who reported that perfusion of intestinal segments *in situ* with nonoxygenated Ringer solution for 4 hr caused loss of intestinal reflexes and degeneration of myenteric neurones. If this were correct, his method would offer the possibility of chronic denervation of the intestine. A number of recent studies (27, 81–83), however, have seriously questioned the effectiveness of his procedure and of various modifications of it in denervating the intestine. Despite good evidence of functional postganglionic cholinergic nerves after this procedure, there were clear changes in function and in the electrical activity of the intestine.

Szurszewski (81, 82) demonstrated recovery of a substantial proportion of nerve cells in the mysenteric (Auerbach's) plexus in intestinal segments perfused 70–90 days earlier. Even a higher proportion of the cells in Meissner's plexus recovered. Clearly the preparation was not denervated. Despite that, the intestinal slow electrical waves were markedly affected. These waves originate from longitudinal muscle cells in the intestine [see (83) for references] and consist of periodic (18–8/min) depolarization and repolarization. They spread (at velocities from 15–2 cm/sec) aborally from the upper duodenum down to about mid-jejunum in the dog and cat (see 83). In the upper intestine, transection, cooling, constriction, and a variety of other procedures prevent aboral spread of slow waves and lead to a drop in their frequency below the level of interruption. However, all segments of the intestine appear to be able to initiate slow waves at an inherent frequency which diminishes distally for reasons as yet unknown. Below the jejunum the frequency of slow waves drops without any experimental intervention and the velocity of aboral propagation, for the short distances over which it can be determined, becomes very slow. The nature and properties of intestinal slow waves have been recently reviewed (83–86) and these publications should be consulted for details and references to early work.

In the postperfusion segments, slow wave frequency was significantly decreased, even below that of distal segments, and propagation into and within the segment was disturbed (81, 82). However, the smooth muscle was histologically normal and, aside from a lower frequency of contraction, mechanically as efficient as in control segments. Szurszewski concluded that the perfused segment generated slow waves at the inherent myogenic frequency and that the myenteric plexus was necessary to raise the excitability of the myogenic system to permit a higher frequency. Further he postulated that an intact myenteric plexus was required for conduction of slow waves in the muscle to enable proximal activity to spread aborally along the intestine and raise the frequency still further. He suggested that release of some excitatory substance from the plexus might account for these results. Previous studies (25–26, 87–89) showing that reserpine (to release 5-HT and noradrenaline), atropine, hexamethonium, or nicotine did not interfere with slow wave amplitude frequency or conduction make the identification of such an excitatory substance with known transmitters unlikely. But none of the above studies has examined the consequences of prolonged withdrawal of mediators or of their effects.

Khin (27) obtained similar effects on slow waves in postperfusion segments, even when attempts were made to eliminate any oxygen from the perfusing media; but she found that these segments responded *in vivo* to drugs such as nicotine and DMPP believed to act indirectly on postganglionic cholinergic nerves. In addition, longitudinal muscle strips from these segments responded *in vitro* to the same drugs and to transmural stimulation. The only clear difference in the activity of strips from postperfusion segments was their lack of segmental movements. Atropine (0.02 µg/ml of the sulphate) or tetrodotoxin prevented the response to transmural stimulation but not that to a high potassium medium. Histological evidence confirmed the presence of functional nerves. Obviously the perfusion damage which altered slow waves was not sufficient to seriously interfere with the function of postganglionic cholinergic nerves. If intrinsic nerves participate at all in maintaining the initiation and propagation of slow waves, then some element other than postganglionic cholinergic fibers is probably involved. Damage to the functional capacity of other intrinsic nerves is more difficult to investigate. If intrinsic nerves are not involved, then we must identify the intestinal component damaged by anoxic perfusion which is essential for normal slow wave activity.

In another study on the dog intestine, Schamaun (83a) showed that clamping the arterial supply, alone or with the venous drainage, for periods up to 20 hr did not prevent recovery of slow waves when the blood supply was restored. Though difficult to evaluate in short experiments of the type used, slow wave frequencies after unclamping seemed not to return to their normal level.

The electrophysiology of intestinal slow waves, their configuration, mode of origin, propagation, and so forth, have recently been reviewed (83–86) and details need not be repeated here. They appear to be propagated electrotonically (89, 90) and perhaps by an active process as well (89), spreading into the circular muscle layer over thin connecting muscle bundles. Moreover, propagation of slow waves in longitudinal muscle may involve cycling from longitudinal muscle to circular muscle and back. Slow waves influence the excitability of circular and longitudinal muscle, diminishing their electrical excitability and perhaps increasing their chemical excitability (89). The possibility should be considered that the low sensitivity to acetylcholine, of isolated circular muscle from guinea pig ileum found by Harry (14) and Kottegoda (15), may result from the disappearance of slow waves from isolated circular muscle.

The general importance of slow waves to motility may be that they cause a propagated band of depolarization (and possibly of increased chemical excitability) to spread synchronously down the intestine. This travelling band would interact with local factors such as release of acetylcholine or inhibitory transmitters either to cause spikes and contractions or inhibit them. Until we know a great deal more about the simultaneous electrical activity of different muscle layers and of intrinsic nerves in and around areas of segmental and peristaltic contraction, this hypothesis cannot be fully tested or elaborated. A recent study (91, 92) suggests that the spikes from longitudinal and circular muscle layers are both recorded from a punctate serosal electrode under slight pressure but that they can be distinguished by their time sequence (longitudinal spikes first), configuration (longitudinal muscle spikes mainly positive-going, because of depolarization from pressure electrode; circular muscle spikes often negative-going), or association with mechanical events. Electrical activity of intrinsic nerves can also be recorded with metal microelectrodes inserted through the serosa (93). The trick will be to obtain all these records under conditions of relatively normal motility.

The best evidence that propagated potential changes in the gut cause the spread of a band of increased chemical excitability comes from studies of antral electrical activity in the dog (25, 26). There, the distally propagated wave (initial potential) is a periodic (5/min) spikelike depolarization which, like the slow wave, does not result in contraction. The velocity of initial potentials increases as they spread into the antrum from the body of the stomach where they seem to originate (25–26, 94–96). The initial potential does, however, result for about 3 sec in an increased susceptibility of the muscle to acetylcholine injected intra-arterially. When injected just after an initial potential wave it causes a secondary prolonged depolarization (second potential), sometimes with secondary spikes, which is associated with contraction. The phase of susceptibility to acetylcholine quickly passes off, leaving a kind of refractory period. Then even large doses of acetylcholine cannot produce second potentials, though premature initial potentials followed by second potentials may be initiated. These premature initial potentials are often propagated in an antiperistaltic direction and may interfere with the normally propagated potential. So far the evidence suggests that the occurrence of second potentials is not required for this change in the response to acetylcholine since it seems to occur in the same way after initial potentials whether or not they are accompanied by second potentials and contractions.

Electrical activities of circular and longitudinal antral muscle have not yet been simultaneously recorded, but the initial potentials have been reported to originate in longitudinal muscle and to be propagated electrotonically into circular muscle (96). There is, however, evidence that interruption of the continuity of the stomach wall followed by reanastomosis disrupts propagation of initial potentials (97–99). Intra-arterial catecholamines in moderate quantities also disrupt propagation (99) by preventing initiation and propagation of initial potentials. In small doses, catecholamines inhibit second potentials and contraction (25, 26). Given intravenously or in large quantities intra-arterially when an intragastric and a duodenal balloon are present, catecholamines can also cause a rapid repetitive discharge of initial potentials, which I have called a 'sympathetic dominance pattern'.

No studies of the role of nerves in regulating electrical activity of the stomach have been made, though it has been found that distention or contractile activity of the duodenum or other portions of the intestine can initiate changes in antral activity similar to those produced by intra-arterial or intravenous catecholamines (31).

At the junction of the antrum and duodenum, initial potential spikes at about 5/min occur less than a millimeter away from intestinal slow waves at 17–18/min. The interaction between these two electrical activities has so far seemed minimal [see (86) for references] but requires further study. An unanswered question is why neither wave is propagated very far past the junction of antrum and duodenum (86, 87, 100–102) *in vivo* since muscle layers seem to be continuous [see (100–102) for references] and since both antral and duodenal electrical activity seem to spread readily from one piece of layer of muscle to another by electrotonic means. Electrotonic spread across this junction has been found *in vitro* (102).

In stomach and intestine, contraction is associated with depolarization or spikes which are poorly propagated (see 25, 26, 83–87, 103, 104). These do not therefore provide a basis for coordination of gastrointestinal motility. The conductance changes accompanying these action potentials are of interest since they are insensitive to tetrodotoxin and may not involve increased sodium conductance (96, 105, 106). However, this area will not be considered further.

In the colon and large bowel, generally very little is known about the electrical coordination of intestinal motility. Despite the intensive and productive study of the electrophysiology of isolated taenia coli [see (84 and 85) for references], we have almost no knowledge of their role in colonic motility. Clearly, *in vivo* studies of the electrical and contractile activity of taenia coli and of other portions of the colonic muscle are required to determine the nature of electrical control of colonic motility.

The esophagus varies greatly from species to species in structure; e.g., in the proportions of smooth and striated muscle in it [see (107) for references]. The upper portion in many species, including men, monkeys, and cats, is composed of striated muscle. In the dog it is nearly all striated muscle. Hellemans et al. (108–110) have found that the *in vivo* electrical activity recorded with bipolar electrodes from the upper portion of the esophagus in the dog and monkey following deglutition resembled that of a skeletal muscle contraction of progressively increasing and decreasing strength. It began with single, identically shaped, spikes; then spikes of different configuration were interposed during an intermediary stage and then the amplitude and number of spikes per unit time rapidly increased so that individual action potentials interfered with one another and were hardly recognizable. The activity waned in reverse order. Activity of single motor units probably accounts for the single type of spike. Spiking rhythm reached a maximum of 35–46/sec and the duration of individual spikes was 4–6 msec. There were usually no spikes before deglutition; spike bursts progressed distally.

In the smooth muscle portion (lower two thirds) of the monkey esophagus, deglutition provoked larger, longer (16–40 msec), and fewer spikes. There was no consistent pattern of frequency changes during the spike bursts accompanying pressure changes.

From some transitional areas, spiking characteristics of both smooth and striated muscles were observed following deglutition. These records probably arise from areas with outer longitudinal striated muscle and inner smooth circular muscle. In some such records a second peristaltic wave contained only smooth muscle spikes. No electrical events accompanied sphincter relaxation and the spike bursts from that region were like those elsewhere in the smooth muscle portion.

The electrical activity of the dog esophagus was characteristic of striated muscle throughout. In the subdiaphragmatic portion of the sphincteric region, the amplitudes and maximal firing rates for spike bursts were lower. No electrical event associated with sphincter relaxation was recorded but the duration of spike bursts was much less in the sphincter region.

A wave of relaxation is believed to precede both primary and secondary peristaltic contraction. Deglutition in a dog during a burst of deglutitive spike activity inhibited all spikes for 0.2 sec simultaneously throughout the esophagus. Thereafter the burst resumed its normal course. Distention of the esophagus, to produce secondary peristalsis, also inhibited spike activity.

In the monkey inhibition followed deglutition and permanently interrupted a spike burst, whether this was occurring in striated or smooth muscle of the body of the esophagus or in the sphincteric region.

In the lower third of the cat esophagus, electrical records resembled those from smooth muscle portions of the monkey esophagus. Spikes accompanied peristalsis following deglutition. Slow waves were not reported but may not have been recorded because of the use of bipolar electrodes and a short time constant.

The longitudinal and circular muscle of the lower 3 cm of cat esophagus *in vitro* manifested similar spikes accompanying drug-induced contraction

(111, 112). Though spontaneous electrical and mechanical activity were rare, each spike burst appeared to be superimposed on a slow wave. Spikes were more difficult to record from circular muscle and did not occur at all sites during contraction. Acetylcholine and other cholinergic stimulants produced contractions prevented by atropine. Atropine also prevented contractions from α-stimulants (as did known α-adrenergic blocking agents), but not those produced by $BaCl_2$. Noradrenaline contractions of longitudinal muscle were selectively inhibited by anoxia, by hemicholinium, and by stripping off adventitial material believed to contain nerves of the lower esophageal plexus. It was proposed that in this organ, α-receptors were in the myenteric plexus and excited contraction by releasing acetylcholine. Inhibitory β-adrenergic receptors were also present. The mechanism of the reflex wave of relaxation is unknown, but it seems unlikely from such evidence that an inhibitory adrenergic reflex is involved in a simple way. Bennett & Whitney (112a) have reported that the sphincteric zone of the human esophagus has excitatory α- and inhibitory β-receptors, when studied *in vitro*, as in the cat. They point out that excitation by adrenergic drugs was found at only one other site, the ileocolic junctional area. The mechanism of the excitatory adrenergic effects in human gut is not known.

Synthesis of Information on Control of Motility

One might postulate that myogenic electrical activity controls intestinal motility by depolarizing muscle cells and initiating contraction, an 'all-or-none' system. However, in the stomach and intestine, myogenic electrical activity depolarizes the smooth muscle cells without necessarily causing contractions; furthermore, at no level of organization have the contractions been shown to be 'all-or-none'. While these observations do not elucidate the mechanism for control of motility, they do suggest the questions, "What controls the electrical activity of muscle cells?" and "What controls the contractile response of the muscle cells to the electrical activity which is present?" It is these questions which will be further elaborated here. In contrast to electrical activity of striated muscle portions of the esophagus which is probably directly controlled by its motor nerves in an 'all-or-none' fashion, that of smooth muscle portions of the gastrointestinal tract seems to be controlled by the spread of electrical activity from cell to cell, slow waves in the intestine, initial potentials in the stomach. However, neither slow waves nor initial potentials are sufficient to cause contraction, which is instead associated with spikes or prolonged depolarization superimposed on or following them. For convenient reference I will call slow waves and initial potentials *control activity* and spikes *response activity*. In most of the stomach and in the intestine, control activity seems to originate at a proximal site in longitudinal muscle (at a pacemaker?) and to spread distally as well as into underlying circular muscle.

One of the difficult and intriguing problems is the mode of propagation of initial potentials in the stomach and of slow waves in the intestine.

Electrotonic spread of these seems to be well established (p. 217). Tetrodotoxin does not interfere with the spread of slow waves, so active excitation by increased sodium conductance in response to local depolarizing currents seems unlikely. The pathways for electrotonic current flow are uncertain. The areas of close contact between intestinal smooth muscle cells [called nexuses by Dewey & Barr (114)] are essential for propagation of action potential spikes (115–116) but their role in propagation of slow waves is undetermined (see 116). Furthermore, the slow wave is positive-going in both intracellular and extracellular recordings, a relationship not expected from volume conductor theory. I have recently discussed (83) two important relevant papers (117, 118). Some difficulties remain in understanding propagation of the potentials.

Inhibition of the sodium pump with ouabain or other agents obliterates slow waves and initial potentials (96, 113). If control activity originates from oscillating activity of a sodium pump, we have to explain how the oscillations in a distal group of cells are phased by oscillations in a proximal group. No studies are available as yet on the effect of slight depolarization on the activity of the sodium pump in intestinal muscle. If the nature of the coupling mechanism is left aside, many of the characteristics of intestinal slow waves can be simulated by treating them as originating from two relaxation oscillators with varying degrees of coupling (86, 113, 117–123). Relaxation oscillators are (123): (a) aperiodic, (b) easily synchronized because frequency pulling occurs readily, (c) different in waveshape from sinusoidal, (d) described by a time period called 'relaxation time', and (e) amplitude stable in contrast to sinusoidal oscillation.

In a recent important study of the application of this model to the slow waves of the small intestine (123), its usefulness was clearly demonstrated. The authors point out that van der Pol's equation for a relaxation oscillator is:

$$\ddot{v} - \alpha (1 - v^2) \dot{v} + w^2 V = 0$$

where

v = the dependent variable, in this case voltage
w = radian frequency of the undamped sinusoid
α = damping coefficient (zero if no damping)
$\dot{v} = dV/dt$ and $\ddot{v} = d^2V/dt = d\dot{v}/dt$

At $\alpha = 0$, the equation reduces to that of a sinusoidal wave with the period $T = 2\pi/w$. The greater the ratio $\alpha/w = \epsilon$, the greater the departure of the waveform from sinusoidal. Slow waves resemble relaxation oscillations with $1 < \epsilon < 10$ and the relaxation time T_{rel} can be calculated from an equation with ϵ as the only variable.

An analog computer was programmed to solve two van der Pol's equations, with α and w in each capable of being adjusted independently. A unidirectional connection from the driving equation to the driven equation provided coupling of the equation solutions.

Increasing ϵ (1 to 10) in a single van der Pol's equation produced waveforms much like those seen in the dog intestine. Unfortunately the authors have chosen slow waves recorded with extracellular electrodes as their model, but these waves appear to be a mixture of an intracellular-like potential after pressure damage or injury and a volume-conducted action potential. In fact, however, the sinusoidal and sawtoothed intracellular potentials (89) are also reproduced by varying ϵ, perhaps even better than are the slow waves of the chosen configurations. However, the values used for ϵ in simulating coupling may be inappropriately high.

In addition, by varying a potentiometer in the coupling circuit, coupling between the solutions of two van der Pol's equations was varied from 0 (no coupling) to 1.000 (no attenuation). At high coupling values one equation could drive the other (both equations showing the same frequency). At low coupling values, the oscillators were independent of each other (oscillating at their uncoupled frequency ratio of 19:13, set to resemble the frequency ratio between the duodenum and ileum). At intermediate coupling values, there was gradual and varying uncoupling of the two rates. The driven equation varied in frequency (or relaxation time) from time to time. This was dependent on having a low value of $\epsilon \leq 3$. At higher values, transitions from the driven to the uncoupled states were abrupt as coupling values were decreased. The variability of the interval between waves increased with decreased values of coupling, as is also the case with increased distance along the intestine according to the authors.

Backward coupling, an effect of the slower frequency oscillator on the frequency of the faster one, also may occur (see 122, 123) but was not studied intensively by the authors. They, like earlier workers, have noted that cutting the upper intestine lowers the slow wave frequency below the cut but does not affect the frequency proximal to the cut. Hence no evidence for backward coupling is available and the authors assume this to be a consequence of refractoriness following each wave in the areas of higher frequency. In such transection experiments, there is very little effect on the ileal rate and this has not been explained by the relaxation oscillation model. It suggests that coupling occurs over limited distances. With pacemakers coupled in series as in the model proposed, the experimental results imply that a set of conditions must exist in which the rate of distal pacemakers (or oscillators) is independent of that of proximal pacemakers. Otherwise the model is incorrect or incomplete.

Backward and forward coupling might be expected to play a role at transitional zones between intestinal areas which have slow waves at different frequencies (antrum at 5/min and duodenum at 19/min). This has not been studied.

Coupling between control activity and response activity has not been studied thoroughly. In the stomach, the propagated initial potential does not seem to be graded (amplitude of initial potentials not influenced by small effective amounts of acetylcholine or noradrenaline) but in the small intestine the slow waves appear to be graded (increased in amplitude by acetylcholine leading to spiking or response activity, or decreased in amplitude by noradrenaline inhibiting response activity). In the stomach, following the passage of the propagated initial potential there is a phase of increased sensitivity to the contracting effect of acetylcholine but it is not clear whether there is also an increased release of acetylcholine. In the stomach, large amounts of noradrenaline can inhibit initial potentials and affect their rhythm. Therefore in the intestine an answer to the first question, "What controls the electrical activity of the muscle cells?" helps to answer the second question, "What controls the contractile response of the muscle cell to that activity?" Anything which increases the amplitude of slow waves is likely to produce spikes. However, this does not seem to be the case in the stomach under physiological conditions. Nevertheless, both in the stomach and in the intestine whether a contraction occurs is not determined exclusively by the arrival of a propagated potential but by the arrival of such a potential when the local chemical or physical environment (acetylcholine, noradrenaline, 5-HT etc.) promotes response activity, i.e., excitation.[2] Local reflexes, usually initiated by distention, appear to determine the balance of chemicals released from nerves and enterochromaffin cells and hence the balance of excitation or inhibition. In some areas (e.g., duodenum) chemical agents may be released into the blood stream to influence distant parts of the gastrointestinal tract.

Obviously, the nature of the coupling between control activity and response activity presents an intriguing and important problem for the understanding of motility. This should be easier to study in the stomach than in the intestine owing to the slower rate of cycling of the control activity and to the greater proportion of each cycle not occupied by the depolarizing control activity.

Coupling between electrical activity (*response activity*) and contraction has also not been studied quantitatively except in taenia coli, probably an inappropriate model for the stomach and other intestinal tissue. In the taenia coli, contractile activity is graded by the frequency of spikes, but many experimental variables have been shown to decouple spikes and contraction (see 83–86).

At present, calcium influx or release is believed to play an important role in coupling response activity to contraction. I feel that the evidence of increased calcium fluxes during response activity presented so far is inadequate

---

[2] Stretch or distention per se depolarizes and excites taenia coli and probably other intestinal muscles but there appears to be no conclusive evidence that stretch can excite intestinal muscle devoid of a source of acetylcholine, 5-HT, or other substances which might be released by distention. However, extreme distention may be sufficient to excite contraction with the participation of propagated potentials or chemicals alone or with neither. Similarly, very high concentrations of chemicals may affect motility without the participation of propagated potentials or distention or both.

to establish their existence. The problems of the effect of a reduced extra-cellular volume during contraction on ^{45}Ca content per gram have not al-ways been considered. Further, in experiments in which ^{45}Ca uptake is estimated only after a period of efflux, it is impossible to say whether a greater residual ^{45}Ca resulted from increased uptake or from a shift of ^{45}Ca from one cellular compartment to another.

LITERATURE CITED

1. Connell, A. M., Texter, E. C., Eds. The International Symposium on Intestinal Motility. Part I, April 1968 and Part II, May 1968. *Am. J. Digest. Diseases*, **13**, 295–496 (1968)
2. Paton, W. D. M., Zar, M. A. *J. Physiol.* (*London*), **194**, 13–33 (1968)
3. Paton, W. D. M. *J. Physiol.* (*London*), **173**, 20P (1964)
4. Gillespie, J. S. *J. Physiol.* (*London*), **162**, 76–92 (1962)
5. Campbell, G. *J. Physiol.* (*London*), **185**, 148–59 (1966)
6. Bennett, M. R. *J. Physiol.* (*London*), **183**, 132–48 (1966)
7. Ohashi, H., Ohgo, A. *Nature*, **216**, 291–92 (1967)
8. Gonella, J. *Compt. Rend. Soc. Biol.*, **158**, 2409–13 (1964)
9. Burnstock, G., Holman, M. E. *Ann. Rev. Physiol.*, **25**, 129–56 (1966)
10. Bennett, M. R., Rogers, D. C. *J. Cell Biol.*, **33**, 573–96 (1967)
11. Pick, J., De Lemos, C., Ciannella, A. *Anat. Record*, **159**, 131–46 (1967)
12. Kosterlitz, H. W., Lees, G. M. *Pharmacol. Rev.*, **16**, 301–39 (1964)
13. Kažić, T., Varagić, V. M. *Brit. J. Pharmacol.*, **32**, 185–92 (1968)
14. Harry, J. *Brit. J. Pharmacol.*, **20**, 399–417 (1963)
15. Kottegoda, S. R. *J. Physiol.* (*London*), (1968)
16. Finkleman, B. *J. Physiol.* (*London*), **70**, 145–57 (1930)
17. Brown, G. L., Davies, B. N., Gillespie, J. S. *J. Physiol.* (*London*), **143**, 41–54 (1958)
18. Norberg, K. A. *Intern. Neuropharmacol.*, **3**, 379–82 (1964)
19. Jacobowitz, D. *J. Pharmacol. Exptl. Therap.*, **149**, 358–64 (1965)
20. Baumgarten, H. G. *Z. Zellforsch.*, **83**, 133–46 (1967)
21. Gillespie, J. S. *J. Physiol.* (*London*), **162**, 54–75 (1962)
22. Bennett, M. R., Burnstock, G., Holman, M. E. *J. Physiol.* (*London*), **182**, 527–40 (1966)
23. Schaumann, W. *Arch. Exptl. Pathol. Pharmakol.*, **233**, 112–24 (1958)
24. Kosterlitz, H. W., Watt, A. J. *J. Physiol.* (*London*), **177**, 11P–12P (1965)
25. Daniel, E. E. *Gastroenterology*, **49**, 403–18 (1965)
26. Daniel, E. E. *Can. J. Physiol. Pharmacol.*, **44**, 951–79 (1966)
27. Khin, J. *Some mechanisms underlying the electrical and mechanical activity of the dog small intestine* (Ph.D. thesis, Univ. Alberta, Edmonton, Alberta, 1967)
28. Lum, K. B., Kermani, M. H., Heilman, R. D. *J. Pharmacol. Exptl. Therap.*, **154**, 463–71 (1966)
29. Sakamoto, S., Nishi, K. *Kumamoto Med. J.*, **20**, 25–38 (1968)
30. Irwin, J., Daniel, E. E. (Unpublished experiments)
31. Daniel, E. E., Wiebe, G. E. *Am. J. Physiol.*, **211**, 634–42 (1966)
32. Gershon, M. D. *J. Physiol.* (*London*), **189**, 317–27 (1967)
33. Bennett, A., Garrett, J. R., Howard, E. R. *Brit. Med. J.*, **1**, 487–89 (1968)
34. Wright, P. G., Shepherd, J. J. *Lancet*, **2**, 1161–63 (1965)
35. Bucknell, A., Whitney, B. *Brit. J. Pharmacol.*, **23**, 164–75 (1964)
36. Martinsson, J., Muren, A. *Acta Physiol. Scand.*, **50**, *Suppl. 175*, 103–4 (1963)
37. Martinsson, J., *Acta Physiol. Scand.*, **62**, 256–62 (1964)
38. Martinsson, J. *Ibid.*, **64**, 453–62 (1965)
39. Martinsson, J. *Ibid.*, **65**, *Suppl. 255*, 1–23 (1965)
40. Paton, W. D. M., Vane, J. R. *J. Physiol.* (*London*), **165**, 10–46 (1963)
41. Greeff, K., Kasperat, H., Osswald, W. *Arch. Exptl. Pathol. Pharmakol.*, **243**, 528–45 (1962)
42. Campbell, G. *J. Physiol.* (*London*), **185**, 600–12 (1966)
43. Bülbring, E., Gershon, M. D. *J. Physiol.* (*London*), **192**, 823–46 (1967)
44. Trendelenburg, U. *Arch. Exptl. Pathol. Pharmakol.*, **230**, 448–56 (1957)
45. Brownlee, G., Johnson, E. S. *Brit. J. Pharmacol.*, **21**, 306–22 (1963)
46. Gyermek, L. Drugs which antagonize 5-hydroxytryptamine and related indolealkylamines. In *Handbuch der Experimentellen Pharmakologie, XIX. 5-Hydroxytryptamine and Related Indolealkylamines*, 471–528 (Erspamer, V., Ed., Springer-Verlag, Berlin, 928 pp., 1966)
47. Daniel, E. E. *Can. J. Physiol. Pharmacol.*, **44**, 981–1019 (1966)
48. Burnstock, G., Campbell, G., Bennett, M., Holman, M. E. *Intern. J. Neuropharmacol.*, **3**, 163–66 (1964)
49. Holman, M. E., Hughes, J. R. *Aus-*

tralian *J. Exptl. Biol. Med. Sci.*, **43**, 277–90 (1965)

50. Day, M. D., Warren, P. R. *Brit. J. Pharmacol.*, **32**, 227–40 (1968)

51. Bennett, A., Bucknell, A., Dean, A. C. B. *J. Physiol. (London)*, **182**, 57–65 (1966)

52. Burnstock, G., Campbell, G., Bennett, M., Holman, M. E. *Nature*, **200**, 581–82 (1963)

53. Burnstock, G., Campbell, G., Rand, M. J. *J. Physiol. (London)*, **182**, 504–26 (1966)

54. Bennett, M. R., Burnstock, G., Holman, M. E. *J. Physiol. (London)*, **182**, 541–58 (1966)

55. Bennett, M. R., Burnstock, G., Holman, M. E. *Ibid.*, **163**, 33P–34P (1963)

56. Bülbring, E., Tomita, T. *J. Physiol. (London)*, **189**, 299–315 (1967)

57. Misiewicz, J. J., Holdstock, D. J., Waller, S. L., *Gut*, **8**, 463–69 (1967)

58. Bennett, A., Misiewicz, J. J., Waller, S. L. *Gut*, **8**, 470–74 (1967)

59. Logan, C. J. H., Connell, A. M. *Lancet*, **1**, 996–99 (1966)

60. Neely, J. *Gut*, **8**, 242–48 (1967)

61. Bennett, A. *Nature*, **208**, 170–73 (1965)

62. Mikos, E., Vane, J. R. *Nature*, **214**, 105–7 (1967)

63. Horton, E. W. *Experientia*, **21**, 113–18 (1965)

64. Coceani, F., Pace-Asciak, C., Volta, F., Wolfe, L. S. *Am. J. Physiol.*, **213**, 1056–64 (1967)

65. Vogt, W. *Biochem. Pharmacol.*, **12**, 415–20 (1963)

66. Vogt, W., Suzuki, T., Babilli, S. *Mem. Soc. Endocrinol.*, **14**, 137–42 (1966)

67. Bennett, A., Friedmann, C. A., Vane, J. R. *Nature*, **216**, 873–76 (1967)

68. Bennett, A., Murray, J. G., Wyllie, J. H., *Brit. J. Pharmacol.*, **32**, 339–49 (1968)

69. Coceani, F., Wolfe, L. S. *Can. J. Physiol. Pharmacol.*, **43**, 445–50 (1965)

69a. Bülbring, E., Crema, A. *J. Physiol. (London)*, **146**, 29–53 (1959)

70. Bennett, A., Bucknell, A., Dean, A. C. B. *J. Physiol. (London)*, **182**, 57–65 (1966)

71. Erspamer, V. Peripheral physiological and pharmacological actions of indolealkylamines. In *Handbuch der Experimentellen Pharmakologie*, **119**, Chap. 7 (Eichler, O., Farah, A., Eds., Springer, Berlin, 1966)

72. Daniel, E. E. Pharmacology of the Gastrointestinal Tract. In *Hand-*

book of Physiology, IV, *Alimentary Canal*, Chap. 108 (Code, C. F., Heidel, W., Eds., Am. Physiol. Soc., Washington, D. C., 1968)

73. Burks, T. F., Long, J. P. *Am. J. Physiol.*, **211**, 619–25 (1966)

74. Burks, T. F., Long, J. P. *J. Pharm. Sci.*, **55**, 1383–86 (1966)

75. Burks, T. F., Long, J. P. *J. Pharmacol. Exptl. Therap.*, **156**, 267–76 (1967)

76. Burks, T. F., Long, J. P. *Brit. J. Pharmacol.*, **30**, 229–39 (1967)

77. Bülbring, E., Lin, R. C. Y. *J. Physiol. (London)*, **140**, 381–407 (1958)

78. Lee, C. Y. *J. Physiol. (London)*, **152**, 405–18 (1960)

78a. Brown, J. C. *Gastroenterology*, **52**, 225–29 (1967)

78b. Brown, J. C., Parks, C. O. *Gastroenterology*, **53**, 731–36 (1967)

78c. Anderson, J. J., Bolt, R. J., Ullman, B. M., Bass, P. *Am. J. Digest. Diseases*, **13**, 157–67 (1968)

79. Hukuhara, T., Sumi, J., Kotani, S. *Japan. J. Physiol.*, **11**, 281–88 (1961)

80. Hukuhara, T., Kotani, S., Sato, G. *Japan. J. Physiol.*, **11**, 635–40 (1961)

81. Szurszewski, J. H. *The relationship of the myenteric plexus to the electrical and mechanical activity of the small intestine in unanesthetized animals* (Ph.D. thesis, Univ. Illinois, Urbana, 1966)

82. Szurszewski, J., Steggerda, F. R. *Am. J. Digest. Diseases*, **13**, 168–77 (1968)

83. Daniel, E. E. *Am. J. Digest. Diseases*, **13**, 297–319 (1968)

83a. Schamaun, M. *Z. Ges. Exptl. Med.*, **141**, 89–162 (1966)

84. Holman, M. E. (See Ref. 72)

85. Kuriyama, H. (See Ref. 72)

86. Daniel, E. E., Irwin, J. (See Ref. 72)

87. Daniel, E. E., Wachter, B. T., Honour, A. J., Bogoch, A. *Can. J. Biochem. Physiol.*, **38**, 777–801 (1960)

88. Daniel, E. E. *Can. J. Physiol. Pharmacol.*, **44**, 981–1019 (1966)

89. Kobayashi, M., Nagai, T., Prosser, C. L. *Am. J. Physiol.*, **211**, 1281–91 (1966)

90. Bortoff, A. *Am. J. Physiol.*, **209**, 1254–60 (1965)

91. Gonella, J., Gignoux, H. *Compt. Rend. Acad. Sci.*, **262**, 570–73 (1966)

92. Gonella, J. *Étude Électrophysiologique de la Motricité Intestinale* (Doctor

of Science thesis, Univ. Aux-Maiseille, 1967)

93. Yokoyama, S. *Pfluegers Arch.*, **288**, 95–102 (1966)

94. Daniel, E. E., Chapman, K. M. *Am. J. Digest. Diseases*, **8**, 54–102 (1963)

95. Carlson, H. C., Code, C. F., Nelson, R. A. *Am. J. Digest. Diseases*, **11**, 155–72 (1966)

96. Papasova, M. P., Nagai, T., Prosser, C. L. *Am. J. Physiol.*, **214**, 695–702 (1968)

97. Shiratori, T., Takakura, K., Kikuchi, S., Takase, S., Kono, H., Sasaki, M. *Tohoku J. Exptl. Med.*, **84**, 228–35 (1964)

98. Shiratori, T., Sugawara, K., Kuroda, S. *Tohoku J. Exptl. Med.*, **85**, 192–200 (1965)

99. Irwin, J. *Proc. Can. Fed. Biol. Soc.*, **10**, 71P (1967)

100. Bass, P., Code, C. F., Lambert, E. H. *Am. J. Physiol.*, **201**, 587–92 (1961)

101. Allen, G. L., Poole, E. W., Code, C. F. *Am. J. Physiol.*, **207**, 906–10 (1964)

102. Bortoff, A., Weg, N. *Am. J. Physiol.*, **208**, 531–36 (1965)

103. Bass, P., Code, C. F., Lambert, E. H. *Am. J. Physiol.*, **201**, 287–91 (1961)

104. Bass, P., Wiley, J. N. *Am. J. Physiol.*, **208**, 908–13 (1965)

105. Nonomura, Y., Hotta, Y., Ohashi, H. *Science*, **152**, 97–99 (1966)

106. Kuriyama, H., Osa, T., Toida, N. *Brit. J. Pharmacol.*, **27**, 366–76 (1966)

107. Christensen, J. (See Ref. 72)

108. Hellemans, J., Vantrappen, G. *Am. J. Digest. Diseases*, **12**, 1240–55 (1967)

109. Hellemans, J., Vantrappen, G., Valembois, P., Janssens, J., Vanden-broucke, J. *Am. J. Digest. Diseases*, **13**, 320–34 (1968)

111. Christensen, J., Daniel, E. E. *Am. J. Physiol.*, **211**, 387–94 (1966)

112. Christensen, J., Daniel, E. E. *J. Pharmacol. Exptl. Therap.*, **159**, 243–49 (1968)

112a. Bennett, A., Whitney, B. *Gut*, **7**, 307–16 (1966)

113. Daniel, E. E. *Can. J. Physiol. Pharmacol.*, **43**, 551–77 (1965)

114. Dewey, M. M., Barr, L. *Science*, **137**, 670–72 (1964)

115. Dewey, M. M., Barr, L. *J. Cell Biol.*, **23**, 553–85 (1964)

116. Barr, L., Berger, W., Dewey, M. M. *J. Gen. Physiol.*, **51**, 347–68 (1968)

117. Bortoff, A. *Am. J. Physiol.*, **213**, 157–62 (1967)

118. Kobayashi, M., Prosser, C. L., Nagai, T. *Am. J. Physiol.*, **213**, 275–86 (1967)

119. van der Pol, B. *Acta Med. Scand. Suppl. 108*, 76–88 (1940)

120. van der Pol, B. *Phil. Mag.*, **2**, 987–92 (1926)

121. van der Pol, B., van der Mark, J. *Phil. Mag. Suppl. 6*, 763–75 (1928)

122. Roberge, F. A., Nadeau, R. A. *Can. J. Physiol. Pharmacol.*, **44**, 301–15 (1966)

123. Nelsen, T. S., Becker, J. C. *Am. J. Physiol.*, **214**, 749–57 (1968)

124. Jacoby, H. I., Bass, P. B., Bennett, D. R. *J. Appl. Physiol.*, **18**, 658–65 (1963)

125. Bass, P., Wiley, J. N. *Am. J. Digest. Diseases*, **10**, 183–200 (1965)

126. Reinke, D. A., Rosenbaum, A. H., Bennett, D. R. *Am. J. Digest. Diseases*, **12**, 113–41 (1967)

LIVER: FUNCTIONAL INTERACTIONS WITHIN THE INTACT ANIMAL[1]

By William C. Shoemaker and David H. Elwyn

*Department of Surgical Research, Hektoen Institute, Cook County Hospital
and Departments of Surgery and Biochemistry, University of Illinois
Chicago, Illinois*

Introduction

Elucidation of the role of the liver in maintenance of normal biochemical homeostasis requires quantitation of manifold, complex hepatic interactions with other organs. Measurements of physiologic and metabolic responses in normal conditions as well as in conditions of stress and disease are difficult to obtain because of the relative anatomic inaccessibility of the hepatic vascular connections with the rest of the body and the extremely subtle nature of hepatic functions. By contrast, evaluation of many other organ functions is simpler; for example, the renal vascular anatomy and the accessibility of the functional endproducts of renal excretion permit precise functional evaluation of the kidney. Hepatic and renal functional interactions with the body as a whole also may be compared. Urinary excretion of metabolites is the major, albeit not the only, essential renal function. By contrast, regulation of energy metabolism and of plasma constituents is the major function of the liver, while biliary excretory functions represent a relatively small part of the total hepatic functional interrelationships.

The liver occupies a central position in body metabolism. It regulates most of the concentrations of plasma constituents, removes metabolic endproducts, clears bilirubin and other hemochromogens resulting from red cell destruction, detoxifies and conjugates abnormally occurring compounds and exogenous poisons, provides a constant source of glucose to meet energy requirements of the peripheral tissues, removes lactic, pyruvic and other organic acids and resynthesizes glucose from them, regulates amino acid metabolism, synthesizes urea and most of the plasma proteins, regulates fat transport, exerts a controlling influence on circulating hormonal concentrations by inactivation, and secretes the bile acids as well as other substances necessary to digestion. Further, the liver is a major site of storage for glycogen as well as for fat-soluble vitamins. In all of these, the liver's metabolic actions must be viewed in relation to the functional activity and demands of the peripheral tissues.

Thus, the ebb and flow of oxidative substrates to vital organs and other

[1] The survey of literature for this review was concluded in January 1968.

peripheral tissues are controlled and regulated by the liver. In part, this is accomplished by removing absorbed glucose, lipids, and amino acids in the postprandial period and releasing them in the postabsorptive period in such a manner as to provide relatively constant circulating blood concentrations. As various plasma constituents are removed by peripheral organs they may be resupplied by the liver, which must make necessary metabolic inter-conversions. In this context, alterations in hepatic hemodynamics, stimulation by various hormones, and various disease states affect hepatic functional relationships with the total body metabolism.

In general, liver function may be approached using a spectrum of preparations which range from subcellular organelles, tissue culture cells, liver slices incubated *in vitro*, the perfused organ, and the hepatectomized animal to the intact animal. These biological preparations provide successive degrees of organization from isolated cell particulates to the whole animal and permit successively decreasing precision of biochemical analyses. The elucidation of metabolic pathways, chemical properties of enzymes, structures of cell organelles, mechanisms of interaction of proteins and nucleic acids, and molecular action of hormones has necessarily come from the study of isolated and purified systems. However, this information is obtained in preparations where the hepatic circulatory and functional interactions with the remainder of the body have been eliminated. The bulk movements of substrates between organs and tissues and the movements between plasma, extracellular fluid, and intracellular spaces also are necessary to the clarification of the functional role of the liver. Eventually, interorgan transport of blood constituents should be related to physiologic and biochemical mechanisms. Recent methodologic approaches permit quantitative estimations of hepatic function in intake aminals in relation to changes in the body as a whole.

Changes in hepatic function frequently are reflections of changes in the normal physiologic rates of metabolic reactions rather than complete elimination or introduction of metabolic pathways. Differences in metabolism of liver cells may consist of changes in the rates of reactions and in the metabolic traffic at key positions along alternative pathways. Similarly, hormonal action, endocrine diseases, hemorrhage, trauma, and other stressful conditions which impose a great functional demand on the liver may produce quantitative changes in the velocity of normally present enzymatic reactions. Hepatic functional changes, which take place during changes in the physiologic state of the normal animal, ultimately must be related to chemical reaction rates. Moreover, regulation of hepatic function ultimately should be understood in terms of the influences of controlling mechanisms on these reaction rates. This review will be limited to studies which primarily relate to quantitative estimations of hepatic functions in relation to changes in the whole body. By and large, the selection of material reflects this orientation toward interactions between liver and other organs in the intact animal; i.e., interorgan transport of blood and plasma constituents.

Methodologic Considerations

Perfusion.—Since Claude Bernard (1) first proposed isolated liver perfusion, this approach has been widely used to investigate the hepatic physiologic and metabolic reactions. Perfusion techniques afford several advantages over other methods for investigation of liver physiology: they make possible differentiation between reactions which are entirely hepatic from those effects which are manifest in the liver but are secondary to extrahepatic influences; they allow a greater control over inflow pressures to the organ, a greater range of concentrations of the prefusate constituents, and a greater control over temperature and other physical conditions than is possible in intact animal preparations; they are ideally suited to acute studies of the progressive hepatic deterioration associated with reduced blood flow, anoxia, metabolic poisons, etc., and to experiments designed to eliminate or control extraneous extrahepatic influences. Descriptions of the various techniques, the biologic limitations of the systems, and criteria for functional evaluation of the perfused liver have been reviewed (2–6).

Classical tests of liver function have been applied to liver perfusions. These included various conjugation and extraction tests such as the bromsulfthalein excretion (7), galactose and ammonia clearance (8), perfusate flow rates, vascular resistance, O_2 consumption, bile flow, glucose and K^+ concentrations of the perfusate, glycogen content of the liver tissues, and release of various enzymes. Concentrations of enzymes of the Krebs cycle (9, 10) rise in acute liver injury and fall during frank cellular necrosis. Drapanas and his associates (11, 12) studied the ability of the isolated perfused calf liver to take up and metabolize intermediates of both glycolytic and oxidative cycles. Other workers (13–15) used the content and regeneration of high energy phosphate compounds in the liver as measures of hepatocyte integrity.

Early investigators noted rapid loss of K^+ from the perfused liver (16–18). The exact role of ionic shifts in the context of liver function is not clear, but Judah et al. (18) in extensive investigations have postulated that this may be a basic mechanism common to all cellular injury.

In all perfusion preparations, gradual deterioration of hepatic function begins at, or shortly after, onset of perfusion. Disharmonic alterations of function occur, but not in an entirely predictable manner. The biologic integrity of the perfusion system may be shown by survival of the animal after re-establishing the normal vascular connections following perfusion (19). However, this does not mean that "normal" hepatic function was maintained during the time of the perfusion.

Deterioration of hepatic function was studied by abrupt discontinuation of O_2 to the perfused calf liver system (4). The perfusate K^+ concentration rapidly increased, SGOT, glucose and lactate concentrations as well as the lactate/pyruvate ratio rose to extremely high levels about an hour after the start of anoxia. Glycogen concentration in the liver diminished and bile output fell to zero within an hour of the start of anoxia; both hepatic arterial and portal venous resistances rose and total blood flow was reduced to approximately one half of the preanoxic values; liver weight increased. The most sensitive indicators appeared to be release of K^+, pyruvate, glucose and SGOT as well as diminished glycogen synthesis (4), increased portal venous and hepatic arterial resistance, liver swelling and engorgement; decreased oxygen consumption, bile output, and BSP extraction are reproducible, although less sensitive, measures of functional integrity of the perfused liver. Light microscopy is of little value in evaluating liver function whereas electron microscopic alterations correlate well with change in chemical tests of liver function. The earliest change in cell ultrastructure is dilatation of the rough endoplasmic reticulum (4).

Rearrangement of hepatic vascular connections.—Hepatic metabolism may be studied in animal preparations with rearrangement of vascular connections by Eck fistual (portacaval anastomosis) with proximal portal vein ligation, reverse Eck fistual (portacaval anastomosis with proximal caval ligation), and portacaval transposition (20, 21). By redirection of routes of inflow to the liver, interrelationships between liver, gut, and other peripheral tissues may be inferred.

Measurement of the rates of hepatic metabolism in the intact conscious animal.—Early estimates of hepatic metabolism consisted of measurements of blood samples taken from the hepatic vessels in "acute" preparations at the time of surgery. Subsequently methods for study of hepatic metabolism in intact unanesthetized animals were devised to eliminate the uncontrollable variables associated with acutely operated anesthetized preparations. London (22) described a two-stage procedure in which free fascial grafts were placed over a hepatic vein and a metal cannula was placed between the fascial grafts and the surface of the abdominal wall. After recovery, hepatic venous blood could be obtained in the conscious animal by introducing a needle through the cannula. Warren & Brannon (23) catheterized hepatic veins in a retrograde fashion.

A technique for chronic implantation of plastic catheters in the major hepatic vessels provided a method for direct measurement of hepatic metabolism in the conscious dog (24). After the animal's recovery, blood samples are readily obtained from the indwelling catheter system. Various components of sampled blood may be analyzed with sufficient accuracy to obtain relatively uniform concentration differences of a given plasma constituent. These differences multiplied by concomitantly measured hepatic blood flow provide an estimate of the net rate of liver output or uptake of the plasma constituent. In a similar manner, the blood pressure in the vessels entering and leaving the liver may be measured through the chronic, indwelling catheter system and used to obtain pressure gradients across the organ. The gradients divided by the simultaneously measured blood flow rate will provide direct measurements of organ resistance (24).

Hepatic Anatomy and Hemodynamics

Hepatic anatomy: blood and plasma volumes, extracellular spaces, hepatic mass.—Hepatic plasma volume (9.3 ± 0.6 ml/100 g wet liver weight), hepatic sucrose-^{14}C space (21.8 ± 0.9 ml/100 g), and exchangeable albumin space in the liver (10.4 ± 0.8 ml/100 g) were measured in anesthetized rabbits (25). After administration of dextran-188, these volumes increased significantly. Goresky & Johns (26) used indicator dilution techniques to determine the sinusoidal blood volume and the extravascular volumes of distribution of diffusible indicators in the livers of anesthetized dogs. A two-compartment mathematical model was developed which assumed that exchange of substances across the sinusoidal walls was very rapid when compared to flow in the sinusoids, and that labeled red cells did not move out of the sinusoids and were completely recoverable in hepatic venous blood. Simultaneous injection of multiple indicators permitted estimation of volume and mean transit time of blood in the sinusoids and the volumes penetrated by albumin, insulin, sucrose, sodium, urea, and water. Excellent agreement between total water volume of the liver determined in this way, and by dry weight determination, confirmed the method. Sinusoidal blood volume, corrected for catheter distortion (27). was found to be 12.8 ± 4.0 per cent of liver weight. Later Goresky & Johns (28) extended this technique to an analysis of the kinetics of sulfobromophthalein uptake by the liver.

Guntheroth & Mullins (29) used four types of transducers to quantify dimensions of the liver in the intact unanesthetized dog. Fright produced no appreciable change in liver size. Epinephrine, norepinephrine, and isoproterenol (average dose 20 μg) caused a variable response with no change in over half of the trials. Angiotensin decreased liver size in one of three trials; acetylcholine produced variable responses; histamine produced no changes and pentobarbital increased liver size in about half of the trials. Rapid hemorrhage caused a gradual decrease in liver size in only half of the animals, but in only one of 18 animals was the decrease considered significant (150 ml). Initial transient decreases in liver size after hemorrhage were followed by return to control levels even though blood volume loss and progressive hypotension continued. The failure of the liver to consistently become smaller with hemorrhagic shock suggested that this organ may be a site of blood pooling; i.e., relatively more blood may accumulate in the liver than in other tissues. Pooling of blood in the liver tissue after hemorrhage also has been observed by radioactive and chemical analyses (30, 31). Increased liver size usually accompanied hypoxia produced by pentobarbital in sufficient quantities to give apnea. After vigorous exercise, the liver released blood in only 4 of 64 experiments; in about half of the excercise periods, the liver actually became larger (29).

Portal and hepatic arterial pressure-flow relations.—Using extracorporeal perfusion circuits and intravascular pressure measurements, Greenway et al. (32) observed that increased resistance in both hepatic arterial (HA) and portal venous (PV) systems followed stimulation of hepatic nerves in the anesthetized cat; HA pressure remained constant while HA flow decreased; PV pressure increased while PV flow was unaltered. These responses were unaffected by pretreatment with atropine and propanolol but were blocked by phenoxybenzamine. Norepinephrine produced changes similar to those from hepatic nerve stimulation except that there was a more prolonged decrease in HA flow (32). In anesthetized, acutely operated dogs, inhalation of a 5 per cent CO_2 to 95 per cent O_2 gas mixture produced increased HA and PV flow (33). Alkalosis induced by hyperventilation decreased HA flow and arterial pressure. These responses were not influenced by HA neurectomy. After HA neurectomy, PV occlusion did not change HA flow. If the nerves were intact, splenectomy produced no change in HA flow; however, denervation of the HA after splenectomy increased HA flow. Superior mesenteric artery occlusion increased HA flow; this increase was greater in animals with prior HA denervation. Both PV occlusion and end-to-side Eck fistula increased HA flow in spite of arterial hypotension; these increases were greater after HA denervation (33). The HA flow also was increased in man after PV occlusion at the time of abdominal surgery (34). The findings suggest intrinsic regulation of HA blood flow by perihepatic arterial nerves only in the presence of severely reduced PV blood flow (33).

With an extracorporeal pump and tube connecting the femoral artery to the distal segment of the severed hepatic artery, the hepatic arterial pressure-flow relations in the acutely operated dog were found to be nonlinear (35). The pressure-flow curve was either predominantly convex to the flow axis or sigmoidal. Increases in pressure above normal resulted in minimal increases in flow. Ganglionic blockade and atropinization did not affect the general shape of this curve (35).

Effect of hormonal stimulation on hepatic hemodynamics.—Injection of epinephrine, 1 to 10 μg/kg, into the femoral vein or inferior vena cava of unanesthetized dogs increased the estimated total hepatic blood flow (HBF) (36). With doses of 10 to 25 μg/kg, a biphasic response was usually seen; this consisted of an initial increase and a subsequent decrease before return to control values. With larger doses there were pronounced decreases in hepatic blood flow and, occasionally, death (36). These findings were confirmed in unanesthetized dogs with an electromagnetic blood flow meter. The increased total hepatic blood flow consisted of an increased portal venous blood flow and an initial decrease followed by an increase in hepatic arterial flow (37). Similar findings were observed in the anesthetized acute preparation (38).

The effects of epinephrine administered by both femoral venous and portal venous routes were compared (36). The rapid rate of epinephrine destruction by the liver allows differentiation of two distinct patterns of epinephrine effects on the hepatic vasculature which depend on the site of administration. Intraportal epinephrine injection produced vasoconstriction of the hepatic vasculature as evidenced by prompt, marked increases in portal venous pressure, portal-hepatic venous pressure gradient, and hepatic vascular resistance to flow (36); there were minimal effects on systemic hemodynamics. On femoral venous injection, epinephrine produced its major action on the heart and arterial circulation. This consisted of an increase in, and redistribution of, cardiac output resulting in greater HBF. There were smaller responses of the hepatic circulation, which consisted of increased pressure gradients across the liver and slightly increased hepatic venous resistance (36).

Norepinephrine (1 to 10 μg/kg) injected into the femoral vein produced prompt decreases in HBF as well as increased PV pressure, portal-hepatic venous pressure gradient, and arterial pressure; the hepatic venous resistance increased (39). The responses reached a maximum 60 sec after injection and were dose dependent. When identical doses were injected into the portal vein under comparable conditions, the arterial pressure and HBF responses were delayed and attenuated. However, increased PV pressure, portal-hepatic venous pressure gradient, and hepatic venous resistance occurred earlier and were more pronounced. Norepinephrine, like epinephrine, constricted the hepatic vasculature, but it had the opposite effect on HBF (39).

Glucagon (0.02 mg/kg) doubled HBF in the conscious dog (40). The increase in flow coincided with hepatic venous hyperglycemia (40) and was associated with decreased hindquarter blood flow (41). Insulin in low doses (0.1 to 0.2 units/kg) produced no significant change in HBF (42). However, insulin in high doses (1.0 unit/kg) resulted in increased HBF associated with pronounced hypoglycemia. This increase was interpreted as a secondary effect to the insulin-induced hypoglycemia, possibly mediated by epinephrine (42). Reduced HBF followed administration of vasopressin (43).

Changes in hepatic blood flow under various physiologic conditions.—Mean HBF for the normal unanesthetized dog averaged 37 ml per kg body weight per min (44). Increased HBF was seen with anxiety, excitement, and muscular activity (44). Feeding 50 g of carbohydrate (glucose and fructose) increased HBF appreciably for 45 to 90 min (45). The increased total hepatic blood flow was largely, if not entirely, attributable to increased portal venous blood flow (45). Changes in HBF throughout the diurnal cycle were observed; major increases were seen after ingestion of a high protein meal (46).

Six normal men weighing an average of 75 kg were subjected to heavy excercise for 60 min (47). The excercise required 10 to 12 kcal/min or 2 to 2.5 liters O_2/min which is an eightfold increase in oxygen consumption over normal values. Splanchnic blood flow decreased to 50 per cent of the normal resting state (average 567 ml/min) but splanchnic O_2 consumption (average 112 ml/min) did not decrease during exercise (47).

Influence of septic and hemorrhagic shock on hepatic hemodynamics.—HA and PV pressures and flow were studied using gated sine-wave flowmeters in acutely operated, anesthetized dogs before and after intravenous administration of *S. enteritidis* endotoxin. This agent produced an immediate rise in PV pressure, as well as decreased HA and PV blood flow, arterial pressure, central venous pressure, cardiac output, and hematocrit. The ratio of PV to HA blood flow fell; the PV and HA resistance both increased. HA flow expressed as a per cent of cardiac output increased while that of PV flow decreased; although total HBF fell, the percentage of cardiac output supplying the liver tended to be maintained near control values (48). In general, there were striking similarities in the pattern of hepatic hemodynamic changes after endotoxin and hemorrhagic shock; however, in hemorrhagic shock PV pressure did not rise until later in the course of shock; i.e., after retransfusion of the shed blood (49).

Decreased HBF, increased PV pressure and portal-hepatic venous pressure gradients, and decreased hepatic venous O_2 saturations were observed in dogs subjected to the Wigger's type of hemorrhagic shock (50). Transient improvement in hepatic blood flow and hepatic venous O_2 followed retransfusion of shed blood. Norepinephrine in sufficient quantities to restore arterial pressures did not increase flow. Dibenamine pretreatment partly sustained hepatic blood flow during hypovolemic shock. Pretreatment of dogs with antibiotics did not significantly alter these hemodynamic effects (50).

Measurement of blood flow in the celiac and superior mesenteric arteries of Macaca monkeys during the Wigger's type of hemorrhagic shock revealed decreased splanchnic blood flow and increased splanchnic resistance in the postinfusion period (51). The ratio of mesenteric resistance to hepatic resistance decreased throughout hemorrhage, and was not significantly increased on retransfusion (51). In the unanesthetized dog (49), the hepatic venous resistance increased moderately after hemorrhage and increased markedly after retransfusion.

In unanesthetized dogs, hepatic blood flow was measured at 10-min intervals throughout all stages of gradual, prolonged exsanguinating hemorrhage (49). Four distinct periods were seen. In the initial period, blood flow values were relatively stable and represented essentially normal values. This period extended until 10 to 20 per cent of the blood volume was withdrawn. A second period characterized by increased HBF then followed. These flow increases were not accompanied by obvious excitement or agitation, although restlessness was sometimes seen. This period of increased flow was brief but definite and its duration depended on the rapidity of the bleeding. A third, and the longest period was characterized by a gradual but continually decreasing HBF. At the end of this period a diminished capacity of the liver to clear bromsulfthalein at the normal or control rates was manifested by modest increases in portal vein bromsulfthalein levels. In the fourth and final period, further reductions in the rate of HBF and progressively decreasing functional capacity of the liver were evidenced by a decreasing ability to clear bromsulfthalein (49).

REGULATION OF HEPATIC POTASSIUM AND OTHER ELECTROLYTE MOVEMENTS

Since the early hepatic perfusion studies (17) and reviews (52), K^+ release has been associated with glycogenolysis and deterioration of hepatic function. Marked K^+ and glucose release has repeatedly occurred upon setting up the isolated perfused liver (3, 5, 17, 53), with deterioration of the functional integrity of the perfused organ (17), and with deliberate anoxia (4). In general, K^+ movements into or out of the hepatic and peripheral cell were related to glucose movements occurring in the same direction. Much of this material has been ably reviewed by Eichler & Farah (54). More recently, quantitative information on K^+ movements in relation to various physiologic states, hormonal stimulation, and movements of other plasma constituents has become available.

Relations between hormone-induced glucose and K^+ movements.—After epinephrine given as a single, intravenous injection into the femoral vein of unanesthetized dogs in doses of 1 to 2 μg/kg, there were increases in the concentrations of glucose and K^+ in hepatic venous plasma and in the rates of output of glucose and K^+ by the liver (55). Maximum glucose release occurred 3 to 5 min after epinephrine injection, but the greatest K^+ response occurred in 40 to 70 sec. Between 0.5 and 1 meq of K^+ was released by the liver in response to 1 μg epinephrine/kg body weight; this was followed by compensatory hepatic uptake of comparable amounts of K^+ (55). Epinephrine in acutely operated anesthetized cats produced similar changes in both arterial and hepatic venous K^+ and glucose concentrations (38). The K^+ efflux was coincident with the arrival of epinephrine at the liver, and synchronous with, or earlier than, the onset of glucose release. However, under these conditions, the onset of hepatic K^+ release preceded that of glucose by only seconds (38).

Elliott et al. (56), using rapid sampling and hypothermia, observed the movements of K^+, Cl^-, Na^+, CO_2, HCO_3^-, and glucose, as well as flow responses, after administration of epinephrine to perfused rabbit livers. There was rapid release of K^+, Cl^-, HCO_3^-, and uptake of Na^+ which began about 10 to 20 sec and reached maximum values in 45 to 90 sec after epinephrine injection. In normothermia, the rate of hepatic glucose output increased to maximal values in 3 to 5 min after epinephrine. In hypothermia, the increased hepatic glucose output was markedly delayed, while the electrolyte movements were not (56). In both normothermia and hypothermia, increased hepatic K^+ release preceded the activation of hepatic phosphorylase by glucagon (57) and epinephrine (37) as well as the subsequent glucose release.

The dissociation of K^+ and glucose movements was also observed by Burton et al. (53, 58) during glucagon-induced glycogenolysis in perfused rat livers. When glucagon was added to preparations which had previously lost K^+ to the perfusate during 60-min perfusions, marked hepatic glucose output occurred without K^+ release (58). Cardiovascular responses from intravenous administration of glucagon were less pronounced than after epinephrine, although glucagon did produce increased hepatic blood flow (40). Relatively large doses of glucagon (0.02 mg/kg) produced significantly increased hepatic venous plasma K^+ levels and hepatic K^+ outputs of 1.0 to

2.7 meq during the first 2 min after injection (37, 55). Cortisol in the properly prepared, adequately fed, nonstressed animal produced increased net hepatic K^+ output (37).

Norepinephrine produced increased hepatic venous plasma K^+ concentrations comparable to those produced by epinephrine (37, 55). However, norepinephrine gave rise to decreased hepatic blood flow (39), and net hepatic K^+ outputs were smaller than after epinephrine (37).

When the perfused liver was pretreated with insulin to restore intracellular K^+, a large K^+ efflux occurred during the onset of glucagon-induced glycogenolysis. After the glucagon administration, insulin caused recovery of K^+ previously lost from the liver and reduced the outflow of glucose (58). Earlier, Kestens et al. (59) reported that insulin produced K^+ uptake in the isolated dog liver without affecting the glucose levels of the perfusate. These data implied that (*a*) despite the initial hypoxia, the perfused liver was responsive to insulin, (*b*) insulin is required by the liver for K^+ recovery, and (*c*) the transfer of K^+ into the liver is dissociated from the transfer of glucose.

In conscious dogs, insulin produced only a modest increase in hepatic K^+ uptake; the effect was maximal 5 min after injection (60). In the barbiturate anesthetized dog, there was a small hepatic K^+ output in the control period. This changed to a hepatic K^+ uptake during the first 20 min after insulin administration. A comparable effect was obtained in the conscious animal pretreated with the blocking agent, phenoxybenzamine HCl. In brief, insulin produced a hepatic K^+ uptake which was greater when epinephrine was blocked by dibenzyline and barbiturate (60). Presumably, insulin-induced hypoglycemia produces counter-regulatory mechanisms including increased epinephrine secretion by the adrenal medulla. In the isolated liver perfused with whole blood, the initial K^+ release and glycogenolytic response, associated with anoxia incident to removal of the liver from the intact animal, subsided in 30 min (53). Subsequently, there was a re-entry of K^+ into the perfused liver and decreased hepatic glucose output. Insulin given during this recovery period resulted in a prompt hepatic K^+ uptake which preceded demonstrable glucose uptake (58). This supports the findings of Mortimore (61) that insulin has a physiologic role in maintaining hepatic intracellular K^+.

Administration of serotonin, as 5-hydroxytryptamine creatinine phosphate, increased portal venous plasma K^+ and K^+ output from the nonhepatic splanchnic area 60 to 90 sec after injection (62). This was followed by hepatic K^+ uptake of almost the equivalent amount of K^+ that was released by the gut.

Effect of hyperventilation with alkalosis on K^+ movements.—Acute respiratory alkalemia, produced by hyperventilation of anesthetized acutely operated dogs for 2 hr, caused temporary increase in plasma K^+ coincident with increase in pH from 7.37 to 7.7 (63). The transient K^+ rise was maximal at about 15 min and was followed by consistent hypokalemia after 45 min.

Arterial plasma K^+ reached an average of 0.6 meq/liter above control in 15 min, while greater increases were seen in portal venous and superior mesenteric venous plasma (1.8 meq/liter) and hepatic venous plasma (1.1 meq/liter). It was concluded that the K^+ was released from the nonhepatic splanchnic area, while the peripheral tissues and the liver removed the liberated K^+; no regional blood flow measurements were made (63).

Effect of hemorrhage on hepatic electrolyte movements.—During both Wigger's type of hemorrhagic shock and gradual prolonged hemorrhage, portal and hepatic venous plasma K^+ concentrations rose parallel with elevations of glucose (49, 64). Increases in K^+ levels were most marked in the hepatic venous plasma, where concentrations of 8 to 12 meq/liter were observed. In gradual hemorrhage, hepatic K^+ output was not initially increased, but as hemorrhage progressed, the rate of K^+ release from the liver increased markedly and paralleled that of glucose (49). When 20 per cent of the blood volume was rapidly removed, there was prompt elevation of hepatic venous plasma K^+ which averaged 2.0 meq/liter more than control values as well as increased net hepatic K^+ output which averaged 2 meq/min over control values (64). This output, if uniformly distributed in the extracellular phase, accounted for the elevated arterial K^+ values (64). Na^+ movements in and out of the liver were of the same order of magnitude but in the opposite direction. These electrolyte movements after hemorrhage were similar to those observed ofter exogenous epinephrine injection and suggest that they may result from epinephrine action (37, 49, 64).

Summary and significance of hepatic K^+ movement.—Studies briefly reviewed here indicate that there are rather well defined patterns of interorgan K^+ movements. Liver output and peripheral uptake of K^+ accompany hepatic glycogenolysis, reduced hepatic blood flow, stimulation by epinephrine, glucagon, steroids and norepinephrine, acute hypokalemia, blood loss, anoxia, stress, and acute disceases. The liver removes K^+ during postprandial obsorption, when K^+ is released by the working muscle, during hyperglycemia, after intravenous glucose load, and with stimulation by insulin especially in the presence of hyperglycemia. Movements of K^+ appear to be related to and almost always in the same direction as movements of glucose. However, while the postulated mechanism of Fenn (49), that K^+ movements are a passive consequence of water movements associated with hepatic glycogen synthesis and breakdown, may operate to a limited extent, it cannot account for the many instances where K^+ movements precede glucose movements, or precede the increased activity of hepatic phosphorylase, or are not accompanied by glucose movement. It would appear, then, that the stimulation of K^+ movement by hormones or stressful stimulation is not mediated by prior glucose movements. In this sense, K^+ movement may be considered as dissociated from carbohydrate movements. Whether hormone effects on carbohydrate metabolism are or are not dependent on K^+ movements is not clear. Since K^+ movements invariably precede glucose movements after stimulation with glucagon or epinephrine, it is possible that they are an obligatory step in activating liver phosphorylase. Alternatively, K^+ movements may be incidentally related to hormone-induced glucose movements but not essential to them.

In the case of glucagon and epinephrine, both K^+ and carbohydrate movements may be postulated to result from hormonal action on adenyl cyclase which catalyzes the reaction;

$$\text{ATP} \xrightarrow{\text{adenyl cyclase}} 3'5'\text{-AMP} + \text{P--P}$$

Liver phosphorylase is activated by $3'5'$-AMP. In addition, significant amounts of K^+ are known to be complexed to the negatively charged ATP molecule (65) and, upon the breaking up of the ATP, may be released. When ATP near the cell membrane is broken down, K ions complexed to it may be washed off into the circulating plasma.

Hepatic Carbohydrate Metabolism and Its Regulation by Hormonal Agents

Hepatic carbohydrate metabolism in the resting state.—Since the early work of Soskin et al. (66), Lipscomb & Crandall (67), Bondy et al. (68), and others, direct and indirect methods have been used to estimate the "normal" resting hepatic glucose output and its regulation by hemodynamic, neural, hormonal, and metabolic factors. Most data accumulated have indicated an average hepatic glucose output of 2 to 4 mg per kg body weight per min in the dog; marked changes occur after hormonal stimulation, food ingestion, starvation, diabetes, hemorrhage, trauma, and other forms of stress.

Under resting postabsorptive conditions in the conscious dog, hepatic glucose output of 5 mg per min per kg was associated with hepatic uptakes of lactate (0.3 mg per kg per min), pyruvate (0.07 mg per kg per min), and citrate (0.1 mg per kg per min) (69). The values for hepatic clearance of organic acids were greater in dogs that were not in optimal nutritional and physiologic condition.

Hepatic carbohydrate metabolism after oral and intravenous glucose administration.—Carbohydrate movements between gut and liver were studied after oral feeding of both 50 g of glucose and 50 g of fructose in the unanesthetized dog with chronically implanted catheters (45). There were rapid elevations in portal venous sugar concentrations until an average of 264 mg/100 ml was reached 30 min after feeding; there were lesser increases in hepatic venous glucose and only modest elevations in arterial levels. Portal venous-arterial concentration differences, hepatic blood flow (measured by a modified bromsulfthalein method), and portal venous blood flow (measured with an electromagnetic flowmeter) were increased up to 180 min after feeding (45). An average of 84 per cent of the ingested carbohydrate was recovered as an output from the gut into the portal vein. The liver removed 31.8 g of sugar (64 per cent of that ingested) from the plasma during the 3-hr period of observation after the carbohydrate meal. The mean control hepatic glucose output averaged 54 mg/min or 3 mg per min per kg. If this were extrapolated over the 3-hr postprandial period, it would be the equivalent of 9.7 g and the net change in the amount of hepatic glucose uptake over control values would be 41.5 g. This value agrees remarkably well with the total measured carbohydrate absorbed by the gut (42.2 g). The data suggest that three fourths of the sugar absorbed by the gut is removed by the liver and the remainder has replaced the glucose which would have been supplied by the liver to the peripheral tissue had the animal continued in the fasting state.

After ingestion of fructose, 42 per cent of this carbohydrate, absorbed by the gut and released into circulating plasma as an output of the gut, was in the form of ketose; the remaining 58 per cent of the absorbed sugar was converted to glucose by the gut during the process of absorption (45).

During glucose and fructose absorption, about 4 per cent of the administered sugar was recovered as lactate; there also was a decreased rate of lactate clearance by the liver during sugar absorption (45).

Some of the factors which determine the rate at which glucose is removed by the liver were evaluated (45). The portal venous glucose concentration correlated well with the portal hepatic venous concentration difference, which suggests that the portal venous glucose concentration was the major factor in determining the portal-hepatic glucose concentration difference. Therefore, the rate of glucose entering the liver was inversely related to the hepatic glucose output and probably a major determinant of the latter. In the unanesthetized dog, portal venous glucose concentrations below 120 mg/100 ml were associated with positive hepatic glucose output, but portal concentrations above this value were associated with uptake of glucose by the liver (45).

Landau et al. (70) observed hepatic glucose output (HGO) during gradually increasing glucose infusion in unanesthetized dogs with indwelling catheters in the hepatic vessels. They noted marked changes in the hepatic response to glucose infusions which were related to the composition of their diets prior to the experiments. In dogs maintained on high protein diets, glucose infusions produced increased blood glucose concentrations and cessation of positive HGO only at hyperglycemic levels. In carbohydrate-fed dogs, glucose infusions produced minimally increased blood glucose concentrations and net hepatic glucose uptakes. In protein-fed dogs, hepatic output changed to an uptake at plasma glucose concentrations between 150 to 200 mg/100 ml, but in carbohydrate-fed dogs this occurred between 100 to 130 mg/100 ml (70). These direct measurements confirm previously held concepts of a strong dependency of glucose assimilation upon the dietary history and suggest adaptive mechanisms. The regulation of plasma glucose concentrations by the liver appeared to be more sensitive in dogs adapted to high carbohydrate feeding.

In general, these data support and amplify Claude Bernard's (71) well-known concept of hepatic regulation of blood sugar concentrations. Using the method of his day, however, Bernard (71) found no sugar in portal blood and believed that the liver was solely responsible for maintaining relatively constant peripheral blood glucose concentrations by the hepatic release of glucose.

Effect of phlorizin.—Kolodny et al. (72) studied the effect of phlorizin on HGO in anesthetized dogs whose hepatic vessels had been acutely catheterized. Phlorizin infusion in these dogs produced glucosuria and increased HGO within 5 to 10 min. These effects preceded significant changes in portal venous glucose concentrations. Phlorizin changed neither HGO nor circulating glucose levels in dogs with bilateral ligation of renal veins and in dogs in which loss of glucose through the urine was prevented by redirecting the urine into the vena cava. Moreover, glucose infusions given at rates sufficient to maintain normal circulating glucose levels also prevented the phlorizin effect on HGO. The data indicate that phlorizin-induced glucose changes are dependent on the loss of glucose from the body, rather than on stimulation of liver, kidney, endocrine glands or on impaired glucose utilization (72).

Glycogenolysis: The effects of glucagon and epinephrine on carbohydrate metabolism.—Intravenous injection of crystalline glucagon, 0.02 mg/kg, to the unanesthetized dog increased HGO about five times that of control values (40). Elevations in hepatic venous glucose concentrations and HGO reached maximal values 10 to 20 min and returned to control values 45 min after glucagon administration. Up to 10 g of glucose was released in response to glucagon stimulation (40). The glucagon-induced glycogenolysis was accompanied by proportional increases in hepatic uptake of lactate, pyruvate, and citrate (69). In the starved animal HGO responses were absent or markedly attenuated (40, 69).

During hepatic glycogenolysis there was increased glucose uptake in the hindquarters and nonhepatic splanchnic area (gut). The increased HGO also was accompanied by increased lactate and citrate output by hindquarters and gut as well as increased pyruvate output by the gut (40). These findings indicate marked acceleration of circulation of the components of the Cori cycle which occurred *pari passu* with glycogenolysis and suggest increased glucogenesis from carbohydrate precursors. The liver also removed amino acids at increased rates, which became maximal 45 min after glucagon injection (75). This suggested the presence of increased gluconeogenesis from noncarbohydrate precursors which followed glycogenolysis; presumably, this may be important to restore glycogen stores (75).

Miller (73, 74) demonstrated effects of insulin and glucagon on carbohydrate and protein metabolism of perfused livers of both fed and fasted rats. Glugacon in small doses provoked glycogenolysis, suppressed oxidation of glucose-^{14}C, and increased protein catabolism as measured by urea output. Pretreatment with insulin during perfusion neutralized the protein catabolic effects of glucagon but did not affect the glucagon-induced glycogenolysis and did not reverse the suppression of oxidation of labeled glucose. The protein catabolic effects of glucagon in the perfused system were due solely to enhanced catabolism of liver proteins and not of plasma proteins (73).

Epinephrine in doses of 1 and 5 μg/kg also produced hepatic glycogenolysis as evidenced by increased HGO (54, 69). The maximum HGO occurred 3 to 5 min after epinephrine injection and was associated with a sixfold increased hepatic uptake of lactate, pyruvate, and citrate, which occurred simultaneously with a threefold increase in HGO. The rates of carbohydrate movements returned to control values within 15 min after injection (69). Epinephrine in the isolated perfused rat liver system produced less complete glycogenolysis than did glucagon (73). Decreased urea output, reduced perfusion flow rates, and suppressed oxidation of labeled glucose occurred after epinephrine administration. It was concluded that epinephrine does not increase protein catabolism (73).

Hyperglycemic and glycogenolytic effects of 3'5'-AMP and its 2'-O-monobutyryl derivative were observed in the perfused rat liver; the latter compound was twice as effective as the former in elevating perfusate glucose concentrations (76). Neither compound increased perfusion flow rates or bile production.

Effect of glucocorticoids.—Livers of normal, adrenalectomized, and hypophysectomized rats were perfused for 4 hr with a substrate-containing, cell-free medium (77). The normal rat liver formed glucose at rates averaging 4.5 mg per g per hr from pyruvate and at similar rates from lactate; this was not altered by adrenalectomy or hypophysectomy. Dexamethasone did not increase glucose synthesis from pyruvate. In livers of intact rats, glucose production from alanine was less than from pyruvate or lactate; hepatic glucose output was further reduced by adrenalectomy, but increased by dexamethasone. Thus, glucocorticoid hormones were thought to increase the conversion of alanine to pyruvate (77). However, others (73, 74) concluded that hydrocortisone was relatively inert on the isolated perfused liver.

Effect of insulin.—The regulatory influence of insulin on hepatic metabolism was studied in the following preparations and conditions: (*a*) the perfused rat, cat, and dog liver; (*b*) the dog whose hepatic inflow vessels have been redirected by Eck fistula (portacaval anastomosis) and by portacaval transposition; (*c*) the dog whose hepatic vessels have been catheterized; (*d*) dilution of ¹⁴C-glucose given by a single injection or constant infusion to the intact dog; and (*e*) the normal man and patients who have been subjected to portacaval shunt and hepatic vein catheterization. Although it is still a controversial question, most investigators and reviewers (78–80) take the position that insulin either suppresses hepatic glucose output or causes hepatic uptake of glucose. Bondy et al. (68) observed a decreased splanchnic glucose output in diabetic patients following insulin administration. This was confirmed by Sherlock and associates (81), who concluded that insulin produced a hepatic as well as a peripheral uptake of glucose. We will attempt to summarize evidence of insulin action on the liver in the frame of reference of hepatic functional interactions with the rest of the body.

Hepatic glucose metabolism in the perfused liver.—Early perfusion studies on cat liver failed to demonstrate diminished hepatic glucose output after insulin administration (82); this was confirmed in the perfused livers of normal dogs and rats (59, 83–85). Haft & Miller (84), using the isolated rat liver perfused with a medium containing 350 mg/100 ml glucose, found that the glucose concentration of the perfusing medium increased to 600 mg/100 ml within an hour and that this increase was unaffected by insulin. But, in livers from alloxan-diabetic rats, insulin increased the removal of glucose from the perfusate at these concentrations after 1.5 to 4 hr of perfusion (84). On the other hand, inhibition of glucose output in the perfused liver was reported (61, 86–90); many of these responses have been small in magnitude, and lacking in consistency and reproducibility. Insulin also produced an immediate inhibition of urea release in livers taken from fasted rats; this suggested reduced gluconeogenesis (73). In the perfused livers of fed animals, insulin had a greater inhibitory effect on glucose release, but a similar effect on urea release (73). However, in subsequent studies, Haft (86) found no insulin effect on glycogen content or urea production.

The effects of various perfusate glucose concentrations on HGO were observed in isolated perfused glycogen-containing rat livers (91). When normoglycemic blood was replaced with hypoglycemic blood, HGO did not increase; it did increase after glucagon stimulation. The authors (91) concluded that the liver does not respond to hypoglycemia directly, but requires extrinsic, extrahepatic stimulation. However, failure to demonstrate this in the perfused livers may have little bearing on the situation in the intact animal.

Ruderman et al. (85) observed glucokinase activity in livers of fed rats which were perfused with and without added insulin. Insulin increased hepatic K^+ uptake and prevented the fall in glucokinase activity, but did not affect hexokinase and glucose-6-phosphatase activities. The magnitude of the glucokinase activity reduction did not correlate with the glucose output or release and was not influenced by variations in the initial glucose concentrations. The net glucose output was not significantly affected by insulin in low doses, but at high doses (1.2 unit/hr) insulin significantly increased net HGO during the first 60 min of perfusion.

Hepatic glucose movements in the dog with vascular rearrangements.—Madison and his associates (92, 93) demonstrated a sharp fall in hepatic glucose output in anesthetized dogs with Eck fistula. They also reported greater decreases in this output as well as decreased peripheral uptake of glucose after intraportally administered insulin as compared with injection of insulin into a foreleg vein. The significance of these results is subject to some reservation, since the dog with an Eck fistula has impaired liver function (94), reduced hepatic blood flow (92, 94, 95), and a modified response to insulin (96). Further, the Eck fistula animals were fed a diet richer in carbohydrate than the customary kennel ration, and anesthesia was used. Moreover, Starzl et al. (96) observed progressively decreasing hypoglycemic responses to insulin during periods up to 8 weeks after production of the Eck fistula. The diminished insulin effect in dogs with Eck fistulae and the rise in insulin requirements after Eck fistula in alloxan-diabetic dogs is important in interpretation of results of this type of experiment; the assumption that Eck fistula dogs respond normally to exogenous and endogenous insulin is severely challenged by these data (94–97).

Insulin infusion reduced hepatic glucose output from an average of 58 to 36 mg/min in dogs with portacaval transportation; this reduction was less than that in dogs with Eck fistula (97). The magnitude and duration of the insulin-induced hypoglycemia in dogs after portacaval transposition was comparable when insulin was given systemically or intraportally and was essentially the same as that of the preoperative response in the same animals (97).

The difference in the hepatic response to insulin in dogs with normal hepatic vascular anatomy, as compared with that in dogs with Eck fistula or portacaval transposition, may be explained, in part, by the difference in availability of glucose to the liver. The carbohydrate and amino acids absorbed from the gastrointestinal tract go first to the peripheral tissues in the animal with Eck fistula and portacaval transposition, in contrast with the normal dog. Limited availability of carbohydrate and carbohydrate precursors to the liver in the Eck fistula and the portacaval transplantation preparation results in reduced glycogen stores (98) and may affect the balance of the rates of carbohydrate movements between the liver and the peripheral tissues in both absorptive and postabsorptive conditions. Further, the hepatic metabolic changes induced by insulin administration in the face of diminished hepatic carbohydrate reserves may limit the capacity of the liver to supply glucose to the periphery; this may reduce the control HGO values as well as hepatic capacity to respond to hormone stimulation. Under these special and limited physiologic conditions, reduced hepatic glucose output after insulin should not necessarily be considered a direct insulin action on the liver, per se. Moreover, though insulin may have an action on hepatic glucose output under conditions of altered hepatic vasculature, it does not necessarily follow that this is a direct hepatic action of insulin which is normally operative.

Hepatic glucose metabolism in the intact dog with chronically implanted catheters.—Arterial, portal, and hepatic venous plasma glucose concentrations, HBF, and HGO were measured in both anesthetized and unanesthetized dogs that were maintained on adequate diets (99–102). Glucagon-free insulin was given by a rapid single injection and by constant infusion in doses from 0.1 to 1.0 units/kg via both portal vein and femoral vein into normal, adrenalectomized, depancreatized, and depancreatized-adrenalectomized dogs all of which were unanesthetized; no significant decrease in HGO was observed after insulin administration in any of these conditions (101, 102). Moreover, there was no increase in hepatic glycogen nor of tissue free-glucose concentrations in hepatic biopsies after insulin; this is consistent with absence of a direct hepatic insulin effect in the dog under the conditions of these experiments. There were only relatively minor changes in the ratios of portal venous to hepatic arterial blood flow to the liver; therefore, redistribution of inflowing blood to the liver could not have masked an insulin effect on HGO (102). Although total splanchnic glucose gradient and total splanchnic glucose output decreased after insulin administration, this was not accompanied by a concomitant decrease in the portal-hepatic glucose gradient and HGO. The assumption that total splanchnic glucose output is equivalent to HGO (68, 81) was not borne out by these experiments (101). Rather, glucose uptake by the nonhepatic splanchnic area after insulin overwhelmed the lack of effect upon the liver and resulted in the observed decrease of total splanchnic glucose output (101).

Leonards et al. (103) measured HGO before and after intravenously administered insulin in unanesthetized dogs with previously implanted catheters. In dogs that had been on a high protein diet, insulin infusion with or without concomitant glucose infusion to maintain circulating glucose levels did not affect HGO. But insulin administration to carbohydrate-fed dogs did decrease HGO. Insulin given together with sufficient glucose to maintain plasma glucose levels decreased HGO and, in some instances, resulted in hepatic glucose uptake. The authors (103) suggested that the threshold for the change from glucose output to uptake by the liver was lowered by insulin. These experiments clearly demonstrate that the action of insulin on the liver's capacity to regulate circulating glucose levels depends on the prior dietary status of the animal. These incisive observations suggest an immediate action of insulin on the liver in carbohydrate-fed dogs and explain the reported disparities in hepatic glucose responses to insulin in intact animals as well as in perfused livers. The pre-existing diet and the flow of carbohydrates at the time the liver is removed for perfusion, as well as the tissue trauma and anoxia associated with removal of the organ in large part, may determine the response or lack of response of HGO to insulin.

The reduced HGO after insulin in dogs fed high carbohyrate diets (103) requires some comment. The dog, normally carnivorous, relies on gluconeogenesis for a large part of his glucose requirements. Insulin administration which tends to drive glucose into peripheral cells would be expected to increase intracellular glucose concentrations. If neural and hormonal regulatory mechanisms are stimulated by circulating glucose levels, it follows that reduced HGO after insulin represents a direct insulin action on the liver. If, by contrast, intercellular glucose concentrations, expecially in pancreatic, adrenal, and neural cells, trigger the hormonal, neural, and hemodynamic mechanisms which regulate HGO, then increased glucose penetration into peripheral cells and the resultant increased intracellular glucose concentrations may evoke feedback mechanisms that depress HGO; this may be mistakenly attributed to a direct insulin action on the liver. Similarly, administration of glucose to maintain normal blood sugar levels given simultaneously with insulin produces the same type of interpretational problems. Artificial maintenance of normal blood glucose concentrations after insulin should not be confused with the maintenance of normally available oxidative substrates in peripheral tissues nor with the normal hepatic-peripheral tissue interactions. Moreover, the effects of simultaneous administration of two experimental variables (glucose and insulin) cannot logically be attributed to only one of them.

   Estimation of HGO in the intact animal by glucose-¹⁴C dilution methods.— Changes in hepatic glucose production after insulin were estimated by Dunn et al. (104) using a ¹⁴C tracer technic first described by Feller et al. (105). Following a single injection of glucose-¹⁴C, plasma glucose specific activity decreased exponentially. After insulin administration, a specific activity "plateau" or a decreased rate of falloff in the specific activity of ¹⁴C-glucose was found (104). Dunn et al. (104) concluded that this plateau was the result of insulin action in stopping the hepatic production of glucose, the latter being predominantly unlabeled. However, in the anesthetized dog, Tarding & Schambye (99) and Henderson et al. (106) observed no appreciable decreases in the rate of decline of plasma glucose-¹⁴C activity after insulin administration.

   Steele, De Bodo and associates (107–111) estimated HGO in dogs by a method based on isotope dilution using constant peripheral intravenous infusions of ¹⁴C-glucose. The calculated rate of dilution of the labeled glucose by unlabeled glucose, presumed to be released almost entirely from the liver, was assumed to represent the rate of HGO; theoretically this calculated rate could become zero, but could not become negative even when a hepatic glucose uptake was present. After a control period, insulin was constantly infused with and without added glucose in sufficient quantities to maintain circulating blood levels. Unanesthetized dogs maintained on a standard (38 per cent) and high (89 per cent) carbohydrate diet were studied during the postabsorptive state (109). Insulin reduced the HGO by about one half during the first hour and by three quarters during the second hour. Glucose infusions at rates between one and one and a half times the resting HGO rates reduced new glucose release by liver by half during the first hour of infusion. In the second or third hour, glucose infused at two to five times the resting HGO rate reduced the unlabeled glucose release by three fourths or more. Animals on the high carbohydrate diet had increased HGO, and increased plasma glucose concentrations in the control period as compared with animals on a low carbohydrate diet. Insulin was reported to decrease the rate of unlabeled glucose production in dogs given both standard and high carbohydrate diets (109). Bishop et al. (110) measured glycogen content of liver and the incorporation into glycogen of glucose-¹⁴C in serial percutaneous biopsies specimens before and during infusions of glucose with and without insulin. Insulin infusions stopped glycogen loss, decreased glucose-¹²C release, and increased glucose-¹⁴C entry into liver glycogen. After glucose infusion, there was an early decrease in net glycogen loss, which was not

brought about by increased uptake of labeled glucose and glycogen synthesis. The authors (110) concluded that endogenous insulin, secreted in
response to hyperglycemia, brought about the early decrease in new glucose
production.

In the single-injection glucose-^{14}C dilution method, the specific activity of
hepatic venous plasma glucose was only slightly lower than that of the
portal vein during the initial control period (101, 112). However, after injection of insulin, the specific activity of the hepatic venous plasma glucose
was significantly lower than that of the portal vein. Moreover, the duration
of the specific activity plateau after insulin was uniformly longer in the
portal blood than in arterial, femoral venous blood and hepatic vein blood
(101, 112). Decreased hepatic venous glucose specific activities observed
during the portal venous specific activity plateau indicate that the portal
blood was more, not less, diluted with unlabeled glucose during passage
through the liver in the postinsulin period. Furthermore, the rate of increase
of the total amount of ^{14}C-glucose on passage through the liver was relatively
unchanged after insulin (101). It appears unlikely that the observed plateau
of glucose specific activity following insulin is due to a cessation of hepatic
glucose production. Among possible alternative interpretations are: (a) an
insulin-caused increase in the rate of bidirectional flux of glucose across cell
membranes, in which case the observed plateau might be expected to result
from the back transfer of glucose of a higher specific activity which had left
the plasma at an earlier point in time (101, 112); (b) a temporary increase in
the size of the pool sampled due to the rapid equilibration of glucose between
plasma and the extracellular fluid; (c) glucagon contamination of the insulin
(108); (d) an acceleration of the Cori cycle giving rise to more rapid rein-
corporation to ^{14}C into newly synthesized hepatic glucose; and (e) re-entry
of ^{14}C-glucose of high specific activity from the cells of the intestinal mucosa.
Since the intestinal mucosa normally transports glucose from gut lumen to
intracellular phase and then into the portal vein plasma during postprandial
absorption, it is likely that labeled glucose enters the mucosal cells and
subsequently is transported back into the plasma. The re-entering glucose
would be of higher specific activity, since a period of time would have
elapsed between leaving and re-entering the plasma, and would explain the
higher portal venous glucose activities in the postinsulin period. This concept is supported by Hetenyi et al. (113).

Tarding & Schambye (99) and Mahler et al. (112) presented evidence
that hepatic glucose outputs estimated simultaneously by the isotope dilution method and by the more direct approach using hepatic catheterization
do not always agree. HGO measured by isotope dilutions in both preinsulin
and postinsulin periods were generally greater than those obtained by catheterization of the hepatic vessels. Only one of four dogs showed comparable
values when the two methods were used simultaneously (112). Furthermore,
after insulin administration, simultaneous HGO estimations by the two
methods changed in different directions; when estimated by isotope dilution,

this output decreased from 80 to 60 mg/min, but when estimated by hepatic catheterization method, it increased from 30 to 40 mg/min (99, 112).

Wrenshall & Hetenyi (113–114) have reviewed and criticized the assumptions and validity of the glucose-^{14}C single-injection and constant-infusion methods for measuring hepatic glucose output.

Hepatic carbohydrate response to hemorrhage and trauma.—Increased blood sugar concentration, as an abnormality of experimental shock, was first observed by Claude Bernard (115) in 1877. The quantitative and temporal relationships of hyperglycemia in shock have since been studied relative to the experimental model, the presence or absence of anesthesia, feeding, fasting, hepatic glycogen content, and other prior conditions of the animal, the presence or absence of the adrenal glands or of the adrenal medulla, and the presence or absence of the liver and abdominal viscera. Hyperglycemia failed to occur in hepatectomized, eviscerated animals and when the liver had been depleted of glycogen by fasting (116–117). Further, both adrenalectomy and adrenal demedullation prevented postinjury hyperglycemia and, on occasion, actually led to hypoglycemia (117–119). However, the hyperglycemia response occurred in fed, adrenalectomized animals which were maintained on saline and DOCA or doses of corticoids that did not, in themselves, elevate blood sugar (117). Glucose mobilization occurred after an initial bleeding in both fed and fasted rats. There was no difference in the mortality between the fed and fasted groups, but the survival time increased significantly in the fed group (119). Hyperglycemia, presumably from hepatic glycogenolysis, occurs after trauma, hemorrhage, stimulation of somatic afferent neurons, and emotional disturbances.

Stoner & Threlfall (120) conducted parallel experiments on fed, fasted, and adrenalectomized or adrenodemedullated rats subjected to tourniquet shock. Fasting accelerated the terminal hypoglycemia and reduced the magnitude of most changes; adrenomedullectomy suppressed the early responses. Hyperglycemia often persisted into the late stages of shock, but eventually blood sugar levels decreased and frequently culminated in hypoglycemia (120). In the final stage, glycogen in heart, liver, brain, and muscle fell, blood glucose decreased, and organic acids rose to their maximal levels (120).

In the unanesthetized dog, the rate of hepatic glucose output was measured continuously throughout the course of gradual prolonged hemorrhage (49): the output began to increase shortly after about 15 per cent of the blood volume had been removed and progressively increased until extremely high rates were reached shortly before death. Glucose concentrations in excess of 700 mg/100 ml were observed in the hepatic venous plasma at this time (49). In brief, experimental shock increases hepatic and peripheral glycogenolysis, blood glucose levels, and peripheral glucose utilization. Late in the course of shock, the rate of glucose utilization exceeded that of HGO and led to decreasing blood sugar levels. Many of these carbohydrate alterations are explicable in terms of epinephrine action.

In the oligemic period of hemorrhagic shock, Seligman et al. (121) and Drucker (118) confirmed the increased lactate and pyruvate and an increased lactate/pyruvate ratio, interpreting it as increased anaerobic metabolism. These carbohydrate abnormalities occurred early (118), but returned toward normal after transfusion of the shed blood, even though the animal went on to die (118, 121).

Clinical depletion states.—Nutritional, metabolic, and physiologic deterioration occurs in acutely depleted clinical states associated with gastroenteric diseases, infections, burns, trauma, and extensive surgical operations followed by multiple complications. Lacking glucose and calories because of inadequate oral or parenteral alimentation, the body may deplete glycogen stores in several days; fat depots are expended more slowly. According to the concept of Soskin & Levine (122), fat burns in the flame of carbohydrate; presumably, fat oxidation requires some concomitant carbohydrate oxidation. When carbohydrate sources have been exhausted, oxalacetate may become rate limiting for Krebs cycle metabolism and ATP production (123). As there is no known pathway in mammals by which lipid can supply the glycolytic or the Krebs cycle intermediates, amino acids from labile proteins maintain the high-priority glycolysis and Krebs cycle metabolism. With prolongation of this situation, additional tissue protein is broken down. This process, while essential to maintain life in the acute illness, eventually may lead to depletion states, inadequate protein synthesis, poor wound healing, inability to resist infection, and other complications. Obviously, more specific and definitive information along these lines in man is needed.

Summary.—Definitive conclusions on the role of the liver in carbohydrate metabolism are limited by the apparent contradictions in the reported data; these frequently center about uncontrolled variables incident to the preparations; e.g., anesthesia and acute operative trauma affect respiration, blood gas content, pH, metabolism of organic acids, adrenal catechol and corticosteroid production, and the integration of neural mechanisms particularly by the higher centers. All of these factors directly and indirectly affect the control state of hepatic hemodynamics and the control rates of hepatic glucose metabolism as well as response to the experimental variable, and must be considered in interpreting results. Artifacts in the isolated perfused liver preparation may be produced by direct injury to the liver itself as well as by effects of the period of interrupted hepatic circulation and hepatic anoxia associated with setting up the perfusion system.

The effects of various hormones on isolated perfused liver may be viewed in terms of their hepatic action as manifest by changes in perfusate and liver tissue concentrations. Data obtained by this type of experiment may imply a direct action of the hormone on the organ. Alternatively, the effect of the hormones may be viewed in terms of their influence on the normally occurring metabolic interactions between the liver and peripheral tissues; i.e., the hepatic regulation of the ebb and flow of oxidative substrates concerned in total-body energy metabolism. The perfused organ approach may have many artificial aspects which limit the conclusions which may be derived. For example, many perfusion experiments are conducted with perfusate glucose levels over 600 mg/100 ml (73, 74). Measurements in the intact conscious animal, while more complex and more difficult to interpret, are more applicable to the normally functioning biologic system. Where discrepancies between the two approaches are clearly evident, the nature of essential hepatic functions regulating body metabolism must be considered. Unequivocal evidence of a hepatic action of a particular hormone is not necessarily provided by perfusion experiments, definite though the data may be. Direct measurements of hepatic metabolic function in relation to peripheral organ function in the intact animal appear to afford more definitive answers.

The concentration of plasma glucose reflects the balance of the rates of release by liver and gut as well as the metabolism by peripheral tissues. The major glucose movements from gut to liver occur in the postprandial period and glucose movements from liver to peripheral tissues occur in the postabsorptive period. In addition to the absorptive and postabsorptive patterns, hepatic glucose output may be influenced by: (a) the past dietary history and pattern of flow of absorbed carbohydrates, lipids, and amino acids along metabolic pathways, (b) the time in the diurnal cycle, (c) the duration of fasting before experiment, (d) the physiologic and hormonal balance at the time of the experiment, and (e) the physiologic status and capacity of the liver itself, which may be profoundly altered by infections, chronic diseases, anesthesia, acute surgical procedures, muscular activity, anxiety, fear, blood loss, and other events immediately before and during the experiment.

Although our present knowledge is extremely sketchy, some tentative clarifying concepts and hypotheses may be proposed within the framework and limitations outlined above. In normal, resting, postabsorptive condition, the liver of the concious dog releases about 2 to 4 mg glucose per kg per min and at the same time removes 20 per cent of this quantity in the form of pyruvate, lactate, and citrate which are returned to the liver to be resynthesized into glucose. There are considerable differences in these rates among various mammalian species. After carbohydrate feeding, the liver removes most of the glucose absorbed by the gut. The removal of glucose by the liver after carbohydrate ingestion and the subsequent slow release in the postabsorptive period is closely related to the glucose concentration in the portal venous blood. In dogs on a high protein diet, glucose concentrations over about 120 mg/100 ml are associated with hepatic uptakes; the higher the level, the greater the uptake. In addition to the changes in carbohydrate movements associated with meals, there are changes during the diurnal cycle which are associated with muscular activity, variations in adrenal steroid release, body temperature, sleep, anxiety, and other physiologic states.

Glucagon and epinephrine stimulate hepatic glycogenolysis, increase hepatic clearance of organic and amino acids, increase protein catabolism and urea output, suppress hepatic oxidation of glucose to CO_2, and alter lipid movements. Evidence favors the concept that glucocorticoids stimulate gluconeogenesis and increased HGO. The hepatic action of insulin has been a favorite controversial subject for symposia; considerable evidence supports a direct hepatic action suppressing HGO in the perfused liver (61, 86–90) in portacaval shunt and portacaval transposition preparations (92, 93, 97) and in man (68, 81). This is partly balanced by reports indicating lack of significant changes in the perfused liver (59, 83–84) and intact animal (99–102). Since significant methodologic and interpretational problems are associated with each of the approaches, a final answer may not be appropriate at this time. However, we favor the view that insulin has a definite action in increasing glucose penetration into peripheral cells; under some special conditions, insulin may also have an effect on HGO which, however, is relatively small, somewhat inconstant, and probably dependent on the state of energy metabolism and the hepatic-peripheral tissue interactions.

REGULATION OF HEPATIC FAT METABOLISM

Bile acid metabolism.—In the neonatal period, bile acids were found to be conjugated mainly with taurine, but during the first week of life the ratio of glycine to taurine conjugates rapidly increased (124). They reached adult values (3.2: 1) after the first years of life (125). In liver disease, especially long-standing obstructive jaundice, this ratio decreased (124).

The homeostatic regulation of bile acid formation was studied in bile duct-cannulated rats during continuous infusion of taurochenodeoxycholic acid into the distal part of the severed bile duct (126, 127). Bile acid metabolism was brought into the normal range with infusions of 5–10 mg per hr; the concentration of bile acids in the portal blood under these conditions was 2 mg per 100 ml (127).

Danielsson et al. (128) observed the distribution and oxidation of 4–^{14}C-cholesterol in isolated perfused livers; the labeled cholesterol was emulsified and added directly to the perfusate or injected into the blood donor animals both 1 and 24 hr before sacrifice. In the latter instance, about 10 per cent of the labeled liver cholesterol (calculated as the per cent of labeled cholesterol present in the liver at the end of perfusion) was converted to taurine-conjugated bile acids; about 80 per cent of this was taurocholic acid and the remainder taurochenodeoxycholic acid. This proportion (8:2) was approximately that found in the intact rat. The artificially emulsified, labeled cholesterol added directly to the perfusate or injected into the blood donor an hour before sacrifice was taken up more rapidly by the liver and oxidized more slowly to bile acids than the physiologic solutions of cholesterol passed through the blood donor animals (128).

Increased biliary excretion of cholesterol was observed in hyperthyroid bile-fistula rats (129, 130).

The hepatic extraction fraction of taurocholate infused in dogs was 92 ± 5 per cent at hepatic blood flow rates of 1.1 to 2.8 ml per min per g liver and the extraction of cholate was 79 ± 8 per cent. This suggests more rapid transfer of cholic acid from blood to bile after prior conjugation (131).

Lipid metabolism of the perfused liver.—Morris (132) observed that palmitic acid both in free form and incorporated into chylomicron triglycerides was taken up by the perfused rat liver and oxidized to CO_2 and ketone bodies; the catabolism of the free palmitic acid occurred more rapidly. Differences in uptake and release of free fatty acids (FFA) and triglycerides were observed in perfused livers of fed and starved rats; the rates of the conversions and oxidation of fat were related to the nutritional state of the animal (132, 133). The level of fat metabolism and the interconversions appear to be related to the availability of oxidative substrates from carbohydrate.

In the perfused rat liver, Heimberg et al. (133) observed greater triglyceride uptake of both synthetic neutral fat emulsions and washed, rat chylomicrons by the perfused rat liver of starved rats as compared with normal fed animals. When no triglyceride was added to the perfusate, triglyceride was released by the perfused livers of fed animals, but was removed by livers of fasted animals. However, these movements were not merely a function of hepatic triglyceride concentrations, since the latter were of the same order of magnitude in both fed and fasted rats. No differences in the uptake of FFA with added albumin-complexed FFA were observed in livers of either fed or fasted animals (133).

In perfusion experiments using fed livers, Morris (132) observed that the perfusate concentration of total esterified fatty acid doubled by the end of 4-hr perfusions, suggesting synthesis of esterified fatty acids from free fatty acids. With added chylomicron triglycerides, the perfusate FFA concentrations increased rapidly to a miximum between 1 and 2 hr. With added FFA as labeled palmitic acid, there was little change in perfusate FFA concentrations, even though the labeled palmitate was rapidly removed; 80 per cent of the radioactivity disappeared in the first hour and only 5 per cent remained after 4 hr. This suggested rapid exchange between perfusate and hepatic FFAs. Breakdown of triglycerides into FFA and synthesis of the former from ^{14}C-palmitic acid were greater in the livers of fed rats than of starved rats (132). The oxidation of both was greater in livers of starved than of fed rats and oxidation of FFA to $^{14}CO_2$ was more rapid than that of chylomicron triglycerides. There were increased concentrations of ketone bodies in the perfusate of both fed and fasted rat livers, but starved rat livers oxidized more fat to $^{14}CO_2$ and ketones than did fed livers. The latter had maximum rates of palmitic acid oxidation at about 2 hr; fed rat livers oxidized most of the labeled triglycerides during the third hour. After 4 hr of perfusion, 90 per cent of the ^{14}C activity was recovered as esterified fatty acid in liver tissue. Most of the radioactivity was recovered in liver phospholipids; lecithin contained 41 to 56 per cent and cephalin 10 to 33 per cent of the total activity. Cholesterol, cholesterol ester, and sphingomyelin fractions each contained very small amounts of activity. The amount of triglyceride radioactivity was less when the labeled palmitic acid was in the free fatty acid form than when it was in triglyceride chylomicrons (132).

In physiologic conditions, free fatty acids and triglycerides are present in the circulation. High concentrations of plasma triglycerides have little influence on hepatic removal of free fatty acids, and its removal from perfusate does not appear to be related to removal of chylomicron triglycerides. This suggests different mechanisms involved with the uptake of these two types of compounds. The difference in fat metabolism in fed and starved livers may be due to differences in hepatic glycogen content. More carbohydrate was available for oxidative metabolism in glycogen-rich livers, and therefore the requirements for fat oxidation were lower than with starved livers. By contrast, in livers with little glycogen, oxidative metabolism occurred largely from fat breakdown. This view is consistent with the observations of Mishkel & Morris (134) on the respiratory quotient of perfused livers; the RQ of livers from starved rats was 0.76, but that of fed rats was close to 1.

In subsequent experiments, Morris (135) observed the effects of concentration, perfusion pressure, and temperature on the metabolism of free ^{14}C-palmitic acid and chylomicron triglycerides in the perfused rat liver. The amount of labeled free fatty acids taken up by the liver depended principally on its concentration in the perfusate and to a lesser extent on the inflow pressure and temperature; the percentage removed by the liver was the same for the three levels of concentration studied. Hepatic removal of chylomicron triglycerides was less efficient at high concentrations and blood flow rates. The percentage of free fatty acids oxidized to ^{14}CO$_2$ was directly related to perfusion inflow pressure, but was unrelated to free fatty acid concentrations and temperature. The percentage of triglyceride oxidized to CO$_2$ was negatively correlated with the concentrations of fat and directly related to perfusion pressure (135). The efficiency of extraction in perfused liver was of the same order of magnitude as in the liver of the intact animal and could account for removal of practically all chylomicron fat which enters the circulation after a fat-rich meal (135, 136).

When Nestel & Steinberg (137) perfused rat livers with high free fatty acid concentrations, the liver removed the fatty acids rapidly and had increased (25 to 60 per cent) glyceride content; the increment corresponded roughly to the amount removed. The glyceride increase was independent of whether palmitate, linoleate, or a combination was added to the perfusate. However, perfusion with labeled palmitic acid increased the percentage of palmitate in liver triglycerides, but only slightly affected perfusate triglycerides. Linoleate, by contrast, had less effect on liver triglyceride patterns, but a greater effect on perfusate triglyceride patterns. High perfusate palmitate concentrations strongly stimulated conversion to ^{14}CO$_2$ and incorporation into glycerides but had less marked effect on incorporation into phospholipids (137).

Lymph chylomicrons of widely different fatty acid compositions were obtained from donor animals fed either cream labeled with palmitic acid or corn oil labeled with linoleic acid. In the perfused rat liver, cream chylomicrons were removed at faster rates than corn oil chylomicrons (138).

Increased incorporation of many lipid fractions, especially cholesterol, was observed in isolated livers of normal and X-irradiated animals (139). Lipids in the livers of partially hepatectomized rats had marked increases in triglyceride content and decreased rates of incorporation into all but the phospholipid fraction. Increased lipid content of regenerating liver was attributed to changes in transport rather than increased synthesis (139).

By adding sodium oleate to the perfusion reservoir, the portal venous FFA concentrations were varied over a wide range (140): portal-hepatic venous FFA concentration difference across the liver was a linear function of portal FFA concentrations over a range of 100 to 1800 μeq/liter; removal of the acids was somewhat greater when the livers of fasted rats were used (140).

Rodbell et al. (141) used triglyceride emulsion labeled with glyceryl tripalmitin-1-^{14}C in the perfused rat liver system to distinguish between unmetabolized substrate and newly formed triglyceride in liver and perfusate. The fractional disappearance of ^{14}C-lipid from blood was inversely related to the triglyceride perfusate concentration. The entry sites were saturated within 5 min, at which time 90 per cent of the ^{14}C in the liver was tripalmitin. During 2-hr perfusions half of the radioactivity removed by the liver was secreted into the blood, principally as triglyceride; the other half remained in the liver as neutral fat, phospholipid, and tripalmitin (141).

Radioactivity distribution after injection of labeled lipid fractions in the intact animal.—After ^{14}C-labeled free fatty acids or triglycerides were injected intravenously in rats, the tissue distribution of radioactivity varied, but a large proportion of the radioactivity appeared in the liver (142, 143). Most of the radioactivity was recovered from the livers of fasting rats after intravenous injection of labeled triglycerides, but most of the radioactivity was found in fat depots in rats fed with carbohydrates (143). Differences in the distribution of radioactivity in various tissues after intravenous injection of these labeled compounds appear to be related to the nutritional state of the animal.

Olivecrona (144, 145) studied the metabolism of 1–^{14}C palmitic acid both as free fatty acids and as chylomicron triglycerides in the rat. After albumin-bound 1-^{14}C-palmitic acid was injected intravenously to carbohydrate-fed rats, 30 per cent was taken up by the liver (144). Five minutes after injection, 97 per cent of the label recovered from the liver was in the esterified form. More of the label was in the hepatic triglyceride pool than in the hepatic tissue phospholipid pool; the turnover of the former was higher than the latter. After 1-^{14}C-palmitic acid-labeled chylomicrons were injected into carbohydrate-fed rats, there was more activity in the liver than when labeled palmitic acid in the free form was given. After 40 min, liver activity declined and subsequently radioactivity accumulated in adipose tissue (145). ³H-labeled palmitic acid chylomicrons in doses of 65 and 124 mg were injected into carbohydrate-fed rats (146). The disappearance curve was more complex, the label disappeared more slowly from the blood, and the percentage of label in the liver was less than at lower doses. It was concluded that, at this dosage, the clearance system was overloaded and the adipose tissue cleared mainly recirculated fatty acids (146). In heparin-treated animals, hepatic uptake of triglyceride radioactivity after intravenous administration of ³H-palmitate-labeled chylomicrons was significantly higher and adipose tissue uptake was lower as compared with saline-treated controls (147).

Morris & Simpson-Morgan (148, 149) continuously infused rat chylomicrons labeled with ¹⁴C-palmitic, ¹⁴C-oleic, and ¹⁴C-linoleic acids into fasting unanesthetized rats and observed that the three labeled fatty acids were taken up and oxidized at essentially the same rates. The rate of $^{14}CO_2$ production reached relative constant values in the second hour of infusion. About 40 per cent of each fatty acid was oxidized to CO_2 during the infusion. The proportion of infused triglyceride oxidized to CO_2 did not change when the rates of infusion of chylomicrons were increased from 5 to 100 mg esterified fatty acids per hour (148, 149).

Hepatic lipid movements in the intact animal.—Chylomicrons transport triglycerides from the gastrointestinal tract via the hymphatic system to the blood during the absorptive period (150). The chylomicrons are taken up rapidly by the liver; chylomicron triglycerides are hydrolyzed rapidly and recirculated in the blood as free fatty acids (FFA) (151). The triglycerides also are released by the liver in very low-density lipoproteins (150). These contain a much larger fraction of polar constituents, are smaller in size, and have proportionally fewer triglycerides, but more cholesterol, cholesterol esters, phospholipids, and protein than do chylomicrons (150).

Dole (152, 153) and Gordon & Cherkes (154) observed decreased FFA levels after glucose administration and increased levels with fasting. In man, concentrations were lowest in the hepatic venous blood as compared with the venous blood from heart, leg, liver, and kidney, indicating a hepatic uptake of FFA (154). In the postabsorptive, unanesthetized dog, the mean rate of hepatic uptake was 0.05 ± 0.016 (SE) meq per min (155). Portal-hepatic venous FFA differences were uniformly positive in the anesthetized acutely operated dog and the rate of hepatic uptake correlated directly with portal FFA levels (156). A similar relationship was seen in diabetic dogs (157).

In intact dogs, cream chylomicrons were removed more rapidly than corn oil chylomicrons (138). The ratio of palmitic acid to linoleic acid in hepatic venous blood was lower than that of both arterial and femoral venous blood; greater percentages of radioactivity of cream chylomicrons were taken up by the liver than of corn oil chylomicrons, but similar amounts were recovered from adipose tissue (139).

Effect of hormones on fat transport in the intact animal and in man.—Portal-hepatic venous plasma FFA concentration differences in dogs were positive in the control state and remained positive after administration of growth hormone, epinephrine, and glucagon (158). No measurable effects of glucagon were observed on FFA uptake by perfused livers from either fasted or glycogen-containing livers (140). Hirsch et al. (159) made rabbits lipidemic by injections of pituitary extract; arteriovenous triglyceride differences across the liver became negative, while most arteriovenous differences across fat depots, intestines, kidney, and leg were usually small and positive. It was concluded that the liver was the principal source of triglycerides and that the fat depots principally clear them (159). Klausner & Heimberg (160) measured the uptake of FFA and release of glucose, triglycerides, ketones, and urea by the isolated perfused livers from fed normal, adrenalectomized, and cortisone-treated rats. Livers from adrenalectomized rats released less triglyceride and glucose, the same amount of FFA and urea, but more ketone than did livers from normal rats. Cortisone, 5 mg, given to the animals daily for 3 days prior to the perfusions and cortisol given *in vitro* into the perfusion system in doses above a critical level (343 μg/min) stimulated triglyceride output from normal rats and restored triglyceride and ketone output in livers of adrenalectomized rats to normal values. Cortisol also induced increased glucose output in livers from normal animals (160).

The influence of insulin administration on the rates of hepatic FFA release or removal was measured simultaneously with that of the gut, omentum, and hindquarters in the postprandial, unanesthetized dog (161). During constant infusion of insulin 0.1 to 0.2 unit per kg per hr, the mean rate of hepatic FFA uptake increased threefold, i.e., from 0.05 to 0.15 meq per min. The hepatic uptake reached maximal values 30 to 40 min after onset of insulin infusion. The small, usually positive, FFA output by the gut decreased slightly, and frequently changed to an uptake during insulin infusion. Similarly, the net rate of omental and hindquarter FFA output decreased. When there was omental and hindquarter FFA uptake in the control period, this uptake increased during insulin infusion (161). On the assumptions that arterial FFA concentrations are representative of the extracellular fluid and that the latter comprises 30 per cent of body weight, 0.68 meq of FFA was removed from the extracellular fluid during the first hour of insulin infusion (155). During this time the net cumulative hepatic FFA uptake was 0.61 meq. This suggests that the greater part of the observed FFA decrease in plasma and extracellular fluid was attributable to increased hepatic clearance; lesser effects were contributed by the slightly increased clearance rates by other tissues and the initially reduced FFA release from fat depots. However, when arterial FFA levels fell significantly, the omental fat depot released FFA at increased rates (159).

In the well-nourished pancreatectomized dog, the time course of FFA concentrations and regional FFA movements was observed over a 4.5-hr period after a single rapid intravenous injection of insulin (161). In the control period, there was a consistently positive hepatic-portal venous concentration difference as well as a positive hepatic FFA output. Almost immediately after insulin administration, there was an abrupt fall in hepatic venous FFA concentrations but not in the portal venous levels; the hepatic-portal venous FFA concentration differences became negative and the liver began to remove FFA. At the same time, the concentration difference across the gut, which was close to zero in the control period, became strongly positive indicating release of FFA by the gut. About 90 min after the insulin injection, rather marked swings occurred in the FFA movements; the hepatic venous levels rose, the portal venous levels fell, the hepatic output again became strongly positive, and the gut output returned toward control values (161).

Summary.—Because of the primary role of fat as an energy source and as an energy store, interorgan lipid transport is of major importance in understanding the metabolic effects of alterations in nutritional state and endocrine balance.

There is considerable interorgan transport of fatty acids in both esterified and unesterified forms. FFA are complexed to albumin and other plasma proteins; triglycerides are transported as chylomicrons as well as low and high density lipoproteins. Chylomicrons which contain essentially all dietary lipid entering the circulation originate primarily in the intestine and are formed in the postprandial period. In addition to dietary intake, cholesterol is synthesized by the liver and other organs, excreted in the bile, and reabsorbed by the gut. After ingestion, triglycerides are broken down to a mixture of FFA and mono-, di-, and triglycerides by pancreatic and other lipases in the presence of bile acids. These compounds together with cholesterol, carotene, and fat-soluble vitamins are absorbed into the cytoplasm of the epithelial cell of the mucosa and merge with the intracellular lipid pools. Triglycerides are resynthesized by the intestinal cell and chylomicra are formed by association of these triglycerides with small amounts of cholesterol, cholesterol esters, phospholipid, and protein; they are extruded into the lacteal, appear in the thoracic duct lymph, and then pass through the pulmonary and systemic circulations before entering the hepatic circulation (162).

The liver plays an active role with respect to all lipid fractions. The liver synthesizes the bulk of plasma phospholipids. FFA, triglycerides, and cholesterol esters may be released or removed by the liver depending on inflow concentrations, nutritional status, hormonal stimulation, and the body's energy demands. Breakdown of triglyceride into FFA, resynthesis of triglyceride from labeled FFA, and catabolism of both fractions to CO_2 are greater in starved than in fed rat liver. The differences in fat metabolism of fed and starved livers may be due in part to the relative availability of carbohydrates for oxidative metabolism, and in part to altered hormonal balance. High plasma triglyceride concentrations appear to have little influence on the hepatic uptake or output of FFA; this suggests different mechanisms of FFA and triglyceride uptake. Labeled triglycerides taken up by the perfused liver are recovered as esterified fatty acid mostly in the phospholipid fraction. The extraction efficiency of the perfused liver is of the same order of magnitude as that of the liver of the intact animal and can account for removal of practically all chylomicron fat which enters the circulation after a fat meal.

The normal postabsorptive hemostatic balance between release of FFA by the fat depots into the circulating plasma and the clearance of FFA by the liver and the muscle may be altered by insulin administration and by the diabetic state. The lipogenic action of insulin, which consists of an uptake of FFA and esterification of glycerol and cholesterol as well as release of triglyceride and cholesterol ester by the liver, is an early response and may precede the effect of insulin on glucose metabolism.

REGULATION OF AMINO ACID AND PROTEIN METABOLISM BY THE LIVER

Munro (163) has provided an extensive summary of the literature, to 1963, and a conceptualization of the interrelations between the liver and other organs in the regulation of mammalian protein metabolism.

Interorgan transport of amino acids.—Elwyn et al. (46) measured gut output and liver uptake of amino acids in unanesthetized dogs, on high protein diets, 4–5 days postoperatively. Liver uptake in all animals responded very sensitively to gut output, maintaining a very constant splanchnic output of most amino acids over 24-hr periods. Although quite constant in each animal, splanchnic outputs of individual amino acids varied considerably between animals and could be either positive or negative, depending on the state of the animal. Carlsten et al. (164) and Onen et al. (165) measured hepatic venous arterial concentration differences in humans in the postabsorptive state. Both groups found consistent net uptake by the splanchnic region of all amino acids except glutamate. Consistent with this are findings of Foley et al. (166) of a net positive output of most amino acids by the human forearm. These data suggest a net transport of free amino acids from the rest of the organism to the splanchnic region.

The liver synthesizes the bulk of plasma proteins (167–169) but probably catabolizes less than half as much (170). Katz et al. (171) have shown rates of albumin degradation in eviscerated rats to be half that in normal rats. This implies a net transport of amino acids in the form of plasma proteins from the liver to peripheral tissues. Since there is net excretion of amino acids in free or bound form from organs such as skin and kidney, net transport of plasma proteins from liver to periphery must be greater than net transport of amino acids from peripheral tissues to the liver.

Regulation of urea synthesis.—Administration of balanced amino acid mixtures to perfused liver of rats (172) or dogs (173), or feeding of protein to dogs (46) caused marked increases in rates of hepatic urea synthesis. In unanesthetized dogs on high protein diets (0.64 to 0.80 g N per kg per day), maximal rates of urea synthesis of 160 mmoles N per hr per kg liver were achieved within an hour after the daily meal. These rates declined gradually to 30 mmoles per hr or less during the nonabsorptive period (46).

Kamin & Handler (174) observed rates of urea synthesis of 270 to 540 mmoles N per hr per kg liver after intravenous infusion of casein hydrolysate, glutamine, arginine, or mixtures of these into anesthetized dogs. In keeping with its role in the Krebs-Henseleit ornithine cycle, stimulation of urea synthesis by arginine was additive to that of either glutamine or casein hydrolysate. Similar effects of arginine have been observed in the intact rat (175, 176). The lower rates of urea synthesis in dogs fed by mouth suggest a role of the gut in regulation of urea synthesis through regulation of the rate of output into portal blood of glutamine and arginine as well as total amino acids.

Miller (73) has shown in perfused rat liver that glucagon stimulates urea production and insulin suppresses this stimulation.

Superimposed on the diurnal variations is the slower adaptation of total daily urea production to changes in the amount of dietary nitrogen. Schimke (177) has shown that activities of all the urea cycle enzymes increase with increasing protein in the diet. In addition, starvation or administration of corticosteroids increases the level of these enzymes over control values.

Protein synthesis and breakdown.—Munro (163, 178) has summarized the evidence indicating that a protein or amino acid meal stimulates net deposition of protein in the liver. Observations of Elwyn et al. (46) in unanesthetized dogs indicate that net protein synthesis may occur after a protein meal but is not an obligatory response. Either net protein synthesis or net breakdown occurred in different animals studied 4 to 5 days postoperatively. McMenamy et al. (173) recorded similar observations in dog liver perfused with fresh dog blood. When a balanced mixture of amino acids was administered immediately after the start of perfusion, considerable net synthesis of protein occurred. When amino acid administration was delayed 90 min, there was no net protein synthesis. Turnover of liver proteins and synthesis of plasma albumin and glycoprotein, as measured by incorporation of radioactive glycine, were not affected by the delay in amino acid administration (179). The loss of net synthetic ability by the perfused liver may reflect loss of circulating hormones in this system. Jeffay et al. (180) have shown, in rats, that steady-state turnover rates of plasma albumin increase as much as two- to threefold with increasing protein in the diet.

Regulation of the rate of net protein synthesis or breakdown in liver could involve changes in rates of either synthesis or catabolism. There is growing evidence that both may be involved. Wunner et al. (181) have shown that the degree of aggregation of rat liver polyribosomes is increased by feeding balanced amino acid mixtures. This is associated with increased incorporation of ^{14}C-amino acids *in vitro*, indicating an increased rate of protein synthesis *in vivo*. Gan & Jeffay (182) infused lysine-^{14}C at a constant rate into rats and found that after 2 hr the ratio of liver to plasma lysine specific activities remained constant. This ratio was 0.5 in control rats, fell to 0.1 on the first and second days of fasting and subsequently, with continued fasting, returned to the fed level. This suggests a marked increase in the production of unlabeled lysine from catabolism of proteins in the liver at a time when maximum net loss of protein was occurring. Schimke (183) has shown that changes in the rates of both synthesis and degradation are involved in the regulation of arginase concentrations in liver.

The concentration of a protein in plasma may affect its rate of synthesis in the liver. Miller et al. (167), with perfused rat liver, demonstrated that the rate of fibrinogen synthesis was equal to normal turnover rates, 0.2 mg per g liver per hr, when the perfused blood contained normal amounts of fibrinogen. Net rates of fibrinogen synthesis increased fourfold when fibrinogen was removed from the perfusing medium.

Valine, leucine, and isoleucine.—Although most essential amino acids appear to be catabolized almost exclusively in the liver (46, 172, 173), this does not appear to be true of the branched-chain amino acids.

When dog (173) or rat (172, 184, 185) liver was perfused without additions, concentrations of most amino acids in the perfusing medium remained in the range of normal plasma values. Valine, leucine, and isoleucine concentrations increased markedly, which indicates that net protein breakdown occurred and that these amino acids were catabolized more slowly than other amino acids. In hepatectomized dogs (186) or eviscerated rats (172), concentrations of most amino acids were higher than in normal animals but concentrations of the branch-chain amino acids were lower, which indicates appreciable catabolism in nonhepatic tissues.

In the unanesthetized dog, production or utilization of valine, leucine, and isoleucine in the liver can be accounted for almost entirely by net breakdown or synthesis of protein (46). Comparison of CO_2 production from labeled amino acids in perfused rat liver or eviscerated rats (172) indicates approximately equal rates of catabolism of valine, leucine, and isoleucine in the two preparations.

Summary.—The liver appears able to absorb the entire gut output of free amino acids after a meal and to maintain an almost constant supply of most essential amino acids to the rest of the organism. Valine, leucine, and isoleucine constitute exceptions which, to a large extent, bypass the liver. The amount of free amino acids supplied or removed from peripheral tissues by the liver, although independent of gut supply, appears to be dependent on the physiologic state of the animal. The two hepatic processes mainly implicated in this regulation are urea synthesis and net synthesis or breakdown of protein; both respond very sensitively to diurnal variations in protein intake. The direction and amount of net protein synthesis seem to be more important than urea synthesis in regulating the free amino acid supply to other tissues.

Conclusions

With respect to carbohydrates and amino acids, the liver plays a dual role. It serves as a buffer for the diurnal variations in supply of nutrients from the gut. In addition, it can respond to tissue requirements by varying the supply of nutrients to other tissues. Unlike other dietary constituents, the lipid supply from the gut bypasses the liver by way of the thoracic duct, and with respect to lipids the liver shares its regulatory role with adipose tissue.

The eventual aims in the study of the liver's role in regulation of inter-organ transport of metabolites must include: (a) a full description of inter-organ transport in normal and stressed situations with particular emphasis on the interrelated movements of carbohydrates, lipids, amino acids, proteins, and inorganic compounds; (b) identification of the cellular processes responsible for these movements; (c) identification of the hormonal and other interorgan regulators of these cellular processes; and (d) utilization of this knowledge for external control of these processes in treatment of disease and injury. At present the available knowledge is too fragmentary and too uneven to permit a cohesive synthesis of this field. In certain areas, such as the study of glucose, O_2, CO_2, and K^+ movements, considerable information has been obtained. Much progress has been made in: (a) describing these movements, in normal and pathological states; (b) determining the influence of hormones and other regulators. In the more complex field of lipid, protein, and amino acid movements, relatively little is known. Hopefully, in another five or ten years, the growing activity in these areas may permit a comprehensive synthesis of metabolic interactions between liver and other organs.

LITERATURE CITED

1. Bernard, C. Sur le mécanisme de la formation du sucre dans la foie. *Compt. Rend. Acad. Sci.*, **41**, 461–79 (1855)
2. O'Donnell, J. F., Schiff, L. Liver perfusion. *Progr. Liver Diseases*, **2**, 41–56 (1965)
3. Shoemaker, W. C. Methods and techniques for measurement of hepatic physiology and metabolism. In Rouiller, Ch., *The Liver*, **II**, 243–66 (Academic Press, New York, 1964)
4. Bombeck, C. T., Biava, C., Condon, R. E., Nyhus, L. M. Parameters of normal liver function in the isolated perfused bovine liver (Norman, J., Ed., Conf. Organ Perfusion and Preservation, New York, Appleton Century Crofts, in press, 1968)
5. Andrews, W. H. H. A technique for perfusion of the canine liver. *Ann. Trop. Med. Parasitol.*, **47**, 146–55 (1953)
6. Kestens, P. J., Farrelly, J. A., McDermott, W. V., Jr. A technique of isolation and perfusion of the canine liver. *J. Surg. Res.*, **1**, 58–63 (1961)
7. Chapman, N. D., Goldsworthy, P. D., Nyhus, L. M., Volwiler, W., Harkins, H. N. Studies in isolated organ physiology; Bromsulphthalein clearance in the isolated perfused bovine liver. *Surgery*, **48**, 111–18 (1960)
8. Eiseman, B., Knipe, P., McColl, H. A., Orloff, M. J. Isolated liver perfusion for reducing blood ammonia. *Arch. Surg.*, **83**, 356–63 (1961)
9. Van Wyck, J. Extracorporeal heterologous liver perfusion in support of patients in hepatic failure. *S. Afr. Med. J.*, **40**, 111–18 (1966)
10. Brown, H., Patel, J., Blair, D. W., Brown, M. E. Biochemical studies with preserved, transplanted canine liver. *J. Am. Med. Assoc.*, **196**, 775–79 (1966)
11. Vang, J. O., Drapanas, T. Metabolism of lactic acid and keto acids by the isolated perfused calf liver. *Ann. Surg.*, **163**, 545–52 (1966)
12. Drapanas, T., Zemel, R., Vang, J. O. Hemodynamics of the isolated, perfused pig liver. *Ann. Surg.*, **164**, 522–37 (1966)

13. Norman, J. C., Hardison, W. G., McDermott, W. V., Jr. Therapeutic and investigational potential of heterologous liver perfusion. *Bull. N. Y. Acad. Med.*, **43**, 967–76 (1967)
14. Norman, J. C., Hardison, W. G., Covelli, V., McDermott, W. V., Jr. Metabolic responses during experimental hepatectomy as related to subsequent perfusion, perservation, or transplantation. *Am. J. Surg.*, **112**, 407–11 (1966)
15. Mieny, C. J., Eiseman, B. Perfusion storage of excised livers. *Surg. Forum*, **18**, 374–76 (1967)
16. Mc Lean, A. E. M. Intracellular potassium in dietary liver necrosis. *Nature*, **185**, 936–37 (1960)
17. D'Silva, J. L., Neal, M. W. The potassium, water, and glycogen content of the perfused rat liver. *J. Physiol. (London)*, **124**, 515–27 (1954)
18. Judah, J. D., Ahmed, K., McLean, A. E. M. Possible role of ion shifts in liver injury. *Cellular Injury. Ciba Found. Symp.* (1964)
19. Shoemaker, W. C., Panico, F. G., Walker, W. F., Elwyn, D. H. Perfusion of the canine liver in vivo. *J. Appl. Physiol.*, **15**, 687–90 (1960)
20. Child, C. G., Barr, D., Halswade, G. R., Harrison, L. S. Liver regeneration following portacaval transposition in dogs. *Ann. Surg.*, **138**, 600–8 (1953)
21. Starzl, T. E., Lazarus, R. E., Schlachter, L., Thornton, F. H., Wendel, R. M., Stearn, B., Scanlan, W. A. A multiple catheter technique for studies of hepatic metabolism and blood flow in dogs with portacaval transposition. *Surgery*, **52**, 654–59 (1962)
22. London, E. S. *Angiostomie und Organstoffwechsel* (All-Union-Instituts, Moscow, 1935)
23. Warren, J. V., Brannon, E. S. Method of obtaining blood samples directly from the hepatic vein in man. *Proc. Soc. Biol. Med.*, **55**, 144–47 (1944)
24. Shoemaker, W. C., Walker, W. F., Van Itallie, T. B., Moore, F. D. A method for simultaneous catheterization of major hepatic vessels in a chronic canine preparation. *Am. J. Physiol.*, **196**, 311–14 (1959)

25. Rothschild, M. A., Oratz, M., Evans, C. D., Schreiber, S. S. Role of hepatic interstitial albumin in regulating albumin synthesis. *Am. J. Physiol.*, **210**, 57–62 (1966)

26. Goresky, C. A., Johns, G. A linear method for determining liver sinusoidal and extravascular volumes. *Am. J. Physiol.*, **207**, 883–92 (1964)

27. Goresky, C. A., Silverman, M. Effect of correction of catheter distortion on calculated liver sinusoidal volumes. *Am. J. Physiol.*, **207**, 883–92 (1964)

28. Goresky, C. A., Johns, G. Initial distribution and rate of uptake of sulfobromphthalein in the liver. *Am. J. Physiol.*, **207**, 13–26 (1964)

29. Guntheroth, W. G., Mullins, G. L. Liver and spleen as venous reservoirs. *Am. J. Physiol.*, **204**, 35–41 (1963)

30. Gibson, J. G., Seligman, A. M., Peacock, W. C., Fine, J., Aub, J. C., Evans, R. D. Circulating red cell and plasma volume and distribution of blood in large and minute vessels by radioactive isotopes of iron and iodine. *J. Clin. Invest.*, **26**, 126–44 (1947)

31. Andersen, D., Shoemaker, W. C. Exchange of injection labeled red cells in liver tissue during hemorrhagic shock. *Proc. Soc. Exptl. Biol. Med.*, **125**, 30–34 (1967)

32. Greenway, C. V., Lawson, A. E., Mellander, S. Effects of stimulation of hepatic nerves, infusions of noradrenalin and occlusion of the carotid arteries on liver blood flow in the anesthetized cat. *J. Physiol. (London)*, **192**, 21–41 (1967)

33. Cohn, R., Kountz, S. Factors influencing control of arterial circulation in the liver of the dog. *Am. J. Physiol.*, **205**, 1260–64 (1963)

34. Schenk, W. G., Jr., McDonald, J. C., McDonald, K., Drapanas, T. Direct measurement of hepatic blood flow in surgical patients. *Ann. Surg.*, **156**, 463–71 (1962)

35. Torrance, H. B. Control of hepatic arterial circulation. *J. Physiol. (London)*, **158**, 39–49 (1961)

36. Shoemaker, W. C., Turk, L. N., Moore, F. D. Hepatic vascular response to epinephrine. *Am. J. Physiol.*, **201**, 58–62 (1961)

37. Shoemaker, W. C. The action of epinephrine and other hormones associated with the stress response on potassium movements with special reference to the development of postoperative depletion states. *Rev. Surg.*, **25**, 9–24 (1968)

38. Craig, A. B., Jr., Honig, C. R. Hepatic metabolic and vascular responses to epinephrine: A unifying hypothesis. *Am. J. Physiol.*, **205**, 1132–38 (1963)

39. Turk, L. N., Shoemaker, W. C. Hepatic vascular responses to norepinephrine. *Am. J. Physiol.*, **202**, 1175–78 (1962)

40. Shoemaker, W. C., Van Itallie, T. B., Walker, W. F. Measurement of hepatic glucose and hepatic blood flow in response to glucagon. *Am. J. Physiol.*, **196**, 315–18 (1959)

41. Shoemaker, W. C., Teel, P. The effect of glucagon on hindquarter blood flow in the dog. *Endocrinology*, **67**, 132–37 (1960)

42. Shoemaker, W. C., Mahler, R., Ashmore, J., Pugh, D. E. Effect of insulin on hepatic blood flow in the unanesthetized dog. *Am. J. Physiol.*, **196**, 1250–52 (1959)

43. Drapanas, T., Crowe, C. P., Shim, T., Schenk, W. G., Jr. Effect of pitressin on cardiac output and coronary, hepatic and intestinal blood flow. *Surg. Gyn. Obst.*, **113**, 484–89 (1961)

44. Shoemaker, W. C. Measurement of hepatic blood flow in the unanesthetized dog by a modified bromsulphthalein method. *J. Appl. Physiol.*, **15**, 473–78 (1960)

45. Shoemaker, W. C., Yanof, H. M., Turk, L. N., Wilson, T. H. Glucose and fructose absorption in the unanesthetized dog. *Gastroenterology*, **44**, 654–63 (1963)

46. Elwyn, D. H., Parikh, H. C., Shoemaker, W. C. Amino acid movements between gut, liver and periphery in unanesthetized dogs. *Am. J. Physiol. (In press)*

47. Rowell, L. B., Masoro, E. J., Spencer, M. J. Splanchnic metabolism in exercising man. *J. Appl. Physiol.*, **20**, 1032–37 (1965)

48. Muller, W., Smith, L. L. Hepatic circulatory changes following endotoxin shock in the dog. *Am. J. Physiol.*, **204**, 641–44 (1963)

49. Shoemaker, W. C., Walker, W. F., Turk, L. N. The role of the liver in the development of hemorrhagic shock. *Surg. Gyn. Obst.*, **112**, 327–33 (1961)

50. Frank, E. D., Frank, H. A., Jacob, S. W., Fine, J. Hepatic blood flow in experimental hemorrhagic shock. *Am. J. Physiol.*, **202**, 7–11 (1962)

51. Abel, F. L., Waldhausen, J. A., Selkurt, E. E. Splanchnic blood flow in the monkey during hemorrhagic shock. *Am. J. Physiol.*, **208**, 265–69 (1965)

52. Fenn, W. O. Role of potassium in physiological processes. *Physiol. Rev.*, **20**, 377–415 (1940)

53. Burton, S. D., Ishida, T. Effect of insulin on potassium and glucose movement in perfused rat liver. *Am. J. Physiol.*, **209**, 1145–61 (1965)

54. Eichler, O., Farah, A. *Handbuch der Experimentellen Pharmakologie* (Springer-Verlag, Berlin, 1960)

55. Shoemaker, W. C., Finder, A. G. Relation of potassium and glucose release from the liver in the unanesthetized dog. *Proc. Soc. Exptl. Biol. Med.*, **108**, 248–52 (1961)

56. Elliott, F. S., Levin, F. M., Shoemaker, W. C. Hepatic electrolyte and glucose responses to epinephrine. *J. Pharmacol. Exptl. Therap.*, **150**, 61–66 (1965)

57. Finder, A. G., Boyme, T., Shoemaker, W. C. Relationship of hepatic potassium efflux to phosphorylase activation induced by glucagon. *Am. J. Physiol.*, **206**, 738–42 (1964)

58. Burton, S. D., Mondon, C. E., Ishida, T. Dissociation of potassium and glucose efflux in isolated perfused rat liver. *Am. J. Physiol.*, **212**, 261–66 (1967)

59. Kestens, P. J., Haxhe, J. J., Lambotte, L., Lambotte, C. The effect of insulin on the uptake of potassium and phosphate by the isolated perfused canine liver. *Metabolism*, **12**, 941–51 (1963)

60. Lambotte, L., Shoemaker, W. C. Effect of insulin on hepatic K movements as influenced by hypothermia, barbiturate and dibenzyline. *Physiologist*, **7**, 184, (1964)

61. Mortimore, G. E. Effect of insulin on potassium transfer in the isolated rat liver. *Am. J. Physiol.*, **200**, 1315–19 (1961)

62. Klechner, H., Galansino, G., Shoemaker, W. C. Effect of serotonin on regional metabolism. *Physiologist*, **4**, 58 (1961)

63. Blesa, E. S., Gonzalez, N. C., Cingolani, H. E. Early increase of plasma potassium in hyperventilation. *Am. J. Physiol.*, **208**, 537–40 (1965)

64. Andersen, D., Shoemaker, W. C. Effect of hemorrhage on hepatic potassium movements. *Proc. Soc. Exptl. Biol. Med.*, **124**, 840–44 (1967)

65. Melchior, N. C. Sodium and potassium complexes of adenosine triphosphate: equilibrium studies. *J. Biol. Chem.*, **208**, 615–27 (1954)

66. Soskin, S., Essex, H. E., Herrick, J. F., Mann, F. C. The mechanism of regulation of the blood sugar by the liver. *Am. J. Physiol.*, **124**, 558–67 (1938)

67. Lipscomb, A., Crandall, L. A., Jr. Hepatic blood flow and glucose output in normal unanesthetized dogs. *Am. J. Physiol.*, **148**, 302–11 (1947)

68. Bondy, P. K., Bloom, W. L., Whitner, V. S., Farrar, B. W. Studies of the role of the liver in human carbohydrate metabolism by the venous catheter technique. II. Patients with diabetic ketosis before and after the administration of insulin. *J. Clin Invest.*, **28**, 1126–33 (1949)

69. Henneman, D. H., Shoemaker, W. C. Effect of glucagon and epinephrine on regional metabolism of glucose, pyruvate, lactate, and citrate in normal conscious dogs. *Endocrinology*, **68**, 889–98 (1961)

70. Landau, B. R., Leonards, J. R., Barry, F. M. Regulation of blood glucose concentration responses of liver to glucose administration. *Am. J. Physiol.*, **201**, 41–46 (1961)

71. Bernard, C. *Nouvelle fonction du foie considéré comme organe producteur de matière sucrée chez l'homme et les animaux* (J.-B. Baillière, Paris, 92 pp., 1853)

72. Kolodny, E. H., Kline, R., Altszuler, N. Effect of phlorizin on hepatic glucose output. *Am. J. Physiol.*, **202**, 149–54 (1962)

73. Miller, L. L. Direct actions of insulin glucagon and epinephrine on the isolated perfused liver. *Fed. Proc.*, **24**, 737–44 (1965)

74. Miller, L. L. Some direct actions of insulin, glucagon and hydrocortisone on the isolated perfused rat liver. *Recent Progr. Hormone Res.*, **17**, 539–68 (1961)

75. Shoemaker, W. C., Van Itallie, T. B. The hepatic response to glucagon

in the unanesthetized dog. *Endocrinology*, **66**, 260–68 (1960)

76. Levine, R. A., Lewis, S. E. Hepatic glycogenolytic activity of cyclic 3′,5′-AMP and its monobutyryl derivative. *Am. J. Physiol.*, **213**, 768–70 (1967)

77. Eisenstein, A. B., Spencer, S. Gluconeogenesis in the isolated perfused rat liver. *J. Clin. Invest.*, **45**, 1004 (1966)

78. de Duve, C. The hepatic action of insulin. *Ciba Found. Colloq. Endocrinol.*, **11**, 203–22 (1956)

79. Lukens, F. D. W. The Pancreas: Insulin and Glucagon. *Ann. Rev. Physiol.*, **21**, 445–74 (1959)

80. Tepperman, J., Tepperman, H. M. Some effects of hormones on cells and cell constituents. *Pharmacol. Rev.*, **12**, 301–53 (1960)

81. Bearn, A. G., Billing, B. H., Sherlock, S. Response of the liver to insulin; hepatic vein catheterization studies in man. *Ciba Found. Colloq. Endocrinol.*, **6**, 350–69 (1953)

82. Lundsgaard, E., Nielsen, N. A., Ørskov, S. L. On the possibility of demonstrating an effect of insulin on isolated mammalian liver. *Skand. Arch. Physiol.*, **81**, 11–19 (1939)

83. Shoemaker, W. C., Mahler, R., Ashmore, J., Pugh, D. E., Hastings, A. B. The hepatic glucose response to insulin in the unanesthetized dog. *J. Biol. Chem.*, **234**, 1631–33 (1959)

84. Haft, D. E., Miller, L. L. Alloxan diabetes and demonstrated direct action of insulin on metabolism of isolated perfused rat liver. *Am. J. Physiol.*, **192**, 33–42 (1958)

85. Ruderman, N. B., Lauris, V., Herrera, M. G. Insulin preservation of glucokinase activity in isolated perfused rat liver. *Am. J. Physiol.*, **212**, 1169–73 (1967)

86. Haft, D. E. Effects of insulin on glucose metabolism by the perfused normal rat liver. *Am. J. Physiol.*, **213**, 219–30 (1967)

87. Gordon, E. R. Factors influencing the net consumption of glucose by the isolated perfused rat liver. *Can. J. Physiol. Pharmacol.*, **43**, 617–26 (1965)

88. Huston, C. J. W., Adams, L. C., Field, R. A., McDermott, W. V., Jr. Effect of insulin on glucose uptake by the isolated perfused liver. *Lancet*, **1**, 357–59 (1962)

89. Mortimore, G. E. Effect of insulin on release of glucose and urea by isolated rat liver. *Am. J. Physiol.*, **204**, 699–704 (1963)

90. Mortimore, G. E., King, E., Jr., Mondon, C. E., Glinsmann, W. H. Effects of insulin on net carbohydrate alterations in perfused rat liver. *Am. J. Physiol.*, **212**, 179–83 (1967)

91. Sokal, J. E., Weintraub, B. Failure of the isolated liver to react to hypoglycemia. *Am. J. Physiol.*, **210**, 63–68 (1966)

92. Madison, L. L., Combes, B., Strickland, W., Unger, R., Adams, R. Evidence for a direct effect of insulin on hepatic glucose output. *Metabolism*, **8**, 469–71 (1959)

93. Madison, L. L., Unger, R. H., Rencz, K. Physiologic significance of the secretion of insulin into portal circulation. II. Effect of rate of administration of glucagon-free insulin on the magnitude of peripheral and hepatic actions. *Metabolism*, **9**, 97–108 (1960)

94. Starzl, T. E., Scanlan, W. A., Shoemaker, W. C., Thornton, F. H., Wendel, R. M., Schlachter, L. Studies on the hepatic blood flow and the rates of bromsulphthalein clearance in dogs with portacaval transposition. *Surgery*, **52**, 660–63 (1962)

95. Heer, F. W., Silvius, D. E., Harper, H. A. The relation between hepatic flow and function in normal dogs and dogs with cirrhosis after portacaval shunt or transposition. *Surg. Forum*, **11**, 282–84 (1960)

96. Starzl, T. E., Butz, G. W., Jr., Meyer, W. H., Jr., Torok, E. E., Dolkart, R. E. Effect in dogs of various portal vein shunts on response to insulin. *Am. J. Physiol.*, **203**, 275–77 (1962)

97. Starzl, T. E., Scanlan, W. A., Thornton, F. H., Wendel, R. M., Stearn, B., Lazarus, R. E., McAllister, W., Shoemaker, W. C. Effect of insulin on glucose metabolism in the dog after portacaval transposition. *Am. J. Physiol.*, **209**, 221–26 (1965)

98. Sexton, A. W., Marchioro, T. L., Waddell, W. R., Starzl, T. E. Liver deglycogenation after portacaval transposition. *Surg. Forum*, **15**, 120–22 (1964)

99. Tarding, F., Schambye, P. The action of sulfonylureas and insulin on

the glucose output from the liver of normal dogs. *Endokrinologie*, **26**, 222–28 (1958)

100. Fine, M. B., Williams, R. H. Effect of an insulin infusion on hepatic output of glucose. *Am. J. Physiol.*, **198**, 645–48 (1960)

101. Shoemaker, W. C., Mahler, R., Ashmore, J. The effect of insulin on hepatic glucose metabolism in the unanesthetized dog. *Metabolism*, **8**, 494–511 (1959)

102. Shoemaker, W. C., Carruthers, P., Powers, I. C., Yanof, H. M. Hepatic effect of insulin in unanesthetized normal, diabetic and adrenalectomized dogs. *Am. J. Physiol.*, **201**, 804–10 (1961)

103. Leonards, J. R., Landau, B. R., Craig, J. W., Martin, F. I. R., Miller, M., Barry, F. M. Regulation of blood glucose concentration; hepatic action of insulin. *Am. J. Physiol.*, **201**, 47–54 (1961)

104. Dunn, D. F. Friedmann, B., Maass, A. R., Reichard, G. A., Weinhouse, S. Effects of insulin on blood glucose entry and removal rates in dogs. *J. Biol. Chem.*, **225**, 225–37 (1957)

105. Feller, D. D., Chaikoff, I. L. Strisower, E. H., Searle, G. L. Glucose utilization in the diabetic dog studied with C^{14}-glucose. *J. Biol. Chem.*, **188**, 865–80 (1951)

106. Henderson, M. J., Wrenshall, G. A., Odense, P. Effects of insulin on rates of glucose transfer in the depancreatized dog. *Can. J. Biochem. Physiol.*, **33**, 926–39 (1955)

107. Steele, R., Wall, J. S., De Bodo, R. C., Altszuler, N. Measurement of size and turnover rate of body glucose pool by the isotope dilution method. *Am. J. Physiol.*, **187**, 15–24 (1950)

108. De Bodo, R. C., Steele, R., Altszuler, N., Dunn, A., Armstrong, D. T., Bishop, J. S. Further studies on the mechanism of action of insulin. *Metabolism*, **8**, 520–30 (1959)

109. Steele, R., Bishop, J. S., Dunn, A., Altszuler, N., Rathgeb, I., De Bodo, R. C. Inhibition by insulin of hepatic glucose production in the normal dog. *Am. J. Physiol.*, **208**, 301–6 (1965)

110. Bishop, J. S., Steele, R., Altszuler, N., Dunn, A., Bjerknes, C., De Bodo, R. C. Effects of insulin on liver glycogen synthesis and breakdown in the dog. *Am. J. Physiol.*, **208**, 307–16 (1965)

111. De Bodo, R. C., Steele, R., Altszuler, N., Dunn, A., Bishop, J. S. On the hormonal regulation of carbohydrate metabolism: studies with C^{14}-glucose. *Recent Progr. Hormone Res.*, **19**, 445–82 (1963)

112. Mahler, R. Shoemaker, W. C., Ashmore, J. Hepatic action of insulin. *Ann. N. Y. Acad. Sci.*, **82**, 452–59 (1959)

113. Hetenyi, G., Jr., Wrenshall, G. A., Best, C. H. Rates of production, utilization, accumulation and apparent distribution space of glucose. *Diabetes*, **10**, 304–11 (1961)

114. Wrenshall, G. A., Hetenyi, G., Jr. Successive measured injections of tracer as a method for determining characteristics of accumulation and turnover in higher animals with access limited to blood. *Metabolism*, **8**, 531–43 (1959)

115. Bernard, C. *Leçons sur le diabète et la glycogénèse animale* (Baillière, Paris, 1877)

116. Engel, F. L., Harrison, H. C., Long, C. N. H. Biochemical studies on shock: Role of the liver and hepatic circulation in the metabolic changes during hemorrhagic shock in the rat and cat. *J. Exptl. Med.*, **79** 9–22 (1944)

117. Engel, F. L., Winton, M. G., Long, C. N. H. Biochemical studies on shock: Metabolism of amino acids and carbohydrates during hemorrhagic shock in the rat. *J. Exptl. Med.*, **77**, 397–410 (1943)

118. Drucker, W. R., Kaye, M., Kendrick, R., Hofmann, N., Kingsbury, B. Metabolic aspects of hemorrhagic shock, *Surg. Forum*, **9**, 49–54 (1960)

119. Strawitz, J. G., Hift, H. Glucose and glycogen metabolism during hemorrhagic shock in the rat. *Surg. Forum*, **11**, 112–14 (1960)

120. Stoner, H. B., Threlfall, C. J., Eds. *Biochemical Responses to Injury*, 467 (Blackwell, Oxford, 1960)

121. Seligman, A. M., Frank, H. A., Alexander, B., Fine, J. Traumatic shock; carbohydrate metabolism in hemorrhagic shock in the dog. *J. Clin. Invest.*, **26**, 536–47 (1947)

122. Soskin, S., Levine, R. *Carbohydrate Metabolism* (Univ. of Chicago Press, Chicago, 1946)

123. White, A., Handler, P., Smith, E. L. *Principles of Biochemistry* (McGraw-Hill, New York, 1964)

124. Encrantz, J. C., Sjövall, J. Bile acids in newborn and adult humans. *Chem. Acta Scand.*, **11**, 1093–96 (1957)

125. Sjövall, J. On the concentration of bile acids in the human intestine during absorption. *Acta Physiol. Scand.*, **46**, 339–45 (1959)

126. Bergström, S. Metabolism of bile acids. *Fed. Proc. Suppl.* **7**, 121–26 (1961)

127. Bergström, S., Danielsson, H. Homeostatic regulation of bile acids formation. *Acta Physiol. Scand.*, **43**, 1–7 (1958)

128. Danielsson, H., Insull, W. Jr., Jordan, P., Strand, O. Metabolism of 4-^{14}C-cholesterol in the isolated perfused rat liver. *Am. J. Physiol.*, **202**, 699–703 (1962)

129. Rosenman, R. H., Friedman, M., Byers, S. O. Observations concerning the metabolism of cholesterol in the hypo- and hyperthyroid rat. *Circulation*, **5**, 589–93 (1952)

130. Erickson, S. Biliary excretion of bile acids and cholesterol in bile fistula rats. *Proc. Soc. Expt. Biol. Med.*, **94**, 578–82 (1957)

131. O'Maille, E. R. L., Richards, T. G., Short, H. H. Influence of conjugation of cholic acid on its uptake and secretion; hepatic extraction of taurocholate and cholate in the dog. *J. Physiol. (London)*, **189**, 337–50 (1967)

132. Morris, B. Metabolism of free fatty acid and chylomicrons triglycerides by the isolated perfused liver of the rat. *J. Physiol. (London)*, **168**, 564–83 (1963)

133. Heimberg, M., Weinstein, I., Klausner, H., Watkins, M. L. Release and uptake of triglycerides by the isolated perfused rat liver. *Am. J. Physiol.*, **202**, 353–58 (1962)

134. Mishkel, M. A., Morris, B. The gaseous metabolism of isolated perfused normal and choline deficient rat liver. *Quart. J. Exptl. Physiol.*, **48**, 202–8 (1963)

135. Morris, B. Some factors affecting the metabolism of FFA and chylomicron triglyceride by the perfused rat liver. *J. Physiol. (London)*, **168**, 584–98 (1963)

136. Borgström, B., Jordan, P. Metabolism of chylomicron glyceride as studied by ^{14}C-glycerol-^{14}C-palmitic acid labeled chylomicrons. *Acta Soc. Med. Upsaliensis*, **64**, 185–93 (1959)

137. Nestel, P. J., Steinberg, D. Fate of palmitate and of linoleate perfused through the isolated rat liver at high concentrations. *J. Lipid Res.*, **4**, 461–69 (1963)

138. Nestel, P. J., Scow, R. O. Metabolism of chylomicrons of differing triglyceride composition. *J. Lipid Res.*, **5**, 46–51 (1964)

139. Bartsch, G. G., Gerber, B. G. Incorporation of acetate-1-^{14}C into lipids by the perfused liver of normal, X-irradiated or partially hepatectomized rats. *J. Lipid Res.*, **7**, 204–9 (1966)

140. Aydin, A., Sokal, J. E. Uptake of plasma free fatty acids by the isolated rat liver: effect of glucagon. *Am. J. Physiol.*, **205**, 667–70 (1963)

141. Rodbell, M., Scow, R. O., Chernick, S. S. Removal and metabolism of triglycerides by perfused liver. *J. Biol. Chem.*, **239**, 385–91 (1964)

142. French, J. E., Morris, B. Removal of ^{14}C-labeled chylomicron fat from the circulation in rats. *J. Physiol. (London)*, **138**, 326–39 (1957)

143. Bragdon, J. H., Gordon, R. S., Jr. Tissue distribution of ^{14}C after intravenous injection of labeled chylomicrons and unesterified fatty acids in the rat. *J. Clin. Invest.*, **37**, 574–78 (1958)

144. Olivecrona, T. Metabolism of 1-^{14}C-palmitic acid in the rat. *Acta Physiol. Scand.*, **54**, 295–305 (1962)

145. Olivecrona, T., Metabolism of 1-^{14}C-palmitic acid labeled chylomicrons in rats. *Ibid.*, **55**, 170–76

146. Belfrage, P., Borgström, B., Olivecrona, T. Tissue distribution of radioactivity following the injection of varying levels of fatty acid labeled chylomicrons in the rat. *Acta Physiol. Scand.*, **58**, 111–23 (1963)

147. Brown, D., Olivecrona, T. Effect of glucose availability and utilization on chylomicron metabolism in the rat. *Acta Physiol. Scand.*, **66**, 9–18 (1966)

148. Simpson-Morgan, M. W., Morris, B. A comparison of the metabolism of palmitic, oleic, and linoleic acids incorporated into chylomicron triglyceride. *Australian J. Exptl. Biol. Sci.*, **40**, 445–54 (1962)

149. Morris, B., Simpson-Morgan, M. W. Oxidation of continuously infused chylomicron fatty acids by unanesthetized rats. *J. Physiol. (London)*, **169**, 729–42 (1963)

150. Havel, R. J. Metabolism of lipids in chylomicrons and very low density lipoproteins. In *Adipose Tissue,* Sect. 5, *Handbook of Physiology,* 499–507 (Renold, A. E., Cahill, G. F. Eds., Am. Physiol. Soc., 1965)

151. Havel, R. J., Fredrickson, D. S. Metabolism of chylomicra. *J. Clin. Invest.,* **35,** 1025–32 (1956)

152. Dole, V. P., Hamlin, J. I. Particulate fat in lymph and blood. *Physiol. Rev.,* **42,** 674–701 (1962)

153. Dole, V. P. Relation between non-esterified fatty acids in plasma and the metabolism of glucose. *J. Clin. Invest.,* **35,** 150–54 (1956)

154. Gordon, R. S., Jr., Cherkes, A. Un-esterified fatty acid in human blood plasma. *J. Clin. Invest.,* **35,** 206–12 (1956)

155. Shoemaker, W. C., Ashmore, J., Carruthers, P. J., Schulman, M. Effect of insulin on rate of hepatic uptake of NEFA. *Proc. Soc. Exptl. Biol. Med.,* **103,** 585–88 (1969)

156. McElroy, W. T., Jr., Siefert, W. L., Spitzer, J. J. Relationship of hepatic uptake of free fatty acids to concentrations. *Proc. Soc. Exptl. Biol. Med.,* **104,** 20–23 (1960)

157. Spitzer, J. J., McElroy, W. T., Jr. Some hormonal influences on the hepatic uptake of free fatty acids in diabetic dogs. *Diabetes,* **11,** 222–26 (1962)

158. Bergen, S., Potheir, L., Van Itallie, T. B. Hepatic removal of free fatty acids following administration of growth hormone, epinephrine and glucagon. *Clin. Res.,* **8,** 236 (1960)

159. Hirsch, R. L., Rudman, D., Travers, R. Movements of lipids into and out of blood during hyperlipidemia induced in rabbits by pituitary extract and fraction H. *J. Lipid Res.,* 182–87 (1966)

160. Klausner, H., Heimberg, M. Effect of adrenalcortical hormones on release of triglycerides and glucose by liver. *Am. J. Physiol.,* **212,** 1236–46 (1967)

161. Shoemaker, W. C., Carruthers, P. J., Elwyn, D. H., Ashmore, J. Effect of insulin on fatty acid transport and regional metabolism. *Am. J. Physiol.,* **203,** 919–25 (1962)

162. Olson, R. E., Vester, J. W. Nutrition endocrine interrelationships in the control of fat transport in man. *Physiol. Rev.,* **40,** 677–733 (1960)

163. Munro, H. N. General aspects of the regulation of protein metabolism by diet and hormones. In *Mammalian Protein Metabolism,* I, 382–482 (Munro, H. N., Allison, J. B., Eds., Academic Press, New York, 566 pp., 1964)

164. Carlsten, A., Hallgren, B., Jagenburg, R., Svanborg, A., Werkö, L. Arterio-hepatic venous differences of free fatty acids and amino acids. *Acta Med. Scand.,* **181,** 199–207 (1967)

165. Onen, K. H., Wade, O. L., Blainey, J. D. Amino acids in hepatic venous and arterial blood. *Lancet,* **271,** 1075–76 (1956)

166. Foley, T. H., London, D. R., Prenton, M. A. Arterial plasma concentrations and forearm clearances of amino acids in myxedema. *J. Clin. Endocrinol. Metab.,* **26,** 781–85 (1966)

167. Miller, L. L., Bale, W. F. Synthesis of all plasma protein fractions except gamma globulins by the liver. *J. Exptl. Med.,* **99,** 125–32 (1954)

168. Miller, L. L., Hanavan, H. R., Tittasiri, N., Chowdhury, A. Dominant role of the liver in biosynthesis of the plasma mucoproteins (seromucoid), ceruloplasmin, and fibrinogen. *Advan. Chem. Ser.,* **44,** 17–40 (1964)

169. Kukral, J. C., Sporn, J., Louch, J., Winzler, R. J. Synthesis of alpha- and beta- globulins in normal and liverless dog. *Am. J. Physiol.,* **204,** 262–64 (1963)

170. MacFarlane, A. S. Metabolism of plasma proteins. In *Mammalian Protein Metabolism,* I, 298–341 (Munro, H. N., Allison, J. B., Eds., Academic Press, New York, 566 pp., 1964)

171. Katz, J., Rosenfeld, S., Sellers, A. L. Sites of albumin catabolism in the rat. *Am. J. Physiol.,* **200,** 1301–6 (1961)

172. Miller, L. L. The role of the liver and the non-hepatic tissues in the regulation of the blood free amino acids levels. In *Amino Acid Pools,* 708–21 (Nolden, J. T., Ed., Elsevier, New York, 815 pp., 1962)

173. McMenamy, R. H., Shoemaker, W. C., Richmond, J. E., Elwyn, D. Uptake and metabolism of amino acids by the dog liver perfused in situ. *Am. J. Physiol.,* **202,** 407–14 (1962)

174. Kamin, H., Handler, P. The metabolism of parenterally administered amino acids. *J. Biol. Chem.*, **188**, 193–205 (1951)

175. du Ruisseau, J. P., Greenstein, J. P., Winitz, M., Birnbaum, S. M. Studies on the metabolism of amino acids and related compounds in vivo. IV. *Arch. Biochem. Biophys.*, **64**, 355–67 (1956)

176. Winitz, M., du Ruisseau, J. P., Otey, N. C., Birnbaum, S. M., Greenstein, J. P. Studies on the metabolism of amino acids and related compuonds *in vivo*. V. *Arch. Biochem. Biophys.*, **64**, 368–73 (1956)

177. Schimke, R. T. Adaptive characteristics of urea cycle enzymes in the rat. *J. Biol. Chem.*, **237**, 459–68 (1962)

178. Munro, H. N. Nutritional and other mechanisms regulating amino acid metabolism in mammals. In *Protein Nutrition and Free Amino Patterns*, 127–49 (Leatham, J. H., Ed., Rutgers Univ. Press, New Brunswick, N. J., 227 pp., 1968)

179. Richmond, J. E., Shoemaker, W. C., Elwyn, D. H. Rates of biosynthesis of plasma and liver proteins. *Am. J. Physiol.*, **205**, 848–56 (1963)

180. Jeffay, H., Winzler, R. J., Donnelly, J. S. The metabolism of serum proteins. II. *J. Biol. Chem.*, **231**, 111–16 (1958)

181. Wunner, W. H., Bell, J., Munro, H. N. The effect of feeding with a tryptophan-free amino acid mixture on rat-liver polysomes and ribosomal nucleic acid. *Biochem. J.*, **101**, 417–28 (1966)

182. Gan, J. C., Jeffay, H. Origins and metabolism of the intracellular amino acid pools in rat liver and muscle. *Biochim. Biophys. Acta*, **148**, 448–59 (1967)

183. Schimke, R. T. The importance of both synthesis and degradation in the control of arginine levels in rat liver. *J. Biol. Chem.*, **239**, 3808–17 (1964)

184. Fisher, M. M., Kerby, M. Amino acid metabolism in the perfused rat liver. *J. Physiol. (London)*, **174**, 273–94 (1964)

185. Schimassek, H., Gerok, W. Control of the levels of free amino acids in plasma by the liver. *Biochem. Z.*, **343**, 407–15 (1965)

186. Freeman, S., Svec, M. Effect of complete hepatectomy upon plasma concentration and urinary excretion of eighteen amino acids. *Am. J. Physiol.*, **167**, 201–5 (1951)

BLOOD CLOTTING MECHANISMS: THREE BASIC REACTIONS[1,2]

By Walter H. Seegers[3]

Department of Physiology and Pharmacology
Wayne State University, School of Medicine
Detroit, Michigan

When considering the phenomenon of blood clotting "one feels that so simple and striking a phenomenon must have a simple and striking explanation, and the urge to discover it is immediate." The discovery forecast by Biggs & Macfarlane (1) has been made. It is now recognized that there are three basic reactions, and all other accessory complexities are designed to support and insure the smooth progression or retardation of these reactions. The following occurs in sequence:

1. Formation of autoprothrombin C
2. Formation of thrombin
3. Formation of fibrin

Recently interest in blood coagulation has spread rapidly because many important clinical manifestations have been explained on the basis of these mechanisms. It plays an important role in the production of all forms of thrombohemorrhagic phenomena (2). There is "solid evidence that well over forty different disease syndromes, allergic phenomena, and traumatic states now may be linked together through a common factor of intravascular coagulation." (3) "Disseminated intravascular coagulation is a fundamental pathogenetic mechanism." (4) These phenomena are conspicuously accelerated through the medium of the blood platelets (5–9).

---

[1] The survey of literature for this review was concluded in March 1968.

[2] Among the terms used autoprothrombin C is considered equivalent to thrombokinase and factor X_a. The precursor is called autoprothrombin III either as found in purified prothrombin or separated therefrom. At convenient sections of the manuscript the word autoprothrombin is reduced to the prefix auto. The term platelet cofactor is used in the same context as F-VIII or antihemophilic factor. Previously it was designated platelet cofactor I, to distinguish from platelet cofactor II, but the latter is now better called autoprothrombin II (F-IX), and thus the Roman numeral is not needed.

[3] Assisted by grants HE-05141-08 and HE-03424-11 from the National Heart Institute, National Institutes of Health, United States Public Health Service.

Formation of Autoprothrombin C and Thrombin in 25 per cent Sodium Citrate Solution

Prothrombin.—The precursor of thrombin is the substrate for the enzyme called autoprothrombin C. Evidence for this already appeared in 1949 when purified bovine prothrombin was placed in 25 per cent sodium citrate solution and thrombin was generated. This was because auto-C was produced first and then thrombin. The process is accelerated by either thrombin or auto-C (10). It is retarded by 3,4,4′–triaminodiphenyl sulfone, and by soybean trypsin inhibitor (11, 12). The former is a competitive inhibitor for auto-C.

Evidently prothrombin itself contains all that is needed to obtain thrombin. It is an aggregate which contains the precursor of two enzymes, namely thrombin and auto-C. The respective precursors are the prethrombin and auto-III of the original prothrombin. The subunits of the molecule are loosely held together, and most likely by van der Waals forces, hydrogen bonds, and/or ionic bonds, but not by covalent bonds. Owing to the mass of information which has accumulated (5, 6, 7, 9) it is out of the question to regard the isolated material as thrombin precursor with multiple random admixtures. Numerous physical-chemical studies have been completed in several laboratories (5), and prothrombin is evidently a single molecular entity. The aggregate occurs in plasma, and Barnhart (13) has shown that antibodies to auto-C form precipitates that remove thrombin precursor from plasma.

Prothrombin preparations.—In the isolation procedure used in my laboratory the integrity of the original subunits and their combination is preserved. Strong salt solutions must be used with care, and DEAE-cellulose is quite disruptive. Reed & Cox (14) have made a plea for care in efforts to remove "contaminating" activities. They say: "If assays for partial reaction are used, it is likely that an individual component of a possible enzyme complex will be purified rather than the intact complex."

When previously purified bovine prothrombin was passed through DEAE-cellulose columns, Seegers & Landaburu (15) produced a thrombin precursor that did not contain auto-III and did not form thrombin in 25 per cent sodium citrate solution, but in the ultracentrifuge it had about the same sedimentation characteristics as the prothrombin applied to the DEAE column. This type of material was evidently obtained from rat blood by Li & Olson (16), and from human plasma (17). Shapiro & Waugh (18) made special comments on the effects of DEAE-cellulose and modified the two-stage assay procedure to increase the thrombin yield. The use of DEAE-cellulose also accounts for the removal of auto-III by Lechner (19). Prothrombin fragments are a different consideration (20). The careful purification work of Moore et al. (21) yielded a product requiring special assay procedures for converting the precursor to thrombin. Presumably auto-III was nearly absent. There is not sufficient information with which to decide whether the crystalline horse prothrombin obtained by Miller & Phelan (22) contains auto-III or not. Crystalline bovine prothrombin evidently contains it (7). All the modified two-stage assay procedures (16, 18, 21) make a difference, but are really not adequate to insure full development of thrombin activity. Shapiro & Waugh (18) obtained a low specific activity for their homogenous product. They tried several ways to explain their low specific activity. Most likely insufficient procoagulant power was used in the assay or alterations were produced, or both. With prethrombin, which has the highest specific activity of any thrombin precursor obtained to date, it was essential to use purified auto-C and purified Ac-globulin (7, 12) for assay purposes. Up to now the procedures used in my laboratory, in contrast to others, have yielded prothrombin most nearly like the native material. From this prothrombin we have produced in excellent yield and high specific activity both thrombin and auto-C and their precursors.

Three distinct thrombin precursors have been obtained in the laboratory and studied extensively. One of these, and the first one obtained, is called prothrombin. It contains the precursor of thrombin and the precursor of auto-C. A second one is DEAE-prothrombin which does not contain the precursor of auto-C. Its sedimentation characteristics in the ultracentrifuge are nearly like prothrombin. A third one is prethrombin which can be derived from either prothrombin or DEAE-prothrombin. Prethrombin has ultracentrifuge sedimentation characteristics more nearly equal to those of thrombin than to those of prothrombin or DEAE-prothrombin. It could be that DEAE-prothrombin contains two prethrombin subunits.

Subunit activation: prethrombin and autoprothrombin III.—With the knowledge that the intact prothrombin would produce auto-C and thrombin, the next step was to dissociate prothrombin and isolate prethrombin as a precursor of thrombin, and auto-III as a precursor of auto-C (12, 23). With these additions to previous technology, five substances, namely prothrombin, auto-III, prethrombin, auto-C, and thrombin, were made available in purified form and these were studied in strong salt solutions. Nothing else was added. The observed effects could thus not be due to unforeseen extraneous factors. All substances were characterized in terms of physical-chemical properties, and amino acid composition. The work of Milstone (24) under the term thrombokinase could be associated with the preparation designated as auto-C (25, 26).

Autoprothrombin III.—The auto-III readily converted to auto-C in 25 per cent sodium citrate solution (11, 12). This process was accelerated by auto-C, trypsin, papain, and Russell's viper venom. The latter fact makes the connection with the work on factor X by Macfarlane and associates (27). The activation was retarded by 3,4,4'-triaminodiphenyl sulfone and soybean trypsin inhibitor (11). Only auto-III was needed to obtain auto C.

Prethrombin.—The prethrombin did not convert to thrombin in 25 per cent sodium citrate solution by itself, but when auto-C was added, thrombin formed by a first-order reaction with respect to the prethrombin substrate

(12, 28–30). Prethrombin also yielded thrombin with trypsin, but not with Russell's viper venom. It is thus clear that auto-C is the enzyme which breaks one or more bonds in prethrombin to form thrombin. This can be outlined as follows:

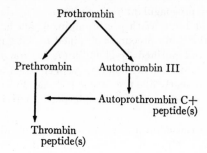

Modified autoprothrombin III.—There is a peculiarity about purified auto-III which is of special interest even though it might be just a laboratory creation. It was found that some preparations would activate in strong salt solutions while others would not. Eventually it was found that failure to activate was related to the use of thrombin for the dissociation of the prothrombin mother substance. Other enzymes did not produce modified auto-III nor would it convert to auto-C with the use of platelet cofactor, calcium ions, and lipids (29, 30). It was quite effective in correcting factor VII "deficient" and Stewart plasma but not hemophilia B plasma. It was, however, possible to convert the auto-III to auto-C in 25 per cent sodium citrate solution when the prethrombin substrate was also present. Either precursor alone did not activate but together both activated. There seems to be some type of reciprocal activation. In any case it is of prime interest to have such a demonstration since it is well known that prothrombin derivatives have procoagulant qualities as well as anticoagulant properties (5, 31). These occur in the form of variants of the prethrombin portion or the auto-III portion of prothrombin (32, 33). In summary, for 25 per cent sodium citrate solutions:

Modified autoprothrombin III———→very little autoprothrombin C
Prethrombin————————————→very little thrombin
The above together ————————→autoprothrombin C+thrombin
DEAE-prothrombin ————————→very little thrombin
Autoprothrombin III ————————→autoprothrombin C
Prethrombin+autoprothrombin C—→thrombin
Prothrombin————————————→thrombin+autoprothrombin C

ACCESSORY SUBSTANCES FOR THROMBIN FORMATION

Prothrombin.—Prothrombin forms thrombin in physiological saline solutions with the addition of only auto-C but the yield is small (24). It is also important to realize that auto-C makes a prothrombin refractory to the two-stage analytical reagents (34–36) and that auto-I forms, and can be isolated and found to be a structural variant of auto-C (32, 37).

Prethrombin.—With the certainty that thrombin can be derived from prethrombin by having only auto-C present it was easy to ask how this is accelerated in physiological integration. Ac-globulin, lipids, and calcium ions are needed. Thromboplastin was without effect (28, 33). It is then necessary to consider the properties of Ac-globulin first. Evidently auto-C forms complexes with lipids and calcium ions as shown by Cole, Koppel & Olwin (38, 39), and the dependence of auto-C activity on Ac-globulin seems to be well known.

Ac-globulin.—In this laboratory we found (5, 7) that thrombin "causes" an increase in Ac-globulin reactivity followed by loss of activity. This has again been confirmed by Hussain & Newcomb (40) and by Bergsagel & Nockolds (41). The Ac-globulin preparations of special interest are those of Hussain & Newcomb (40), Esnouf & Jobin (42), Barton & Hanahan (43), and Aoki, Harmison & Seegers (44). This work leaves no doubt that Ac-globulin is a protein, in which blocking of SH groups destroys activity (44). The molecular weight is uncertain, perhaps 100,000 or greater. Two amino acid analyses (42, 44) show low methionine and tryptophan values, but in general the results do not correspond exactly. Unfortunately, we are again confronted with the common failure to use methods and units that make specific activity comparisons possible. Barton & Hanahan (43) obtained a precipitate with calcium ions that was fabulously active, but we tried many times and failed to get that precipitate in this laboratory.

In the "cascade" (45) and "waterfall" (46) outlines for "intrinsic" blood clotting, Ac-globulin was supposed to become an active enzyme. This has been reaffirmed by Breckenridge & Ratnoff (47), but is not agreed to by Jobin & Esnouf (48), by Barton, Jackson & Hanahan (49), or by Hemker et al. (50). They find that it is a protein which supports the function of auto-C, in agreement with work from this laboratory (5, 7, 9, 10, 51). The "cascade" (45) and "waterfall" (46) sequence could not be adapted to standard methods of enzyme kinetics as studied by Hemker, Hemker & Loeliger (52).

Prethrombin, Ac-globulin, lipids, calcium, and autoprothrombin C.—Baker & Seegers (53) capitalized on the advantages of studying prethrombin instead of prothrombin and described the kinetics for thrombin generation. In their experiments purified prethrombin was converted to thrombin in an activating system consisting of purified auto-C, purified Ac-globulin, lipid activator, and calcium chloride. With the concentration of calcium and pH fixed, the effect of varying the concentration of the other three procoagulants was studied. Best thrombin yields were obtained with the simultaneous presence of auto-C, Ac-globulin, and lipid. Reducing any one of the three toward zero concentration decreased the rate of formation and the yield of thrombin. Under the conditions where thrombin formed most rapidly and the yields were the highest, Ac-globulin and auto-C were represented in approximately a 1:1 molar ratio. Autoprothrombin C is the enzyme and Ac-globulin determines its reaction specificity. For these conditions the Michaelis constant for auto-C on prethrombin as a substrate was $3.14 \times 10^{-6} M$. In this work the lipids from platelets, from thromboplastin, and from other natural sources were suitable, but no studies were done with purified or synthetic phospholipids. The main point to appreciate is that lipids of platelets are the only ones utilized when thromboplastin is excluded. The lipids in plasma are not adequate. In other words, the lipids of platelets are essential. There are substitutes only under experimental conditions. Hemolyzed red cells can also supply lipids.

Accessory Substrates for Autoprothrombin C Formation

Thromboplastin.—The transformation of purified auto-III to auto-C occurs readily and efficiently with calcium ions and repeatedly sedimented brain thromboplastin. No auto-III remains in serum if sufficient thromboplastin is used (54). That much seems certain, and is fundamental to our whole perspective.

Properties of thromboplastin.—What about the word "thromboplastin"? Does it require something additional called factor VII? Is prothrombin capable of contributing something important to tissue extracts? Purified bovine prothrombin can be infused into the veins of a dicumarolized dog to correct the hemostatic functions and the prothrombin time. Deutsch, Lechner & Schmer (55) did not succeed in proving that factor VII exists in plasma, nor did Voss (56–58). In agreement with the work from this laboratory he considers a prothrombin molecule the source of factors VII, IX, and X. In the work of Williams (59) lung microsomes were in the position of thromboplastin and he obtained a fraction associated with factor X which was necessary for their function. In this area of work there are peculiarities related to species. It may be that factor VII is merely a property of auto-C.

Seegers et al. (12) used sedimentable brain thromboplastin and found no difficulty in obtaining auto-C from highly purified auto-III. The latter readily corrected plasmas designated as factor VII, IX, or X deficient (12, 30). This purified auto-III seems to be the most active source known to date for correcting plasmas called factor VII, IX, or X deficient (7, 12, 30). A modified form of this auto-III corrected VII and X, but not the F-IX plasma. Thrombin was used to destroy the function (7, 12, 30) which corrects hemophilia B plasma. In the work of Nemerson (60) auto-C activity generated rapidly with thromboplastin, but he thought that a plasma component inhibited by DFP and soybean trypsin inhibitor generated procoagulant activity with thromboplastin. He suggested a separate factor VII, but like all others could not rule out prothrombin. Repeatedly prothrombin is found to be a molecule which is uniform with respect to physical properties and the source of several "factor" activities before and after dissociation into subunits.

The chemical composition of brain thromboplastin has been given extensive attention by Hecht & Oosterbaan van Lit (61) who were astonished by the claim of Irsigler (62) and Deutsch et al. (63) that brain thromboplastin is a lipoprotein that can be separated to obtain a protein which can be made active by reassociation with the original lipid or a suitable substitute. Hecht & Oosterbaan van Lit (61) found substantial objections to the previous work (62, 63), but found a significant amount of nitrogenous material. Perhaps this nitrogenous material is of very real importance. It will take a while to bring more insight to bear on these questions, and relate them to the fact that prothrombin is an aggregate that can be dissociated and degraded to give active procoagulants and at least one anticoagulant.

Platelet cofactor and lipids.—If tissue extracts are excluded, blood clots slowly and most of the auto-III portion of prothrombin remains in human serum (64, 65) as well as in the serum of many other species (54). Since only auto-C produces thrombin this implies a low yield of auto-C. What accounts for this limited yield? It seems to be produced slowly and in limited amounts by platelet cofactor (F-VIII) (10, 12, 51, 64, 66). Depending upon whether the platelet cofactor was obtained from human or bovine sources, the production of auto-C was absolutely or to a lesser degree dependent upon phospholipid. For all practical purposes this means platelet factor 3 as derived from platelets. The lipids in plasma are not sufficient. In addition, the platelet cofactor activity disappears during the clotting process because of thrombin and inhibitor source material, and this loss must subsequently be replaced by a substitute. This substitute comes into operation through the appearance of auto-II, which is derived from prothrombin (7), and is a platelet cofactor.

Urine component.—In addition to tissue components, platelet cofactor, trypsin, Russell's viper venom, and other enzymes, there is a substance in urine that can convert purified auto-III to auto-C. Calcium ions are essential for this but lipids are not (67). It makes purified prothrombin refractory to the two-stage analytical reagents, and in due course sensitivity is regained. Concentrates of this material have been made by Aoki & von Kaulla (68). The physiological significance is not understood. It is less abundant in urine during uremia (69) and kidney diseases (70).

Miscellaneous.—It seems to me that we can feel quite certain that tissue thromboplastin, platelet cofactor (F-VIII), a prothrombin derivative, and material from urine are concerned directly with the generation of auto-C activity. In addition enzymes such as cathepsin, papain, trypsin, and Russell's viper venom are effective. More needs to be known about the function of these substances.

The present preparations of F-VIII are not adequate for firm conclusions about basic theoretical considerations. It generally has been the aim to make something for clinical use and this has met with gratifying success (71–77), but there is still the struggle to make a separation from fibrinogen (78, 79). There is an anomalous behavior of hemophilia A fibrinogen during centrifugation (80). Except in papers from this laboratory, it was formerly stated that thrombin inactivates F-VIII, but now it does not (80), and in one study the conclusion was reached that thrombin activates F-VIII (81). We (5, 7, 9) have shown that platelet cofactor is not in serum because of inactivation by thrombin *and* inhibitor source material. This latter material is not found in PTA plasma. Ether extraction regenerates platelet cofactor activity of serum. The question whether hemophilia A is an inhibitor or deficiency disease has been reviewed by Hecht (82, 83) with the balance toward the former view, which is supported by many experiments from this laboratory (5, 7, 9). Very interesting is the release of this activity from storage areas in tissues (84, 85).

Summary

An outline of the events which take place with prothrombin alone was produced at the end of the discussion of prothrombin activation in sodium citrate solution. This outline can be expanded to indicate how forces on the periphery of prothrombin have their effect.

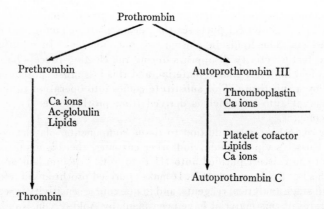

The Platelets

Function.—I want to stress my impression that platelets are most generally the point of beginning for the series of events that leads to fibrin formation. Their role in *formation* of auto-C and in the *function* of auto-C has been outlined above. Any "start" or acceleration elsewhere at least must converge on the platelets, unless red cells hemolyze, or a snake bites, or trypsin gains access to the circulation, or a staphylococcus flourishes to pathogenic proportions. In the "cascade" (45) and "waterfall" (46) sequence, Hageman factor is supposed to begin a series of reactions leading to fibrin formation. Now active Hageman factor has again been isolated (86), and one preparation (87) was infused intravenously in large quantities. There was no disseminated intravascular clotting, and thus facts do not fit predictions. Contrawise myocardial infarction has been observed in Hageman deficiency (88, 89). Hageman factor is, however, concerned with the activation of plasma kinins and with platelets (86, 90) and it functions as a platelet cofactor (86) in much the same way as platelet cofactor (F-VIII) does, and that can account for the production of thrombi with ellagic acid (91). Fibrinogen split products serve as platelet cofactor (92). Thus to regard platelets as the most common point of beginning for clotting is consistent with the numerous clinical conditions in which there is disseminated intravascular clotting.

Stimulating platelets.—Evidently ADP (93, 94) is commonly involved in platelet adhesiveness (95–102) and perhaps even with catecholamines (103–105), and can be released from red cells through mechanical damage (106). In congenital fibrinogen deficiencies much more ADP was needed for the abnormal aggregation (107). Dextran of suitable molecular weight reduces platelet adhesiveness and for that reason is of practical value (108–112). Bleeding times are prolonged (113). Fibrinogen split products (114) produce platelet aggregation, provided the digestion is not allowed to progress too far. In high concentration, aggregation may be inhibited (114). Eventually products form that only inhibit aggregation (115, 116).

The ionic charge and especially the electric charge of glass surfaces and other materials including collagen, stearic acid, and cholesterol have a role in promoting coagulation (117). Heparin bound to artificial surfaces reduces the extent of thrombus formation (118). Sawyer et al. (119) demonstrated the deposition of formed elements of the blood at polarized metal electrodes when the electrode potential became more positive than a critical value. Electrodes were inserted through side branches into the carotid artery for thirty to forty minutes. Magnesium, aluminum, and cadmium, which established a negative interfacial potential, produced no thrombus deposition (120). Others with a positive charge surface did. Magnesium tubes continued to be patent for long periods of time when inserted into the aorta. In this connection Cowan & Monkhouse (121) studied electrically induced thrombosis by applying metal electrodes to the *surface* of mesenteric vessels and applied microampere currents. There was electrolyte dissociation and gas formation accompanied by thrombosis. Thrombosis was produced as a result of pH change, and especially with a decrease (more acid) at the positive pole. Heparin does not easily prevent this formation of thrombi because of its inactivation at the pH produced (3).

Endothelial supporting function.—Before we continue with platelets in blood coagulation it seems important to give attention to the endothelial supporting function of platelets. Fibrin formation alterations, and degranulation of platelets occurred only when the endothelial barrier was interrupted. Contact with subendothelial connective tissue seems to be essential (122). Johnson et al. (123) used the electron microscope to study ultrathin sections and concluded that platelets enter the endothelial cell. Even purified platelet factor 3 was adequate for this function. In thrombocytopenia produced by irradiation, erythrocytes passed through the endothelial cells of capillaries (124). Carbon particles were found to escape transcellularly, and apparently not through endothelial junctions (125). Platelets were incorporated into the cytoplasm of the endothelial cells (126).

Platelet or plasma lipids.—According to Quick (127), platelet homogenates must function with contact plasma to be procoagulant. Massive quantities of auto-C, purified to a degree that can be detected in nanogram quantities, do not produce disseminated intravascular coagulation, unless platelet homogenates or platelet factor 3 are simultaneously administered (128). The lipids of plasma are not effective in meeting the requirements for auto-C, because these lipids are predominantly anticoagulant, the chief component being lecithin (129). The clotting defect in hibernating ground squirrels is not a plasma inhibitor but is associated with a low number of platelets (130).

Platelet components.—The antiheparin material has again been dissociated from the enzyme (?) that sensitizes fibrinogen to thrombin (131). The lipase inhibitor is different from antiheparin of platelets (132). Platelet factor 3, a lipoprotein, is commonly confused with lipids derived therefrom or those that might be free of protein. For example, platelet factor 3 and calcium ions make purified prothrombin refractory to the two-stage analytical reagents, whereas the lipid portion does not. Platelet granules and membranes have this activity (133). By using the electron microscope White & Krivit (134) found that phospholipid micells can become available without destroying the cells. Lipid micells were apparently ejected through the membrane. During coagulation of blood the greater fraction of platelet factor 3 remained with particulate platelet fragments, and 5 to 25 per cent was released in a nonsedimentable form (135). Silver (136) made suspensions of phospholipids and observed the formation of aggregates and "plugs" in a simple flowing system. Calcium ions alone mediated the aggregation, and he suggested that platelet aggregation during thrombus formation might occur in like manner.

Lipids in Prothrombin Activation

Whether the lipids are in the complicated thromboplastin as studied by Hecht (137) or in any other natural form, their position is at the beginning of events in blood coagulation. I am at odds with a sentence in the review by Marcus (138) which states: "There is no evidence that they initiate the coagulation process." Certainly the events cannot progress without them, and why be committed to the concept of *one* initiating factor? Convergence on platelets is over multiple routes. When red cells hemolyze, it is the lipids of the membranes that function in prothrombin activation, and under certain conditions the result may be fatal (3). A combination of materials from two anatomic compartments is needed. Even fatty acids are of importance through the route of platelets (139) and activation of Hageman protein (140). It is thus important to continue the synthesis and study of phospholipids (141, 142). The reports of Grisdale & Okany (143), Silver et al. (144), and Daemen et al. (145) are of great value and I do not pretend to encapsulate their contents.

Synthetic phosphatidyl serine (PS) had anticoagulant activity when solubilized (141) and weak procoagulant activity in simple suspension. The effectiveness of PS combined with phosphatidyl ethanolamine (146) continues to be confirmed. Emphasis is placed on the need for an acidic or negatively charged phospholipid. *In vitro* activity is not to be attributed to a certain type of phospholipid or a defined mixture. Daemen et al. (145), however, state that "optimal coagulant activity was produced by mixtures of synthetic phospholipids viz, phosphatidyl ethanolamine with phosphatidyl serine, phosphatidic acid or (isolated) cardiolipin and by certain combinations of lecithin and phosphatidyl serine." Grisdale & Okany (143) emphasize that "in aqueous media the zwitterionic phospholipid molecules are responsible for the following intermolecular forces: van der Waals attractive forces and ionic, ion-dipole, and dipole-dipole attractive or repulsive forces. A balancing of all these leads to stable micell formation." This means that a micell is needed with optimal surface charge density. It bears repeating that the clot-promoting property of platelet phospholipid linked with protein was more effective than lipids alone (135).

Authors have been most careful with the selection of a substrate. It is now, however, possible to study auto-III activation and prethrombin activation separately. Stated another way, it is now possible to study separately the *formation* and auto-C and its *enzyme activity*. It will then be interesting to ascertain whether the requirements differ in each case. What happens if phosphatidyl ethanolamine (PE) and PS are alone or combined in each case?

PHYSIOLOGICAL INTEGRATION OF CHEMICAL REACTIONS

In two of the main events in blood clotting the molecular biology has the recurring pattern of duality. Two molecules, Ac-globulin and platelet lipids, support the enzyme activity of auto-C. Two molecules, platelet cofactor (F-VIII) and platelet lipids, are needed for the formation of auto-C. Each pair comes from two anatomic compartments. This is analogous to having a reagent in two beakers one of which sits in the other. Break the inner one (injury) and the reagents are mixed and can function together. The main breaks in the barriers are platelet alterations, and the cutting or bruising of blood vessels and juxtavascular cells. It is one of several weaknesses of the "cascade" (45) and "waterfall" (46) hypotheses to fail in specifying the role of platelets or to give attention to the anatomic compartments. I take satisfaction in pointing to the latter consideration in my Harvey Lecture of 1952 (147).

I attempted to make a chart (Figure 1) of the facts related to blood clotting, and then divided it into four major divisions to consider the following:

1. Changes prothrombin undergoes
2. Accessories for changes in prothrombin
3. Neutralization of procoagulants
4. Transformations of fibrinogen

I think this representation subsumes what was stated in the cascade and waterfall projections, which have not been defended successfully. The intention is to represent a dynamic process which is counterbalanced by fibrinoly-

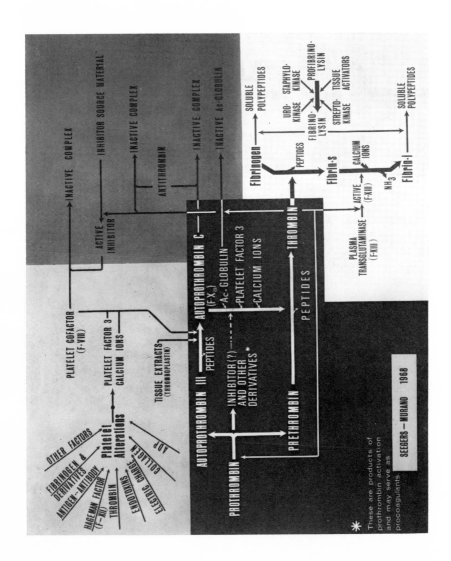

sis. Even with extreme amplification at the local levels, the procoagulant power can be neutralized rather rapidly. Despite elaboration on a neutral point of view (148), I doubt any possibility of survival without continuous latent clotting. For evidence there is the rapid turnover of prothrombin, of its derivatives (149–151), and of platelet cofactor. Prethrombin and fibrino-peptides are found in plasma. Fibrinogen solubilizes fibrin by interacting competitively with sites involving polymerization (152). Platelet cofactor levels (F-VIII) rise rapidly in response to epinephrine. This response is elimi-nated by blocking β-receptors (153).

The homeostasis maintained by opposing continuous clotting with fibrinolysis and neutralization of coagulation products requires the dynamic process of flow which is so well considered by Dintenfass and associates (154, 155). The clotting of blood depends upon the velocity gradient (156)

←◂◂◂

FIG. 1. Design of illustration is in four parts: as related to (a) changes prothrombin undergoes (*lower left*); (b) conditions to which prothrombin responds (*upper left*); (c) transformations of fibrinogen (*lower right*); and (d) neutralization of procoagulant activity (*upper right*). A prothrombin molecule can undergo several kinds of trans-formations, and not every molecule is activated in the same way.

In the first step some auto-III becomes activated to auto-C by tissue extracts and/or platelets plus platelet cofactor plus calcium ions. For this it is immaterial whether the auto-III is in the original prothrombin aggregate or separate. If throm-boplastin is excluded much auto-III remains in serum. Many stimuli make platelet materials available. Prothrombin derivatives (formed by platelets, thrombin, or auto-C and not diagramed in detail) accelerate the function of platelet and tissue substances.

In the second step auto-C generates thrombin activity. The precursor is here desig-nated as prethrombin with the meaning that it is a thrombin precursor. This can be one of several forms of the precursor as, for example, prothrombin which is not disso-ciated, or a dissociation product comparable to the DEAE-prothrombin which has been produced in the laboratory. In the generation of thrombin from one or another precursor by auto-C, the process is accelerated by the simultaneous presence of Ac-globulin, calcium ions, and platelet lipoprotein. Red cell lipoprotein is also possible. Note that the generation and the function of auto-C require a pair of substances originating from two anatomic compartments.

In the third main reaction thrombin removes fibrinopeptides from fibrinogen, and the resulting fibrin polymerizes. Thrombin also activates plasma transglutamin-ase. The latter forms crosslinks in fibrin with release of ammonia and the clot is stabilized.

The fourth provision concerns neutralization of procoagulant activity. In this function the reticuloendothelial system is important (not indicated). Fibrinolysin removes fibrin, and fibrinogen is also a substrate for that enzyme. The potent pro-coagulants which form have a short life and are rapidly neutralized. Thrombin first "activates" and then inactivates Ac-globulin; it also is important in producing in-active platelet cofactor through the medium of inhibitor source material. Thrombin itself is inactivated by antithrombin and heparin accelerates this. Likewise heparin accelerates the inactivation of auto-C by antithrombin.

The viscosity of blood from patients suffering from myocardial infarction and arterial thrombosis was appreciably higher than in normal persons (157). One can speak of high blood viscosity syndromes (158). With circulatory arrest the pH goes down (159). Crowell & Smith (160) demonstrated that dogs given a fibrinolytic activator could withstand circulatory arrest for longer periods of time than control animals. Crowell et al. (161) reported that the "mechanism of death" involves minute clots, and the central nervous system is not as sensitive to anoxia as previously believed. If clotting is ruled out by asanguineous total-body perfusion (162), survival is rather long and brain damage is reduced (163).

REMOVAL OF COAGULATION PRODUCTS

Leucocytes and liver.—Henry (164) reported that leucocytes migrated into a thrombus and their number increased with time. Eosinophils are a source of profibrinolysin of importance in acute inflammatory disease (165), and Riddle & Barnhart (166) observed the migration of leucocytes toward fibrin particles under skin windows. Fibrin was produced with thrombin, and using the electron microscope Prose, Lee & Balk (167) found fibrin on or near the cytoplasmic membrane of hypertrophied Kupfer cells. Fibrin was found within the cytoplasmic vacuoles. According to Barnhart (168, 169), Barnhart & Cress (170), and Barnhart & Riddle (171), neutrophylic leucocytes take up fibrin but not fibrin split products. Leucocytes are strongly attracted to fibrin. On the other hand the reticuloendothelial (RE) cells pick up both, namely aggregates and soluble products. Gans and co-workers (172–175) experimented with the perfusion of rat livers and advanced quantitative concepts of prime importance. Fibrin was taken up far more rapidly from the blood than soluble fibrin degradation products. Soluble fibrinogen derivatives are even competitive inhibitors of thrombin (176). Thrombin, a toxic agent, is cleared very rapidly by the liver and more rapidly than the innocuous thrombin neutralized by antithrombin. The RE system is marvelously selective, and its life-saving importance is seen in cases of disseminated intravascular coagulation.

Antithrombin.—There are now several new reports of a thrombosing tendency in association with low blood levels of antithrombin III (177–180). This is exactly what should follow from a latent continuous activation of prothrombin. Antithrombin neutralizes thrombin. Furthermore, Seegers et al. (181) found that it destroys auto-C, which is one of the most potent procoagulants known. Antithrombin III itself is destroyed by ether, there being no separate substance for the antithrombin IV effect (182). On the basis of experiments done with plasma deficient in antithrombin III (183), and with purified material (184–186), it seems that antithrombin III and heparin-cofactor are one and the same substance. Cofactor combines with heparin to form an active complex (187) that can block the enzymatic action of thrombin. Thrombin activity can be released from the complex by adding protamine (188). Henstell & Kligerman (189) think that antithrombin is bound to an inhibitor and postulate the following:

(a) Antithrombin−inhibitor+heparin = antithrombin−heparin+inhibitor
(b) Antithrombin−heparin+thrombin = antithrombin−thrombin+heparin

Through the purification work of Monkhouse & Milojevic (184) and Heimburger (185), antithrombin III is known to be an α_2-globulin with 6.9 per cent hexose, 4.5 per cent acetylhexosamine, and 3.3 per cent sialic acid, with molecular weight in the range 80,000–100,000. It inhibits trypsin, plasmin, and thrombin (185), and auto-C (181).

Other plasma components.—α_2-Antitrypsin evidently also inactivates thrombin (190, 191). A third substance seems to be involved, namely α_2-macroglobulin (α_2-M). It has been obtained as a purified component by Mehl et al. (192). It neutralizes trypsin, chymotrypsin (193), and fibrinolysin (194). In serum, α_2-M is destroyed by 0.25 M methylamine (195) and by ammonium sulfate (193). The binding with thrombin is unusual because it neutralizes thrombin C but not thrombin E activity (193).

THROMBIN, FIBRINOGEN, AND FIBRIN

Thrombin.—During the past ten years methods have been made available for producing bovine (5, 7, 9) and human (196, 197) thrombin of purity sufficient for chemical studies. Bovine thrombin has been studied by many (5, 7, 9). Practically all criteria for testing homogenicity were exhausted, and it was found to be a single substance. Nevertheless, Seegers, McCoy & Kipfer (198) were able to strip off 75 residues predominantly rich in Asp and Glu. This doubled the specific activity, reduced the total amino acid residues to 183, raised the isoelectric point to 6.2, and reduced the molecular weight from 33,700 to 25,000. $S^0_{20,w}$ was reduced from 3.7 to 3.15. During ultracentrifugation the molecule associated to form larger units. The K_m $=9.5\times10^{-5}$ M on TAMe and the N-terminal amino acids were found to be isoleucine and threonine, which is in line with what had previously been indicated by Magnusson (199) who worked with the 3.7 material. Hopefully this helps to clear up confusion about bothersome peptides associated with thrombin (200). For a molecular weight of 25,000 the amino acid residues found were as follows: Lys 14, His 4, Arg 13, Asp 16, Thr 8, Ser 10, Glu 20, Pro 9, Gly 15, Ala 9, 1/2 Cys 6, Val 11, Met 3, Ile 8, Leu 16, Tyr 7, Phe 8, and Trp 6. This analysis was the same as found for acetylated thrombin. The latter did not associate to form larger units during ultracentrifugation. Acetylated thrombin did not clot fibrinogen, it did not make prothrombin refractory to the two-stage analytical reagents, and it did not destroy the ability of purified prothrombin to correct prothrombin consumption in hemophilia B. The $K_m=4.85\times10^{-4}$ on TAMe, and the acetylated enzyme is thus not as effective as the original thrombin (198).

Kézdy, Lorand & Miller (201) used human thrombin to hydrolyze nitrophenyl N-benzyloxycarbonyl-L-tyrosinate and N-benzoyloxycarbonyl-Llysinate with formation of acylthrombin as an intermediate in the reaction which probably involves the DFP-sensitive serine residue of thrombin. They point to similarity of kinetic specificity with trypsin and α-chymotrypsin. Thrombin is sensitive to 1-chloro-3-tosylamido-7-amino-2-heptanone (TLCK) and this is consistent with the possibility that a histidine residue is essential for enzyme function (7, 202).

Human thrombin produced by activation of prothrombin with staphylo-coagulase has not been obtained in pure form, but evidently has unusual characteristics (203, 204). It is insensitive to antithrombin III, heparin, and hirudin, but removes the usual peptides from fibrinogen. It does not produce active plasma transglutaminase (F-XIII).

Fibrinogen.—The fibrinogen molecule (205, 206) contains an α-poly-peptide chain to which there is attached the short A-fibrinopeptide chain. There is a β-chain with B-peptide attached, and a third γ-chain from which thrombin does not remove a peptide. All this is duplicated as a dimer. By following the preliminary suggestion of the International Committee on Hemostasis and Thrombosis one can write as follows: for half the molecule (bovine) $\alpha(A)\beta(B)\gamma$, for the whole molecule $(\alpha(A)\beta(B)\gamma)_2$, for fibrin mono-mer $(\alpha\beta\gamma)_2$, for fibrin polymer $[(\alpha\beta\gamma)_2]_n$, for crosslinked urea insoluble trans-glutaminase produced fibrin polymer $[(\alpha\beta\gamma)_2]_n^x$, and for reptilase fibrin $[(\alpha\beta(B)\gamma)_2]_n$. The latter indicates that reptilase does not remove the B-peptide, and incidentally such clots do not retract (207). For the postulated (201) acylation reaction with thrombin (E-OH) and fibrinogen one could write

$$\alpha(A)\alpha(A)[\beta(B)\gamma]_2 + \text{E-OH} \rightarrow \alpha(A \cdot \text{E-OH})\alpha(A)[\beta(B)\gamma]_2 \rightarrow \text{A-O-E} + \alpha\alpha(A)[\beta(B)\gamma]_2$$

Fibrinopeptides.—Primarily from the work of Blombäck (208), Laki (209), and their associates we know the amino acid sequences for many fibrinopeptides. In man the composition for peptide A is: H-Ala·Asp·Ser·Gly·Glu·Gly·Asp·Phe·Leu·Ala·Glu·Gly·Gly·Gly·Val·Arg-OH. The ninth residue from Arg–OH is always Phe from species to species, and pre-sumably the arrangement is essential for thrombin activity. This Arg–OH attaches to Gly on the α-chain. This α-chain has been sequenced further by Blombäck et al. (210) and is as follows: Gly·Pro·*Arg*·Val·Val·Glu·Arg·His etc. up to 50. This is of special interest because eight cases of congenital dysfibrinogenemia have been reported, and in fibrinogen Detroit the argi-nine, third residue from bond split by thrombin, is replaced by serine (211). This fibrinogen had other characteristics different from normal.

Bovine peptide B has vasoconstrictor activity (212). In several animals this peptide and human peptide A caused pulmonary hypertension, de-creased effective pulmonary flow and related phenomena (213). They are thus not just discards in the clotting process, but exert physiological pres-sures and are subsequently broken down in serum (214). According to Lorand, Urayama & Lorand (215) the fibrinopeptides are relatively new in evolution. The blood of the lobster clots without producing them. The enzyme involved functions like the transpeptidase of vertebrates which is found in platelets and plasma of higher animals. Species specificity is observed at the lamprey level of development. Its thrombin releases two fibrinopeptides from lamprey fibrinogen at about the same rate, but bovine thrombin releases only fibrinopeptide B. The other can subsequently be removed by lamprey thrombin (216).

Plasma transglutaminase.—There was a difficult struggle to determine the nature of acceptor groups in transpeptidation. From these brilliant works (217–221) the evidence seems to favor the conclusion that the enzyme (F-XIII) properly be called plasma transglutaminase (220). The amide acceptor is a γ-glutamyl residue (220) and the donor is an ϵ-amino group of lysine (218). This is outlined below. It may be that the pattern of inheritance is like classical hemophilia; namely on the X chromosome (222).

Carbohydrates of fibrinogen are probably not released by either thrombin (223) or transglutaminase (224). Crosslinking of fibrin is also produced by a transglutaminase concentrated from liver tissue (225). Lorand & Konischi (226) demonstrated that papain functions by modifying fibrinogen so that it will polymerize and be crosslinked to form urea insoluble fibrin. Lorand & Jacobson (227) produced inhibitors of crosslinking that attach to end-amino groups (glycine ethyl ester) and compounds with carbonylamide functions (carbobenzoxy-L-asparagine amide). Thrombi produced in the presence of these inhibitors were more susceptible to lysis by fibrinolysin than crosslinked fibrin thrombi (228). Interesting ideas about fibrinogen and thrombin in tumor growth have been advanced (205).

Vitamin K and Dicumarol

Reports on the effects of vitamin K and Dicumarol (bishydroxycoumarin) generally tend to be dogmatic and are not critical with respect to the facts about blood clotting mechanisms. This also applies to discussions of the genetic aspects (229). Commonly one reads approximately as follows: "Vitamin K stimulates the appearance of several coagulation proenzymes (Factors II, VII, IX and X)." By borrowing from the phraseology of Koller (230) one can say that this seems "to be one of the many erroneous statements which are taken over from one author to the other." It could be called the lore of the unverified. It is self evident from the facts reviewed above that prothrombin is the protein requiring vitamin K for its synthesis. When liver slices produce a procoagulant (231) it is important to realize that tissue substances such as thromboplastin or cathepsin or both can convert auto-III to auto-C. From that point of view it seems possible to conclude that actinomycin D and puromycin (231–236) interfere with prothrombin synthesis. The site of action of vitamin K is at the ribosomal level (235), and thus at or near the translational stage in protein synthesis (236, 237). Barnhart (238) used immunological technics and structural studies to conclude that vitamin K functions at the translational level in prothrombin synthesis. Dicumarol produced changes in the organization of the endoplasmic reticulum. There was disorganization of membrane arrangement and a decrease in the number of ribosomes. Normal conditions were promptly restored after administration of vitamin K. Müller-Berghaus & Seegers (239) used the two-stage assay for prothrombin and the new prethrombin assay. Even with normal rabbit plasma the latter assay gave 20 per cent more thrombin than the other. At the height of the Dicumarol effect the thrombin yield was 200 per cent higher by the prethrombin assay. Reno & Seegers (54) developed an assay for auto-III and at the height of the Dicumarol effect in dogs the first response to intravenous vitamin K was an increase in the concentration of thrombin precursor and this was followed by the auto-III precursor. An effect was noticed within thirty minutes after the vitamin K was given. Within three hours the *proportions* of the two were the same as in normal plasma. Each precursor is thus synthesized independently of the other. Long before the prethrombin, prothrombin, and auto-III titres were very high, the prothrombin time was very much shortened. One does not necessarily need to assume a third factor to account for that result, because, as pointed out in connection with sodium citrate experiments, either precursor alone may not activate but when the two are together the prethrombin substrate influences the formation of auto-C. The shortening of the prothrombin time could be due to the simple fact that the two are together. In any case this possibility must be taken into account. In recent work we have found that the prothrombin which remains after synthesis is stopped by

Dicumarol or the purified prothrombin infused to restore the prothrombin level is rapidly transformed to a thrombin precursor assayed only by the prethrombin test and not by the regular two-stage assay. One path of degradation is thus from prothrombin to prethrombin. Prothrombin remains in circulation no more than six to eight hours (149, 240).

The response to Dicumarol was as follows: Prothrombin synthesis in the parenchymal cells of the liver was stopped. The material responding to two-stage analysis and the material responding to auto-III analysis dropped in concentration at the same rate over a period of two days. The precursor responding to the two-stage prethrombin assay tended to increase temporarily during the metabolic runoff. When the high dosages of Dicumarol were continued after prothrombin levels were extremely low and purified prothrombin was infused, this infused prothrombin corrected the hemostatic defect and it decayed in the same way as the original prothrombin, and was gone in about ten hours. When vitamin K was given to counteract the Dicumarol, prethrombin increased in concentration first, but within three hours prethrombin and auto-III were found in the same *proportions* as in purified prothrombin or in normal plasma. The prothrombin time was already quite short in three hours and approached normal by six hours while the prothrombin concentration continued to rise for ten to sixteen hours. By using fluorescent antibodies for prothrombin it could be demonstrated that fluorescence began on liver parenchymal cells within thirty to sixty minutes and was maximum in two to four hours (238). Barnhart (238) made some interesting calculations: prothrombin molecules synthesized per minute $= 1.27 \times 10^{15}$, and 17,900 are synthesized by each hepatocyte.

The minimal daily requirement for vitamin K_1 in adult man is near 0.03 μg/kg body weight (241). In the earliest work with oral anticoagulants it was found that some rabbits are resistant to the drug. Some rats are astonishingly resistant (242), and perhaps that is also true for sheep (243), and for mice (244). O'Reilly et al. (245, 246) made a study of resistance in man where there was great sensitivity to the antidotal action of vitamin K. Resistance appeared to be transmitted by a dominant allele. They stated that their study documents the first instance of genetically determined drug resistance in man to be reported in the literature.

ACKNOWLEDGMENTS

I hope I have conveyed a little of the spirit of progress since the last review in this series by Daniel L. Kline (247). To me it is a pleasant way to commemorate thirty years of continuous study in this field. Frank C. Mann was a previous contributor to this series and has recently written on further evidence for a simpler view of the coagulation of blood (248). I hope this review also contributes in that direction. Another important paper on fibrin crosslinking has appeared (249). I overlooked the paper by Suttie (250) in which it is also stated that vitamin K functions at the translation level of protein synthesis. I appreciate the help of Bea Blum with the checking of references, the secretarial assistance of Catherine Smetanka, and the work of Gene Murano on the illustration. Valuable suggestions were made by each of my colleagues: Marion I. Barnhart, Raymond Henry, Eberhard F. Mammen, Ewa Marciniak, Lowell McCoy, and Demetrios C. Triantaphyllopoulos.

LITERATURE CITED

1. Biggs, R., Macfarlane, R. G. *Human Blood Coagulation and Its Disorders* (Blackwell, Oxford, 474 pp., 1962)
2. Selye, H. *Thrombohemorrhagic Phenomena* (Thomas, Springfield, Ill., 337 pp., 1966)
3. Hardaway, R. M. III. *Syndromes of Disseminated Intravascular Coagulation* (Thomas, Springfield, Ill., 466 pp., 1966)
4. McKay, D. G. *Disseminated Intravascular Coagulation* (Harper, New York, 493 pp., 1965)
5. Seegers, W. H. *Blood Clotting Enzymology* (Academic Press, New York, 628 pp., 1967)
6. Seegers, W. H., Johnson, S. A. *Physiology of Hemostasis and Thrombosis* (Thomas, Springfield, Ill., 338 pp., 1967)
7. Seegers, W. H. *Prothrombin in Enzymology, Thrombosis and Hemophilia* (Thomas, Springfield, Ill., 181 pp., 1967)
8. Schulz, H. *Thrombocyten und Thrombose im elektronmikroskopischen Bild* (Springer-Verlag, New York, 125 pp., 1968)
9. Seegers, W. H. *Prothrombin* (Harvard Univ. Press, Cambridge, Mass., 728 pp., 1962)
10. Seegers, W. H., McCoy, L., Marciniak, E. *Clin. Chem.*, 14, 97–115 (1968)
11. Kipfer, R., Seegers, W. H. *Thromb. Diath. Haemorrhag.* (In press, 1968)
12. Seegers, W. H., Marciniak, E., Kipfer, R. K., Yasunaga, K. *Arch. Biochem. Biophys.*, 121, 372–83 (1967)
13. Barnhart, M. I. In *Blood Clotting Enzymology*, 217–77 (Seegers, W. H., Ed., Academic Press, New York, 628 pp., 1967)
14. Reed, L. J., Cox, D. J. *Ann. Rev. Biochem.*, 35, 79–82 (1966)
15. Seegers, W. H., Landaburu, R. H. *Can. J. Biochem. Physiol.*, 38, 2405–10 (1960)
16. Li, L., Olson, R. E. *J. Biol. Chem.*, 242, 5611–16 (1967)
17. Lanchantin, G. F., Friedmann, J. A., Hart, D. W. *J. Biol. Chem.*, 243, 476–86 (1967)
18. Shapiro, S. S., Waugh, D. F. *Thromb. Diath. Haemorrhag.*, 16, 469–90 (1966)
19. Lechner, K. *Thromb. Diath. Haemorrhag. Suppl.*, 17, 259–62 (1965)

20. Aronson, D. L., Menache, D. *Biochemistry*, 5, 2635–40 (1966)
21. Moore, H. C., Lux, S. E., Malhotra, O. P., Bakerman, S., Carter, J. R. *Biochim. Biophys. Acta*, 111, 174–80 (1965)
22. Miller, K. D., Phelan, A. W. *Biochem. Biophys. Res. Commun.*, 27, 505–10 (1967)
23. Seegers, W. H., Cole, E. R., Aoki, N., Harmison, C. R. *Can. J. Biochem.*, 42, 229–33 (1964)
24. Milstone, J. H. *Fed. Proc.*, 23, 742–56 (1964)
25. Marciniak, E., Seegers, W. H. *Can. J. Biochem. Physiol.*, 40, 597–605 (1962)
26. Seegers, W. H., Heene, D. L., Marciniak, E. *Thromb. Diath. Haemorrhag.*, 15, 1–11 (1966)
27. Macfarlane, R. G. *Oxford Med. Sch. Gaz.*, 17, 100–15 (1965)
28. Seegers, W. H., Marciniak, E. *Life Sci.*, 14, 1721–26 (1965)
29. Seegers, W. H., Marciniak, E., Heene, D. *Texas Rept. Biol. Med.*, 23, 675–704 (1965)
30. Marciniak, E., Seegers, W. H. *New Istanbul Contrib. Clin. Sci.*, 8, 117–33 (1965)
31. Marciniak, E., Murano, G., Seegers, W. H. *Thromb. Diath. Haemorrhag.*, 18, 161–66 (1967)
32. Seegers, W. H., Kagami, M. *Can. J. Biochem.*, 42, 1249–62 (1964)
33. Marciniak, E., Seegers, W. H. *Nature*, 209, 621–22 (1966)
34. Seegers, W. H., Aoki, N., Marciniak, E. *New Istanbul Contrib. Clin. Sci.*, 5, 170–76 (1962)
35. Seegers, W. H. *Thromb. Diath. Haemorrhag.*, 14, 213–28 (1965)
36. Seegers, W. H., Cole, E. R., Aoki, N. *Can. J. Biochem. Physiol.*, 41, 2441–61 (1963)
37. Seegers, W. H. *Fed. Proc.*, 23, 749–56 (1964)
38. Cole, E. R., Koppel, J. L., Olwin, J. H. *Can. J. Biochem.*, 42, 1595–1603 (1964)
39. Cole, E. R., Koppel, J. L., Olwin, J. H. *Thromb. Diath. Haemorrhag.*, 14, 431–44 (1965)
40. Hussain, Q. Z., Newcomb, T. F. *Ann. Biochem. Exptl. Med.*, 23, 569–76 (1967)
41. Bergsagel, D. E., Nockolds, E. R.

Brit. J. Haematol., **11**, 395–410 (1965)

42. Esnouf, M. P., Jobin, F. *Biochem. J.*, **102**, 660–65 (1967)

43. Barton, P. G., Hanahan, D. J. *Biochim. Biophys. Acta*, **133**, 506–18 (1967)

44. Aoki, N., Harmison, C. R., Seegers, W. H. *Can. J. Biochem. Physiol.*, **41**, 2409–21 (1963)

45. Macfarlane, R. G. *Nature*, **202**, 498–99 (1964)

46. Davie, E. W., Ratnoff, O. D. *Science*, **145**, 1310–11 (1964)

47. Breckenridge, R. T., Ratnoff, O. D. *J. Clin. Invest.*, **44**, 302–14 (1965)

48. Jobin, F., Esnouf, M. P. *Biochem. J.*, **102**, 666–74 (1967)

49. Barton, P. G., Jackson, C. M., Hanahan, D. J. *Nature*, **214**, 923–24 (1967)

50. Hemker, H. C., Esnouf, M. P., Hemker, P. W., Swart, A. C. W., Macfarlane, R. G. *Nature*, **215**, 248–51 (1967)

51. Seegers, W. H. *Pfluegers Arch.* (In press, 1968)

52. Hemker, H. C., Hemker, P. W., Loeliger, E. A. *Thromb. Diath. Haemorrhag.*, **13**, 155–75 (1965)

53. Baker, W. J., Seegers, W. H. *Thromb. Diath. Haemorrhag.*, **17**, 205–13 (1967)

54. Reno, R. S., Seegers, W. H. *Thromb. Diath. Haemorrhag.*, **18**, 198–210 (1967)

55. Deutsch, E., Lechner, K., Schmer, G. *Thromb. Diath. Haemorrhag. Suppl.*, **20**, 275–77 (1966)

56. Voss, D. *Blut*, **15**, 214–20 (1967)

57. Voss, D. *Klin. Wochschr.*, **9**, 449–52 (1967)

58. Voss, D. *Z. Physiol. Chem.*, **348**, 1172–78 (1967)

59. Williams, W. J., Norris, D. G. *J. Biol. Chem.*, **241**, 1847–55 (1966)

60. Nemerson, Y. *Biochemistry*, **5**, 601–08 (1966)

61. Hecht, E., Oosterbaan van Lit, W. L. *Thromb. Diath. Haemorrhag.*, **18**, 223–40 (1967)

62. Irsigler, K. *Thromb. Diath. Haemorrhag. Suppl.*, **13**, 433–35 (1964)

63. Deutsch, E., Irsigler, K., Lomoschitz, H. *Thromb. Diath. Haemorrhag.*, **12**, 12–34 (1964)

64. Macfarlane, R. G., Ash, B. J. *Brit. J. Haematol.*, **10**, 217–24 (1964)

65. Niemetz, J. *Thromb. Diath. Haemorrhag.*, **18**, 332–41 (1967)

66. Lundblad, R. L., Davie, E. W. *Biochemistry*, **4**, 113–20 (1965)

67. Marciniak, E., Seegers, W. H. *Thromb. Diath. Haemorrhag.* (In press, 1968)

68. Aoki, N., von Kaulla, K. N. *Thromb. Diath. Haemorrhag.*, **16**, 586–605 (1966)

69. Matsumura, T., von Kaulla, K. N. *Experientia*, **22**, 318–19 (1966)

70. Joist, H., Alkjaersig, N. *Thromb. Diath. Haemorrhag.*, **18**, 425–32 (1967)

71. Hattersley, P. G. *J. Am. Med. Assoc.*, **198**, 243–47 (1966)

72. Pool, J. G., Hershgold, E. J., Pappenhagen, A. R. *Nature*, **203**, 312 (1964)

73. Abildgaard, C. F., Simone, J. V., Corrigan, J. J., Seeler, R. A., Edelstein, G., Vanderheiden, J., Schulman, I. *New Engl. J. Med.*, **275**, 471–75 (1966)

74. Simson, L. R., Oberman, H. A., Penner, J. A., Lien, D. M., Warner, C. L. *Am. J. Clin. Pathol.*, **45**, 373–76 (1966)

75. Michael, S. E., Tunnah, G. W. *Brit. J. Haematol.*, **12**, 115–32 (1966)

76. Hershgold, E. J., Pool, J. G., Pappenhagen, A. R. *J. Lab. Clin. Med.*, **67**, 23–32 (1966)

77. Prentice, C. R. M., Breckenridge, R. T., Forman, W. B., Ratnoff, O. D. *Lancet*, **1**, 457–60 (1967)

78. Barrow, E. M., Amos, S. M., Heindel, C., Graham, J. B. *Proc. Soc. Exptl. Biol. Med.*, **121**, 1001–5 (1966)

79. Rizza, C. R., Chan, K. E., Henderson, M. P. *Nature*, **207**, 90–91 (1965)

80. Blombäck, B., Blombäck, M., Laurent, T. C., Persson, H. *Biochim. Biophys. Acta*, **97**, 171–73 (1965)

81. Ozge-Anwar, A. H., Connell, G. E., Mustard, J. F. *Blood*, **26**, 500–9 (1965)

82. Hecht, E. *Med. Welt*, **17**, 2139–49 (1966)

83. Hecht, E. *Klin. Wochschr.*, **14**, 797–803 (1966)

84. Muhrer, M. E., Lechler, E., Cornell, C. N., Kirkland, J. L. *Am. J. Physiol.*, **208**, 508–10 (1965)

85. Webster, W. P., Reddick, R. L., Roberts, H. R., Penick, G. D. *Nature*, **213**, 1146–47 (1967)

86. Mammen, E. F., Grammens, G. L. *Thromb. Diath. Haemorrhag.*, **18**, 306–7 (1967)

87. Schoenmakers, J. G. G., Matze, R., Haanen, C., Zilliken, F. *Biochim. Biophys. Acta*, **101**, 166–76 (1965)

88. Hoak, J. C., Swanson, L. W., Warner,

E. D., Connor, W. E. *Lancet*, **2**, 884–86 (1966)

89. Glueck, H. I., Roehll, W., Jr. *Ann. Internal Med.*, **64**, 390–96 (1966)

90. Iatridis, P. G., Ferguson, J. H., Iatridis, S. G. *Thromb. Diath. Haemorrhag.*, **11**, 355–71 (1964)

91. Nordoy, A., Chandler, A. B. *Lab. Invest.*, **16**, 3–12 (1967)

92. Triantaphyllopoulos, D. C., Triantaphyllopoulos, E. *Life Sci.*, **6**, 601–8 (1967)

93. Gaarder, A., Jonsen, J., Laland, S., Hellem, A., Owren, P. A. *Nature*, **192**, 531–32 (1961)

94. Morita, H., Asada, T. *Acta Haematol. Japon.*, **19**, 426–49 (1956)

95. Born, G. V. R., Haslam, R. J., Goldman, M., Lowe, R. D. *Nature*, **205**, 678–80 (1965)

96. Johnson, S. A., Van Horn, D. L., Pederson, H. J., Marr, J. *Transfusion*, **6**, 3–17 (1966)

97. Caen, J. P. *Nature*, **205**, 1120–21 (1965)

98. Philp, R. B., Wright, H. P. *Lancet*, **2**, 208–9 (1965)

99. Brinkhous, K. M., Read, M. S., Mason, R. G. *Lab. Invest.*, **14**, 335–42 (1965)

100. Sharp, A. A. *New Engl. J. Med.*, **272**, 89–92 (1965)

101. Marr, J., Barboriak, J. J., Johnson, S. A. *Nature*, **205**, 259–62 (1965)

102. Silver, M. D., Stehbens, W. E., Silver, M. M. *Nature*, **205**, 91–92 (1965)

103. O'Brien, J. R. *Nature*, **202**, 1188–90 (1964)

104. Thomas, D. P. *Nature*, **215**, 298–99 (1967)

105. Roswell, H. C., Hegardt, B., Downie, H. G., Mustard, J. F., Murphy, E. A. *Brit. J. Haematol.*, **12**, 66–73 (1966)

106. Harrison, M. J. G., Mitchell, J. R. A. *Lancet*, **2**, 1163–64 (1966)

107. Inceman, S., Caen, J., Bernard, J. *J. Lab. Clin. Med.*, **68**, 21–32 (1966)

108. Fadhli, H. A., Fine, D. P., Mazuji, M. K. *J. Thorac. Cardiov. Surg.*, **53**, 496–99 (1967)

109. Barnhart, M. I., Quintana, C. *Blood*, **30**, 541 (1967)

110. Bennett, P. N., Dhall, D. P., McKenzie, F. N., Matheson, N. A. *Lancet*, **2**, 1001–3 (1966)

111. Bygdeman, S., Eliasson, R. *Scand. J. Clin. Lab. Invest.*, **20**, 17–23 (1967)

112. Cronberg, S., Robertson, B., Nilsson, I. M., Nilehn, J. E. *Thromb. Diath. Haemorrhag.*, **16**, 384–94 (1966)

113. Thompson, W. L., Gadsden, R. H. *Transfusion*, **5**, 440–46 (1965)

114. Barnhart, M. I., Cress, D. C., Henry, R. L., Riddle, J. M. *Thromb. Diath. Haemorrhag.*, **17**, 78–98 (1967)

115. Larrieu, M. J., Inceman, S., Marder, V. *Nouvelle Rev. Franc. Hematol.*, **7**, 691–704 (1967)

116. Kopec, M., Budzynski, A., Stachurska, J., Wegrzynowicz, Z., Kowalski, E. *Thromb. Diath. Haemorrhag.*, **15**, 476–90 (1966)

117. Hubbard, D., Lucas, G. L. *J. Appl. Physiol.*, **15**, 265–70 (1960)

118. Salzman, E. W., Austen, W. G., Lipps, B. J., Merrill, E. W., Gilliland, E. R., Joison, J. *Surgery*, **61**, 1–10 (1967)

119. Sawyer, P. N., Wu, K. T., Wesolowski, S. A., Brattain, W. H., Boddy, P. J. *Proc. Natl. Acad. Sci. U. S.*, **53**, 294–300 (1965)

120. Chopra, P. S., Srinivasan, S., Lucas, T., Sawyer, P. N. *Nature*, **215**, 1494–95 (1967)

121. Cowan, C. R., Monkhouse, F. C. *Can. J. Physiol. Pharmacol.*, **44**, 881–86 (1966)

122. Ashford, T. P., Freiman, D. G. *Am. J. Pathol.*, **50**, 257–73 (1967)

123. Johnson, S. A., Balboa, R. S., Dessel, B. H., Monto, R. W., Siegesmund, K. A., Greenwalt, T. J. *Exptl. Mol. Pathol.*, **3**, 115–27 (1964)

124. Van Horn, D. L., Johnson, S. A. *Am. J. Clin. Pathol.*, **46**, 204–13 (1966)

125. Van Horn, D. L., Johnson, S. A. *J. Lab. Clin. Med.* (In press, 1968)

126. Johnson, S. A., Balboa, R. S., Greenwalt, T. J. *Bibl. Haematol.*, **23**, 1362–65 (1965)

127. Quick, A. J. *Thromb. Diath. Haemorrhag.*, **16**, 318–30 (1966)

128. Marciniak, E., Rodriguez-Erdmann, F., Seegers, W. H. *Science*, **137**, 421–22 (1962)

129. Cohen, J., Reed, C. F., Troup, S. B. *Thromb. Diath. Haemorrhag.*, **13**, 531–42 (1965)

130. Lechler, E., Penick, G. D. *Am. J. Physiol.*, **205**, 985–88 (1963)

131. Farbiszewski, R., Niewiarowski, S., Poplawski, A. *Biochim. Biophys. Acta*, **115**, 397–403 (1966)

132. Poplawski, A., Niewiarowski, S. *Biochim. Biophys. Acta*, **90**, 403–5 (1964)

133. Marcus, A. J., Zucker-Franklin, D., Safier, L. B., Ullman, H. L. *J. Clin. Invest.*, **45**, 14–28 (1966)

134. White, J. G., Krivit, W. *Blood*, **27**, 167–86 (1966)
135. Horowitz, H. I., Papayaanou, M. F. *J. Lab. Clin. Med.*, **69**, 1003–12 (1967)
136. Silver, M. J. *Am. J. Physiol.*, **209**, 1128–36 (1965)
137. Hecht, E. *Nature*, **214**, 197–98 (1967)
138. Marcus, A. J. *Advan. Lipid Res.*, **4**, 1–37 (1966)
139. Haslam, R. J. *Nature*, **202**, 765–68 (1964)
140. Hoak, J. C., Connor, W. E., Eckstein, J. W., Warner, E. D. *J. Lab. Clin. Med.*, **63**, 791–800 (1964)
141. Turner, D. L., Silver, M. J., Baczynski, E., Giordano, N., Rodalewicz, I. *J. Lipid Res.*, **5**, 616–23 (1964)
142. Turner, D. L., Silver, M. J., Baczynski, E. *J. Med. Chem.*, **9**, 771–72 (1966)
143. Grisdale, P. J., Okany, A. *Can. J. Biochem.*, **43**, 1465–70 (1965)
144. Silver, M. J., Turner, D. L., Rodalewicz, I., Giordano, N., Holburn, R., Herb, S. F., Luddy, F. E. *Thromb. Diath. Haemorrhag.*, **10**, 164–89 (1963)
145. Daemen, F. J. M., van Arkel, C., Hart, H. C., van der Drift, C., van Deenen, L. L. M. *Thromb. Diath. Haemorrhag.*, **13**, 194–217 (1965)
146. Hecht, E. R. *Lipids in Blood Clotting* (Thomas, Springfield, Ill., 328 pp., 1965)
147. Seegers, W. H. *Harvey Lectures*, *Ser.* **47**, 180–220 (1952)
148. Hjort, P. F., Hasselback, R. *Thromb. Diath. Haemorrhag.*, **6**, 580–612 (1961)
149. Bowie, E. J. W., Thompson, J. H., Jr., Didisheim, P., Owen, C. A., Jr. *Transfusion*, **7**, 174–84 (1967)
150. Dodds, W. J., Packham, M. A., Roswell, H. C., Mustard, J. F. *Am. J. Physiol.*, **213**, 36–42 (1967)
151. Kazmier, F. J., Spittell, J. A., Jr., Thompson, J. H., Jr., Owen, C. A., Jr. *Arch. Internal Med.*, **115**, 667–73 (1965)
152. Shainoff, J. R., Page, I. H. In *Natl. Conf. Cardiov. Disease, 2nd, Washington, D. C.*, 373–75 (1964)
153. Ingram, G. I. C., Jones, R. V. *J. Physiol. (London)*, **187**, 447–54 (1966)
154. Dintenfass, L., Rozenberg, M. C. *J. Atheroscler. Res.*, **5**, 276–90 (1965)
155. Rozenberg, M. C., Dintenfass, L.

156. Dintenfass, L. *Angiology*, **15**, 333–43 (1964)
157. Dintenfass, L., Julian, D. G., Miller, G. E. *Am. Heart J.*, **71**, 587–600 (1966)
158. Dintenfass, L. *Arch. Internal Med.*, **118**, 427–35 (1966)
159. Crowell, J. W., Kaufmann, B. N. *Am. J. Physiol.*, **200**, 743–45 (1961)
160. Crowell, J. W., Smith, E. E., *Am. J. Physiol.*, **186**, 283–85 (1956)
161. Crowell, J. W., Sharpe, G. P., Lambright, R. L., Read, W. L. *Surgery*, **38**, 696–702 (1955)
162. Neely, W. A., Turner, M. D., Haining, J. L. *J. Am. Med. Assoc.*, **184**, 718–21 (1963)
163. Neely, W. A., Youmans, J. R. *J. Am. Med. Assoc.*, **183**, 1085–87 (1963)
164. Henry, R. L. *Thromb. Diath. Haemorrhag.*, **13**, 35–45 (1965)
165. Riddle, J. M., Barnhart, M. I. *Blood*, **25**, 776–94 (1965)
166. Riddle, J. M., Barnhart, M. I. *Am. J. Pathol.*, **45**, 805–23, (1964)
167. Prose, P. H., Lee, L., Balk, S. D. *Am. J. Pathol.*, **47**, 403–17 (1965)
168. Barnhart, M. I. *Biochem. Pharmacol.*, **16**, 1–16 (1967)
169. Barnhart, M. I. *Fed. Proc.*, **24**, 846–53 (1965)
170. Barnhart, M. I., Cress, D. C. In *The Reticuloendothelial System and Atherosclerosis*, 492–502 (Di Luzio, N. R., Paoletti, R., Eds., Plenum Press, New York, 516 pp., 1967)
171. Barnhart, M. I., Riddle, J. M. *Thromb. Diath. Haemorrhag. Suppl.*, **26**, 87–105 (1967)
172. Gans, H., Lowman, J. T. *Blood*, **29**, 526–39 (1967)
173. Gans, H., Subramanian, V., Lowman, J. T., Tan, B. H. *Surgery*, **62**, 698–703 (1967)
174. Gans, H., Subramanian, V., Tan, B. H. *Science*, **159**, 107–10 (1968)
175. Gans, H. *J. Surg. Res.*, **6**, 87–92 (1966)
176. Triantaphyllopoulos, D. C., Triantaphyllopoulos, E. *Brit. J. Haematol.*, **12**, 145–51 (1966)
177. Egeberg, O. *Thromb. Diath. Haemorrhag.*, **13**, 516–30 (1965)
178. von Kaulla, E., von Kaulla, K. N. *Am. J. Clin. Pathol.*, **48**, 69–80 (1967)
179. Koszewski, B. J., Vahabzadeh, H. *Thromb. Diath. Haemorrhag.*, **11**, 485–96 (1964)
180. von Kaulla, K. N., Paton, B. C.,

Rosenkrantz, J. G., von Kaulla, E., Wasantapruek, S. *Arch. Surg.*, **94**, 107–11 (1967)

181. Seegers, W. H., Cole, E. R., Harmison, C. R., Monkhouse, F. C. *Can. J. Biochem.*, **42**, 359–64 (1964)

182. Monkhosue, F. C., Milojevic, S. *Can. J. Physiol. Pharmacol.*, **43**, 819–23 (1965)

183. Egeberg, O. *Thromb. Diath. Haemorrhag.*, **14**, 473–89 (1965)

184. Monkhouse, F. C., Milojevic, S. *Can. J. Physiol. Pharmacol.* (In press, 1968)

185. Heimburger, N. *First International Symposium on Tissue Factors in the Homeostasis of the Coagulation-Fibrinolysis System*, 33–62 (Firenze-Maggio, Behringwerke A. G., Marburg/Lahn, Germany, 1967)

186. Abildgaard, U. *Scand. J. Clin. Lab. Invest.*, **19**, 190–95 (1967)

187. Porter, P., Porter, M. C., Shanberge, J. N. *Biochemistry*, **6**, 1854–63 (1967)

188. Porter, P., Porter, M. C., Shanberge, J. N. *Clin. Chim. Acta*, **17**, 189–200 (1967)

189. Henstell, H. H., Kligerman, M. *Thromb. Diath. Haemorrhag.*, **18**, 167–78 (1967)

190. Gans, H., Tan, B. H. *Clin. Chim. Acta*, **17**, 111–17 (1967)

191. Schwick, H. G., Heimburger, N., Haupt, H. *Z. Inn. Med.*, **7**, 193–98 (1966)

192. Mehl, J. W., O'Connell, W., de Groot, J. *Science*, **145**, 821–22 (1964)

193. Lanchantin, G. F., Plesset, M. L., Friedmann, J. A., Hart, D. W. *Proc. Soc. Exptl. Biol. Med.*, **121**, 444–49 (1966)

194. Ganrot, P. O., Nilehn, J. E. *Clin. Chim. Acta*, **17**, 511–13 (1967)

195. Steinbuch, M., Blatrix, C., Jasso, F. *Nature*, **216**, 500–1 (1967)

196. Lanchantin, G. F., Friedmann, J. A., Hart, D. W. *J. Biol. Chem.*, **242**, 2491–2501 (1967)

197. Miller, K. D., Copeland, W. H. *Exptl. Mol. Pathol.*, **4**, 431–37 (1965)

198. Seegers, W. H., McCoy, L., Kipfer, R. *Arch. Biochem. Biophys.* (In press, 1968)

199. Magnusson, S. *Arkiv Kemi*, **23**, 271–283 (1964)

200. Landaburu, R. H., Abdala, O., Morrone, J. *Science*, **148**, 380–81 (1965)

201. Kézdy, F. J., Lorand, L., Miller, K. D. *Biochemistry*, **4**, 2302–8 (1965)

202. Shaw, E., Mares-Guia, M., Cohen, W. *Biochemistry*, **4**, 2219–24 (1965)

203. Kopec, M., Wegrzynowicz, Z., Budzynski, A. Z., Jeljaszewicz, J., Latallo, Z. S., Lipinski, B., Kowalski, E. *Thromb. Diath. Haemorrhag.*, **18**, 475–86 (1967)

204. Soulier, J. P., Prou, O. *Thromb. Diath. Haemorrhag. Suppl.*, **20**, 255–67 (1966)

205. Laki, K. *Fibrinogen* (Marcel Dekker, Inc., New York, 398 pp., 1968)

206. Blombäck, B. In *Blood Clotting Enzymology*, 143–215 (Seegers, W. H., Ed., Academic Press, New York, 628 pp., 1967)

207. Morse, E. E., Jackson, D. P., Conley, C. L. *J. Lab. Clin. Med.*, **70**, 106–15 (1967)

208. Blombäck, B., Blombäck, M., Henschen, A., Hessel, B., Iwanga, S., Woods, K. R. *Nature* (In press, 1968)

209. Laki, K. *Fed. Proc.*, **24**, 794–99 (1965)

210. Blombäck, B., Blombäck, M., Hessel, B., Iwanga, S. *Nature*, **215**, 1445–48 (1967)

211. Blombäck, M., Blombäck, B., Mammen, E. F., Prasad, A. S. *Nature* (In press, 1968)

212. Colman, R. W., Osbahr, A. J., Morris, R. E., Jr. *Nature*, **215**, 292–93 (1967)

213. Bayley, T., Clements, J. A., Osbahr, A. J. *Circ. Res.*, **21**, 469–84 (1967)

214. Teger-Nilsson, A. C., Blombäck, B. *Acta Chem. Scand.*, **21**, 307–9 (1967)

215. Lorand, J., Urayama, T., Lorand, L. *Biochem. Biophys. Res. Commun.*, **23**, 828–34 (1966)

216. Doolittle, R. F. *Biochem. J.*, **94**, 735–41 (1965)

217. Loewy, A. G. Matacic, S., Darnell, H. J. *Arch. Biochem. Biophys.*, **113**, 435–38 (1966)

218. Fuller, G. M., Doolittle, R. F. *Biochem. Biophys. Res. Commun.*, **25**, 694–700 (1966)

219. Lorand, L., Ong, H. H. *Biochem. Biophys. Res. Commun.*, **23**, 188–93 (1966)

220. Matacic, S., Loewy, A. G. *Biochem. Biophys. Res. Commun.*, **24**, 858–66 (1966)

221. Doolittle, R. F., Fuller, G. M. *Biochem. Biophys. Res. Commun.*, **26**, 327–34 (1967)

222. Hampton, J. W., Cunningham, G. R., Bird, R. M. *J. Lab. Clin. Med.*, **67**, 913–21 (1966)

223. Raisys, V., Molnar, J., Winzler, R. J.

Arch. Biochem. Biophys., **113**, 457–60 (1966)

224. Tyler, H. M. *Nature*, **210**, 1045–46 (1966)

225. Tyler, H. M., Laki, K. *Biochemistry*, **6**, 3259–63 (1967)

226. Lorand, L., Konishi, K. *Biochemistry*, **3**, 915–19 (1964)

227. Lorand, L., Jacobsen, A. *Biochemistry*, **3**, 1939–43 (1964)

228. Lorand, J., Pilkington, T. R. E., Lorand, L. *Nature*, **210**, 1273–74 (1966)

229. Kerr, C. B. *J. Med. Genet.*, **2**, 254–303 (1965)

230. Koller, F. *Acta Haematol.*, **36**, 133–40 (1966)

231. Merskey, C., Wohl, H. *Proc. Soc. Exptl. Biol. Med.*, **118**, 703–6 (1965)

232. Olson, R. E. *Can. J. Biochem.*, **43**, 156–73 (1965)

233. Hill, R. B., Paul, F., Johnson, B C. *Proc. Soc. Exptl. Biol. Med.*, **121** 1287–90 (1966)

234. Lowenthal, J., Simmons, E. L. *Experientia*, **23**, 421–22 (1967)

235. Johnson, B. C., Hill, R. B., Alden, R., Ranhotra, G. S. *Life Sci.*, **5**, 385–92 (1966)

236. Olson, R. E. *Advan. Enzyme Reg.*, **4**, 181–96 (1966)

237. Olson, J. P., Miller, L. L., Troup, S. B. *J. Clin. Invest.*, **45**, 690–701 (1966)

238. Barnhart, M. I. *J. Histochem. Cytochem.*, **13**, 740–51 (1965)

239. Müller-Berghaus, G., Seegers, W. H. *Thromb. Diath. Haemorrhag.*, **16**, 707–22 (1966)

240. Spector, I., Corn, M., Ticktin, H. E. *New Engl. J. Med.*, **275**, 1032–37 (1966)

241. Frick, P. G., Riedler, G., Brogli, H. *J. Appl. Physiol.*, **23**, 387–89 (1967)

242. Lund, M. *Nature*, **203**, 778 (1964)

243. Linton, J. H., Goplen, B. P., Bell, J. M., Jaques, L. B. *Can. J. Animal Sci.*, **43**, 353–60 (1963)

244. Rowe, F. P., Redfern, R. *J. Hyg.*, **63**, 417–25 (1965)

245. O'Reilly, R. A., Aggeler, P. M., Hoag, M. S., Leong, L. S., Kropatkin, M. L. *New Engl. J. Med.*, **271**, 809–15 (1964)

246. O'Reilly, R. A., Aggeler, P. M. *Fed. Proc.*, **24**, 1266–73 (1965)

247. Kline, D. L. *Ann. Rev. Physiol.*, **27**, 285–306 (1965)

248. Mann, F. D. *Am. J. Clin. Pathol.*, **46**, 612–15 (1966)

249. Lorand, L., Rule, N. G., Ong, H. H., Furlanetto, R., Jacobsen, A., Downey, J., Öner, N., Bruner-Lorand, J. *Biochemistry*, **7**, 1214–23 (1968)

250. Suttie, J. W. *Arch. Biochem. Biophys.*, **118**, 166–71 (1967)

OVERALL CIRCULATORY REGULATION[1,2]

By Kiichi Sagawa[3]

Department of Physiology and Biophysics, University of Mississippi
School of Medicine, Jackson, Mississippi

INTRODUCTION

Since this is the first systematic review under the title "Overall Circulatory Regulation", I will begin by delineating the subject matter and stating my criteria for selection of papers. The period to be reviewed is May 1966 to April 1968.

The function of the circulatory system is to transport the blood and a minute amount of lymph throughout the body. In this manner the system transports respiratory gases, metabolites, humoral agents, and heat from one part of the body to another. Admittedly, the ultimate end served by this transport is homeostasis of the tissue environment. From this axiom immediately follows an important thesis related to the current subject: In the discussion of overall circulatory regulation, any particular aspect of the system's behavior ultimately has to be evaluated with quantitative reference to homeostasis of individual tissues and the whole body. To emphasize this objective, the subject of the review may be rephrased as circulatory adaptation toward overall homeostasis. Studies on the behavior of the circulatory system as correlated with respiratory, metabolic, and thermal activities during exercise, at high altitude, during heat stress, etc. are good examples of overall circulatory regulation. Studies on hypertension as a disease of regulation are also pertinent. In essence, the subject is a circulatory version of *systems physiology* which brings into sharp focus the interactions and equilibria among the related subsystems (1).

The term overall circulatory regulation has also been used in a different context for years. It has often meant, particularly to students of circulatory

[1] Supported in part by United States Public Health Service grants HE-09644 and HE-10581.

[2] For supplementary bibliographic material (171 references, 28 pages), order NAPS Document 00020 from ASIS National Auxiliary Publications Service, c/o CCM Information Sciences, Inc., 22 West 34th Street, New York, New York, 10001. Remit with your order $1.00 for microfiche or $3.00 for photocopies.

[3] Present address: Department of Biomedical Engineering, Schools of Engineering and Medicine, Case Western Reserve University, Cleveland, Ohio 44106.

physiology, an analysis of circulatory dynamics in terms of the lumped (overall) variables such as cardiac output, central arterial and venous pressures. Obviously, analysis of the complex mechanical structure of this closed-loop hydraulic system, whose behavior is further complicated by multiple neural and humoral parallel feedback loops, requires a fair degree of skill. Although such analyses have no direct bearing on the overall homeostasis of the body, they may provide a solid physical basis for the latter approach. In control engineering such analysis is termed plant identification. It is the first step toward designing the controller in engineering; it has been, in the minds of conventional circulatory physiologists, the very last end.

Compared with mechanical hydraulic devices, every component in the circulatory system is extremely "soft" and equipped with an abundance of autoregulatory features. In fact, it is often impossible to separate the controller and the controlled system except as a matter of concept. Therefore, identification of the isolated cardiac pump or the vascular conduit constitutes a substantial part of the analysis of circulatory regulation; it has to be advanced along with the analysis of the controller. Many papers which deal with only a part of the circulatory system have nevertheless been cited here because of their implications for the overall system's behavior.

No attempt has been made to be comprehensive, yet almost one quarter of the papers published on circulation appeared to have some valid information concerning the present subject. Aided by personal bias and limitation of the allotted space, I succeeded in cutting the number of citations to some one hundred. To those whose works were not cited despite their significant contribution, my sincere apology. To those who kindly responded to a request for reprint or manuscript, my deep appreciation. During this period excellent review articles appeared in *Physiological Reviews* with regard to human circulatory regulation during exercise (2) and the role of the sympathetic nervous system in hemorrhage (3). In addition, proceedings of important symposiums on the following relevant topics were published: the physical bases of circulatory transport (4), the baroreceptor reflex (5), exercise and the heart (6), the physiology of muscular exercise (7), and neurohumoral mechanisms and hypertension (8–11). In addition, a monograph on hormones and hypertension (12) and two textbooks of circulation (13, 14) were published.

MODELS

The review period is noteworthy for the ever increasing use of computer technics for simulation and data processing in every corner of circulatory physiology. A brief account of the state of the art in the realm of overall circulatory regulation will be given in a few examples.

Computer modeling.—Beneken & DeWit (15) summarized the major characteristics of a large analog computer model of the entire human circulatory system. The circulatory system was compartmentalized into nineteen segments, and approximately forty equations were derived to describe the basic properties of these segments. The amount of physiological information put into this model, as well as the rigorous mathematical formulations from the physics standpoint, distinguishes this from similar models of the overall circulation. Many classes of control mechanisms are introduced, including various factors affecting contractility of the myocardium, effect of intra-thoracic and abdominal pressure changes on the venous conductance and ventricular distention, baroreceptor reflex control of the cardiac pump and the vascular resistance, autoregulation in various vascular beds, capillary fluid shift, and stress relaxation phenonemon. By virtue of being an analog computer, the model permits quick solutions to parametric sensitivity tests. This feature was fully exploited in simulating hemorrhagic shock, Valsalva maneuvers, and other examples of altered hemodynamic situations where input disturbance was well defined and experimental data were available to compare with the computer solutions. The capability of computer simula-tion as a tool for checking the validity of hypotheses and assumptions was well demonstrated with this detailed and flexible model. Beneken & Ride-out (16) further discussed the advantage of using such a model to study the transport function of oxygen, CO_2, dye, and heat. In so doing, combination with the perturbation technic helps greatly to amplify the relatively small changes in variables in the original set of analog circuits into large enough signals in the second set. This perturbation technic will be an asset, provided one can afford two sets of computers and the manner in which perturbation signals modify the system parameters is known with such mathematical precision that he can derive the perturbation equations. Even with the ac-celerated use of computer facilities at research institutes, it may take a while before the average investigator will be able to enjoy the merits of the technic.

Guyton & Coleman (17) presented an analog model of long-term circula-tory regulation into which the interactions between the circulatory system and the renal body fluid control system were explicitly incorporated. The following are the main features of this model, used to test the authors' con-cepts on the mechanism of renoprival hypertension. The first feature to be emphasized is the integration of a long-term autoregulation of the systemic vascular system into the basic scheme as the most powerful control mecha-nism for tissue homeostasis over an extended period of time. The second is the negative feedback loop between kidney function and the circulation. Briefly, the magnitude of arterial pressure determines the urinary output, which in turn determines the blood volume and thereby the mean circulatory pressure. The latter pressure is a determinant of cardiac output and cardiac output is, of course, a determinant of arterial pressure. In this closed loop of cause and effect, renal urine formation function was disturbed by a renoprival proce-dure to cause a shift in the arterial pressure-urinary output relationship. The new equilibrium state following this shift will involve increased blood volume and cardiac output, and elevated arterial pressure, if vascular autoregulation does not alter the systemic vascular resistance. However, because of the vascular autoregulation, an eventual hypertensive equilibrium state is reached in a few days with only a slightly increased cardiac output and blood volume. This prediction was confirmed by the animal experiment conducted by the authors. The third unique feature is that despite a large number of blocks representing the key components in the system, input and output of these blocks feed back and forth in other blocks in such a way that only a few independent parametric variables remain open ended. In other words, the model is self-contained regarding the parametric controls and resembles the real biological system in the floating nature of its pursuit of a goal.

The most important of the many carrier functions of the circulatory system is oxygen transport. Thus Pennock & Attinger (18) proposed a mathematical model to analyze the overall performance of the oxygen transport system within the limits set by the physical chemical properties of the individual subjects. The model is characterized by (a) division of the whole-body tissue mass into three compartments—the respiratory pump tissue, the cardiac pump tissue, and the rest of the body tissues; (b) the oxygen extraction fractions in the lung and the tissue compartments expressed by four parametric constants, which collectively consider the effect of perfusion-ventilation ratio in the lung or the shunt flow in the tissue compartments; and (c) the use of previously obtained experimental data on the efficiency of the respiratory and cardiac pumps under varied conditions. Six equations were derived to describe the oxygen transfer and transport, and the normal performance was computed. Then, stressful conditions such as high altitude, obstructive respiratory diseases, anemia, and strenuous exercise were introduced by changing the respective parameters. The effects of these changes on the interactions between the subsystems and on optimization with respect to the flexibility and maximal limits of performance of the oxygen transport system were examined. The model simulated the available experimental data reasonably well, which indicates that the basic framework was satisfactory. Being so simple in structure, it has potential provision for further sophistication. This potentiality should be fully exploited by the student of overall circulatory regulation.

To economize on programing effort and to establish bases for comparison of efficiency among various types of computer models of the circulation, McLeod proposed an experiment to test a concept—a physiological simulation benchmark experiment, or PHYSBE. A year later, he summarized the responses to his proposal (19). Although the basic idea is sound, the practical value of such standardization of circulatory models remains to be seen since most circulatory physiologists have such drastically different concepts of which parameters in circulatory dynamics should be emphasized and which should be disregarded.

Hydraulic analog.—Osborn, Hoehne & Badia (20) constructed an elaborate hydraulic analog for clinical training and medical student education. The ventricles are represented by pneumatically driven, diastolic volume-sensitive, variable pulse rate, and variable duty ratio pumps. The vascular circuits consist of arterial Windkessel, resistance tube, and venous and atrial capacitance cylinders. After rendering various parts of this hydraulic system ill, the authors state, "It is surprising how much more obvious they (the pathological hemodynamic situations) are by hindsight than before observing the reaction of the model." If so, it is obviously a powerful tool to transfer the teacher's concepts to the student.

SHORT-TERM REGULATION

Simply for convenience, an arbitrary distinction is made between short-term regulatory mechanisms, observed within 24 hours, and long-term regulations, revealed over several days or weeks. With the advent of implantable transducers and cardiac output measuring technics on the one hand and the accumulation of endocrinological knowledge on the other, the duration of experiments has been continually prolonged. This is an obvious advance toward a more complete understanding of circulatory regulation which operates continuously in conjunction with many other slow-acting systems.

BLOOD VOLUME

Physical impact.—To examine the immediate mechanical effects, Harlan, Smith & Richardson (21) very rapidly changed the blood volume of the dog between 140 and 85 per cent of the control; then they stopped the heart, occluded the ascending aorta and pulmonary artery, and transferred the blood from the systemic artery to the vein. The equilibrated ("mean") pressures measured in the pulmonary and systemic vascular beds reflected the degree of filling of each bed with blood. Both pressures were found to be approximately linearly related to the imposed blood volume changes. The data suggest that if neurohumoral reflex compensatory mechanisms fail to reduce the systemic and pulmonary vessel capacitances and thereby to redistribute the blood more centrally to better fill the cardiac pump, the areflex circulatory system will be unable to cause any flow as a result of reduction of venous return and consequent poor preloading of the heart, when only 12 per cent of its normal blood volume is lost.

Neural regulation.—Chien (3) comprehensively reviewed the role of the sympathetic nervous system in hemorrhage of various degrees of severity.

To determine the primary receptor site for blood volume changes, Gupta et al. (22) analyzed the relative importance of the afferent signals from the cardiac low pressure receptors and those from the sinoaortic high pressure receptors. During nonhypotensive hemorrhage (cardiac output decreased but mean arterial pressure maintained), the impulse discharge frequency per unit time from the low pressure receptors was reduced in proportion to the bled volume. On the other hand, the sinoaortic discharge frequency per beat decreased but the total number of impulses per unit time remained nearly identical because of the increased heart rate. On the basis of these and earlier experimental findings the authors concluded that the low pressure receptors inform the cardiovascular center of the imposed blood loss. Although the well controlled experimental preparations leave little doubt as to the value of the information obtained from the few selected afferent fibers, a question remains as to whether the whole spectrum of the receptors responds in the same manner to changes in mean arterial and pulse pressures.

To analyze the relative importance of the rate-sensitive and the static components of the carotid baroreceptor afferent signals during similar non-hypotensive hemorrhage, Sagawa (23) conducted an experiment in which the isolated carotid sinuses were perfused by (a) natural arterial pressure, (b) nonpulsatile pressure which followed the mean arterial pressure of the body, and (c) constant static pressure. The magnitude of the reduction in blood pressure under these three conditions reflects the uncompensated offset of three different states of feedback control systems with various combinations of rate-sensitive signals and afferent signals. The results suggested that the unidirectionally rate-sensitive signals play a significant role in the maintenance of arterial pressure during mild hemorrhage. Thus much still remains to be clarified concerning the quantitative, as well as the qualitative, importance of high and low pressure receptor reflexes in the control of arterial pressure.

Using unanesthetized rabbits, Chalmers, Korner & White (24) made detailed observations for 24 hours on the cardiovascular effects of acute hemorrhage amounting to 26 per cent of the control blood volume. The blood volume and cardiac output recovered completely within three to four hours by absorption of tissue fluid, whether or not the adrenals, the sympathetic ganglia, or the sinoaortic nerves remained intact. However, this was not true of the systemic vascular resistance, or consequently of the systemic arterial pressure. Even in normal rabbits, there was little tendency for the arterial pressure to recover to the control level by five hours after bleeding despite the fully recovered cardiac output. Failure of the peripheral resistance to recover was most marked in sinoaortic deafferented rabbits, whereas the magnitude of the systemic arterial pressure fall was greatest in guanethidine-treated, deafferented animals. After 24 hours, the systemic arterial pressure recovered to the control level in most rabbits with the cardiac output still at the level observed three to four hours after bleeding. The question arises: What factor caused the decrease in total peripheral resistance and its sluggish recovery? There seem to be at least two factors: (a) lowered viscosity of the blood after bleeding and during recovery and (b) vascular autoregulation due to the gradual reduction in oxygen content of the arterial blood resulting from dilution. At any rate, the conventional view that both the sympathetic and the vagal efferent limbs contribute to minimizing the reduction in arterial and right atrial pressures and to maintaining the increased heart rate is well supported by these pharmacological denervation experiments.

Conway (25) made similar prolonged observations in trained conscious dogs. The blood volume was acutely expanded or reduced to a mild degree. The cardiac output, mean arterial pressure, total blood volume, and right ventricular pressure were measured at intervals of 2.5 hours for seven to ten hours. The central blood volume and right ventricular end diastolic pressure returned to normal in three hours after hemorrhage. In striking contrast to the conventional picture apparently confirmed by Korner's rabbit experiment, the cardiac output fell insignificantly and returned in three hours to control levels, but thereafter it continued to increase with the gradual increase in central blood volume. Most intriguing was the finding that as cardiac output returned to the control level, the total peripheral resistance began to decrease, so that the arterial pressure, which had not previously shown significant depression, started to fall. An almost exact mirror image of this picture was observed when the blood volume was expanded by three blood transfusions given within three hours. The peripheral resistance and right ventricular pressure increased proportionally and the mean arterial pressure rose slightly. However, the cardiac output did not increase significantly. Two hours after transfusion a second marked rise in peripheral resistance occurred, accompanied by a return of the cardiac output to control levels. This strange second increase in total peripheral resistance after transfusion and the corresponding decrease after hemorrhage intrigued the investigator so much that he refrained from giving any immediate explanation for it. These changes were still observed at the end of the tenth hour, and were unaffected by ganglionic blockade.

In eleven human subjects, Price et al. (26) studied the effects of subacute bleeding of 15 to 20 per cent of the measured control blood volume over a period of 35 minutes. The central blood volume decreased by a statistically insignificant 10 per cent. When central blood volume, cardiac output, total peripheral resistance, and systemic arterial pressure were measured 20 to 35 minutes after hemorrhage, none showed a statistically significant difference. The only significant change was a 40 per cent reduction in splanchnic blood volume. Decreased hepatic blood flow was also suggested by a diminished indocyanin clearance and the low oxygen content of hepatic venous blood. There was no significant change in the hepatic oxygen consumption.

When one compares the findings in conscious rabbits, dogs, and humans, he gets the impression that, after an acute adjustment period is over, man has the best developed circulatory compensation for a mild blood loss, whereas the dog's vascular system shows a strange delayed response. Closer inspection, however, reveals that different volumes and rates of bleeding were used and that the period of observation differed from continuous observation by Korner to spot measurements by Price. Also different statistical methods of evaluation were used. The apparent inconsistency of the peripheral resistance response may result from such divergent methods or from different psychic stress on top of species differences. Clearly, the 24-hour sequence of circulatory and body fluid responses to mild and moderate hemorrhage or transfusion must be reinvestigated with standardized technics and data analysis.

Flow distribution.—Besides Price's work on humans (26), a number of animal experiments have been performed to study the systemic flow distribution after hemorrhage. Using unanesthetized rabbits, Chalmers, Korner & White (27) investigated the roles of the autonomic nervous system during the five hours following 26 per cent hemorrhage. In normal rabbits the most prominent response was increased renal resistance which persisted to the end of the observed period. In contrast, when animals were deefferented with autonomic blockers, a progressive and marked reduction in resistance occurred in the portal bed and, with a lag, in the renal bed. Despite such differences in flow and resistance responses, the mean arterial pressure and total peripheral resistance were not significantly different in the two groups. In sinoaortic deafferented animals, the decrease in portal resistance was even greater. These findings indicate that the maintenance of normal portal resistance after hemorrhage depends heavily upon the sinoaortic baroreceptor reflex, and the efferent paths of this reflex are mediated by both neural and humoral mechanisms. In a separate study on renal vascular response and functions, Korner's group (28) confirmed that the sympathoadrenal system was essential for the renal vascular constriction and that the role of the adrenal humoral mechanism increased progressively with the degree of blood loss. Carriere et al. (29) used a ^{85}Kr washout technic to demonstrate that progressive renal cortical ischemia occurred in the face of well maintained medullary blood flow as graded degrees of hemorrhage were imposed.

The splenic contribution to the maintenance of red cell volume during acute hemorrhage was studied by Guntheroth, McGough & Mullins (30) in conscious and anesthetized dogs. The splenic dimension, venous hematocrit, and blood flow were continuously monitored together with the systemic arterial pressure and hematocrit. Graded losses of blood were accompanied one to three minutes later by progressive splenic contraction and persistent elevation of the arterial hematocrit, up to 51 per cent, in the absence of a measurable change in systemic arterial pressure. Sodium pentobarbital was found to cause splenic contraction rather than dilatation as suggested by earlier investigators. To avoid errors in densitometric and other measurements caused by the changing hematocrit after splenic contraction, Buckley et al. (31) studied the effects upon cardiac output, central blood volume, and hepatic and renal blood flow of 25 ml/kg bleeding in splenectomized and chloralosed dogs, with or without simultaneous infusion of epinephrine and norepinephrine. There were no statistically significant differences between the infusion group and the control group in any of the measured variables. The same investigators (32) then studied the posthemorrhagic response to 10 ml/kg bleeding after blocking the autonomic nervous system at three different sites, ganglia, α-receptors, and β-receptors. The authors concluded that, since only propranolol caused a significant reduction in cardiac output and heart rate, the circulatory adjustments to meet the stress of hemorrhage depend mainly on the enhanced cardiac activity, rather than on vascular changes in resistance and flow distribution. These two reports are a bit difficult to reconcile because in one the importance of cardiac receptor stimulation was emphasized while in the other stimulation of the receptor with catecholamine caused no significant change in cardiac output. In addition, the absence of a differential in hepatic flow between the blocked and control groups is in sharp contrast to Price's observations in man and those of Chalmers et al. in rabbits.

ADH, renin, and cortisol.—The thesis that there are stretch receptors in the cardiac chambers which sense blood volume changes and affect ADH secretion continues to receive support. Gilmore & Daggett (33) demonstrated attenuation of natriuretic and diuretic responses to acute volume expansion in dogs with denervated hearts. Henry et al. (34) extended their long search for the role of low pressure stretch receptors to ADH secretion during hemorrhage. Carefully trained, unanesthetized dogs were bled in steps of 10 per cent of their calculated blood volume. In spite of well maintained mean arterial pressure and only a slightly decreased pulse pressure, the plasma ADH titer rose severalfold. Referring to their electroneurographic findings under similar conditions, the authors concluded that reflex control of ADH release is indeed one of the many effects of homeostatic reflex triggered by the low pressure receptor. Direct evidence of the effects of stimulating identified low pressure receptors is, however, lacking.

Share & Levy demonstrated two other afferent signals which reflexly influence ADH secretion. They are the carotid sinus chemoreceptor (35) and the rate-sensitive element of the baroreceptor impulses (36). To prevent activation of the low pressure and aortic stretch receptor reflex, dogs were thoracotomized, vagotomized, and artificially ventilated. Perfusion of the isolated carotid sinuses with deoxygenated blood then caused a significant increase in ADH secretion. When a concomitant mean arterial pressure rise was prevented by bleeding, the ADH response was even greater. As hemorrhagic hypotension is known to cause increased chemoreceptor discharge, this may be one of the multiple afferent signals for ADH secretion. In contrast, changing the pressure in the isolated sinus from a pulsatile pressure of large amplitude (85 mm Hg peak to peak and 156 cycles/min) to a static pressure with the identical mean level caused an 89 per cent increase in ADH titer and a 56 per cent rise in mean systemic arterial pressure. When the latter hypertension was prevented by bleeding, the ADH level further increased by 160 per cent of the control level. Since hypotensive or nonhypotensive hemorrhage invariably results in a reduced cardiac output and therefore a decreased pulse pressure, this receptor mechanism probably exerts a negative feedback control effect on blood volume. Quantitatively, the physiological significance of a feedback mechanism evoked by such tremendous pulsation or complete anoxia in the sinuses is somewhat dubious.

An increased renin release in response to mild hemorrhage has been repeatedly observed. McKenzie, Lee & Cook (37) determined the arterial plasma renin levels of lightly anesthetized rabbits before and after brisk bleeding. The activity was 2.5 times the control level immediately after bleeding, and five times as great forty minutes after. Nephrectomized rabbits gave negative results. A similar renin release after hemorrhage was observed by Bunag, Page & McCubbin (38) in anesthetized dogs. Ganglionic blockade or anesthetization of the renal nerve abolished the response, which indicates the neural nature of the stimulus. Common carotid occlusion triggered a renin release even when renal arterial pressure was maintained. The post-hemorrhagic release was independent of changes in arterial pressure or renal blood flow but dependent on the diet. Dogs fed a low sodium diet gave more consistent results.

For an account of the interactions between the cardiovascular system and the ACTH-adrenocortical hormone release system, the reader is referred to Gann (39). The complexity of the interactions required his group and others to develop a new class of mathematical models, which are obviously powerful tools for clarifying the multitude of perplexing observations in this and other fields. There are few formal models of the hemorrhagic response.

Hemorrhagic shock.—The review period encompassed a large number of papers on this severe disorder in which the limit of circulatory regulation is approached and passed. The balance between the extreme stress of oxygen deficit and the maximally exploited physiologic compensations is so delicate that opinions remain diverse as to the basic factor or factors dividing reversibility and irreversibility.

Fell's (40) studies on plasma volume changes at various stages of hemorrhage and during the postreinfusion period indicated that hemodilution occurred in the early stages of hemorrhage but that the plasma volume was reduced after reinfusion. During the postreinfusion a continued, but quite variable, loss was detected in most dogs. The author's conclusion was that the observed plasma loss in itself was not sufficient to cause the postreinfusion decline of cardiac output.

To determine whether the failing heart is the initiating and decisive factor, Rothe (41) studied the effect of massive blood transfusion which maintained the right atrial pressure at the control level throughout the postreinfusion period. "Frank" heart failure was seen only rarely although "weakening" was often evident. A massive and continued loss of fluid was consistently found. These findings incline the author toward a multifactor hypothesis rather than a single-factor theory, either cardiac or peripheral. Rothe (42) performed another experiment to reinvestigate the correlation between survival rate and oxygen debt, the amount of lost blood reabsorbed, the postreinfusion arterial pressure, and the rate of oxygen consumption. Survival was correlated, not with a critical amount of oxygen debt, but with the postreinfusion oxygen consumption. Thus he doubts the validity of whole-body oxygen debt as a predictor of irreversible shock, although the importance of the oxygen deficit in the vital organs as a primary causative factor was appreciated.

Brand, Suh & Avery (43) examined the reversing effect of massive transfusions of (*a*) water containing physiologic electrolytes and glucose, (*b*) homologous blood, and (*c*) dextran solution on otherwise irreversible hemorrhagic shock. Cats were used because this animal does not suffer from trypsin enteritis as the dog does. Right atrial pressure was maintained as in Rothe's experiment above control levels for four hours after retransfusion. Although all three fluid infusions prolonged the survival time, only fluid (a) resulted in definite reversal. A group from the same laboratory (44) claim that a specific myocardial depressant factor is present in the cat's plasma during late hemorrhagic shock. It is low molecular weight and heat stable.

Lack of unified criteria of hemorrhagic stress appears to be partly responsible for the confusion of findings and opinions concerning the irreversibility of shock. Chien (3) proposes a constant amount of blood loss in proportion to the measured blood volume. The reduction of cardiac output to a standard level for a fixed period may be an alternate criterion, since tissue hypoxia is fairly widely agreed to be the primary cause of irreversible shock.

Variations in the hemodynamic status of vascular beds in different tissues during shock have been emphasized by several groups. Abel et al. (45) found no sign of pulmonary pooling of blood, while Lintermans et al. (46) observed blood pooling in the mesenteric bed in half of the hemorrhaged dogs. This pooling, however, was not significantly correlated with survival time. Bond, Manley & Green (47) studied the roles of the sympathetic nervous system and the hormones in cutaneous and skeletal muscle vascular responses to moderate and irreversible hemorrhage. They conclude that in these beds the local metabolic deficit eventually overpowers the neural or hormonal vasomotor controls in prolonged hypotension.

Blood Gases

Hypoxia.—Smith & Crowell (48) studied in anesthetized dogs the effects of hypoxia on mean circulatory pressure (for the definition of and technic for measuring the mean circulatory pressure, see the section on blood volume) and cardiac output. After inhalation of 9 per cent oxygen for five minutes, mean circulatory pressure rose from 6 to 8 mm Hg and the cardiac output increased 45 per cent in spite of a lowered right atrial pressure. When dogs were rendered areflexic, the mean circulatory pressure dropped to 4 mm Hg, whereas the cardiac output and right atrial pressure remained at control levels. Since the mean circulatory pressure chiefly reflects the compliance of the small veins, it was presumed that hypoxia caused relaxation of the capacitance vessels in areflexic animals but contraction when the central nervous system was active. The unaltered cardiac output in the face of a reduced mean circulatory pressure in areflxic animals was explained in terms of decreased resistance for the venous return due to both arteriolar and venular vasodilation. That the inotropic effect of hypoxia on the cardiac pump is mediated by the central nervous system was confirmed by Downing, Talner & Gardner (49). This explains part of the increase in cardiac output in animals with an intact CNS. Thus the net effect on mean arterial pressure is a slight rise above the control level.

Kontos et al. (50) made similar observations in man and unanesthetized dogs. The main differences in the human response were a more intense reduction in total peripheral resistance and the consequent lack of a significant change in systemic arterial pressure despite a similar increase in cardiac output. The reason for these differences is not clear. Richardson et al. (51) further investigated the role of the β-adrenergic system in the response of man to hypoxia. They found that β-adrenergic blockade attenuated the increase in cardiac output but not the fall in peripheral resistance, again confirming direct vasodilator action and centrally mediated augmentation of cardiac pumping capacity.

There are many complicating factors in the circulatory response to hypoxia. First, hypoxia is likely to be associated with hypocapnia, which is known to cause variation in central nervous activity. Second, hypoxia exerts diametrically opposite influences on the cardiac pump and vascular segments; its direct action is inhibitory and relaxing whereas its effects via the chemoreceptor reflex and direct action on the higher centers are acceleratory and constrictive. Chalmers, Korner & White (52, 53) attacked the problem by using unanesthetized rabbits and multiple combinations of surgical and pharmacologic denervations involving both afferents and efferents. In a serial study, they compared the respiratory and circulatory responses of three groups of rabbits whose carotid sinus nerves or aortic nerves or both had been cut with the responses to hypoxia of a normal group. Their main conclusions were that (a) in rabbits the chemoreceptor reflex is mediated chiefly through the carotid sinus nerves, (b) the main effect is strong peripheral vasodilation, which in turn facilitates cardiac pumping, (c) the circulatory effect of concomitant hypocapnia is rather weak, and (d) the reflex constrictor effect counteracts the peripheral vasodilation and maintains the arterial pressure slightly above baseline. Regrettably, information on venous or atrial pressure was not included in these well conducted experiments, which renders interpretation of the factors affecting cardiac pumping somewhat obscure. These investigators also reported on the distribution of systemic flow during hypoxia. The susceptibilities of the various beds to the local dilator effects of hypoxia, assessed from the responses of animals without sinoaortic nerves or autonomic effectors, were markedly different; the vasodilation was by far the greatest in the portal bed, followed in descending order by the renal, skin, and muscle beds. The chemoreceptor reflex from the sinoaortic area exerted such an intense vasoconstrictor effect on portal and renal beds that in intact rabbits, the net effect was a marked reduction in portal flow and a moderate reduction in renal flow. In the muscle and skin of the limbs, the net vasomotor effects were small.

Our knowledge of the chemoreceptor reflex control of circulation has been further enriched by Daly & Robinson's continued work (54) with elaborate dog preparations. They focused their attention on the distinction and synergism of carotid sinus and aortic chemoreceptor reflexes. The aortic arch and carotid sinuses were isolated and exposed to combinations of hypoxia and hypercapnia while the animal's systemic vascular bed was perfused with a constant flow of blood with controlled P_{O_2} and P_{CO_2}. Among many findings the authors emphasized two observations: (a) the superposition of hypercapnia on hypoxia enhanced the systemic vasoconstrictor responses from both areas, and (b) the pressor response to hypoxic stimulation of the carotid bodies was weaker than that evoked by aortic body stimulation because the carotid sinus reflex was normally masked by the lung inflation-systemic vasodilator reflex. The abolition of the lung inflation reflex by lung denervation revealed an equally potent pressor response from stimulation of the carotid body. The reason for the absence of the interference by the lung inflation-vasodilator reflex in aortic body stimulation was accounted for as follows: The chief effect on respiration of the aortic body reflex is acceleration of the frequency and not of the tidal volume. In contrast, the carotid chemoreceptor reflex causes much greater increases in tidal volume as well as tachypnea, this provoking the lung inflation reflex. When either one of the chemoreceptive areas was exposed to venous blood, the magnitude of the pressor response ranged from 5 to 60 mm Hg. When both areas were stimulated simultaneously, the effect was synergistic and gave a pressor response as large as 100 mm Hg in one case.

Stern & Rapaport (55) elaborated on the comparison of the cardiac effects elicited from combined or separate stimulation of the aortic and carotid chemoreceptors with nicotine in dogs after artificial ventilation. Aortic chemoreceptor stimulation caused an increase in heart rate and an augmentation of myocardial contractility which were confirmed to be independent of the rate effect or the effect of varied afterload pressure. Carotid chemoreceptor stimulation decreased heart rate and increased stroke volume. Systemic vascular resistance was increased by aortic chemoreceptor stimulation but not by carotid sinus stimulation. Thus the combined stimulation resulted in an initially marked, then attenuated, bradycardia and in persistently increased cardiac output, peripheral resistance, and mean arterial pressure.

Browse & Shepherd (56) studied, in dog's limb preparation and using sodium cyanide as chemoreceptor stimulant, the effect of aortic and carotid sinus chemoreceptor reflexes on venous tone. The response was a moderate venoconstriction in either of the reflexes, and the mode of ventilation did not affect the response. With repetition of stimulation, however, the venoconstriction became attenuated in half the animals and finally reversed into a significant venodilation. Since the respiratory effect and systemic pressor response of the reflex were not diminished by the repeated stimulation, the unexplained diminution and reversal must have occurred in the effector path of the reflex.

With regard to the effects of the lung inflation-vasodilation reflexes on the circulatory responses to generalized hypoxia, Kontos et al. (57) made further studies. They repeated hypoxic experiments with and without the pulmonary vagal afferent. Hypoxic responses such as tachycardia, increased aortic flow, and decreased systemic resistance were greatly attenuated after pulmonary denervation. Thus, they conclude that the enhanced lung inflation associated with the respiratory reflex is a major, if not the sole, contributing factor to the commonly observed circulatory responses to hypoxia.

Vogel & Harris (58) studied cardiac output in resting men as they were exposed to simulated altitudes of 600, 3345, and 4570 m above sea level. The increase in cardiac output was noted as early as one hour after exposure to hypoxia and was better correlated with arterial oxygen saturation than with arterial Po_2, Pco_2, or pH. The latter finding was interpreted as evidence that the peripheral vasodilator action of hypoxia, rather than reflex or direct stimulation of the cardiovascular center, is responsible for the increase in cardiac output. This interpretation was based on an earlier finding by Korner that arterial hypoxia did not elicit reflex enhancement of cardiac output until arterial Po_2 fell below 30 mm Hg.

Carbon dioxide.—Suutarinen (59) made systematic observations on the effects of hyper- and hypocapnia in dogs lightly anesthetized with thiopental. Briefly, definite correlations were found between the arterial Pco_2 and the heart rate, stroke volume, and right atrial pressure. The elevation of right atrial pressure by a high arterial Pco_2 suggests the possibility of reflex constriction of venous capacitance vessels in the face of the local dilator action of carbon dioxide. The changes in cardiac output, mean arterial pressure, and systemic total resistance were not significantly correlated with the arterial Pco_2. This was interpreted as the result of varied balances among the directionally opposite neural effects and direct effects of the gas on the heart and the vessels. Wendling, Eckstein & Abboud (60) analyzed the role of the autonomic and the β-adrenergic system in hypercapnic response. In their hands, the anesthetized dog's cardiac output and heart rate fell while total peripheral resistance and mean arterial pressure rose in response to 10 per cent CO_2 inhalation. After ganglionic blockade with hexamethonium, the cardiac output tended to increase, whereas total peripheral resistance decreased to such an extent that the mean arterial pressure also dropped. After propranolol was combined with the ganglionic blocker, almost identical results were obtained. Thus the vasoconstrictor effect of moderate hypercapnia mediated by chemoreceptor reflex or via excitatory action on the vasomotor center was amply evidenced. On the other hand, the direct effect of hypercapnia on the heart remains obscure. These investigators interpreted the increased cardiac output after the ganglionic blockade as the result of diminished arterial pressure. Compared with the effects of hypoxia, the effects of hypercapnia remain much more elusive.

PHYSICAL STRESSES

Muscle and respiratory pumping.—Stegall (61) showed that the muscle pumps of the dependent legs contribute more than 30 per cent of the total energy expended to circulate blood during stationary running. In making a model of the overall circulation during exercise, such information will be extremely valuable. Moreno et al. (62) analyzed quantitatively the influence of respiration on venous return in dogs. From simultaneous measurements of portal and hepatic venous flow, they conclude that diaphragmatic compression of the liver during inspiration causes a valve action on the hepatic venules. This interrupts hepatic venous outflow and thus moderates the phasic surge of venous return during inspiration from other abdominal viscera into the right heart. Increased hepatic venous return during expiration then compensates for the meager venous return from the other abdominal area. Thus the abdominal portion of the respiratory pump can provide a fairly smooth venous return into the thoracic caval vein rather than an intermittently squeezed flow.

Positive and negative pressure breathing.—Feisal, Abboud & Eckstein (63) studied the effector mechanism of the circulatory adjustments associated with positive pressure breathing in dogs. The normal circulatory response, characterized by a moderate decrease in cardiac output, an increase in heart rate, and a slight but insignificant fall in arterial pressure, was exaggerated after α-receptor, but not β-receptor, blockade. Elevation of right atrial pressure in α-receptor blocked dogs was smaller than the control. Accordingly, it was concluded that the reflex adjustments are effected via α-adrenergic vasoconstrictor response. The influences of negative pressure breathing on cardiovascular and renal functions were reinvestigated by Godley, Myers & Rosenbaum (64). Although the usual diuresis and natriuresis accompanied by elevation of mean arterial pressure were observed with iso-osmotic hydration, no significant change was detected in renal plasma flow, glomerular filtration rate, free water clearance, and other hemodynamic variables. Also in their cross-circulation experiments, in which one of the dogs breathed against negative pressure while the other dog's free water clearance was examined, no detectable change was found. Consequently, the authors proposed that the response observed in their experiments was either an effect of the increased arterial pressure mediated by the arterial baroreceptor on intrarenal flow redistribution, or a natriuretic hormone other than ADH.

Gravity.—Myers & Godley (65) studied cardiovascular and renal functions of dogs during total-body water immersion. Loss of gravity, so simulated, caused a significant diuresis due to an increase in the excretion fraction of filtered sodium. Here again found unaltered were renal plasma flow glomerular filtration, and free water clearance, which indicates that the underlying mechanism primarily suppressed sodium reabosrption. In contrast, a simulation of gravitational pull of the blood into the lower part of the body by applying a negative pressure of -60 mm Hg proved to be a potent stimulus to salt and fluid retention. However, Gilbert et al. (66), who conducted lower-body negative pressure experiments in man, feel that the mechanism of salt and fluid retention under the circumstances may be explained chiefly in terms of the considerable decrease in renal plasma flow and glomerular filtration that they detected, although participation of ADH and aldosterone can not be utterly excluded. The paper of Martino & Earley (67) is of interest to those concerned with the interrelationships of renal functions and blood volume changes. They suggest that the relationships depend upon the state of the renal vascular bed (and consequently upon the tubular loading conditions) before the volume changes are introduced.

Gilbert & Stevens (68) reported an elevated venous vascular tone in the human forearm during negative pressure application to the lower body and during upright tilting. This finding contradicts the findings from a similar experiment by Samueloff, Browse & Shepherd (69), who noted only a temporary elevation of venous tone. That this discrepancy might have arisen from the difference in the methods used was suggested by Newberry & Bryan (70). When venous capacitance is measured by the occluded limb technic as it was by Samueloff's group, nervous reflex control can reach the measured venous segment but not humoral agents which may be reflexly released within the trunk. In contrast, when Gilbert's group used four different methods of measurement, venous tone elevation persisted with those allowing the access of humoral agents. Newberry & Bryan applied a periodic flow-impeding pressure to the limb and measured the increases in venous pressure and volume in the arm. They observed persistent venous constriction, particularly when the hydrostatic stress was intensified by increasing the magnitude of headward acceleration or by combining tilting with lower-body negative pressure. They conclude that the postural reflex adjustment of venous tone consists of a phasic neural constriction and a slower, continued constriction due to the release of a humoral constrictor agent. The receptor of the reflex is perhaps an arterial baroreceptor but the humoral agent remains unidentified. Cohen, Conn & Rovner (71) propose that the slow humoral mechanism is enhancement of plasma renin activity and aldosterone excretion. The augmentation was found to be independent of the subject's level of sodium intake. Epstein, Stampfer & Beiser (72) studied the venous tone in vasovagal syncope and found that exaggerated bradycardia and marked decrease in total peripheral resistance caused an acute fall in arterial pressure but the venous bed, by constricting, tended to maintain the cardiac filling pressure and cardiac output during the syncope.

In addition, Epstein et al. (73) warn those who investigate venous tone in man of the possible complication by psychic reaction to the added procedure. When lower-body negative pressure was applied to twelve awake subjects, venous tone increased temporarily; when these men were anesthetized, no response was seen in six of them despite the persistent inspiratory constrictor response. The seemingly reflex venoconstriction, therefore, might have simply been a psychic reaction to the unpleasant sensation.

Temperature.—The effects of a brief and intense heat pulse on human circulation were studied by Murray (74) simulating the thermal environment during re-entry of the space ship. The wall temperature was quickly raised to 205° C and held for about twelve minutes. The skin temperature remained at around 42.5° C, and the sweat rate exceeded one liter per hour. Cardiac output increased by nearly 50 per cent, with accelerated heart rate and a pronounced reduction in total peripheral resistance. At the end of exposure, cardiac output was considerably reduced from the peak value in the presence of significantly rising venous pressure, further diminished total peripheral resistance, and slightly falling heart rate. There is little doubt that the decrease in cardiac output is related to 8 per cent loss of plasma volume, and the further fall in peripheral resistance is associated with dermal vasodilation. However, the concomitant high venous pressure makes the whole picture difficult to understand unless one assumes a fairly strong reflex inhibition on the cardiac pump and a reflex constriction of the venous capacitance vessels. The slight elevation of the mean arterial pressure and pulse pressure appears to be insufficient to fully explain the cardiac depression in terms of the baroreceptor reflex.

Evonuk (75) made a shrewd analysis of physiological response to hypothermia using a cross-circulation technic. While the donor dog was exposed to cold stress, part of its blood was continuously exchanged with the normothermic recipient dog's blood. The cold blood coming from the donor dog was rewarmed through a heat exchanger so that only the humoral signal produced in the hypothermic dog would be passed to the normothermic dog. With a cold stress which lowered the donor dog's core temperature by 3° C, the recipient dog's cardiac output decreased by an average of 50 per cent. Heart rate was reduced to varied degrees and arterial pressure showed falls less than 10 per cent below control. The identity of the humoral agents is unknown but they are likely to be histamine and norepinephrine. Interestingly, when cold-acclimatized dogs were used as the recipients, they did not respond with significant decrease in cardiac output. Accordingly, the author suggests that a shift of cardiovascular threshold to the humoral substance is involved in cold acclimatization.

EXERCISE

In normal environment.—Whether the maximum limit of cardiac output is set by the pumping capacity of the heart itself or by the vascular system's capability to return the blood to the heart and sufficiently fill the cardiac pump was investigated by Robinson et al. (76) in man. The maximum cardiac output achieved during near-maximum exercise was compared before and after rapid transfusion of one liter of the subject's own blood. Despite a large increase in central venous pressure (+7.4 mm Hg) during the exercise, no significant increase in cardiac output or oxygen uptake occurred. This finding demonstrates that the upper limit of circulatory transport is determined by the pumping capacity of the heart rather than by extracardiac factors. When the dog was bled 10 to 35 per cent of its blood volume prior to a moderate excercise, Vanhoutte & Leusen (77) found that cardiac output did not reach the same level as the control. However, the absolute increment of cardiac output and the absolute decreases in total peripheral resistance were greater after the hemorrhage than in the control experiment, which indicates that the cardiovascular system adjusted to a greater extent after the hemorrhage and exercise. The qualitative aspects of the response did not differ significantly whether the dogs were unanesthetized or anesthetized, with the sinoaortic reflex intact or abolished (78).

The importance of the vascular response, i.e., a drastic decrease in arterial resistance, in bringing about the large increase in cardiac output during exercise was substantiated by Warner & Topham (79). When the dog's total resistance was maintained by a servomechanism during exercise, no increase of cardiac output occurred. The authors emphasize the unloading effect on the heart (or absence of rising aortic pressure) of the decreased vascular resistance as the mechanism for increased cardiac output. The sinoaortic baroreceptor reflex was considered to operate via a central resetting mechanism in their model.

The importance of circulating catecholamines as the cardiovascular stimulant during exercise was well demonstrated by Mayo cardiologists (80). Greyhound racing dogs were deprived of both the cardiosympathetic nerves and the β-adrenergic receptors. Their cardiac output, heart rate, and racing record were all lowered, and when the race was finished they were on the verge of collapse. Evidence was also gained for another cardiac stimulant during exercise. Mitchell et al. (81) electrically stimulated the cut central end of the quadriceps nerve and observed increased heart rate, cardiac output, and arterial pressure. Since the left ventricular preparation with controlled input and output load exhibited signs of augmented contractility, participation of the afferent impulse from the exercising muscles during exertion is very likely, although the extent of contribution to the actively working heart was not determined. Stegemenn, Ulmer & Boning (82) suggest that the source of stimulation which causes the above afferent impulses might be CO_2 produced in the exercising muscle. They observed a marked increase in ventilation, heart rate, and arterial pressure in response to the insufflation of CO_2 gas into lower abdominal aortic flow. Stenberg et al. (83) compared the pattern of cardiopulmonary responses when a fixed submaximal amount of work was performed with arms, legs, and both. Their findings indicate that arm work involves higher heart rate, higher arterial pressure, and greater ventilation than does leg or combined work. Optimization of the overall oxygen transport system is designed apparently for leg or generalized exercise rather than for arm exercise alone.

Castenfors (84) systematically analyzed renal function during exercise: he observed in man an increased plasma renin activity which was not altered by renal vasodilation induced with dihydralazine or by increase in distal tubular sodium load induced with ethacrynic acid. It was prevented, however, by ganglionic blocking. Consequently, the investigator proposes that a direct sympathetic nervous stimulation of the juxtaglomerular apparatus is mainly responsible for the increased plasma renin activity.

In heat and cold.—Rowell et al. (85) studied in detail how thermal stress (43° C) affects the overall circulatory regulation during four intensities of exercise. In comparison with control values at 25.6° C, oxygen consumption was unaffected but cardiac output was significantly decreased, particularly at high work loads. Central blood volume was reduced 16 per cent below the the control, as was stroke volume. Heart rate on the other hand increased greatly, the maximum level being attained at the third work load. From these findings the authors explained the thermal adaptation of circulatory regulation during exercise in terms of a repartitioning of flow and blood volume from the core to the skin, rather than an increasing cardiac output to meet the added demand for heat dissipation. The blood volume shift limits the normal increase in cardiac output, and the high work load is tolerated by extracting more oxygen from an identical amount of flow, thus leading the muscle to anaerobic metabolism earlier than in cooler conditions. The flow redistribution involved decrease in mesenteteric and hepatic flow and increase in dermal flow, according to earlier work. If this redistribution could be achieved without repartitioning of blood volume from the central circulation and therefore with maintained cardiac filling pressure, reduction in cardiac output would be prevented and work capacity would be restored. Whether this occurs in acclimatization was further investigated by the same group, with negative findings (see the section on long-term regulation).

With regard to the influence of cold stress, Dawson et al. (86) made an interesting observation on rats swimming in cold water. After an initial rise, 50 per cent above control levels, cardiac output kept falling down to 80 per cent of the resting value in proportion to the diminishing heart rate and core temperature. This reduction in cardiac output was accompanied by progressive increases in total peripheral resistance, keeping arterial pressure almost unaltered. The colder the water, the earlier the exhaustion occurred. While the exact reason for this early succumbing of the circulatory system to cold stress remains unexplained, factors such as decreasing heart rate and increasing blood viscosity due to the falling core temperature appear to be important in causing both the poor pumping by the heart and the tremendous hindrance to flow, particularly in the low pressure segments of the vascular bed. Thus, the reduced oxygen transport curtailed the time to exhaustion. At a given time point or core temperature during the swim, there was no significant difference in cardiac output between good and bad swimmers; thus, the apparent determinant for exhaustion time is either local flow adjustment in the muscle or efficiency of oxygen extraction, the capacity for anaerobic metabolism of the contractile machine, or a combination of these factors.

Hypoxia.—Stenberg, Ekblom & Messin (87) compared cardiopulmonary responses of man to exercise at sea level and simulated altitude of 4000 m. At simulated altitude, maximum oxygen transport was reduced by 72 per cent, while maximum heart rate and cardiac output were unaltered compared to the sea level values. The reduction in oxygen uptake was therefore due to the lowered arterial oxygen saturation from 90 per cent at sea level to 70 per cent at the high altitude. Maximum pulmonary ventilation was equal in the two conditions, which indicates poorer oxygen exchange in the hypoxic conditions. Since the observed maximum ventilation is considerably below the voluntary maximum breathing capacity measured for two minutes without simultaneous exercise, there seems to be a factor which suppresses ventilatory effort beyond the observed maximum level. It may be decreased arterial P_{CO_2} or the rapid deterioration in efficiency of the respiratory pump due to precipitous increase in oxygen cost of the ventilation pump itself, as suggested by Hughes et al. (88). At any rate, the human circulatory system does not appear to be primarily responsible for the diminished oxygen transport under the hypoxic conditions, even if it may be blamed for the lack of further effort to compensate for the limitation of the respiratory pump under hypoxic conditions. In the dog, however, Piiper et al. (89) found that the maximum cardiac output is dependent on inspired oxygen concentration; the ceiling of cardiac output with 11 per cent oxygen in air was approximately 80 per cent of the value during air breathing.

SINOAORTIC BARORECEPTOR REFLEXES

Considered here are works whose primary aim was to define the transducer characteristics of the sinoaortic baroreceptors or the cardiovascular effects of the sinoaortic reflexes evoked by pressure changes isolated in these receptor areas (open-loop analysis). Studies on modifications by these reflexes of circulatory responses to other disturbances such as hemorrhage, posture, hypoxia, and hypertension (closed-loop analysis) will be found in the respective sections on primary disturbances.

Carotid sinus.—The aforementioned symposium proceedings (5) provide us with the recent advances in knowledge of reflex functions. Particularly impressive is the paper by Gero & Gerova (90) which presents the receptor transducer characteristics and overall barostatic transfer characteristics of the carotid sinus reflex in terms of every parameter of the input pressure variables, and the sophisticated computer analysis that Christensen, Warner & Pryor (91) developed to study the transducer characteristics of the receptor without isolating the sinus. In another symposium (4) Scher et al. (92) summarized their and others' work chiefly on the unidirectional rate-sensitive characteristics of the overall reflex action, and Hatakeyama (93) discussed the problem of summation of parallel baroreceptor feedback loops.

Kezdi's group (94, 95) reported on the frequency response characteristics of the various neural components of the reflex and showed a considerably more uniform increase of mean impulse frequency over an extensive pressure range when the receptor was driven by pulsating pressure than when forced by static pressure. In contrast, Ninomiya & Irisawa's study (96) on the cat's aortic baroreceptor transducer characteristics indicated little evidence for such a difference in the averaged multifiber discharge frequency between pulsatile and nonpulsatile pressure forcings of the receptor. Koushanpour & McGee (145) obtained an intermediate result; there was a greater amount of activity during pulsation than during static pressure in the normal and subnormal ranges but no difference when the mean level of input pressure exceeded 150 mm Hg. Irisawa & Ninomiya (97) compared carotid sinus and aortic baroreceptor firing using the same multifiber recording technic.

The most common and annoying experience among students of the carotid sinus reflex is the variability of the reflex effect from dog to dog and from time to time. That this variability is not necessarily due to varying effects of anesthesia among individuals and with time was demonstrated by Olmsted, McCubbin & Page (98). Using carefully trained dogs with an exteriorized common carotid artery, these investigators examined the relative contributions of the cardiac output and the vascular resistance components in pressor responses to carotid occlusion. A considerable variability of the relative contribution with time and individual was revealed in these unanesthetized animals, too. The authors maintain that the pre-existing hemodynamic state conditions the mechanism of the response pattern, quite a reasonable thesis suggesting the need for a systems analysis approach in dealing with even single feedback loop analysis. Search for the effect of the carotid sinus baroreceptor reflex was extended to the dynamics of capillary fluid shift by Baker (99). Using a dog forelimb preparation technic he gained evidence that carotid occlusion increases the permeable surface area of the vascular bed.

Aortic arch.—Ninomiya & Irisawa's work on the transducer characteristics of the aortic arch receptor was mentioned above (96, 97). Levy, Ng & Zieske (100) isolated the dog's aortic arch from the arterial circulation with functioning left ventricle and studied the aortic arch baroreceptor reflex effect on cardiac performance. Compared with the carotid sinus receptor, the aortic arch reflex receptor appears to operate over a much higher input pressure range (100 to 300 mm Hg) as far as cardiac effects are concerned. A similar high operating pressure range and relatively low static gain with considerable rate sensitivity were shown by Allison & Sagawa (101) for this reflex with respect to the vascular resistance response. A start has been made in overcoming the surgical difficulty which has hampered the overall openloop analysis of this reflex, although still with the severe insult of the openchest preparation.

LONG-TERM REGULATION

Polycythemia and Anemia

Weisse et al. (102) followed for eight days the circulatory adjustments resulting from acute normovolemic polycythemia in splenectomized dogs. The animals' red cell volume was expanded by 50 per cent whereas the plasma volume was reduced by 40 per cent. Immediate responses included a significant fall in stroke volume and cardiac output with a marked rise in systemic and pulmonary resistance to flow, but insignificant changes in heart rate, arterial pressure, and left ventricular end diastolic pressure. As a result, oxygen transport decreased to approximately 50 per cent of the normal. Within the following 24 hours, however, plasma volume returned to the control level with increased total blood volume, and these expanded volumes continued to the eighth day. Accompanying this was a complete recovery of cardiac output with bradycardia and recovered stroke volume above the control level. From these observations, one may envision the following chain of events: Polycythemia disturbs the circulation by increasing the hematocrit and thereby the viscosity factor of flow resistance, with a resultant decrease in cardiac output. To rescue the diminished oxygen transport accompanying the decreased cardiac output, some unknown mechanism operates to recover the reduced volume. It reverses the disturbing effect of polycythemia in two ways: (a) return of hematocrit to the normal optimal range and (b) enhanced filling of the cardiovascular system with blood. Both help venous return and cardiac pumping. The blood volume control system appears to be subordinated to the demand for oxygen transport under the circumstances. The quantitative roles of vascular autoregulation, chemo- and baroreceptor reflexes, and the state of renal functions are subjects for further studies.

The adaptation of renal functions to the opposite directional disturbance, i.e., a week-long anemia produced by repeated hemorrhage, was investigated by Aperia, Liebow & Roberts (103). Renal blood flow was unaltered, while glomerular filtration, renal oxygen consumption, and cortical tissue Po_2 were reduced. The authors postulate that anemic hypoxia leads, through an intrarenal mechanism, to preglomerular arteriolar constriction and reduction of glomerular filtration. Thus the kidney adapts to lowered oxygen transport by diminishing the blood flow to the cortex with its high oxygen demand, and at the same time decreasing the reabsorption work load on this area and reducing the oxygen consumption. In addition, increased titers of erythropoietin could be demonstrated from the renal venous blood. Thus the kidney contributes to the recovery of both plasma and cell volumes in anemic conditions.

Acclimatization

Exercise in heat.—Rowell's group (104) asked themselves which of the following three mechanisms are involved in acclimatization to combined heat and exercise stress: (a) central redistribution of blood volume from the body surface, (b) decreased demand for cutaneous blood flow, or (c) decreased cardioacceleration resulting from a cooler functional environment. The changes in central blood volume and cardiac output during exercise in a hot environment hardly differed after one week of acclimatization from those before. Therefore the cooler functional environment was discerned to be a more plausible mechanism than others. Since measurements were not done on the intermediate days, the authors reserve the possibility of an intermediary temporary cardiovascular adjustment, i.e., increased venomotor tone which increases central blood volume and cardiac output, before enhanced sweating and lower surface and core temperatures are established.

Exercise at altitude.—Reflecting the approaching 1968 Olympic games in Mexico City (2268 m above sea level), Pike's Peak and other high altitude areas over the world witnessed groups of physiologists come, stay, and conduct heavy exercise experiments with catheters in young athletes' or in their own hearts. With 24 students divided into six groups and brought to altitude at various rates, Vogel, Hansen & Harris (105) analyzed the effect of physical conditioning and rate of ascent on cardiovascular responses to graded work load. Compared with sea level values in rest and exercise, the general response during the first four days after the ascent was an increase in cardiac output, accompanied by increase in heart rate, and a slight fall in arterial pressure and in total peripheral resistance.

The increase in cardiac output depended on the rate of ascent, the abrupt group showing twice as great an increase, but it did not depend on physical conditioning. On the other hand, the increase in heart rate was not affected by the rate of ascent. All measurements returned to sea level or near-sea level values by the third week except for heart rate. Resting cardiac output of the acute ascent group returned to sea level after two weeks as arterial oxygen tension and venous oxygen content increased. At variance with Alexander et al.'s report (106), the authors could detect no sign of suppressed cardiac contractility at high altitude. At the maximum work level, after acclimatization, they observed a slightly larger cardiac output with a slightly lower heart rate but greater stroke volume than at sea level. Thus they presume a mechanism which optimizes the heart rate-stroke volume relationship in lieu of the idea that moderate hypoxia of 4300 m has direct suppressive action on the sinoauricular node of the myocardium. In view of the finding by Sugimoto, Sagawa & Guyton (107) that the descending limb of the cardiac output-heart rate relationship curve above 160 beats per minute could be shifted toward a much higher heart rate range as ventricular filling pressure and catecholamine level were elevated simultaneously with tachycardia, lack of data on preloading factors of the heart in the report of Vogel et al. makes their discussion a bit vague. Also, further studies on the efficiency of ventricular work in terms of cardiac oxygen consumption seem necessary to support the concept of optimization.

The same group also reported on the metabolic aspects of the above experiment (108). The main findings are: (a) Mean maximum oxygen uptake at 4300 m was 83 per cent of the sea level value, and was not affected by the rate of ascent. (b) Total amount of work to exhaustion was also proportionally decreased below the sea level value and acclimatization did not improve it, despite increase in maximum pulmonary ventilation and arterial oxygen content. (c) Arterial lactate content during maximum work was prominently decreased by acclimatization below the sea level value. (d) Venous oxygen content was higher during maximum exercise at high altitude than at sea level regardless of the duration of stay. From these findings, the authors maintain that acclimatization includes decreased capacity of the peripheral tissues to extract oxygen from the blood. Since the subjects stopped the maximum exercise in the presence of arterial lactate and venous oxygen concentrations higher than the sea level maximum exercise values, it is possible that some event outside the homeostasis of muscular tissue stopped or slowed down the work. It may be the overwhelming sensation of breathlessness. On return to sea level, the acclimatized subjects indicated no significant increase in maximum oxygen uptake so that the training effect specific to high altitude was doubted by the investigators as well as by others (89).

From the above and other studies, altitude acclimatization does not seem to increase the oxygen transport capacity of the cardiovascular system. It may remain depressed throughout one's life. This is a conclusion from serial studies by Grover's group (106, 109) in which they attempted to confirm the smaller cardiac output and stroke volume of high altitude residents or newcomers to high altitude compared with those at sea level. In the first study (109), the subjects were residents of Leadville, Colorado (3100 m above sea level). Cardiac output as well as oxygen consumption, at rest and during graded work load, was measured in the supine position by the direct Fick method for oxygen, first in the town and then at sea level. Cardiac output increased 8 per cent ten days after descent to sea level. At the same time heart rate decreased slightly and stroke volume increased 15 per cent. After eliminating many probable factors in the subnormal cardiac output, the authors hypothesize that low arterial oxygen tension or reduced coronary flow causes a depression of myocardial contractility which together with accelerated heart rate results in reduced stroke volume. The depression, or the recovery from it after descent, develops slowly, taking more than one day. Oxygen inhalation at altitude further decreased cardiac output, rather than increasing it. In the second study (106), sea level residents were taken to Leadville to compare cardiac output during rest and exercise. The results were similar to those in the first study; cardiac output was reduced by 9 per cent at high altitude. Hematocrit increased because of diminished plasma volume. However, acute expansion of plasma volume with dextran did not restore cardiac output to the sea level value, which casts doubt on the importance of ventricular filling factor as the cause.

The reports from these two groups of investigators disagree regarding the most basic variable, cardiac output response to altitude ascent. Whether this is due to the difference in method (dye-dilution technic vs. Fick method), in altitude (4300 vs. 3100 m), or in posture (sitting vs. supine) remains undetermined.

HYPERTENSION

Numerous papers appeared as usual concerning the role of hormonal, neural, and dietary factors in causing, accelerating, or suppressing hypertensive state. Only a dozen are discussed here because of their appeal to my personal interest. The reader is encouraged to refer to several symposium proceedings cited in the introduction and the supplementary reference list.

Baroreceptor reflex.—Today, most investigators look upon the arterial baroreceptor reflex as a mechanism that adapts itself to the progress of hypertension rather than initiating it, but at least a few physiologists still challenge this attitude (110). That the arterial baroreceptor reflex has apparently normal reflex sensitivity over a shifted high input pressure range does not conclusively eliminate it as a cause of hypertension; the shift of operating range may be the result of adaptation, but it may well be the primary cause of essential hypertension. Interesting in this connection is Bader's finding on the human aorta that with age, the tangential wall stress linearly decreased (111). According to the author this means that in order to maintain an identical amount of stress on the stretch receptor, some active adjustment has to be made continuously in normal man as hardening occurs in the aortic wall with age (92).

However, when hypertension is produced by some other means, the carotid sinus reflex seems to adapt very quickly. Alexander & DeCuir (112) compared the speed of the development of hypertension acutely induced by plastic bag encapsulation and compression of the kidney in normal and sino-aortic denervated rabbits. Since the slope of the pressor response to rising capsule pressure did not differ detectably between the two groups, the authors inferred that the reflex adapts to the rapidly rising arterial pressure within one day. Christensen, Warner & Pryor (91) also reported that the carotid sinus baroreceptor itself appeared to adapt to some extent to changing mean sinus input pressure within a period of seconds.

Renal hypertension.—Guyton & Coleman (17) closely followed the course of hemodynamic changes after unilateral nephrectomy in those dogs whose other kidney had previously been deprived of one half to two thirds of its tissue. In contrast to earlier reports based on measurements made a few days after the surgery, cardiac output did increase considerably in the first two days together with expansion of blood volume; after the third day it decreased nearly to normal as total peripheral vascular resistance increased, presenting the pattern of typical renal hypertension. A similar initial and transient increase in cardiac output, followed by increasing peripheral resistance and return of cardiac output nearly to normal level with sustained arterial pressure, was observed by Ledingham & Pelling (113) in the course of Goldblatt hypertension in rats. The central idea of the previously described computer model of renoprival hypertension proposed by Guyton & Coleman is that with diminished renal function, blood volume and body fluid expand, with a resultant increase in cardiac output. In response to the supernormal cardiac output, vascular autoregulation occurs and further raises arterial pressure, which in turn augments urinary output toward the normal amount and thus blood volume returns toward the control. This decrease in blood volume then diminishes cardiac output and a new equilibrium is established. Although these experiments and the model are an impressively quantitative step toward a deeper understanding of renal hypertension, a long list of questions must be answered before the etiology of essential hypertension can be clarified.

Renin angiotensin system.—Untiring search continues for explanations to the discrepancy between the pharmacological dose of angiotensin needed to cause a pressor response and the low plasma renin activity found in hypertensive patients. For example, Dickinson & Yu (114) observed in conscious rabbits a complete abrogation of the pressor response to angiotensin after autonomic ganglionic blockade. They hypothesize that angiotensin acts primarily on the vasomotor control center which in turn causes resetting of the arterial baroreceptor reflex and thereby a new equilibrium state at a hypertensive level. However, a diametrically opposite result was obtained by Gordon & Stephenson (115). They found increased vascular response to angiotensin during ganglionic blockade and maintain that adrenergic impulses normally inhibit the vasoconstrictive action of angiotensin. Ross & White (116), on the other hand, demonstrated that adrenalectomy or propranolol prevented the vasodilating phase of the angiotensin effect and therefore hold that angiotensin stimulates adrenal secretion of catecholamine.

Similar conflicts exist as to the involvement of the carotid sinus reflex and renal functions in the pressor effect of angiotensin. Thus, Geller & Kendrick (117) noted a marked reduction in the renal vasoconstrictor response to angiotension as the background sympathetic activity was reduced by raising carotid sinus pressure. Masson, Aoki & Page (118) observed a synergism between sinoaortic denervation and the cardiovascular response to renin and angiotensin. Gabelman & Rondell (119), on the other hand, obtained negative findings concerning the neurogenic influence on the protracted pressor response to angiotensin infusion. McGiff (120) adduced some presumptive evidence that although angiotensin produces antinatriuresis in intact dogs, it has a renal tubular action which works toward natriuresis and is uncovered after the administration of guanethidine or reserpine.

Concerning the influence of the state of sodium balance on the overall vascular response to angiotensin, the literature is less controversial. Baum & Shropshire (121) as well as McCaa et al. (122) showed that sodium retention caused by deoxycorticosterone or aldosterone accelerated the vasoconstrictor response of the systemic vascular bed.

The principal interest of researchers, however, has now been directed to the mechanism of renin release which appears to bear some close relation to juxtaglomerular cell function and tubular reabsorption of sodium. Brown et al. (123) as well as Brubacher & Vander (124), among many others, made convincing observations that changes in plasma sodium level rather than renal arterial pressure variations are very well correlated with the plasma activity level of renin. Hypotheses advanced range from a purely intrarenal sodium-sensitive mechanism [Nash et al. (125)] to a multiple feedback loop theory including high and low pressure cardiovascular receptors [Vander & Luciano (126)].

COMMENTARY

Untouched topics.—This review has left untouched many important areas, the most actively cultivated of which is perhaps the pulmonary circulation. The demonstration of zonal difference in perfusion of the upright human lung by West excited a revival of interest among experimenters. A few models based on the concept of vascular waterfall have explained pressure and flow distribution in the excised lung reasonably well, but fail to predict some phenomena observed *in vivo* (e.g. 127). The model is being made more sophisticated by considering the effect of intrapleural pressure. Also essential for the model building is accurate knowledge of the relative magnitudes of arterial and venous resistances and compliances. New approaches to assess these parameters have been devised (e.g. 128 and 129), and mathematical modeling in turn aids in the analysis (e.g. 130). The effect of lung volume changes was studied (131) and a generalized mathematical formulation was tested (132). Knowledge of the dynamics of pressure and flow propagation contributed to understanding of left ventricular filling (133, 134). Pulmonary tissue pressure was measured (135) and the dynamics of transcapillary fluid shift was studied in terms of pulmonary edema formation and the isogravimetric technic (136, 137). Also remarkable is the abundance of experimental data concerning the hypoxic increase of pulmonary vascular resistance. Fifteen published papers on this single topic accumulated on my desk. Since the pulmonary vascular bed is simpler by far in structure than the systemic vascular bed, and the extramural pressure can be manipulated via intra-alveolar pressure, sweeping progress in the understanding of this vascular bed can be expected.

Another topic that should be covered is the control of the cardiovascular function by the central nervous system. Steady efforts have been made in electroneurophysiological study of the medullary and higher centers (e.g. 138–140). Although the direct neural controls of circulatory functions are in general phasic and less powerful over long periods of time, the central nervous system is undoubtedly highly influential on the long-term overall circulatory regulation via the neurohumoral and neurosecretory mechanisms. Active studies were also carried out on the effect of various ions, peptides, and autonomic blockers. The reader may find some of these in the supplementary references.

Methodological note.—The following discussion is a methodological notion, as well as a review of papers, concerning the basic identification of the circulatory system performance. It is axiomatic that the important factors in circulatory dynamics are the variable behavior of the cardiac pump and the variable impedance that the vascular system loads on the heart. The basic mechanical determinants of cardiac output, and thereby the means of regulating the circulatory transport, are the input load (the Frank-Starling mechanism), the heart rate, and the output load or aortic pressure. In turn, the determinant of these loading parameters is the set of externally coupled vascular parameters, as well as cardiac output itself.

A point of importance often disregarded by the student of circulation is that both the pump and the vascular conduit are coupled to each other at inflow and outflow ends simultaneously. Figure 1 explains this bilateral coupling in a schematic way. The upper block may represent either the cardiac pump or the perfusion pump, while the lower block represents either the real vascular system or an artificial conducting vessel. As seen in the

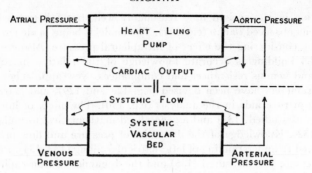

FIG. 1. Circulatory system as a *bilaterally* coupled pump and conduit system.

foregoing review, it is conventional to lump the system components into two major segments (the heart lung pump and systemic vascular circuit) as illustrated. The measured variables are the mean levels of aortic flow and arterial, venous, and atrial pressures. The two pairs of lines connecting these blocks on both terminals represent the bilateral coupling of the two segments. The direction of the arrows signifies whether the coupling is an input or output variable.

Because of the principle of duality, either the pressure or the flow signal can be assigned as input or output. If flow is chosen as the input variable, pressure has to be the output variable and vice versa. One important restriction is that blood volume cannot change very quickly; accordingly, when one of the two segments is expected to have a far greater compliance than the other, a set of identical flow variables as the input to the more compliant segment is preferable to a set of independent pressure variables. For example, when one wishes to study pressure-flow relationships in the systemic vascular bed of an experimental animal with a constant normal blood volume, one cannot load 5 mm Hg of venous pressure while loading a mean arterial pressure of 120 mm Hg; the result will be a tremendous amount of blood accumulated in the capacitance vessels and profound modification of the peripheral resistance and capillary fluid exchange.

Most investigators of vascular resistance have maintained venous pressure at zero while they changed arterial inflow. By so doing, they changed the blood volume in the preparation to an unknown degree whenever they altered the arterial inflow. In addition, this type of experiment omits valuable information on the transient behavior of the capacitance vessels. On the other hand, if the vascular circuit impedance is studied by forcing an identical flow variable into the arterial end and out of the venous end, two output variables (i.e., arterial pressure and venous pressure) will be obtained. Both of these pressures are quite relevant variables as the input forcing for the pump segment. For example, in an attempt to clarify the effect of humoral agents on the venous segment of the systemic circuit, Emerson (141) measured venous outflow, coupling the caval venous pressure to zero potential as Rashkind and many others did. Thus, he shunted the major venous capacitance to ground, and changes in this capacity parameter were determined in terms of the alterations of the reservoir blood volume. Considering the nonlinear nature of the venous capacitance, the alternative measurement of venous capacitance in terms of varying venous pressure, holding venous outflow at a constant level, would have given us more direct information on the response of the venous capacitance vessel as a determinant of the cardiac pump's input load parameter.

In study of the cardiac pump segment, diametrically opposite constraints and input-output preference hold. The input variables are now a number of independently chosen combinations of venous (or atrial) pressure and arterial pressure. The single output variable then is aortic flow or venous return.

The importance of venous pressure as the driving force for the cardiac pump has been known for a century. The impact of the venous pressure on venous return and cardiac output was demonstrated in systematic experiments by Guyton and elaborated mathematically by Grodins only a decade ago. Since both of these studies were static analyses, we do not yet have good experimental information on the dynamic performance of the systemic or pulmonary vascular bed, as seen from the venous end in particular, over the frequency range below the cardiac cycle. During the period of review, rigorous analyses of dynamic frequency characteristics were performed on the systemic and pulmonary arterial impedances over the frequency range above the cardiac cycle. These power spectra yield valid information on the impedance variable to be coupled with the mechanical source impedance of the ventricles studied on a beat-to-beat basis. As a matter of fact, many known neurohumoral mechanisms work on the peripheral resistance and venous capacitance so slowly that the frequency spectrum of the magnitude and phase component of the resistance term over a frequency range far below one cycle per second is even more important information for understanding overall circulatory regulation. Fortunately, Taylor (142) extended his interest into such an "ultralow" frequency range and found extremely interesting nonlinear alterations of resistance modulus magnitude as aortic inflow was varied by stimulating the cardiac nerve for long intervals. After sympathetic ganglion blockade, the nonlinear characteristics observed in intact animals were greatly attenuated, which indicates that the nonlinearity derives from neural control, very probably from the baroreceptor reflex. It is all the more regrettable that he did not simultaneously analyze impedance characteristics seen from the venous side of the systemic circuit.

As indicated in Figure 1, the static and dynamic characteristics of the pump segment may be studied by imposing multiple combinations of mean atrial and arterial pressures on the heart. The mean flow output responding to combinations of the input and output pressure loads will be expressed as a three-dimensional surface as Beneken's model proposed (15). Sagawa (143) examined the left heart in this manner and found that the dependency of steady-state aortic flow on the output (mean arterial) pressure load is a function of the input (mean atrial) pressure load. A high aortic flow was considerably influenced by a change in aortic pressure, whereas it was almost independent of aortic pressure when the input load was subnormal. Plotted on a three-dimensional graph, cardiac output represents a complex surface against venous and arterial pressure load coordinates. The significance of such a cardiac output surface will not be appreciated unless it is graphically equated with a vascular impedance curve which can be studied as discussed above and expressed in the same three-dimensional plot. The intersection of the curve and the surface represents equilibrated aortic flow, venous pressure, and arterial pressure. Both the surface and the curve will alter in shape and position as heart rate, inotropic background, tone of the resistance and capacitance vessels, or total blood volume is varied or repartitioned between the two segments. This alteration then illustrates the shift of static equilibrium points between the pump and the conduit segments coupled bilaterally. Analysis of transient dynamics, on the other hand, requires the aid of a computer even with such a simplified model.

Concluding remarks.—The physiologist today stands under the tremendous pressure of multidisciplinary training. For him, Engelberg (144) wrote a consoling thought: "The physiologist is a pioneer; and pioneers travel light. Pioneers and craftsmen rely on simple and basic tools; complicated, specialized tools are the counterpart of the comfort loving town dweller or the amateur craftsman."

The review on overall circulatory regulation reflects the ever deepening recognition by the investigators of the complicated reality as opposed to the simple, principal purpose of the circulation. The interaction of the circulatory system with other colleague subsystems for homeostasis occurs at multiple levels of organization of these subsystems. The ranking of subsystems in the hierarchy of physiological regulation is dynamic rather than stereotypic. Signs of cohesiveness and unification are not impossible to find. But the majority of existing data directs us toward the opposite: multiple inputs, multiple outputs, multilevel parametric controls of the circulatory black box. Thus, endless repetition of careful experiments, modeling, verifying experiments, and remodeling appears the only right path for the systems physiologist. He then will have to travel heavy, with wit in mind, computer in hand and sweat all over.

LITERATURE CITED

1. A view of systems physiology. *Physiologist*, **11**, 115–33 (1968)
2. Bevegård, B. S., Shepherd, J. T. Regulation of the circulation during exercise in man. *Physiol. Rev.*, **47**, 178–213 (1967)
3. Chien, S. Role of the sympathetic nervous system in hemorrhage. *Physiol. Rev.*, **47**, 214–88 (1967)
4. *Physical Bases of Circulatory Transport: Regulation and Exchange* (Reeve, E. B., Guyton, A. C., Eds., Saunders, Philadelphia, 381 pp., 1967)
5. *Baroreceptors and Hypertension* (Kezdi, P., Ed., Pergamon, Oxford, 460 pp., 1967)
6. *Physical Activity and the Heart*

(Karvonen, M. J., Barry, A. F., Eds., Thomas, Springfield, Ill., 1966)

7. *Physiology of Muscle Exercise. Circ. Res.,* **20,** *Suppl. I* (226 pp., 1967)

8. *Renin Mechanisms and Hypertension (Hypertension,* **XV**). *Circ. Res.,* **21,** *Suppl. II* (226 pp., 1967)

9. *Catecholamines in Cardiovascular Physiology and Disease. Circ. Res.,* **21,** *Suppl. IV* (247 pp., 1967)

10. *Renin, Angiotensin, Aldosterone and Hormonal Regulation of Arterial Pressure and Salt Balance. Fed. Proc.,* **26,** 39–69 (1967)

11. *Renal Hypertension* (Page, I. H., McCubbin, J. W., Eds., Year Book Med. Publ., Chicago, 493 pp., 1968)

12. *Hormones and Hypertension* (Manger, W. M., Ed., Thomas, Springfield, Ill., 265 pp., 1966)

13. Berne, R. M., Levy, M. N. *Cardiovascular Physiology* (Mosby, St. Louis, 254 pp., 1967)

14. Marshall, R. J., Shepherd, J. T. *Cardiac Function in Health and Disease* (Saunders, Philadelphia, 409 pp., 1968)

15. Beneken, J. E. W., DeWit, B. A physical approach to hemodynamic aspects of the human cardiovascular system (See Ref. 4), 1–45

16. Beneken, J. E. W., Rideout, V. C. The use of multiple models in cardiovascular system modeling: Transport and perturbation methods. *Trans. IEEE,* **BME-15,** No. 4

17. Guyton, A. C., Coleman, T. G. Long-term regulation of the circulation: Interrelationships with body fluid volumes (See Ref. 4), 179–201

18. Pennock, B., Attinger, E. D. Optimization of the oxygen transport system. *Biophys. J.,* **8,** 879–96 (1968)

19. McLeod, J. PHYSBE. . . . a year later. *Simulation,* **10,** 37–45 (1968)

20. Osborn, J. J., Hoehne, W., Badia, W. Ventricular function in the basic regulation of the circulation: Studies with a mechanical analog (See Ref. 4), 47–60

21. Harlan, J. G., Smith, E. E., Richardson, T. Q. Pressure-volume curves of systemic and pulmonary circuit. *Am. J. Physiol.,* **213,** 1499–503 (1967)

22. Gupta, P. D., Henry, J. P., Sinclair, R., Van Baumgarten, R. Responses of atrial and aortic baroreceptors to nonhypotensive hemorrhage and to transfusion. *Am. J. Physiol.,* **211,** 1429–37 (1966)

23. Sagawa, K. Relative roles of the rate sensitive and proportional control elements of the carotid sinus during mild hemorrhage (See Ref. 5), 97–105

24. Chalmers, J. P., Korner, P. I., White, S. W. The effects of hemorrhage in the unanesthetized rabbit. *J. Physiol. (London),* **189,** 367–91 (1967)

25. Conway, J. Hemodynamic consequences of induced changes in blood volume. *Circ. Res.,* **18,** 190–98 (1966)

26. Price, H. L., Deutsch, S., Marshall, B. E., Stephan, G. W., Behar, M. G., Neufeld, G. R. Hemodynamic and metabolic effects of hemorrhage in men, with particular reference to the splanchnic circulation. *Circ. Res.,* **18,** 469–74 (1966)

27. Chalmers, J. P., Korner, P. I., White, S. W. Effects of hemorrhage on the distribution of the peripheral blood flow in the rabbit. *J. Physiol. (London),* **192,** 561–74 (1967)

28. Korner, P. I., Stokes, G. S., White, S. W., Chalmers, J. P. Role of the autonomic nervous system in the renal vasoconstriction response to hemorrhage in the rabbit. *Circ. Res.,* **20,** 676–85 (1967)

29. Carriere, S., Thorburn, G. D., O'Morchoe, C. C. C., Barger, A. C. Intrarenal distribution of blood flow in dogs during hemorrhagic hypertension. *Circ. Res.,* **19,** 167–79 (1966)

30. Guntheroth, W. G., McGough, G. A., Mullins, G. L. Continuous recording of splenic diameter, vein flow, and hematocrit in intact dogs. *Am. J. Physiol.,* **213,** 690–94 (1967)

31. Buckley, N. M., Frank, M. H., Zeig, N. J., Bass, B. G., Macy, J., Jr. Effects of acute hemorrhage during catecholamine infusion in splenectomized dogs. *Am. J. Physiol.,* **212,** 579–88 (1967)

32. Zeig, N. J., Buckley, N. M., Macy, J., Jr. Effects of acute hemorrhage after adrenergic blockade in splenectomized dogs. *Am. J. Physiol.* **214,** 33–40 (1968)

33. Gilmore, J. P., Daggett, W. M. Response of the chronic cardiac denervated dog to acute volume expansion. *Am. J. Physiol.,* **210,** 509–12 (1966)

34. Henry, J. P., Gupta, P. D., Meehan,

J. P., Sinclair, R., Share, L. The role of afferents from the low pressure system in the release of anti-diuretic hormone during nonhypotensive hemorrhage. *Can. J. Physiol. Pharmacol.*, **46**, 287–95 (1968)

35. Share, L., Levy, M. N. Effect of carotid chemo-receptor stimulation on plasma antidiuretic hormone titer. *Am. J. Physiol.*, **210**, 157–61 (1966)

36. Share, L., Levy, M. N. Carotid sinus pulse pressure, a determinant of plasma antidiuretic hormone concentration. *Ibid.*, **211**, 721–24

37. McKenzie, J. K., Lee, M. R., Cook, W. F. Effect of hemorrhage on arterial plasma renin activity in the rabbit. *Circ. Res.*, **19**, 269–73 (1966)

38. Bunag, R. D., Page, I. H., McCubbin, J. W. Neural stimulation of release of renin. *Circ. Res.*, **19**, 851–58 (1966)

39. Gann, D. S. Systems analysis in the study of homeostasis. *Am. J. Surg.* **114**, 95–102 (1967)

40. Fell, C. Plasma loss in dogs in irreversible hemorrhagic shock. *Am. J. Physiol.*, **211**, 885–89 (1966)

41. Rothe, C. F. Cardiac and peripheral failure in hemorrhagic shock treated with massive transfusions. *Am. J. Physiol.*, **210**, 1347–61 (1966)

42. Rothe, C. R. Oxygen deficit in hemorrhagic shock in dogs. *Ibid.*, **214**, 436–42 (1968)

43. Brand, E. D., Suh, T. K., Avery, M. C. Reversal of postoligemic shock in the cat by hypervenobaric massive fluid therapy. *Am. J. Physiol.*, **211**, 1232–40 (1966)

44. Lefer, A. M., Cowgill, R., Marshall, F. F., Hall, L. M., Brand, E. D. Characterization of a myocardial depressant factor present in hemorrhagic shock. *Am. J. Physiol.*, **213**, 492–98 (1967)

45. Abel, F. L., Waldhausen, J. A., Daly, W. J., Pearce, W. L. Pulmonary blood volume in hemorrhagic shock in the dog and primate. *Am. J. Physiol.*, **213**, 1072–78 (1967)

46. Lintermans, J. P., Appel, A. J., Bloom, R. S., Mullins, G. L., Guntheroth, W. G. Mesenteric blood flow and vascular volume in hemorrhagic shock. *Am. J. Physiol.*, **212**, 482–87 (1967)

47. Bond, R. F., Manley, E. S., Jr., Green, H. D. Cutaneous and skeletal muscle vascular responses to hemorrhage and irreversible shock. *Am. J. Physiol.*, **212**, 488–97 (1967)

48. Smith, E. E., Crowell, J. W. Influence of hypoxia on mean circulatory pressure and cardiac output. *Am. J. Physiol.*, **212**, 1067–69 (1967)

49. Downing, S. E., Talner, N. S., Gardner, T. H. Influences of hypoxemia and acidemia on left ventricular function. *Am. J. Physiol.*, **210**, 1327–34 (1966)

50. Kontos, H. A., Levasseur, J. E., Richardson, D. W., Mauck, H. P., Jr., Patterson, J. L., Jr., Comparative circulatory responses to systemic hypoxia in man and in unanesthetized dog. *J. Appl. Physiol.*, **23**, 381–86 (1967)

51. Richardson, D. W., Kontos, H. A., Raper, A. J., Patterson, J. C., Jr. Modification by beta-adrenergic blockade of the circulatory responses to acute hypoxia in man. *J. Clin. Invest.*, **46**, 77–85 (1967)

52. Chalmers, J. P., Korner, P. I., White, S. W. The relative roles of the aortic and carotid sinus nerves in the rabbit in the control of respiration and circulation during arterial hypoxia and hypercapnia. *J. Physiol. (London)*, **188**, 435–50 (1967)

53. Chalmers, J. P., Korner, P. I., White, S. W. Local and reflex factors affecting the distribution of the peripheral blood flow during arterial hypoxia in the rabbit. *Ibid.*, **192**, 537–48

54. Daly, M. D., Robinson, B. H. An analysis of the reflex systemic vasodilator response elicited by lung inflation in the dog. *J. Physiol. (London)*, **195**, 387–406 (1968)

55. Stern, S., Rapaport, E. Comparison of the reflexes elicited from combined or separate stimulation of the aortic and carotid chemoreceptors on myocardial contractility, cardiac output and systemic resistance. *Circ. Res.*, **20**, 214–27 (1967)

56. Browse, N. L., Shepherd, J. T. Response of veins of canine limb to aortic and carotid chemoreceptor stimulation. *Am. J. Physiol.*, **210**, 1435–41 (1966)

57. Kontos, H. A., Goldin, D., Richardson, D. W., Patterson, J. L., Jr. Contribution of pulmonary vagal reflexes to circulatory response to hypoxia. *Am. J. Physiol.*, **212**, 1441–46 (1967)

58. Vogel, J. A., Harris, C. W. Cardio-pulmonary responses of resting man during early exposure to high altitude. *J. Appl. Physiol.*, **22**, 1124–28 (1967)

59. Suutarinen, T. Cardiovascular response to changes in arterial carbon dioxide tension. *Acta Physiol. Scand.*, **67**, *Suppl. 266*, 1–76 (1966)

60. Wendling, M. G., Eckstein, J. W., Abboud, F. M. Cardiovascular response to carbon dioxide before and after beta-adrenergic blockade, *J. Appl. Physiol.*, **22**, 223–26 (1967)

61. Stegall, H. F. Muscle pump. *Circ. Res.*, **18**, 180–90 (1966)

62. Moreno, A. H., Burchell, A. R., Van Der Woude, R., Burke, J. H. Respiratory regulation of splanchnic and systemic venous return. *Am. J. Physiol.*, **213**, 455–65 (1967)

63. Feisal, K. A., Abboud, F. M., Eckstein, J. W. Effect of adrenergic blockade on cardiovascular responses to increased airway pressure. *Am. J. Physiol.*, **213**, 127–33 (1967)

64. Godley, J. A., Myers, J. W., Rosenbaum, D. A. Cardiovascular and renal function during continuous negative pressure breathing in dogs. *J. Appl. Physiol.*, **22**, 568–72 (1967)

65. Myers, J. W., Godley, J. A. Cardiovascular and renal function during total body water immersion of dogs. *J. Appl. Physiol.*, **22**, 573–79. (1967)

66. Gilbert, C. A., Bricker, L. A., Springfield, W. T., Jr., Stevens, P. M., Warren, B. H. Sodium and water excretion and renal hemodynamics during lower body negative pressure. *J. Appl. Physiol.*, **21**, 1699–1704 (1966)

67. Martino, J. A., Earley, L. E. Demonstration of a role of physical factors as determinants of the natriuretic response to volume expansion. *J. Clin. Invest.*, **46**, 1963–78 (1967)

68. Gilbert, C. A., Stevens, P. M. Forearm vascular responses to lower body negative pressure and orthostasis. *J. Appl. Physiol.*, **21**, 1265–72 (1966)

69. Samueloff, S. L., Browse, N. L., Shepherd, J. T. Response of capacity vessels in human limbs to head-up tilt and suction on lower body. *J. Appl. Physiol.*, **21**, 47–54 (1966)

70. Newberry, P. D., Bryan, A. C. Effect on venous compliance and peripheral vascular resistance of headward (+Gz) acceleration. *J. Appl. Physiol.*, **23**, 150–56 (1967)

71. Cohen, E. L., Conn, J. W., Rovner, D. R. Postural augmentation of plasma renin activity and aldosterone excretion in normal people. *J. Clin. Invest.*, **46**, 418–28 (1967)

72. Epstein, S. E., Stampfer, M., Beiser, G. D. Role of the capacitance and resistance vessels in vasovagal syncope. *Circulation*, **37**, 524–33 (1968)

73. Epstein, S. E., Beiser, G. D., Stampfer, M., Braunwald, E. Role of the venous system in baroreceptor mediated reflexes in man. *J. Clin. Invest.*, **47**, 139–52 (1968)

74. Murray, R. H. Cardiopulmonary effects of brief, intense thermal exposures. *J. Appl. Physiol.*, **21**, 1717–24 (1966)

75. Evonuk, W. Cardiovascular effects in normothermic dogs cross circulated with hypothermic dogs. *Am. J. Physiol.*, **211**, 38–42 (1966)

76. Robinson, B. F., Epstein, S. E., Kahler, R. L., Braunwald, E. Circulatory effects of acute expansion of blood volume: studies during maximal exercise and at rest. *Circ. Res.*, **19**, 26–32 (1966)

77. Vanhoutte, P., Leusen, I. The cardiovascular adaptation of the dog to muscular exercise after graded hemorrhages. *Arch. Intern. Physiol. Biochem.*, **74**, 185–200 (1966)

78. Vanhoutte, P., Lacroix, E., Leusen, I. The cardiovascular adaptation of the dog to muscular exercise.—Role of the arterial pressoreceptors. *Arch. Intern. Physiol. Biochem.*, **74**, 201–22 (1966)

79. Warner, H. R., Topham, W. S. Regulation of cardiac output during transition from rest to exercise (See Ref. 5), 77–88

80. Donald, D. E., Ferguson, D. A., Milburn, S. E. Effect of β-adrenergic receptor blockade on racing performance of greyhounds with normal and with denervated hearts. *Circ. Res.*, **22**, 127–34 (1968)

81. Mitchell, J. H., Mierzwiak, D. S., Wildenthal, K., Willis, D. W., Jr., Smith, A. M. Effect on left ventricular performance of stimulation of an afferent nerve from muscle. *Circ. Res.*, **22**, 507–16 (1968)

82. Stegemann, J., Ulmer, H.-V., Böning, D. Auslösung peripherer neurogener Atmungs- und Kreislaufantriebe

durch Erhöhung des CO_2-Druckes in grösseren Muskelgruppen. *Pflügers Arch.*, **293**, 155–64 (1967)

83. Stenberg, J., Astrand, P., Ekblom, B., Royce, J., Saltin, B. Hemodynamic response to work with different muscle groups, sitting and supine. *J. Appl. Physiol.*, **22**, 61–70 (1967)

84. Castenfors, J. Renal function during exercise. *Acta Physiol. Scand.*, **70**, *Suppl. 293*, 1–44 (1967)

85. Rowell, L. B., Marx, H. J., Bruce, R. A., Conn, R. D., Kusumi, F. Reduction of cardiac output, central blood volume and stroke volume with thermal stress in normal men during exercise. *J. Clin. Invest.*, **45**, 1801–16 (1966)

86. Dawson, C. A., Nadel, E. R., Morvath, S. M. Cardiac output in the cold-stressed swimming rat. *Am. J. Physiol.*, **213**, 320–25 (1968)

87. Stenberg, J., Ekblom, B., Messin, R. Hemodynamic response to work at simulated altitude, 4,000 m. *J. Appl. Physiol.*, **21**, 1589–94 (1966)

88. Hughes, R. L., Clode, M., Edwards, R. H. T., Goodwin, T. J., Jones, N. L. Effect of inspired O_2 on cardiopulmonary and metabolic responses to exercise in man. *J. Appl. Physiol.*, **24**, 336–47 (1968)

89. Piiper, J., Cerretelli, P., Cuttica, F., Mangili, F. Energy metabolism and circulation in dogs exercising hypoxia. *J. Appl. Physiol.*, **21**, 1143–49 (1966)

90. Gero, J., Gerova, M. Significance of the individual parameters of pulsating pressure in stimulation of baroreceptors (See Ref. 5), 17–30

91. Christensen, B. N., Warner, H. R., Pryor, T. A. A technique for the quantitative study of carotid sinus behavior (See Ref. 5), 41–50

92. Scher, A. M., Franz, G. N., Ito, C. S., Young, A. C. Studies on the carotid sinus reflex (See Ref. 4), 113–20

93. Hatakeyama, I. Analysis of baroceptor control of the circulation (See Ref. 4), 91–112

94. Spickler, J. W., Kezdi, P. Dynamic response characteristics of carotid sinus baroceptors. *Am. J. Physiol.*, **212**, 474–76 (1967)

95. Kezdi, P., Geller, E. Baroceptor control of postganglionic sympathetic nerve discharge. *Am. J. Physiol.*, **214**, 427–35 (1968)

96. Ninomiya, I., Irisawa, H. Aortic nervous activity in response to

pulsatile and nonpulsatile pressure. *Am. J. Physiol.*, **213**, 1504–11 (1967)

97. Irisawa, H., Ninomiya, I. Comparison of the averaged nervous activities of aortic and carotid sinus nerves. *Ibid.*, 504–10

98. Olmsted, F., McCubbin, J. W., Page, I. H. Hemodynamic cause of the pressor response to carotid occlusion. *Am. J. Physiol.*, **210**, 1342–46 (1966)

99. Baker, C. H. Effects of carotid occlusion on dog forelimb vascular volume. *Am. J. Physiol.*, **213**, 477–82 (1967)

100. Levy, M. N., Ng, M. L., Zieske, H. Cardiac and respiratory effects of aortic arch baroreceptor stimulation. *Circ. Res.*, **19**, 930–39 (1966)

101. Allison, J. L., Sagawa, K. An openloop analysis of the aortic arch and brachiocephalic baroreceptor reflex. *Physiologist*, **10**, 108 (1967)

102. Weisse, A. B., Regan, T. J., Nadimi, M., Hellems, H. K. Late circulatory adjustments to acute normovolemic polycythemia. *Am. J. Physiol.*, **211**, 1413–18 (1966)

103. Aperia, A. C., Liebow, A. A., Roberts, L. E. Renal adaptation to anemia. *Circ. Res.*, **22**, 489–500 (1968)

104. Rowell, L. B., Kraning, K. K. II, Kennedy, J. W., Evans, T. O. Central circulatory responses to work in dry heat before and after acclimatization. *J. Appl. Physiol.*, **22**, 509–18 (1967)

105. Vogel, J. A., Hansen, J. E., Harris, C. W. Cardiovascular responses in man during exhaustive work at sea level and high altitude. *J. Appl. Physiol.*, **23**, 531–39 (1967)

106. Alexander, J. K., Hartley, L. H., Modelski, M., Grover, R. F. Reduction of stroke volume during exercise in man following ascent to 3,100 m altitude. *J. Appl. Physiol.*, **23**, 849–58 (1967)

107. Sugimoto, T., Sagawa, K., Guyton, A. C. Effect of tachycardia on cardiac output during normal and increased venous return. *Am. J. Physiol.*, **211**, 288–92 (1966)

108. Hansen, J. E., Vogel, J. A., Stelter, G. P., Consolazio, F. Oxygen uptake in man during exhaustive work at sea level and high altitude. *J. Appl. Physiol.*, **23**, 511–22 (1967)

109. Hartley, L. H., Alexander, J. K., Modelski, M., Grover, R. F. Sub-

normal cardiac output at rest and during exercise in residents at 3,100 m altitude. *J. Appl. Physiol.*, **23**, 839–48 (1967)

110. Horrobin, D. F. A theory of hypertension. *Lancet*, **I**, 574–79 (1966)

111. Bader, H. Dependence of wall stress in the human thoracic aorta on age and pressure. *Circ. Res.*, **20**, 354–61 (1967)

112. Alexander, N., DeCuir, M. Sino-aortic baroreflex system and early pressure rise in renal hypertensive rabbits. *Am. J. Physiol.*, **213**, 701–5 (1967)

113. Ledingham, J. M., Pelling, D. Cardiac output and peripheral resistance in experimental renal hypertension. *Circ. Res.*, **20–21**, *Suppl. II*, 187–99 (1967)

114. Dickinson, C. J., Yu, R. Mechanisms involved in the progressive pressor response to very small amounts of angiotensin in conscious rabbits. *Circ. Res.*, **20–21**, *Suppl. II*, 157–65 (1967)

115. Gordon, D. B., Stephensen, M. P. Increased vascular response to angiotensin during ganglionic blockade. *Am. J. Physiol.*, **212**, 1033–36 (1967)

116. Ross, G., White, F. N. Role of catecholamine release in cardiovascular responses to angiotensin. *Am. J. Physiol.*, **211**, 1419–23 (1966)

117. Geller, R. G., Kendrick, J. E. Reduction in renal vascular responses to angiotensin and norepinephrine during carotid sinus stimulation. *Circ. Res.*, **20**, 321–27 (1967)

118. Masson, G. M. C., Aoki, K., Page, I. H. Effects of sino-aortic denervation on renal and adrenal hypertension. *Am. J. Physiol.*, **211**, 99–104 (1966)

119. Gabelman, E. H., Rondell, P. A. Protracted pressor response to angiotensin after bilateral nephrectomy in rats. *Circ. Res.*, **18**, 705–13 (1966)

120. McGiff, J. C. Natriuretic effect of angiotensin in dogs revealed after administration of reserpine and guanethidine. *Circ. Res.*, **20**, 664–75 (1967)

121. Baum, T., Shropshire, A. T. Sympathetic and humoral vasoconstrictor responses in deoxycorticosterone hypertension. *Am. J. Physiol.* **213**, 499–503 (1967)

122. McCaa, R. E., Richardson, T. Q.,

Langford, H. G., Douglas, B. H. Circulatory changes following angiotensin administration. *Am. J. Physiol.*, **212**, 565–68 (1967)

123. Brown, T. C., Davis, J. O., Olickney, M. J., Johnston, C. I. Relation of plasma renin to sodium balance and arterial pressure in experimental renal hypertension. *Circ. Res.*, **18**, 475–83 (1966)

124. Brubacher, E. S., Vander, A. J. Sodium deprivation and renin secretion in unanesthetized dogs. *Am. J. Physiol.*, **214**, 15–21 (1968)

125. Nash, F. D., Rostorfer, H. H. Bailie, M. D., Wathen, R. L., Schneider, E. G. Renin release: Relation to renal sodium load and dissociation from hemodynamic changes. *Circ. Res.*, **22**, 473–87 (1968)

126. Vander, A. J., Luciano, J. R. Effects of mercurial diuresis and acute sodium depletion on renin release in dog. *Am. J. Physiol.*, **212**, 651–56 (1967)

127. Guntheroth, W. G., Morgan, B. C., Lintermans, J. P. Postural effects on lobar pulmonary and systemic flow: a flowmeter study in dogs. *J. Appl. Physiol.*, **23**, 859–64 (1967)

128. Caro, C. G., Bergel, D. H., Seed, W. A. Forward and backward transmission of pressure waves in the pulmonary vascular bed of the dog. *Circ. Res.*, **20**, 185–93 (1967)

129. Brody, J. S., Stemmler, E. J., DuBois, A. B. Longitudinal distribution of vascular resistance in the pulmonary arteries, capillaries, and veins. *J. Clin. Invest.*, **47**, 783–99 (1968)

130. Wilner, F., Morkin, E., Skalak, R., Fishman, A. P. Wave propagation in the pulmonary circulation. *Circ. Res.*, **19**, 834–50 (1966)

131. Pain, M. C. F., West, J. B. Effect of the volume history of the isolated lung on distribution of blood flow. *J. Appl. Physiol.*, **21**, 1545–50 (1966)

132. Lloyd, T. C., Jr. Analysis of the relation of pulmonary arterial or airway conductance to lung volume. *J. Appl. Physiol.*, **23**, 887–94 (1967)

133. Szidon, J. P., Ingram, R. H., Fishman, A. P. Origin of the pulmonary venous flow pulse. *Am. J. Physiol.*, **214**, 10–14 (1968)

134. Cohn, J. N., Pinderson, A. L., Tristani, F. E. Mechanism of pulses paradoxus in clinical shock. *J. Clin. Invest.*, **46**, 1744–55 (1967)

135. Myer, B. J., Myer, A., Guyton, A. C. Interstitial fluid pressure: V. Negative pressure in the lungs. *Circ. Res.*, **22**, 263–71 (1968)

136. Gaar, K. A., Jr., Taylor, A. E., Owens, L. J., Guyton, A. C. Effect of capillary pressure and plasma protein on development of pulmonary edema. *Am. J. Physiol.*, **213**, 79–82 (1967)

137. Levine, O. B., Mellins, R. B., Senior, R. M., Fishman, A. P. The application of Starling's law of capillary exchange to the lung. *J. Clin. Invest.*, **46**, 934–44 (1967)

138. Kahn, N., Mills, E. Centrally evoked sympathetic discharge: a functional study of medullary vasomotor areas. *J. Physiol. (London)*, **191**, 339–52 (1967)

139. Aoki, V. S., Brody, M. J. Medullary control of vascular resistance: An electrophysiological analysis. *Circ. Res.*, **18–19**, *Suppl. I*, 73–85 (1966)

140. Folkow, B., Lisander, B., Tuttler, R. S., Wang, S. C. Changes in cardiac output upon stimulation of the hypothalamic defense area and the medullary depressor area in the cat. *Acta Physiol. Scand.*, **72**, 220–33 (1968)

141. Emerson, T. E., Jr. Effects of angiotensin, epinephrine, norepinephrine, and vasopressin on venous return. *Am. J. Physiol.*, **210**, 933–42 (1966)

142. Taylor, M. G. Use of random excitation and spectral analysis in the study of frequency-dependent parameters of the cardiovascular system. *Circ. Res.*, **18**, 585–95 (1966)

143. Sagawa, K., Analysis of the ventricular pumping capacity as a function of input and output pressure loads (See Ref. 4), 141–48

144. Engelberg, J. Physiological regulation: The steady state. *Physiologist*, **9**, 69–88 (1968)

145. Koushanpour, E., McGee, J. P. Demodulation of electrical activity in the carotid sinus baroceptor nerve. *J. Appl. Physiol.*, **24**, 262–66 (1968)

HEMODYNAMICS[1]

By Paul C. Johnson

Department of Physiology, College of Medicine, University of Arizona
Tucson, Arizona

Dr. D. A. McDonald inaugurated this section on hemodynamics last year with the mild complaint that he had no precedent on which to base his discussion. In providing his successor with a precedent he has shown little mercy in making it one which is difficult to match or even approach in lucidity and candor.

Hemodynamics[2] may be classified as applied fluid mechanics but empirical and descriptive studies still provide most of the basic framework for our present understanding of this area. However, to appreciate more fully the significance of experimental findings, a good knowledge of the mechanics of fluids and elastic and plastic bodies is most useful. Unfortunately, the physiologist who attempts a detailed examination of the physical properties of the peripheral circulation finds himself beset by two difficulties: first, his formal training in mechanics is often not sufficient to allow a basic attack on the problem from the standpoint of fluid mechanics; second, if he is intrepid or foolhardy enough to remedy this deficiency he finds that many classical concepts in mechanics are not directly applicable to physiological problems. Sometimes this is due to certain "simplifying assumptions" which the physical scientist may find permissible but which the physiologist knows are not acceptable for his system. For example, Fung (2) points out that much of present elastic theory depends upon the assumption of an infinitesimal strain. This is not generally true of biological systems; therefore, computations of elastic modulus are inadequate for biological systems except within a narrow range, since the apparent modulus of elasticity varies greatly when the strain is a sizable fraction of the initial length. In addition, the rigorous analysis of nonhomogeneous, nonisotropic media is exceedingly complex. Simplifying assumptions in this regard may seriously compromise the validity of the analysis.

The analytical solution of the problem of a non-Newtonian liquid flowing in a pulsating nonsinusoidal manner through a series of branching, tapered tubes which possess complex rheological characteristics is not readily available. Much remains to be learned from experiment regarding the elastic.

---

[1] The survey of literature for this review was concluded in June 1968.

[2] A more inclusive term for the material to be covered here would be hemorheology, which includes the mechanics of the blood and the vessels, as expressed by Wayland (1).

viscous, and plastic properties of the wall material and of the fluid. However, certain portions of the system are being rigorously examined and we may expect these studies to lead to certain deductions regarding their contributions to the behavior of the total system. Fortunately the problem of hemodynamics not only holds the attention of physiologists but has attracted engineers and physical scientists as well, thus their experimental and theoretical techniques are being brought to bear on the problems of blood flow in the circulation. Since the literature of hemodynamics is increasingly taking on the character of the studies in engineering and physical sciences, those who would pursue research in this area need an understanding of some of the basic concepts of the physical sciences. A simple conceptual framework for understanding physical properties of tissues is presented in a monograph on rheology by Reiner (3).[3] Several interpretive articles by Wayland which discuss rheological concepts as applied to the microcirculation are also quite useful (1, 4, 5).

Since considerable emphasis was placed by Dr. McDonald upon the characteristics of the aorta and larger vessels, we will deal only lightly with that area and will attempt to summarize some of the current thinking regarding the rheology of the smaller segments of the circulation.

RHEOLOGY OF RED BLOOD CELLS

The mechanical properties of the red cell must be considered in any analysis of the flow properties of blood. Red cells twist and bend to form diverse shapes as they pass through the capillaries. Presumably the same is true in larger vessels as cells collide and deform under the influence of a velocity gradient. Yet when the stress is removed the cells return to their normal biconcave shape. Judging from the degree of deformation which the red cell undergoes in passing through the capillary, it would appear that the red cell is radically deformed when a small force or shear stress is applied.

However, the apparent flexibility of the red cell applies primarily to bending; it is more difficult to change the shape if red cell volume is altered in the process. Two recent symposia have brought conflicting views of red cell elastic properties and tensile strength into clearer focus. Rand points out (6) that the red cell can tolerate large bending strains without damage, but small tangential strains of the membrane cause rupture of the cell and hemolysis. From studies of tangential stress on the red cell, Rand deduces a viscosity for the red cell membrane of 10^7 to 10^{10} poise. He also concludes that the elastic modulus of the red cell membrane lies between 10^6 and 10^8 dynes/cm^2.

Fung (7) has examined the theoretical basis of red cell mechanical behavior and finds Rand's assumption that the red cell interior is liquid to be consistent with the known properties of red cells. Fung has, however, challenged Rand's computation of red cell membrane elastic modulus since that

---

[3] Now out of print but available from H. K. Lewis & Co., Ltd., London.

deduction was based on extrusion of red cells in a pipette from which the elastic modulus was computed by assuming the La Place relationship to hold. Fung contends that the La Place relationship is not applicable in this circumstance.

Fung & Tong (8) have recently considered the theory of the sphering of red cells. They have developed a rigorous mathematical solution of the sphering of a red cell under the assumption that the red cell is a fluid-filled shell which may swell into a perfect sphere in an appropriate hypotonic medium. They point out that a biconcave disc composed of material of constant elastic modulus cannot swell into a sphere without buckling at the equator. However, a red cell forms a perfect sphere. This indicates that the elastic modulus is not constant over the red cell surface but probably is increased in areas where stress is increased.

Burton (9) has considered the role which the mechanical properties of the red cell may play in determining its life span. He suggests that in the spleen there may be a filtering system which requires the red cells to pass through an orifice of small size. Young cells, he suggests, are more distensible and are able to squeeze through the restrictive opening without damage, but older, more fragile cells are hemolyzed and removed from the circulation.

A recent study by Canham & Burton (10) has shown that red cell diameter, area, and volume are linearly interrelated. They describe a theoretical, geometric parameter, *the minimum cylindrical diameter*, as the thinnest cylindrical channel through which individual cells could pass. This diameter has a value of 3.66 μ and represents the smallest channel through which 95 per cent of the cells could pass. In two splenectomized patients with hereditary spherocytosis, the minimal cylindrical diameter was increased to approximately 4.0 μ, which suggests that the severest restriction to red cell passage is located in the spleen.

Zajicek (11) has analyzed a simple model of red cell behavior by computer techniques. By assuming that red cell volume increases with age and that cells reaching a critical size or volume are eliminated from the system, he is able to mimic the behavior of the red cell population *in vivo*.

The matter of red cell deformation reduces ultimately to a basic question of the properties of the cell interior and the cell membrane. Studies of deformability of cells of other types have indicated that the surface charge of the membrane plays an important role in determining the mechanics of the cell. For example, in studying the deformability and electrophoretic mobilities of three types of cells, Weiss (12) has shown that the surface charge of the membrane is related to the deformability of the cells. Neuraminidase makes the cells more easily deformable and reduces their net negativity. The relation of this finding to red cell mechanics is not clear since Seaman & Swank (13) find no change in rheological characteristics of blood in the cone and plate viscometer after reducing surface charge with neuraminidase or uranyl nitrate. Viscometric measurements may not be the method of choice to determine flexibility of the red cell, however.

Rheology of Whole Blood

The rheological characteristics of whole blood may be analyzed in terms of the individual characteristics of the several constituents and their interactions. In a viscometer, red cells in saline behave as a nearly Newtonian fluid and show no yield shear stress (14). Plasma (15) behaves in a similar fashion. However, when red cells and plasma are combined, a yield shear stress appears. Studies of the properties of blood in a Couette viscometer by Merrill and associates have shown that the yield shear stress of blood is due to the aggregation of red cells and occurs only in the presence of fibrinogen (16). If fibrinogen is removed from the blood, the yield shear stress disappears and aggregation no longer occurs. Measurement of yield shear stress with the Couette viscometer must be done by extrapolation to zero of a plot of shear stress vs. shear rate.

At low rates of shear, blood flow can be described in terms of the Casson equation $\tau^{1/2} = a^{1/2}\dot{\gamma}^{1/2} + \tau_y^{1/2}$ where τ is the shear stress, $\dot{\gamma}$ is the gradient of shear, τ_y is the yield shear stress, and a is a constant related to the viscosity of the fluid. Inertial forces are neglected. Cokelet and co-workers (17) have determined from these studies that τ_y is about 0.02 dynes/cm² at a hematocrit of 40. The adherent force between red cells was computed on the basis of the Casson equation to be of the order of 3 dynes/cm². In a recent study using a balance method, Benis & Lacoste (18) found yield shear stresses one-half to one-third those reported by Merrill's group.

When blood is flowing at low rates of shear (less than 100 inverse sec) the apparent viscosity increases as the flow rate decreases. At a shear rate of 100 inverse sec the viscosity is approximately 6 centipoise, while at 0.1 inverse sec the apparent viscosity is 200 centipoise and at 0.01 inverse sec the viscosity is 800 centipoise (19). The tendency of red cells to form aggregates is reflected in the increase in apparent viscosity. The Casson equation was developed to describe the flow behavior of printing ink particles which would reversibly aggregate at low flows. With blood the equation fits the data satisfactorily below 20 inverse sec. Above 100 inverse sec blood behaves as a Newtonian fluid while 20 to 100 inverse sec is a transitional zone. Schmid-Schönbein et al. (20) have observed in a special transparent cone-plate viscometer that red cell aggregates formed at low shear rates but dispersed when the shear rate reached 46 sec⁻¹. The process was readily reversible.

Gelin and others (21) have shown that Dextran 40 alters the rheological characteristics of blood and have suggested that Dextran 40 reduces the aggregation tendency of blood. However, studies with the GDM viscometer indicate that Dextran 40 does not improve the rheological characteristics of blood (22) when hematocrit is held constant. On the other hand, studies on the optical properties of blood (23) indicate that the tendency toward cell aggregation is diminished by Dextran 40 in man and dog but not in rabbit. Thus the conclusions to be drawn from optical studies and rheological studies regarding the effects of Dextran 40 appear to conflict.

Goldsmith (24, 25) examined the behavior of red cell rouleaux under the microscope in a flowing stream and showed that the bending modulus of red cell aggregates is very low compared with that of fibers of comparable size.

Two recent studies have raised the question of the influence of red cell shape and size on its flow characteristics. Meiselman and co-workers (26) found that when human red cells were swollen in a hypotonic medium, the viscosity of the suspension decreased while the yield stress increased. This was true if the hematocrit was held constant. However, when the hematocrit was not adjusted back to control values after swelling, yield stress was greater in the hypotonic suspension but viscosity was about the same. By contrast, red cells in normal plasma show an increase in both yield stress and viscosity when the hematocrit is increased. The authors suggest that the fibrinogen bonding between red cells which presumably causes aggregation and a finite yield shear stress is more effective as the cells expand and the curvature of the surface decreases. The changes in viscosity would be a consequence of alteration in membrane stiffness and perhaps the viscosity of the cell contents as well. One would expect the swollen cells to be stiffer and thus the viscosity higher. However, the cell contents are more diluted and that may cause the viscosity of the suspension to decrease. Stone et al. (27) compared the relative viscosity of the elliptical cells of camel and llama with that of goat, sheep, dog, and human. With constant hematocrit the viscosity increased with decreasing cell size, in accordance with the findings reported above for human red cells. These findings were not altered when the studies were repeated with washed red cells in saline, which suggests that the protein content of the plasma was not a factor. The elliptical shape of camel and llama red cells did not appear to affect viscosity. Yield stress was not measured.

Blood Flow in Tubes

The rheological characteristics of blood have important consequences for its flow through the peripheral vessels. For example, the velocity of red cells in capillaries and adjacent vessels waxes and wanes from 0 to 5 mm/sec (28). During periods of low flow, aggregation in the arterioles and venules is evident. As flow starts and stops, there must be changes in the apparent viscosity of the blood. If flow stops completely in the microvessels, the yield stress of the blood would have to be exceeded before flow could resume. However, the yield stress is thought to be due to formation of a three-dimensional aggregate or structure of red cells. The importance of this factor would depend upon the vessel size and the flow rate.

It is not obvious that the yield stress measured in a viscometer or large tube would be important in flow through the capillary network. However, it might have an effect in the arterioles and be an important factor in the venules.

Whitmore's (29) analysis of some of the problems of red cells flowing through capillaries of dimensions comparable to those of the cells indicates that smaller cellular elements should accumulate behind larger ones in transit. This may be the cause of red cell "trains" often seen in the microcirculation (30). Sutera & Hochmuth (31) find in model experiments that rigid particles produce 30–40 per cent less pressure drop when in groups than the same particles would traveling separately. With respect to larger vessels, Deakin discusses (32–34) erythrocyte distribution in arterial blood flow and the possible effects of radial differences in the hematocrit. He points out that though blood may be almost Newtonian in large arteries, the fact there is a small non-Newtonian effect may alter erythrocyte distribution in the artery and produce hematocrit differences in the branches of the arterial tree.

Charm et al. (35) found that hemodynamic data on flow of blood through small tubes could be better related to a radial distribution model which assumed unequal concentration of red cells across the velocity profile than to a marginal zone model. This raises the venerable question of the supposed tendency of red cells to accumulate in the center of a tube. This so-called axial streaming of red cells has been observed in the microcirculation and in glass tubes by many workers. However, careful studies have brought the accuracy of these visual observations into question. Bloch (36) has clearly shown with high speed photography that what appears to be a cell-free marginal layer does contain red cells. Occasionally there are plasma gaps in the vicinity of the wall which at high speeds apparently give the visual impression of a cell-free layer in that area. Since there can be no red cells having their centers at the wall, it is quite possible that the hematocrit in the wall region is reduced (wall exclusion effect). Red cells apparently extend to the wall of a tube in which the blood is flowing as determined in studies with the flying spot microscope (37). Bayliss (38) found that the marginal zone, if one exists, is of the order of 1 to 2 μ wide in a tube of 78 μ diameter.

It is possible to obtain the impression under appropriate lighting of a cell-poor core in the center of the flow stream in small vessels, which would suggest that the cells may be congregated in a ring about a central core. Also Segré & Silberberg found that polymethyl methacrylate spheres would concentrate into an annulus when they flowed down a tube of uniform bore (39). Very high flow rates were required. However, this is a visual impression only in a red cell flow stream, for Wiederhielm (40) has shown that red cells are distributed throughout the flow stream. The appearance is probably due to red cell orientation in the flow stream as shown by Yanami et al. (41).

A further example of the deceptive nature of the apparent opacity of flowing red cells is pointed out in a recent paper by Hocherman & Palti (42). They performed extensive studies to compare the finger blood volume by plethysmography and simultaneously recorded photoelectric finger opacity. They found the patterns were similar but a quantitative correlation did not exist; in some instances plethysmographic volume increased while opacity decreased and vice versa. They conclude that the opacity record follows alterations in blood distribution between vessels, rather than blood volume changes. D'Agrosa & Hertzman (43) have recently studied the opacity pulse of individual minute arteries in several microcirculatory beds. The authors find an appropriate linear relation between flow in an arterial vessel and the opacity pulse. The mean opacity changes in accordance with the volume of a particular vessel.

In my own observations of the microcirculatory bed, the occurrence of red cell aggregation at low flows changes the red cell distribution to such a degree that an opacity reading could hardly be expected to follow volume changes. At low flows aggregation of red cells causes plasma gaps to form in the flow stream, making measurement of vessel diameter with the flying spot microscope difficult and sometimes impossible (37). A general measurement of opacity over a large region, as used in studies of the finger, would present this problem unless shear rate everywhere in the microcirculation was fast enough to prevent aggregates from forming. In studies of the reflection coefficient of blood with a fiber optic system, Mook and co-workers (44) found a significant effect of blood flow on the apparent oxygen saturation of the blood. Moreover, as flow increased from 0 to 10 ml per min in their system, reflection increased 2.5 times. As flow increased to 25 and 40 ml per min, there was a drop in the reflection coefficient. They suggest that the effect of flow on the reflection coefficient is due to rouleaux formation and secondarily to a directional effect on red cell orientation as a function of flow.

MORPHOLOGY OF THE VASCULATURE

A rigorous analysis of the mechanical properties of the terminal vascular bed depends in part upon a precise description of the geometry of the peripheral circulation. Anatomical studies unfortunately usually do not readily lend themselves to this kind of analysis.

In a recent paper, Wiedeman (45) discusses the geometry of the terminal vascular bed in the bat wing. In this vascular bed a major artery gives rise to a number of smaller arteries having a diameter about one half of the parent vessels. These branches send off small ramifications which are only about one fifth of the length of their parent vessels and in turn give rise to a relatively large number of arterioles having a diameter approximately one-third that of the small arteries. Wiedeman points out that the capillaries in this area are typically much smaller than ordinarily supposed, 4 to 6 μ. On the postcapillary side the smallest venules are formed by coalescence of capillary nets and are approximately twice as large as the capillaries. These vessels in turn join to form venules which are about $3 \times$ larger than the adjacent arterioles. In the bat wing the total cross-sectional area increases successively from the artery through the arteriolar capillary network and on to the postcapillary venules and the venules. Thus, an interesting finding in these studies is that the greatest cross-sectional area actually is found in the venules from whence it decreases both upstream and downstream.

A precise quantitative definition of the composition of the blood vessel wall would aid in understanding its mechanical properties. It would need to encompass not only the relative proportion of the constituents, but also the geometric arrangement of the components in the wall. Moreover, in the case of the microvessels (especially capillaries) the surrounding tissue matrix probably contributes a significant portion of the load-bearing ability (7). Wiederhielm (46) has analyzed the structure of arteriolar wall and finds it consists of endothelium, 20 per cent; internal elastic membrane, 4 per cent; smooth muscle, 55 per cent; and interstitial collagen, 21 per cent. Apter (47) found that isolated elastic lamellae of blood vessels had a larger circumference than the internal circumference of the same artery when intact and the lamellae were less wrinkled. The adventitia was twice the circumference of the elastic lamellae from the same vessel. The difference in initial length of these elements undoubtedly contributes to the observation that collagen has an important role at larger extensions. Associated studies of mechanical properties reveal that creep is associated more with muscle than elastin or collagen, the latter being of least importance.

The ultrastructure of the microvessels has been studied to varying degrees. The classical work of Bennett and co-workers (48) defined certain morphological characteristics of capillaries which could be related to the relative permeability and filtration characteristics of the organ involved. Rhodin (49) has combined light and electron microscope studies to determine the structure of the capillaries and the arterial tree. Arterioles of 100 μ internal diameter have a media 5 μ thick with several layers of smooth muscle arranged in a circular fashion within the wall. As the diameter decreases, the amount of smooth muscle is reduced and at 50 μ the intima is only one layer thick. Each cell appears to cover about one-tenth the vessel circumference. In 100 μ vessels the cells of the inner layer are pitched normal to the vessel axis while the outermost cells are spirally oriented at a pitch of 18° (72° to the vessel axis). The endothelial cells have a thickness of about 2 μ in the region of the nucleus and 0.15 μ elsewhere, with a large amount of filamentous material. Membrane contact is of the tight junction type. The elastica interna averages 0.3 μ in thickness. Collagen shows up in the adventitial layer as loosely arranged bundles of fibrils. Small collagen bundles also appear between muscle cells in the media. Clefts are seen on the surfaces of some muscle cells which apparently serve as an anchoring point for collagen.

Arterioles 50 μ or less have a single layer of smooth muscle cells 0.5 to 1.0 μ thick. They are wider and flatter than in larger vessels. A basement membrane surrounds each muscle cell but lateral contacts between smooth muscle are frequent, every cell making membrane contact with its neighbors.

Rhodin was especially impressed by the fact that in the small arterioles (usually about 30 μ) a direct membrane-to-membrane contact was occasionally established for a distance of 0.5 to 1.0 μ between the smooth muscle cell and the adjacent endothelial cell. At a level of 30 μ diameter the small arterioles give off branches of 10–15 μ inside diameter which taper to about

7 μ over a distance of 50–100 μ. These vessels branch in turn to form the capillary network. The muscle cells in the precapillary sphincter have a circular arrangement and are usually one or two in number. At this level the myoendothelial junctions become even more pronounced and numerous.

Electron microscopy has also demonstrated cross-striated fibrils in vascular endothelium which may have functional importance. Röhlich & Oláh (50) have demonstrated that endothelial cells of myometrial arterioles contain filaments in parallel arrays which have periodic dense bends similar to the Z-lines of the myofibril. They suggest that this structure may be contractile. However, the bundle lies parallel to the longitudinal axis of the arteriole, which would reduce the vessel lumen only indirectly, by shortening the endothelial cell and causing it to bulge inward. Moffat (51) has shown that the perivascular cells of the kidney, which lie between the ascending and descending vasa recta, contain fibrils which resemble myofibrils on the side facing the descending vessel and pinocytotic vesicles on the side facing the ascending vessel. Similar fibrillar structures have been reported by Bensch et al. (52) in pulmonary arterial vessels where the long axis of the filament was generally normal to the axis of the vessel. Majno (53) has noted similar structures in the endothelial cells of small venules and suggests that histamine causes these cells to contract, allowing partial detachment of intracellular connections and consequent plasma exudation. Thus it appears that the absence of smooth muscle cells in certain microvessels would not rule out the possibility of some type of contractile behavior. But there is no evidence that such contractile behavior actually changes the vessel diameter. Majno's hypothesis suggests that such contractile behavior would constitute a shutter mechanism, opening and closing a pathway for flow between plasma and interstitial fluid.

THE RHEOLOGICAL PROPERTIES OF ARTERIAL VESSELS

Typically blood vessels exhibit elastic, plastic, and viscous behavior. Attempts have been made to relate these properties to the principal constituents of the blood vessel wall: smooth muscle, elastin, and collagen. However, the mechanical behavior of the arterial vessels, at least in the microcirculation, may be determined in part by the make-up of the surrounding tissues (7). Recent studies by Apter (47) and by Kimoto & Goto (54) have emphasized the separate roles of the individual constituents of the blood vessel wall in determining its mechanical properties. Apter compared the mechanical properties of aorta and pulmonary artery with isolated elastin, collagen, and smooth muscle at temperatures between 0 and 70° C. Intact arteries stimulated by phenylephrine and stretched to a moderate degree behave like smooth muscle. When the artery was stretched to a greater degree (20–70 per cent) it behaved like elastin, while arteries stretched to a very high degree (100 per cent) behaved like collagen. The load-bearing function of collagen was not discernible until the internal pressure had exceeded 300 mm Hg. These findings thus assign a much lesser role to collagen in determining the mechanics of blood vessels than Roach & Burton (55) previously suggested.

Kimoto & Goto performed their studies on aorta of the toad. They also found that the mechanical characteristics of the blood vessel resembled those of elastin with about 40 per cent extension while they resembled those of collagen when the vessel was stretched in the vicinity of 100 per cent. Hysteresis loops of the toad aorta and vena abdominalis became small at normal temperature while they increased greatly at low (2 to 5° C) and at high temperatures (40 to 42° C). These loops bore certain similarities to the behavior of tendon and to vessels treated with formic acid. Laszt (56) has studied the elastic properties of the carotids and various peripheral blood vessels in the relaxed and contracted states. The elastic modulus of blood vessels varies with the mode and degree of contraction. The elastic properties were different when the vessels were stimulated with KCl and when they were excited with catecholamines. Moreover the carotids behave differently from other blood vessels. But in all cases the contracted vessel, when put under a tension similar to that encountered with normal blood pressure, yielded a smaller modulus of elasticity than the relaxed vessel.

Leitz & Arndt (57) have studied the diameter-pressure relationship of unexposed carotid arteries by an X-ray technique. They found that the pulsatile changes in artery diameter were approximately 15 per cent, a value larger than reported in exposed or isolated arteries (58). The authors suggest that manipulation of arteries causes constriction and reduction of distensibility.

Dynamic renal arterial compliance and conductance have been examined recently by Rothe & Nash (59) using on-line computation of parameters in an analog model. These workers were able to predict the renal arterial flow pattern, the arterial compliance, and preglomerular conductance from the measured renal arterial pressure pulse pattern. The model consists of large artery resistance, inertance and compliance, preglomerular arteriolar conductance, and a steady glomerular pressure.

Knowledge of the mechanical properties of arterioles and other precapillary elements in the microcirculation is quite limited. Baez, Lamport & Baez some years ago (60) described the dimensional changes of arterioles, metarterioles, and precapillary sphincters with changes in static pressure head. They found that vessels retracted as pressure was reduced although in some vessels a region of pressure was found in which no dimensional change occured. This "flat-top phenomenon" they related to active adjustments in the contractile state of the smooth muscle (myogenic response). Baez has recently utilized a television split-image technique to follow these changes precisely (61). Wiederhielm (46) has investigated the mechanical properties of frog mesenteric arterioles, using a television scanning system and a servo-controlled system for inflating a segment of arteriole to the desired pressure. In these studies all arterioles were passive, that is, diameter increased as a function of pressure over the full range. The elastic modulus increased with strain from 1.2×10^6 dynes/cm^2 with 5 per cent strain to 45×10^6 dynes/cm^2 with 31 per cent strain. The nonlinear elastic properties of the arteriole thus resemble those of large arteries and other types of tissue as well.

From an associated study of the wall structure and consideration of the elastic modulus of smooth muscle, collagen, elastin, and endothelium, Wiederhielm concludes that the stiffness of the relaxed vessel is due almost entirely to collagen. When the vessel was stimulated to contract with epinephrine, the viscosity of the vessel increased dramatically; a fortyfold change was seen at zero strain. Wiederhielm points out that an arrangement of springs and dashpots is not a satisfactory mechanical model for the arteriole. He suggests instead a reaction rate kinetic model in which transition of contractile elements from a long to a short state occurs in a single step.

The pressure-diameter relations of arterioles in cat mesentery have recently been reported from our laboratory (62); primary emphasis was on the autoregulatory phenomenon. When arterial pressure was reduced, the arteriole first became smaller, and then dilated. Assuming arteriolar pressure was a constant fraction of large artery pressure, tension-radius diagrams were constructed for autoregulatory vessels. This analysis showed that the stress-strain diagram for an autoregulating arteriole is actually a family of curves. At low pressures, the vessel follows the distensibility curve for a relaxed vessel. At moderate pressures the curve followed is that for a partially contracted vessel, while under high pressures the vessel behaves as if the smooth muscle is strongly contracted. When arterial pressure is suddenly altered, the diameter of the arteriole changes along the stress-strain curve appropriate to the existing state of vascular tone. However, if the new pressure is maintained for more than 5 sec, the smooth tone changes and the vessel shifts to a new curve reflecting the altered mechanical properties.

Hochberger & Zweifach (63) have examined experimentally the evidence for *critical closing pressure* in the rabbit ear. Critical closure could not be demonstrated in ears taken from rabbits pretreated with phenoxybenzamine and in a state of low vascular tone, during perfusion either with plasma having a vasoconstrictor action or with an albumin solution lacking vasotonic properties. They found that flow stopped in the system at a perfusion of approximately 3 cm H_2O with both perfusing fluids and attribute this stoppage to back pressure from the venous system caused by surface tension effects at the outflow orifice rather than by critical closure.

The rheological properties of the cardiovascular system have lately been considered from the standpoint of optimal design. Taylor (64) has pointed out that the distribution of elastic properties and other features of the arterial system permit circulation of blood by the heart with a minimum expenditure of energy. Crowell & Smith (65) have considered the optimal blood viscosity and hematocrit for efficient oxygen transport; in both instances they assumed that the primary role of the system is to deliver nutrients to the tissues. The delivery of an appropriate pressure to each capillary bed should also be important in design considerations.

RHEOLOGY OF THE VENOUS SYSTEM

The mechanical properties of the venous vessels have usually been examined from the standpoint of their role as the capacitance part of the vascular system. However, this portion of the network also plays an important role in determining the pressure in the capillary bed and thus in the exchange of fluid between blood and tissue.

Alexander (66) has examined the mechanical properties of a strip of portal vein which is alternately stretched and relaxed. He found the work dissipated in the stretch cycle to be described by the expression $a + b(c)^x$ where x is the unstretched muscle length. Catecholamines and other vasoactive agents gave solutions to the equation in which a, b, and c were unchanged. If a second contractile mechanism were activated by any of these agents, a change in the constants would have been expected. Potassium did produce a different pattern compatible with the notion of a second contractile system at very high concentrations of the ion. In further studies (67) the viscous resistance to stretch was evaluated from the work dissipated in the stretch cycle. Elevations of the concentration of calcium in the bathing medium increased viscous resistance to stretch. The results suggest that calcium may be involved in the excitation of the contractile machinery or the inhibition of a relaxing factor.

Ardill and co-workers (68) indicate that changes in volume of a congested limb may be used to study active changes in the capacitance portion of the vascular network in instances where the associated change in blood flow is a reduction from the basal level rather than an increase. Walker et al. (69) observed that during acute venous occlusion of the forearm, plethysmographic blood flow records show a biphasic vascular response consisting first of a vasodilator reaction and then vasoconstriction. Their results suggest that in the vasodilator phase there may be accumulation of vasodilator material as well as a physical distention of the blood vessels. The constrictor phase was thought to be a myogenic response to the increase in wall tension. The pattern of inflow may influence the rapid and slow phases of vascular filling, which suggests that computations of capacity by this technique should be interpreted in this light. Öberg (70) indicates that the relative contribution of active constriction and passive recoil of the veins differs radically at various distending pressures. At high venous pressures nervous stimulation causes a reduction in blood flow and in volume of the organ. Secondary to the reduction in blood flow there is a decrease in the internal pressure of the veins leading to a passive recoil. However, the diminution of volume in this circumstance is due more to an active constriction of the smooth muscle in the wall than to a decrease in internal pressure. However, when venous pressure is low the relative importance of these two factors is reversed: that of the passive recoil of the veins is considerable, that of the active constriction minimal.

Nagle et al. (71) have studied the changes in venous resistance in skin and skeletal muscle under various circumstances. They find that venous resistance is importantly determined by transmural pressure, although the relation was not invariant. In most instances venous resistance fell as venous pressure rose, but not during reactive hypermia. Zsotér et al. (72) found the distensibility of veins taken from patients with varicosities to be markedly greater than in control groups. This was true whether the segment studied was varicose or not. Hysteresis was also greater in vessels from varicose subjects. Lutz et al. (73) recently explored the hemodynamic changes in the liver circulation that result from pressure changes in each of the three vascular circuits. Elevation of hepatic vein pressure caused an increase in hepatic arterial resistance, but portal pressure elevation was more effective. The authors conclude that a myogenic response of the arterial vessels produces the change in resistance when venous pressure is altered. These findings agree with earlier reports (74, 75). Dorr & Brody (76) have studied the hemodynamic mechanisms involved in penile erection. Their results do not support the notion that mechanical compression of venous drainage is responsible. Rather, the magnitude of the increased blood flow seemed sufficient to explain erection.

Extravascular Hydrostatic Pressure

The pressure outside the vascular tree is an important determinant of vessel diameter and thus of blood flow. Shulman & Verdier (77) have studied the effect of cerebrospinal fluid (CSF) pressure on cerebral blood flow. In the range studied (0–40 cm H_2O), alterations in CSF pressure did not influence steady-state blood flow. Simultaneous measurement of subarachnoid venous pressure enabled the authors to show that venous resistance fell as CSF pressure was elevated. These findings may be explained in terms of autoregulatory dilatation of arterioles and passive collapse of the veins.

Elevation of ureteral pressure is known to cause a marked dilatation of blood flow (78). Hársing and co-workers (79) found that this increase in flow was accompanied by a reduction in extraction of PAH and in magnitude of flow as determined by ^{86}Rb. They suggest therefore that the increase in flow is due to the opening of shunts. Gray & Staub (80, 81) have investigated the effect of skeletal muscle contraction on the vasculature: Blood flow fell as muscle tension rose; the former could be due to a rise in tissue pressure. The microcirculation opened during tetany but the larger arterioles and veins were often compressed and pinched as they entered the muscle mass or passed between fasciculi. Thus the increase in vascular resistance during muscle contraction is chiefly a consequence of closure of large vessels, rather than of compression of the microcirculation.

Flow in the Microcirculation

The matter of intra-organ flow distribution was mentioned above with respect to ureteral pressure elevation. The question of shunt flow vs. capillary flow is one aspect of this problem. Friedman (82) has measured ^{86}Rb uptake by skeletal muscle under conditions of regulated flow. Under control conditions Rb extraction is inversely related to flow. There is, moreover, incomplete extraction at low flow rates and a positive intercept at zero flow. However, Friedman suggests that this inverse relation does not mean that Rb extraction is flow limited. In further studies of extraction during papaverine infusion and reactive hyperemia, he finds extraction to be very nearly independent of flow rate. The existence of a positive intercept suggests that impermeable shunts exist in the microcirculation, while the variation of extraction with flow in the control situation suggests that flow shifts from the shunts to the capillary network at low flows.

Sejrsen & Tønneson (83) measured blood flow in the gastrocnemius muscle by direct and isotopic (^{133}Xe) methods. They found fairly good agreement between the two techniques, indicating that shunts do not exist in the skeletal muscle. The deviation of their clearance curves from true exponentials they suggest is due to counter-current exchange between vessels rather than shunt flow. Renkin has studied ^{86}Rb and ^{42}K uptake by skeletal muscle in a variety of circumstances. In reviewing his findings (84), he notes that the quantity PS (the product of permeability times surface area of exchange vessels) changes greatly as vasomotor activity is altered. Measurements of PS indicate that about 50 per cent of the capillary surface is functional in the control state. Under conditions of sympathetic vasoconstriction 25 per cent or fewer of the capillaries are open, while in metabolic vasodilatation (exercise) the entire bed is open. He proposes that this variation is due to opening or closure of precapillary sphincters.

Changes in capillary surface area may also be assessed from the capillary filtration coefficient (CFC). Kjellmer has found a large increase in CFC of skeletal muscle with exercise (85), which he attributes to opening of precapillary sphincters. Dresel et al. (86) measured simultaneously the PS product and capillary filtration coefficient (CFC) in the cat intestine. During sympathetic stimulation, CFC fell more than PS, hence the former may be the more sensitive index of change in available capillary surface.

Sonnenschein et al. (87) have studied effects of a variety of vasoactive agents on the hemodynamics of the isolated perfused gastrocnemius-soleus. They find evidence that isoproterenol and histamine cause redistribution of blood in the parallel flow channels of muscle. Acetylcholine may have a similar effect but in addition it appears to reduce the number of capillaries being perfused.

Studies at the microcirculatory level are required to answer the question of what element or elements control flow distribution in skeletal muscle. There are no data presently available on skeletal muscle; however, studies on capillary flow in the mesentery which we performed with Dr. Harold Wayland may provide a partial answer (28). We found that when arterial pressure to the mesentery was reduced, flow in the true capillaries was maintained or even increased in some instances. This must have occurred at the expense of flow through other channels since total blood flow through the intestine decreases as arterial pressure is reduced (88). The finding would explain Friedman's observation that extraction increased as flow was reduced.

Observations on isotope extraction from other vascular beds indicate different vascular behavior. Häggendal & Sivertsson (89) studied the extraction of ^{85}Kr by the salivary gland, before, during, and after chorda tympani stimulation. They found no evidence of shunt flow in this organ.

Kampp and co-workers (90) have examined the ^{85}Kr washout curves of the cat small intestine. The elimination curve could be resolved into four components whose individual natures could be determined. The first (most rapid) component appears to reflect a countercurrent exchange between arterial and venous blood in the mucosa. The second component reflects flow through the mucosa, while the third is attributed to muscularis flow. The fourth component is attributed to perivascular fat in the mesentery and absorption from the intestinal lumen. In further studies (91) Kampp & Lundgren determined the fractional distribution of the total flow among the several tissue areas. In the resting state, 70–80 per cent of flow is through mucosa and submucosa with most of the remainder through the muscularis. When the flow rate is increased by isopropylnorepinephrine, the proportion of total flow to the mucosa-submucosa increases and that to the muscularis decreases.

CAPILLARY FILTRATION AND PERMEABILITY

Present-day concepts of the hydrodynamics of the capillary membrane are based on the original hypothesis of Starling, its experimental verification by Landis, and its elaboration in terms of the pore theory by Pappenheimer. While electron microscopists have not identified channels which could be considered as pores through the endothelial cells lining the capillary, the intercellular junction remains an area highly suspect (92). As improved quantitative techniques for study of the microcirculation are developed, it is inevitable that our present understanding will be vastly improved. Vargas & Johnson (93) have studied the permeability characteristics of rabbit heart capillaries to nonelectrolytes. They weighed the heart during coronary perfusion and suddenly introduced an osmotically active material into the perfusion solution. The heart then lost weight as a function of time. The weight transient was analyzed to determine the capillary permeability coefficients. Values obtained varied from 0.5×10^{-5} cm sec^{-1} for insulin to 9.7×10^{-5} for urea. The results are consistent with the pore theory of capillary permeability. The technique represents a promising new approach to a difficult problem.

The manner in which large molecules pass the capillary membrane has recently been quantified in the frog mesentery by Wiederhielm (94) using a TV-microscope system. Diffusible dyes were injected into the circulation and their rate of movement into the tissue spaces was followed from the change in optical density. From this data the diffusion coefficient for the dye in the tissue was derived. Another interesting aspect of this study was the observation that the dye diffused across the wall of the venules most rapidly, next it appeared outside the venous capillary, and finally it crossed the wall of the arterial capillary. In further studies (95), Wiederhielm measured the rate of water movement out of single capillaries in response to an osmotically active solution placed on the mesentery. He found that water moved out of the venous capillary twice as fast as the arterial capillary. Water permeated the venular walls as well, moving out of these vessels as rapidly as it did from the arterial capillaries.

In a recent report, Zweifach & Intaglietta (96) have reviewed their findings on movement of fluid across the walls of single capillaries in rat and rabbit omentum. The filtration constant was lower on the arterial side of the capillary (2 to 8 $\times$ 10^{-3} μ/sec) than on the venous side (16 to 25 $\times$ 10^{-3} μ/ sec). This finding, in agreement with Wiederhielm's results, suggests that the center of fluid exchange is located on the venous side of the capillaries. But they also found the hydrostatic pressure in the capillaries is well above the colloid osmotic pressure of the plasma, which suggests a constant outward movement of fluid across the capillary wall. This finding is somewhat puzzling unless one assumes the venules are involved in the filtration process, since volumetric and gravimetric techniques have ordinarily shown that the organs under study will assume a constant volume if arterial and venous pressures are normal. They also point out that the mean capillary pressure as determined by the isogravimetric technique (88) may not represent the midpoint of the capillaries but may be situated in the venous portion of the capillary bed. However, the precise location of the filtration mid-point would also depend upon the pressure profile in the capillaries.

Diana et al. (97) have reported a modification of the weight technique for determining capillary filtration. The limb was made isogravimetric before and after a period of increased venous pressure; the difference in limb weight in the two isogravimetric periods represents the amount of fluid filtered while venous pressure was elevated. This technique obviates some of the problems encountered in using the slope of the slow component of weight gain to measure filtration.

Solomon & Hinshaw (98) have found that endotoxin reduces the isogravimetric mean capillary pressure of the forelimb from 16 mm Hg in the control state to 6 mm Hg 4 hr post endotoxin and 9 mm Hg 20 hr post endotoxin. The authors suggest that endotoxin changes capillary permeability by a direct effect or indirectly by ischemia. The reduction in isogravimetric capillary pressure could be due in part to the loss of limb weight known to occur after endotoxin (99). Absorption of water from the tissue spaces ought to increase the colloid osmotic pressure of the interstitial fluid, creating an isogravimetric state at low capillary pressure.

STRUCTURAL AND RHEOLOGICAL PROPERTIES OF THE LUNG

The hemodynamic properties of the lung differ in many important respects from those of the peripheral circulation, in part, perhaps, because of the geometry of the blood vessels. The pulmonary vessels are usually considered to branch dichotomously. However, Sobin & Tremer (100) found right-angle branchings in the arterial and venous microvasculature. This perpendicular branching begins in vessels of 500 μ diameter and is repeated down to, but does not include, the capillary level. The pulmonary vasculature thus forms an orthogonal network. The pulmonary capillaries have been ordinarily described as a parallel series of interconnected cylinders but in Sobin's preparations the capillaries appeared as endothelial sheets separated and supported by numerous septa. Recently Sobin & Fung (101, 102) have explored the nature of "sheet flow" which would occur in such a network.

The lung is also unique in that its large dimensions, coupled with the low perfusion pressure, cause a wide variation in flow distribution within the organ. In recent studies of this phenomenon, Maloney and co-workers (103) investigated the effect of pulsatile arterial pressure on the distribution of blood flow in the isolated dog lung. The pattern of blood flow varied during pulsatile perfusion with more blood passing through the upper zones of the lung during pulsatile as opposed to nonpulsatile perfusion. However, as the frequency of the pulsation increased from 0.03 to 3 Hz the flow pattern changed and the height to which the blood rose in the lung decreased. At low frequencies the blood rose to a level corresponding to approximately 70 per cent of the peak arterial hydrostatic pressure. At upper frequencies this was reduced to 30 per cent. The authors suggest that transmission of artery pressure pulse by the blood vessels of the lung is frequency dependent and this alters distribution of blood flow in the lung.

The Johns Hopkins group has reported recently on further studies of the vascular waterfall effect in the lung (104). Blood flow stopped when pulmonary artery pressure equaled alveolar pressure if transpulmonary pressure was about 5 mm Hg. If blood pH was lowered or P_{CO_2} of the alveolar gas was increased, blood flow stopped at a higher pressure level, i.e., before pulmonary artery pressure had fallen to alveolar pressure. The authors suggest that high CO_2 or increased acidity cause *critical closure* in the pulmonary vessels. Their use of the term critical closure may not be appropriate since they did not demonstrate the fundamental condition of instability which Burton postulated would exist in small muscular vessels at low pressure (105). Their evidence is convincing for *closure*[4] of small vessels at low pressures with high CO_2 or reduced pH. But vessels may close for reasons other than Burton's postulate.

McDonald & Butler (106) have used the vascular waterfall effect to assess the pressure drop in arterial, capillary, and venous segments of the isolated perfused dog lung. They find that the major site of vascular resistance varies with the rate of blood flow and the proportion of alveolar vessels which are in the collapsed state. As flow increases, the perfusion pressure

---

[4] Closure in these experiments must be considered in a functional sense; that is, when the vessel lumen is too narrow for red cells to pass, the flow of whole blood will cease.

rises, apparently because of the increased pressure drop across the arterial and venous portions of the circuit. If venous pressure was high enough to keep all alveolar vessels open, pressure drops across all these segments of the vasculature were approximately equal when flow was 500 ml/min. When all the alveolar vessels were in the waterfall state, the pressure drop in the capillary network accounted for about 80 per cent of the total pressure gradient in the system.

Gaar et al. (107) determined by the isogravimetric technique that the mean capillary pressure in the dog lung averaged 7 mm Hg, while vascular resistance was divided between the arterial and venous segments in the ratio of 56 per cent to 44 per cent. Before the determination was made, the lung was allowed to collapse to its minimal volume so that alveolar pressure was zero.

Miscellany.—The search for a painless and simple method of measuring circulatory function in the periphery received another setback with the publication of a critical analysis of electrical impedance techniques used in some laboratories as a tool for plethysmography (108). According to Hill and co-workers (109) this technique cannot be calibrated for plethysmographic measurements and responds primarily to changes in outward directed pressure from the tissue onto the electrode. The effects of blood volume upon tissue impedance are, according to their studies, too small to be measured accurately.

LITERATURE CITED

1. Wayland, H. Rheology and microcirculation. *Bibl. Anat.*, **5**, 2–22 (1965)
2. Fung, Y. C. Elasticity of soft tissues in simple elongation. *Am. J. Physiol.*, **213**, 1532–44 (1967)
3. Reiner, M. *Deformation, Strain and Flow* (Interscience, 2nd ed., 1960)
4. Wayland, H. Rheological measurements applicable to the microcirculation. *Bibl. Anat.*, **5**, 33–46 (1965)
5. Wayland, H. Rheology and the microcirculation. *Gastroenterology*, **52**, 342–55 (1967)
6. Rand, R. P. Some biophysical considerations of the red cell membrane. *Fed. Proc.*, **26**, 1780–84 (1967)
7. Fung, Y. C. Theoretical considerations of the elasticity of red cells and small blood vessels. *Fed. Proc.*, **25**, 1761–72 (1966)
8. Fung, Y. C. B., Tong, P. Theory of the sphering of red blood cells. *Biophys. J.*, **8**, 175–98 (1968)
9. Burton, A. C. Role of geometry, of size and shape, in the microcirculation. *Fed. Proc.*, **25**, 1753–60 (1966)
10. Canham, P. B., Burton, A. C. Distribution of size and shape in populations of normal human red cells. *Circ. Res.*, **22**, 405–22 (1968)
11. Zajicek, G. A computer model simulating the behavior of adult red blood cells. Red cell model. *J. Theoret. Biol.*, **19**, 51–66 (1968)
12. Weiss, L. Studies on cell deformability: V. Some effects of ribonuclease. *J. Theoret. Biol.*, **18**, 9–18 (1968)
13. Seaman, G. V. F., Swank, R. L. The influence of electrokinetic charge and deformability of the red blood cell on the flow properties of its suspensions. *Biorheology*, **4**, 47–59 (1967)
14. Wells, R. E., Jr., Merrill, E. W., Gabelnick, H. Shear rate dependence of visosity of blood: Interaction of red cells and plasma proteins. *Trans. Soc. Rheol.*, **6**, 19–24 (1962)
15. Merrill, E. W., Benis, A. M., Gilliland, E. R., Sherwood, T. K., Salzman, E. W. Pressure-flow relations of

human blood in hollow fibers at low flow rates. *J. Appl. Physiol.*, **20**, 954–67 (1965)

16. Merrill, E. W., Gilliland, E. R., Lee, T. S., Salzman, E. W. Blood rheology: effect of fibrinogen deduced by addition. *Circ. Res.*, **18**, 437–46 (1966)

17. Cokelet, G. R., Merrill, E. W., Gilliland, E. R., Shin, H., Britten, A., Wells, R. E., Jr. Rheology of human blood: measurement near and at zero shear rate. *Trans. Soc. Rheol.*, **7**, 303–17 (1963)

18. Benis, A. M., Lacoste, J. Study of erythrocyte aggregation by blood viscometry at low shear rates using a balance method. *Circ. Res.*, **22**, 29–41 (1968)

19. Replogle, R. L., Meiselman, H. J., Merrill, E. W. Clinical implications of blood rheology studies. *Circulation*, **36**, 148–60 (1967)

20. Schmid-Schönbein, H., Gaehtgens, P., Hirsch, H. On the shear rate dependence of red cell aggregation in vitro. *J. Clin. Invest.*, **47**, 1447–54 (1968)

21. Gelin, L-E., Ingelman, B. Rheomacrodex—a new dextran solution for rheological treatment of impaired capillary flow. *Acta Chir. Scand.*, **122**, 294–302 (1961)

22. Meiselman, H. J., Merrill, E. W., Salzman, E. W., Gilliland, E. R., Pelletier, G. A. Effect of dextran on rheology of human blood: low shear viscometry. *J. Appl. Physiol.*, **22**, 480–86 (1967)

23. Engeset, J., Stalker, A. L., Matheson, N. A. Objective measurement of the dispersing effect of Dextran 40 on red cells from man, dog, and rabbit. *Cardiovasc. Res.*, **1**, 385–88 (1967)

24. Goldsmith, H. L. Red cells and rouleaux in shear flow. *Science*, **153**, 1406–7 (1966)

25. Goldsmith, H. L. Microscopic flow properties of red cells. *Fed. Proc.*, **26**, 1813–20 (1967)

26. Meiselman, H. J., Merrill, E. W., Gilliland, E. R., Pelletier, G. A., Salzman, E. W. Influence of plasma osmolarity on the rheology of human blood. *J. Appl. Physiol.*, **22**, 772–81 (1967)

27. Stone, H. O., Thompson, H. K., Jr., Schmidt-Nielsen, K. Influence of erythrocytes on blood viscosity. *Am. J. Physiol.*, **214**, 913–18 (1968)

28. Johnson, P. C., and Wayland, H. Regulation of blood flow in single capillaries. *Am. J. Physiol.*, **212**, 1405–15 (1967)

29. Whitmore, R. L. A theory of blood flow in small vessels. *J. Appl. Physiol.*, **22**, 767–71 (1967)

30. Monro, P. A. G. The appearance of cell-free plasma and "grouping" of red cells in normal circulation in small vessels observed in vivo. *Biorheology*, **1**, 239–46 (1963)

31. Sutera, S. P., Hochmuth, R. M. Large scale modeling of blood flow in the capillaries. *Biorheology*, **5**, 45–73 (1968)

32. Deakin, M. A. B. Erythrocyte distribution in arterial blood ffow: I. Basic equations and anisotropic effects. *Bull. Math. Biophys.*, **29**, 549–63 (1967)

33. Deakin, M. A. B. Erythrocyte distribution in arterial blood flow: II. The hypothesis of minimal energy dissipation. *Bull. Math. Biophys.*, **29**, 565–74 (1967)

34. Deakin, M. A. B. Erythrocyte distribution in arterial blood flow: III. Physiological considerations. *Bull. Math. Biophys.*, **29**, 649–56 (1967)

35. Charm, S. E., Kurland, G. S., Brown, S. L. The influence of radial distribution and marginal plasma layer on flow of red cell suspensions. *Biorheology*, **5**, 15–44 (1968)

36. Bloch, E. H. A quantitative study of the hemodynamics in the living microvascular system. *Am. J. Anat.*, **110**, 125–53 (1962)

37. Johnson, P. C. Measurement of microvascular dimensions in vivo. *J. Appl. Physiol.*, **23**, 593–96 (1967)

38. Bayliss, L. E. The flow of suspensions of red blood cells in capillary tubes. Changes in the 'cell free' marginal sheath with changes in the shearing stress. *J. Physiol.*, **179**, 1–25 (1965)

39. Segré, G., Silberberg, A. Radial particle displacements in poiseuille flow of suspensions. *Nature*, **189**, 209–10 (1961)

40. Wiederhielm, C. A., Billig, L. Effects of erythrocyte orientation and concentration on light transmission through blood flowing through microscopic blood vessels. In *Proc. 1st Intern. Conf. Hemorheol.* (Copley, A. L., Ed., Pergamon, New York, 1968)

41. Yanami, Y., Intaglietta, M., Frasher,

W. G., Jr., Wayland, H. Photo-metric study of erythrocytes in shear flow. *Biorheology*, **2**, 165–68 (1964)

42. Hocherman, S., Palti, Y. Correlation between blood volume and opacity changes in the finger. *J. Appl. Physiol.*, **23**, 157–62 (1967)

43. D'Agrosa, L. S., Hertzman, A. B. Opacity pulse of individual minute arteries. *J. Appl. Physiol.*, **23**, 613–20 (1967)

44. Mook, G. A., Osypka, P., Sturm, R. E., Wood, E. H. Fibre optic reflection photometry on blood. *Cardiovasc. Res.*, **2**, 199–209 (1968)

45. Wiedeman, M. P. Architecture of the terminal vascular bed. *Physical Bases of Circulatory Transport: Regulation and Exchange*, 307–12 (Saunders, Philadelphia, 1967)

46. Wiederhielm, C. A. Distensibility characteristics of small blood vessels. *Fed. Proc.*, **24**, 1075–84 (1965)

47. Apter, J. T. Correlation of viscoelastic properties with microscopic structure of large arteries: IV. Thermal responses of collagen, elastin, smooth muscle, and intact arteries. *Circ. Res.*, **21**, 901–18 (1967)

48. Bennett, H. S., Luft, J. H., Hampton, J. C. Morphological classifications of vertebrate blood capillaries. *Am. J. Physiol.*, **196**, 381–90 (1959)

49. Rhodin, J. A. G. The ultrastructure of mammalian arterioles and precapillary sphincters. *J. Ultrastruct. Res.*, **18**, 181–223 (1967)

50. Röhlich, P., Oláh, I. Cross-striated fibrils in the endothelium of the rat myometrial arterioles. *J. Ultrastruct. Res.*, **18**, 667–76 (1967)

51. Moffat, D. B. The fine structure of the blood vessels of the renal medulla with particular reference to the control of the medullary circulation. *J. Ultrastruct. Res.*, **19**, 532–45 (1967)

52. Bensch, K. G., Gordon, G. B., Miller, L. Fibrillar structures resembling leiomyofibrils in endothelial cells of mammalian pulmonary blood vessels. *Z. Zellforsch.*, **63**, 759–66 (1964)

53. Majno, G., Gilmore, V., Leventhal, M. On the mechanism of vascular leakage caused by histamine-type mediators. *Circ. Res.*, **21**, 833–47 (1967)

54. Kimoto, Y., Goto, M. The effects of temperature on tension, hysteresis loop and stress-relaxation of the blood vessels. *Japan. J. Physiol.*, **17**, 365–76 (1967)

55. Roach, M. R., Burton, A. C. Reason for the shape of the distensibility curves of arteries. *Can. J. Biochem. Physiol.*, **35**, 681–90 (1957)

56. Laszt, L. Untersuchungen über die elastischen Eigenschaften der Blutgefässe im Ruhe- und im Kontraktionszustand. *Angiologica*, **5**, 14–27 (1968)

57. Leitz, K. H., Arndt, J. O. Die Durchmesser-Druck-Beziehung des intakten Gefässgebietes der A. carotis communis von Katzen. *Pflügers Arch.*, **301**, 50–69 (1968)

58. Peterson, L. H., Jensen, R. E., Parnell, J. Mechanical properties of arteries in vivo. *Circ. Res.*, **8**, 622–39 (1960)

59. Rothe, C. F., Nash, F. D. Renal arterial compliance and conductance measurement using on-line self-adaptive analog computation of model parameters. *Med. Biol. Engr.*, **6**, 53–69 (1968)

60. Baez, S., Lamport, H., Baez, A. Pressure effects in living microscopic vessels. In *Flow Properties of Blood*, 122–36 (Pergamon, New York, 1960)

61. Baez, S. Vascular smooth muscle: quantitation of cell thickness in the wall of arterioles in the living animal in situ. *Science*, **159**, 536–38 (1968)

62. Johnson, P. C. Autoregulatory responses of cat mesenteric arterioles measured in vivo. *Circ. Res.*, **22**, 199–212 (1968)

63. Hochberger, A. I., Zweifach, B. W. Analysis of critical closing pressure in the perfused rabbit ear. *Am. J. Physiol.*, **214**, 962–68 (1968)

64. Taylor, M. G. The elastic properties of arteries in relation to the physiological functions of the arterial system. *Gastroenterology*, **52**, 358–63 (1967)

65. Crowell, J. W., Smith, E. E. Determinant of the optimal hematocrit. *J. Appl. Physiol.*, **22**, 501–4 (1967)

66. Alexander, R. S. Contractile mechanics of venous smooth muscle. *Am. J. Physiol.*, **212**, 852–58 (1967)

67. Alexander, R. S. Role of calcium in the plasticity of venous smooth muscle. *Am. J. Physiol.*, **213**, 287–94 (1967)

68. Ardill, B. L., Bhatnagar, V. M.,

Fentem, P. H. Observation of changes in volume of a congested limb as a means of studying the behavior of capacity vessels. *J. Physiol.*, **194**, 627–44 (1968)

69. Walker, R. L., MacKay, I. F. S., Van Loon, P. Vascular responses to venous congestion. *J. Appl. Physiol.*, **22**, 889–99 (1967)

70. Öberg, B. The relationship between active constriction and passive recoil of the veins at various distending pressures. *Acta Physiol. Scand.*, **71**, 233–47 (1967)

71. Nagle, F. J., Scott, J. B., Swindall, B. T., Haddy, F. J. Venous resistances in skeletal muscle and skin during local blood flow regulation. *Am. J. Physiol.*, **214**, 885–91 (1968)

72. Zsotér, T., Moore, S., Keon, W. Venous distensibility in patients with varicosities: in vitro studies. *J. Appl. Physiol.*, **22**, 505–8 (1967)

73. Lutz, J., Peiper, U., Bauereisen, E. Auftreten und Verhalten venovasomotorischer Reaktionen in der Leberstrombahn. *Pflügers Arch.*, **299**, 311–25 (1968)

74. Hanson, K. M. Experiments on autoregulation of hepatic blood flow in the dog. *Circ. Res.*, **15** (*Suppl. 1*), 222–24 (1964)

75. Hanson, K. M., Johnson, P. C. Local control of hepatic arterial and portal venous flow in the the dog. *Am. J. Physiol.*, **211**, 712–20 (1966)

76. Dorr, L. D., Brody, M. J. Hemodynamic mechanisms of erection in the canine penis. *Am. J. Physiol.*, **213**, 1526–31 (1967)

77. Shulman, K., Verdier, G. R. Cerebral vascular resistance changes in response to cerebrospinal fluid pressure. *Am. J. Physiol.*, **213**, 1084–88 (1967)

78. Nash, F. D., Selkurt, E. E. Effects of elevated ureteral pressure on blood flow. *Circ. Res.*, **15** (*Suppl. 1*), 142–46 (1964)

79. Hársing, L., Szántó, G., Bartha, J. Renal circulation during stop flow in the dog. *Am. J. Physiol.*, **213**, 935–38 (1967)

80. Gray, S. D., Staub, N. C. Resistance to blood flow in leg muscles of dog during tetanic isometric contraction. *Am. J. Physiol.*, **213**, 677–82 (1967)

81. Gray, S. D., Carlsson, E., Staub, N. C. Site of increased vascular resistance during isometric muscle contraction. *Am. J. Physiol.*, **213**, 683–89 (1967)

82. Friedman, J. J. Muscle blood flow and ^{86}Rb extraction: [86]Rb as a capillary flow indicator. *Am. J. Physiol.*, **214**, 488–93 (1968)

83. Sejrsen, P., Tønnesen, K. H. Inert gas diffusion method for measurement of blood flow using saturation techniques. *Circ. Res.*, **22**, 679–93 (1968)

84. Renkin, E. M. Blood flow and transcapillary exchange in skeletal and cardiac muscle. *Intern. Symp. Coronary Circulation and Energetics of the Myocardium, Milan, 1966*, 18–30

85. Kjellmer, I. The effect of exercise on the vascular bed of skeletal muscle. *Acta Physiol. Scand.*, **62**, 18–30 (1964)

86. Dresel, P., Folkow, B., Wallentin, I. Rubidium clearance during neurogenic redistribution of intestinal blood flow. *Acta Physiol. Scand.*, **67**, 173–84 (1966)

87. Sonnenschein, R. R., Wright, D. L., Mellander, S. Effects of vasodilators on filtration coefficient and distal arterial pressure in muscle. *Am. J. Physiol.*, **213**, 706–10 (1967)

88. Johnson, P. C., Hanson, K. M. Effect of arterial pressure on arterial and venous resistance of intestine. *J. Appl. Physiol.*, **17**, 503–8 (1962)

89. Häggendal, E., Sivertsson, R. About arterio-venous shunts in salivary glands: A study with krypton elimination technique in dogs. *Acta Physiol. Scand.*, **71**, 85–88 (1967)

90. Kampp, M., Lundgren, O., Sjöstrand, J. On the components of the Kr wash-out curves from the small intestine of the cat. *Acta Physiol. Scand.*, **72**, 257–81 (1968)

91. Kampp, M., Lundgren, O. Blood flow and flow distribution in the small intestine of the cat as analyzed by the Kr wash-out technique. *Acta Physiol. Scand.*, **72**, 282–97 (1968)

92. Luft, J. H. Fine structures of capillary and endocapillary layer as revealed by ruthenium red. *Fed. Proc.*, **25**, 1773–83 (1966)

93. Vargas, F., Johnson, J. A. Permeability of rabbit heart capillaries to nonelectrolytes. *Am. J. Physiol.*, **213**, 87–93 (1967)

94. Wiederhielm, C. A. Transcapillary and interstitial transport phenomena in

the mesentery. *Fed. Proc.*, **25**, 1789–98 (1966)

95. Wiederhielm, C. A. Analysis of small vessel function. *Physical Bases of Circulatory Transport: Regulation and Exchange*, 313–26 (Saunders, Philadelphia, 1967)

96. Zweifach, B. W., Intaglietta, M. Mechanics of fluid movement across single capillaries in the rabbit. *J. Microvasc. Res.*, **1**, 83–101 (1968)

97. Diana, J. N., Colantino, R., Haddy, F. J. Transcapillary fluid movement during vasopressin and bradykinin infusion. *Am. J. Physiol.*, **212**, 456–65 (1967)

98. Solomon, L. A., Hinshaw, L. B. Effect of endotoxin on isogravimetric capillary pressure in the forelimb. *Am. J. Physiol.*, **214**, 443–47 (1968)

99. Hinshaw, L. B., Solomon, L. A., Reins, D. A. Comparative vascular responses to endotoxin, tourniquet removal and hemorrhage. *J. Trauma*, **7**, 678–90 (1967)

100. Sobin, S. S., Tremer, H. M. Functional geometry of the microcirculation. *Fed. Proc.*, **25**, 1744–52 (1966)

101. Sobin, S. S. A sheet-flow concept of the pulmonary alveolar microcirculation. *Physiologist*, **10**, 308 (1967)

102. Fung, Y. C. B. Sheet-flow concept of pulmonary alveolar microcirculation. *Fed. Proc.*, **27**, 578 (1968)

103. Maloney, J. E., Bergel, D. H., Glazier, J. B., Hughes, J. M. B., West, J. B. Effect of pulsatile pulmonary artery pressure on distribution of blood flow in isolated lung. *Resp. Physiol.*, **4**, 154–67 (1968)

104. Lopez-Muniz, R., Stephens, N. L., Bromberger-Barnea, B., Permutt, S., Riley, R. L. Critical closure of pulmonary vessels analyzed in terms of Starling resistor model. *J. Appl. Physiol.*, **24**, 625–35 (1968)

105. Burton, A. C. The physical equilibrium of small blood vessels. *Am. J. Physiol.*, **164**, 319–29 (1951)

106. McDonald, I. G., Butler, J. Distribution of vascular resistance in the isolated perfused dog lung. *J. Appl. Physiol.*, **23**, 463–74 (1967)

107. Gaar, K. A., Jr. Taylor, A. E., Owens, L. J., Guyton, A. C. Pulmonary capillary pressure and filtration coefficient in the isolated perfused lung. *Am. J. Physiol.*, **213**, 910–14 (1967)

108. Nyboer, J. *Electrical Impedance Plethysmography* (Thomas, Springfield, Ill., 1959)

109. Hill, R. V., Jansen, J. C., Fling, J. L. Electrical impedance plethysmography: A critical analysis. *J. Appl. Physiol.*, **22**, 161–68 (1967)

THE ENDOCRINE FUNCTION OF THE PANCREAS[1,2]

By Lawrence A. Frohman

Department of Medicine, State University of New York at Buffalo
Buffalo, New York

During the three-year period with which this review is concerned notable advances were made in many areas of research pertaining to both insulin and glucagon. The total synthesis of both hormones has been accomplished and, at least with insulin, considerable information is now available concerning structural-functional relationships. Recent reports relating to the biosynthesis of insulin have identified and characterized a precursor substance. Abnormal physical-chemical characteristics of insulin from diabetics have been reported. The control of insulin secretion was studied extensively and the spectrum of stimulators and inhibitors has become enormous. Considerable insight into the mechanism of action of these substances has been gained though much remains to be determined. Studies of the effects of insulin and glucagon on isolated tissues, cells, and subcellular particles have contributed to an overall understanding of the action of these hormones in the intact organism. Methods for measuring glucagon by immunoassay have been improved but serious limitations still exist. Abnormalities of insulin secretion and action in human diabetes and obesity have been described although considerable controversy exists as to interpretation.

This article, by design selective rather than exhaustive, is an attempt to review the general topics mentioned. Because of space limitations many excellent papers had to be omitted, and certain areas have been covered in greater detail because of their inherent interest to the author.

Structure and Synthesis of Insulin

Structure-function relationships.—Variations in the amino acid sequence of insulins from different species have been established, and with one notable exception, the insulins of all mammalian species studied differed by only a few amino acids in selected positions from a proposed common insulin molecule (1). Guinea pig insulin, the exception, differs from pig insulin by 17 amino acids among the 51 residues. This difference is greater than that of chicken insulin and comparable to that of the fish insulins studied. Small variations in chain length have been observed in both fish and mammalian insulins. These involve primarily the N-terminal end of the B-chain but have also been observed at the C-terminal end of the A-chain.

[1] The survey of literature for this review was concluded in June 1968.

[2] The preparation of this manuscript and the work by the reviewer referred to in it were supported in part by grant AM-11456 from the National Institutes of Health.

The availability of purified preparations from different species has permitted an assessment of biologic activity using numerous combinations of insulins and recipients. The more distant the insulin species is from the recipient animal, and hence the more different the insulin structure, the less the biologic activity (2). Even in mammals, guinea pig insulin is only one fourth as active as bovine insulin when assayed in the mouse, yet fully active in the guinea pig (1). Reduced immunologic reactivity of guinea pig insulin has also been shown (3). This explains both the unique success achieved in producing antibodies to porcine and bovine insulin and the lack of alteration in carbohydrate metabolism observed in immunized animals of this species.

Experiments which utilized acid and enzymatic degradation have shown that the C-terminal alanine of the B-chain of bovine insulin and the amide group on the C-terminal asparagine of the A-chain are of little importance in determinining biologic activity (4). The presence of the C-terminal asparagine (or aspartic acid), however, is very important, although slight activity remains even when this residue is removed. Interestingly, all insulins isolated contain an asparagine or aspartic acid residue next to the terminal half-cysteine residue of the A-chain. With regard to the B-chain, it appears that the heptapeptide next to the arginine is necessary for full biologic expression although certain substitutions are compatible with an active molecule. Modifications of the insulin molecule resulting in loss of biologic activity are accompanied by changes in molecular conformation. This makes it doubtful that specific amino acid groups truly function as active sites, but rather that certain of these groups are essential in preserving the three-dimensional structure required for full biologic activity.

Further evidence for the importance of the C-terminal end of the A-chain in maintaining biologic activity has been reported by Arquilla et al. (5) using radioiodinated insulin. As little as 0.2 atoms of iodine per insulin molecule results in attenuation of biologic activity and the first site of iodine attachment is the A-19 tyrosine residue, immediately adjacent to the C-terminal asparagine.

The heterogeneity of crystalline insulin from numerous species has been shown by electrophoretic techniques (6). Major components were both biologically and immunologically active. This suggests either that the differences in structure may exist within individual species or that alterations occur in the process of extraction which may not affect activity. A true structural difference occurs in the rat: insulin molecules from individual rat pancreases may contain either methionine or lysine at the 29-position of the B-chain (1).

The injection of both homologous and heterologous insulins into cows (7, 8) and rabbits (9) has resulted in the production of antibodies, islet histopathologic changes by light and electron microscopy, and varying degrees of insulin insensitivity and carbohydrate intolerance. These findings after injection of homologous insulin suggest either that a difference exists between the state of pancreatic and circulating insulin or that alterations in the conformational structure of insulin due to extraction have rendered it immunogenic. The latter concept has been supported by a report (10) that serum from an insulin-resistant diabetic individual (anti-insulin serum) reacted *in vivo* both with human plasma insulin which was extracted and reinjected and with synthetic human insulin, but not with unaltered human plasma insulin.

Synthesis.—The complete synthesis of both sheep and human insulin has been described by Katsoyannis (11) and his associates. Each individual chain was synthesized separately and combined with natural bovine chains to prove the correctness of the sequence. The chains were finally combined with one another to produce a totally synthetic insulin exhibiting the expected biologic activity. The synthesis of this molecule represented the first chemical synthesis of a human protein.

The insulin biosynthetic pathway has been studied to determine whether the two chains are synthesized individually and then combined or whether the hormone is synthesized as a single chain. Using tritiated and ^{14}C-proline both singly and in sequential combination and measuring the isotope ratios in the two chains, Humbel (12) obtained data supporting the double-chain theory of insulin biosynthesis. The demonstration that the specific activity of the proline located in the middle of the A-chain was intermediate between those of the prolines on the opposite ends of the B-chain was felt to be incompatible with single-chain synthesis.

Because of the possibility that asynchronous synthesis and release of the individual chains into the peripheral circulation could occur, attempts have been made to measure the chains and to study their biologic activity. A radioimmunoassay for A- and B-chains has been reported (13) which is capable of detecting levels in human plasma. The values reported for A- and B-chains in fasting normal subjects were 20 ng/ml and 5 ng/ml, which would be 25 and 4 times the concentration of insulin on a molar basis. B-chain, but not A-chain, was reported to increase after a glucose load. Glucose uptake by the rat hemidiaphragm was impaired by both A- and B-chains (14), but neither prevented the stimulation by insulin. A-chain but not B-chain stimulated glucose oxidation in adipose tissue (14) and isolated fat cells (15), but no lipogenic effect was seen. The large amount of A-chain required to produce this effect on glucose oxidation (30,000 times that of insulin) and the lack of effect observed with a synthetic A-chain containing an intact disulfide bridge raise the question of the biologic significance of these observations.

An insulin precursor has been discovered by Steiner et al. (16) using both rat and human islet tissue incubated with labeled amino acids. Radioactivity was first noted in the precursor which had some immunologic crossreactivity with insulin, and subsequently observed in insulin itself. The latter step was shown to be independent of protein synthesis. This protein, named "proinsulin", was separated from crystalline bovine insulin (17) and converted by limited trypsin treatment to a protein believed to be insulin. Amino acid analysis of proinsulin revealed no residues absent in bovine insulin. In addition it contained an excess of glutamate, glycine, and proline. Sedimentation equilibrium studies (18) have revealed a molecular weight of about 9000 and a variety of physical-chemical studies have confirmed the similarity to, but not the identity with, insulin. Proinsulin behaved as a single-chain polypeptide on both electrophoresis and gel filtration (19). Through use of trypsin digestion, desalanine insulin, with a high biologic potency (23–26 U/mg) and a peptide of 31 residues, was isolated (20). The structures of both porcine and bovine proinsulin were reported (20, 21) just as this review was completed. The species difference in structure of the connecting peptide appears to be considerably greater than in that of either the A- or B-chains. These observations suggest that insulin is derived from a single-chain precursor by proteolytic cleavage of a peptide linking the C-terminus of the B-chain to the N-terminus of the A-chain. An explanation is still needed to integrate Humbel's results supporting separate chain synthesis (12) with the single-chain theory based on proinsulin. Porcine proinsulin has been shown to stimulate glucose oxidation and conversion into lipids in rat adipose tissue *in vitro* (22). This action, but not that of insulin, is blocked by trypsin inhibitors. This suggests that proinsulin itself is inactive but is cleaved by tissue proteases to true insulin.

Endogenous plasma insulin from humans when subjected to gel filtration revealed two components, one of which was of larger molecular weight and exhibited diminished immunoreactivity (23). This larger component, named "big insulin" and of pancreatic origin, comprises only a small fraction of total plasma insulin under fasting conditions. However, by one to two hours after glucose ingestion, big insulin represents up to 40 per cent of the total circulating insulin. It is tempting to speculate on the identity of big insulin and proinsulin because of their many similarities. However, the biologic function of such a molecule, which is at its highest concentration at the time plasma insulin levels are returning toward baseline values, remains to be determined.

Abnormal insulin.—Elliott et al. (24) have investigated the possibility that a structurally abnormal insulin might exist in diabetes. Plasma insulin from untreated diabetic children isolated by immunochemical methods was found to be relatively resistant to destruction by insulinase. The authors implied that the same structural change might also be responsible for decreased biologic activity. Studies on sera from parents of diabetics (25) showed an intermediate range of resistance to destruction and suggested a distribution other than unimodal. The similarities of these observations to those related to the synalbumin antagonist (26) led to the investigation of the biological activity of the abnormal insulin. Considerably less glucose was incorporated into glycogen *in vivo* with insulin from diabetics than from normals (27).

A possible isoleucine-lysine interchange in the A-chain of insulin obtained from the pancreas of a diabetic has also been reported (28). If confirmed, this would represent a significant advance in the study of the pathogenesis of diabetes.

CONTROL OF INSULIN SECRETION

Synthesis vs. release.—The list of factors which stimulate the secretion of insulin has increased substantially since the last review three years ago. Stimulation by glucose of RNA synthesis in the isolated islets of the rat has been shown (29) as has the incorporation of labeled amino acids into insulin in slices of rabbit and ox pancreas (30). The latter finding helps to explain why constant glucose stimulation does not deplete pancreatic insulin content. Further studies have permitted the differentiation of insulin which is released from that which is synthesized in response to glucose (31). With constant glucose stimulation, newly synthesized insulin is not immediately released, but rather remains within the β-cell for one to two hours, after which it can be detected in the media. Prior to release the hormone is believed to move from the endoplasmic reticulum to the Golgi complex where granule formation occurs and then to the periphery of the β-cell. The time required is consistent with that noted for the release of proteins from other types of secretory cells and supports the concept that the pathway for the secretion of newly synthesized insulin must involve β-granule formation. The intensity and duration of the glucose stimulus required for insulin synthesis are not known, nor has the duration of effect been determined once the stimulation has been discontinued. Release of insulin, however, occurs within thirty seconds of glucose stimulation (32) and stops within thirty seconds of the termination of the stimulus.

Carbohydrates, amino acids, and lipids.—The glucose molecule itself does not mediate the release of insulin, as has been shown using inhibitors such as 2-deoxyglucose. Glucosamine, which competitively inhibits glucose phosphorylation, also inhibits the stimulatory effect of glucose (33). Fructose stimulates insulin secretion, but in normals this may simply result from its conversion to glucose. Insulin secretion is not stimulated by fructose in patients with essential fructose intolerance, where a deficiency of 1-phosphofructoaldolase exists. This enzyme converts fructose-1-phosphate to dihydroxyacetone phosphate and glyceraldehyde. Since fructose will stimulate insulin secretion in patients with glucose-6-phosphatase deficiency despite the absence of an increase in blood glucose (34), it would appear that the trioses or subsequent intermediates in the glycolytic cycle may actually be responsible for insulin secretion. Xylitol, a pentitol which enters the pentose-phosphate pathway through D-xylulose, is more potent than glucose in stimulating insulin release (35), though the exact mechanism of its stimulation remains to be clarified.

Insulin secretion occurs in response to protein ingestion (36) and to intravenous administration of essential amino acids (37). Since insulin stimulates amino acid membrane transport and incorporation into protein, the relationship is analogous to that of glucose stimulation. There are, however, a number of differences between these two stimuli. First, amino acid-stimulated insulin secretion is not suppressed by inhibitors of glucose-stimulated insulin secretion such as epinephrine (38) and diazoxide (benzothiadiazine) (39). In addition, one amino acid, leucine, appears to act differently from the others. Insulin secretion in response to leucine, but not to the other essential amino acids, is enhanced by chlorpropamide treatment and diminished by diazoxide (39, 40). The pattern of response to leucine is similar to that seen using glucose and suggests that a common pathway may exist in the intermediary metabolism of these two compounds.

Both long- and short-chain fatty acids have been implicated in the secretion of insulin. Butyrate and proprionate release insulin in the sheep (41), a species in which short-chain fatty acids are an important metabolic fuel. Octanoate causes a release of insulin both from rat pancreas *in vitro* (42) and after duodenal installation in man (43). Elevation of long-chain fatty acids without changes in blood ketones in the dog (44) results in increased insulin secretion. This might explain the mechanism by which insulin is involved in controlling the rate of lipolysis.

The hypothesis, however, is considerably more complicated inasmuch as in the fasting state, where free fatty acid levels are elevated, pancreatic insulin content as well as glucose-stimulated insulin secretion *in vivo* and *in vitro* are decreased in the rat (45). In man after prolonged fasting and despite rises in free fatty acids and blood ketones, Genuth (46) has shown that the initial insulin response to glucose is not maintained despite persistent hyperglycemia. This also implies a diminished capacity for sustained insulin secretion in the fasting state. A diurnal variation in plasma insulin levels during the course of a prolonged fast in normal humans has also been noted (47), despite the absence of similar changes in blood glucose. The significance of this observation remains to be determined. A seasonal variation in basal and postglucose insulin levels in the rat also occurs (48). Maximal plasma insulin values under both conditions were found in June and minimal levels in November. The percentage increase in response to glucose was greater during winter, and a cold environment further increased this response. These changes were associated with an increase in both glucose turnover and insulin sensitivity in the cold-exposed animal.

Muscular exercise, which enhances glucose uptake by muscle independent of insulin, has generally not been found to stimulate insulin secretion (49). However, subjects with coronary artery disease and a reduced work capacity showed a striking increase in insulin secretion in response to exercise (50). Whether this is merely an exaggeration of the normal metabolic response or whether it is peculiar to this group of patients remains to be determined. A disease of skeletal muscle, myotonic dystrophy, is also associated with an increased insulin response to glucose (51). The authors suggest the intriguing possibility that the increased insulin secreted may be a compensatory mechanism aimed at facilitating muscle regeneration.

Cations.—Cation requirements for the secretion of insulin have been investigated using the isolated perfused rat pancreas (52) and the rabbit pancreas *in vitro* (53, 54). In both systems calcium was found to be crucial in permitting the insulin response to glucose although it did not stimulate insulin directly. Potassium, on the other hand, did stimulate insulin secretion, but only in the presence of calcium. Sodium is also necessary for insulin release in response to glucose, leucine, tolbutamide, and glucagon. Inhibition of the sodium pump by ouabain or by omission of potassium results in insulin release *in vitro* only in the presence of sodium. Since both sodium and calcium are necessary for a variety of stimuli, it would appear that both must act at the β-cell membrane or enter the cell before insulin can be released.

Hormones and cyclic AMP.—Numerous reports have described the effects of hormones upon insulin secretion, but in many of these it is difficult to distinguished physiologic from pharmacologic effects. If doses used are far in excess of those believed possible by endogenous secretion, or if the effect is demonstrable with exogenously administered hormone but not with endogenously secreted hormone, then the physiologic significance must be questioned. The comments are applicable to many of the following reports.

The effect of growth hormone has been studied in a large variety of conditions. In general, the most sensitive systems compared a growth hormone deficiency state with and without therapy to the normal state. The pancreas of hypophysectomized as compared to normal rats contains and secretes less insulin *in vitro* (55) and does not respond to preincubation with growth hormone (56). Pretreatment of the animal with growth hormone corrects both of these defects. In humans with growth hormone deficiency, the decreased insulin release in response to glucose could be corrected along with the concomitant improvement in the glucose disappearance rate within five minutes of growth hormone administration (57). No direct stimulatory effect of growth hormone on insulin secretion could be shown. These studies all suggest that the action of growth hormone on the β-cell results in a greater response to glucose stimulation. When large amounts of growth hormone are administered, a further rise in insulin secretion is observed, but this is associated with marked carbohydrate intolerance, insulin antagonism, and a diabetes-like state (58). In a most fascinating experiment (59), insulin secretion in acromegalics was first increased and later almost completely abolished as the disease progressed. In one patient, however, after successful therapy and return of growth hormone levels to normal, the insulin secretory response to glucose returned.

Human placental lactogen which is in many ways similar to growth hormone was infused in normal humans at a rate comparable to the placental secretory rate during pregnancy (60). Insulin secretion in response to glucose was increased but glucose tolerance was impaired. When lactogen was given by intermittent injection to two hypophysectomized diabetics, similar effects were noted (61). In a third patient the increased insulin secretion was associated with improved glucose tolerance, which suggests an effect similar to that of growth hormone on the β-cell.

Porte et al. (62) have demonstrated that infused epinephrine in humans inhibits insulin secretion in response to hyperglycemia produced by epinephrine itself, by concomitant glucose infusion, or by glucagon. The response to tolbutamide was similarly suppressed. After the epinephrine infusion was terminated, insulin levels promptly rose. Results of similar studies on monkeys by Kris et al. (63) were identical. In addition, they found decreased levels of portal vein insulin and no effects of infused epinephrine on insulin disappearance from plasma. Carotid infusion of epinephrine was no more effective than systemic infusion, which suggests that the brain was not the primary site of action. The direct inhibition of pancreatic insulin secretion *in vitro* by epinephrine and norepinephrine has been demonstrated (64). The receptor mechanism in man was studied with the aid of α- and β-adrenergic blocking agents (65, 66). Propranolol, a β-blocker, did not block the epinephrine suppression of insulin release despite its inhibition of epinephrine-stimulated lipolysis and hyperglycemia. When given alone, propranolol actually resulted in a fall in plasma insulin from previously established basal levels. Phentolamine, an α-blocker, in combination with epinephrine partially inhibited the rise in glucose but resulted in a marked rise in insulin, which suggests that the epinephrine inhibition of insulin secretion is an α-effect. Phentolamine alone caused no change in plasma insulin levels in man. In anesthetized dogs, on the other hand, phentolamine by itself will stimulate insulin secretion (67). Whether this represents a species difference in responsiveness to the blocking agents or merely the alteration in circulating epinephrine levels due to anesthesia has not been determined. Isoproterenol, a synthetic catecholamine with pure β-effect, produced a rise in insulin levels without changing blood glucose (66). This stimulation was abolished by simultaneous propranolol administration. These experiments provide good evidence for separating the effects of epinephrine on insulin secretion into an α-effect which is inhibitory and a β-effect which is stimulatory. Under normal physiologic conditions the α-effect appears to predominate.

Evidence for the role of the adenyl cyclase system in insulin secretion was presented by Malaisse et al. (68) using the *in vitro* rat pancreas. Isoproterenol, in contrast to its *in vivo* effects, inhibited insulin secretion *in vitro* (64), but was stimulatory in combination with an α-blocker (phenoxybenzamine). Theophylline, caffeine, 3′,5′-cyclic AMP, glucagon, ACTH, and TSH, all believed to act through adenyl cyclase in liver and adipose tissue, stimulated insulin release, but only when media glucose concentrations were greater than 100 mg per cent. Pancreatic islet tissue containing no demonstrable glycogen showed a reduced effect and insulin secretion was abolished by mannoheptulose or 2-deoxyglucose. Glycogen-containing tissue was stimulated by theophylline, a phosphodiesterase inhibitor, even in the absence of glucose and this effect was reduced by 2-deoxyglucose but not by manno-heptulose. These workers believe that the β-cell contains an adenyl cyclase system which is involved in the activation of phosphorylase and possibly phosphofructokinase. Insulin secretion is felt to be regulated by substances influencing the rate at which glycolysis proceeds within the β-cell. This concept explains why mannoheptulose, which blocks glucose phosphoryla-tion, inhibits insulin secretion only in the fasted state since no glycogen is available for glycolysis. It also explains why 2-deoxyglucose, which blocks the metabolism of glucose-6-phosphate, is effective in both fed and fasted states. One might expect that the stimulatory effect of fructose would not be altered by these blockers.

Further evidence for the adenyl cyclase system has been presented by Turtle et al. (69) using the fasted adrenalectomized rat. Theophylline, whether injected alone or during an epinephrine infusion, increased insulin secretion. α-Adrenergic blockade enhanced the insulin response and β-adrenergic blockade abolished it. The results suggest that α-receptors in-hibit and β-receptors stimulate the generation of cyclic AMP.

The mechanism by which ACTH stimulates insulin secretion was studied in mice by Lebovitz & Pooler (70, 71) using puromycin and aminophylline. When administered by itself, puromycin inhibited protein synthesis but had no effect on insulin secretion. When injected with ACTH, puromycin poten-tiated the ACTH-stimulated insulin release. Similar augmentation was seen with glucagon-stimulated insulin secretion but not with glucose or tolbuta-mide. Puromycin aminonucleoside, an analog of puromycin which does not block protein synthesis, was ineffective in potentiating insulin secretion. Recent studies have indicated that puromycin and its analog both inhibit phosphodiesterase and this may well explain the potentiating effect of puro-mycin on insulin secretion. It does not explain why puromycin aminonu-cleoside was inactive. Similar experiments using aminophylline showed a potentiation of both ACTH and glucagon. In addition, aminophylline also enhanced glucose-mediated insulin secretion and in some experiments, the effect of tolbutamide as well. Although the theory contains certain weak-nesses, an action of ACTH on the adenyl cyclase system of the β-cell would best explain the results obtained.

Glucagon has been shown by Crockford et al. (72) to stimulate insulin secretion in man, independent of its hyperglycemic action. In patients with hepatic phosphorylase deficiency, glucagon produced an elevation of insulin levels despite the lack of hyperglycemia. In normal subjects a constant glucagon infusion preceding an acute glucagon injection abolished the hyper-glycemic response to the latter but not the insulin stimulatory effect. The return of insulin values toward the baseline during continuous infusion of glucagon was felt by the authors to be due to the concomitant stimulation by glucagon of epinephrine. Samols et al. (73) noted in similar studies that the insulinogenic effect of small amounts of glucagon given as a constant infusion was apparent only if blood glucose levels were raised. In addition, forearm arterial-venous blood glucose differences were unaltered by the increased concentration of insulin during the glucagon infusion. No obvious explanation is available for this observation, although if catecholamine levels were elevated, their effects could counterbalance those of insulin.

The stimulatory effect of glucagon, like that of ACTH, is believed to be mediated by adenyl cyclase. Supporting evidence includes the potentiation by aminophylline (71) and the inhibition by epinephrine (62). The lack of suppression by propranolol (66) remains unexplained. Inhibition of the glycolytic pathway by 2-deoxyglucose (74) also blocks the stimulatory effect of glucagon in the absence of glucose, which implies that β-cell glycogen stores participate in the process.

The physiologic importance of both ACTH- and glucagon-stimulated insulin secretion still requires clarification. With a few exceptions, the doses of hormones required to evoke the response are beyond physiologic limits and the recognized biologic functions of these hormones are not enhanced by insulin secretion. The conditions under which glucagon secretion occurs, in particular, would not appear to be served by a concomitant insulin release.

McIntyre et al. (75) found higher insulin and lower arterial glucose levels in humans after intraduodenal installation of glucose than after intravenous infusion of identical amounts. Rapid infusion by both routes led to an exaggeration of this response. They attributed their findings to an intestinal factor(s) which affected insulin secretion. One such factor extracted from hog duodenal mucosa has been shown to be secretin, which stimulates insulin secretion both in the anesthetized dog (76) and in man (77). Pancreozymin (78–80) and gastrin (78) have also been observed to stimulate insulin secretion in man and dog. Thus, at least three specific enteric hormones are capable of stimulating insulin secretion which might be required for disposal of a substrate load. The mechanism by which these enteric hormones act is unknown but might well be via the adenyl cyclase system. There are conflicting reports, though, on the effect of epinephrine on the stimulatory nature of secretin. In the dog, Unger et al. (78) were able to abolish the effect with epinephrine. In man, Milson et al. (81) found the stimulatory effect of secretin unmodified by epinephrine. It is in these same two species that differences in phentolamine effects have been noted (65, 67), which suggests a difference in these two species in the role of adrenergic agents on insulin secretion. An important question has been raised, however, as to the physiologic significance of the enteric hormones in stimulating insulin secretion. Neither Mahler & Weisberg (80) nor Boyns et al. (82) observed any change in insulin levels after the administration of oral or intraduodenal acid in humans to stimulate the release of endogenous secretin. The same subjects did respond to exogenous secretin. Although neither group actually measured secretin levels after acid stimulation, the procedures followed were standard methods. These reports again raise the question of physiologic vs. pharmacologic effects and will require further study using physiologic amounts of hormones.

It may be significant that the patterns of insulin secretion in response to several of the hormones mentioned exhibit certain similarities. Insulin secretion decreases substantially after repeated injections of ACTH (83) and pancreozymin (79). Similarly, when constant infusions of either glucagon (73) or isoproterenol (66) do not elevate blood glucose levels, the insulin response is short lived. This response can be increased by giving glucose between pancreozymin injections (79) or along with the glucagon infusion (73). These observations all support the hypothesis that hormonal stimulation of insulin secretion utilizes substrate within the β-cell (glycogen) without stimulating replenishment. Once the substrate is depleted, the stimulus is no longer effective. Further evidence obtained by measuring insulin synthesis will be necessary before this concept can be fully accepted.

Both oxytocin and vasopressin have also been shown by Kaneto et al. (84) to release insulin in the dog. The oxytocin effect was prompt and independent of changes in blood glucose. The response to vasopressin was more gradual and less marked than that to oxytocin and was probably evoked through a different mechanism. Insulin release after vasopressin injection could occur as a consequence of its corticotropin releasing factor-like activity. The mechanism of the oxytocin effect remains to be determined. Once again, doses in the pharmacologic range of both hormones were necessary to demonstrate insulin release.

Angiotensin II will diminish the insulin response to glucose and to tolbutamide in man (85). This effect is not blocked by phentolamine and, therefore, is independent of epinephrine. Diminished blood flow to the islets may be responsible for this phenomenon.

Thyroxine *in vitro* had no effect on insulin secretion (86). However, both thyroidectomy and treatment with pharmacologic doses of thyroxine decreased insulin output. Since thyroxine stimulates glucose uptake by peripheral tissues, the reduced insulin secretion probably accounts for the variable rates of glucose utilization observed in the hyperthyroid state.

Ovulatory suppressants (combined estrogen and progesterone derivatives) given in a cyclic manner to normal women increased insulin secretion in response to intravenous glucose without altering the net glucose disappearance rate (87). Since estrogens increase growth hormone levels in plasma, the elevated insulin levels may be secondary to the insulin antagonistic action of growth hormone.

The question whether exogenous insulin can impair β-cell function was studied by Chu & Goodner (88). Rats treated with insulin for a five-month period showed identical blood glucose responses to intravenous glucose and to tolbutamide, as did controls. Only in animals treated with enough insulin to produce persistent hypoglycemia were pancreatic insulin stores reduced. This was attributed to a reduced glycemic stimulus for insulin synthesis. Even in this group, the secretory response was unimpaired.

Central nervous system.—The central nervous system control of insulin secretion, after having been studied briefly 25 to 40 years ago, has become a topic of renewed interest. Suppression of insulin secretion after central nervous system stimulation dates back to the classic "piqûre hyperglycemia" of Claude Bernard over 100 years ago and is mediated through the sympathetic nervous system. Central nervous system stimulation of insulin secretion has been convincingly demonstrated to be mediated via the vagus nerve in studies by Frohman et al. (67) and Kaneto et al. (89) in the dog, and by Daniel & Henderson in the baboon (90). Both cervical vagi and the dorsal subdiaphragmatic vagal trunk, when stimulated, cause an immediate release of insulin. The duration of insulin release is brief and levels return toward the baseline despite a persistence of stimulation. Upon repeated stimulation the insulin response is significantly diminished. In these two respects vagal-stimulated insulin release is similar to hormonal-stimulated and implies the rapid exhaustion of some endogenous substrate. The vagal effect is blocked by atropine (67) as is the slight increase in blood glucose, which may be due to a concomitant glucagon release. Similar effects have been observed *in vitro* with the rat pancreas using cholinergic and anticholinergic agents (64). Specific histochemical stains for cholinesterase have demonstrated cholinergic nerve fibers surrounding the islet cells (90). No impairment in glucose-mediated insulin secretion was demonstrable after vagotomy despite a small drop in basal insulin levels (67). Furthermore, the transplanted denervated pancreas secretes insulin and is capable of maintaining a normal blood glucose for weeks (91).

The central nervous system pathways controlling insulin secretion have not been completely identified but the ventral hypothalamus appears to be involved. Electrolytic destruction of the ventromedial hypothalamic nuclei in weanling rats results in hyperinsulinemia, hyperlipemia, and excessive fat deposition despite normoglycemia and an absence of increased food intake or excessive weight gain (92). In addition, such animals exhibit growth hormone deficiency and impaired linear growth. Insulin levels are significantly elevated as early as the fourth postoperative day despite a reduced food intake and relative hypoglycemia at that time (93). No evidence for tissue resistance to insulin action has been found *in vivo* or during *in vitro* studies of liver and adipose tissue metabolism (94). A detailed investigation of the hypothalamus has not revealed any area other than the ventromedial nucleus which when destroyed results in this syndrome (95). The ventromedial nucleus is generally considered as part of the sympathetic nervous system and is believed to inhibit the ventrolateral nucleus which is a part of the parasympathetic nervous system. The mechanism by which insulin levels are elevated after ventromedial nucleus destruction might involve either a diminution of sympathetic inhibition or a parasympathetic (vagus)-mediated stimulation.

Insulin injected into the cerebrospinal fluid of the dog caused a decline in glucose in both the cerebrospinal fluid and the blood (96). Similar injections in vagotomized animals produced almost no fall in blood glucose. The results suggest that increased glucose utilization by the central nervous system may have stimulated the vagus-mediated insulin secretion.

Stimulation of the rostral and dorsal sections of the cingulate gyrus increased the insulin-like activity of pancreatic vein blood in the dog two hours after glucose infusion but not in the fasting state (97). The mechanism responsible for this effect is not known.

INSULIN METABOLISM AND DISTRIBUTION

Removal from plasma.—The plasma disappearance rate of crystalline porcine insulin in man was studied in normals and noninsulin-treated diabetics by Stimmler (98) using immunoassay methods. The half-life in normals was 3.3 minutes, significantly shorter than that seen in diabetics (4.8 minutes). No correlation with age or weight existed in normals, or with duration of disease in diabetics. The slower disappearance rate seen in diabetics has not been explained. It is tempting to speculate that an abnormal insulin which is relatively resistant to insulinase (24) might decrease the activity of the enzyme *in vivo*, thereby accounting for the difference. Tomasi et al. (99), using a similar procedure, found the insulin half-life to vary from 6.5 to 9 minutes and observed no difference between normals and diabetics. The explanation for the longer half-life and the lack of distinction between normals and diabetics in the latter study is not apparent. What should be noted is that the half-lives reported in both studies are substantially shorter than the 20 to 30 minute values previously reported after the injection of radioactive insulin and measurement of trichloroacetic acid precipitable radioactivity as an index of intact insulin. The explanation appears to be that some of the products of iodoinsulin degradation which appear within the plasma compartment are still trichloroacetic acid precipitable but more slowly cleared, resulting in a falsely prolonged plasma half-life.

The kinetics of radioiodinated insulin disappearance from plasma in dogs was studied by Arnould et al. in a series of elegant experiments (100). Insulin was isolated by chromatographic procedures or immunoprecipitated, both methods giving identical results. It was not possible to draw a straight line through even the initial portion of the disappearance curve on semilogarithmic paper. With a digital computer the disappearance curve could be adjusted to a multiexponential function. From these data, an analog computer determined the expected curve for a constant infusion, which was verified experimentally. The mathematical function implies the existence of one or several feedbacks of the labeled insulin toward the plasma compartment and at least two additional peripheral compartments. Each exponential function represents the result of various movements of labeled insulin to and from the different compartments. Similarly, none of the compartments by themselves corresponds to any physiologic space. Only the sum of all intercepts together approaches the plasma volume, which indicates early mixing of the labeled insulin with plasma. The results, therefore, preclude the use of any component of the disappearance curve for a direct calculation of a so-called half-life of radioiodinated insulin.

The discrepancy between this study and those using nonradioactive insulin where a first-order decay rate was observed (98, 99) may be explained by the many differences between the two types of experiments performed. First, even though the radioiodinated insulin injected was of low specific activity [considerably below that studied by Arquilla et al. (5)], its metabolism may not have been identical to that of unlabeled insulin, as is indicated by other studies (100). Second, the kinetics of insulin disappearance may vary with the plasma insulin concentrations, which were considerably greater in the studies with unlabeled insulin. Measurements of hepatic insulin extraction have revealed that the percentage of insulin removed increases by two to threefold during periods of elevated insulin secretion (101). Growth hormone has been shown not to alter the rate of removal of nonradioactive insulin from the plasma of depancreatized dogs (102).

Insulin has been found in bile of many species (103, 104). The concentrations in gallbladder are proportional to but greater than can be explained by bile concentration. Insulin levels often exceed 1000 $\mu U/ml$ in gallbladder bile, whereas in bile not retained by the gallbladder the concentration is equal to or lower than plasma. It would appear that the gallbladder can either secrete or differentially concentrate insulin. After intravenous glucose or injection of insulin into the portal vein, peak bile concentrations occurred at 30 to 45 minutes. The significance of these observations is not known.

Kidney.—The role of the kidney in the metabolism of endogenous insulin was studied in normal human subjects and in patients with renal disease (105). A renal arterial-venous insulin concentration difference of approximately 29 per cent suggested renal insulin clearance to be greater than glomerular filtration rate. The excreted insulin of normals never exceeded 1.5 per cent of the filtered load. The data suggest that insulin is normally filtered at the glomerulus and is completely reabsorbed or destroyed in the proximal tubule. Reabsorption probably occurs, but the insulin is utilized in renal metabolism along with insulin taken directly from the blood. The 24-hour renal insulin requirement was calculated to be about four units. In patients with renal disease an increased urinary insulin output occurred, probably on the basis of impaired renal tubular reabsorption. Urinary insulin clearance calculated on the basis of urinary flow rate and urinary and arterial insulin concentrations was less than 1 per cent of values obtained using arterial-venous differences. Values obtained by the former method are inaccurate and provide a poor index of plasma insulin levels or insulin secretion (105).

Further evidence for the proximal tubular reabsorption of insulin was obtained using radioiodinated insulin in mice (106). Radioautographic studies indicated that after intravenous administration, maximal insulin concentrations were first present in the glomeruli, then in the proximal tubule lumina, and finally in the proximal tubule cells.

Distribution.—Rasio et al. (107, 108) have studied the migration of insulin into extracellular fluid (lymph) in anephric patients and in dogs. The vascular and extravascular pools behaved as a single unit with regard to glucose. Insulin, after it had crossed the capillary membrane, did not reenter the vascular compartment but was carried into the lymphatics. The half-life of injected insulin was significantly longer in lymph than in serum and the distribution volume of insulin approximated that of extracellular fluid. After intravenous glucose, lymph insulin peaked at 50 to 60 minutes in contrast to the five-minute peak in blood. After pancreatectomy, the decrease in lymph insulin was slower than that of serum insulin. Lymph insulin levels correlated better with glucose assimilation rates than did serum insulin levels, which suggests that the former is the major determinant of the net glucose disappearance rate.

Studies on the distribution of radioiodinated insulin in striated muscle were reviewed by Edelman & Schwartz (109). They found radioactive insulin to be associated primarily with the sarcolemmal and soluble fractions of the muscle cell. Binding possibly occurs to the transverse tubular extensions of the sarcolemmal membrane, causing swelling. This is generally associated with hyperpolarization and it is interesting to compare this work with the findings of Zierler (110) that insulin hyperpolarizes the muscle cell membrane. Stretching of this sarcolemma could explain the membrane transport effects of insulin and its stimulation of protein synthesis by facilitating translocation and interactions of substrates, enzymes, cofactors, and mobile templates within the cell.

INSULIN ACTIONS

Carbohydrates.—It has been more difficult to demonstrate insulin effects on carbohydrate metabolism in the liver than in adipose tissue or in muscle. The problem has usually been approached in one of two ways: to compare insulin deficiency states with the normal, or to observe the effect of added insulin using the normal state as a reference. Both methods have now been successful in demonstrating effects of insulin although the most striking changes have been shown in states of insulin deficiency.

Insulin deficiency has generally been produced by injecting insulin antisera rather than alloxan because of the rapidity and selective action of the former. Exton et al. (111) were unable to demonstrate any effects by adding insulin antisera to the rat liver perfusate system, except the neutralization of added insulin. However, by injecting the antisera one hour before removing the liver, they demonstrated a doubling of net glucose production and increased conversion of lactate to glucose. Both effects were reversed by the addition of insulin. Antisera also resulted in an immediate and sustained rise in cyclic AMP levels in the liver and in adipose tissue. Using a similar method, Haft (112) has found a decrease in glycogen content, fatty acid synthesis, and glucose oxidation. Insulin, added to the perfusate, restored the rate of glucose oxidation to normal levels and stimulated fatty acid synthesis. Increased urea production was seen only when initial glycogen content was low. Insulin decreased urea production whether the initial rate was elevated or normal. The effects observed in the isolated perfused liver which have been attributed to the prior injection of insulin antisera are identical to those produced by glucagon. Measurement of circulating glucagon after administration of insulin antisera would distinguish between these two possibilities.

The addition of insulin to perfusates of livers from normal rats stimulated the incorporation of radioactive glucose into glycogen (113) and fatty acids (114). The reduction of glucose output was found to correlate well with the amount of glycogen spared (115). The latter accounted for more than 70 per cent of the combined net inhibitory effect of insulin on the accumulation of perfusate glucose and lactate. In dogs with an Eck fistula, a portacaval transposition, the portal or systemic infusion of insulin produced a decreased hepatic glucose output (116). The fistula consists of a side to side anastamosis of the portal vein and the inferior vena cava so that a portion of blood flow from the former enters the systemic circulation and from the latter enters the liver. Similar infusions of insulin into unoperated dogs had no observable effect on hepatic glucose output. This suggests two possibilities. The diversion of pancreatic blood flow would reduce the effect of glucagon and perhaps other intestinal hormones which might otherwise mask the effect of insulin. In addition, the decreased hepatic glycogen content which occurs after portacaval transposition might limit the capacity of the liver to supply glucose to the periphery and thus make the insulin effect more easily demonstrable. It does not necessarily follow that insulin has similar effects under normal conditions.

The effect of sudden insulin deprivation was studied in dogs which had previously been subtotally pancreatectomized, with the remaining portion grafted subcutaneously (117). When the pedicle of the autograft was clamped, the rate of disappearance of radioactive glucose from plasma decreased to one third within one minute and plasma glucose accumulation doubled within the same period of time. The initial increase in the rate of glucose production appeared to result from glycogenolysis. In fasted animals blood glucose levels began to rise within four to ten minutes. When blood flow was restored after a 30 to 60 minute occlusion, several hours were required for a return of glucose output and disappearance rates to preclamping values. The results indicate that continuous secretion of insulin is required, to prevent glucose accumulation.

Effects of insulin on glucose metabolism by the kidney have been demonstrated with the aid of techniques designed to decrease insulin destruction by renal glutathione-insulin transhydrogenase (insulinase) (118). Both adding alloxan, which appears to decrease the enzyme activity, and incubating tissues at low temperature permit observation of the stimulatory effect of insulin on glucose uptake. The rate of glycogen synthesis *in vitro* by brain slices of alloxan diabetic rats is reduced despite a high initial glycogen content. Synthesis is returned to normal by insulin both *in vivo* or *in vitro* (119), resulting in an even greater level of glycogen. Considerable species variation exists in the response of adipose tissue glucose metabolism to insulin (120). Progressively less stimulation by insulin of total glucose utilization and lipogenesis *in vitro* was seen in the guinea pig, rabbit, and hamster when compared to the rat, despite the use of insulin from four species. Among the possible explanations are varying degrees of insulin-inactivating mechanisms, the possibility of species variation in insulin structure, especially the guinea pig (1), the role of glucose in the endogenous metabolic pattern of the species, and differences in the viability of the tissues.

Lipids.—The antilipolytic effect of insulin on isolated fat cells from rats was studied by Fain et al. (121). The effect of insulin was independent of the presence of glucose, and as little as 0.1 μU/ml prevented the lipolytic effect of growth hormone and dexamethasone. This insulin level is 10–100 times less than that required to stimulate glucose metabolism. Insulin reduced the lipolytic effects of small amounts of ACTH and theophylline, but this could be reversed by larger doses. Insulin did not suppress the lipolytic effect of glucagon; small amounts of insulin actually potentiated the effect. In contrast to the immediate lipolytic effects of ACTH, theophylline, and glucagon, the effects of growth hormone and dexamethasone are delayed. Actinomycin must be added to the incubation media at an early stage to inhibit the lipolysis of growth hormone but insulin is effective even at late stages, which indicates that the insulin effect is at a relatively late step in the activation of lipolysis. Since ACTH and aminophylline are believed to stimulate lipolysis by increasing cyclic AMP, the authors believe that insulin inhibition occurs at this level as long as the system is not operating maximally. The results with glucagon, though, are incompatible unless glucagon-induced lipolysis is not mediated through cyclic AMP. A similar dissociation between the antilipolytic and glucose stimulatory effects of insulin has been demonstrated by Chlouverakis (122) with the aid of 2-deoxyglucose. Insulin not only failed to inhibit the high lipolytic rate induced by high concentrations of epinephrine but actually produced a slight potentiation. The same stimulatory effect of insulin could be demonstrated at low concentrations of epinephrine in tissues of fasted rats. These seemingly paradoxical effects of insulin on glucagon- and epinephrine-stimulated lipolysis remain to be clarified.

The role of insulin in promoting triglyceride synthesis was investigated in humans with endogenous hypertriglyceridemia by Reaven et al. (123). Significant correlations were observed between the insulin response to glucose and the degree of hypertriglyceridemia as well as between individual insulin and triglyceride levels. The authors suggest that an impairment of peripheral glucose uptake results in secondary hyperinsulinemia which in turn leads to elevated plasma triglyceride levels.

Protein synthesis.—Wool et al. (124) have suggested that the synthesis of an initial protein is necessary for the subsequent stimulation of ribosomal protein synthesis by insulin. This hypothetical protein serves to modify the translation of other species of stable messenger RNA. This hypothesis is based on the observation that puromycin and cyclohexamide block the hormone's effect while actinomycin does not. It would also explain why insulin fails to act *in vitro* in a cell-free ribosomal system since it would be the specific protein rather than insulin itself which is responsible for modifying ribosomal function. Although insulin does increase RNA synthesis in muscle (125), the actinomycin results indicate that RNA synthesis is not a requisite for hormone-mediated protein synthesis. The authors also exclude increased amino acid transport, increased turnover of high energy phosphate compounds, or effects on the cellular cytostructure as the basis for accelerated protein synthesis. Insulin increases the percentage of polyribosomes and decreases the proportion of lighter ribosomal aggregates in rat skeletal muscle within two hours (126). This effect is not altered by a protein-free diet but is abolished by a 48-hour fast.

The stimulation of amino acid incorporation into adipose tissue protein occurs at insulin concentrations ranging from 10–800 μU/ml and is not dependent upon the presence of glucose (127). Although a higher concentration of insulin appears necessary for this effect than for inhibition of lipolysis or stimulation of glucose utilization in adipose tissue, all three actions have now been shown to occur within the physiologic range of plasma insulin levels.

Hepatic glucose-6-phosphate dehydrogenase and, to a lesser extent, 6-phosphogluconate dehydrogenase activity were decreased during states of hypoinsulinism (fasting or diabetes) and restored to normal levels by appropriate therapy (128). Actinomycin blocked the insulin-induced increase, which suggests that the effect is due to *de novo* enzyme biosynthesis involving new RNA production.

Insulin Secretion in Obesity and Diabetes

The relative frequency of obesity and diabetes in man and the inability to reproduce their exact pathophysiology in animals have led to numerous investigative efforts in human subjects. An extensive discussion of this topic is beyond the scope of this review, but certain observations deserve comment.

Obesity, per se, has been recognized to result in an increased insulin response to both oral and intravenous glucose. Fasting insulin levels correlate both with the per cent of ideal weight and the magnitude of the insulin rise after glucose (129). If the insulin response to glucose is expressed as a per cent of fasting level, similar values are observed in both obese and nonobese subjects. An increased insulin response has been reported in obesity after both glucagon (130) and tolbutamide (131). A degree of peripheral insensitivity to endogenous insulin exists in obesity as evidenced by the absence of increased glucose disposal in the presence of the increased insulin secretion. Isolated fat cells from obese subjects show a relative insensitivity to the stimulation of glucose oxidation by insulin and a return of insulin sensitivity after reduction of weight to normal levels (132). There have been attempts to quantitate the extent of the insulin insensitivity by various types of insulin/glucose ratios (131, 133–135). This concept of a ratio has been useful inasmuch as it presumably relates the insulin response to a certain level of glucose stimulation. In all instances, insulin/glucose ratios are increased in obesity although separation of non-obese from obese individuals may not be as great as by measurements of absolute insulin levels (133). The ratio is also of limited usefulness when simultaneous changes occur in both the numerator, an index of insulin secretory capacity, and the denominator, a reflection of both insulin secretion and sensitivity.

Insulin secretion is absent or almost absent in the "juvenile onset" type of diabetes. In "maturity onset" diabetes (to which all of the following applies) considerable controversy exists as to (a) whether increased insulin secretion actually occurs, and (b) whether insulin resistance exists. The problem is complicated because many diabetics are obese and a portion of their insulin secretory response as well as some insulin insensitivity is related to their obesity. Perley & Kipnis (135), using oral glucose tolerance tests and intravenous glucose infusions designed to match the blood glucose levels of the oral tests, concluded that diabetes per se was unassociated with insulin resistance and that insulin secretion was diminished. Seltzer et al. (133) had previously come to similar conclusions using standard oral and intravenous glucose tolerance tests. Cerasi & Luft (134), using a computer analysis of the response to a sustained high glucose infusion, concluded that a combined defect of impaired insulin secretion and peripheral insensitivity was present. They showed that significant impairment of insulin secretion alone could be compatible with normal glucose tolerance in subjects genetically determined to become diabetic (identical twins of diabetics and children of two diabetic parents). This observation, however, could be interpreted as showing an increased peripheral sensitivity to insulin. Soeldner et al. (136) observed a similar diminution in insulin secretion in genetic prediabetic men with normal glucose tolerance.

Floyd et al. (137) reported a progressive decrease in amino acid-stimulated insulin release in subclinical diabetics (normal glucose tolerance test but abnormal cortisone glucose tolerance test) and diabetics. In response to oral glucose, insulin secretion in subclinical diabetics was reduced despite normal glucose tolerance while in diabetics, glucose intolerance was associated with insulin levels similar to those in subjects with subclinical diabetes. Berger & Vongaraya (138) found a threefold increase in insulin responses to ingested protein in diabetics. It is not clear if the obesity factor was controlled in this study despite identical mean weights of the diabetics and controls. The elevated fasting insulin levels in the diabetics could, but do not necessarily, suggest coexistent obesity. Adequate insulin secretion, associated with insulin insensitivity, was suggested by the results of Graber et al. (139) in which constant glucose infusions for as long as a week in diabetics and normals resulted in comparable insulin levels despite elevated glucose values in the diabetics. Kreisberg et al. (131) found higher fasting insulin values; greater insulin responses to tolbutamide and to oral and intravenous glucose; and greater insulin/glucose ratios in obese diabetics than in obese non-diabetics. Paulsen et al. (140) reported greater insulin responses to oral glucose in obese children with a positive family history of diabetes than in those with a negative family history despite comparable glucose levels. Frohman et al. (141) studied Seneca Indians, where the prevalence of diabetes is 34 per cent. Diabetics, who were weight matched to nondiabetics, exhibited higher fasting insulin levels and a greater insulin response to oral glucose suggesting the presence of insulin resistance. A correlation existed between per cent of ideal weight and fasting insulin levels in normals but not in diabetics.

The results of these ten studies do not provide a clear answer to the question of insulin secretion and insensitivity in diabetes. The studies are not comparable as they include subjects varying in age, prediabetics, racially semi-isolated groups, etc. Further evaluation of these populations, using a variety of techniques, might indicate whether they are truly distinct from one another with respect to the character of their diabetes.

GLUCAGON

Synthesis and structure.—The complete synthesis of glucagon has been described by Wunsch (142) who synthesized and then combined five partial peptides of the 29 amino acid sequence. Identical with the native hormone in chromatographic and electrophoretic behavior, the product showed hyperglycemic activity in the dog about 50 per cent that of crystallized bovine glucagon. This accomplishment has opened the door for the synthesis of structurally modified hormones to permit the study of structure-function relationships of glucagon. Optical rotatory dispersion studies of glucagon suggest that the hormone exists as a random coil with perhaps one turn of an α-helix near the C-terminal end of the molecule (143). There was no evidence of a defined tertiary structure in solution. Upon standing in acid solution, large aggregates form which eventually become a precipitate consisting of long fibrils in the form of antiparallel β-chains.

Morphologic studies of the α-cell by Lazarus et al. (144) have indicated that the synthesis and release of glucagon are in many aspects similar to that of insulin. α-Cell granules form in the Golgi complex rather than in the endoplasmic reticulum where insulin is formed. The granules then migrate to the cell membrane and are extruded intact to the capillary border of the cell between the plasma membrane and the basement membrane. At this point the granules appear to undergo dissolution and resorption.

Control of secretion.—The quantitation of circulating glucagon levels requires the sensitivity of the radioimmunoassay since levels in the peripheral blood are beneath the limits of bioassay (145). However, problems in three specific areas have plagued the immunoassay. These relate to the difficulty in producing high affinity, high titer antiglucagon sera, plasma peptidases and proteases which degrade the labeled hormone, and the presence in plasma of a nonpancreatic immunologic cross reactant.

The relatively poor antigenicity of glucagon probably relates to its small size and to a limited, but not yet proven, difference in structure between species. The problem has been solved by complexing glucagon to albumin by means of carbodiamide (146) or gluteraldehyde (147). Both methods have resulted in the production of antisera in guinea pigs and rabbits which are suitable for immunoassay. Antibodies produced by the latter method, when preincubated with glucagon, proved capable of neutralizing its effects in the intact rat and the perfused rat liver (147).

Enzymatic destruction of labeled but not of endogenous glucagon has been reported to elevate the circulating glucagon values artificially. Trasylol, a kallikrein inhibitor, is effective in preventing this damage and when added to the immunoassay system results in lower measurable levels (148, 149). These levels (0.4 to 2.0 mμg/ml) are greater than those believed to exist by bioassay (0.03 to 0.1 mμg/ml) (145), and imply that most "immunoreactive glucagon" is not actually glucagon (149).

Immunoreactive glucagon has been identified in all segments of the alimentary tract from the stomach to the colon (150, 151). Varying degrees of immunologic identity exist, with the material from the stomach being least similar, that from the duodenum intermediate, and that from the colon being the most similar to glucagon (146, 151, 152). The variations observed between laboratories relate to the specific characteristics of the individual antisera used and raise the possibility that antisera will be found which will not react with the gut factors. These crossreactants are believed to exist in plasma since immunoreactive glucagon, unlike immunoreactive insulin, persists in plasma after pancreatectomy (153, 154). Consequently, the unknown contribution of the extrapancreatic crossreactant to the total immunoreactive glucagon level restricts the value of the determination.

Attempts to circumvent this difficulty have required the collection of blood from both pancreatic and mesenteric or portal veins. By these methods, Buchanan et al. (153) and Unger et al. (154) have shown that alimentary glucose stimulates the release of the intestinal cross reactant. On the other hand, glucose infusions depress and hypoglycemia stimulates pancreatic glucagon secretion (154, 155). The complete dissociation of glucagon and insulin secretion *in vivo* has been shown with respect to high and low media glucose concentrations (156). The observations force a reconsideration of the significance of glucagon-induced insulin secretion.

Pancreozymin, but not secretin or gastrin, stimulates glucagon secretion when administered intravenously (78). Since all four hormones stimulate insulin release, the authors postulate the existence of an "entero-insular axis" which augments insulin secretion and prevents high substrate concentrations that would otherwise follow ingestion of large meals. Stimulation of glucagon secretion by amino acids has also been reported (157).

Neutral red (aminodimethylaminotoluaminozine hydrochloride) stimulates the release of glucagon resulting in hyperglycemia and glycogenolysis (158, 159). The destructive effect on the α-cells noted with chronic administration suggests that the acute release of glucagon may result from cellular injury. Rats so treated exhibit fasting hypoglycemia and a prolonged hypoglycemic response to insulin, compatible with glucagon deficiency (158).

Actions.—In addition to the well-known effects of the activation of

hepatic phosphorylase and glycogenolysis, glucagon stimulates gluconeogenesis from amino acids (160), pyruvate, and lactate (160, 161) in the
isolated perfused rat liver. The absence of a glucagon effect on gluconeogenesis from fructose suggests that the glucagon-sensitive step lies prior to the
formation of the 3-carbon intermediates (111). In the same system, glucagon
decreases hepatic glucose oxidation and incorporation into protein (114,
162) and stimulates urea production (160, 162, 163). Activation of hepatic
lipase after either *in vivo* or *in vitro* glucagon treatment has been suggested
as the mechanism of its ketogenic action (164). Increased hepatic utilization
of free fatty acids has also been observed after glucagon (165).

Many of the hepatic effects of glucagon are integrated with or antagonized by other hormones. The stimulation of tryptophan transaminase
induction is potentiated by hydrocortisone although the steroid by itself is
inactive (166). This may explain why hydrocortisone alone does not stimulate urea production but enhances the effect of glucagon. The glucagon
effects on hepatic glucose output and urea production are both antagonized
by insulin at several concentrations (167). Insulin is much more effective
in suppressing glucagon-stimulated urea production than hepatic glucose
output.

Moderate to large doses of glucagon (1–50 $\mu g/kg$) resulted in a fall in
plasma free fatty acids in unanesthetized dogs, presumably mediated by the
stimulation of insulin secretion (168). With large doses a rebound occurred
at one hour, possibly because of stimulation of catecholamine release. With
a dose calculated to reproduce the endogenous secretion rate (1 $m\mu g/kg/min$)
a persistent elevation of plasma free fatty acids was observed (169). This
suggests that the adipokinetic effect of glucagon may be important under
the physiologic conditions that stimulate its secretion, such as fasting and
hypoglycemia.

A comparison of the effects of glucagon and epinephrine on liver glycogen
and blood glucose has been made in the dog (170). Glucagon was 10 to 25
times more active than epinephrine on a weight basis when injected intravenously and more than 100 times as active when administered by portal
vein. Epinephrine produced greater results when infused in the femoral vein
as compared to the portal vein. No rise in lactate (indicating muscle glycogenolysis) occurred during endoportal infusion, which indicates that very
little of the hormone escaped hepatic inactivation. Previous studies from the
same laboratory showed similar results in the perfused rat liver and the
overall conclusion was that only glucagon is a physiologic glycogenolytic
agent for the liver. These experiments also indicate the potential hazards in
the interpretation of results using pharmacologic amounts of hormones. A
convincing argument for the role of glucagon as an essential hormone has
been presented by Sokal (171).

Pharmacologic doses of glucagon stimulate the secretion of catecholamines
from the human adrenal (172). This has prompted the use of glucagon as a
provocative agent for the diagnosis of pheochromocytoma. When given to

patients with pheochromocytomas, glucagon resulted in a greater rise in plasma catecholamines three minutes after injection than in controls (173). The rise in insulin levels was similar in both groups and no correlation existed between the level of pressor amines and the insulin level.

The effects of glucagon on myocardial function were studied because catecholamines are believed to exert their actions on the myocardium through the formation of cyclic AMP. Augmented contractility and increased heart rate could be demonstrated by glucagon in man, dog, and cat (174). Similar effects of glucagon and isoproterenol were observed in the isolated perfused rat heart with two exceptions: propranolol blocked the effect of isoproterenol but not that of glucagon; and glucagon produced no net change in cyclic AMP but the concentration was doubled by isoproterenol (175). Therefore, the effects of glucagon on the heart, although similar to those of β-adrenergic agents, may occur through different mechanisms. Future experiments will have to determine the exact relationship between the effect of glucagon on the adenyl cyclase system and its effects on carbohydrate and lipid metabolism.

LITERATURE CITED

1. Smith, L. F. Species variation in the amino acid sequence of insulin. *Am. J. Med.*, **40**, 662–66 (1966)

2. Falkmer, S., Wilson, S. Comparative aspects of the immunology and biology of insulin. *Diabetologica*, **3**, 519–28 (1967)

3. Berson, S. A., Yalow, R. S. Insulin in blood and insulin antibodies. *Am. J. Med.*, **40**, 676–90 (1966)

4. Carpenter, F. H. Relationship of structure to biological activity of insulin as revealed by degradative studies. *Am. J. Med.*, **40**, 750–58 (1966)

5. Arquilla, E. R., Ooms, H., Mercola, K. Immunological and biological properties of iodoinsulin labeled with one or less atoms of iodine per molecule. *J. Clin. Invest.*, **47**, 474–87 (1968)

6. Mirsky, I. A., Kawamura, K. Heterogeneity of crystalline insulin. *Endocrinology*, **78**, 1115–19 (1966)

7. Renold, A. E., Steinke, J., Soeldner, J. S., Antoniades, H. N., Smith, R. E. Immunological response to the prolonged administration of heterologous and homologous insulin in cattle. *J. Clin. Invest.*, **45**, 702–13 (1966)

8. LeCompte, P. M., Steinke, J., Soeldner, J. S., Renold, A. E. Changes in the islets of Langerhans in cows injected with heterologous and homologous insulin. *Diabetes*, **15**, 586–96 (1966)

9. Grodsky, G. M., Feldman, R., Toreson, W. E., Lee, J. C. Diabetes mellitus in rabbits immunized with insulin. *Diabetes*, **15**, 579–85 (1966)

10. Patterson, R., Lucena, G., Metz, R., Roberts, M. The use of reaginic antibody to demonstrate induced autoantibodies against insulin. Program. *Am. Soc. Clin. Invest. Ann. Meeting, May 1968, Atlantic City, N. J., Abstr. No. 228*

11. Katsoyannis, P. G. The chemical synthesis of human and sheep insulin. *Am. J. Med.*, **40**, 652–61 (1966)

12. Humbel, R. E. Biosynthesis of the two chains of insulin. *Proc. Natl. Acad. Sci. U.S.*, **53**, 853–59 (1965)

13. Meek, J. C., Doffing, K. M., Bolinger, R. E. Radioimmunoassay of insulin A and B chains in normal and diabetic human plasma. *Diabetes*, **71**-61–66 (1968)

14. Meek, J. C., Bolinger, R. E. The biologic activity of insulin A and B chains as determined by the rat diaphragm and epididymal fat pad. *Biochemistry*, **5**, 3198–203 (1966)

15. Marglin, A., Cushman, S. W. A biological activity of the A-chain of insulin and the inactivity of a synthetic analog containing an intact intrachain disulfide bridge. *Bio-*

chem. Biophys. Res. Commun., **29**, 710–16 (1967)

16. Steiner, D. F., Cunningham, D., Spigelman, L., Aten, B. Insulin biosynthesis: evidence for a precursor. *Science*, **157**, 697–700 (1967)

17. Yip, C. C., Lin, B. J. Amino acid composition of bovine "proinsulin". *Biochem. Biophys. Res. Commun.*, **29**, 382–87 (1967)

18. Frank, B. H., Veros, A. J. Physical studies on proinsulin—molecular weight, association behavior and spectral studies. *Fed. Proc.*, **27**, 392 (1968)

19. Chance, R. E., Ellis, R. M. Isolation and characterization of porcine proinsulin. *Fed. Proc.*, **27**, 392 (1968)

20. Chance, R. E., Ellis, R. M., Bromer, W. W. Porcine proinsulin: characterization and amino acid sequence. *Science*, **161**, 165–67 (1968)

21. Steiner, D. F., Cho, S., Bayliss, C., Hallund, O. On the isolation and some properties of bovine proinsulin. *Diabetes*, **17**, 309 (1968)

22. Shaw, W. N., Chance, R. E. The effect of porcine proinsulin *in vitro* on glucose oxidation and fatty acid synthesis by adipose tissue of the rat. *Diabetes*, **17**, 310 (1968)

23. Roth, J., Gorden, P., Pastan, I. "Big insulin": a new component of plasma insulin in man. Program. *Am. Soc. Clin. Invest. Ann. Meeting, May 1968, Atlantic City, N. J., Abstr. No. 249*

24. Elliott, R. B., O'Brien, D., Roy, C. C. An abnormal insulin in juvenile diabetes mellitus. *Diabetes*, **14**, 780–87 (1965)

25. Roy, C. C., Elliott, R. B., Shapcott, D. J., O'Brien, D. Resistance of insulin to insulinase, a genetic discriminate in diabetes mellitus. *Lancet*, **II**, 1433–35 (1966)

26. Vallance-Owen, J. Insulin antagonists. *On the Nature and Treatment of Diabetes*, 340–53 (Leibel, B. S., Wrenshall, G. A., Eds., Excerpta Med. Found., Amsterdam, Netherlands, 804 pp., 1965)

27. O'Brien, D., Shapcott, D., Roy, C. C. Further studies on an abnormal insulin of diabetes mellitus. *Diabetes*, **16**, 572–75 (1967)

28. Kimmel, J. R., Pollock, H. G. Studies of human insulin from nondiabetic and diabetic pancreas. *Diabetes*, **16**, 687–94 (1967)

29. Jarrett, R. J., Keen, H., Track, N.

30. Parry, D. G., Taylor, K. W. The effects of sugars on incorporation of ³H-leucine into insulins. *Biochem. J.*, **100**, 2C–4C (1966)

31. Howell, S. L., Taylor, K. W. The secretion of newly synthesized insulin *in vitro*. *Biochem. J.*, **102**, 922–27 (1967)

32. Grodsky, G. M., Bennett, L. L., Smith, D. F., Schmid, F. G. Effect of pulse administration of glucose or glucagon on insulin secretion *in vitro*. *Metabolism*, **16**, 222–33 (1967)

33. Martin, J. M., Bambers, G. Insulin secretion in glucosamine-induced hyperglycemia in rats. *Am. J. Physiol.*, **209**, 797–802 (1965)

34. Hug, G., Schubert, W. K. Serum insulin in type 1 glycogenosis. Effect of galactose or fructose administration. *Diabetes*, **16**, 791–95 (1967)

35. Kuzuya, T., Kanazawa, Y., Kosaka, K. Plasma insulin response to intravenously administered xylitol in dogs. *Metabolism*, **15**, 1149–52 (1966)

36. Floyd, J. C., Jr., Fajans, S. S., Conn, J. W., Knopf, R. F., Rull, J. Insulin secretion in response to protein ingestion. *J. Clin. Invest.*, **45**, 1479–86 (1966)

37. Floyd, J. C., Jr., Fajans, S. S., Conn, J. W., Knopf, R. F., Rull, J. Stimulation of insulin secretion by amino acids. *Ibid.*, 1487–1502

38. Rabinowitz, D., Merimee, T. J., Burgess, J. A., Riggs, L. Growth hormone and insulin release after arginine: indifference to hyperglycemia and epinephrine. *J. Clin. Endocrinol.*, **26**, 1170–72 (1966)

39. Fajans, S. S., Floyd, J. C., Jr., Knopf, R. F., Guntsche, E. M., Rull, J. A., Thiffault, C. A., Conn, J. W. A difference in mechanism by which leucine and other amino acids induce insulin release. *J. Clin. Endocrinol.*, **27**, 1600–6 (1967)

40. Fajans, S. S., Floyd, J. C., Jr., Knopf, R. F., Rull, J., Guntsche, E. M., Conn, J. W. Benzothiadiazine suppression of insulin release from normal and abnormal islet tissue in man. *J. Clin. Invest.*, **45**, 481–92 (1966)

41. Manns, J. G., Boda, J. M. Insulin release by acetate, propionate, butyrate, and glucose in lambs and

adult sheep. *Am. J. Physiol.*, **212**, 747–55 (1967)

42. Sanbar, S., Martin, J. M. Stimulation by octanoate of insulin release from isolated rat pancreas. *Metabolism*, **16**, 482–84 (1967)

43. Linscheer, W. G., Slone, D., Chalmers, T. C. Effects of octanoic acid on serum levels of free fatty acids, insulin, and glucose in patients with cirrhosis and in healthy volunteers. *Lancet*, **I**, 593–97 (1967)

44. Seyffert, W. A., Jr., Madison. L. L. Physiologic effects of metabolic fuels on carbohydrate metabolism. 1. Acute effect of elevation of plasma free fatty acids on hepatic glucose output, peripheral glucose utilization, serum insulin, and plasma glucagon levels. *Diabetes*, **16**, 765–76 (1967)

45. Malaisse, W. J., Malaisse-Lagae, F., Wright, P. H. Effect of fasting upon insulin secretion in the rat. *Am. J. Physiol.*, **213**, 843–48 (1967)

46. Genuth, S. M. Effects of prolonged fasting on insulin secretion. *Diabetes*, **15**, 798–806 (1966)

47. Freinkel, N., Mager, M., Vinnick, L. Cyclicity in the interrelationships between plasma insulin and glucose during starvation in normal young men. *J. Lab. Clin. Med.*, **71**, 171–78 (1968)

48. Howland, R. J., Nowell, N. W. Seasonal changes of plasma insulin concentration in the rat. *J. Endocrinol.*, **40**, vi–vii (1968)

49. Schalch, D. S. The influence of physical stress and exercise on growth hormone and insulin secretion in man. *J. Lab. Clin. Med.*, **69**, 256–69 (1967)

50. Nikkila, E. A., Taskinen, M. R., Miettinen, T. A., Pelkonen, R., Poppius, H. Effect of muscular exercise on insulin secretion. *Diabetes*, **17**, 209–18 (1968)

51. Huff, T. A., Horton, E. S., Lebovitz, H. E. Abnormal insulin secretion in myotonic dystrophy. *New Engl. J. Med.*, **277**, 837–41 (1967)

52. Grodsky, G. M., Bennett, L. L. Cation requirements for insulin secretion in the isolated perfused pancreas. *Diabetes*, **15**, 910–13 (1966)

53. Milner, R. D. G., Hales, C. N. Cations and the secretion of insulin. *Biochim. Biophys. Acta*, **150**, 165–67 (1968)

54. Hales, C. N., Milner, R. D. G. The role of sodium and potassium in insulin secretion from rabbit pancreas. *J. Physiol. (London)*, **194**, 725–43 (1968)

55. Martin, J. M., Gagliardino, J. J. Effect of growth hormone on the isolated pancreatic islets of rat *in vitro*. *Nature*, **213**, 630–31 (1967)

56. Bouman, P. R., Bosboom, R. S. Effects of growth hormone and of hypophysectomy on the release of insulin from rat pancreas *in vitro*. *Acta Endocrinol.*, **50**, 202–12 (1965)

57. Frohman, L. A., MacGillivray, M. H., Aceto, T., Jr. Acute effects of human growth hormone on insulin secretion and glucose utilization in normal and growth hormone deficient subjects. *J. Clin. Endocrinol.*, **27**, 561–67 (1967)

58. Campbell, J., Rastogi, K. S. Growth hormone-induced diabetes and high levels of serum insulin in dogs. *Diabetes*, **15**, 30–43 (1966)

59. Sonksen, P. H., Greenwood, F. C., Ellis, J. P., Lowy, C., Rutherford, A., Nabarro, J. D. N. Changes of carbohydrate tolerance in acromegaly with progress of the disease and in response to treatment. *J. Clin. Endocrinol.*, **27**, 1418–30 (1967)

60. Beck, P., Daughaday, W. H. Human placental lactogen: studies of its acute metabolic effects and disposition in normal man. *J. Clin. Invest.*, **46**, 103–10 (1967)

61. Samaan, N., Yen, S. C. C., Gonzalez, D., Pearson, O. H. Metabolic effects of placental lactogen (HPL) in man. *J. Clin. Endocrinol.*, **28**, 485–91 (1968)

62. Porte, D., Jr., Graber, A. L., Kuzuya, T., Williams, R. H. The effect of epinephrine on immunoreactive insulin levels in man. *J. Clin. Invest.*, **45**, 228–36 (1966)

63. Kris, A. O., Miller, R. E., Wherry, F. E., Mason, J. W. Inhibition of insulin secretion by infused epinephrine in rhesus monkeys. *Endocrinology*, **78**, 87–97 (1966)

64. Malaisse, W., Malaisse-Lagae, F., Wright, P. H., Ashmore, J. Effects of adrenergic and cholinergic agents upon insulin secretion *in vitro*. *Endocrinology*, **80**, 975–78 (1967)

65. Porte, D., Jr. A receptor mechanism for the inhibition of insulin release by epinephrine in man. *J. Clin. Invest.*, **46**, 86–94 (1967)

66. Porte, D., Jr. Beta adrenergic stimu-

lation of insulin release in man. *Diabetes*, **16**, 150–55 (1967)

67. Frohman, L. A., Ezdinli, E. Z., Javid, R. Effect of vagotomy and vagal stimulation on insulin secretion. *Diabetes*, **16**, 443–48 (1967)

68. Malaisse, W. J., Malaisse-Lagae, F., Mayhew, D. A possible role for the adenylcyclase system in insulin secretion. *J. Clin. Invest.*, **46**, 1724–34 (1967)

69. Turtle, J. R., Littleton, G. K., Kipnis, D. M. Stimulation of insulin secretion by theophylline. *Nature*, **213**, 727–28 (1967)

70. Lebovitz, H. E., Pooler, K. Puromycin potentiation of corticotropin-induced insulin release. *Endocrinology*, **80**, 656–62 (1967)

71. Lebovitz, H. E., Pooler, K. ACTH-mediated insulin secretion: effect of aminophylline. *Ibid.*, **81**, 558–64

72. Crockford, P. M., Porte, D., Jr., Wood, F. C., Jr., Williams, R. H. Effect of glucagon on serum insulin, plasma glucose and free fatty acids in man. *Metabolism*, **15**, 114–22 (1966)

73. Samols, E., Marri, G., Marks, V. Interrelationship of glucagon, insulin and glucose. The insulinogenic effect of glucagon. *Diabetes*, **15**, 855–66 (1966)

74. Devrim, S., Recant, L. Effect of glucagon on insulin release *in vitro*. *Lancet*, **II**, 1227–28 (1966)

75. McIntyre, N., Holdsworth, C. D., Turner, D. S. Intestinal factors in the control of insulin secretion. *J. Clin. Endocrinol.*, **25**, 1317–24 (1965)

76. Unger, R. H., Ketterer, H., Eisentraut, A., Dupre, J. Effect of secretin on insulin secretion. *Lancet*, **II**, 24–26 (1966)

77. Dupre, J., Rojas, L., White, J. J., Unger, R. H., Beck, J. C. Effects of secretin on insulin and glucagon in portal and peripheral blood in man. *Lancet*, **II**, 26–27 (1966)

78. Unger, R. H., Ketterer, H., Dupre, J., Eisentraut, A. M. The effects of secretin, pancreozymin, and gastrin on insulin and glucagon secretion in anesthetized dogs. *J. Clin Invest.*, **46**, 630–45 (1967)

79. Meade, R. C., Kneubuhler, H. A., Schulte, W. J., Barboriak, J. J. Stimulation of insulin secretion by pancreozymin. *Diabetes*, **16**, 141–44 (1967)

80. Mahler, R. J., Weisberg, H. Failure of endogenous stimulation of secretin and pancreozymin release to influence serum-insulin. *Lancet*, **I**, 448–51 (1968)

81. Nelson, J. K., Rabinowitz, D., Merimee, T. J. Effect of epinephrine on insulin release in man induced by secretin. *Nature*, **215**, 883–84 (1967)

82. Boyns, D. R., Jarrett, R. J., Keen, H. Intestinal hormones and plasma insulin: an insulinotropic action of secretin. *Brit. Med. J.*, **2**, 676–78 (1967)

83. Ohsawa, N., Kuzuya, T., Tanioka, T., Kanazawa, Y., Ibayashi, H., Nakao, K. Effect of administration of ACTH on insulin secretion in dogs. *Endocrinology*, **81**, 925–27 (1967)

84. Kaneto, A., Kosaka, K., Nakao, K. Effects of the neurohypophysial hormones on insulin secretion. *Endocrinology*, **81**, 783–90 (1967)

85. Mintz, D. H., Finster, J., Stept, M. Effect of angiotensin II on immunoreactive insulin. *J. Clin. Endocrinol.*, **27**, 671–78 (1967)

86. Malaisse, W. J., Malaisse-Lagae, F., McCraw, E. F. Effects of thyroid function upon insulin secretion. *Diabetes*, **16**, 643–46 (1967)

87. Spellacy, W. N., Carlson, K. L., Birk, S. A. Carbohydrate metabolic studies after six cycles of combined type oral contraceptive tablets. Measurement of plasma insulin and blood glucose levels. *Diabetes*, **16**, 590–94 (1967)

88. Chu, P. C., Goodner, C. J. Lack of functional suppression of pancreatic beta cells during chronic insulin replacement in the rat. *Endocrinology*, **82**, 296–302 (1968)

89. Kaneto, A., Kosaka, K., Nakao, K. Effects of stimulation of the vagus nerve on insulin secretion. *Endocrinology*, **80**, 530–36 (1967)

90. Daniel, P. M., Henderson, J. R. The effect of vagal stimulation on plasma insulin and glucose levels in the baboon. *J. Physiol. (London)*, **192**, 317–27 (1967)

91. Ota, K., Mori, S., Inou, T., Kanazawa, Y., Kuzuya, T. Endocrine function of the pancreatic allograft. *Endocrinology*, **82**, 731–41 (1968)

92. Frohman, L. A., Bernardis, L. L. Growth hormone and insulin levels in weanling rats with ventromedial hypothalamic lesions. *Endocrinology*, **82**, 1125–32 (1968)

93. Frohman, L. A., Bernardis, L. L., Schnatz, J. D., Burek, L. Effect of ventromedial hypothalamic nucleus destruction on carbohydrate and lipid metabolism in weanling rats. Program *3rd Intern. Congr. Endocrinol., July 1968, Mexico City, Abstr. No. 239*

94. Goldman, J. K., Bernardis, L. L., Frohman, L. A., Schnatz, J. D. Glucose and fatty acid utilization by tissues of weanling rats with ventromedial hypothalamic lesions. *Diabetes,* **17,** 301 (1968)

95. Bernardis, L. L., Frohman, L. A. Insulin secretion and obesity after hypothalamic lesions in weanling rats. *Fed. Proc.,* **27,** 320 (1968)

96. Chowers, I., Lavy, S., Halpern, L. Effect of insulin administered intracisternally on the glucose level of the blood and the cerebrospinal fluid in vagotomized dogs. *Exptl. Neurol.,* **14,** 383–89 (1966)

97. Kaneto, A., Miki, E., Kosaka, K., Okinaka, S., Nakao, K. Effects of stimulation of the cingulate gyrus on insulin secretion. *Endocrinology,* **77,** 617–24 (1965)

98. Stimmler, L. Disappearance of immunoreactive insulin in normal and adult-onset diabetic subjects. *Diabetes,* **16,** 652–55 (1967)

99. Tomasi, T., Sledz, D., Wales, J. K., Recant, L. Insulin half-life in normal and diabetic subjects. *Proc. Soc. Exptl. Biol. Med.,* **126,** 315–17 (1967)

100. Arnould, Y., Cantraine, F., Ooms, H. A., Delcroix, C., Franckson, J. R. M. Kinetics of plasma disappearance of labelled iodoinsulins following intravenous injection. *Arch. Intern. Pharmacodyn.,* **166,** 225–37 (1967)

101. Field, J. B., Webster, M., Drapanas, T. Evaluation of factors regulating hepatic control of insulin homeostasis. Program. *Am. Soc. Clin. Invest. Ann. Meeting, May 1968, Atlantic City, N. J., Abstr. No. 99*

102. Campbell, J., Rastogi, K. S. Effects of growth hormone on the rate of disappearance of insulin from blood in depancreatized and Houssay dogs. *Metabolism,* **16,** 562–71 (1967)

103. Lopez-Quijada, C., Goni, P. M. Liver and insulin: presence of insulin in bile. *Metabolism,* **16,** 514–21 (1967)

104. Daniel, P. M., Henderson, J. R. Insulin in bile and other body fluids. *Lancet,* **I,** 1256–57 (1967)

105. Chamberlain, M. J., Stimmler, L. The renal handling of insulin. *J. Clin Invest.,* **46,** 911–19 (1967)

106. Beck, L. V., Fedynskyj, N. Evidence from combined immunoassay and radioautography procedures that intact insulin-^{125}I molecules are concentrated by mouse kidney proximal tubule cells. *Endocrinology,* **81,** 475–85 (1967)

107. Rasio, E. A., Hampers, C. L., Soeldner, J. S., Cahill, G. F., Jr. Diffusion of glucose, insulin, inulin, and Evans blue protein into thoracic duct lymph of man. *J. Clin. Invest.,* **46,** 903–10 (1967)

108. Rasio, E. A., Hill, G. J., Soeldner, J. S., Herrera, M. G. Effect of pancreatectomy on glucose tolerance and extracellular fluid insulin in the dog. *Diabetes,* **16,** 551–56 (1967)

109. Edelman, P. M., Schwartz, I. L. Subcellular distribution of I^{131}-insulin in striated muscle. *Am. J. Med.,* **40,** 695–708 (1966)

110. Zierler, K. L. Possible mechanisms of insulin action on membrane potential and ion fluxes. *Am. J. Med.,* **40,** 735–39 (1966)

111. Exton, J. H., Jefferson, L. S., Jr., Butcher, R. W., Park, C. R. Gluconeogenesis in the perfused liver. The effects of fasting, alloxan diabetes, glucagon, epinephrine, adenosine $3',5'$-monophosphate and insulin. *Am. J. Med.,* **40,** 709–15 (1966)

112. Haft, D. E. Effects of insulin on metabolism of perfused livers of rats made acutely diabetic by anti-insulin serum injection. *Diabetes,* **17,** 251–55 (1968)

113. Snyder, P. J., Cahill, G. F., Jr. Selective effect of insulin on glucose-U-C^{14} metabolism in rabbit liver slices. *Am. J. Physiol.,* **209,** 616–20 (1965)

114. Williamson, J. R., Garcia, A., Renold, A. E., Cahill, G. F., Jr. Studies on the perfused rat liver. I. Effects of glucagon and insulin on glucose metabolism. *Diabetes,* **15,** 183–87 (1966)

115. Mortimore, G. E., King, E., Jr., Mondon, C. E., Glinsmann, W. A. Effects of insulin on net carbohydrate alterations in perfused rat liver. *Am. J. Physiol.,* **212,** 179–83 (1967)

116. Starzl, T. E., Scanlan, W. A., Thornton, F. H., Wendel, R. M., Stearn, B., Lazarus, R. E., McAllister, W., Shoemaker, W. C. Effect of insulin on glucose metabolism in the dog after portacaval transposition. *Am. J. Physiol.*, **209**, 221–26 (1965)

117. Wrenshall, G. A., Vranic, M., Cowan, J. S., Rappaport, A. M. Effects of sudden deprivation and restoration of insulin secretion on glucose metabolism in dogs. *Diabetes*, **14**, 689–95 (1965)

118. Mahler, R. J., Szabo, O. Insulin action upon insulin-insensitive tissues following impaired degradation of the hormone. *Proc. Soc. Exptl. Biol. Med.*, **125**, 879–82 (1967)

119. Prasannan, K. G., Subrahmanyam, K. Effect of insulin on the synthesis of glycogen in cerebral cortical slices of alloxan diabetic rats. *Endocrinology*, **82**, 1–6 (1968)

120. DiGirolamo, M., Rudman, D. Species differences in glucose metabolism and insulin responsiveness of adipose tissue. *Am. J. Physiol.*, **210**, 721–27 (1966)

121. Fain, J. N., Kovacev, V. P., Scow, R. O. Antilipolytic effect of insulin in isolated fat cells of the rat. *Endocrinology*, **78**, 773–78 (1966)

122. Chlouverakis, C. Factors affecting the inhibitory action of insulin on lipolysis in a glucose-free medium. *Endocrinology*, **81**, 521–26 (1967)

123. Reaven, G. M., Lerner, R. L., Stern, M. P., Farquhar, J. W. Role of insulin in endogenous hypertriglyceridemia. *J. Clin. Invest.*, **46**, 1756–67 (1967)

124. Wool, I. G., Cavicchi, P. Insulin regulation of protein synthesis by muscle ribosomes: effect of the hormone on translation of messenger RNA for a regulatory protein. *Proc. Natl. Acad. Sci. U.S.*, **56**, 991–98 (1966)

125. Wool, I. G., Rampersad, O. R., Moyer, A. N. Effect of insulin and diabetes on protein synthesis by ribosomes from heart muscle. Significance for theories of the hormone's mechanism of action. *Am. J. Med.*, **40**, 716–23 (1966)

126. Young, V. R., Chen, S. C., MacDonald, J. The sedimentation of rat skeletal-muscle ribosomes. Effect of hydrocortisone, insulin and diet. *Biochem. J.*, **106**, 913–19 (1968)

127. Miller, L. V., Beigelman, P. M. Effects of varying concentrations of insulin upon protein synthesis in isolated fat cells. *Endocrinology*, **81**, 386–89 (1967)

128. Weber, G., Convery, H. J. H. Insulin: inducer of glucose-6-phosphate dehydrogenase. *Life Sci.*, **5**, 1139–46 (1966)

129. Bagdade, J. D., Bierman, E. L., Porte, D., Jr. The significance of basal insulin levels in the evaluation of the insulin response to glucose in diabetic and nondiabetic subjects. *J. Clin. Invest.*, **46**, 1549–57 (1967)

130. Benedetti, A., Simpson, R. G., Grodsky, G. M., Forsham, P. H. Exaggerated insulin response to glucagon in simple obesity. *Diabetes*, **16**, 666–69 (1967)

131. Kreisberg, R. A., Boshell, B. R., DiPlacido, J., Roddam, R. F. Insulin secretion in obesity. *New Engl. J. Med.*, **276**, 314–19 (1967)

132. Salans, L. B., Knittle, J. L., Hirsch, J. The role of adipose cell size and adipose tissue insulin sensitivity in the carbohydrate intolerance of human obesity. *J. Clin. Invest.*, **47**, 153–65 (1968)

133. Seltzer, H. S., Allen, E. W., Herron, A. L., Jr., Brennan, M. T. Insulin secretion in response to glycemic stimulus: relation of delayed initial response to carbohydrate intolerance in mild diabetes mellitus. *J. Clin. Invest.*, **46**, 323–35 (1967)

134. Cerasi, E., Luft, R. "What is inherited-what is added" hypothesis for the pathogenesis of diabetes mellitus. *Diabetes*, **16**, 615–27 (1967)

135. Perley, M. J., Kipnis, D. M. Plasma insulin responses to oral and intravenous glucose: studies in normal and diabetic subjects. *J. Clin. Invest.*, **46**, 1954–62 (1967)

136. Soeldner, J. S., Gleason, R. E., Williams, R. F., Garcia, M. J., Beardwood, D. M., Marble, A. Diminished serum insulin response to glucose in genetic prediabetic males with normal glucose tolerance. *Diabetes*, **17**, 17–26 (1968)

137. Floyd, J. C., Jr., Fajans, S. S., Conn, J. W., Thiffault, C., Knopf, R. F., Guntsche, E. Secretion of insulin induced by amino acids and glucose in diabetes mellitus. *J. Clin. Endocrinol.*, **28**, 266–76 (1968)

138. Berger, S., Vongaraya, N. Insulin response to ingested protein in diabetes. *Diabetes*, **15**, 303–6 (1966)

139. Graber, A. L., Wood, F. C., Jr., Wil-

liams, R. H. Serum immunoreactive insulin response during prolonged glucose infusions in nondiabetic and diabetic humans. *Diabetes*, **16**, 145–49 (1967)

140. Paulsen, E. P., Richenderfer, L., Ginsberg-Fellner, F. Plasma glucose, free fatty acids, and immunoreactive insulin in sixty-six obese children. Studies in reference to a family history of diabetes mellitus. *Diabetes*, **17**, 261–69 (1968)

141. Frohman, L. A., Doeblin, T. D., Emerling, F. G. Glucose and insulin measurements in normal and diabetic Seneca Indians. *Diabetes*, **17**, 324 (1968)

142. Wunsch, E. The complete synthesis of glucagon (in German). *Z. Naturforsch.*, **22**, 1269–76 (1967)

143. Gratzer, W. B., Beaven, G. H., Rattle, H. W. E., Bradbury, E. M. A confirmational study of glucagon. *European J. Biochem.*, **3**, 276–83 (1968)

144. Lazarus, S. S., Shapiro, S., Volk, B. W. Secretory granule formation and release in rabbit pancreatic A-cells. *Diabetes*, **17**, 152–60 (1968)

145. Sokal, J. E., Ezdinli, E. Z. Basal plasma glucagon levels of man. *J. Clin. Invest.*, **46**, 778–85 (1967)

146. Assan, R., Rosselin, G., Tchobroutsky, G. Glucagon in blood and immunological specificity of glucagon molecule. *Protein and Polypeptide Hormones*, Part 1, *Proc. Intern. Symp., May 1968, Liège*, 87–90 (Margoulies, M., Ed., Excerpta Med. Found., Amsterdam, Netherlands, 325 pp., 1968)

147. Frohman, L. A., Sokal, J. E., Reichlin, M. Inhibition of biologic activity of glucagon by anti-glucagon serum. *Protein and Polypeptide Hormones*, Part 3, *Proc. Intern. Symp., May 1968, Liège* (Excerpta Med. Found., Amsterdam, Netherlands, 1968) (In press)

148. Eisentraut, A. M., Whissen, N., Unger, R. H. Incubation damage in the radioimmunoassay for human plasma glucagon and its prevention with "trasylol". *Am. J. Med. Sci.*, **255**, 137–42 (1968)

149. Hazzard, W. R., Crockford, P. M., Buchanan, K. D., Vance, J. E., Chen, R., Williams, R. H. A double antibody immunoassay for glucagon. *Diabetes*, **17**, 179–86 (1968)

150. Unger, R. H., Ketterer, H., Eisentraut, A. M. Distribution of immunoassayable glucagon in gastrointestinal tissues. *Metabolism*, **15**, 865–67 (1966)

151. Samols, E., Tyler, J., Megyesi, C., Marks, V. Immunochemical glucagon in human pancreas, gut, and plasma. *Lancet*, **II**, 727–29 (1966)

152. Schopman, W., Hackeng, W. H. L., Steendijk, C. The purification of ^{125}I-glucagon of high specific activity for radioimmunochemical estimation of glucagon and a qualitative comparison of glucagon from different sources. *Acta Endocrinol.*, **54**, 527–40 (1967)

153. Buchanan, K. D., Vance, J. E., Aoki, T. Williams, R. H. Rise in serum immunoreactive glucagon after intrajejunal glucose in pancreatectomized dogs. *Proc. Soc. Exptl. Biol. Med.*, **126**, 813–15 (1967)

154. Unger, R. H., Ohneda, A., Valverde, I. Eisentraut, A. M. Exton, J. Characterization of the responses of circulating glucagon-like immunoreactivity to intraduodenal and intravenous administration of glucose. *J. Clin. Invest.*, **47**, 48–65 (1968)

155. Ohneda, A., Parada, E., Eisentraut, A., Unger, R. H. Control of pancreatic glucagon secretion by glucose. *Diabetes*, **17**, 312 (1968)

156. Vance, J. E., Buchanan, K. D., Challoner, D. R., Williams, R. H. Effect of glucose concentration on insulin and glucagon release from isolated islets of Langerhans of the rat. *Diabetes*, **17**, 187–93 (1968)

157. Ohneda, A., Parada, E., Eisentraut, A., Unger, R. Aminogenic hyperglucagonemia: demonstration of a new physiologic role of pancreatic glucagon. Program. *Am. Soc. Clin. Invest., Ann. Meeting, May 1968, Atlantic City. N. J., Abstr. No. 219*

158. Okuda, T., Grollman, A. Action of neutral red on the secretion of glucagon and glucose metabolism in the rat. *Endocrinology*, **78**, 195–203 (1966)

159. Nevis, H. C., Stiller, A., Woll, J., Lawrence, A. M. Neutral red induced hyperglucagonemia. *Endocrinology*, **82**, 1042–46 (1968)

160. Garcia, A., Williamson, J. R., Cahill, G. F., Jr. Studies on the perfused rat liver. II. Effect of glucagon on gluconeogenesis. *Diabetes*, **15**, 188–93 (1966)

161. Exton, J. H., Park, C. R. The stimu-

lation of gluconeogenesis from lactate by epinephrine, glucagon, and cyclic 3',5'-adenylate in the perfused rat liver. *Pharmacol. Rev.*, **18**, 181–88 (1966)

162. Miller, L. L. Direct actions of insulin, glucagon, and epinephrine on the isolated perfused rat liver. *Fed. Proc.*, **24**, 737–44 (1965)

163. Sokal, J. E. Effect of glucagon on gluconeogenesis by the isolated perfused rat liver. *Endocrinology*, **78**, 538–48 (1966)

164. Bewsher, P. D., Ashmore, J. Ketogenic and lipolytic effects of glucagon on liver. *Biochem. Biophys. Res. Commun.*, **24**, 431–36 (1966)

165. Gorman, C. K., Salter, J. M., Penhos, J. C., Effect of glucagon on lipids and glucose in normal and eviscerated rats and on isolated perfused rat livers. *Metabolism*, **16**, 1140–57 (1967)

166. Greengard, O., Baker, G. T. Glucagon, starvation, and the induction of liver enzymes by hydrocortisone. *Science*, **154**, 1461–62 (1966)

167. Mackrell, D. *Antagonism between effects of insulin and glucagon on glycogenolysis and gluconeogenesis in the isolated perfused rat liver* (Master's thesis, State Univ. New York at Buffalo, 1968)

168. Sokal, J. E., Aydin, A., Kraus, G. Effect of glucagon on plasma free fatty acids of normal and pancreatectomized dogs. *Am. J. Physiol.*, **211**, 1334–38 (1966)

169. Lefebvre, P. The physiological effect of glucagon on fat-mobilisation. *Diabetologia*, **2**, 130–32 (1966)

170. Ezdinli, E. Z., Sokal. J. E. Comparison of glucagon and epinephrine effects in the dog. *Endocrinology*, **78**, 47–54 (1966)

171. Sokal, J. E. Glucagon—an essential hormone. *Am. J. Med.*, **41**, 331–41 (1966)

172. Kuschke, H. J., Klusmann, H., Scholkens, B. Studies of the effect of glucagon on the sympatho-adrenal system in man. (in German) *Klin. Wochschr.*, **44**, 1297–1300 (1966)

173. Cremer, G. M., Molnar, G. D., Moxness, K. E., Sheps, S. G., Maher, F. T., Jones, J. D. Hormonal and biochemical response to glucagon administration in patients with pheochromocytoma and in control subjects. *Mayo Clin. Proc.*, **43**, 161–76 (1968)

174. Glick, G., Parmley, W. W., Wechsler, A. S., Sonnenblick, E. H. Glucagon: its positive inotropic and chronotropic properties as studied in the cat papillary muscle preparation, intact dog heart, and conscious human subjects. *Am. J. Cardiol.*, **21**, 99–100 (1968)

175. LaRaia, P. J., Craig. R. J., Reddy, W. J. Glucagon: biochemical mechanisms and contractility effects on the heart. *Am. J. Cardiol.*, **21**, 107 (1968)

NEUROENDOCRINE ASPECTS OF MAMMALIAN REPRODUCTION[1,2,3]

By John W. Everett

Department of Anatomy, Duke University School of Medicine
Durham, North Carolina

The concept set forth long ago by Hohlweg & Junkmann (1) that gonadotropic functions of the adenohypophysis are regulated by a sexual center in the hypothalamus was useful as a first approximation. However, in the light of present knowledge the hypothesis that one center controls all reproductive functions of the gland can be held only in loose application to the medial basal region of the hypothalamus immediately adjacent to the infundibulum, the "hypophyseotropic area" (2). This region contains the final neural station through which central neural controls of the various secretions are carried out. Axons originating there pass to the median eminence and infundibular stem to end near the primary capillary plexus of the hypophyseal portal system. Even within this neurovascular complex, however, a regional division of labor appears likely. According to the generally accepted hypothesis, all neural controls of the pars distalis of the adenohypophysis are accomplished by neurohumoral agents passing from the median eminence and the stem via the portal vessels. Since the pars distalis produces at least six tropic hormones, the secretion of each being regulated in a highly selective manner and to large extent through this neurovascular link, there is much current interest in the detailed microanatomy, histochemistry, biochemistry, and physiology of the hypothalamohypophyseal system.

Median Eminence, Portal Vessels, Neurosecretion

It is generally agreed that nerve fibers destined for the median eminence and infundibular stem arise from the arcuate and other nuclei of the medial basal tuberal region. Multitudes of these fine tuberoinfundibular fibers move into the external zone where they terminate in synapselike endings about the penetrating capillary loops of the primary plexus of the hypophyseal

---

[1] The survey of literature for this review was concluded in June 1968.

[2] Abbreviations used include the following: FSH (follicle-stimulating hormone); LH (luteinizing hormone); PMS (pregnant mare serum gonadotropin); HCG (human chorionic gonadotropin); FSH-RF (FSH-releasing factor); LH-RF (LH-releasing factor); PIF (prolactin-inhibiting factor).

[3] Preparation of this review was aided by a grant from the National Science Foundation (GB-1737).

portal vessels or in palisade fashion at the outer surface, where they are in close relation to the rich capillary bed of the Mantelplexus (2). Also present in this region are the processes of a seemingly specialized ependyma that present some evidence of secretory activity and that have been considered as possible agents in the transfer of materials from the third ventricle to the portal vessels (3–5).

The content of these nerve terminals, as well as that of adjacent glia and ependyma, has been examined with the electron microscope by a number of authors (2, 6–12). It is especially significant that several recent studies have dealt specifically with the rat, for in this species we have the greatest hope at the present time of correlating changes in fine structure with specific changes in endocrine function. The excellent papers by Rinne (6) and Monroe (7) are particularly noteworthy. Both authors describe within the nerve terminals abundant small vesicles of the synaptic variety having diameters of 200–600 Å, either by themselves in some endings or in association with granules and vesicles of larger size. Small vesicles which Rinne says measure about 420 Å are said to be dominant over all others. However, there are many granules and vesicles in the 700–1000 Å range, averaging about 875 Å. Many of the vesicles have dense cores, separated from the enclosing membranes by clear halos. These dense-core vesicles are similar in size and appearance to objects regularly seen in adrenergic nerve terminals of the autonomic system, a suggestive correlation with the fact that the external zone of the median eminence is exceedingly rich in monoamines (10, 13, 14). Relatively few dense granules and vesicles ranging up to 2000 Å are found in this region of the neurohypophysis, a fact differentiating the endings of the tuberoinfundibular tract from the endings of fibers in the neural lobe deriving from the magnocellular hypothalamic nuclei.

The histochemical technique of selectively detecting monoamines by fluorescence (15) has been extensively exploited by Fuxe and associates in locating monoaminergic neurons, pathways, and terminals within the brain (13). Abundant fibers which they identify as dopaminergic are characteristic of the tuberoinfundibular tract and its terminals in the median eminence in the monkey, cat, dog, guinea pig, rat, and mouse (14). Identity of these dopamine stores with the material in the dense-core vesicles has been postulated, but not yet established to everyone's satisfaction. Thus, Fuxe et al. (16) concluded that monoamine storage occurs in the small agranular vesicles. Matsui (11) and Rinne & Arstila (17), however, report changes after reserpine treatment in only the granulated vesicles (dense-core) in the 1000-Å range. Sano et al. (10) have made comparative fluorescence and electron microscope studies of the infundibular region in dogs, noting the effects of reserpine. They describe, as principal elements of the nerve terminals, dense granules 600–1500 Å in diameter and "synaptic vesicles" measuring 250–600 Å. Reserpine treatment selectively discharged the former, producing many empty vesicles of corresponding size. Since it also caused complete loss of fluorescence, the logical conclusion was that these dense granules carry the monoamines. Some of the problems of identification may relate to methods of fixation (12) for electron microscopy.

Attempts have been made to correlate changes in reproductive status with visible changes in fine structure and monoamine content of the nerve terminals in the median eminence. There are many speculations but little hard fact. Zambrano & De Robertis, studying the effect of castration on the median eminence and the arcuate nucleus in rats (8), noted that 30 days after gonadectomy in either sex, the nerve terminals of the outer zone exhibited an increase of dense-core vesicles, accentuated at 6 months. A high correlation was postulated between the population of dense-core vesicles and the content of dopamine. The authors speak of the "probable regulatory effect" of monoamines on the secretion of gonadotropins. Kobayashi et al. (9) had earlier reported an increase of the small dense granules and small vesicles 2 weeks after castration in this same species. However, Fuxe et al. (18) reported a loss of fluorescence, in distinct contrast to the postulate of Zambrano & De Robertis. In the castrated male guinea pig, Barry & Leonardelli (19) described a greatly diminished fluorescence of the median eminence.

In extracts of the hypothalamus, Donoso et al. (20) noted that in the anterior hypothalamus of castrated rats (a region containing the rostral end of the hypophyseotropic area) a differential change occurs in the assayable content of norepinephrine and dopamine, the former being increased and the latter diminished. The effect was detectable by day 10 and day 20, but not by day 5. No change was noted in other regions of the hypothalamus or in the frontal cortex. Anton-Tay & Wurtman (21), however, by the use of ^{3}H-norepinephrine injected into the lateral ventricle, ascertained that although endogenous brain norepinephrine increases somewhat within 2 days after gonadectomy, there is actually an increased turnover with increased synthesis.

Changes in norepinephrine levels in both the anterior and middle third of the hypothalamus during the rat estrous cycle have been recognized, the lowest levels occurring during estrus and the highest on the day of proestrus, at both 0800 and 1700 hr.[4] Fuxe et al. (19) detected little visible change in the dopaminergic neurons of the median eminence during the cycle, although a slight drop was suggested during diestrus. A pronounced increase in dopamine content during pseudopregnancy, pregnancy, and lactation was reported.

It has been known for years that certain drugs having antiadrenergic action will, on the one hand, block ovulation in rats and, on the other hand, induce pseudopregnancy (22 for references). For this reason, special interest attaches to the effects of reserpine on the monoamines of the hypothalamus and neurohypophysis. When reserpine is injected into a proestrous female

---

[4] All times given in this review are in terms of the schedule of illumination and according to the 24-hr clock, with the zero hour at the midpoint of the dark period.

a few hours in advance of the "critical period" for LH release, it will prevent the ovulation that would otherwise follow. If, however, the timing of injection is such that the ovulatory release of LH is not blocked, the drug will cause the secretion of prolactin and a period of pseudopregnancy. Reserpine implantation in the hypothalamus has also induced pseudopregnancy (23), an effect that could be blocked by iproniazide. The conclusion was that, therefore, monoamine oxidase depletion is causal and the dopaminergic component of the tuberoinfundibular system acts to inhibit prolactin release from the pars distalis. Pseudopregnancy has also been induced by α-methyldopa (23) and by α-methyl-p-tyrosine (24), both of which are inhibitors of catecholamine synthesis. Lippmann et al. (24, 25) discovered that while the latter drug or reserpine depressed hypothalamic catecholamine content, blocked ovulation, and induced pseudopregnancy, iproniazide prevented all three effects. Bretylium did not, supposedly because it lacks central activity. Interestingly, pargyline increased the hypothalamic content of catecholamines with no apparent effect on either LH or prolactin. The rate of synthesis, uptake, or release of the amines was judged to be more important, however, than the absolute concentrations. It was proposed that gonadotropin secretion may be regulated by a "sympathetic tone originating in the hypothalamus" and that as this increases, the hypothalamic output of gonadotropin-releasing and prolactin-inhibiting factors is increased, the opposite effect occurring with reduction in the "sympathetic tone" (25). Myerson & Sawyer (26) confirmed that the ovulation-blocking action of reserpine can be prevented by monoamine-oxidase inhibitors (pargyline and nialamide). Increased dosage of pargyline by itself prevented ovulation. Significantly, neither nialamide nor nialamide-dopa, which are known to increase monoamine levels, advanced the timing of the ovulation surge of LH.

HYPOTHALAMIC NEUROHUMORAL AGENTS REGULATING GONADOTROPIN SECRETION

While it is generally accepted that selective neural control of gonadotropic secretions from the pars distalis is effected by chemicals transmitted to the gland by the portal vessels, the chemical nature of these materials remains obscure. The technical problems inherent in their isolation, identification, and definition of function have been detailed in recent extensive reviews (27–29), hence no attempt will be made here to present another thorough treatment.

At least three agents are generally considered to be involved in control of gonadotropin secretion, two that provoke the release of FSH and LH (FSH-RF and LH-RF, respectively) and a factor that inhibits release of prolactin (PIF). Whether the two releasing factors also cause synthesis of the respective gonadotropins is not yet known. Evidence that PIF is distinct from FSH-RF and LH-RF (29) is now reasonably definite.

A fundamental problem encountered in attempts at chemical characterization stems from the exceedingly small amounts of the active substances obtainable by extraction from the hypothalamus, median eminence, and pituitary stalk. Adding to the problem is the tendency for the more highly purified materials to deteriorate rapidly, even when frozen.

Methods of assay present awkward difficulties, for the neurohumors cannot yet be measured directly and their activities can be determined only by secondary assay of the tropic hormones liberated (or blocked from release) from the pars distalis *in vivo* or *in vitro*. While for FSH the Steelman-Pohley assay and for prolactin the pigeon crop gland assay are considered adequately specific, their sensitivity leaves much to be desired. For LH (ICSH), the commonly used ovarian ascorbic acid depletion (OAAD) assay is indirect and, under some circumstances, has given nonspecific responses (30). A recent modification (31) of the ovarian cholesterol depletion assay (32) may prove to have greater sensitivity and specificity. An assay which in the biologic sense is surely specific is that of Fawcett et al. (33), in which the material to be tested is infused into the pituitaries of estrous female rabbits, the endpoint being ovulation or the production of hemorrhagic follicles. Clearly this method has limitations both in sensitivity and in the numbers of animals that can practically be used. It also assumes that only LH is reflected in the induced ovarian changes. The specificity and the sensitivity of the method can be considerably enhanced by introducing the measurement of ovarian venous output of 20α-hydroxypregn-4-en-3-one (20α-OHP) at some fixed interval after intrapituitary infusion of the test material (cf. 34).

Greatly heightened sensitivity is inherent in radioimmunoassays. To the extent that these techniques may be used to measure activities of the hypothalamic neurohumors, they will still be measuring secondary responses instead of the neurohumors themselves. It seems unlikely that the latter will be amenable to direct evaluation by immunoassay, and until their chemical make-up is known there is little likelihood of direct measure by any method.

It was first thought that the releasing factors are polypeptides related to vasopressin and oxytocin. But with increased purification the apparent molecular dimensions and the amino acid residues have diminished (35, 36). Recent reports indicate that FSH-releasing materials in hypothalamic extracts may consist, not of one substance, but to a large extent of a family of polyamines (37). Five polyamines (histamine, spermidine, spermine, lysine, and putrescine) isolated from porcine hypothalamic extracts had FSH-depleting action *in vivo* when injected intravenously or via the carotid artery. When separately tested for their abilities to release FSH, the order of activity was that listed, histamine having the lowest potency and putrescine the highest. At this writing I have seen no evidence that these polyamines are active *in vitro*, hence it may be that their actions are to release the releaser, so to speak, thus differing from the agent(s) in hypothalamic extracts active *in vitro* (38, 39).

Even though a crude or even highly purified material from hypothalamic extracts may act in *in vitro* systems with demonstrable specific ability to discharge or inhibit discharge of a particular tropic hormone, there is no assurance that it is an agent normally delivered to the pars distalis via the portal vessels. Only its isolation from the portal blood can demonstrate this. Moves in this direction are now possible with the exquisite techniques of Fink et al. (40) and of Porter & Smith (41), affording means to obtain portal blood of rats in significant quantity. The latter method appears to have the advantage that collection of blood can be continued for considerable periods of time. It also eliminates the possibility of contamination with pars distalis secretions through backflow, admittedly a complication in the other method. Fink (42) has reduced this hazard by adding a procedure that eliminates substances having molecular weights over 5000. He demonstrated that the portal blood truly contains a factor that when infused into the pituitary of an estrous rabbit will produce ovulation.

In their review on Hypothalamus, Adenohyphysis and Adrenal Cortex in *Annual Review of Physiology* 1958, Sayers, Redgate & Royce classified a variety of ways by which ACTH secretion might be regulated. Obviously, these also apply to other tropic hormones. With current interest so strongly focused on "releasing factors" and the inhibition of release of prolactin, it is easy to lose sight of the real possibilities of the existence of (*a*) agents that are specifically essential for cytologic differentiation and hormone synthesis; (*b*) hemodynamic and physicochemical factors; or (*c*) a combination of several factors influencing one activity.

Recent studies on the release of pars distalis hormones in *in vitro* systems have disclosed that release of ACTH, TSH, and LH into the medium was potentiated by an excess of K^+, provided that Ca^{++} was also present (39, 43–45). The effects of K^+ and LH-RF were additive, but the latter was only partially inhibited by the absence of calcium (39). Whereas the releasing factors for the tropins mentioned were specific, the effect of K^+ was apparently indiscriminate. Neither the "resting level" of release (leakage?) nor the increase after LH-RF action seemed to be influenced by the addition of other releasing factors to the preparation. The extent to which the normal actions of the hypophyseotropic factors may involve membrane depolarization has yet to be evaluated. However crude and unphysiologic the *in vitro* incubations of whole gland or pieces thereof may be, as employed in these studies, they can at least indicate directions and pose definitive questions for more exact investigations.

ATTEMPTS AT LOCALIZATION OF FUNCTION BY SELECTIVE DESTRUCTION OF HYPOTHALAMUS OR MEDIAN EMINENCE

There has long been speculation about the ability of an island of hypothalamic tissue to maintain the various functions of the pars distalis. Halász and associates (2), with the use of a small curved knife stereotaxically moved about within the basal hypothalamus of rats, succeeded in producing this type of preparation with apparent ease. When the medial basal tuber was completely circumscribed and thus neurologically dissociated from the remainder of the brain, gonadotropin secretion was retained. The extent of the cut was such that the major portion of the hypophyseotropic area was retained within the island. In female rats so treated, the ovaries developed large follicles but failed to ovulate. When cuts were made lateral to and behind the tuber, but incomplete rostrally, the rats continued to have ovulatory estrous cycles. However, when simple, arching cuts were made bilaterally across the rostral hypothalamus immediately behind the optic chiasma, the results were blockage of ovulation and a persistence of vaginal cornification. Halász (46) recently reported that cyclic ovulation was obtained in island preparations if the rostral limit of the cut extended anteriorly to include the medial preoptic area. This region has often been proposed as the seat of cyclic activity and possibly of positive feedback action of ovarian steroids essential for the "spontaneous" ovulatory discharge of gonadotropin. If this important observation by Halász can be confirmed, there would seem to be no question that the preoptic area is capable of autonomous activity in cyclically driving the hypophyseotropic area. There is, as yet, no evidence whether preparations of this type retain the clearly defined circadian rhythm characteristic of the cyclic LH-release apparatus of the intact rat.

Halász' observations on the rostral cuts behind the optic chiasma confirmed that the preopticotuberal pathway concerned with ovulation control in rats is a diffuse system (22). Tejasen (47) has examined this pathway by using a combination of unilateral frontal cuts of varying extent, together with an electrochemical stimulus applied later to the preoptic area of the same or opposite side. To block the ovulation-inducing action of an ipsilateral preoptic stimulus it was necessary that a cut at the frontal plane of the suprachiasmatic nucleus extend medially to 0.3 mm of the midline and laterally to 1.4 mm from the midline. There was evidence that in the retrochiasmatic region there exists a partial decussation, such that the effect of the unilateral stimulus is distributed to the two sides of the median eminence and, hence, to the two sides of the pars distalis. The data support the hypothesis that an approximate point-to-point relationship exists between the medial preoptic area and the hypophyseotropic complex. Whether the decussating elements lie within the hypophyseotropic complex itself was not disclosed.

In spite of the strong evidence that spontaneous ovulation, at least in the rat, is governed by a rostral, preopticotuberal neuronal system, two recent studies, one in the rat (48) and one in the ewe (49, 50), indicate that posterior input may also be important. The importance of the amygdala in gonadotropin regulation is brought out once more by the work of Eleftheriou and associates in the deermouse *Peromyscus maniculatus bairdii* (51–55).

FSH AND LH SECRETION IN DIFFERENT PHYSIOLOGICAL CIRCUMSTANCES

Sensitive techniques of radioimmunoassay now permit the measurement of low levels of circulating pituitary hormones. This work is being actively pursued in a number of laboratories and in various species including man and the several large domestic animals, from which relatively pure FSH, LH, and prolactin are available as antigens. The recent availability of purified rat LH has made it possible to extend the studies to that species (56, 57).

Several years ago, Ramirez & McCann demonstrated with the OAAD assay that in cyclic female rats LH was detectable in significantly large amounts in the blood plasma late in the afternoon of proestrus but not at other times, save possibly on the morning of proestrus when there was evidence of a slight increase (cf. 29). These data were confirmed by Anderson & McShan, who noted in addition that the levels of circulating LH remained high until after 2000 hr, i.e. for some 5 or 6 hr after the beginning of the ovulatory surge in the critical period (58). This work and other available data on LH content of the rat hypophysis (59) indicate that a considerable excess of LH is released during the ovulation surge, well above the minimal ovulation quota. Hypophyseal content of LH is known to be lower on the morning after ovulation than at any other time during the estrous cycle. Midgely and associates (56, 57) have refined the radioimmunoassay for rat LH, employing it for serial blood samples on individual animals. The details of their observations are awaited with much interest.

Whether FSH is a part of the ovulation-inducing complex remains unsettled. The FSH content of the pars distalis of the cyclic female rat was reported to be high during estrus, diestrus, and the morning of proestrus, but with a marked drop by 1700 hr on the afternoon of proestrus (60). The administration of atropine sulfate or pentobarbital at 1200 hr during proestrus, in dosage known to block ovulation, prevented the drop otherwise present later that day. The same result was found after ovariectomy at 0900 hr, but the injection of progesterone at 1100 hr gave a 50 per cent depression of FSH by 1700 hr. Goldman & Mahesh (61) likewise noted a sharp drop in hypophyseal FSH on the afternoon of proestrus in rats. They also described experiments in the hamster with antiserum having high titers to both LH and FSH. Administered at 1300 hr on the day of proestrus, this blocked ovulation in most animals. When 80–90 per cent of the anti-FSH component had been neutralized with FSH, however, the material failed to prevent ovulation in any animal.

Circulatory levels of LH and FSH have been studied by several investigators with radioimmunoassay during the menstrual cycle in women (62–64). Marked rises of both gonadotropins were described at mid-cycle about the time of the nadir in basal body temperature. According to Faiman & Ryan (62) the peak of FSH sometimes preceded the LH peak, and sometimes was coincidental or a little later. An additional peak during the early proliferative phase was also reported. The LH peak appeared 12 to 18 days after the onset of menses, 10 to 13 days before the next menstruation.

It seems appropriate to review certain aspects of the earlier literature having a bearing on the critical timing of release of the ovulation-inducing hormone(s). Workers in this field have tended to interpret our experiments in the rat (cf. 22) as having demonstrated a surge of secretion, and of the stimulus causing it, beginning more or less exactly at 1400 hr on the afternoon of proestrus and lasting almost precisely 2 hr. This is not true. Actually, the blocking agents, or hypophysectomy, have simply defined the range of time during which action of the release mechanisms is most likely to begin (not be completed). The term critical period is empirical and applies strictly to a particular set of animals under particular circumstances. Thus, the critical period for the spontaneous surge of gonadotropin in 4-day cyclic rats of the Osborne-Mendel strain is ~ 2 hr beginning at about 1400 hr, while in 5-day cyclic rats of the same strain it seems to last a little longer. In Sprague-Dawley rats of the CD strain (65), the critical period in 4-day cyclic rats begins at about 1300 hr and is spread over the following 4 hr. In postpartum rats the critical time for hormone release is said to be broader than in cyclic rats (66). Rebar & Nakane (57) noted two instances in which LH release began as early as 1200 hr, as determined by radioimmunoassay of the blood serum. After estrogen administration on the second day of the 3-day diestrus in 5-day cyclic rats of the Osborne-Mendel strain (67), blocking experiments with atropine disclosed that the critical period began at 1400 hr on the day following injection of estrogen, but lasted considerably longer than 2 hr. An extreme variation can be seen after the administration of progesterone on the day of proestrus (68); injection at 0800 hr brought about the release of enough gonadotropin before 1100 hr to produce full ovulation in one of ten rats and partial activation of the ovaries in four others. Limits of the critical period will necessarily vary also with the chosen endpoint: full ovulation, ovulation of one or more follicles, detectable luteinization, or prelutein changes in one or more follicles. Finally, as a corollary of the above argument, it should be emphasized that the individual female does not have a critical period. She does have a surge of gonadotropin.

Several questions may be posed about the time course of the naturally occurring surge of gonadotropin which have a bearing on the normal stimulus that the ovary receives, the stimulus to which the ovary must be assumed to be best adapted. How high must the blood level rise to bring about a preovulatory response? Is that response a function of a given level of gonadotropin or is there primarily a need for a rapid increment? If the former, how long must that level be maintained to produce minimal recognizable lutein or prelutein changes, on the one hand, or full ovulation, on the other hand? If the latter, how rapid must the increment be for these respective results? Neither the rapid intravascular injection of a dose of exogenous hormone nor its slow infusion at a steady rate would seem to simulate the pattern of hormone release from the pars distalis adequately. Although the appropriate neural signal might begin abruptly to activate the nerve terminals that discharge releasing factor(s) into the hypophyseal portal vessels, the process of such discharge would lag behind and rise more slowly to its maximum, then gradually fall as available releasing factor(s) diminish. Gonadotropin release would display a further lag. The rate of that release could best be measured by frequent sampling of jugular blood as the nearest practical approach to the hypophyseal effluent. The systemic levels at any given time would depend on both the rate of release and the rate of disappearance. Interaction of these two factors would mean that unless the clearance were extemely slow there would be a marked difference in the pattern of the hormone surge as determined in the jugular blood and in the peripheral circulation. Gay & Bogdanove (69) estimate that in castrated rats, circulating endogenous LH following hypophysectomy has a half-life of ∼30 min. There is no indication, however, whether the disappearance rate is independent of concentration. Whether or not that is true, it would seem that to maintain a given level once it was reached would require a much lower rate of secretion than that needed to bring about a rapid rise from base levels such as indicated by the available data on the ovulation surge.

Ovarian Output of Steroids in the Reproductive Cycle, Pseudopregnancy, and Pregnancy

Several recent studies of plasma levels of progesterone in peripheral blood during the menstrual cycle of women and rhesus monkeys have been carried out by means of a technique of competitive protein binding. During four normal cycles in women (70) there were low progesterone levels during the proliferative phase, followed by a rapid rise after the mid-cycle peak of LH. Although LH declined, progesterone levels remained high for 4 to 6 days. An abrupt fall was later seen 24 hr before menstruation. In the monkey, also, progesterone levels were low during the proliferative phase (71, 72). An abrupt increase occurred on the day before ovulation, presumably after the LH surge. Some monkeys showed a drop in progesterone on the day of ovulation, others not, and in some there was an increase. Maximal amounts were observed 3 to 4 days after ovulation. There was a decline to extremely low levels 3 days before menstruation, somewhat earlier than in the human cycles.

For the study of ovarian function in the ewe, Goding et al. (73) devised a technique of autotransplantation of the ovary to the neck of the animal, where revascularization was established by connections to the aorta and jugular vein. Output of progesterone was less than 5 μg/hr during estrus, contrasted with ∼200 μg/hr during the luteal phase of the cycle. In the cow, the progesterone content of ovarian venous effluent (74) similarly was very low on day 1, high on days 14–15, and then rapidly declined to the day of ovulation. In the guinea pig (75) a brief surge of progesterone, as measured in the arterial blood, was observed 8 to 12 hr before ovulation, coincident with estrous behavior. It then declined to a low level about ovulation time, gradually rose thereafter to a maximum on day 9, decreased somewhat by day 11, markedly declined by day 13, and was undetectable on day 15.

Secretion rates in rats of both progesterone and 20α-OHP were recently determined in ovarian venous blood in a wide variety of reproductive states (76). During the 4-day estrous cycle the output of progesterone, in terms of μg/hr/ovary was comparatively small (0.5–4.4 μg) compared with 20α-OHP (10.2–18.1 μg). The low and high values for progesterone were both seen on the day of proestrus, at 1000 and 1900 hr. In view of the question whether a progesterone rise precedes or merely follows the proestrus surge of LH, it is unfortunate that measurements were not made nearer the critical period. During pregnancy, not surprisingly, the progesterone output rose progressively to a maximum at day 14 (counting the day that spermatozoa were found in the vagina as day 0). The production of 20α-OHP, meanwhile, was usually less than during the estrous cycle. In contrast to pregnancy, during pseudopregnancy (induced by mechanical stimulation of the cervix) the output of both progestins was low, progesterone rising only to two or three times the diestrus values from day 6 to day 9. Hysterectomy on day 5 resulted in a two- to threefold increase of progesterone secretion on day 6 although the increase was not sustained. A comparable increase following the induction of deciduomata was sustained into the second week, however. The data on the two steroids during the estrous cycle are in approximate agreement with those of Lindner & Zmigrod (77) based on progestin content of the ovary. They noted that the progesterone/20α-OHP ratio was generally low during the cycle. On the day of proestrus, however, from a low value at 0900 hr it rose moderately between 1500 and 2100 hr, the shift in favor of progesterone being supposedly in response to the LH surge.

An earlier report by Fajer & Barraclough (78) agrees with that of Hashimoto et al. (76) in showing a marked distinction between pregnancy and pseudopregnancy, although some details differ, possibly because of procedural differences. They (78) reported that both steroids decline sharply on pregnancy day 5, although the progesterone drop is transient. That particular day was not studied by the other workers (76). The data on pseudopregnancy show a transient high on day 4 and then a gradual increase on days 5–9 to values two to three times higher than the amount found on day 2. A transient decline of 20α-OHP was noted on day 7. Both reports are at variance with the data of Lindner & Zmigrod (77) if one takes the determinations of ovarian content to correspond with output, a doubtful assumption. They presented progesterone/20α-OHP ratios of 1.7, 1.2, 1.4, and 1.2, on days 4 to 7. De Groot et al. (79), at the other extreme, stated that on day 7 of pseudopregnancy the blood level of progesterone (and also of prolactin) was less than at estrus.

Some of these points of difference are certain to be eliminated by the improvement of technique. A double isotope procedure for progesterone (80) is said to possess sensitivity greater than that of the gas-liquid chromatographic method by a factor of 10, with potential further improvement in equal degree. The authors find it adequate for determination of ovarian output in 5-min samples.

Differences between pregnancy and pseudopregnancy with respect to progestin outputs and other aspects of ovarian function have also been described in the rabbit (81). In pseudopregnancy, progesterone output was never higher than that of 20α-OHP. Other differences were noted in the weight of corpora lutea and in the content of cholesterol in corpora lutea and the interstitial tissue. It now appears that the interstitial tissue is a primary source of 20α-OHP (82), that this secretion is partly under the influence of prolactin in this species (83), and that this progestin, unlike progesterone, cannot maintain pregnancy (82).

STEROID FEEDBACK

It is generally recognized that gonadectomy is followed by a marked increase in gonadotropin secretion and that this can be prevented by administering androgen or estrogen. This negative feedback action occurs in species as widely separated as the ferret (84) and the desert iguana (85).

According to Keever & Greenwald (86) the administration of either progesterone or estrogen or of a combination of the two on a single day (day 1) of the hamster estrous cycle can have profound effects on gonadotropin secretion several days later. Estrogen caused atresia of all vesicular follicles by 48 hr and a depression of pituitary LH content. Progesterone prevented the ovulatory surge of gonadotropin on day 4. The combination of the two hormones appeared to inhibit both synthesis and release of LH.

In rats, Bodganove & Gay (87) have studied in detail both the pituitary and plasma levels of FSH and LH following the withdrawal of androgen treatment in castrated animals of both sexes. FSH in plasma rose sooner and higher than plasma LH. The pituitary content of LH also increased, thus indicating synthesis. An interesting side issue developed from the unexpected finding that after 5 weeks of treatment with testosterone propionate, the FSH content exceeded the control level by a factor of 3, although few gonadotrophs could be found in histologic sections and those that remained were very small (88).

The compensatory hypertrophy of the remaining gonad after unilateral gonadectomy presents certain anomalies discussed by Greenwald (89). This was in relation to his investigation of the effect of a given combined dosage of PMS and HCG on ovarian weight and number of eggs produced in hypophysectomized immature rats bearing a single ovary, compared with those having two ovaries. The single ovaries weighed about half as much as the pairs and produced about half as many eggs. Schreiber's view (90) that the inhibition of compensatory ovarian hypertrophy by goitrogens is based on competitive inhibition has been examined by Florsheim et al. (91). The inhibitory effects were prevented by thyroid feeding. In rats subjected to "rostral deafferentation" of the median eminence with the Halász knife, there were exceedingly wide variations in ovarian and thyroid weight, with no correlation between the two. Hence, it appeared that there is no interaction between FSH and TSH control mechanisms. The result argues against the hypothesis that TSH regulation has a privileged position in pituitary economy.

In a study of compensatory ovarian hypertrophy in rats of different ages, it was noted (92) that 10 days after the operation performed at 23 days of age, hypertrophy was slight. When the operation was performed about the time of puberty, maximal increase of the remaining ovary was seen. There was a lessened response to the operation at 75–210 days and none at 270 days of age. Age changes of gonadotropin secretion in rats before and after puberty have received attention in four laboratories (93–96). Shiino & Rennels (93) combined an immunocytologic study of the pituitary with functional tests of FSH secretion by means of the ovarian augmentation response to HCG. The cytologic findings indicated that some FSH may be synthesized as early as 7 to 15 days of age, with a marked increase at about days 19–20. Active secretion of FSH was also detected at 19 days. Although some augmentation of ovarian weight was obtained as early as day 15, follicle development was not then much different from that of controls. Maximal follicle development following HCG treatment was obtained at day 21. Age changes of the FSH concentration in the female rat pituitary and corresponding changes of FSH-RF were studied by Corbin & Daniels (94). There was a progressive rise from the fetal age at 20 days of gestation (3.5 μg/pituitary) to a maximum at 33 days after birth (65.3 μg/pituitary). At the approximate time of puberty (39–40 days), both the total content and concentration were considerably lower, especially in those rats already having open vaginas. At 70 days of age the concentration was further reduced, but the total content had not greatly changed. FSH-RF in the stalk-median eminence presented a progressive increase to the age of 25 days, then little change until there was a marked drop at 39–40 days in animals with open vaginas. It was high again at 70 days. According to Lisk (95) the pituitary LH stores of male and female rats were alike at the age of 40 days, the approximate time of puberty, although the female had twice the content of the male at 30 days. Another study presented markedly different data (96), indicating LH content in males exceeding that of females at both 33 and 40 days; there was no drop in the male pituitary content at 40 days.

Smith & Davidson (97, 98) investigated the induction of precocious puberty in male and female rats by implants of testosterone propionate or estradiol benzoate in the hypothalamus. Male rats receiving implants near the median eminence at 30 days of age, and hemicastrated at the same time, later showed inhibition of compensatory hypertrophy of the remaining testis, a reduction in weight of seminal vesicles and prostate compared with the controls, and a depression in the pituitary content of LH. When the operations were carried out at 55 days of age or in the adult, very little effect was seen, however. Analogous results were observed in females in which estrogen implants contained in steel tubes were placed near the median eminence at 26 days of age or later. In both sexes the prepuberal median eminence region was thus more sensitive to androgen and estrogen than after puberty. The data thus support the concept first stated by Hohlweg &

Junkmann (1), and now expressed in control-system terminology, that at the time of puberty there is an increased "set-point" for negative feedback of the sex steroids to the hypothalamus. This change appears to be reflected in the comparative effects of experimental cryptorchidism in the rat (99) on pituitary cytology. Signet-ring gonadotrophs were not seen until after puberty.

The effect of "deafferentation" of the medial basal hypothalamus in infantile female rats, either by anterior cuts alone or by complete encircle-ment, was to induce precocious opening of the vagina and immediate onset of persistent vaginal cornification (100). The deafferented hypophyseotropic region can thus sustain precocious maturation but not regular ovulatory cycles. There was no ovulation when PMS was administered, which recalls an older observation by Quinn & Zarrow (101). The influence of afferent pathways to the hypothalamus on sexual maturation is suggested by the observation (102) that significant advancement in the times of vaginal opening, of the first vaginal estrus, and of the first mating was produced in female mice by the presence of an adult male, especially in the period after weaning. The adult female was much less effective. A related observation (103) was that female rats on a restricted food intake of 50–62.5 per cent of normal came into heat faster than otherwise expected, when in the presence of a male rat.

The sites of feedback action of the gonadal steroids are not yet well defined. Data such as those of Smith & Davidson (97, 98) point to a locus primarily in the hypophyseotropic area for negative feedback, although the possibility of diffusion of steroids into the portal vessels and, thence, passage to the pars distalis, is an ever-present hazard whenever implants are made near the median eminence. However, when implants of estradiol benzoate were made into the rostral anterior hypothalamic area or medial preoptic area and removed 48 hr later, there was a significant advancement of the time of vaginal opening and of the initiation of normal ovarian cycles (98). The conclusion was reached that while systemic effects of estrogen may have some direct influence on the pars distalis, it is not likely that puberty is triggered by estrogen action at that site. Dörner & Döcke (104) hold the contrary view that in promoting gonadotropin secretion, estrogen increases the hypophyseal sensitivity to gonadotropin-releasing factors. Döcke & Dörner (105) also propose that gestagens, in suppressing ovulation, act at the pituitary level by blocking estrogen receptor sites, thus preventing sensitization of the gland.

The fact that radioactive estrogen is taken up in large amount by the pars distalis is well recognized, but uptake in the anterior hypothalamus and other portions of the brain is also significant. Kato & Villee (106) gave evi-dence in rats for specific estradiol-binding receptors in both the pars distalis and anterior hypothalamus, with preference for the latter, noting that in both sites the uptake of 17β-estradiol-^{3}H was reduced by the concomitant administration of unlabeled estradiol. In a similar study (107), clomiphene citrate caused a marked reduction in uptake of labeled estradiol by the anterior pituitary, but its effect in the hypothalamus was considerably less, which suggests that this agent may have its major site of action in the pars distalis. Kato & Villee demonstrated not only that estradiol was taken up more avidly by the hypothalamus than by cortex and cerebellum, but that it was retained longer. There was no evidence of its having been metabolized to estrone during the 4-hr limit of the study. McGuire & Lisk (108) noted that both the hypothalamus and pituitary retain labeled estradiol for at least 6 hr. Pfaff (109), in an autoradiographic study, ascertained that 30 to 75 min after injection of 17β-estradiol-^{3}H the radiochemical was concentrated by neurons and glia throughout the brain. By the end of 2 hr, however, it had diminished in the olfactory bulb and nonlimbic structures, while remaining high in the limbic system and hypothalamus (the dentate gyrus of the hippocampus and the ventromedial nucleus of the hypothalamus were illustrated). Another autoradiographic study (110) disclosed that the specialized ependyma in the floor of the third ventricle retained strong activity 12 hr after injection of labeled estradiol. The significance of that is unknown.

An attempt to find sites of specific uptake of radioactive progesterone (111) disclosed higher radioactivity at 2, 5, and 60 min in the anterior and posterior hypothalamus than in the cerebral cortex. However, the 60-min counts were generally quite low. There appeared to be no specific binding sites.

Electrical activity of the brain under different functional conditions, in particular in the hypothalamus, has been the subject of a number of recent studies. In an investigation of the effects of estrogen on unit firing rates in the septum, preoptic area, and hypothalamus of rats, Lincoln & Cross (112) noted inhibition of activity in the preoptic area and anterior hypothalamus. Unit activity was also studied by Ramirez et al. (113), with respect both to the effects of hormones (progesterone and LH by intravenous injection) and to the influence of vaginal stimulation. Progesterone injection was followed by marked inhibition of the electroencephalogram and moderate inhibition of unit activity in the hypothalamus. Somewhat surprisingly the effects were sustained for periods of only 10 to 45 min. Arai et al. (114) likewise described comparatively short periods of slow wave activity in the cortical EEG of female rats intravenously injected with progesterone. In intact females the peak of activity was reached 7 to 9 min after injection of 300 μg; in ovariectomized subjects the peak activity was obtained 10 to 15 min after 75 μg. Ovariectomy resulted in a marked increase in sensitivity to progesterone after 2 to 3 weeks, an effect that was prevented by the administration of estrogen during the 3 days before progesterone injection. Endröczi et al. (115) studied evoked potentials in the female rat hypothalamus in response to stimulation of the midbrain reticular core. Thresholds for response in the preoptic area were high in castrates, but normal after injection of 100 μg 17β-estradiol for 4 days. In some cases unilateral implantations of estradiol were made in the preoptic area opposite control implants of cholesterol. Under these circumstances the thresholds were significantly lower on the side of the estrogen implants. Kawakami & Terasawa (116) investigated the influence on evoked potentials in the arcuate nucleus and reticular formation in castrated cats treated with estrogen or progesterone, or both. Stimuli were applied to the sciatic nerve, to a dorsal sacral spinal root, to the hippocampus, or to the amygdala. Animals primed with the two hormones exhibited facilitation of the potentials evoked by stimulation of the sciatic nerve and the amygdala, and inhibition of potentials evoked from the other sites. Contrary effects were seen after administration of progesterone alone. It was concluded that "estrogen dominance" enhances somatosensory transmission, via the reticular formation, and suppresses viscerosensory transmission, while "progesterone dominance" has the opposite effects. According to Cross & Kitay (117), hypothalamic islands prepared with the Halász knife showed increased firing rates when explored 5 hr after the operation. This increased rate could be prevented by the administration of barbiturates.

SHORT-LOOP FEEDBACK

There is continuing research interest in the so-called "short-loop" or "internal" feedback actions whereby pituitary hormones seem to have the power to control their own secretion. According to Ramirez et al. (113), the intravenous injection of LH had a specific depressant effect on unit firing rates in the ventromedial hypothalamic nucleus of rats. There was little effect of LH inactivated by boiling. The depressant action was sustained for periods that seem rather short (8, 11, 18 min in illustrated examples) inasmuch as the half-life of LH is $\sim$30 min. Terasawa & Sawyer (118) report activity in the arcuate nucleus, peaking at 85 min and lasting for 200 min. Activity in the anterior hypothalamus and preoptic area was inhibited. The intravenous dosage of 20–40 μg NIH-LH-S$_{11}$ is far in excess of that believed to be normally secreted.

Corbin & Story (119) detected an internal feedback effect of FSH in immature female rats. The hormone was mixed with cholesterol and implanted in the brain at different sites. Implants near the median eminence caused a drop in both the stalk-median eminence content of FSH-RF and the pituitary content of FSH. Ovarian weight was not greatly changed from the control values, but the ovaries had few mature follicles. Implants of either FSH or PMS near the median eminence of neonatally androgenized female rats (120) inhibited compensatory ovarian hypertrophy after unilateral ovariectomy, whereas no effect was obtained with LH, HCG, TSH, or ACTH. Indirect evidence was claimed in the hamster (121) from comparison of pituitary FSH content of bilaterally ovariectomized animals with that of similarly treated animals that also received PMS.

Prolactin implants near the median eminence are said to inhibit both the synthesis and release of the endogenous hormone (122, 123). The stalk-median eminence content of the prolactin-inhibiting factor is increased. The first evidence that high blood levels of prolactin suppress prolactin secretion, reported by Chen et al. (124), was based on studies of the effects in rats of transplanted tumors secreting proclactin.

Feedback actions of estrogen and progesterone as they particularly concern ovulation will be dealt with in the following section.

Ovulation

The subject of ovulation has come up for discussion in several other segments of this review in connection with: monoamines of the median eminence, regions and pathways in the brain, releasing factors, the ovulation-inducing surge of gonadotropin, and the effects of steroids and other agents on the sexual differentiation of the hypothalamus. Here the special interest will attach to the so-called spontaneous and reflex types of ovulation, and to the influences of estrogen and progesterone, other hormones, diurnal rhythms, and copulatory stimuli.

Like the rabbit, the female ferret is a "reflex ovulator". She also resembles the rabbit in that ovulation will sometimes spontaneously follow treatment with estrogen or combination of estrogen and progesterone (84). Five among twenty ferrets that were primed with estradiol or estradio benzoate ovulated, as well as two of three that also received progesterone.

The importance of estrogen in the spontaneous ovulatory release of gonadotropin in rats was shown by the results of treatment with an estrogen antagonist, MER-25. When it was given (125) on the day before proestrus, there was either partial or complete interference with ovulation, depending on the time of injection and the dosage. The uterine distention characteristic of proestrus was usually prevented and the vaginas usually failed to cornify as otherwise expected. By contrast with these results, the injection of pentobarbital or phenobarbital at approximately noon on the day before proestrus prevented neither ovulation nor the other estrogen effects (126, 127). Either hypophysysectomy or ovariectomy before midafternoon usually prevented the uterine distention and consistently prevented the vaginal cornification. The conclusion was drawn (124) that no surge of gonadotropin occurs on the day before proestrus comparable with that inducing ovulation. However, evidence (128) of a 24-hr periodicity in plasma LH was observed by the same authors under the special circumstances offered by the ovariectomized rat. Alternative explanations submitted are a periodic fluctuation in the release rate or a rhythmic fluctuation in the processes responsible for removal of the hormone from circulation.

Early investigations in this laboratory (22) demonstrated that ovulation would consistently follow the administration of estrogen to pregnant rats on day 4 of leukocytic vaginal smears. Ovulation in the 5-day cyclic rat could also be advanced 24 hr by the injection of estrogen on day 2 of the diestrous interval. Until recently, it had never been determined whether the ovulatory surge of gonadotropin under either of these circumstances occurs at the time of day corresponding with the critical period for spontaneous discharge in the proestrous animals. That information is now available, in the affirmative (67,129), for both pseudopregnant and cyclic rats of the Osborne-Mendel strain. After injection of estradiol benzoate on day 4 of pseudopregnancy or on day 2 of diestrus in the 5-day cyclic rat, the administration of atropine sulfate at 1400 hr on the next afternoon consistently blocked the ovulation that would otherwise occur on the second night. Injection of atropine at later times disclosed that the critical period was roughly comparable to that of the proestrous animal. Furthermore, the time of gonadotropin release apparently did not depend on the time of day at which the estrogen was administered, equivalent results occurring in the cyclic rats after injection at either 0830 or 1230 hr.

Redmond (68) investigated the ability of progesterone to induce the ovulatory discharge of gonadotropin following injection early on the day of proestrus. The usual method was to make the injection at 0530, 0800, or 1100 hr and in each case to follow this after a 3-hr interval with a blocking dose of atropine sulfate (4-day cycle, Osborne-Mendel rats). Progesterone injected at 1100 hr caused full ovulation in nearly every rat. Injection at 0800 hr induced complete ovulation in only one of ten rats and partial ovulation in four others. A few eggs were shed by seven of the twenty rats injected with progesterone at 0530 and atropine at either 0800 or 1100 hr. Also investigated was the effect of "large" vs. small single doses of progesterone (1 or 2 mg/100 g body wt vs. 0.25 mg/100 g). Both dosages prevented ovulation at the normally expected time. Evidence from preoptic stimulation of the brain and from injection of LH on the day after progesterone injection indicated that the higher dosages interfered not only with the ovulatory surge of intrinsic gonadotropin, but also with the basal secretion necessary for follicle growth. Brown-Grant (130) likewise observed that progesterone injected on the day before proestrus of the 4-day cycle delayed ovulation one or more days, while in the 5-day cycle it advanced ovulation. In the latter circumstance, there was a rise in thyroid/serum ratio of ^{131}I, but significantly less than that normally occurring with spontaneous ovulation. According to his admittedly speculative hypothesis, under normal circumstances there is a considerable secretion of TSH following the proestrus LH surge. This view is based on observed shifts in ^{131}I in thyroid, uterus, and oviduct relative to the blood levels.

New evidence adduced by Meyer & McCormack (131) supports their view that in the immature rat, if the ovaries are prepared by exogenous follicle-stimulating gonadotropin (in this case purified pituitary FSH instead of the usual PMS), the eventual ovulatory discharge of endogenous LH occurs during afternoon hours comparable to the adult proestrus critical period. Twice-daily FSH injections having been started at age 21 days, superovulation was seen on day 25. It was consistently blocked by injection of phenobarbital on day 24 at 1330 hr, but not usually by injection at 1730 hr. A regimen of continuous light prevented the "spontaneous" ovulation, but treatment with progesterone induced it in spite of this illumination.

Rothchild (132) considered in depth the special physiology of the luteal phase of the female cycle, pregnancy, and lactation, with special regard to the effects of progesterone on ovulation, appetite, motor activity, sexual receptivity, body temperature, and prolactin secretion.

As noted previously, Döcke & Dörner (105) proposed that progestins, acting when estrogens are at low level, block the estrogen receptors in the pars distalis, preventing sensitization to gonadotropin-releasing factors. If estrogen-induced sensitization has already proceeded, the primary action of progesterone may be to lower the median eminence threshold, thus increasing the amount of releasing factor discharged. However, would it not be difficult to explain the estrogen stimulation of ovulation in pseudopregnant or pregnant rats on this hypothesis?

A study by Exley et al. (34) was aimed at location of the site of action of the synthetic progestin, chlomadinone acetate, in blocking ovulation in the rabbit. They feel that the data indicate that the drug acts in the central nervous system above the level of the median eminence. Administered 24 hr before mating, the drug blocked ovulation in 72 per cent of the rabbits and reduced the number of ova in the others. But there was no loss of response to exogenous LH. Therefore, the ovaries were not impaired. Unipolar or bipolar stimulation through indwelling electrodes in the posterior median eminence (X-ray control of implantation site) caused ovulation as readily in rabbits treated with the progestin as in the controls. Likewise the amount of LH liberated was at least as great in the treated group as in the controls, as estimated by the amounts of 20α-OHP in the ovarian effluent. An anterior hypothalamic site of antiovulatory action of another synthetic progestin is indicated by Ectors & Pasteels (133).

A study of the excretion of FSH and LH in women during lactation (134), showing that secretion of these hormones continued in significant amounts, led to the proposal that the amenorrhea and anovulation of lactation may be due to ovarian refractoriness. Although several investigations cited by Exley et al. (34) indicate that the progestins do not impair the ability of the ovary to respond to gonadotropin, none of the studies was carried out with graded doses of the hormones. The distinct possibility remains that ovarian thresholds are influenced by progestin activity.

The ovulatory response of the rabbit ovary has been measured quantitatively in numbers of follicles caused to ovulate by varying amounts of gonadotropins (135). In animals of assorted strains the response increased more or less linearly with logarithmic increase of dosage.

In contrast to the rat, mouse, and hamster in which ovulation is spontaneous, the rabbit shows no change in the ^{131}I of the peripheral blood over a period of 5 hr following the mating stimulus for ovulation (136, 137). The time course of the changes in hypophyseal content of several tropic hormones following the copulatory stimulus in female rabbits was studied by Desjardins et al. (138). LH concentration exhibited some reduction at 15 min, loss of about 40 per cent at 45 min and of 50 per cent at 3 hr. Prolactin was increased at 15 min and then fell precipitously by 45 min. ACTH dropped only at 15 min, and FSH presented no significant change.

Behavioral factors in the reflex induction of ovulation in rabbits were critically examined by Staples (139). In over 240 cases, mounting by the male failed to cause ovulation whenever vaginal penetration was prevented, although lordosis occurred. Proximity to the male, in addition to daily mounting for 2 weeks, also failed. Submissive does mounted by anestrous or estrous does while caged in pairs for 1-17 days did ovulate, whereas the dominant female did not. However, in male rabbits (140) 400–500 per cent increase in plasma testosterone concentration occurred within 30 min after copulation and even "precoital behavior" by itself brought about comparable increases.

Whereas the rat normally ovulates spontaneously as the result of the feedback action of gonadal steroids, ovulation can also be induced in this species by copulation or even by artificial stimulation of the cervix under some circumstances (22). There has been increasing interest in this phenomenon. Aron et al. (141) have reviewed their extensive studies carried out in Strasbourg in recent years. A linear relationship was discerned between the response, measured by frequency of luteinization, and the logarithm of the number of copulations. In further examination of the afferent stimuli involved in the reflex (142), intromission appeared to be unnecessary, for when the vaginal orifice was covered with tape 47 per cent of the animals showed a luteinization response to a single copulation, the same frequency as in animals in which intromission occurred. On the other hand, a significant number of rats showed luteinization merely after glass-rod stimulation of the vagina. The basic procedure in all these experiments was to inject estradiol on the first day of diestrus in 4-day cyclic rats, to subject the animal to one or another stimulus between 1700 and 1900 hr on the following day, and to observe the result a day later.

Meanwhile, Harrington et al. (143) have followed up their initial observation that rats blocked with chlorpromazine during the proestrus critical period will copulate when presented to the male that evening. Bilateral section of the pelvic nerves prevented the reflex response. A second dose of chlorpromazine before exposure to the male reduced the proportion of females copulating and blocked ovulation in those that did copulate. Thus we now know that both chlorpromazine and atropine at high dosage will block both reflex and spontaneous ovulation in this species. Zarrow & Clark (144) have shown that even in the immature rat primed with PMS on day 28 and with spontaneous ovulation blocked by chlorpromazine on day 30, copulation during exposure to a male overnight usually induced ovulation. Large numbers of such animals also ovulated following mechanical stimulation of the vaginal cervix and significant numbers ovulated after electrical stimulation. The ovulatory response was quantitatively related to the amount of mechanical stimulation. The observation that the reflex is prevented by bilateral section of the pelvic nerves was confirmed. Some interesting speculation about the phylogenetic aspects of reflex versus spontaneous ovulation was presented.

SEXUAL DIFFERENTIATION OF THE HYPOTHALAMUS

One of the most fascinating questions in the physiology of reproduction concerns the process whereby the hypothalamohypophyseal apparatus differentiates during fetal or early postnatal life to eventuate after puberty either in the steady "tonic" secretion of gonadotropin characteristic of the male or in the complex cyclic secretion characteristic of the female. The extensive literature on this subject and the related one of the differentiation of sexual behavior continues to grow (145). Inasmuch as in the rat the critical time at which differentiation is influenced by gonadal hormones and other agents extends into the few days immediately after birth, experimental work is largely confined to that species.

Since the pioneer studies by Pfeiffer (cf. 22, 145) it has been recognized that exposure of the newborn rat to testicular hormone prevents subsequent development of the cyclic female type of gonadotropin secretion. The effect is now known to be exerted principally, if not exclusively, in the central nervous system. It has been shown (a) that the pituitary gland of a male rat when transplanted to the median eminence region of a hypophysectomized female rat will maintain cyclic function; (b) that injection of androgen into a female rat within a few days after birth causes differentiation in the male direction so that after puberty the ovaries fail to ovulate and persistent estrus ensues; (c) that castration of a newborn male rat allows the subsequent development of cyclic function if an ovary is transplanted to the animal; (d) that not only androgen but estrogen administered neonatally will cause differentiation in the male direction; (e) that the acyclic ovary of the neonatally androgenized rat will become cyclic if transplanted into an ovariectomized female; and (f) that once the animal has passed the critical age and meanwhile has been exposed or not exposed to androgen the effect is irreversible.

Gorski (146) addressed himself to the question whether there is a sharply defined critical period of days for the androgen effect in postnatal life of the rat. A low dose of 10 μg testosterone propionate (TP) was given to females on one of the first 10 days of life, except day 9. Injection on days 1 to 4 prevented even an initial ovulation after puberty, whereas injection on days 5 or 6 led to the anovulatory state only after a few ovulatory cycles had transpired. Gorski commented that the "concept of a critical period during which hypothalamic neurons are competent to respond to TP lacks specific and clear definition." In other studies, Arai & Gorski (147, 148), following administration of androgen, examined the exposure time in hours necessary for the production of the persistent estrus syndrome. They injected 30 μg TP on day 5 as the basic procedure, following that treatment at different intervals with pentobarbital, phenobarbital (147), or the antiandrogen cyproterone acetate (148). Earlier work cited had shown protection against the action of androgen by simultaneous administration of the barbiturates. The data are roughly comparable, indicating that the full effect of the androgen had been accomplished by 12 hr. Protection afforded by reserpine, chlorpromazine, progesterone, deoxycorticosterone acetate, or 5β-pregnane-3, 20-dione (149) was less marked than that given by the barbiturates. The additional administration of Metrazol (pentylentetrazol), an antibarbiturate, tended to counteract the protective action of pentobarbital. According to Wollman & Hamilton (150), cyproterone protected rats against the administration of androgen (TP, day 5) but not against the development of persistent estrus resulting from daily injection of HCG (2–20 IU) beginning on day 6. They interpreted this to mean that the HCG effect was not due to androgen secretion stimulated by the gonadotropin. However, there were no comparable daily treatments with TP on corresponding days.

The question whether androgens are present in detectable amounts in the testis and blood of the infant rat during these critical days after birth has been answered in the affirmative by Resko et al. (151) in a study of rats ranging in age from 1 to 120 days. On day 1 the testosterone concentration in plasma was 0.027 μg/100 ml, descending to a baseline of 0.010–0.015 μg/100 ml at 10 to 30 days, then rising after puberty. Androstenedione was not detectable in plasma until day 30. Concentrations in the testis exhibited roughly similar changes, although androstenedione was abundant there on day 1.

The evidence is strong that in promoting the postpuberal steady state of gonadotropin secretion the perinatal action of androgen is essentially limited to the central nervous system. Circumstantially, the preoptic area is indicated to be the principal locus of the "deleterious" action (145). Yet in this laboratory we have seen that ovulation can readily be induced by stimulation of the medial preoptic area either in castrated adult male rats bearing ovarian grafts (152) or in persistent estrous females neonatally treated with 1.25 mg TP on day 5 (153). The stimulus applied in these circumstances was of the order of magnitude that will cause a normal cyclic female rat to ovulate. This clearly implies that there was no impairment of preoptic neurons, no lessening of their ability to act upon the "tonic center" in the hypophyseotropic area, no deficiency in the gonadotropin-releasing factor(s) in the median eminence, and no deficiency in the resulting surge of gonadotropin secretion. The deficiency may better be ascribed to modified input to the preoptic area than to damage in the preoptic area itself. One is reminded of the observation by Tima & Flerkó (154) that in rats made persistent-estrous by anterior hypothalamic cuts with the Halász knife, ovulation was produced in nearly every case by removing the pituitary, homogenizing it, and injecting it within 2 hr into the same animal. Hence, in at least this variety of persistent estrus, there was enough gonadotropin stored in the pituitary but it was not being released.

Arai & Kusama (155), like others before them, have described changes in neuron nuclear volume in the hypothalami of rats neonatally treated with a steroid (in this instance, estrone for 30 days). In such work, there is no assurance that the abnormalities observed are causal to the endocrine disturbances which they accompany. This also applies to the observation by Moguilevsky & Rubinstein (156) that *in vitro* the anterior hypothalamus of the neonatally androgenized rat had a higher O_2 uptake than that of the normal female and reacted differently to addition of LH or FSH to the medium. Differences in O_2 uptake (157) and steroidogenesis (145) have also been recognized in the follicular ovaries of neonatally androgenized rats in comparison with normal ovaries, yet the follicular ovaries will acquire cyclic, ovulatory function if transplanted to the environment offered by a normal (spayed) female.

Related to the considerations of sex differentiation is the finding by De Moor & Denef (158) that in the male rat at puberty a shift takes place in liver catabolism of steroids, such that the 20-carbonyl group becomes the major site of attack. Before puberty and in the adult female, the Δ^4-3-keto reduction to 3α-OH metabolites is dominant. Castration of immature males on days 20–24 did not prevent the shift at puberty, but in newborn males castrated at ages of 5 days or less, subsequent development of the male pattern was more and more limited as the age at operation was lowered to a minimum of 10–14 hr.

Possibly also relevant to the critical perinatal period for sexual differentiation in the rat is the fact that the hypophyseal portal system undergoes its principal development after day 4. On that day, only slight indication of the intrusion of capillary loops of the primary plexus can be recognized microscopically (159). Attempts at perfusing the vessels with "spherocytes" of known diameter showed progressively increasing penetrability of the portal system from day 4 to day 25 (160). This probably reflects the increase of caliber of capillaries in the primary bed.

PROLACTIN

To discuss in systematic fashion the secretion of prolactin, its control mechanisms, and the roles that the hormone plays in reproduction, presents awkward problems. With respect to lactation, one is confronted with a phenomenon in which prolactin serves not alone, but at best as an indispensable element in a galactopoietic complex of hormones, whose composition appears to differ somewhat from species to species. Consequently the higher control mechanisms for lactation are complex and must involve interaction of a multitude of regulatory processes. One's problem is amplified with respect to the roles of prolactin in ovarian steroidogenesis, especially as a luteotropin. Although prolactin appears as a primary agent in luteotropic hormone complexes in rats and a few other mammals, its possible role in corpus luteum regulation in the majority is doubtful, to say the least. In the last two volumes of *Annual Review of Physiology* the present understanding of corpus luteum biochemistry and of the pituitary hormones that influence it has been lucidly and authoritatively portrayed from the standpoint of the corpus luteum itself. No attempt will be made on this occasion to cover that territory again. Instead, the focus of interest will be on the brain and pituitary gland, primarily with respect to control of prolactin secretion and only secondarily with respect to prolactin's peripheral roles to the extent that they serve as indicators of the operation of the central mechanisms. Control of prolactin in the respective roles in lactation and as a luteotropin in the rat presents certain challenging points of difference.

There seems to be general agreement that in mammals the neural control of prolactin secretion is regulated by an inhibitory factor (PIF) of hypothalamic origin (22, 29). Although, like the releasing factors, this material has not been chemically isolated and characterized, the specificity of the pigeon crop gland assay for prolactin gives reasonable assurance of specificity when employed as a secondary assay for PIF. Whether the hypothalamus also produces a specific prolactin-releasing factor in mammals is not yet known, although Mishkinsky et al. (161) obtained evidence of *in vivo* release by homogenates of the pituitaries of postpartum rats. The possible existence of a prolactin-releasing factor has also been raised by Grosvenor et al. (162).

The pituitary content of prolactin during the estrous cycle of the rat was reported by Sar & Meites (163) to be 64 to 71 per cent higher during proestrus and estrus than during diestrus. The hypothalamus also had a higher content of PIF. The implication is that some of this larger supply of PIF, by finding its way to the pars distalis, inhibits release of the store of prolactin. According to Kwa & Verhofstad (164), on the other hand, during proestrus there is a surge of prolactin in the blood plasma, detectable by radioimmunoassay. It is difficult to bring this into line with the former observations without further information. Other reports from Meites' laboratory support a generalization that an elevated hypothalamic content of PIF is correlated with a retention of prolactin in the pars distalis, while a low PIF level is correlated with prolactin release. Mittler & Meites (165) observed that treatment of female rats twice daily for 5 days with either epinephrine or acetylcholine, which previous work had shown to increase prolactin secretion, resulted in a reduction in PIF in the hypothalami. Sar & Meites (166), after treating ovariectomized female rats for 10 days with progesterone, testosterone propionate, or cortisol, found an increase in both hypothalamic PIF and pituitary prolactin.

Quantitative relationships between PIF and the release of prolactin *in vitro* were examined by Kragt & Meites (167). Male rat pituitaries were used because they proved to be more sensitive and less variable than female pituitaries. The prolactin-inhibiting material was in the form of hypothalamic extracts rather than purified PIF. Negative dose-response relationships were observed.

Quantitative relationships have also been examined *in vivo* between neural factors and the extent of prolactin synthesis and release, by making use of the suckling stimulus. Grosvenor, Mena & Schaefgen (168), in a study of changes in the pituitary prolactin in lactating rats in response to suckling after different intervals of isolation from their litters, discovered a marked difference between rats isolated for 8 hr and those isolated for 16 hr. In the former, suckling by six pups for periods of either 2 or 30 min caused rapid depletion of prolactin independent of the duration of the stimulus. After isolation for 16 hr, on the other hand, stimulation by 30-min suckling failed to deplete prolactin even when the number of pups was increased. Milk ejection, however, was normal. This and other evidence indicates that pituitary prolactin content is not necessarily an inverse measure of prolactin release or lack thereof. According to Mena & Grosvenor (169) prolactin concentration, after 30-min suckling following isolation for 8 1/2 hr, was three times higher after suckling by ten pups than by only two. Yet the milk yield, being approximately the same per pup, was greatly increased.

A quantitative relationship between the neural stimulus and the endocrine response in lactation was shown by Edwardson & Eayrs (170) by means of selective thelectomy, partial or complete denervation of nipples, and variation of the number of suckling pups. When suckling was restricted to a single pair of nipples, their complete denervation arrested lactation; partial denervation related directly to the amount of residual innervation. Two pups were enough to sustain lactation, provided they could suckle more than two nipples.

Grosvenor et al. (162), in confirmation of earlier work in the same laboratory, reported that not only the suckling stimulus but other exteroceptive factors contributed by the proximity of a litter served to increase prolactin synthesis. Milk supply was first depleted by a 30-min period of suckling and treatment with oxytocin. The mothers were isolated for 16 hr and then exposed to another (test) period of suckling. Administration of either an extract of stalk-median eminence or purified PIF before the first suckling reduced the milk supply at the second suckling. Addition of prolactin after the first suckling, however, fully restored the milk supply at the end of the 16-hr isolation. It was also restored if pups were placed under the mothers with contact prevented by wire screening. Possible roles of contamination of the hypothalamic preparations with FSH-RF and LH-RF were ruled out, since the reduction of milk supply took place in ovariectomized females as well as in normal rats.

An interesting development concerning the suckling stimulus is that a significant depletion of pituitary concentration of growth hormone occurred after 30 min of suckling (171). No clue to the mechanism was found. Indirectly relevant information is that, according to fluorescent antibody procedures carried out by Shiino & Rennels (172), prolactin and growth hormone are contained in distinctly separate cells in the pituitaries of both the rat and the rabbit.

Knowledge remains fragmentary about the central nervous pathways and nuclei that take part in regulating prolactin secretion (cf. 22). It seems likely that the suckling reflex for prolactin release and the milk ejection reflex involving the release of oxytocin operate through closely similar, if not identical, ascending pathways in the spinal cord and brainstem. Details on the pathways through the brainstem are supplied in part by the excellent review of Tindal (173) and recent reports from his laboratory (174, 175). Whereas these pathways can evidently be traced to the immediate vicinity of the magnocellular nuclei of the hypothalamus from which the neurosecretory fibers that form oxytocin take origin, the processes by which selective controls of oxytocin and vasopressin are carried out remain obscure. Far deeper obscurity beclouds prolactin controls.

It has long been recognized (cf. 22) that pseudopregnancy or the progravid phase of pregnancy in the rat involves an extended period of prolactin secretion triggered in the manner of a reflex by a brief stimulus. Thus, the central neural process must differ greatly from those mediating the suckling reflex, which must be activated more or less continually on a day to day basis to sustain prolactin secretion. An approach to analyzing the pseudopregnancy mechanism is offered by the regional separation of hypothalamic sites that upon stimulation will induce ovulation or pseudopregnancy. Sites giving the pseudopregnancy response selectively are to be found in the premamillary complex, the dorsomedial nucleus, and the adjacent portion of the ventromedial nucleus. Especially noteworthy is the finding by Quinn (176) that the effect of electrical stimulation of this region was retained for a week or more. If competent corpora lutea were eliminated during this interval, a delayed pseudopregnancy was initiated when a new set of follicles ruptured and luteinized at that later time. There was evidence of a quantitative relationship between the length of stimulation and the length of time that the effect of the stimulus was retained. It is not yet known whether prolactin secretion is elevated by the initial stimulus and maintained during the interval in such experiments. Whether it is or not, the initial stimulus must establish some prolonged change in the physiologic state of the brain. It seems likely that further analysis of this phenomenon will give insight into the general question of prolactin regulation. What bearing it might have on the role of the nervous system in regulating corpus luteum function in species that do not employ prolactin as a luteotropin is problematical.

Acknowledgments

I am pleased to acknowledge the careful assistance of the following persons in the preparation of this manuscript: Marian Everett, Karen Robertson, and Robert F. Daugherty.

LITERATURE CITED

1. Hohlweg, W., Junkmann, K. Die hormonal-nervöse Regulierung der Funktion des Hypophysenvorderlappens. *Klin. Wochschr.*, **11**, 321–23 (1932)

2. Szentágothai, J., Flerko, B., Mess, B., Halász, B. *Hypothalamic Control of the Anterior Pituitary*, 3rd ed. (Akad. Kiadó, Budapest, 399 pp., 1968)

3. Löfgren, F. The infundibular recess, a component in the hypothalamo-adeno-hypophysial system. *Acta Morphol. Neerl-Scand.*, **3**, 55–78 (1960)

4. Leveque, T. F., Stutinsky, F., Porte, A., Stoeckel, M.-E. Morphologie fine d'une différenciation glandulaire du recessus infundibulaire chez le rat. *Z. Zellforsch.*, **69**, 381–94 (1966)

5. Stutinsky, F., Ed. *Neurosecretion*, Proc. IVth Intern. Symp. Neurosecretion, Strasbourg, July 25–27, 1966 (Springer-Verlag, Berlin/Heidelberg/New York, 253 pp., 1967)

6. Rinne, U. K. Electron microscopic studies on the neurosecretory nerve endings in the median eminence. *Acta Neurol. Scand.*, **43**, 205–6 (1967)

7. Monroe, B. G. A comparative study of the ultrastructure of the median eminence, infundibular stem and neural lobe of the hypophysis of the rat. *Z. Zellforsch.*, **76**, 405–32 (1967)

8. Zambrano, D., De Robertis, E. The effect of castration upon the ultrastructure of the rat hypothalamus. II. Arcuate nucleus and outer zone of the median eminence. *Z. Zellforsch.*, **87**, 409–21 (1968)

9. Kobayashi, T., Kobayashi, T., Yamamoto, K., Kaibara, M., Kameya, Y. Electron microscopic observation on the hypothalamo-hypophyseal system in the rat. II. Ultrafine structure of the median eminence and of the nerve cells of the arcuate nucleus. *Endocrinol. Japon.*, **14**, 158–77 (1967)

10. Sano, Y., Odake, G., Taketomo, S. Fluorescence microscopic and electron microscopic observations on the tubero-hypophyseal tract. *Neuroendocrinology*, **2**, 30–42 (1967)

11. Matsui, T. Effect of reserpine on the distribution of granulated vesicles in the mouse median eminence. *Neuroendocrinology*, **2**, 99–106 (1967)

12. Hökfelt, T. The possible ultrastructural identification of tubero-infundibular dopamine-containing nerve endings in the median eminence of the rat. *Brain Res.*, **5**, 121–23 (1967)

13. Fuxe, K., Hökfelt, T. The influence of central catecholamine neurons on the hormone secretion from the anterior and posterior pituitary. *Neurosecretion*, Proc. IVth Intern. Symp. Neurosecretion, Strasbourg, July 25–27, 1966, 165–75 (Stutinsky, F., Ed., Springer-Verlag, Berlin/Heidelberg/New York, 1967)

14. Odake, G. Fluorescence microscopy of the catecholamine-containing neurones of the hypothalamohypophyseal system. *Z. Zellforsch.*, **82**, 46–84 (1967)

15. Carlsson, A., Falck, B., Fuxe, K., Hillarp, N.-Å. Cellular localization of monoamines in the spinal cord. *Acta Physiol. Scand.*, **54**, 385–86 (1963)

16. Fuxe, K., Hökfelt, T., Nilsson, O. A fluorescence and electron microscopic study on certain brain regions rich in monoamine terminals. *Am. J. Anat.*, **117**, 33–46 (1965)

17. Rinne, U. K., Arstila, A. U. Electron microscopic evidence on the significance of the granular and vesicular inclusions of the neurosecretory nerve endings in the median eminence of the rat. I. Ultrastructural alterations after reserpine treatment. *Med. Pharmacol. Exptl. (Basel)*, **15**, 357–69 (1966)

18. Fuxe, K., Hökfelt, T., Nilsson, O. Activity changes in the tubero-infundibular dopamine neurons of the rat during various states of the reproductive cycle. *Life Sci.*, **6**, 2057–62 (1967)

19. Barry, J., Leonardelli, J. Etude comparée des neurones et des fibres monoaminergiques de la région tubéro-infundibulaire chez le cobaye mâle normal ou castré. *Compt. Rend. Acad. Sci.*, **266**, 15–17 (1968)

20. Donoso, A. O., Stefano, F. J. E., Biscardi, A. M., Cukier, J. Effect

of castration on hypothalamic catecholamines. *Am. J. Physiol.*, **221**, 737–39 (1967)

21. Anton-Tay, F., Wurtman, R. J. Norepinephrine: turnover in rat brain after gonadectomy. *Science*, **159**, 1245 (1968)

22. Everett, J. W. Central neural control of the reproductive functions of adenohypophysis. *Physiol. Rev.*, **44**, 373–431 (1964)

23. Van Maanen, J. H., Smelik, P. G. Depletion of monoamines in the hypothalamus and prolactin secretion. *Acta Physiol. Pharmacol. Neerl.*, **14**, 519–20 (1967)

24. Lippmann, W., Leonardi, R., Ball, J., Coppola, J. A. Relationship between hypothalamic catecholamines and gonadotrophin synthesis in rats. *J. Pharmacol. Exptl. Therap.*, **156**, 258–66 (1967)

25. Coppola, J. A. The apparent involvement of the sympathetic nervous system in the gonadotrophin secretion of female rats. *J. Reprod. Fertility Suppl. 4*, 35–45 (1968)

26. Meyerson, B. J., Sawyer, C. H. Monoamines and ovulation in the rat. *Endocrinology*, **83**, 170–76 (1968)

27. Guillemin, R. Hypothalamic factors releasing pituitary hormones. *Recent Progr. Hormone Res.*, **20**, 89–130 (1964)

28. Guillemin, R. The adenohypophysis and its hypothalamic control. *Ann. Rev. Physiol.*, **29**, 313–48 (1967)

29. McCann, S. M., Dhariwal, A. P. S., Porter, J. C. Regulation of the adenohypophysis. *Ann. Rev. Physiol.*, **30**, 589–640 (1967)

30. Gibson, W. R., Frankel, A. I., Graber, J. W., Nalbandov, A. V. An ovarian ascorbic acid depletion factor in starch gel preparations following electrophoresis. *Proc. Soc. Exptl. Biol. Med.*, **120**, 143–46 (1965)

31. Clark, J. H., Zarrow, M. X. Effect of pretreatment with androgen in the neonatal rat on LH-induced ovarian cholesterol depletion. *Proc. Soc. Exptl. Biol. Med.*, **127**, 626–29 (1968)

32. Bell, E. T., Lunn, S. F. The pretreatment of animals in the ovarian cholesterol depletion test for luteinizing hormone. *J. Endocrinol.*, **35**, 327–28 (1966)

33. Fawcett, C. P., Reed, M., Charlton, H. M., Harris, G. W. Purification

of LH-releasing factor with some observations on its properties. *Biochem. J.*, **106**, 229–36 (1968)

34. Exley, D., Gellert, R. J., Harris, G. W., Nadler, R. D. The site of action of 'chlormadinone acetate' (6-chloro-Δ⁶-dehydro-17α-acetoxyprogesterone) in blocking ovulation in the mated rabbit. *J. Physiol.*, **195**, 697–714 (1968)

35. Schally, A. V., Bowers, C. Y., White, W. F., Cohen, A. I. Purification and *in vivo* and *in vitro* studies with porcine luteinizing hormone-releasing factor (LRF). *Endocrinology*, **81**, 77–87 (1967)

36. Schally, A. V., Saito, T., Arimura, A., Sawano, S., White, W. F., Cohen, A. I. Purification and *in vitro* and *in vivo* studies with porcine hypothalamic follicle-stimulating hormone-releasing factor. *Endocrinology*, **81**, 882–92 (1967)

37. White, W. F., Cohen, A. I., Rippel, R. H., Story, J. C., Schally, A. V. Some hypothalamic polyamines that deplete pituitary follicle stimulating hormone. *Endocrinology*, **82**, 742–52 (1968)

38. Watanabe, S., Dhariwal, A. P. S., McCann, S. M. Effect of inhibitors of protein synthesis on the FSH-releasing action of hypothalamic extracts *in vitro*. *Endocrinology*, **82**, 674–84 (1968)

39. Wakabayashi, K., Schneider, H. P. G., Watanabe, S., Creighton, D. B., McCann, S. M. Studies on the mechanism of action of the gonadotrophin releasing factors on the pituitary. *Fed. Proc.*, **27**, 269 (1968)

40. Fink, G., Nallar, R., Worthington, W. C. The demonstration of luteinizing hormone releasing factor in hypophysial portal blood of prooestrous and hypophysectomized rats. *J. Physiol.*, **191**, 407–16 (1967)

41. Porter, J. C., Smith, K. R. Collection of hypophysial stalk blood in rats. *Endocrinology*, **81**, 1182–85 (1967)

42. Fink, G. Nature of LH releasing factor in hypophysial portal blood [rats]. *Nature*, **215**, 159–61 (1967)

43. Vale, W., Amoss, M., Burgus, R., Guillemin, R. On the mode of action of hypothalamic releasing factors in their stimulating release of pituitary hormones (Intern. Symp. Pharmacol. Hormonal Polypeptides, Sept. 14–16, 1967, Milan)

44. Samli, M. H., Geschwind, I. I. Some

effects of the hypothalamic luteinizing hormone releasing factor in the biosynthesis and release of luteinizing hormone. *Endocrinology*, **81**, 835–48 (1967)

45. Samli, M. H., Geschwind, I. I. Some effects of energy-transfer inhibitors and of Ca^{++}-free or K$^+$-enhanced media on the release of luteinizing hormone (LH) from the rat pituitary gland *in vitro*. *Ibid.*, **82**, 225–31 (1968)

46. Halász, B. *Endocrine Function of Hypothalamic Islands* (Proc. 3rd Intern Congr. Endocrinol., Mexico City, 1968: Excerpta Med. Found., New York, 1969)

47. Tejasen, T., Everett, J. W. Surgical analysis of the preoptico-tuberal pathway controlling ovulatory release of gonadotropins in the rat. *Endocrinology*, **81**, 1387–96 (1967)

48. Kordon, C. Contrôle nerveux du cycle ovarien. *Arch. Anat. Microscop. Morphol. Exptl.*, **57**, 458–74 (1968)

49. Radford, H. M. The effect of hypothalamic lesions on reproductive activity in sheep. *J. Endocrinol.*, **39**, 415–22 (1967)

50. Radford, H. M. Electrical stimulation of ovulation in the ewe. *Ibid.*, **38**, 477–78

51. Eleftheriou, B. E., Zolovick, A. J., Norman, R. L. Effects of amygdaloid lesions on plasma and pituitary levels of luteinizing hormone in the male deermouse. *J. Endocrinol.*, **38**, 469–74 (1967)

52. Eleftheriou, B. E. Effects of amygdaloid nuclear lesions on hypothalamic luteinizing hormone-releasing factor in the male deermouse. *J. Endocrinol.*, **38**, 479–80 (1967)

53. Eleftheriou, B. E., Zolovick, A. J. Effect of amygdaloid lesions on plasma and pituitary levels of luteinizing hormone. *J. Reprod. Fertility*, **14**, 33–37 (1967)

54. Eleftheriou, B. E. Effect of amygdaloid nuclear lesions on hypothalamic luteinizing hormone-releasing factor in the male deermouse. *J. Endocrinol.*, **38**, 479–80 (1967)

55. Eleftheriou, B. E., Pattison, M. L. Effect of amygdaloid lesions on hypothalamic follicle-stimulating hormone-releasing factor in the female deermouse. *J. Endocrinol.*, **39**, 613–14 (1967)

56. Monroe, S. E., Rebar, R. W., Midgley, A. R., Jr. Radioimmunoassay determination of LH levels in the rat during the estrous cycle. *Fed. Proc.*, **27**, 371 (1968)

57. Rebar, R. W., Nakane, P. K. Postpartum LH release in the rat studied with radioimmunoassay. *Fed. Proc.*, **27**, 371 (1968)

58. Anderson, R. R., McShan, W. H. Luteinizing hormone levels in pig, cow and rat blood plasma during the estrous cycle. *Endocrinology*, **78**, 976–82 (1966)

59. Schwartz, N. B. The effects of ovariectomy on pituitary LH, uterine weight, and vaginal cornification. *Am. J. Physiol.*, **207**, 1251–59 (1964)

60. Caligaris, L., Atrada, J. J., Taleisnik, S. Pituitary FSH concentrations in the rat during the estrous cycle. *Endocrinology*, **81**, 1261–66 (1967)

61. Goldman, B. D., Mahesh, V. B. Fluctuations in pituitary FSH during the ovulatory cycle in the rat and a possible role of FSH in the induction of ovulation. *Endocrinology*, **83**, 97–106 (1968)

62. Faiman, C., Ryan, R. J. Serum follicle-stimulating hormone and luteinizing hormone concentration during the menstrual cycle as determined by radioimmunoassays. *J. Clin. Endocrinol. Metab.*, **27**, 1711–16 (1967)

63. Saxena, B. B., Demura, H., Gandy, H. M., Peterson, R. E. Radioimmunoassay of human follicle-stimulating and luteinizing hormones in plasma. *J. Clin. Endocrinol. Metab.*, **28**, 518–34 (1968)

64. Odell, W. D., Ross, G. T., Rayford, P. L. Radioimmunoassay for luteinizing hormone in human plasma or serum: physiological studies. *J. Clin. Invest.*, **46**, 248–55 (1967)

65. Everett, J. W., Tejasen, T. Time factor in ovulation blockade in rats under differing lighting conditions. *Endocrinology*, **80**, 790–92 (1967)

66. Hoffmann, J. C., Schwartz, N. B. Timing of post-partum ovulation in the rat. *Endocrinology*, **76**, 620–25 (1965)

67. Everett, J. W., Nichols, D. C. The timing of ovulatory release of gonadotropin induced by estrogen in pseudopregnant and diestrous cyclic rats. *Anat. Record*, **160**, 346 (1968)

68. Redmond, W. C. *Ovulatory Response*

to Brain Stimulation or Exogenous Luteinizing Hormone in Progesterone-Treated Rats (Ph.D. dissertation, Duke Univ., Durham, N.C., 1968)

69. Gay, V. L., Bogdanove, E. M. Disappearance of endogenous and exogenous luteinizing hormone activity from the plasma of previously castrated, acutely hypophysectomized rats: An indirect assessment of synthesis and release rates. Endocrinology, 82, 359–68 (1968)

70. Neill, J. D., Johansson, E. D. B., Datta, J. K., Knobil, E. Relationship between the plasma levels of luteinizing hormone and progesterone during the normal menstrual cycle. J. Clin. Endocrinol. Metab., 27, 1167–73 (1967)

71. Neill, J. D., Johansson, E. D. B., Knobil, E. Levels of progesterone in peripheral plasma during the menstrual cycle of the rhesus monkey. Endocrinology, 81, 1161–64 (1967)

72. Johansson, E. D. B., Neill, J. D., Knobil, E. Periovulatory progesterone concentration in the peripheral plasma of the rhesus monkey with a methodological note on the detection of ovulation. Ibid., 82, 142–48 (1968)

73. Goding, J. R., McCracken, J. A., Baird, D. T. The study of ovarian function in the ewe by means of a vascular autotransplantation technique. J. Endocrinol., 39, 37–52 (1967)

74. Dobrowolski, W., Stupnicka, E., Domanski, E. Progesterone levels in ovarian venous blood during the oestrous cycle of the cow. J. Reprod. Fertility, 15, 409–14 (1968)

75. Feder, H. H., Resko, J. A., Goy, R. W. Progesterone concentrations in the arterial plasma of guinea-pigs during the oestrous cycle. J. Endocrinol., 40, 505–13 (1968)

76. Hashimoto, I., Henricks, D. M., Anderson, L. L., Melampy, R. M. Progesterone and pregn-4-en-20α-ol-3-one in ovarian venous blood during various reproductive states in the rat. Endocrinology, 82, 333–41 (1968)

77. Lindner, H. R., Zmigrod, A. Microdetermination of progestins in rat ovaries: Progesterone and 20α-hydroxypregn-4-en-3-one content during proestrus, oestrus and pseudopregnancy. Acta Endocrinol., 56, 16–26 (1967)

78. Fajer, A. B., Barraclough, C. A. Ovarian secretion of progesterone and 20α-hydroxypregn-4-en-3-one during pseudopregnancy and pregnancy in rats. Endocrinology, 81, 617–22 (1967)

79. de Groot, C. A., Kwa, H. G., van Rees, G. P. Progesterone and prolactin blood levels during pseudopregnancy. Acta Endocrinol. Suppl. 119, 190 (1967)

80. Siiteri, P. K., Tippit, P., Yates, C., Jr., Porter, J. C. A double isotope procedure for the determination of progestins in rat ovarian vein blood. Endocrinology, 82, 837–43 (1968)

81. Hilliard, J., Spies, H. G., Sawyer, C. H. Cholesterol storage and progestin secretion during pregnancy and pseudopregnancy in the rabbit. Endocrinology, 82, 157–65 (1968)

82. Keyes, P. L., Nalbandov, A. V. Endocrine function of the ovarian interstitial gland of rabbits. Endocrinology, 82, 799–804 (1968)

83. Hilliard, J., Spies, H. G., Lucas, L., Sawyer, C. H. Effect of prolactin on progestin release and cholesterol storage by rabbit interstitium. Endocrinology, 82, 122–31 (1968)

84. Donovan, B. T. The feedback action of ovarian hormones in the ferret. J. Endocrinol., 38, 173–79 (1967)

85. Lisk, R. D. Neural control of gonad size by hormone feedback in the desert iguana Dipsosaurus dorsalis dorsalis. Gen. Comp. Endocrinol., 8, 258–66 (1967)

86. Keever, J. E., Greenwald, G. S. Effect of oestrogen and progesterone on pituitary gonadotrophic content of the cyclic hamster. Acta Endocrinol., 56, 244–54 (1967)

87. Bogdanove, E. M., Gay, V. L. Changes in pituitary and plasma levels of LH and FSH after cessation of chronic androgen treatment. Endocrinology, 81, 930–33 (1967)

88. Bogdanove, E. M. Analysis of histophysiologic responses of the rat hypophysis to androgen treatment. Anat. Record, 157, 117–36 (1967)

89. Greenwald, G. S. Influence of one or two ovaries on ovulation and ovarian weight in the hypophysec-

tomized rat. *Endocrinology*, **82**, 591–96 (1968)

90. Schreiber, V., Kmentová, V. L'hypertrophie de l'hypophyse du rat après surrénalectomie, castration, thyroïdectomie et leurs combinaisons. *Compt. Rend. Acad. Sci.*, **258**, 4251–53 (1964)

91. Florsheim, W. H., Rudko, P., Corcorran, N. L., Bodfish, R. E. On the mechanism of the inhibition of compensatory ovarian hypertrophy by goitrogens. *Endocrinology*, **81**, 771–78 (1967)

92. Labhsetwar, A. P. Age-dependent changes in the pituitary-gonadal relationship: a study of ovarian compensatory hypertrophy. *J. Endocrinol.*, **39**, 387–93 (1967)

93. Shiino, M., Rennels, E. G. Pituitary follicle stimulating hormone *in vivo* and ovarian development in the infant rat. *Endocrinology*, **81**, 1379–86 (1967)

94. Corbin, A., Daniels, E. L. Changes in concentration of female rat pituitary FSH and stalk-median eminence follicle stimulating hormone releasing factor with age. *Neuroendocrinology*, **2**, 304–14 (1967)

95. Lisk, R. D. Luteinizing hormone in the pituitary gland of the albino rat: concentration and content as a function of sex and age. *Neuroendocrinology*, **3**, 18–24 (1968)

96. Grossberg, C., Schwartz, N. B. Patterns in pituitary LH content in male and female rats from infancy to puberty. *Fed. Proc.*, **27**, 371 (1968)

97. Smith, E. R., Davidson, J. M. Differential responses to hypothalamic testosterone in relation to male puberty. *Am. J. Physiol.*, **212**, 1385–90 (1967)

98. Smith, E. R., Davidson, J. M. Role of estrogen in the cerebral control of puberty in female rats. *Endocrinology*, **82**, 100–8 (1968)

99. Morehead, J. R., Morgan, C. F. Cryptorchidism: its pre- and postpubertal effects on the hypophysis of the rat. *Fertility Sterility*, **18**, 530–37 (1967)

100. Ramaley, J. A., Gorski, R. A. The effect of hypothalamic deafferentation upon puberty in the female rat. *Acta Endocrinol.*, **56**, 661–74 (1967)

101. Quinn, D. L., Zarrow, M. X. Inhibition of the release of the ovulating hormone in immature rats with hypothalamic lesions. *Endocrinology*, **77**, 255–63 (1965)

102. Vanderbergh, J. G. Effect of the presence of a male on the sexual maturation of female mice. *Endocrinology*, **81**, 345–49 (1967)

103. Cooper, K. J., Haynes, N. B. Modification of the estrous cycle of the under-fed rat associated with the presence of the male. *J. Reprod. Fertility*, **14**, 317–20 (1967)

104. Dörner, G., Döcke F. Influence of intrahypothalamic and intrahypophyseal implantation of estrogen or progestogen on gonadotrophin release. *Endocrinol. Exptl.*, **1**, 65–72 (1967)

105. Döcke, F., Dörner, G. Mechanism of the gestagen effect on ovulation. *Acta Endocrinol. Suppl. 119*, 163 (1967)

106. Kato, J., Villee, C. A. Factors affecting uptake of estradiol-6,7-^{3}H by the hypophysis and hypothalamus. *Endocrinology*, **80**, 1133–38 (1967)

107. Kato, J., Kobayashi, T., Villee, C. A. Effect of clomiphene on the uptake of estradiol by the anterior hypothalamus and hypophysis. *Endocrinology*, **82**, 1049–52 (1968)

108. McGuire, J. L., Lisk, R. D. Evidence for estrogen receptors in hypothalamus and pituitary of the intact rat. *Fed. Proc.*, **27**, 270 (1968)

109. Pfaff, D. W. Uptake of ^{3}H-estradiol by the female rat brain. An autoradiographic study. *Endocrinology*, **82**, 1149–55 (1968)

110. Kumar, T. C., Knowles, F. System linking the third ventricle with the pars tuberalis of the rhesus monkey [incl. possible connection with anterior pituitary function]. *Nature*, **215**, 54–55 (1967)

111. Seiki, K., Higashida, M., Imanishi, Y., Miyamoto, M., Kitagawa, T., Kotani, M. Radioactivity in the rat hypothalamus and pituitary after injection of labelled progesterone. *J. Endocrinol.*, **41**, 109–10 (1968)

112. Lincoln, D. W., Cross, B. A. Effect of oestrogen on the responsiveness of neurones in the hypothalamus, septum and preoptic area of rats with light-induced persistent oestrus. *J. Endocrinol.*, **37**, 191–203 (1967)

113. Ramirez, V. D., Komisaruk, B. R., Whitmoyer, D. I., Sawyer, C. H. Effects of hormones and vaginal

stimulation on the EEG and hypothalamic units in rats. *Am. J. Physiol.*, **212**, 1376–84 (1967)

114. Arai, Y., Hiroi, M., Mitra, J., Gorski, R. A. Influence of intravenous progesterone administration on the cortical electroencephalogram of the female rat. *Neuroendocrinology*, **2**, 275–82 (1967)

115. Endröczi, E., Babichev, V., Hartmann, G., Korányi, L. Changes in evoked potentials of the hypothalamus to brainstem stimulation in female rats. *Endocrinol. Exptl.*, **2**, 1–10 (1968)

116. Kawakami, M., Terasawa, E. Differential control of sex hormone and oxytocin evoked potentials in the hypothalamus and midbrain reticular formation. *Japan. J. Physiol.*, **17**, 65–93 (1967)

117. Cross, B. A., Kitay, J. I. Unit activity in diencephalic islands. *Exptl. Neurol.*, **19**, 316–30 (1967)

118. Terasawa, E., Sawyer, C. H. Effects of luteinizing hormone (LH) on multiple unit activity in the rat hypothalamus. *Fed. Proc.*, **27**, 269 (1968)

119. Corbin, A., Story, J. C. "Internal" feedback mechanism: response of pituitary FSH and stalk-median eminence follicle stimulating hormone releasing factor to median eminence implants of FSH. *Endocrinology*, **80**, 1006–12 (1967)

120. Arai, Y., Gorski, R. A. Inhibition of ovarian compensatory hypertrophy by hypothalamic implantation of gonadotrophin in androgen-sterilized rats: Evidence for "internal feedback". *Endocrinology*, **82**, 871–73 (1968)

121. Grady, K. L., Greenwald, G. S. Studies on interactions between the ovary and pituitary follicle-stimulating hormone in the Golden Hamster. *J. Endocrinol.*, **40**, 85–90 (1968)

122. Clemens, J. A., Meites, J. Inhibition by hypothalamic prolactin implants of prolactin secretion, mammary growth and luteal function. *Endocrinology*, **82**, 878–81 (1968)

123. Chen, C. L., Voogt, J. L., Meites, J. Effect of median eminence implants of prolactin, LH and FSH on luteal function in the rat. *Fed. Proc.*, **27**, 269 (1968)

124. Chen, C. L., Minaguchi, H., Meites, J. Effects of transplanted pituitary

tumors on host pituitary prolactin secretion. *Proc. Soc. Exptl. Biol. Med.*, **126**, 317–20 (1967)

125. Shirley, B., Wolinsky, J., Schwartz, N. B. Effects of a single injection of an estrogen antagonist on the estrous cycle of the rat. *Endocrinology*, **82**, 959–68 (1968)

126. Lawton, I. E., Sawyer, C. H. Timing of gonadotrophin and ovarian steroid secretion at diestrus in the rat. *Endocrinology*, **82**, 831–36 (1968)

127. Schwartz, N. B., Lawton, I. E. Effects of barbiturate injection on the day before proestrus in the rat. *Neuroendocrinology*, **3**, 9–17 (1968)

128. Lawton, I. E., Schwartz, N. B. A circadian rhythm of luteinizing hormone secretion in ovariectomized rats. *Am. J. Physiol.*, **214**, 213–17 (1968)

129. Everett, J. W. (Unpublished)

130. Brown-Grant, K. The effect of a single injection of progesterone on the oestrous cycle. thyroid gland activity and uterus-plasma concentration ratio for radioiodide in the rat. *J. Physiol.*, **190**, 101–21 (1967)

131. Meyer, R. K., McCormack, C. E. Ovulation in immature rats treated with ovine follicle-stimulating hormone: facilitation by progesterone and inhibition by continous light. *J. Endocrinol.*, **38**, 187–94 (1967)

132. Rothchild, I. The neurologic basis for the anovulation of the luteal phase, lactation and pregnancy. In *Reproduction in the Female Mammal*, 30–54 (Lamming, G. E., Amoroso, E. C., Eds., Butterworths, London, 1967)

133. Ectors, F., Pasteels, J. L. Action antiovulatoire de la médroxyprogestérone, implantée en quantités minimes dans l'hypothalamus antérieur de la Ratte. *Compt. Rend. Acad. Sci.*, **265**, 758–60 (1967)

134. Keller, P. J. Excretion of FSH and LH during lactation. *Acta Endocrinol.*, **57**, 529–35 (1968)

135. Fox, R. R., Krinsky, W. L. Ovulation in the rabbit related to dosage of human chorionic gonadotropin and pregnant mare's serum. *Proc. Soc. Exptl. Biol. Med.*, **127**, 1222–27 (1968)

136. Brown-Grant, K. Ovulation and thyroid function in the rabbit. *J. Endocrinol.*, **41**, 85–89 (1968)

137. Brown-Grant, K., El Kabir, D. J.,

Fink, G. The effect of mating on pituitary luteinizing hormone and thyrotrophic hormone content in the female rabbit. *J. Endocrinol.*, **41**, 91–94 (1968)

138. Desjardins, C., Kirton, K. T., Hafs, H. D. Anterior pituitary levels of FSH, LH, ACTH and prolactin after mating in female rabbits. *Proc. Soc. Exptl. Biol. Med.*, **126**, 23–26 (1967)

139. Staples, R. E. Behavioural induction of ovulation in the oestrous rabbit. *J. Reprod. Fertility*, **13**, 429–35 (1967)

140. Saginor, M., Horton, R. Reflex release of gonadotropin and increased plasma testosterone concentration in male rabbits during copulation. *Endocrinology*, **82**, 627–30 (1968)

141. Aron, C., Asch, G., Roos, J. Triggering of ovulation by coitus in the rat. *Intern. Rev. Cytol.*, **20**, 139–72 (1966)

142. Aron, C., Roos, J., Asch, G. New facts concerning the afferent stimuli that trigger ovulation by coitus in the rat. *Neuroendocrinology*, **3**, 47–54 (1968)

143. Harrington, F. E., Eggert, R. G., Wilbur, R. D. Induction of ovulation in chlorpromazine-blocked rats. *Endocrinology*, **81**, 877–81 (1967)

144. Zarrow, M. X., Clark, J. H. Ovulation following vaginal stimulation in a spontaneous ovulator and its implications. *J. Endocrinol.*, **40**, 343–52 (1968)

145. Barraclough, C. A. Modifications in reproductive function after exposure to hormones during the prenatal and early postnatal period. In *Neuroendocrinology*, **2**, 62–95 (Martini, L., Ganong, W. F., Eds., Academic Press, New York, 1967)

146. Gorski, R. A. Influence of age on the response to paranatal administration of a low dose of androgen. *Endocrinology*, **82**, 1001–4 (1968)

147. Arai, Y., Gorski, R. A. Critical exposure time for androgenization of the developing hypothalamus in the female rat. *Endocrinology*, **82**. 1010–14 (1968)

148. Arai, Y., Gorski, R. A. Critical exposure time for androgenization of the rat hypothalamus determined by antiandrogen injection. *Proc. Soc. Exptl. Biol. Med.*, **126**, 590–93 (1968)

149. Arai, Y., Gorski, R. A. Protection against the neural organizing effect of exogenous androgen in the neonatal female rat. *Endocrinology*, **82**, 1005–9 (1968)

150. Wollman, A. L., Hamilton, J. B. Prevention by cyproterone acetate of androgenic, but not of gonadotropic elicitation of persistent estrus in rats. *Endocrinology*, **81**, 350–56 (1967)

151. Resko, J. A., Feder, H. H., Goy, R. W. Androgen concentrations in plasma and testis of developing rats. *J. Endocrinol.*, **40**, 485–91 (1968)

152. Quinn, D. L. Luteinizing hormone release following preoptic stimulation in the male rat. *Nature*, **209**, 891–92 (1966)

153. Everett, J. W., Zeilmaker, G. H., Redmond, W. C., Quinn, D. L. (Unpublished)

154. Tima, L., Flerkó, B. Ovulation induced by autologous pituitary extracts in persistent estrous rats. *Endocrinol. Exptl.*, **1**, 193–99 (1967)

155. Arai, Y., Kusama, T. Effect of neonatal treatment with estrone on hypothalamic neurons and regulation of gonadotrophin secretion. *Neuroendocrinology*, **3**, 107–14 (1968)

156. Moguilevsky, J. A., Rubinstein, L. Gylcolytic and oxidative metabolism of hypothalamic areas in prepuberal androgenized rats. *Neuroendocrinology*, **2**, 213–21 (1967)

157. Rubinstein, L., Moguilevsky, J. A. "In vitro" effects of gonadotrophins on the glycolytic and oxidative metabolism of prepuberal rat ovaries of androgenized rats. *Acta Physiol. Latinoam.*, **18**, 80–95 (1968)

158. De Moor, P., Denef, C. The "puberty" of the rat liver. Feminine pattern of cortisol metabolism in male rats castrated at birth. *Endocrinology*, **82**, 480–92 (1968)

159. Daikoku, S., Morishita, H., Hashimoto, T., Takahashi, A. Light-microscopic studies on the development of the interrelationship between the neurosecretory pathway and the portal system in rats. *Endocrinol. Japon.*, **14**, 209–24 (1967)

160. Florsheim, W. H., Rudko, P. The development of portal system function in the rat. *Neuroendocrinology*, **3**, 89–98 (1968)

161. Mishkinsky, J., Khazen, K., Sulman, F. G. Prolactin-releasing activity

of the hypothalamus in post-partum rats. *Endocrinology*, **82**, 611–13 (1968)

162. Grosvenor, C. E., Mena, F., Dhariwal, A. P. S., McCann, S. M. Reduction of milk secretion by prolactin-inhibiting factor: further evidence that exteroceptive stimuli can release pituitary prolactin in rats. *Endocrinology*, **81**, 1021–28 (1967)

163. Sar, M., Meites, J. Changes in pituitary prolactin release and hypothalamic PIF content during the estrous cycle of rats. *Proc. Soc. Exptl. Biol. Med.*, **125**, 1018–21 (1967)

164. Kwa, H. G., Verhofstad, F. Prolactin levels in the plasma of female rats. *J. Endocrinol.*, **39**, 455–56 (1967)

165. Mittler, J. C., Meites, J. Effects of epinephrine and acetylcholine on hypothalamic content of prolactin inhibiting factor. *Proc. Soc. Exptl. Biol. Med.*, **124**, 310–11 (1967)

166. Sar, M., Meites, J. Effects of progesterone, testosterone, and cortisol on hypothalamic prolactin-inhibiting factor and pituitary prolactin content. *Proc. Soc. Exptl. Biol. Med.*, **126**, 426–29 (1968)

167. Kragt, C. L., Meites, J. Dose-response relationships between hypothalamic PIF and prolactin release by rat pituitary tissue *in vitro*. *Endocrinology*, **80**, 1170–73 (1967)

168. Grosvenor, C. E., Mena, F., Schaefgen, D. A. Effect of non-suckling interval and duration of suckling on the suckling-induced fall in pituitary prolactin concentration in the rat. *Endocrinology*, **81**, 449–53 (1967)

169. Mena, F., Grosvenor, C. E. Effect of number of pups upon suckling-induced fall in pituitary prolactin concentration and milk ejection in the rat. *Endocrinology*, **82**, 623–26 (1968)

170. Edwardson, J. A., Eayrs, J. T. Neural factors in the maintenance of lactation in the rat. *J. Endocrinol.*, **38**, 51–59 (1967)

171. Grosvenor, C. E., Krulich, L., McCann, S. M. Depletion of pituitary concentration of growth hormone as a result of suckling in the lactating rat. *Endocrinology*, **82**, 617–19 (1968)

172. Shiino, M., Rennels, E. G. Cellular localizations of prolactin and growth hormone in the anterior pituitary glands of the rat and rabbit. *Texas Rept. Biol. Med.*, **24**, 659–73 (1967)

173. Tindal, J. S. Studies on the neuroendocrine control of lactation. In *Reproduction in the Female Mammal*, 79–109 (Lamming, G. E., Amoroso, E. C., Eds., Butterworths, London, 1967)

174. Tindal, J. S., Knaggs, G. S., Turvey, A. The afferent path of the milk-ejection reflex in the brain of the guinea pig. *J. Endocrinol.*, **38**, 337–49 (1967)

175. Tindal, J. S., Knaggs, G. S., Turvey, A. Preferential release of oxytocin from the neurohypophysis after electrical stimulation of the afferent path of the milk-ejection reflex in the brain of the guinea pig. *Ibid.*, **40**, 205–14 (1968)

176. Quinn, D. L., Everett, J. W. Delayed pseudopregnancy induced by selective hypothalamic stimulation. *Endocrinology*, **80**, 155–62 (1967)

SOMATIC SENSATION

By Ian Darian-Smith

*Department of Physiology, The Johns Hopkins University School of Medicine
Baltimore, Maryland*

In the orderly analysis of sensory function an early step must be the precise definition of *what* is perceived, so that the functional boundaries of performance are known for the relevant neural mechanisms. Tacit to these investigations is the assumption of a measurable correspondence between the end results of the perceptual process—which includes the detection, recognition and discrimination of certain physical characteristics of the stimulus—and the activity evoked by the stimulus in particular neural elements, at a succession of levels in the nervous system. Usually there will be considerable, and often drastic, selection of the features of the total stimulus pattern which are perceived and further, the contribution of specific neural populations activated by the stimulus may be restricted to the transmission of information concerning even fewer stimulus parameters. To define these functional boundaries, correlative analysis of a subjective response and the activity evoked in the particular neurons studied is essential; and as a result, both sets of data must be available in a form which allows these comparisons, independent of the metrics and dimensions of the responses.

In this review I have concentrated on two aspects of sensory function relevant to the above considerations. Firstly, recent developments in the concepts underlying techniques for measuring sensory capacities in man and animals are considered, particularly in relation to their usefulness in the comparison of neural and sensory activity. Selected aspects of recent work on neural mechanisms of somatic sensory processes published prior to April 1968 are then reviewed.

PERCEPTUAL DISCRIMINATIVE CAPACITIES

Detection and recognition of signals in the sensory systems (1–7).—One of the basic data in the study of sensory processes, both at the physiological and behavioral levels, is the minimal stimulus intensity which can be detected, either relative to the background or to some reference intensity. This provides a measure of the 'sensitivity' of the system. The detection process at the observer level may be conveniently represented by a model which partitions it into two successive stages: a *sensory* or neural stage, independent of the motives of the observer and reflecting the nervous mechanisms of the appropriate sensory pathways, and a *decision* stage at which a response is selected according to the observer's bias. Because of 'noise', either input or neural, the sensory response even at the receptor level must be correlated with the stimulus in statistical terms, and at low stimulus intensities the neural information concerning the occurrence of the stimulus will be equivocal: stimulus occurrence may then be defined as a probability. The decision process will be based on this statistical information but will also be influenced by the goals of the observer—his decision criteria. For example, his aim may be to maximize the correct decisions, with a combined maximal value for 'hits' and a minimum for 'false alarms'. Alternatively, he may wish to obtain a maximal number of 'hits' even at the expense of a somewhat higher 'false alarm' rate. The sensory physiologist focuses his attention on the 'neural' stage of the sensory process, that stage determining the inherent detectability of the signal, and is primarily interested in those psychophysical methods which will allow its selective study. Unfortunately, the methods of classical psychophysics developed and refined by Fechner (8) confound the sensory and decision stages in a single statistical construct—the sensory threshold. However, in appropriately designed experiments in which 'noise' introduced by uncontrolled stimulus variability and a fluctuating decision criterion have been reduced to a minimum, this measure has certainly provided a useful, if approximate, index of the observer's 'sensitivity'. Recent experiments of this type are considered later in this review (9).

The alternate approach to detection behavior has been to develop procedures which measure independently the inherent detectability of a signal and the decision criterion of the observer. The signal detection theory recently reviewed and developed by Green & Swets (1) attempts this partition. The information available in the neural activity evoked by a stimulus is considered to be distributed along a continuum, and not to be a discrete process. In this theory the decision as to whether the stimulus has occurred, when the two states are equally likely, is based on the odds for the occurrence of the particular neural response in these alternate situations. For the decision goals commonly aimed at, it may be shown from statistical decision theory that a strategem based on the likelihood ratio—the ratio of the probability of the sensory (neural) response occurring coincident with the stimulus and that for its independent occurrence in the absence of the stimulus—is the most efficient. Signal detection theory applied to human decision tasks assumes that the decision process is based on neural information monotonically related to the likelihood ratio. This theory has now been applied to a large number of human decision tasks, but not to the examination of coincidental neural and subjective behavior. Clearly the likelihood ratio for a particular neural response to a stimulus could be estimated directly, providing a specific test of a fundamental assumption of the theory. The model would appear to have greatest interest when one is considering neural responses superposed on a background of activity, the usual situation in central sensory pathways. Preliminary investigations in such a situation were reported by Fitzhugh (10) several years ago, but appear not to have been developed.

Experimental procedures for estimating the detectability of a signal, independent of observer bias (1, 2), have been developed by modifications of the classical psychophysical techniques which allow an estimate not only of the probability of correct identification, but also of the probability of 'false alarm' responses; these two measures specify the observer response, including the decision bias. By varying the a priori probability of occurrence of the stimulus, or the observer's decision goal, a succession of these conditional probabilities may be generated to define a function termed the Receiver Operating Characteristic (ROC) curve by Petersen, Birdsall & Fox (11). Luce (5) calls this function the Iso-sensitivity Curve, because it is generated under conditions of fixed signal intensity in which the observer's sensitivity is fixed. When plotted on a unit square, the area under such a curve is a measure of observer sensitivity (1). Powerful supporting evidence for the signal detection theory is that estimates of observer 'sensitivity' for a specific task are independent of the experimental procedure used; this is not true for the estimates of 'threshold' using the classical psychophysical methods. For example, the probability of correct identification of the signal in the two-alternative forced-choice experiment (1), a measure of 'sensitivity', is identical to the area bounded by the ROC curve, within the limits of experimental error (1). This measure of the inherent detectability of the signal is also independent of the form of the distribution of the neural 'noise' and response; a normal distribution is not assumed. The signal detection model may be summarized by the statement that the 'response threshold' (a term not used in the theory) is determined by the structure of the *decision stage* and not by the neural or sensory response, which is assumed to vary continuously with the stimulus intensity.

Boneau & Cole (12) have developed a decision-theory model applicable to signal detection by animals, and used it to study color discrimination in the pigeon. In this model a decision rule was constructed for the 'minimally informed observer' rather than for the 'ideal observer' as is the case in signal detection theory (1, 2). Even though different strategies were proposed for the actual decision-making process by the human and animal observer, it was shown that the decision rules were equivalent and monotonically related to the likelihood ratio.

The alternate and much older view of a 'peripheral or neural threshold' determining the detection process assumes that the sensory process is discrete rather than continuous. In the neural quantum theory developed by Stevens, Morgan & Volkmann (13), fluctuations in the neural response to a fixed stimulus will, however, occur because of changing excitability of the nervous system. Only when this sensory response increases by a fixed, quantal amount, or some integral multiple of this, will the observer detect the signal; if the sensory response falls below this criterion no signal is detected. Specific predictions concerning the form of the psychometric function derive from the neural quantum theory (13, 14), but have been experimentally realized only within the framework of a very limited set of experimental conditions. These findings have provided a basis for severe criticism (15), but also for extension and development of the theory, in which a more elaborate decision structure is grafted to the original model (16, 17). No definitive experimental testing of the modified 'high threshold' theories has yet been achieved.

Several 'low threshold' theories have been proposed also (1) in which the neural threshold response may be exceeded on occasion by spontaneous activity ('noise'). The associated decision structure in such models has much in common with that proposed in the signal detection theory. These have been extensively reviewed (1, 4, 5).

Discrimination along intensive continua: the psychophysical function.— The development of concepts and methods for the measurement of the magnitude of the subjective response to a stimulus of varying intensity is usually traced back to Fechner (8), but the bulk of the work in this field has been done since 1950. The techniques which have received most attention in recent years are the 'direct' estimation methods of Stevens (18–20). These 'direct' methods fall into two general classes—in the magnitude methods the observer is presented with a series of stimuli, and asked to assign a number to each stimulus so that this number is proportional to his estimate of its intensity; alternately, he may be presented with a standard stimulus also, and asked to report the *ratio* of intensities of the variable and test stimuli. With the category methods the observer is instructed to assign a number to each stimulus so that the intervals between the subjective magnitudes correspond to the difference between the respectively assigned numbers. Typically, with this scaling procedure based on apparently equal intervals of subjective intensity, an anchoring stimulus is presented at the upper end of the range examined. By contrast, in the classical psychophysical techniques developed by Fechner, equal measurements or distances along the subjective continuum are equated with the just noticeable difference between pairs of stimuli, i.e. the unit of this subjective scale is one of resolving power. Clearly, such a scale will not be linearly related either to a ratio scale or to an equal-appearing interval scale, as variability in the sensory response, the determinant of resolving power, increases with the magnitude of the response.

With intensive, or 'prothetic' (19) sensory continua, the estimated subjective magnitude along the ratio, equal interval, or discriminability scales are each differently related to the stimulus scale. The well-known 'power law' of Stevens describes this stimulus-response (S-R) relation to a first approximation for subjective intensity estimates along the ratio scale; Fechner's logarithmic function describes the relationship for subjective estimates along the sensory scale based on resolving power, while the relation when responses are based on category scaling typically assumes a form intermediate between these (19). With extensive sensory continua, or those involving quality differentiation, the S-R relations based on the three sensory scales have a different relationship to each other; with both ratio and equal interval scaling the S-R relation is now best described by a power function.

Although Stevens has insisted on the 'directness' of the measurement of the sensory magnitude along the ratio scale, the psychophysical evidence for this is equivocal. The reported magnitude may well be a nonlinear transform of the primary sensory response to the stimulus (21). Garner (22) has suggested that the subject's reported estimate of stimulus magnitude involves his matching of the sensory response with the subjective correlate of a number, which, presumably based on experience, may be scaled in a nonlinear manner.

Ekman et al. (23, 24) have extended this view and suggest that the power law is simply a special case of Fechner's law. It was assumed, for discussion, that Fechner's law is generally valid and describes the relation between any stimulus variable, including the variable of number, and the corresponding subjective magnitude. Let S denote any stimulus variable, N the particular stimulus variable consisting of numbers, and R_S and R_N the corresponding subjective variables. Then, from Fechner's law:

$$R_S = a + b \log S \quad \text{and} \quad R_N = c + d \log N$$

In a typical ratio scaling experiment, using Stevens' method, the subject is instructed to give a numerical estimate such that R_N matches with R_S, i.e. $R_N = R_S$. It follows that

$$\log N = \alpha + n \log S$$

where

$$\alpha = (a - c)/d, \quad \text{and} \quad n = b/d$$

or

$$N = \gamma S^n \quad \text{where} \quad \gamma = \text{antilog } \alpha$$

This is the power law, in its simplest form, derived from Fechner's law. If, instead of the response R_S being matched to a numerical scale, it is matched with the response to a second independent stimulus, then the situation becomes that of the many cross-modality matching experiments which Stevens has reported and interpreted as supporting the power law. However, they may equally well be interpreted as supporting Fechner's law for the relation between R and S. Somewhat related views have been stated by Treisman (25, 26). These enquiries emphasize that the true subjective variable is not directly observable, and the quantitative estimates of this variable, although retaining a monotonic relation with R, may undergo transformation, indeterminate by these methods.

What emerges from these investigations of subjective judgement of stimulus magnitude? As with measurements of the 'threshold' for detecting a signal, the available techniques for estimating this subjective dimension confound the sensory or neural mechanisms subserving this function and the decision behavior of the observer. Stevens contends that the latter component becomes negligible in a well-designed experiment and that the power relationship then defines the transducer characteristics of the neural mechanisms. However, the experimental fact that the exponent of this relationship may be modified by the range of stimuli presented, by the location of the reference stimulus within this range, by the size of the stimulus modulus, and by several other experimental variables (27) indicates that judgement bias introduced by the observer may be very significant. Ideally, the sensory physiologist requires a technique in which the 'transducer' or neural component and the judgement criterion are partitioned and measured separately; no such methods are yet available. Such a two-stage model of perception, of course, is a serious simplification of a complex process, which may well involve a succession of stages; the different transformations of the S-R relationship reflected in the different scales of the subjective dimension may depend on the particular level in the perceptual process at which information is utilized (26).

Notwithstanding the possible nonlinear transformations of the neural and subjective responses to a stimulus, not only those inherent, but also those transformations introduced by the measuring procedures, Stevens' view of the 'direct' relation of subjective responses along a ratio scale and the underlying neural response certainly receives support from the available neurophysiological data. Werner, Mountcastle and colleagues (28–30) and Darian-Smith et al. (31) have shown that a power relation with an invariant exponent (to a first approximation) describes the S-R relation at several levels in the neural pathways and also at the subjective level for the intensity of sustained indentation of the skin by a probe 2 mm in diameter. The assumptions made in these experiments were that the stimulus intensity was signalled at successive neural levels by the mean discharge frequency of specific mechanoreceptive neurons, and that interspecies comparison of data was valid. A power relation with the same exponent described the S-R relation at the level of the receptor (28–31) and of the second-order medial lemniscal neuron (31, 32) and in the postcentral gyrus (33), as well as the subjective magnitude estimate in man. Whether such a 'direct' relation exists for other discriminative behavior remains to be determined.

Neural and subjective responses to identical changes in stimulus intensity have been correlated in recent investigations on gustatory sensation (34) and on electrical stimulation of the skin (35). Measures of neural activity in the chorda tympani and the sensory cortex, respectively, have been of neural populations and, as a consequence, were influenced by changes in both the number of active units and their individual discharge patterns. This ambiguity limits their usefulness in the analysis of mechanisms of coding of stimulus intensity.

Transmission of sensory information.—One question of importance in the consideration of the stimulus-response relation, either at the behavioral or neural levels, is: how efficiently does the observer (or neural response) define a particular stimulus parameter?

Information theory (36–38) provides a technique for investigating such problems. The formal theory, developed in relation to physical communication systems, is not a model of discriminative behavior; it promises, however, to prove useful in the development of such a model, particularly in the analysis of correlated neural and behavioral responses. This theory provides a measure of information, allows the identification of equivalences among messages, and enables the determination of the limits to the degree of correlation or association between such messages. In essence the communication system considered in this theory consists of three parts: (a) the source; (b) the channel, which is a fixed transmission system connecting the source with the third component; (c) the destination. The source may be considered multiple, including the 'signal' source and a 'noise' source, the characteristic of the latter being that it introduces messages into the channel which neither the original source nor the destination can predict in detail.

There is much common to the analysis of information transmission and to the analysis of variance (39). The 'amount of information' is very similar in concept to the variance. If, for example, only two possible values of the input occur, with equal probability, then the input information (and variance) is low. But, if any one of a number of input values is equally likely to occur, then the stimulus uncertainty or input information (and variance) is much higher. At the output side of the last-named system there may also be considerable variability in the response to the input, i.e. the output information will be high. However, the output information, or response uncertainty, may be partitioned: one part, the 'noise' of the system, will provide no information concerning the input, while a second component will be correlated with the input (and covary with the stimulus signal). It is this correlated component of the output information which gives a measure of the amount of information transmitted by the system—the *information transmission* of the system. These measures of the different components of the output information are invariant, and independent of the metric of the output, and thus have important advantages over the isomorphic analysis of variance. For example, the information transmitted by the behavioral responses to a stimulus and by the discharge of appropriate neurons in response to the same stimulus may be directly compared. Details of the procedures for calculating information transmission are outlined in Garner's monograph (37).

If the amount of input information is small (i.e. the possible alternate values of the signal are few, and equally likely), even a poor communication channel may permit unequivocal identification of the stimulus, and the transmitted information then equals the input information. When, however, the number of possible alternate values of the signal is progressively increased, a stage will be reached when the information transmitted by the response no longer defines the input, and uncertainty occurs. The transmitted information is then less than the input information. With further increases in the possible values of the signal the information transmission will fall progressively below the input information and asymptotically approach a fixed upper value. This limit to the amount of information which may be transmitted characterizes the communication channel and is termed its *channel capacity*. The channel capacity for sensory pathways, unlike that for physical communication systems, falls off with increasing stimulus presentation rates and, because of this dependency, is expressed as the maximal amount of information transmitted per stimulus presentation, at the stimulus frequency of the particular experiment.

The sensory pathways may be regarded as multichannel communication systems; hence if these channels operate independently of each other, and not conditionally, then estimates of the channel capacity of the total system will be that of the most efficient channel. Single neuron recording within these sensory pathways allows examination of separate transmission channels, and so it becomes possible to compare information transmission not only within the one channel which uses different coding schemes, but also within parallel channels which use a common coding procedure to relay information about the signal (31). Such analyses become possible because the measure of information transmission is invariant and quite independent of the metric of the different responses.

Experimental analysis of information transmission at the neuronal level has to the present been restricted to a consideration of unidimensional intensive stimulus parameters. Earlier investigations (40) had demonstrated that the human observer has quite restricted capacity for differentiating unequivocally a succession of categories along the stimulus continuum—usually not more than six to seven separate categories (about $2^{2.5}$ or 2.5 bits of information). Perceptual anchors provided by reference stimuli interposed along the stimulus continuum may greatly improve the resolution, but this is not a simple additive effect (37). Werner & Mountcastle (28, 29) estimated the capacity for discrimination along the intensive continuum by slowly adapting cutaneous mechanoreceptors. The stimulus was a controlled rectangular indentation of the skin of the receptive field; the neural code was the number of impulses in the individual response (mean firing frequency). The channel capacity for individual receptors was ~2.5 bits, which indicates that the human observer's discrimination of the intensity of skin indentation when other stimulus parameters are defined can be entirely accounted for by the information transmitted by individual receptors. Similar observations have been made on the different types of slowly adapting mechanoreceptors in hairy skin of the cat's face (31, 32). In this investigation the relative efficiency of the parallel trigeminothalamic channels for relaying information about the stimulus intensity was also measured. The findings are discussed on pages 430–32.

No analysis at the neural level of multidimensional stimulus discrimination has yet been reported. Behavioral studies (37), however, provide a pointer to the types of neural coding to be anticipated. For situations such as pattern discrimination these imply that an observer, faced with a complex discriminative task, can cope more efficiently with a number of separate stimulus dimensions, within each of which few categories need to be differentiated, rather than the alternative situation in which a large number of stimulus categories must be differentiated within each of a few separate stimulus dimensions.

PRETHALAMIC MECHANISMS OF SOMATIC SENSATION

Tactile and Kinesthetic Sensibility

Notwithstanding our concern with increasingly elaborate measures of sensory behavior, knowledge of somatic sensory capacities is in certain areas quite limited. An example quoted by Weinstein (41) concerns a figure in the chapter on somatic sensation in a standard textbook of physiology (42) which illustrates the threshold for two-point discrimination for different regions of the body surface. On tracing the source of the data from which this was constructed, it was found to be Ruch's interpretation of Sherrington's translation of Weber's data published in 1835. No small tribute to this transmission line is that Weinstein's observations substantially confirm Weber's! Weinstein used the classical method of limits to measure pressure sensitivity, two-point discrimination, and point localization in different regions of the body surface of man, in order to examine several generalizations embedded in the literature concerning regional tactual sensitivities. One, concerning the proximal-distal gradient of sensitivities along a limb, the lowest thresholds being anticipated in the most distal parts, was essentially confirmed for the spatial discriminative measures. However, the gradient was reversed for pressure sensitivity, the lowest thresholds in the forelimb occurring at the shoulder and the highest at the palm, a surprising finding in view of the known innervation densities of these areas of skin. Comparison of the tactual sensitivities of a particular peripheral region with the extent of its representation on the primary cortical projection area in the post central gyrus also confirmed for the extensive stimulus variables the widely expressed view that these are correlated; again, regional pressure sensitivies were not correlated in this way.

Cutaneous mechanoreceptors.—The differentiation of the rapidly adapting and slowly adapting mechanoreceptor types found in glabrous and hairy skin continues (43–46). The separate functional entities among mechanoreceptors in hairy skin have proved the more difficult to define, but some differentiation has been achieved, based on the hair follicle type innervated, the stimulus-response profile, the spatial characteristics of the receptive field, and the conduction velocity of the myelinated afferent fiber. In hairy skin, with the exception of Pacinian corpuscles, all rapidly adapting mechanoreceptors innervated by myelinated fibers are functionally associated with hair follicles. Brown & Iggo (44) recognize three types within the skin field of the saphenous nerve in both primates and subprimates, innervating the three common follicle types, which are those of fine down hairs (type D), guard hairs (type G), and the less common but distinctive tylotrich sensory hairs (type G) (47, 48). Rapidly adapting receptors also innervate vibrissal follicles on the face of the cat (32). Burgess et al. (46) attach less significance to the type of sensory hair follicle associated with the receptor and more to the characteristics of the discharge pattern in the differentiation of their G_1 and G_2 receptor types. The type D receptor is identical in Iggo's and Burgess' classifications. The precise relation of these receptors to the follicle has not been defined, but presumably they constitute part of the terminal plexus surrounding the deeper part of the hair shaft (44, 45). Regional differences in the population of rapidly adapting mechanoreceptors would appear to parallel the distribution of the different hair types (49–51). It should be observed that the differentiation of tylotrich and guard hair follicles by the microscopic examination of the skin surface may be uncertain; in the phase of active growth of tylotrich hairs the distinguishing features of these follicle types are poorly developed. In the quiescent phrase of hair growth, however, the tylotrich is readily identified by its enlarged 'hair disc'.

Slowly adapting mechanoreceptors in hairy skin may also be differentiated into several types. Fitzgerald (52) first described such receptors innervating the vibrissal follicles in the cat, and similar slowly adapting units have been recently observed in association with the specialized tactile hairs in the carpal region in the cat (53). The 'hair disc' of Pinkus overlying displacement-sensitive receptor terminals (type I of Brown & Iggo) were considered independent of adjacent hair follicles in earlier neurophysiological investigations, but Straile (47, 48) and Mann & Straile (54) have insisted that the 'hair disc' and tylotrich follicle constitute a structural entity. Recent observations of Brown & Iggo (44) illustrate their responsiveness to movement of an adjacent tylotrich, which may synchronously but in unequal degree excite a rapidly adapting type T receptor. In tactually sensitive regions in the cat, such as the face (32), and in most areas in mice, rats, and guinea pigs (55), the 'hair disc' commonly surrounds the tylotrich hair follicle. Smith (55) observed that in 15–40 per cent of hair discs more than one slowly adapting mechanoreceptive fiber innervated the structure. Dorsal root section produced degeneration of myelinated fibers innervating Merkel cells in the hair disc, but no change in the ultrastructure of these cells was seen up to ninety days after the section. Chambers & Iggo describe a third slowly adapting receptor type (type II) (56) in the hairy skin of primates and subprimates, also with a localized receptive field. Slowly adapting units have been observed in the skin of the cat's face (31, 32) which have a larger field than that of 'hair discs' and which include several down hair follicles within their field limits. Such receptors are probably type II units. Type II receptors have been tentatively identified with interfollicular intradermal encapsulated terminals (56), but the available evidence does not preclude a structural and functional association with down hair follicles. If this were so, all hair follicle types would be innervated by both rapidly adapting and slowly adapting receptors, providing a structural basis for the remarkably uniform response characteristics within the two functional groups.

Apart from the differentiating spatial characteristics of the receptive fields associated with each hair follicle type, one might anticipate functional uniformity within the two major groups of slowly and rapidly adapting receptors. Within the resolution of recent investigation this appears to be so. With all three types of slowly adapting receptor the stimulus-response relation along the intensive continuum is near-linear (31, 32), their sensitivities are similar, and information transmission concerning this stimulus parameter has the same upper limits for each receptor type. Likewise, with rapidly adapting receptors, the dynamic response characteristics, defined by their 'tuning curve' in response to a sinusoidal vibratory stimulus (31; see below), are similar and independent of the follicle type innervated. Note that one highly sensitive mechanoreceptor responsive to cutaneous stimulation has been unequivocally identified and does not innervate a hair follicle—the rapidly adapting Pacinian corpuscle. This terminal is, however, uncommon in the subdermal tissues underlying hairy skin, except near joints. Because of its extreme sensitivity to skin movement and consequently ill-defined and extensive receptive field (9, 57) the Pacinian corpuscle contributes little information about the stimulus location.

Vibratory sensation has been the focus of several recent psychophysical (58–62) and neurophysiological studies (9, 57, 63, 64). A sustained dynamic component is present in a vibratory pattern of stimulation: the skin is moving throughout the period of stimulation, and as a result those receptors and central pathways relevant to the appreciation of skin movement will be selectively and uniquely engaged for the duration of the stimulus. The resultant unique sensation, with stimulus frequencies above 5 cps, is not one of local repetitive skin movement but a derived tactile sensation characterized by a 'pitch' or roughness ('flutter' below about 60 cps and 'vibration' above this stimulus frequency), and an intensity. In glabrous skin Mountcastle et al. (9, 57) have shown that dermal rapidly adapting and slowly adapting receptors, as well as the deeper Pacinian corpuscles, all respond to vibratory stimulation, but each has a different stimulus-frequency range in which it responds optimally. Detection and recognition of the vibratory stimulus applied to glabrous skin depends on the two rapidly adapting receptor types—dermal rapidly adapting units (?Meissner's corpuscles) and the subcutaneously located Pacinian corpuscles. Each has a distinctive and complementary 'tuning curve', the dermal receptor responding optimally to stimulus frequencies of 30–40 cps and the Pacinian corpuscle at frequencies of 200–300 cps. The detection-stimulus frequency function in man can be accounted for only if both receptor types contribute to the process. Sinusoidal vibratory stimulation may also modulate in phase the discharge of slowly adapting receptors innervating glabrous skin (9). At stimulus frequencies below 10 cps this occurs at amplitudes below the human detection threshold, but at higher frequencies this modulation occurs at stimulus intensities dependent on the steady state firing rate, occurring most readily when the steady state discharge frequency and the stimulus frequency are identical. Unlike dermal rapidly adapting receptors, these slowly adapting units have no characteristic stable 'tuning curve' dependent only on the parameters of the sinusoidal deformation of the skin. Talbot et al. (9) concluded that slowly adapting dermal receptors contribute little if at all to the detection of sinusoidal deformation of glabrous skin.

Human detection thresholds of vibratory stimulation for hairy skin are higher than in glabrous skin at all frequencies (59), but the form of the frequency-threshold curve is similar in other respects. The 'tuning curves' of rapidly adapting receptors innervating the different types of hair follicle (32) suggest that these receptors alone could account for the subjective detection of vibratory stimuli over the frequency range 5–300 cps. Lindblom & Tapper (64), however, conclude that the slowly adapting receptors innervating the hair disc of Pinkus may also contribute to this function.

Subjective estimation of the intensity of a sinusoidal stimulus of fixed frequency is related in an approximately linear fashion to the stimulus sine-wave amplitude (9) over the stimulus frequency range of 40–250 cps. However, the intensity function for individual receptors is not monotonic but stepwise, response plateaus occurring when the discharge frequency exactly equals or doubles that of the stimulus sinewave. Typically, the plateau for 1:1 firing extends over a wide stimulus intensity range, so that at any particular stimulus intensity a very significant proportion of the receptor population engaged by the stimulus will be firing with a frequency exactly that of the stimulus sinewave. Furthermore it would appear likely from the observations of Talbot et al. (9) that the proportion of the neural population firing at this frequency does not alter greatly with changes in stimulus intensity. Such a stable discharge pattern, largely independent of the stimulus intensity, would effectively code stimulus frequency at the receptor level. Signalling of the stimulus intensity, however, must presumably depend on recruitment of units and not on the internal patterning of the receptor discharge.

Bessou, Burgess & Perl (65, 66) have recently examined the response characteristics of 220 unmyelinated fibers innervating cat skin, a tour de force vindicating the microelectrode technique for fiber analysis. One of the mechanoreceptor types innervated by C-fibers responded uniquely to skin deformation, signalling the amount but not the rate of deformation. Iggo & Kornhuber (67) report that the discharge frequency of such receptors is linearly related to the indentation, as with other slowly adapting mechanoreceptors (30–32).

The medial lemniscal system (33).—In considering the somatotopic representation of the body surface within planar sections of ascending pathways and interposed nuclei, difficulties have arisen in finding adequate descriptive models which account for the continuities and discontinuities observed experimentally. Werner & Whitsel (68) have overcome some of the difficulties encountered in the analysis of the projection of the hindlimb of the primate to the fasciculus gracilis. In addition to defining precisely the dermatomal sequence and the ventroaxial line, a concept introduced by Sherrington, they have used a classical topological figure—the Möbius band—to describe the experimentally determined projection. This planar pattern accounts for (a) the homotopic projection of the foot, in which any two points in the central representation can be joined by a straight line which cuts across the projections of only those regions which would be crossed by a comparable anatomical line drawn on the limb surface; and (b) the nonhomotopic projection of the hindlimb as a whole, in which discontinuity occurs along the ventroaxial line. Comparison of this trajectory with that of the medial lemniscal system to the ventrobasal complex of the thalamus and to the post-central gyrus suggests that these are not exactly isomorphic. Discontinuities occur in the more rostral projections which are not apparent in the dorsal column.

Werner & Whitsel (68) observed close correspondence between derma-tomes and sclerotomes, and no segregation within these of fibers driven by the different mechanoreceptor types. However, the proportion of fibers innervating superficial and deep structures, such as joints, varied with the dermatome. Uddenberg (69) described segregation in the dorsal column of the cat of fibers innervating superficial and deep structures in the forelimb, but as this was not demonstrated within a single dermatome the observation must be viewed with caution.

Petit & Burgess (70) have examined the projections of cutaneous afferents to the dorsal column nuclei, identified by their antidromic discharge following electrical stimulation of the dorsal column at C2. Not unexpectedly, those high threshold mechanoreceptors, thought to be nociceptive in function (71, 72), did not project rostrally to this level, but the surprising observation was that both the highly sensitive type D rapidly adapting mechanorecep-tors and the type I slowly adapting units in the sural nerve terminated caudal to T10. The dorsal column fiber population relative to that of cuta-neous nerves was biased in favor of rapidly adapting mechanoreceptors. By contrast, all cutaneous mechanoreceptor types project to the trigeminal nucleus caudalis (31, 32); presumably this is true also for the analogous spinal projection to the dorsal horn. Preliminary investigation of single neuron activity in the human dorsal column (73) has revealed a few slowly adapting cutaneous mechanoreceptor afferents, but the majority of driven units were proprioceptive in function.

In addition to mechanoreceptive primary fibers, Uddenberg (74) reports synaptically activated second-order afferents in the cervical dorsal column of the cat. Such neurons had a restricted cutaneous receptive field, but exci-tatory inputs from all the mechanoreceptive types within its limits; an input to the same cell was also commonly observed from deep structures in the fore-limb. The supraspinal termination of these ascending fibers was not deter-mined.

The spinocervicothalamic system.—Goldberg & Lavine (75) have reviewed recent work on this system.

The existence of a spinocervicothalamic projection system in man and other primates remains uncertain. Mizuno and colleagues (76) describe a small, poorly differentiated lateral cervical nucleus in the Japanese and owl monkeys, but they were uncertain about the existence of such a differen-tiated lateral cervical nucleus in the Japanese and owl monkeys, but they were uncertain about the existence of such a differentiated structure in man and the apes, as were Ha & Morin (77) earlier. Detailed examination of the effects of partial section of the cervical cord in the macaque (78–82) on limb movement and on tactile and proprioceptive discrimination, however, imply that ascending fibers in the dorsolateral part of the spinal-lateral column are

relevant to these functions in the hindlimb. The sensory information transmitted by fibers of the dorsolateral column of the spinal cord apparently
complements that relayed in the dorsal column from the hindlimb; sensory
loss was severe only when both pathways were sectioned. To further assess
the relative importance of these ascending pathways, single neuron studies
in the primate are required which analyse their capacities for coding both
spatial and intensive characteristics.

   Anterolateral system.—The somatotopic organization of the input to the
first synaptic relay in the anterolateral system and its brainstem analogue
appears to be as precise as that of the dorsal column. The accumulated observations on more than 200 patients with trigeminal tractotomies which
were performed at various levels caudal to the obex (83) reflect a well-defined
spatial projection of the primary fiber input to the nucleus caudalis. This
representation of the ipsilateral face in the trigeminal spinal tract, deduced
from the patterns of cutaneous analgesia produced by tractotomy, corresponds remarkably with that determined by electrophysiological methods
(84).

   Wall and colleagues (85–87) and Fetz (88) have examined transmission
within the lumbar spinal dorsal horn of the cat and freely moving rat, and
report a correlation between the structural lamination described by Rexed
(89) and the functional characteristics of the cells located within them. No
unitary activity was observed in laminae 1, 2, and 3. In laminae 4, 5, and 6,
neurons responding to mechanical stimulation of the appropriate dermatome
were isolated. Cells in lamina 4 had small cutaneous receptive fields, with
inputs from both rapidly and slowly adapting mechanoreceptors; the projection to the lamina was topographically organized. About 40 per cent of
these neurons had long axon projections into the dorsolateral column (88),
and probably contributed to the spinocervical tract. Neurons in laminae 5
and 6 had larger cutaneous receptive fields, still restricted however to the
appropriate dermatome. In addition, many lamina 6 units also responded to
movements of adjacent joints. The rat differed from the cat in that some
lamina 6 units had a purely proprioceptive input. About 20 per cent of lamina
5 cells projected to the dorsoalteral column, but none of the lamina 6 neurons
had such a trajectory. Stimulation of the pyramidal tract affected most of
these neurons. Inhibition of the spontaneous activity of two thirds of the
lamina 4 contrasted with the predominantly excitatory action on lamina 6
neurons; lamina 5 cells were intermediate in behavior; inhibition of activity
evoked by cutaneous stimulation was uncommon.

   Wall (87) presents a model to explain these results with cutaneous afferents terminating only on lamina 4 cells. Lamina 5 cells have a convergent
input from several lamina 4 neurons, and in turn these converge together
with proprioceptive afferents on lamina 6 cells. Earlier proposals of a presynaptic gating circuit involving neurons of the sustantia gelatinosa and
lamina 3 are incorporated into this model.

   Nucleus caudalis in the brainstem trigeminal complex is structurally (90),
and in many ways functionally, homologous with the more dorsal laminae

of the spinal dorsal horn (84). The mechanoreceptive population in this nucleus is rather similar to that observed in lamina 4 of the dorsal horn by Wall (85, 87), but there are important differences. Firstly, 30–40 per cent of the trigeminal population have a direct axon projection to the contralateral posterior thalamus (84), whereas fewer than 1 per cent of neurons with a mechanoreceptor input in the dorsal horn of C7 and C8 of the cat have such an axon projection (unpublished experiments—Darian-Smith, Rowe & Sessle). The receptive fields of caudalis cells also differ from those of lamina 4 units described by Wall (87). Fields are small and indistinguishable from those in the medial lemniscal homologue of the trigeminal complex (main sensory nucleus and nucleus oralis). The convergence of specific afferent fibers is of a fixed pattern, either from rapidly adapting or from slowly adapting mechanoreceptors. A few trigeminothalamic neurons, both in nucleus oralis and nucleus caudalis, may have an even more exclusive input from a single sensory hair follicle type, such as a vibrissa. Responses to changes in skin temperature could be entirely accounted for by the thermal responsiveness of the convergent mechanoreceptive afferents, and did not imply an input from specific thermoreceptors.

With such similar receptive field characteristics, trigeminothalamic neurons in both ascending pathways may be equally effective in signalling the spatial characteristics of the cutaneous stimulus. However, intensive and temporal stimulus parameters are not equally well coded within these systems. Information transmission about the intensity of skin indentation, signalled by the mean discharge frequency of slowly adapting mechanoreceptive neurons, differs very considerably. This has been demonstrated in single receptors by analysing the stimulus-response relations, and in trigeminothalamic cells within nucleus oralis and nucleus caudalis (31, 32) by using the statistical procedures of information theory outlined earlier (36–38).

The information transmitted by single slowly adapting mechanoreceptors and trigeminothalamic units can account for the subjective discrimination along this intensive continuum observed in man (~2.5 bits of information). Very little loss of information accompanies synaptic transmission within nucleus oralis (the medial lemniscal homologue), but synaptic transmission in nucleus caudalis introduces much neural noise into the relayed signal, which now correlates poorly with the stimulus intensity. The information relayed by such caudalis cells typically allows the unequivocal identification of the stimulus only if its amplitude is 500–600 μ (microns); over the same stimulus range oralis cells may enable the discrimination of five to six levels of intensity.

Further evidence of an impaired capacity of caudalis cells to relay mechanoreceptive information is apparent from their response to sinusoidal vibratory stimulation of hairy skin (31, 91). Oralis neurons have been isolated whose 'tuning curve' matches that of the most responsive receptors but no such units have been observed in nucleus caudalis.

Primary afferent depolarization (PAD) elicited in the dorsal horn (92–96) and in the dorsal column nuclei (97) of the cat has recently been analysed to determine the patterns of interaction between different mechanoreceptive fiber types. Schmidt and colleagues (92–96) demonstrated that PAD is readily evoked in the central terminals in the spinal dorsal horn of myelinated fibers innervating both rapidly and slowly adapting mechanoreceptors in hairy skin and in the foot pad. The most effective stimuli were those engaging rapidly adapting receptors in the skin; a transient indentation of the skin evoked PAD, graded with the stimulus intensity over the range 0–15 μ, but which increased only slightly with further deformation of the skin. If the rapidly adapting mechanoreceptors in hairy skin were engaged continuously by a vibratory stimulus with a frequency of 40 cps, then the PAD, evident from the dorsal root potential, was also sustained with little attenuation (92). However, continuing PAD was elicited in cutaneous mechanoreceptive fibers by sustained deformation of the footpad only if the deforming pressure was 100g/sec cm or more (95), a stimulus intensity far in excess of that necessary to active cutaneous slowly adapting mechanoreceptors. The skin field from which PAD could be elicited in a single afferent included and surrounded the primary field (94); maximal effects were elicited from this latter region. A similar 'surround' pattern was previously observed with single trigeminal primary afferents (98).

Vyklicky & Tabin (99) reported similar findings with transient mechanical stimuli. Tactile stimuli evoked PAD from a purely ipsilateral 'surround' skin field, but nociceptive stimuli were effective over a considerably larger, bilateral field.

Zimmermann has recently reported (100) that PAD of the central terminals of myelinated fibers in the dorsal horn may be produced by a pure C-fiber volley set up by electrical stimulation of a cutaneous nerve with selective blocking of the A-fiber activity. This contrasts with Mendell & Wall's earlier proposal (101) that such a volley hyperpolarizes these myelinated afferents.

The dominance of phasic rather than tonic action of the PAD elicited in somatic afferent pathways by 'tactile' stimulation of the skin may benefit the relay of information about transient stimuli by helping to retain spatial and temporal resolution or contrast. However, intermittent activation of the pathways mediating PAD by quite minute inputs may well produce fluctuations in the excitability of the presynaptic terminals and hence in synaptic transmission, i.e. 'noise' may be introduced into the transmission line. Rudomin & Dutton (102, 103) have demonstrated that presynaptic action of this type on 1a terminals accounts for much of the variability in the monosynaptic reflex response of motoneurons to a fixed input.

Thermal and pain sensation (104).—Kenshalo and colleagues have used a conditioning technique to measure the thermal sensitivities of hairy skin and that of the perioral region in the cat (105, 106), and compared these with response thresholds in man (107). In the cat, sensitivity of the perioral skin to warming approached that of man, but in regions of hairy skin its response to warming appeared to be purely aversive, occurring only when the skin temperature rose to 48–51° C, well above the temperature evoking pain in man. Cooling of the cat's hairy skin evoked a detection response which was apparently not aversive; nevertheless, the response threshold was about sixty times greater than that of man.

The contribution of each of the thermally sensitive receptor types to the subjective detection and discrimination of changes in skin temperature is still not clear. Specific 'cold' and 'warm' thermoreceptors innervated by C-fibers are found in both glabrous and hairy skin in both primates and sub-primates (108, 109). In the cat similar thermoreceptors innervated by Aδ-fibers have been observed only in the tongue and in perioral skin (109), but in the primate 'cold' receptors of this type are found also in hairy skin. Kenshalo & Gallegos (110) have recently examined such receptors in the skin fields of the radial and saphenous nerves in the macaque. In their experiments these units typically had a punctuate receptive field, consisting of three to eight discrete responsive spots less than 1 mm in diameter, and extending over an area of up to 1.7 cm². Their response to cooling consisted of a dynamic and a tonic component, the frequency of the latter being related to the final steady temperature of the skin. Summation of the phasic component of the response to the cooling of individual sensitive spots in the receptive field was observed. It would appear that the known thermoreceptors innervated by Aδ-fibers can alone account for the behavioral responses to changes in skin temperatures observed in the different skin regions in different species; thermoreceptive C-fibers probably have a nonsensory function, and do not contribute to the animal's awareness of changes in skin temperature. This conclusion parallels that based on the effects of selective nerve block in man.

Recent comparative studies of interest have been the demonstration of infrared thermoreceptors in the facial pits of an Australian python (111) and an examination of the response characteristics of cutaneous thermoreceptors in hibernating hamsters (112). Reflex thermoregulatory mechanisms operate in these animals at body temperatures as low as 5° C. With many Aδ and C-fiber thermoreceptive units in these animals, maximal responsiveness occurs in the range 2–5° C; this is a species characteristic and is unchanged during the summer.

The earlier description by Burgess & Perl (71) of cutaneous nociceptors in the cat's hairy skin which are innervated by Aδ-fibers has been extended to include primate skin (72). Each of these fibers innervated a number of discrete spots of skin, each about 1 mm in diameter, which were distributed over a circular or oval skin field up to 20 mm in diameter. Only these receptors responded maximally to noxious mechanical stimuli, for such stimuli failed to evoke maximal or unique activity in the more sensitive mechanoreceptors. These nociceptors failed to respond to intense thermal stimuli, however, and also to the topical application of bradykinin.

Some of the proposed central neural mechanisms of pain perception have been extensively reviewed in recent symposia. A restatement and extension of the 'gate control theory' was presented at the symposium on *The Skin Senses* (113). Changes in human pain threshold accompanying the selective engagement of myelinated cutaneous fibers by electrical stimulation of nerve (114) and by vibratory stimulation of skin (115) have been interpreted as supportive evidence for this theory. New and relevant neurophysiological data continue, however, to be elusive.

THALAMIC MECHANISMS OF SOMATIC SENSATION

A valuable general account of this subject will be found in Mountcastle & Poggio's chapter in the former's text of physiology (116).

Input to the thalamus.—Using reversible cold block of synaptic transmission in the juxtaposed dorsal column nuclei and trigeminal nucleus caudalis, Rowe & Sessle (117) were able to partition the input to mechanoreceptive cells in the posterior thalamus of the cat. Lemniscal block consistently suppressed a response evoked by cutaneous stimulation in 85 per cent of neurons isolated in VPL; in the remainder suppression of activity was incomplete, consistent with an anterolateral input. With VPM cells, block of transmission in nucleus caudalis affected only 15 per cent of the units examined, and five of these eight cells were now more responsive to the cutaneous stimulus, which suggests a tonic inhibitory interaction between the parallel ascending systems in the normal animal. Similar blocking experiments indicated that the input to neurons in the posterior nuclear group (PO) was usually more complex, and varied: some neurons' responses suggested a lemniscal input, a finding compatible with recent anatomical observations (118, 119).

Ventrobasal complex.—In Golgi preparations of the mammalian ventrobasal complex, at least six components of the presynaptic neuropil may be identified (120, 121). Individual medial lemniscal fibers radiate out from the hilar entry zone, suggesting an onionskin arrangement from which the terminals flare out to form a succession of 'arbors' or 'glomeruli' of fine unmyelinated terminals. Each glomerulus envelops from ten to fifty ventrobasal cells, many of which have their dendritic trees orientated parallel to the axon terminals—an arrangement optimal for ensuring replication of the axo-dendritic synaptic linkage between a single presynaptic terminal and a dendrite. Analysis of the ultrastructure of the glomerulus (122) has confirmed such a 'climbing fiber' system, which provides a structural basis for the potent synaptic linkage and the somatotopic organization so characteristic of the ventrobasal complex. Axosomatic synaptic junctions are uncommon. None of the other presynaptic terminals in this complex has such intimate contact with the postsynaptic elements; spinothalamic terminals, for example, have a much more diffuse distribution in the form of discs radiating out from the stem axon, and their density of synaptic contact with individual neurons is much lower (120).

Postsynaptic elements in the ventrobasal complex can be differentiated in Golgi preparations into three types: large thalamocortical relay cells (often with recurrent collaterals), Golgi type II interneurons, and a small number of long-axon fusiform cells (the 'integrative' cells of the Scheibels). Axoaxonal synapses, anticipated from functional studies of presynaptic inhibition in the nucleus (123), have been demonstrated by electron micros-copy(122).

Maekawa & Purpura (124, 125) used intracellular recordings to analyse the highly secure synaptic linkage between medial lemniscal terminals and ventrobasal neurons. Lemniscal volleys evoked EPSPs in these cells which were commonly all-or-none in character, and which typically did not increase in amplitude when the soma membrane was hyperpolarized by injected cur-rent. This contrasted with IPSPs which were inverted by depolarization of the membrane. These findings might be anticipated if the axodendritic synapses remote from the soma were excitatory, and the less common axo-somatic synapses inhibitory in function, when impedance changes in the soma membrane would then influence only the IPSP. A similar model has been proposed for synaptic activation of spinal motoneurons; although inhibitory input is largely restricted to the region of the soma, Rall et al. (126) present evidence that effective excitatory input from 1a fibers occurs also at dendri-tically remote synapses. EPSPs which were all-or-none, such as were evoked by lemniscal action, have also been recorded in Purkinje cells activated by climbing fibers (127); activation of a large part of the postsynaptic membrane by a single presynaptic axon would account for this behavior. Slowly re-peated electrical stimulation of the intralaminar nuclei, which elicits power-ful recruiting responses in the cat's precruciate cortex and modulates the activity of neurons in the ventrolateral nucleus, proved to have only slight effects on ventrobasal cells (125).

Andersen, Andersson & Lømo (128, 129) conclude from their analysis of barbiturate spindling in the cat that this thalamocortical activity is initiated in thalamic structures beyond the intralaminar nuclei previously postulated by Morrison and his colleagues. With 'moderate' barbiturate anaesthesia a point-to-point relation was established between localized regions of thala-mus and vertical columns of the cerebral cortex in which coincident rhythmic activity was recorded: this correspondence disappeared in the lightly anaes-thetized animal. The relevance of these findings to normal thalamocortical relations is not clear.

Thermally responsive neurons with small receptive fields on the tongue were isolated in the ventrobasal complex of the squirrel monkey (130). These were of two types, both of which were excited by cooling of the tongue, but the more common group responded also to mechanical stimulation, adapting slowly to the stimulus. The specific thermally receptive cells (T-units) re-sponded to stepwise cooling with both a phasic and a sustained component in the discharge. The steady discharge was maintained over a broad tempera-ture range, falling off at extreme temperatures of 15 and 45°; only a few bi-modal neurons (T+M units) had a similar steady state response. Both neuron types responded to rapid cooling of the tongue with increased dis-charge rates. T-units had a temperature response profile with a peak in the range 31–21° but with all T+M units the discharge frequency progressively increased as the tongue temperature fell to 17° C. The sensitivity of T-units was not influenced by the preadapted temperature of the tongue, in parallel with behavioral responses in primates, but T+M cells were differentially sensitive, as the response thresholds were lowest when the preadapted temperature of the tongue was below 30° C. No units excited by warming of the tongue were found. The orderly behavior of the T+M cells closely reflects that of bimodal receptors in the tongue. A comparable relationship has been observed between bimodal receptors in the cat's hairy skin and trigemino-thalamic cells in both rostral and caudal trigeminal muclei (unpublished data of Darian-Smith, Rowe & Sessle).

Posterior nuclear group and intralaminar nuclei of the thalamus.—Mehler (131) has recently reviewed the evidence concerning structural and functional correspondence in the posterior thalamic region in primates and subprimates. Much uncertainty exists, largely because most neurophysiological investigations have been confined to subprimates, whereas the sensory effects of localised lesions in this region have been studied in man.

From a comparative study of the dorsal thalamus, Erickson and colleagues (132) conclude that the progressive emergence of the ventrobasal complex, with its precise modal and spatial organization from a more 'primitive' multisensory neuronal population, is evident within the mammalian phyletic series. In the marsupial ventrobasal complex they observed a neuron population which included not only typical 'lemniscal' cells but also multimodal units of the type observed in the adjacent posterior nuclear group. The proportion of unspecialized neurons in the ventrobasal complex decreased successively in the opossum, hedgehog, cat, and monkey.

Other investigations have not supported these findings. Pubols & Pubols (133), for example, report a somatotopically organized ventrobasal complex in the Virginia opossum, with a preponderant projection from the contralateral face; the resolution within this projection was entirely comparable with that seen in 'higher' mammals. These authors rank the different species in terms of behavioral specialization, the most precise representation in the dorsal thalamus being of those peripheral organs directly involved in this special behavior, such as the forepaw of the raccoon and the snout of the rabbit. The organization of thalamocortical projections from the ventrobasal complex and the posterior nuclear group of the Virginia opossum is quite comparable with that of more developed mammals (134). The sterotaxic maps of the opossum diencephalon (*D. aurita* and *D. virginiana*), prepared by Oswaldo-Cruz & Rocha-Miranda (135, 136), will be of considerable help to future investigations of this marsupial.

An earlier study from the author's laboratory (137) on the cortical dependence of neurons in the posterior nuclear group (PO) failed to demonstrate antidromic invasion of these cells following electrical stimulation of the somatic sensory cortex of the cat. This was unexpected in view of the anatomical evidence (116). Recently, with more effective cortical stimulation, Rowe & Sessle (117) in this laboratory have shown that about 35 per cent of PO neurons with a mechanoreceptive input from the skin are thalamocortical relay cells. The 'antidromic fields' of most of these cells were confined to the specific somatic sensory cortex (SI and SII), but a proportion projected beyond this, particularly to the auditory cortex. A bifid axon projection, with discrete cortical fields in the somatic sensory (SII), and auditory regions, was observed with a few cells—a 'sustaining projection' (138). A reciprocal corticothalamic projection in the cat to the posterior nuclear group has been reported from the cortical area SII (139) together with a less dense projection from SII to the ventrobasal complex.

Considerable uncertainty continues regarding the relation of the different intralaminar nuclei to the somatic sensory system. Much of the apparent conflict concerning the input to the region appears to have resulted from semantic confusion in the classification of the nuclei, and in the differentiation of terminal degeneration and the degeneration of fibers of passage in Nauta studies (118, 140). The main issues are as follows.

(a) Termination of the paleospinothalamic tract. After earlier disagreement the prevailing view is that this tract projects principally to the "nucleus centralis lateralis of Olszewski and a number of caudally located cytologically similar cell clusters probably belonging to this nucleus" (118). It is now generally recognized that no projection occurs to other intralaminar nuclei including the centromedian nucleus-parafascicular complex.

(b) Input to the centromedian-parafascicular complex. Mehler (118, 140) contends that the only significant afferent projections to these nuclei are from the forebrain, including the postcentral gyrus (141, 142) and the globus pallidus (143). However, Petit & Mallart (144) and recently Bowsher, Mallart, Petit & Albe-Fessard (145) have presented electrophysiological evidence that an ascending excitatory projection to the centromedian-parafascicular complex of the cat is localized in the anterolateral column in the spinal cord, and relays in nucleus reticularis gigantocellularis at the level of the inferior olive. The neuron populations at the medullary and thalamic levels have matching static functional characteristics, including a multimodal input. No projection from large-diameter muscle afferents to the centromedian nucleus, however, was reported (146). Stimulation of the caudate nucleus modulates activity in this system, both excitatory and inhibutory actions apparently being affected at prethalamic levels (147, 148). Albe-Fessard and colleagues (149) have developed the hypothesis that this ascending system, including the centromedian-parafascicular complex, contributes to the appreciation of the 'protopathic' type of pain. Isolated destruction of this region in man is insufficient to abolish pain (150) but may prove an essential component of more extensive thalamic lesions directed to this end.

The terminations of efferents emerging from the intralaminar nuclei have also proven difficult to define. Lesions of the frontal lobe produce cell shrinkage and pallor, but not cell loss, in the rostral intralaminar nuclei (151); no changes occur in the centromedian-parafascicular complex, even following extensive decortication. Severe cellular degeneration occurs in all the intralaminar nuclei only following destruction of parts of the internal capsule or striatum. Powell & Cowen (151) favor the view that each of the intralaminar nuclei projects widely to different parts of the striatum only and that cell changes following cortical ablation do not reflect a cortical dependency, but rather transneuronal degeneration, secondary to the interruption of the heavy corticothalamic projection to these nuclei.

CORTICAL MECHANISMS OF SOMATIC SENSATION

A number of investigations have now shown that short-latency responses to 'tactile' stimulation occur in regions of the cerebral cortex beyond the somatic sensory areas SI and SII. In the squirrel monkey (152) five direct projection areas have been described, in the postcentral, the precentral gyri, and the second sensory area, and also in the supplementary 'motor' area and the supplementary 'sensory' area of Penfield. In the cat three areas have been reported (83, 117, 153–155), each of which has an axon projection from the ventrobasal complex, is somatopically organized, and has a predominantly lemniscal neuron population. These projections in the cat (117, 137, 153) are to the second somatic sensory area (SmII), and to the architectonic fields 1, 2, and 3b, and to field 4, respectively, as defined by Hassler & Muhs-Clement (153, 156). Accordingly, the latter projections may be considered analogous to the areas SmI and MsI of the primate, as defined by Woolsey (157). Ruffini receptors of the cat's elbow joint have a similar triple projection (158), but the evidence concerning the cortical projection of Golgi-type endings is equivocal. Group 1 muscle afferents project to field 3a (153) just behind the classical 'motor' area (field 4) and to the anterior part of the suprasylvian fold (159). The anterior suprasylvian gyrus also receives vestibular, cochlear, and joint inputs and possibly is concerned with the regulation of movement (154).

T. A. Woolsey (160) has shown that the somatic sensory projection pattern in the mouse cerebral cortex has much in common with that of other rodents.

Recent electrophysiological investigations of the 'nonprimary' cortex of the cat have been reviewed by Buser & Bignall (161). In the lightly anaesthetized animal many neurons in the 'association' areas of cortex have a polymodal excitatory input, but the response profile to these inputs differs with the particular neuron population and the anaesthetic used. For example, ready visual responsiveness typifies cells in the anterior suprasylvian gyrus of the cat, although they do commonly also respond to auditory and somatic inputs (162, 163). The pathways for this visual response, unlike that to the visual cortex, are multiple (164, 165) and thought to include projections from other polymodal subcortical structures, such as the reticular formation, as well as from the lateral geniculate body and also the visual cortex. Dubner & Brown (163) showed that some of these neurons responded to localized illumination of the retina, but the visual fields were large, and delimited only with threshold stimuli. Convergence occurs, within the multiple projections to each 'association' area, probably at both subcortical and cortical levels (166, 167).

Ablation studies.—A two-stage model of the perceptual process in which a purely sensory stage leads to a second more elaborate cognitive stage has formed the basis for much of the traditional analysis of cortical function, the two stages being thought to be subserved by the primary cortical receiving areas and the 'association' cortex, respectively (168). As proposed by this model, removal of part of the primate postcentral gyrus does permanently impair tactile discriminative capacities such as two-point discrimination, point localization, and to a lesser degree the detection of changes in stimulus intensity on the side opposite the cortical lesion (196). There is an obvious relationship between this sensory loss and the known functional properties of the neuron population of the postcentral gyrus. However, ipsilateral sensory loss, particularly of point localization (170), is not readily accounted for in terms of these neuron characteristics. Correlation of elementary sensory function with the specific somatic cortex is further blurred in relation to cutaneous thermal sensibility. Cragg & Downer (171) found that the perception of changes in skin temperature by the macaque depended on an intact specific sensory cortex, but the dependency was complex. Ablations of SmI and SmII did not significantly impair the differential threshold in the contralateral hand, but transfer of trained discrimination in the one hand to the other did require an intact postcentral gyrus. Either section of the corpus callosum, an entirely intercortical pathway, or removal of the pre- and postcentral gyri on the side opposite the trained hand, prevented the transfer of the learned discrimination to the ipsilateral hand.

Analysis of the somatic sensory function of the second sensory (SmII) and the other somatic afferent projection areas is at an impasse because no perceptual loss has been correlated with their destruction (172).

Perceptual loss associated with ablation of frontal, temporal, and parietal lobes may in each situation include impaired tactual function. The losses resulting from frontal, infratemporal, and mediotemporal (173) ablations appear to be secondary, supramodal, perceptual defects. Ablation of the posterior parietal lobe, however, is thought by Wilson (174) to produce a modality-specific cognitive loss of perception. Monkeys with such a lesion fail to recognize the significance of a particular tactual cue, useful to them in a reward situation, although their ability to detect tactual stimuli and to utilize helpful visual cues is not impaired—behavior which approximates that termed visual agnosia in man.

Semmes, from her studies of the lasting effects of penetrating brain wounds of the parietal lobe in man (175, 176), has reached somewhat different conclusions. As in the animal experiments and previously reported clinical observations, she observed impaired tactual shape discrimination in the absence of elementary sensory, motor, or cognitive loss. However, this loss of tactual shape discrimination is explained in terms of two independent factors, one the status of the somatic sensory capacities, and the other depending on a generalized sensory spatial disorientation—apparent in any test which depends on spatial orientation and which is independent of the sensory modality tested. According to this interpretation there is a nontactual component in astereognosis. Unfortunately, serious uncertainties concerning

the extent and depth of the lesion are inherent in the study of patients with
brain injury.

   Corticofugal influences on transmission in somatic sensory pathways.—
Since the initial observations of Andersen and colleagues (177, 178) demonstrating that electrical stimulation of the somatic sensory cortex may induce
primary afferent depolarization (PAD) of the central terminals of cutaneous
myelinated fibers, a number of investigations have been directed to the definition of the feedback pathways involved and their functional characteristics. The areas of cerebral cortex from which PAD may be elicited most
readily have been located within the specific somatic sensory cortex, with
evidence of somatotopic organization of the corticospinal (177, 178, 179),
corticofunicular (180), and corticobulbar (137, 181–183) linkages. Parallel
cortically evoked inhibitory effects have also been observed in the second-
order neurons in the somatic sensory pathways at both spinal (185–188) and
brainstem levels, not only in interneurons but also in medial lemniscal (187)
and trigeminothalamic relay neurons (184, 189–192) as well as those projecting into the dorsolateral spinal column of the cat (88). Corticofugal,
latency excitatory responses have also been observed in all these cell types.

   There is increasing evidence that corticofugal pathways affecting the
PAD of cutaneous fibers include not only direct pyramidal projections to
the sensory relays but also projections via the brainstem reticular formation.
Electrical stimulation of the somatic sensory cortex effectively elicits PAD
in terminals in the spinal dorsal horn (179, 188) and in the brainstem (183,
185, 188, 193) following acute and chromic pyramidotomy, although Carpenter and colleagues (179) observed such action only with high intensity
stimulation of the cortex. Hongo & Jankowska (188) also reported somewhat
higher cortical stimulus thresholds for evoking PAD in cutaneous afferents
via extrapyramidal pathways; they concluded from the effects of localized
spinal cord lesions that the rubrospinal and possibly the reticulospinal pathways mediate these changes. Direct electrical stimulation of the brainstem
reticular formation, after degeneration of the corticospinal and corticobulbar
projections (bilateral ablation of the sensorimotor cortex), also evokes primary afferent depolarization of dorsal column afferents (194). Stimulation
of the caudalmost regions of the brainstem reticular formation proved the
most effective in evoked PAD in the dorsal column nuclei (194), in the spinal
dorsal horn (195), and in the trigeminal complex (196). Nyberg-Hansen (197)
has summarized his Nauta studies of the sites of termination in the spinal
cord of the cat of the various descending supraspinal fiber systems with
reference to the laminar organization of the cord. Engberg, Lundberg &
Ryall (198, 199) have obtained evidence suggesting differential effects of the
corticospinal, the rubrospinal, and the 'dorsal reticular system' on interneurons in the dorsal horn, and also on spinal reflexes. Differential effects of this
type possibly also operate on the ascending somatic sensory pathways.

   Reversible cold block of descending pathways in the spinal cord has been
shown by Wall (85, 87) to modify the excitability of dorsal horn cells. Coinci-

dent with this block, sustained increase in their excitability occurred, evident as an expansion of the receptive fields of neurons in laminae V and VI of Rexed. Wall (86) also reported an expansion of the response profile of these cells so that some units, previously responsive to 'tactile' stimuli only, also responded to proprioceptive inputs during block of these supraspinal projections. With some neurons actual 'switch' in the modality was reported. Somewhat comparable results were observed in the dorsal horn cells in unrestrained rats. It appeared that when the rat's attention was directed to the skin regions adjacent to the receptive field of such a cell its excitability was increased, but when his attention was specifically directed elsewhere, the neuron's responsiveness to the test stimulus was reduced. Wall and colleagues (86) suggest that forebrain regulating mechanisms, operating largely at presynaptic sites, account for these changes in excitability of dorsal horn neurons.

COMMENT

Now that modern data processing methods permit the detailed description of the internal patterns of on-going activity in single neurons, the responses of these cells to physiological stimuli may be studied with the aim of identifying the coding mechanisms of the different stimulus characteristics. This advance provides major advantages, the most important in my view being that neural and subjective responses to identical stimuli may now be compared quantitatively. Examination of the observer's sensory capacities in this situation provides precise definition of the limits to detection, recognition, and discrimination within which the appropriate neural mechanisms operate—any proposed neural code must account both for these boundaries to the perceptual process and for the subjective behavior within them. Several problems are associated with experiments of this type. Firstly, precise, controlled stimulation simulating inputs common in the observer's experience must be developed—a soluble, practical problem. Secondly, appropriate statistical procedures for analysing the patterning of the neural response, and its correlation with the stimulus parameters, have already received considerable attention (200) but will require further expansion for specific experimental situations. Probably the most formidable group of problems is that concerned with the measurement of subjective responses. With the psychophysical methods available, any transformation occurring at stages in the perceptual process beyond that stage being examined at the neural level, or any transformation introduced by the experimental scaling of the subjective response, limits the value of the comparison of synchronous neural and subjective responses; such experimental situations pose problems for the immediate future. Fortunately for the neural/subjective response comparisons recently reported (28–32), nonlinear transformation other than of the transducer type was apparently negligible, but this cannot be anticipated with all such comparisons.

The methods considered here are most readily applicable to situations where the neural channels operate independently of each other; the information relayed by appropriate single neurons will then be reflected in the observer's sensory capacities. However, it is likely that in many situations the response profile of a population of neurons determines the information transmitted, that is, the separate neural channels of the sensory pathway do not operate independently but are closely coordinated in their activity. When the coding mechanisms are of this type the available single neuron recording techniques have limited application, for the population response must be synthesized, and then incompletely, from independent observations on separate neurons. Synchronous recording of the activity in more than one isolated neuron will be essential in these analyses.

Books.—Recent books relevant to this chapter include: *Medical Physiology*, edited by Mountcastle (201), in which most of the section in neurophysiology has been rewritten; an excellent symposium, with extensive coverage on *The Skin Senses*, edited by Kenshalo (202); a Ciba Symposium on *Myotatic Kinaesthetic and Vestibular Mechanisms*, edited by Reuck & Knight (203); *Contributions to Sensory Physiology*, edited by Neff (204); *Recent Advances in Clinical Neurophysiology*, edited by Widen (205); *Sensory Inhibition* by Bekesy (206); *Oral Sensation and Perception* edited by Bosma (207); Howard & Templeton's *Human Spatial Orientation* (208); a Henry Ford Hospital Symposium on *Pain*, edited by Knighton & Dumke (209); Moore's *Interval Analysis* (210); and *The Statistical Analysis of Series of Events*, by Cox & Lewis (211). A very readable translation of Fechner's classic *Elements of Psychophysics* has also appeared (8).

Although this review has focused on somatic sensory mechanisms, the recent work of Eccles, Ito & Szentagothai, summarized in *The Cerebellum as a Neuronal Machine* (127), is of considerable relevance to any electrophysiological neuronal circuit analysis. In this work functional cell identification has been developed to a level seldom previously achieved in the mammalian nervous system. The detailed structural and functional analysis of the cerebellar glomerulus, with inputs from the mossy fiber rosette and the Golgi cell axon collaterals to both granule and Golgi cell dendrites, should prove of considerable interest in relation to the organization of glomeruli in the posterior thalamus (122). Other novel neuron circuits proposed by Eccles, Ito & Szentagothai, and supported by extensive experimental data, include the 'de passage' excitatory linkage of parallel fibers with dendrites extending into the molecular layer of the cerebellar cortex, and the climbing fiber input to Purkinje cells, with its monitoring function of providing an instantaneous measure of the excitability of these neurons. Analogous circuits have not yet been looked for in the sensory systems.

Acknowledgements. This review was completed in the Department of Physiology, The John Curtin School of Medical Research, The Australian National University. I sincerely thank Professor P. O. Bishop for his generous hospitality. Mrs. Helen Kerns and the staff of the Biomedical Library of the University of New South Wales helped greatly with the assembling of references.

LITERATURE CITED

1. Green, D. M., Swets, J. A. *Signal Detection Theory and Psychophysics* (Wiley, New York, 445 pp., 1966)
2. Swets, J. A., Ed. *Signal Detection and Recognition by Human Observers* (Wiley, New York, 702 pp., 1964)
3. Treisman, M., Watts, T. R. Relation between signal detectability theory and the traditional procedures measuring sensory thresholds. *Psychol. Bull.*, **66**, 438–54 (1966)
4. Luce, R. D. Detection and recognition. In *Handbook of Mathematical Psychology*, **1**, 107–89 (Luce, R. D., Bush, R. R., Galanter, E., Eds., Wiley, New York, 491 pp., 1963)
5. Luce, R. D. A threshold theory for simple detection experiments. *Psychol. Rev.*, **70**, 61–79 (1963)
6. Blackwell, H. R. Neural theories of simple visual discrimination. *J. Opt. Soc. Am.*, **53**, 129–60 (1963)
7. Corso, J. F. A theoretico-historical review of the threshold concept. *Psychol. Bull.*, **60**, 356–70 (1963)
8. Fechner, G. *Elements of Psychophysics*, **1** (Transl. Adler, H. E.; Howes, D. H., Boring, E. G., Eds., Holt, Rinehart & Winston, New York, 286 pp., 1966)
9. Talbot, W. H., Darian-Smith, I., Kornhuber, H. H., Mountcastle, V. B. The sense of flutter-vibration: comparison of the human capacity with response patterns of mechanoreceptive afferents from the monkey hand. *J. Neurophysiol.*, **31**, 301–34 (1968)
10. Fitzhugh, R. The statistical detection of threshold signals in the retina. *J. Gen. Physiol.*, **40**, 925–58 (1957)
11. Peterson, W. W., Birdsall, T. G., Fox, W. C. The theory of signal detectability. *Trans. IRE Professional Group on Information Theory PGIT-4*, 171–212 (1954)
12. Boneau, C. A., Cole, J. L. Decision theory, the pigeon, and the psychophysical function. *Psychol. Rev.*, **74**, 123–35 (1967)
13. Stevens, S. S., Morgan, C. T., Volkmann, J. Theory of the neural quantum in the discrimination of loudness and pitch. *Am. J. Psychol.*, **54**, 315–35 (1941)
14. Miller, G. A., Garner, W. R. Effect of random presentation on the psychometric function: implications for a quantal theory of discrimination. *Am. J. Psychol.*, **57**, 451–67 (1944)

15. Duncan, C. J., Sheppard, P. M. Continuous and quantal theories of sensory discrimination. *Proc. Roy. Soc. (London) B*, **158**, 343–63 (1963)
16. Larkin, W. D., Norman, D. A. An extension and experimental analysis of the neural quantum theory. In *Studies in Mathematical Psychology*, 188–200 (Atkinson, R. C., Ed., Stanford Univ. Press, Stanford, Calif., 1964)
17. Norman, D. A. Sensory thresholds, response biases, and the neural quantum theory. *J. Math. Psychol.*, **1**, 88–120 (1964)
18. Stevens, S. S., Galanter, E. H. Ratio scales and category scales for a dozen perceptual continua. *J. Exptl. Psychol.*, **54**, 377–411 (1957)
19. Stevens, S. S. The psychophysics of sensory function. In *Sensory Communication*, 1–34 (Rosenblith, W. A., Ed., Mass. Inst. Technol. Press and Wiley, New York, 844 pp., 1961)
20. Stevens, S. S. On the operation known as judgement. *Am. Sci.*, 385–401 (1966)
21. Attneave, F. Perception and related areas. In *Psychology: a Study of a Science*, **4**, 619–59 (Koch, S., Ed., McGraw-Hill, New York, 731 pp., 1962)
22. Garner, W. R. A technique and a scale for loudness-measurement. *J. Acoust. Soc. Am.*, **26**, 73–88 (1954)
23. Ekman, G. Is the power law a special case of Fechner's law? *Percept. Motor Skills*, **19**, 730 (1964)
24. Ekman, G., Sjöberg, L. Scaling. *Ann. Rev. Psychol.*, **16**, 451–74 (1965)
25. Treisman, M. What do sensory scales measure? *Quart. J. Exptl. Psychol.*, **16**, 387–91 (1964)
26. Treisman, M., Irwin, R. J. Auditory intensity discriminal scale 1. Evidence derived from binaural intensity summation. *J. Acoust. Soc. Am.*, **42**, 586–92 (1967)
27. Poulton, E. C. The new psychophysics: six models for magnitude estimation. *Psychol. Bull.*, **69**, 1919 (1968)
28. Werner, G., Mountcastle, V. B. Neural activity in mechanoreceptive cutaneous afferents: stimulus-response relations, Weber functions, and information transmission. *J. Neurophysiol.*, **28**, 359–97 (1965)
29. Werner, G., Mountcastle, V. B. Quantitative relations between me-

chanical stimuli to the skin and neural responses evoked by them. In *The Skin Senses*, 6, 112–37 (Kenshalo, D. R., Ed., Thomas, Springfield, Ill., 636 pp., 1968)

30. Mountcastle, V. B., Talbot, W. H., Kornhuber, H. H. The neural transformation of mechanical stimuli delivered to the monkey's hand. In *Touch, Heat and Pain*, 325–45 (Reuck, A. V. S. de, Knight, J., Eds., Churchill, London, 389 pp. 1966)

31. Darian-Smith, I., Rowe, M. J., Sessle, B. J. "Tactile" stimulus intensity: information transmission by relay neurons in different trigeminal nuclei. *Science*, **160**, 791–94 (1968)

32. Darian-Smith, I. The neural coding of 'tactile' stimulus parameters in different trigeminal nuclei. In *Trigeminal Neuralgia* (Walker, A. E., Hassler, Eds.) (In press) (1968)

33. Mountcastle, V. B., Darian-Smith, I. Neural mechanisms in somethesis. In *Medical Physiology*, 12th ed., Chap. 62 (Mountcastle, V. B., Ed., Mosby, St. Louis, 1968)

34. Borg, G., Diamant, H., Ström, L., Zotterman, Y. The relation between neural and perceptual intensity: a comparative study of the neural and psychophysical response to taste stimuli. *J, Physiol. (London)*, **192**, 13–20 (1967)

35. Rosner, B. S., Goff, W. R. Electrical responses of the nervous system and subjective scales of intensity. *Contrib. Sensory Physiol.*, **2**, 169–221 (1967)

36. Attneave, F. *Applications of Information Theory to Psychology* (Holt, Rinehart & Winston, New York, 120 pp., 1959)

37. Garner, W. R. *Uncertainty and Structure as Psychological Concepts* (Wiley New York, 369 pp., 1962)

38. Frisk, F. C. Information theory. In *Psychology: a Study of a Science*, **2**, 611–36 (Koch, S., Ed., McGraw-Hill, New York, 706 pp., 1959)

39. Garner, W. R., McGill, W. J. The relation between information and variance analysis. *Psychometrika*, **21**, 219–28 (1956)

40. Miller, G. A. The magic number seven, plus or minus two: some limits on our capacity for processing information. *Psychol. Rev.*, **63**, 81–97 (1956)

41. Weinstein, S. Intensive and extensive aspects of tactile sensitivity as a function of body part, sex, and laterality (See Ref. 29), 195–222

42. Ruch, T. C., Patton, H. D., Woodbury, J. W., Towe, A. L., Eds. *Neurophysiology* (Saunders, Philadelphia, Pa., 316, 1965)

43. Iggo, A. Cutaneous receptors with a high sensitivity to mechanical displacement (See Ref. 30), 237–60

44. Brown, A. G., Iggo, A. A quantitative study of cutaneous receptors and afferent fibres in the cat and rabbit. *J. Physiol. (London)*, **193**, 707–33 (1967)

45. Iggo, A. Electrophysiological and histological studies of cutaneous mechanoreceptors (See Ref. 29), 84–111

46. Burgess, P. R., Petit, D., Warren, R. M. Receptor types in cat hairy skin supplied by myelinated fibers. *J. Neurophysiol.* (In press) (1968)

47. Straile, W. E. Sensory hair follicles in mammalian skin: the tylotrich follicle. *Am. J. Anat.*, **106**, 133–48 (1960)

48. Straile, W. E. The morphology of tylotrich follicles in the skin of the rabbit. *Ibid.*, **109**, 1–13 (1961)

49. Miller, S., Weddell, G. Mechanoreceptors in rabbit ear skin innervated by myelinated fibres. *J. Physiol. (London)*, **187**, 291–305 (1966)

50. Miller, S. Excitation of mechanoreceptor units in the skin of the rabbit ear. *Arch. Ital. Biol.*, **105**, 290–314 (1967)

51. Brown, A. G., Iggo, A., Miller, S. Myelinated afferent nerve fibres from the skin of the rabbit ear. *Exptl. Neurol.*, **18**, 338–49 (1967)

52. Fitzgerald, O. Discharges from the sensory organs of the cat's vibrassae and the modification of their activity by ions. *J. Physiol. (London)*, **98**, 163–78 (1940)

53. Nilsson, B. Y., Skoglund, C. R. The tactile hairs on the cat's foreleg. *Acta Physiol. Scand.*, **65**, 364–69 (1965)

54. Mann, S. J., Straile, W. E. Tylotrich (hair) follicle: association with a slowly adapting tactile receptor in the cat. *Science*, **147**, 1043–46 (1965)

55. Smith, K. R. The structure and function of the *haarscheibe*. *J. Comp. Neurol.*, **131**, 459–74 (1968)

56. Chambers, M. R., Iggo, A. Slowly

adapting cutaneous mechanoreceptors. *J. Physiol.* (*London*), **192**, 26–27P (1967)

57. Mountcastle, V. B., Talbot, W. H., Darian-Smith, I., Kornhuber, H. H. Neural basis of the sense of flutter-vibration. *Science*, **155**, 597–600 (1967)

58. Verrillo, R. T. Effect of spatial parameters on the vibrotactile threshold. *J. Exptl. Psychol.*, **71**, 570–75 (1966)

59. Verrillo, R. T. Vibrotactile thresholds for hairy skin. *Ibid.*, **72**, 47–50

60. Verrillo, R. T. A duplex mechanism of mechanoreception (See Ref. 29), 139–59

61. Goff, G. D. Differential discrimination of frequency of cutaneous mechanical vibration. *J. Exptl. Psychol.*, **74**, 294–99 (1967)

62. Calne, D. B., Pallis, C. A. Vibratory sense: a critical review. *Brain*, **89**, 723–46 (1966)

63. Lindblom, U., Lund, L. The discharge from vibration-sensitive receptors in the monkey foot. *Exptl. Neurol.*, **15**, 401–17 (1966)

64. Lindblom, U., Tapper, D. N. Terminal properties of a vibro-tactile sensor. *Exptl. Neurol.*, **17**, 1–15 (1967)

65. Bessou, P., Burgess, P. R., Perl, E. R. The specificity of cutaneous receptors with unmyelinated afferent fibers (In press) (1968)

66. Bessou, P., Perl, E. R. Activation specifique de fibres afférentes amyeliniques d'origine cutanée chez le chat par des stimuli nociceptifs mécaniques ou thermiques (In press) (1968)

67. Iggo, A., Kornhuber, H. H. A quantitative analysis of non-myelinated cutaneous mechanoreceptors. *J. Physiol.* (*London*), P (1968)

68. Werner, G., Whitsel, B. L. The topology of dermatomal projection in the medial lemniscal system. *J. Physiol.* (*London*), **192**, 123–44 (1967)

69. Uddenberg, N. Differential localization in dorsal funiculus of fibres originating from different receptors. *Exptl. Brain Res.*, **4**, 367–76 (1968)

70. Petit, D., Burgess, P. R. Dorsal column projection of receptors in cat hairy skin supplied by myelinated fibers. *J. Neurophysiol.* (In press) (1968)

71. Burgess, P. R., Perl, E. R. Myelinated afferent fibers responding specifically to noxious stimulation of the skin. *J. Physiol.* (*London*), **190**, 541–62 (1967)

72. Perl, E. R. Myelinated afferent fibres innervating the primate skin and their response to noxious stimuli. *J. Physiol.* (*London*) (In press) (1968)

73. Puletti, F., Blomquist, A. J. Single neuron activity in posterior columns of the human spinal cord. *J. Neurosurg.*, **27**, 255–59 (1967)

74. Uddenberg, N. Functional organization of long, second-order afferents in the dorsal funiculus. *Exptl. Brain Res.*, **4**, 377–82 (1968)

75. Goldberg, J. M., Lavine, R. A. Nervous system: afferent mechanisms. *Ann. Rev. Physiol.*, **30**, 319–58 (1968)

76. Mizuno, N., Nakano, K., Imaizumi, M., Okamoto, M. The lateral cervical nucleus of the Japanese monkey (macaca fuscata). *J. Comp. Neurol.*, **129**, 375–84 (1967)

77. Ha, H., Morin, F. Comparative anatomical observations of the cervical nucleus, N. cervicalis lateralis, of some primates. *Anat. Record*, **148**, 374–75 (1964)

78. Gilman, S., Denny-Brown, D. Disorders of movement and behaviour following dorsal column lesions. *Brain*, **89**, 397–418 (1966)

79. Christiansen, J. Neurological observations on macaques with spinal lesions. *Anat. Record*, **154**, 330 (1966)

80. Levitt, M., Schartzmann, R. Spinal sensory tracts and two-point tactile sensibility. *Anat. Record*, **154**, 377 (1966)

81. Vierck, C. J. Spinal pathways mediating limb position sense. *Anat. Record*, **154**, 437 (1966)

82. Schwartzman, R. J., Bogdonoff, M. D. Behavioral and anatomical analysis of vibration sensibility. *Exptl. Neurol.*, **20**, 43–51 (1968)

83. Kunc, Z. Significance of fresh anatomic data on spinal trigeminal tract for possibility of selective tractotomy. In *Pain*, 351–64 (Knighton, R. S., Dumke, P. R., Eds., Little, Brown, Boston, 636 pp., 1966)

84. Darian-Smith, I. Neural mechanisms of facial sensation. *Intern. Rev. Neurobiol.*, **9**, 301–95 (1966)

85. Wall, P. D. The laminar organization of dorsal horn and effects of de-

scending impulses. *J. Physiol.* (*London*), **188**, 403–23 (1967)

86. Wall, P. D., Freeman, J., Major, D. Dorsal horn cells in spinal and freely moving rats. *Exptl. Neurol.*, **19**, 519–29 (1967)

87. Wall, P. D. Organization of cord cells which transmit sensory cutaneous information (See Ref. 29), 512–33

88. Fetz, E. E. Pyramidal tract effects on interneurons in the cat lumbar dorsal horn. *J. Neurophysiol.*, **31**, 69–80 (1968)

89. Rexed, B. Some aspects of the cytoarchitectonics and synaptology of the spinal cord. *Progr. Brain Res.*, **11**, 58–92 (1964)

90. Kerr, F. W. L. The ultrastructure of the spinal tract of the trigeminal nerve and the substantia gelatinosa. *Exptl. Neurol.*, **16**, 359–76 (1966)

91. Rowe, M. J., Sessle, B. J., Darian-Smith, I. Stimulus-response relations and central projections of mechanoreceptors in the hairy skin of the cat's face. *Proc. Australian Physiol. Pharmacol. Soc.*, P22 (1968)

92. Schmidt, R. F., Trautwein, W., Zimmermann, M. Dorsal root potentials evoked by natural stimulation of cutaneous afferents. *Nature*, **212**, 522–23 (1966)

93. Schmidt, R. F., Senges, J., Zimmermann, M. Excitability measurements at the central terminals of single mechanoreceptor afferents during slow potential changes. *Exptl. Brain Res.*, **3**, 220–33 (1967)

94. Schmidt, R. F., Senges, J., Zimmermann, M. Presynaptic depolarization of cutaneous mechanoreceptor afferents after mechanical stimulation. *Ibid.*, 234–47

95. Janig, W., Schmidt, R. F., Zimmerman, M. Presynaptic depolarization during activation of tonic mechanoreceptors. *Brain Res.*, **5**, 514–16 (1967)

96. Janig, W., Schmidt, R. F., Zimmermann, M. Two specific feedback pathways to the central afferent terminals of phasic and tonic mechanoreceptors. *Exptl. Brain Res.* (In press) (1968)

97. Andersen, P., Etholm, B., Gordon, G. Presynaptic depolarization of dorsal column fibers by adequate stimulation. *J. Physiol.* (*London*), **194**, 83–84P (1968)

98. Darian-Smith, I. Presynaptic component in the afferent inhibition observed within trigeminal brainstem nuclei of the cat. *J. Neurophysiol.*, **28**, 695–709 (1965)

99. Vyklicky, L., Tabin, V. Primary afferent depolarization evoked by adequate stimulation of skin receptors. *Physiol. Bohemoslov.*, **15**, 89–97 (1966)

100. Zimmermann, M. Dorsal root potentials after C-fiber stimulation. *Science*, **160**, 897–98 (1968)

101. Mendell, L. M., Wall, P. D. Presynaptic hyperpolarization: a role for fine afferents. *J. Physiol.* (*London*), **172**, 274–94 (1964)

102. Rudomin, P., Dutton, H. Effects of presynaptic and postsynaptic inhibition on the variability of the monosynaptic reflex. *Nature*, **216**, 292–93 (1967)

103. Rudomin, P., Dutton, H. The effects of primary afferent depolarization on excitability fluctuations of 1a terminals within the motor nucleus. *Experientia*, **24**, 48–50 (1968)

104. Mountcastle, V. B. Pain and temperature sensibilities (See Ref. 33), 1424–64

105. Kenshalo, D. R., Duncan, D. G., Weymark, C. Thresholds for thermal stimulation of the inner thigh, footpad, and face of cats. *J. Comp. Physiol. Psychol.*, **63**, 133–38 (1967)

106. Kenshalo, D. R. Behavioral and electrophysiological responses of cats to thermal stimuli (See Ref. 29), 400–22

107. Kenshalo, D. R., Decker, T., Hamilton, A. Spatial summation on the forehead, forearm, and back produced by radiant and conducted heat. *J. Comp. Physiol. Psychol.*, **63**, 510–15 (1967)

108. Iggo, A. An electrophysiological analysis of afferent fibers in primate skin. *Acta Neuroveg.* (*Wien*), **24**, 225–40 (1963)

109. Hensel, H. Electrophysiology of cutaneous thermoreceptors (See Ref. 29), 384–99

110. Kenshalo, D. R., Gallegos, E. S. Multiple temperature-sensitive spots innervated by single nerve fibers. *Science*, **158**, 1064–65 (1967)

111. Warren, J. W., Proske, U. Infrared receptors in facial pits of the Australian python Morelia spilotes. *Science*, **159**, 439–41 (1968)

112. Raths, P., Hensel, H. Cutane Ther-

moreceptoren bei Winterschläfern. *Pfluegers Arch.*, **293**, 281–302 (1967)

113. Melzack, R., Casey, K. L. Sensory, motivational, and central control determinants of pain (See Ref. 29), 423–43

114. Wall, P. D., Sweet, W. H. Temporary abolition of pain in man. *Science*, **155**, 108–9 (1967)

115. Sullivan, R. Effect of different frequencies of vibration on pain-threshold detection. *Exptl. Neurol.*, **20**, 135–42 (1968)

116. Mountcastle, V. B., Poggio, G. F. Structural organization and general physiology of thalamo-telencephalic systems (See Ref. 33), 1277–1314

117. Rowe, M. J., Sessle, B. J. Somatic afferent input to posterior thalamic neurones and their axon projection to the cerebral cortex. *J. Physiol. (London)*, **196**, 19–35 (1968)

118. Mehler, W. R. Some observations on secondary ascending afferent systems in the central nervous system (See Ref. 83), 11–32

119. Lund, R. D., Webster, K. E. Thalamic afferents from the spinal cord and trigeminal nuclei. *J. Comp. Neurol.*, **130**, 313–28 (1967)

120. Scheibel, M. E., Scheibel, A. B. Patterns of organization in specific and nonspecific thalamic fields. In *The Thalamus*, 13–46 (Purpura, D. P., Yahr, M. D., Eds., Columbia Univ. Press, New York, 438 pp., 1966)

121. Tömböl, T. Short neurons and their synaptic relations in the specific thalamic nuclei. *Brain Res.*, **3**, 307–26 (1967)

122. Pappas, G. D., Cohen, E. B., Purpura, D. P. Fine structure of synaptic and non-synaptic neuronal relations in the thalamus of the cat (See Ref. 120), 47–76

123. Eccles, J. C. Properties and functional organization of cells in the ventrobasal complex of the thalamus (See Ref. 120), 129–41

124. Maekawa, K., Purpura, D. P. Intracellular study of lemniscal and non-specific synaptic interactions in thalamic ventrobasal neurons. *Brain Res.*, **4**, 308–23 (1967)

125. Maekawa, K., Purpura, D. P. Properties of spontaneous and evoked synaptic activities of thalamic ventrobasal neurons. *J. Neurophysiol.*, **30**, 360–81 (1967)

126. Rall, W., Burke, R. E., Smith, T. G., Nelson, P. G., Frank, K. Dendritic location of synapses and possible mechanisms for the Synaptic EPSP in motoneurons. *J. Neurophysiol.*, **30**, 1169–93 (1967)

127. Eccles, J. C., Ito, M., Szentagothai, J. *The Cerebellum as a Neuronal Machine* (Springer-Verlag, New York, 335 pp., 1967)

128. Andersen, P., Andersson, S. A., Lømo, T. Some factors in the thalamic control of spontaneous barbiturate spindles. *J. Physiol. (London)*, **192**, 257–81 (1967)

129. Andersen, P., Andersson, S. A., Lømo, T. Nature of thalamocortical relations during spontaneous barbiturate spindle activity. *Ibid.*, 283–307

130. Poulos, D. A., Benjamin, R. M. Response of thalamic neurons to thermal stimulation of tongue. *J. Neurophysiol.*, **31**, 28–43 (1968)

131. Mehler, W. R. The posterior thalamic region in man. *Confinia Neurol.*, **27**, 18–29 (1966)

132. Erickson, R. P., Hall, W. C., Jane, J. A., Snyder, M., Diamond, I. T. Organization of the posterior dorsal thalamus of the hedgehog. *J. Comp. Neurol.*, **131**, 103–30 (1967)

133. Pubols, B. H., Pubols, L. M. Somatic sensory representation in the thalamic ventrobasal complex of the Virginia opossum. *J. Comp. Neurol.*, **127**, 19–34 (1966)

134. Pubols, B. H. Retrograde degeneration study of somatic sensory thalamocortical connections in brain of Virginia opossum. *Brain Res.*, **7**, 232–51 (1968)

135. Oswaldo-Cruz, E., Rocha-Miranda, C. E. The diencephalon of the oppossum in stereotaxic coordinates. I. The epithalamus and dorsal thalamus. *J. Comp. Neurol.*, **129**, 1–38 (1967)

136. Oswaldo-Cruz, E., Rocha-Miranda, C. E. The diencephalon of the opossum in stereotaxic coordinates. II. The ventral thalamus and hypothalamus. *Ibid.*, 39–48

137. Darian-Smith, I. Cortical projections of thalamic neurones excited by mechanical stimulation of the face of the cat. *J. Physiol. (London)*, **171**, 339–60 (1964)

138. Rose, J. E., Woolsey, C. N. Cortical connections and functional organization of the thalamic auditory

system of the cat. In *The Biological and Biochemical Bases of Behavior*, 127–50 (Harlow, H. F., Woolsey, C. N., Eds., Univ. Wisconsin Press, Madison, 476 pp., 1958)

139. DeVito, J. L. Thalamic projection of the anterior ectosylvian gyrus (Somatic Area 11) in the cat. *J. Comp. Neurol.*, **131**, 67–78 (1967)

140. Mehler, W. R. Further notes on the centre median nucleus of Luys (See Ref. 120), 109–27

141. Petras, J. M. Some fiber connections of the precentral cortex (areas 4 and 6) with the diencephalon of the monkey (Macaca mulatta). *Anat. Record*, **148**, 322 (1964)

142. Sakai, S. Some observations on the cortico-thalamic fiber connections in the monkey. *Proc. Japan Acad.*, **43**, 822–26 (1967)

143. Nauta, W. J. H., Mehler, W. R. Projections of the lentiform nucleus in the monkey. *Brain Res.*, **1**, 3–42 (1966)

144. Petit, D., Mallart, A. Voies spinales afférentes vers le noyau centre médian du thalamus chez le chat. *J. Physiol. (Paris)*, **56**, 423–24 (1964)

145. Bowsher, D., Mallart, A., Petit, D., Albe-Fessard, D. A bulbar relay to the centre median. *J. Neurophysiol.*, **31**, 288–300 (1968)

146. Mallart, A. Thalamic projections of muscle nerve afferents in the cat. *J. Physiol. (London)*, **194**, 337–53 (1968)

147. Feltz, P., Krauthamer, G., Albe-Fessard, D. Neurons of the medial diencephalon. I. Somatosensory responses and caudate inhibition. *J. Neurophysiol.*, **30**, 55–80 (1967)

148. Krauthamer, G., Feltz, P., Albe-Fessard, D. Neurons of the medial diencephalon. II. Excitation of central origin. *Ibid.*, 81–97

149. Albe-Fessard, D. Organization of somatic central projections. *Contrib. Sensory Physiol.*, **2**, 101–67 (1967)

150. Spiegel, E. A., Wycis, H. T., Szekely, E. G., Gildenberg, P. L. Medial and basal thalamotomy in so-called intractable pain (See Ref. 83), 503–17

151. Powell, T. P. S., Cowan, W. M. The interpretation of the degenerative changes in the intralaminar nuclei of the thalamus. *J. Neurol. Neurosurg. Psychiat.*, **30**, 140–53 (1967)

152. Blomquist, A. J., Lorenzini, C. A.

Projections of dorsal roots and sensory nerves to cortical sensory motor regions of squirrel monkey. *J. Neurophysiol.*, **28**, 1195–1205 (1965)

153. Oscarrson, O. The projection of Group 1 muscle afferents to the cat cerebral cortex. In *Nobel Symposium 1: Muscular Afferents and Motor Control*, 307–16 (Granit, R., Ed., Wiley, New York, 466 pp., 1966)

154. Landgren, S., Silfvenius, H., Wolsk, D. Vestibular, cochlear and trigeminal projections to the cortex in the anterior suprasylvian sulcus of the cat. *J. Physiol. (London)*, **191**, 561–73 (1967)

155. Aubert, M. Aspect spatio-temporal des projections de la patte antérieure sur le cortex cérébral du chat. *Compt. Rend. Soc. Biol.*, **160**, 1907 (1966)

156. Hassler, R., Muhs-Clement, K. Architektonischer Aufbau des sensomotorischen und parietalen Cortex der Katze. *J. Hirnforsch.*, **6**, 377–20 (1964)

157. Woolsey, C. N. Organization of somatic sensory and motor areas of the cerebral cortex (See Ref. 138), 63–81

158. Andersen, H. T., Korner, L., Landgren, S., Silfvenius, H. Fibre components and cortical projections of the elbow joint nerve in the cat. *Acta Physiol. Scand.*, **69**, 373–82 (1967)

159. Landgren, S., Silfvenius, H., Wolsk, D. Somato-sensory paths to the second cortical projection area of the group 1 muscle afferents. *J. Physiol. (London)*, **191**, 543–59 (1967)

160. Woolsey, T. A. Somatosensory, auditory and visual cortical areas of the mouse. *Bull. Johns Hopkins Hosp.*, **121**, 91–112 (1967)

161. Buser, P., Bignall, K. E. Nonprimary sensory projections on the cat neocortex. *Intern. Rev. Neurobiol.*, **10**, 111–66 (1967)

162. Dubner, R. Single cell analysis of sensory interaction in anterior lateral and suprasylvian gyri of the cat cerebral cortex. *Exptl. Neurol.*, **15**, 255–73 (1966)

163. Dubner, R., Brown, F. J. Response of cells to restricted visual stimuli in an association area of cat cerebral cortex. *Exptl. Neurol.*, **20**, 70–86 (1968)

164. Bignall, K. E. Comparison of optic

afferents to primary visual and polysensory areas of cat neocortex. *Exptl. Neurol.*, **17**, 327–43 (1967)

165. Bignall, K. E. Effects of subcortical ablations on polysensory cortical responses and interactions in the cat. *Ibid.*, **18**, 56–67

166. Bignall, K. E., Singer, P., Herman, C. Interaction of cortical and peripheral inputs to polysensory areas of the cat neocortex. *Exptl. Neurol.*, **18**, 194–209 (1967)

167. Bignall, K. E., Singer, P. Auditory, somatic and visual input to association and motor cortex of the squirrel monkey. *Exptl. Neurol.*, **18**, 300–12 (1967)

168. Teuber, H. L. Preface: disorders of higher tactile and visual functions. *Neuropsychologia*, **3**, 287–94 (1965)

169. Corkin, S., Milner, B., Rasmussen, T. Effects of different cortical excisions on sensory thresholds in man. *Trans. Am. Neurol. Assoc.*, **89**, 112–16 (1964)

170. Semmes, J., Mishkin, M. Somatosensory loss in monkeys after ipsilateral cortical ablation. *J. Neurophysiol.*, **28**, 473–86 (1965)

171. Cragg, B. G., Downer, J. de C. Behavioral evidence for cortical involvement in manual temperature discrimination in the monkey. *Exptl. Neurol.*, **19**, 433–42 (1967)

172. Orbach, J., Chow, K. L. Differential effects of resection of somatic area I and II in monkeys. *J. Neurophysiol.*, **22**, 195–203 (1959)

173. Iverson, S. D. Tactile learning and memory in baboons after temporal and frontal lesions. *Exptl. Neurol.*, **18**, 228–38 (1967)

174. Wilson, M. Tactual discrimination learning in monkeys. *Neuropsychologia*, **3**, 353–61 (1965)

175. Semmes, J. A. Non-tactual factor in astereognosis. *Neuropsychologia*, **3**, 295–315 (1965)

176. Semmes, J. Manual stereognosis after brain injury. In *Symposium on Oral Sensation and Perception*, 137–48 (Bosma, J. F., Ed., Thomas, Springfield, Ill., 360 pp., 1967)

177. Andersen, P., Eccles, J. C., Sears, T. A. Presynaptic inhibitory action of cerebral cortex on the spinal cord. *Nature*, **194**, 740–41 (1962)

178. Andersen, P., Eccles, J. C., Sears, T. Cortically evoked depolarization of primary afferent fibers in the spinal

cord. *J. Neurophysiol.*, **27**, 63–77 (1964)

179. Carpenter, D., Lundberg, A., Norrsell, U. Primary afferent depolarization evoked from the sensorimotor cortex. *Acta Physiol. Scand.*, **59**, 126–42 (1963)

180. Andersen, P., Eccles, J. C., Schmidt, R. F., Yokota, T. Slow potential waves produced in the cuneate nucleus by cutaneous volleys and by cortical stimulation. *J. Neurophysiol.*, **27**, 78–91 (1964)

181. Darian-Smith, I., Yokota, T. Cortically evoked depolarization of trigeminal cutaneous afferent fibers in the cat. *J. Neurophysiol.*, **29**, 170–84 (1966)

182. Hammer, B., Tarnecki, R., Vyklicky, L., Wiesendanger, M. Corticofugal control of presynaptic inhibition in the spinal trigeminal complex of the cat. *Brain Res.*, **1**, 216–18 (1966)

183. Wiesendanger, M., Hammer, B., Tarnecki, R. Corticofugal control of the presynaptic in the spinal trigeminal nucleus of the cat. *Arch. Neurol. Psychiat.*, **100**, 39–60 (1967)

184. Shende, M. C., King, R. B. Excitability changes of trigeminal afferent preterminals in brainstem nuclear complex of squirrel monkey (Saimiri sciureus). *J. Neurophysiol.*, **30**, 949–63 (1967)

185. Levitt, M., Carreras, M., Liu, C. N., Chambers, W. W. Pyramidal and extrapyramidal modulation of somatosensory activity in gracile and cuneate nuclei. *Arch. Ital. Biol.*, **102**, 197–229 (1964)

186. Harris, F., Jabbur, S. J., Morse, R. W., Towe, A. L. Influence of the cerebral cortex on the cuneate nucleus of the monkey. *Nature*, **208**, 1215–16 (1965)

187. Winter, D. N. Gracilis of cat. Functional organization and corticofugal effects. *J. Neurophysiol.*, **28**, 48–70 (1965)

188. Hongo, T., Jankowska, E. Effects from the sensorimotor cortex on the spinal cord in cats with transected pyramids. *Exptl. Brain. Res.*, **3**, 117–34 (1967)

189. Darian-Smith, I., Yokota, T. Corticofugal effects on different neuron types within the cat's brain stem activated by tactile stimulation of the face. *J. Neurophysiol.*, **29**, 185–206 (1966)

190. Hammer, B.   Electrophysiologische

Untersuchung von peripheren corticalen und thalamischen Verbindungen zu Neuronen der bülbaren Trigeminuskerne der Katze. *Pfluegers Arch.*, **299**, 261–84 (1968)

191. Tarnecki, R., Hammer, B. Funktionelle Eigenschaften von Neuronen des spinalen Trigeminuskerns der Katze. *Helv. Physiol. Acta* (In press) (1968)

192. Dubner, R. Interaction of peripheral and central input in the main sensory trigeminal nucleus of the cat. *Exptl. Neurol.*, **17**, 186–202 (1967)

193. Wiesendanger, M., Hammer, B., Hepp-Reymond, M. C. Corticofugal control mechanisms of somatosensory transmission in the spinal trigeminal nucleus of the cat. *Symposium on Trigeminal Neuralgia* (In press) (Walker, A. E., Hassler, R., Eds., 1968)

194. Cesa-Bianchi, M. G., Mancia, M., Sotgiu, M. L. Depolarization of afferent fibers to the Goll and Burdach nuclei induced by stimulation of the brainstem. *Exptl. Brain Res.*, **5**, 1–15 (1968)

195. Carpenter, D., Engberg, I., Lundberg, A. Primary afferent depolarization evoked from the brainstem and the cerebellum. *Arch. Ital. Biol.*, **104**, 73–85 (1966)

196. Baldissera, F., Broggi, G., Mancia, M. Depolarization of trigeminal afferents induced by stimulation of brainstem and peripheral nerves. *Exptl. Brain Res.*, **4**, 1–17 (1967)

197. Nyberg-Hansen, R. Functional organization of descending supraspinal fibre systems to the spinal cord. Anatomical observations and physiological correlations. *Ergeb. Anat. Entwicklungsgesch.*, **39**, 6–48 (1966)

198. Engberg, I., Lundberg, A., Ryall, R. W. Reticulospinal inhibition of transmission in reflex pathways. *J. Physiol. (London)*, **194**, 201–24 (1968)

199. Engberg, I., Lundberg, A., Ryall, R. W. Reticulospinal inhibition of interneurones. *Ibid.*, 225–36

200. Moore, G. P., Perkel, D. H., Segundo, J. P. Statistical analysis and functional interpretation of neuronal spike data. *Ann. Rev. Physiol.*, **28**, 493–522 (1966)

201. Mountcastle, V. B., Ed. *Medical Physiology*, 12th ed. (Mosby, St. Louis, 1968)

202. Kenshalo, D. R., Ed. *The Skin Senses* (Thomas, Springfield, Ill., 636 pp., 1968)

203. Reuck, A. V. S. de, Knight, J., Eds. *Myotatic, Kinesthetic and Vestibular Mechanisms* (Churchill, London, 331 pp., 1967)

204. Neff, W. D., Ed. *Contributions to Sensory Physiology*, 2 (Academic Press, New York, 263 pp., 1967)

205. Widen, L., Ed. *Recent Advances in Clinical Neurophysiology. Proc. 6th Intern. Congr. Electroencephalog. Clin. Neurophysiol., 1965* (Elsevier, Amsterdam, 308 pp., 1967)

206. Bekesy, G. von. *Sensory Inhibition* (Princeton Univ. Press, Princeton, N. J., 265 pp., 1967)

207. Bosma, J. F., Ed. *Oral Sensation and Perception* (Thomas, Springfield, Ill., pp., 1967)

208. Howard, I. P., Templeton, W. B. *Human Spatial Orientation* (Wiley, New York, 533 pp., 1966)

209. Knighton, R. S., Dumke, P. R., Eds. *Pain, Henry Ford Hospital International Symposium* (Little, Brown, Boston, 636 pp., 1966)

210. Moore, R. E. *Interval Analysis* (Prentice-Hall, Englewood Cliffs, N. J., 145 pp., 1966)

211. Cox, R. D., Lewis, P. A. W. *The Statistical Analysis of Series of Events* (Wiley, New York, 285 pp., 1966)

MOTOR MECHANISMS OF THE CNS: CEREBROCEREBELLAR INTERRELATIONS[1]

By E. V. Evarts and W. T. Thach

*Laboratory of Clinical Science, National Institute of Mental Health
Bethesda, Maryland*

Introduction

What chain of neuronal events precedes voluntary movement? It is known that neurons of motor cortex and cerebellum are links in the chain, but over what pathways and in what sequence are they excited? How do the motor cortex and cerebellum interact in initiating movement? These were the questions to which this review is addressed.

The review will consist of three sections:

I: Connections from Cerebrum to Cerebellum
II: Connections from Cerebellum to Cerebrum
III: The Role of Cerebrocerebellar Interconnections in the Initiation of Movement

We will first list some of the previous reviews of various aspects of our subject: on cerebellar anatomy and connections: Crosby, Humphrey & Lauer (1); Jansen & Brodal (2); Larsell (3); Voogd (4)—on the function of cerebrocerebellar interconnections: Bremer (5); Brookhart (6); Dow & Moruzzi (7); Jansen (8); Kreindler & Steriade (9); Stoupel (10)—on intrinsic cerebellar mechanisms: Bell & Dow (11); Dow (12); Eccles, Ito & Szentagothai (13)—on the role of the cerebellum in sensory processes as opposed to movement: Fadiga & Pupilli (14); Snider (15)—on the various "relay stations" linking cerebellum and cerebrum: the thalamus [Ajmone-Marsan (16)]; the red nucleus and ventralis lateralis [Massion (17, 18)]; the thalamus [Purpura & Yahr (19)]—on more general aspects of movement: the neurophysiological basis of motor activity [Yahr & Purpura (20)]; muscle receptors [Barker (21)]; muscle afferents [Granit (22)].

I. CONNECTIONS FROM CEREBRUM TO CEREBELLUM

This description of the cerebral input to the cerebellum is organized in the form of the following six questions.

A. What Areas of the Cortex Project to the Cerebellar Cortex, and to What Parts of the Cerebellum Are They Linked?

This section will summarize data which show the following: much but not all of the cerebral cortex projects to the cerebellum; almost all of the

---

[1] The survey of literature for this review was concluded in May 1968.

cerebellar cortex receives at least some input from the cerebral cortex; and
certain parts of the cortex project preferentially to certain parts of the cerebellum. These findings are derived in large part from cerebral stimulation-
cerebellar recording experiments in which the patterns of linkage between
the two structures were studied by moving one electrode with respect to the
other. The results of such experiments are greatly influenced by strength of
stimulation, depth of anesthesia, and dimensions of recording electrodes
(cf. 23). In the experiments of Dow (24), Jansen (8), Deura (25), and
Provini et al. (26), these parameters were adjusted to allow detection of
even slight projections from cerebrum to cerebellum. The results for the
monkey are summarized in Table I (24), and for the cat in Tables II (8) and
III (25).

A small zone of cerebral cortex (especially SM) may project to very wide
areas of cerebellar cortex. Conversely, a small zone of cerebellar cortex
(especially L zone) may receive information from many different parts of
cerebral cortex. There are exceptions, however: NSM (prefrontal, posterior
temporal, posterior parietal) may project to relatively small areas of cerebellum, and M-IM zones of the cerebellum may receive from relatively
restricted portions of the cortex. This relationship may be roughly schema-
tized in the following diagram, where "+" may be taken as an index of the
"strength" of projection:

	M-IM	L
SM	++++	++
NSM	0-+	+++

Not all parts of the cerebrum project to the cerebellum. This is true, in
the cat, for the more posterior cerebral cortical regions—on the lateral as well
as the medial surface of the hemisphere. In the monkey, nonprojecting areas
would appear to include the anterior temporal lobe and the striate cortex.
All regions of the cerebellar cortex thus far investigated have been shown to
receive inputs from the cerebral cortex; the lingula, nodulus, and flocculus
have not yet been studied, in part because of their inaccessibility.

B. "Point-to-Point" Patterns of Projection

In Dow's study (24) of cerebrocerebellar projections, a slight tendency to
somatotopically organized projections was observed within certain cerebellar
areas. By comparing the percentage of low threshold points in the face, arm,
and leg subdivisions of the cerebral sensory cortex, Dow was able to detect
certain differences indicative of a slight preponderance of connections to
certain cerebellar lobules from these somatotopic divisions of the cerebral
cortex. In contrast, mere presence or absence of cerebeller responses failed
to provide evidence for the existence of different cerebellar areas receiving
differentially from face, arm, and leg divisions of the cerebral sensory cortex.

The subsequent studies of Adrian (27), Hampson (28), Snider & Eldred
(29–31), Jansen (8), Jansen & Fangel (32), and Provini, Redman &
Strata (26, 33) have provided additional data on this tendency to somato-

TABLE I

CEREBELLAR RESPONSES TO CEREBRAL STIMULATION

Cerebellar Area Recorded

Cerebral Area Stimulated		Anterior lobe		Pyramis M	Para-median IM	Crus II L
		anterior M	posterior IM-L			
4	M_1	++	+++	+++	+++	+
1, 2, 3	S_1	++	+++	++/0	+++	++
21	Temporal lobe	0	0	0	+/0	0/+
22	Temporal lobe	0	0	0/+	0/+	++/0
17	Occipital lobe	0	0	0	0	0
18	Occipital lobe	0	0	0	+	0
19	Occipital lobe	0	0	0/++	0/++	0/++
5	Posterior parietal lobe	+++	+++	+/0	+++	++/0
7	Posterior parietal lobe	+/0	++/0	0/+	++/0	++/0
4s	Premotor area	+	++	+++	+	+++
6	Premotor area	++/0	++	+++	++	+++
9	Prefrontal lobe	0	0	0/+	++/0	0/+
10	Prefrontal lobe	0	0	0/+	0/+	++/0
6a	Frontal operculum	0/+	+++	+++	+++	+++
6b	Frontal operculum	+	0	+++	0/++	+++
3	Frontal operculum	0	+++	++	++	++

Legend:
0 = stimulation evoked no response in cerebellum.
+ = stimulation evoked response in cerebellum.
0/+ = no response was more common than response.
+/0 = response was more common than no response.
+ to +++ = a grading of response by the intensity of threshold stimulation and the amplitude of response. +++ denotes lowest threshold and highest amplitude (the two were related); +, the highest thresholds and lowest amplitudes. The values given here are averages of the many Dow gave for each area to area projection, and are rounded off to the next highest "+".
M = medial
IM = intermediate
L = lateral
SM = sensorimeter

[From data of Dow (24) for the monkey.]

TABLE II

CEREBELLAR RESPONSES TO CEREBRAL STIMULATION

Cerebellar Area Recorded

Cerebral Area Stimulated		Paramedian		Crus I		Crus II		Paraflocculus	
		contr.	ips.	contr.	ips.	contr.	ips.	contr.	ips.
Anterior sigmoid gyrus	M_I	S L SL	S L	S L SL	L	S L SL	L SL	S L	L
Posterior sigmoid gyrus	S_I	L	L	SL		SL	SL		
Anterior ectosylvian gyrus	S_{II}	S SL	S SL	S SL		S SL	SL		
Posterior part of posterior sigmoid gyrus	S_{III}	S							
Anterior lateral gyrus	2S	S				S		S	S
Orbital gyrus		S L SL / L	L	SL / L		S / L SL / L	L SL / L	S / L SL / L	S
Proreate and limbic gyrus								S	
Middle suprasylvian gyrus		S				S		S	
Anterior sylvian gyrus		S				S		S	
Middle ectosylvian gyrus		S L SL				S			

Legend: S = short-latency response.
 L = long-latency response.
 SL = combined short- and long-latency response.
 Blanks = no cerebellar response to cortical stimulation.
[From data of Jansen (8) for the cat.]

TABLE III

CEREBELLAR RESPONSES TO CEREBRAL STIMULATION

Cerebellar Area Recorded

Cerebral Area Stimulated	Anterior lobe		Simplex		Tuber		Pyramis		Paramedian		Crus I		Paraflocculus	
	contr.	ips.	contr.	ips.	contr.	ips.	contr.	ips.	contr.	ips.	contr.	ips.	contr.	ips.
Anterior sigmoid gyrus M₁	SL		SL		S		S		SL	S	S			
Posterior sigmoid gyrus S₁	SL		S		S		S		SL		S			
Anterior lateral gyrus	S		S						S					
Anterior suprasylvian gyrus	S		SL		S		S		SL		S		S	
Middle ectosylvian gyrus	S				SL				S				SL	
Middle suprasylvian gyrus														
Posterior lateral gyrus														
Posterior suprasylvian gyrus														
Posterior ectosylvian gyrus														
Posterior sylvian gyrus														

Legend: S = short-latency response.

L = long-latency response.

Blanks = no cerebellar response to cerebral stimulation.

[From data of Deura (25) for the cat.]

topic projection. Much of this work is reviewed and discussed in Jansen & Brodal (2), Dow & Moruzzi (7), Dow (12), Brookhart (6), and Fadiga & Pupilli (14). Most authors agree that detection of point-to-point projections requires special attention to kind and amount of anesthetic, use of near-threshold short-duration stimuli, and proper condition of the preparation (cf. 23). Even then, the somatotopic nature of the input pattern may be evident not in terms of presence or absence of responses, but only in terms of the relative amplitudes of responses. Moreover, even when so defined, somatotopic "point-to-point" projection has been found only within certain area-to-area linkages. These are principally projections of the motor (M_1) and sensory (S_1, S_2, auditory, visual) areas of the cerebral cortex to the medial and intermediate zones of the cerebellar cortex.

Anterior lobe and lobulus simplex.—Both M_1 (26, 27, 29–31, 33) and S_1 (26, 28–31, 33) project to the contralateral anterior lobe (at least in the intermediate zone) in a point-to-point pattern that preserves the somatotopic organization of the cortical "sending" areas. The pattern is clearly somatotopic only in the sagittal dimension and only in the intermediate zone, with hindlimb cortex represented anteriorly in centralis, head cortex posteriorly in simplex, and forelimb cortex between head and hindlimb in culmen. The projection would thus seem to overlap that from the peripheral somatosensory receptors (27, 34, 35). But the projection patterns of peripherally evoked potentials and the results of ablation studies (36, 37) suggest that the body is also represented in the coronal dimension, with the limbs in the intermediate zone and the trunk and axial musculature in the vermis. It is not yet clear how the cerebral cortex projects to the vermis; most authors have not commented on representation in the coronal dimension. Provini et al. (26) do, and conclude that the limbs are again represented in the vermis but in a pattern different from that in the intermediate zone: there is not only a tendency for hindlimb cortex to be represented anteriorly and forelimb cortex posteriorly (as in the intermediate zones), but also for hindlimb to be closer to the midline and forelimb more lateral (near the paravermian vein). The authors note (see their Figure 6), however, that these patterns are much less obvious than those seen in the intermediate zone.

It seems probable that the vermis of the cerebellar cortex receives mainly from trunk rather than limb areas of the cerebral sensorimotor cortex. As cortical areas representing the trunk are small and poorly defined, and as most authors have tended to place stimulating electrodes within limb or face areas of cortex (26), a cortical projection of "trunk" areas to the vermis of the anterior lobe (corresponding to that pattern of input from the peripheral nerves) might have been overlooked.

Paramedian lobes.—The paramedian lobe also receives a somatotopically organized projection from the cerebral cortex, not only from M_1 (29–31) and S_1 (29–31), but also from S_2 (8, 28, 32). Snider & Eldred (30, 31) failed to detect a somatotopically organized projection from S_2. A paramedian lobe may be activated from either cerebral hemisphere; one hemisphere thus projects to both paramedian lobules, but the contralateral projection shows the clearer somatotopic organization.

Simplex, folium, tuber.—Auditory and visual receiving areas of the cerebral cortex of cats (28, 30) and of monkeys (31) project to medial simplex, folium, and tuber, and often extend laterally into simplex and the rostral paramedian lobes (14), thus overlapping each of the two head projections from motor and sensory areas of the cortex. The projection also overlaps an input from the cerebral cortical frontal eye fields (31), and the peripheral inputs from head, retina, and cochlea. The auditory cortex would appear to project to a more localized zone of cerebellum than the visual cortex (14, 28, 30, 31).

C. Cerebral Cortical Projections via Mossy and Climbing Fibers

In much of the early work on cerebellar evoked potentials it was recognized that cerebellar responses fell into two categories with regard to latency. Jansen (8) systematically studied "short latency" (SL, 2–6 msec) and "long latency" (LL, 12–25 msec) responses, and with Fangel (32) obtained evidence that the SL response was due to mossy fiber activation of granule cells and the LL response due to climbing fiber action on Purkinje cells. The anatomical experiments of Szentagothai & Rajkovits (38) showed that olivocerebellar fibers terminate as climbing fibers, and abundant evidence from physiological experiments has confirmed the proposal of Jansen & Fangel that the climbing fiber input causes the LL response (39, 40–42). Since the distinction between the two inputs is important in much of the recent work on cerebellar physiology, the methods of distinguishing mossy from climbing fiber activity and the evidence that climbing fibers are terminals of olivary inputs and that mossy fibers are terminals of all other fibers will be briefly reviewed.

1. Cajal (43) described climbing fibers as having a one-to-one projection to Purkinje cells, and mossy fibers as dividing to contact many granule cells.

2. Jansen (8) observed that a short-latency (SL) cerebellar response to cerebral cortical stimulation reversed polarity in the granule layer, while a long-latency (LL) response reversed in the Purkinje layer. Jansen & Fangel (32) showed that cerebellar cortical stimulation lateral to the recording electrode (thus activating parallel fibers) evoked the SL but not the LL response, and that the SL response to parallel fiber stimulation blocked the SL response to cerebral cortical stimulation. Single-unit recording further confirmed the localization of the SL response in the granule layer and the LL response in the Purkinje layer, and showed that the SL response was followed by a "simple spike" from Purkinje cells while the LL response involved an "inactivation response" [the two different types of Purkinje cell responses described by Granit & Phillips (44)]. Jansen & Fangel concluded that the SL response is produced by mossy fibers exciting granule cells which in turn generate a simple spike in Purkinje cells (over rapidly conducting pathways),

while the LL response is caused by a more slowly conducting climbing fiber pathway which excites the Purkinje cell so as to produce the "inactivation response" of Granit & Phillips.

3. The recent work of Bell & Grimm (42) supports these conclusions. They recorded the activity of two adjacent Purkinje cells simultaneously and noted that while the simple spikes of each cell tended to fire together, the complex spikes did not—which suggests that simple spikes were produced by a shared input (the parallel fibers), while the complex spikes were produced by unshared inputs (the climbing fibers).

4. Szentagothai & Rajkovits (38) gave direct anatomical evidence that climbing fibers are terminals of the olivocerebellar projection and that mossy fibers were the terminals of all other inputs. This evidence led Jansen & Fangel (32) to conclude that their LL response was mediated by climbing fiber input to the Purkinje cell from the inferior olive, and (by exclusion) that the SL response was due to mossy fiber input to the granule cells from the pons.

5. Eccles et al. (40) stimulated the olive and produced in the Purkinje cell the inactivation response of Granit & Phillips (the LL response of Jansen & Fangel) and (with the evidence of Szentagothai & Rajkovits on climbing fiber origin) concluded that the inactivation response was due to climbing fiber activation of Purkinje cells.

6. Armstrong & Harvey (39), Crill & Kennedy (41), and Bell & Grimm (42) recorded single-unit activity from the inferior olive and found that the pattern of discharge is similar (see section 4) to the climbing fiber response in the Purkinje cell [but see Sedgwick & Williams (45)].

The evidence above shows (a) that the "simple" spike (ordinary spike; parallel fiber response) of the Purkinje cell is mediated by parallel fiber input, and that the "complex" spike (inactivation response; long-latency response; climbing fiber response) is mediated by input from a climbing fiber, and (b) that climbing fibers are the intracerebellar terminals of olivary neurons, whereas other cerebellar inputs terminate as mossy fibers. The above conclusions are generally accepted [except for the olive being the *exclusive* source of climbing fibers; see Bell & Dow (11)], but there remain certain unexplained observations. Thus, in the work of Jansen (8) and Deura (25), LL responses to cortical stimulation persisted after section of the olivary efferents at their midline decussation (8) and in the inferior peduncle (8, 25), but were abolished by section of the middle cerebellar peduncle. Since olivocerebellar fibers cross the midline and ascend to the cerebellum solely in the inferior peduncle, these experiments suggest that another structure—one which projects to the cerebellum via the middle peduncle—may be able to initiate the "complex" spike in the Purkinje cell. These conflicts need be to resolved before the current hypothesis that all climbing fibers arise in the olive can be wholly accepted.

Tentatively accepting the hypothesis, however, one can interpret the cerebrocerebellar mapping studies of Jansen (8), Deura (25), and Provini et al. (26) (all in the cat) as showing that both mossy and climbing fibers carry impulses from the cerebrum to the cerebellum. Granted that both sorts of fibers are involved in the cerebrocerebellar projection, there remains the question as to whether the short-latency (SL, mossy fiber) and long-latency (LL, climbing fiber) responses have the same or different topographical distributions in the cerebellar cortex.

Jansen studied SL (2–6 msec) and LL (12–25 msec) projection patterns in cats anesthetized with a mixture of nembutal and chloralose. Suprathreshold stimulation was used to study extent of projection, and threshold stimulation to study differences in projection from two adjacent stimulating or to two adjacent recording sites. The entire cerebral cortex was stimulated, but recordings were obtained only from the hemispheric portions of the cerebellar cortex (crus I, crus II, paraflocculus, and paramedian—not from anterior lobe, flocculus, nodulus, or any part of the vermis). Within these regions, the distribution of projection was variable, depending on depth of anesthesia and condition of the animal. Nevertheless, the following conclusions were reached:

1. Cerebellar responses to stimulation of somatic area II were generally SL, with only rare instances of LL responses. In contrast, stimulation of somatic area I evoked predominantly LL responses.

2. The classical motor area of the anterior sigmoid gyrus projected most widely to the cerebellum, and its stimulation evoked both SL and LL responses.

3. Most cerebellar areas could show SL, LL, or combined responses, depending on the site of cerebral stimulation. Crus II, for example, showed pure SL responses to anterior suprasylvian stimulation, combined SL-LL responses to anterior ectosylvian stimulation, and predominantly LL responses to stimulation of a number of other cerebral areas.

4. The paramedian lobes received SL and LL inputs from many different parts of the cerebral cortex, while crus I had a relatively restricted input field. For any one major cerebellar lobule, both SL and LL impulses could be received from at least two and usually more large areas of the cerebral cortex.

5. SL and LL responses were received from ipsilateral as well as contralateral cortical hemispheres, but the contralateral projection was the stronger. For contralateral cerebral stimulation, the SL response was usually evoked from more areas then the LL response. For ipsilateral cerebral stimulation, the LL response was as common if not more so than the SL response.

Deura (25) has also studied SL (6 msec) and LL (15 msec) cerebellar responses to cerebral stimulation in cats anesthetized with nembutal. It was found that:

1. From any one cerebral cortical area the SL response was more widely distributed than the LL response: one area (anterior lateral gyrus) evoked only SL responses; no area was found to evoke only LL responses.

2. S_1 projected as widely as did M_1 and sent more SL impulses than LL impulses (but see Jansen, 8).

3. Each cerebellar area received SL inputs from wide areas of the cerebral cortex, whereas LL inputs were received from relatively restricted cerebral areas; two areas (pyramis and crus I) received *only* SL inputs.

4. Ipsilateral projection was found only in the paramedian lobe and there only from M_1.

Deura concluded that for stimulation of a given cerebral point, the SL response had a wider cerebellar distribution than the LL response. For cerebellar receiving areas at the center of a major cerebral projection field, both SL and LL responses are evoked; for cerebellar receiving areas in the periphery, only the SL response is evoked. This finding is consistent with the anatomy: the olivocerebellar projection is point-to-point and the pontocerebellar projection is diffuse (cf. 2). Deura attributed the differences between his observations and those of Jansen (8), Adrian (27), Hampson (28), and Snider & Eldred (30, 31) to differences in the type and depth of anesthesia. (Deura found no somatotopic organization in anterior lobe, simplex, or paramedian lobes—either for SL or for LL inputs.)

Provini et al. (26) studied SL (3–3.5 msec) and LL (13–16 msec) projection patterns in cats anesthetized with nembutal and stimulated with currents six times threshold. Only the forelimb and hindlimb areas (as defined by evoked potentials from stimulating peripheral nerves) of the sensorimotor cortex (no distinction was made between M_1 and S_1) were stimulated, and recordings were from only the cerebellar anterior lobe. It was found that:

1. Stimulation of a point in the sensorimotor cortex evoked both SL and LL responses in overlapping zones of the anterior lobe. There was, however, a tendency for the SL response to be more widespread than the LL response.

2. For cerebellar cortical receiving areas the LL response was evoked by stimulation of a relatively restricted zone of the cortex (e.g., forelimb only), while the SL response could be evoked from a wider cerebral area (e.g., forelimb plus hindlimb cortex).

3. These patterns of projection from limb areas in the sensorimotor cortex were demonstrated in the intermediate zone of the anterior lobe only and not the vermis (a possible reason for this has already been given). Provini et al. (26) conclude that SL and LL projections from cerebral cortex to cerebellar cortex (for the areas studied) overlap, though the SL projection is slightly wider than the LL.

In the results of Jansen (8), Deura (25), and Provini et al. (26), the areas of cerebellar recording were not the same in the three studies; and further, certain differences may be related to the recording sites. Thus, it appears that the projection pattern of cerebral association cortex onto cerebellar hemisphere is most diffuse, whereas transmission from sensorimotor cortex to anterior lobe, simplex, and paramedian lobe is most focused.

D. Pathways from the Cerebral Cortex to the Cerebellar Cortex

Climbing fiber pathways.—The evidence that the olive gives rise to climbing fibers is discussed in Section C. Brodal (46) showed that the inferior olive is unique among sources of cerebellar input in that it projects quite strictly in a point-to-point fashion to the entire contralateral cerebellar cortex. The inputs to the olive are also well localized (2), such that the caudal half receives a spinal input (47), and the rostral half a "descending" input (48–50). The descending input to the olive consists of projections from caudate nucleus, globus pallidus, red nucleus, mesencephalic reticular formation, and periaqueductal gray, and from the cerebral (chiefly SM) cortex proper—and each of these projections is apparently restricted to its own portion of the anterior part of the olive, with relatively little overlap (48–50). By comparing the projection of olive to cerebellum with that of cerebrum to olive, Walberg (48–50) inferred that parts of the cerebrum were linked predominantly to certain areas of the cerebellar cortex. Thus, the cerebral cortex (chiefly SM) projects bilaterally to the cerebellar nuclei and to the intermediate zone of the anterior lobe (and to lesser extents to lobulus simplex, crus II, the paramedian lobes, the pyramis, and the uvula). These are thus areas in which long-latency responses should be easily produced by stimulation of the cerebral cortex, particularly the sensorimotor cortex (Tables II, III). Cerebral information could get to crus I of the cerebellum via the olive by first going through the red nucleus or the mesencephalic periaqueductal gray. Several recent studies on the projection of the cerebral SM cortex to the red nucleus (51–56) further show that the red nucleus may serve as a "relay" from cerebral cortex to olive and thence to cerebellar cortex. But the role of the red nucleus is not solely this, as it also receives an input from the interposed and dentate cerebellar nuclei (57–63) and transmits to nuclei other than the inferior olive [the interposed nucleus (64, 65), the lateral reticular nucleus (66, 67), and the spinal cord (43, 68, 69)]. Less is known about the connections of the other cerebral structures which may (or may not) "relay" cerebral cortical information to the olive.

There are physiological observations that the above anatomical studies do not explain. One is that cortical stimulation can evoke LL potentials in the vermis of the anterior lobe as well as in the intermediate zone (25, 26, 33). The vermis has been shown to receive only from the caudal or "spinal" portion of the olive (2, 46), and the cortico-olivary fibers do not terminate in the "spinal" portion of the olive (48–50). However, Crill & Kennedy (41) and Sedgwick & Williams (45) all report recording from single olivary cells (in various positions in the olive) that could be driven by *both* spinal and cerebral cortical inputs. If cerebral cortical and spinal inputs overlap (as is suggested by these experiments), the cerebral cortex may project to the entire olive, and thus have direct access to greater portions of the cerebellar cortex than is apparent from the anatomical studies.

Mossy fiber pathways.—There are two major nuclear groups which receive cerebral cortical inputs and relay to the cerebellum via mossy fibers.

These are the pontine nuclei and the reticular nuclei (lateral and para-median).

The pontine nuclei.—First we shall summarize certain of the major features of the cerebropontocerebellar pathway as presented by Jansen & Brodal (2).

1. The entire cerebellar cortex receives fibers from the pons, except possibly the flocculonodular lobe and lingula. However, the projection is greatest to the more lateral portions of the cerebellar cortex.

2. No one pontine nucleus projects exclusively to a single cerebellar lobule: a small portion of pons projects to a relatively large area of cortex and a small area of cortex receives from a large portion of pons. Compared with the olivocerebellar projection, the pontine projection is diffuse and divergent.

3. There is some tendency for localized projection, in the sagittal plane at least, such that the vermis receives mainly from medial and lateral portions of the pons, while the hemispheres receive mainly from an intermediate portion.

4. The hemispheres receive chiefly crossed fibers, while the vermis receives both crossed and uncrossed fibers.

5. Following ablation of the cerebellar cortex, all of the cells in the pontine nuclei degenerate, showing that all cells project to the cerebellar cortex.

Jansen & Brodal (2) also review the work on the inputs to the pons, and conclude that:

1. The main input to the pons is from the cerebral cortex.

2. The cortical projection terminates diffusely, though there is a tendency to topical localization in the coronal plane.

3. Going from medial to lateral, the pons receives serially from:

    frontal lobe: especially areas 4 and 6, but also areas 9, 10, 11, 12
    parietal lobe: areas 3, 1, 2, 5, 7
    occipital lobe: mainly areas 18 and 19, with few or no fibers from 17
    temporal lobe: mainly its posterior part, and possibly its anterior tip

These conclusions are chiefly based on the study of Nyby & Jansen (70) on the monkey. More recent studies in the monkey have shown that both the supplementary motor area (mesial frontal cortex) (71) and the prefrontal area project to the pons (72). The temporal lobe, however, except possibly its most posterior part, sends few fibers to the pons (73).

P. Brodal (74), using silver impregnation methods following small cortical lesions in the cat, has recently found a more complex pattern of corticopontine projection. The anterior (M_1) and posterior (S_1) sigmoid gyri each project onto each of two longitudinal columns of pontine nuclear cells located on either side of a corticospinal fiber tract. M_1 and S_1 each project to different parts of these columns: the medial column receives M_1 fibers at its medial and caudal portion and S_1 fibers at its lateral and rostral portions; the lateral column receives M_1 fibers at its ventral and caudal and S_1 fibers at its dorsal and rostral portions. Within each column there is furthermore a strong tendency for both M_1 and S_1 to end somatotopically: the medial column receives from "face" cortex dorsally and "hindlimb" cortex ventrally; the lateral column receives from "face" cortex rostrally and "hindlimb" cortex caudally. How these subdivisions of the pontine nuclei in turn project onto the cerebellar cortex is not known in comparable detail, but it would seem that these connections may mediate the somatotopic corticocerebellar projections that are evident in the evoked potential studies described in Section IB.

Analysis of the projection of cerebral cortex to pons and of pons to cerebellum reveals a tendency to localization of the projection from cerebral cortex to cerebellar cortex, with the frontal cortex projecting somewhat more to vermis than to the hemispheres, and the parietal association cortex projecting predominantly to the hemispheres. Jansen & Brodal (2) conclude that the diffuse nature of the corticopontocerebellar projection is more in keeping with the results of Dow (24) (showing a diffuse projection) than with those of Adrian (27), Hampson (28), and Snider & Eldred (29–31) (showing a more localized projection). Also, Deura (25) and Provini et al. (26) observed that the short-latency cerebrocerebellar responses (presumably mediated by the pontine mossy fiber input) are more diffusely distributed than the long-latency responses (presumably mediated by the climbing fiber inputs). One may further see a basis for Dow's (24) observation that the frontal lobes project widely but most intensely to the vermis and intermediate zones, while occipital and temporal lobes project narrowly and most intensely to lateral and posterior cerebellum.

In addition to the "direct" corticopontocerebellar pathways described above, there are several "indirect" corticopontocerebellar projections. Jansen & Brodal (2) review the evidence for projections from the superior and inferior colliculi to the lateral parts of the pons in rat, guinea pig, rabbit, and cat. Recent physiological and anatomical studies confirm a projection from the cortical visual and auditory areas to the superior and inferior colliculi (75–78). The superior colliculus has been shown to project to a medial portion of the pons (79) which, from Jansen & Brodal's (2) pontocerebellar projection map, should project mainly to vermal portions of the cerebellar cortex. Snider (80) stimulated the superior colliculus and recorded responses in the cerebellar cortex, mainly in tuber and simplex near the midline. There would thus seem to be *two* paths whereby signals from visual and auditory cortex can reach the cerebellar cortex—a direct corticopontocerebellar and an indirect corticocolliculopontocerebellar projection. Since the point-to-point visual and auditory responses were recorded near the midline rather than in the lateral lobes (28–31), the path traversed by these might be indirect rather than direct (81). This would account for the midline visual response having a slightly longer latency than other responses (30, 31) and seeming to require chloralose or no anesthesia for its demonstration (23). On the other hand, the midline auditory response which is evoked by stimulation of the temporal lobe has a shorter latency (28–31) and a relative insensitivity to anesthetics (28), and may travel over both a direct and an indirect path to vermal portions of the cerebellar cortex. More precise determinations of latency in further such experiments might distinguish between direct and indirect pathways.

The reticular nuclei.—The lateral reticular nucleus lies just lateral to the inferior olive, and like the olive, projects to the entire cerebellar cortex (82). Unlike the localized olivary projection, however, the projection of the lateral reticular nucleus is diffuse. The projection is entirely contralateral; an anterior small-celled part ("subtrigeminal") projects chiefly to the opposite flocculus, a ventrolateral small-celled part chiefly to the opposite vermis, and a dorsomedial large-celled part to the opposite hemisphere. Inputs to the lateral reticular nucleus arise from the spinal cord, the cerebral cortex, the red nucleus, and the fastigial nucleus. The spinal input consists of crossed and uncrossed fibers that ascend in the lateral funiculus of the cord. These fibers were originally thought (2) to terminate within a restricted part of the small-celled and adjacent large-celled regions, though recent information (83) suggests that the distribution may be more widespread. The rostral one third of the contralateral fastigial nucleus projects mainly to the dorsomedial large cells of the lateral reticular nucleus (84). The caudal two thirds of the red nucleus projects uncrossed to the lateral portions of all three sectors of the nucleus (66, 67). Some but not all of the cerebral cortex projects to the lateral reticular nucleus: mainly the anterior sigmoid, and to a lesser extent the posterior sigmoid, the anterior ectosylvian, the proreate gyri, and the mesial wall of the anterior lobe, with no projection from occipital, temporal, or posterior parietal areas and very little from the cingulate gyrus. The projection is mostly crossed, terminating largely in the rostral, dorsal part of the large-celled sector without somatotopic localization (85). "Apparently each of the four contingents of afferents (spinal, cortical, cerebral and cerebellar) has its main terminal region within the nucleus, although there is ample overlapping between the regions" (85). There is evidence that at least the spinal and the cortical and possibly all four afferent pathways converge on single cells of the lateral reticular nucleus (86). Because the various inputs overlap as they terminate and because the nucleus projects diffusely to the cerebellar cortex, no attempt has been made to link the four inputs to circumscribed cerebellar zones.

The paramedian reticular nucleus is just *medial* to the inferior olive, and projects to restricted portions of the cerebellum (87)—the anterior lobe (possibly the vermis only), the pyramis, uvula, and possibly the fastigial nuclei. It does not project to hemispheric portions (crus I, crus II, paramedian, paraflocculus, flocculus, or dentate). The projection is apparently diffuse. There are at least five inputs to the paramedian reticular nucleus (88): crossed and uncrossed fibers from the spinal dorsal column nuclei, the vestibular nerve, probably the fastigial nucleus, probably the pontine reticular formation, and crossed and uncrossed fibers from the sensorimotor cortex (a large input). These inputs apparently overlap as they end in the nucleus, and since the nucleus itself projects diffusely the inputs do not have restricted target zones within the overall projection toward the vermis.

The reticular nucleus of the tegmentum of the pons is considered by Jansen & Brodal (2) to be a dorsal extension of the pontine nuclei proper. It projects both to the vermis and the hemisphere. It receives a spinal input, but its descending connections have not been worked out (2).

To summarize this account of the anatomy of the different mossy fiber pathways:

1. The projections are diffuse, both from cortex to nuclear relay and from nuclear relay to cerebellar cortex. This diffuseness contrasts with the more localized projection of the corticoolivocerebellar system, and is in accord with the relative diffuseness of short-latency responses (as compared to long-latency responses) evoked in the cerebellar cortex by stimulation of the cerebral cortex.

2. There is a slight *tendency* to somatotopic projection for some of the mossy fiber inputs, and it appears that certain anesthetic agents may enhance this somatotopic organization of the short-latency responses.

3. It is not possible to say to what extent each of the "direct" mossy fiber pathways contributes to the short-latency cerebrocerebellar evoked response, except that the pons would seem to carry information from SM and NSM cortex, while the reticular nuclei would carry mainly from SM cortex.

4. Each of the "relays" has from one to four other inputs in addition to the input from cerebral cortex, and in some experiments these inputs have been shown to converge on single cells (56, 86).

E. Physiology of Single Cells Within the Cerebrocerebellar Pathway

Climbing fiber pathways.—An individual olivary climbing fiber contacts a single Purkinje cell and excites it (8, 32, 38–40, 42, 43). A single shock to the olive evokes a climbing fiber response (CFR) in the Purkinje cell. The CFR, first described by Granit & Phillips (44) as an "inactivation response", has a unique configuration, consisting of an initial spike followed by a prolonged depolarization lasting between 5 and 10 msec on which may be superimposed one or several wavelets of the same duration but of smaller amplitude than the initial spike (40). The CFR waveform also occurs spontaneously; the same Purkinje cell also generates individual spikes of simple waveform (44). In the anesthetized cat (42) and the unanesthetized monkey (89, 90), the CFR occurs sporadically and at a mean rate of close to 1/sec. It seems likely that the simple spike and the initial deflection of the CFR are conducted down the Purkinje axon, but whether the small wavelets of the CFR are conducted is uncertain. There are several hypotheses as to the nature of the CFR wavelets: they are EPSPs from repetitive climbing fiber firing (which may or may not initiate conducted impulses in Purkinje axons); they are soma spikes which are conducted down the Purkinje cell axon; they are axon hillock spikes which are conducted (40); they are dendritic spikes which are not conducted (90a). The intra- and extracellular spikes of inferior olive cells resemble the CFR of Purkinje cells in having an initial spike followed by a prolonged afterwave on which might be superimposed several wavelets (39, 41, 42, 45). Crill (91) has evidence from antidromic-orthodromic impulse collision experiments that all of the smaller wavelets are conducted up the olivary climbing fiber; thus they all must generate EPSPs in the Purkinje cell. By analogy, one might infer that the CFR of the Purkinje cell may also send several spikes down its axon, but this is not certain.

Several recent studies have dealt with responses of olivary cells (39, 41, 45, 92). Anatomical studies had suggested that the different inputs (cortical, spinal, etc.) to the olive terminated in different olivary regions. However, Sedgwick & Williams (45) and Crill & Kennedy (41) have shown that many olivary units receive both cerebral and spinal inputs regardless of their position in the olive. Sedgwick & Williams (45) also found olivary cells driven from the caudate nucleus in addition to cerebral cortex and periphery.

Oshima et al. (92) have shown that there are monosynaptic connections from corticobulbar neurons to olivary cells. Only the more slowly conducting (20 m/sec) corticobulbar fibers are directed toward the olive, whereas the pons receives inputs from both rapidly and slowly conducting fibers.

Thach (89, 90) recorded the CFR of Purkinje cells (an index of olivary input to cerebellum) during rest and movement in the awake monkey, and found that during one kind of movement (a self-paced rapidly alternating movement of the arm) the CFR continued as during rest even though the simple spike discharge altered in relation to the movement. During another kind of movement (requiring rapid reaction to a light or buzzer) the CFR often occurred in association with the movement, commonly preceding it. This indicates that the climbing fiber under certain conditions may be activated prior to movement, possibly by cerebral cortical input. But the olive would appear to be more involved in certain movements than in others. It is possible that the olive cell generates an output only when its tonic inputs reach very high frequencies, as might occur during "maximum efforts" or "startle reactions".

The overall function of the climbing fiber system is far from clear. The effect of input by the climbing fiber into the Purkinje cell is not fully known: the climbing fiber could cause a burst of spikes to go down the axon (excitation) or it could cause a single spike followed by a prolonged pause (inhibition). Thus, it is not known how the climbing fiber influences Purkinje cell output and hence, how it controls the cerebellar output generated by the nuclear cell. Studies of the effects of olivary lesions on movement reveal a range of deficits including laryngeal myoclonus, hypermetria, extensor hypertonus, and hypotonia of trunk and limb girdle (cf. 7). But olivary lesions also damage the long tracts that pass through the olive. Orioli & Mettler (93) attempted to damage *only* the olive efferent fibers so as to discover the specific role of the olive in motor activity. After severing olivocerebellar connections by midline medullary incisions in monkeys, they concluded that the only deficit specifically due to olive damage was "hypokinesis"—a poverty of movement; but they commented that the animals did not recover the ability to walk or run properly, or to jump.

In summary, ablation experiments have failed to reveal a specific role for the inferior olive, and neurophysiological experiments have yet to show how climbing fiber inputs to the cerebellum control the circuits on which they impinge.

Mossy fiber pathways.—Mossy fibers control the simple spike discharge in the Purkinje cell (cf. 13), and as the discharge frequency of the simple spike may be finely modulated over a wide range, it would seem likely that mossy fiber discharge frequencies should also be modulated over a broad range. Kitai et al. (83) studied spinal inputs to lateral reticular nucleus (LRN) cells in urethane-chloralose anesthetized cats and found response frequencies as high as 40–60/sec. Crichlow & Kennedy (86) also studied LRN cell responses in chloralose anesthetized cats and found convergence of spinal and cerebral inputs to single cells.

Oshima et al. (92) have found that cells of the pontine nuclei receive inputs from both rapidly conducting and slowly conducting corticobulbar neurons. If these are analogous to the large ("phasic") and small ("tonic") pyramidal tract neurons studied by Evarts (94), then the pons would have an input with a frequency range of from 0 to about 100/sec.

Functional differences between the pontine, the reticular, and the other mossy fiber inputs to cerebellum are not yet known. Szentagothai (13) has found that the distribution in the granule layer of lateral reticulocerebellar and dorsal spinocerebellar tract mossy fibers is quite different: the reticular mossy fibers end superficially and the spinal mossy fibers end only in deeper parts of the granule layer. How pontine fibers end in the granule layer with respect to these other two mossy fiber inputs is not known. These different patterns of termination within the granule layer are probably clues to further differences in the way that the different mossy fiber inputs are connected through to Purkinje cells. Some inputs may be preferentially linked to Purkinje cell excitors, and others to Purkinje cell inhibitors, and thus affect the Purkinje cell in entirely different ways.

The role of the pontine and reticular mossy fibers in motor behavior is also obscure. Turner & German (95) studied motor deficits in monkeys following unilateral severance of the middle peduncle. They observed transient symptoms including "curvature of the head and spine, spiralling and circus movements toward the side of the lesion; awkwardness of the lower extremities in locomotion, with incoordination between hindlimbs and forelimbs; slight hypotonia of both lower extremities"—disappearing in three to four weeks. No permanent deficits were noted and some of the transient deficits may even have been due to injury of the vestibular nuclei (7). Bilateral interruption of the middle peduncles was studied in one monkey only (95). After four months (during which symptoms similar to the above were noted) an abnormality of gait persisted. The animal seemed to have to "constantly watch its step"; and when forced to run, developed increased incoordination between the hindlimbs and forelimbs and fell. A year after the operation the incoordination became progressively worse (also seen in one of the unilaterally operated monkeys). At autopsy, no new lesions were found.

F. Pathways to Cerebellar Nuclei from Cerebral Cortex

From anatomical studies (43) the main driving input to the intracerebellar nuclei has appeared to be that from Purkinje cells. Ito (13) showed that Purkinje cells inhibit nuclear cells, and that in spite of this inhibition, nuclear cells have maintained discharge. These studies imply that nuclear cells (unless they are spontaneously active pacemaker cells) must have excitatory inputs from an extracerebellar source in order to overcome the tonic inhibitory input from Purkinje cells. Cajal and others have described extracerebellar inputs to the nuclei, but these inputs seemed sparse and, at the time, unimportant. There are a number of more recent reports of extracerebellar inputs to nuclear cells [inferior olive to cerebellar nuclei (46); red nucleus to interpositus nucleus (64); vestibular nuclei to fastigial nucleus (96)—but see (97); possibly *all* cerebellar afferent systems (13)]. [Reviewed in (11) and (13).]

It is not known whether impulses of cerebral cortical origin reach the cerebellar nuclei by paths not involving the cerebellar cortex. There is some preliminary evidence that they might. Ito et al. (13, 98) have stimulated the inferior olive and recorded monosynaptic EPSPs in the cerebellar nuclei; it is possible that a cerebral (SM) cortical input to the olive could achieve the same result. Snider (cf. 11) has stimulated the brachium pontis and recorded increased activity in brachium conjunctivum fibers at latencies so short as to imply monosynaptic excitation of nuclear cells. The red nucleus of the cat has been shown to project to the interposed nucleus (64), and to receive from the cerebral SM cortex (51–54, 56). Szentagothai (13) has concluded that although the number of collaterals is not very large, one can nevertheless trace collaterals from almost all afferent systems to one or several of the cerebellar nuclei. Szentagothai also stated that pontocerebellar, olivocerebellar, and the reticulocerebellar systems supply the cerebellar nuclei with abundant collaterals.

As formulated by Ito (13), the discharge of cerebellar nuclear cells is not necessarily dependent on input from any afferent system. It could be truly spontaneous, and modulations in nuclear cell output could be produced entirely by modulated inhibitory input from Purkinje cells.

II. CONNECTIONS FROM CEREBELLUM TO CEREBRUM

A. PROJECTION OF CEREBELLAR CORTEX TO CEREBELLAR NUCLEI

Fibers projecting from cerebellum to cerebrum arise in the cerebellar nuclei and (for the most part) pass rostrally via the ascending branch of the brachium conjunctivum (BC). We shall first consider the pattern of projection of cerebellar cortex onto the cerebellar nuclei. Within recent years several investigators have used silver techniques to reexamine the original proposal of Jansen & Brodal (99), who, on the basis of the original Marchi studies in rabbits, cats, and monkeys, concluded that the corticonuclear projection is organized according to the following pattern: the vermis projects to the medial (fastigial) nucleus; a paravermian, medial part of the hemisphere (pars intermedia) projects to the nucleus interpositus; and the lateral part of the hemisphere projects to the lateral nucleus (dentate). The corticonuclear projection has since been reexamined with silver methods to determine terminal degeneration with greater accuracy. Eager (100), using the Nauta-Laidlaw stain in the cat, confirmed the longitudinal organization found by Jansen & Brodal (99), but found considerable overlap of the three corticonuclear zones. Projection from vermis to fastigial nucleus and from anterior paravermal cortex to interpositus was almost identical to that reported by Jansen & Brodal, but Eager found a stronger projection from the lateral portion of the anterior lobe (anterior intermediate zone) to the dentate than had been apparent in the earlier Marchi studies. Greater differences were found for the paramedian lobule (posterior intermediate zone), which was seen to project not only to the interposed but also to the dentate and fastigial nuclei. Moreover, the paramedian lobule was found to project to fastigial nuclei bilaterally. Another difference between results obtained with Marchi and with silver techniques was seen in the manner in which corticonuclear fibers passed to the area of their ultimate termination. It was found that fibers from a small cortical area could project to almost the entire length of a nucleus. Eager's results have important implications for interpreting effects of nuclear lesions: a small lesion not only cuts the cortical connections to the small nuclear area in question but also severs cortical fibers passing through the damaged region to other nuclear levels.

The corticonuclear projection has also been reexamined by Walberg & Jansen (101), who reached five general conclusions. (a) The projection from the cerebellar vermis is confined to the fastigial nucleus. Projections to the other cerebellar nuclei do not occur. (b) The strictly ipsilateral nature of the corticonuclear projection found in earlier Marchi studies was also confirmed; the authors speculated that Eager's finding of bilateral projections to the fastigial nucleus might have resulted from inadvertent bilateral cortical damage. (c) The nuclear projections of anterior and posterior lobe vermal regions overlapped in the fastigial nuclei rather than projecting to mutually exclusive fastigial zones. (d) It was found that there is a narrow paravermal zone which projects exclusively to nucleus interpositus, but that the more lateral parts of the anterior lobe project to the dentate as well. (e) It was found that there was a projection gradient whereby only the lateralmost parts of simplex, crura I and II, paramedianus, and paraflocculus projected to the dentate exclusively, with less lateral parts of these lobules projecting to both dentate and interpositus.

In general, the silver studies of Eager and of Walberg & Jansen point to a more diffuse corticonuclear projection than had been revealed by the earlier Marchi studies. The two studies referred to above were carried out in the cat. A recent study by Eager (102) in the monkey also shows diffuse rather than focal corticonuclear projection: there was significant overlap of corticonuclear projections, with small cortical areas commonly sending fibers to at least two nuclei. Goodman et al. (103) studied the corticonuclear projection in the rat using silver methods and found a more diffuse corticonuclear projection than might have been anticipated from the simple concept of three longitudinal zones with sharp borders. Nevertheless, these investigators felt that their results supported the general concept that the cerebellar cortex is anatomically organized into longitudinal corticonuclear zones.

The recent summary by Brodal (104) has emphasized that the overlap of output of cerebellar cortical areas to nuclei is paralleled by an overlap of inputs to vestibulocerebellum, spinocerebellum, and pontocerebellum. Thus, it is pointed out that the spinocerebellum, when defined as that region which receives impulses from the cord, extends into what was originally referred to as the "pontocerebellum". This does not mean that the pontocerebellum is reduced in size; on the contrary, if defined as that region which receives fibers from the pons, the "pontocerebellum" overlaps with the spinocerebellum and even includes parts of the vermis proper. Dow (12) and Jansen & Larsell (105a) also point out that in phylogenetically higher mammals the pons not only projects to hemispheres but also projects to the intermediate and midline cerebellum. The pontine projection is thus not simply "added on" laterally in higher mammals, but also tends to influence "spinocerebellar" areas more than in lower mammals.

In conclusion, it would appear that in spite of the newer findings of overlap between corticonuclear zones, the original plan expounded by Jansen & Brodal remains useful. It has support in the work of Chambers & Sprague (36, 37) on behavioral deficits following cerebellar ablations, which suggests that there are three longitudinal zones each with a different motor function. The sharp borders separating a medial "vestibulocerebellum" projecting via the fastigial nucleus, an intermediate "spinocerebellum" projecting via interpositus, and a "pontocerebellum" projecting via the dentate have now been replaced by gradients, but the fact of the longitudinally organized projection remains important for studies on the cerebellum. Indeed, Jansen & Brodal (2, p. 350) long ago emphasized that cerebellar localization was a matter of degree—that there was "a functional gradient, within the anterior lobe, from an almost purely spinal medial region, the vermis proper, via the intermediate part, less heavily impinged upon by spinal impulses, but being to a greater extent than the vermis dependent also on the cerebral cortex, to the lateral part, entirely or at least almost entirely devoid of spinal influxes but being solely dependent on the cortex and possibly other supracerebellar structures, resembling in this respect the ansiform lobule."

Finally, overlapping gradients of localization rather than sharp borders between functionally separate zones have been demonstrated for projections of motor cortex pyramidal tract neurons onto spinal cord alpha-motoneurons (cf. 105), and it would seem likely that gradients rather than sharp borders are a general feature of patterns of central organization in the motor system as in other systems: localization is more-or-less rather than all-or-none.

The physiology of the cerebellar corticonuclear synaptic connections has been clarified by Ito and his colleagues; their experiments on this topic are fully reviewed by Eccles et al. (13) and for this reason will not be dealt with in detail in this review. In summary, it was found that Purkinje cells exert only inhibitory effects on their target neurons and thus act entirely by inhibition and disinhibition, both in the cerebellar nuclei and in Deiters' nucleus. In contrast, the nuclear output is excitatory, as shown by recordings in vestibular nuclei, nucleus ventralis lateralis, and the red nucleus.

B. Connections from Cerebellar Nuclei to Cerebral Cortex via the Thalamus and Reticular Formation

Cerebellocerebral influences are mediated both by the brachium conjunctivum (BC) (via the thalamus, or the red nucleus and the thalamus) and the inferior peduncle (via the bulbar reticular formation). [See (2, 7, 12, 106) for a review of the older literature.]

New information on the pattern of the cerebellar nuclear projection into the BC has been provided by the retrograde degeneration study of Flood & Jansen (107). All three cerebellar nuclei send fibers into the BC, though it is mostly formed by fibers from interpositus and dentate; most fastigial fibers go into the inferior peduncle. It would appear that, as for corticonuclear projection, BC composition involves a gradient: lateral (dentate) and intermediate (interposed) nuclei project mostly via the BC, whereas the medial (fastigial) nucleus projects mostly via the inferior peduncle. Though the more lateral neocerebellar regions dominate the cerebellocerebral projection, the vermal portion of the cerebellar cortex also has access to the cerebral cortex by at least three routes: the vermal projection to interpositus and thence through BC; the vermal projection to the fastigial nucleus and thence through BC; the fastigiobulbar tract, which reaches all levels of the brainstem reticular formation and can influence the cerebral cortex via the ascending elements of this system (108).

The terminal distribution of efferent cerebellar nuclear fibers has been reexamined with silver methods. The results of Niimi et al. (109) show that the BC projection to the thalamus is bilateral and widespread. Following unilateral lesions of the cerebellar nuclei in the cat, terminal degeneration was seen bilaterally (most heavily contralaterally) in nucleus parafascicularis, laminaris, medialis dorsalis, lateralis ventralis, pulvinaris, centre median, zona incerta, and most abundantly in nucleus ventralis. McCance et al. (110) further confirmed that BC projects bilaterally to thalamus by stimulating the BC and recording synaptically evoked cell spikes in thalamus bilaterally. Thalamic terminations of ipsilateral and contralateral BC fibers overlapped but were not coincident. Evidence that the nuclei project bilaterally was also provided by Li & Tew (111) who stimulated the dentate of unanesthetized cats and recorded responses in cells bilaterally in motor cortex. Flood & Jansen (107) also showed that nuclear projection is bilateral: about one quarter of the cells of the lateral and interposed nuclei, most of them located in the caudal half of the nuclei, failed to degenerate following midline cut of the decussating BC, which indicates that a considerable number of axons (or at least axon collaterals) from these nuclei do not decussate. All of these studies confirm the observations of Carrea & Mettler (106) that a limb of the BC ascends without crossing.

Thomas et al. (112) studied terminal degeneration following nuclear lesions and showed that the fastigial nucleus has a particularly strong uncrossed thalamic projection. This projection via the crossed and uncrossed limbs of the BC terminated much more widely than had previously been suspected, reaching the following thalamic structures: VPL, VM, VL, VA, subparafascicular, centralis lateralis, centre median, and reuniens. Bowsher et al. (113) also found bilateral terminations of the fastigial nucleus in the thalamus, but failed to detect terminal degeneration in the thalamus following ipsilateral dentate or interpositus lesions.

Though many studies demonstrate the bilateral thalamic distribution of the BC, there are a number of discrepancies in the literature. Thus, Carpenter & Stevens (114) failed to see any uncrossed fibers in the BC. Using electroanatomical techniques, Combs & Dennery (115) failed to detect any consistent ipsilateral evoked responses to cerebellar stimulation in the monkey, and Combs (116) and Combs & Saxon (117) found only small and inconstant ipsilateral projections in the cat, although Whiteside & Snider (118) had found a widespread bilateral thalamic distribution of cerebellar-evoked responses.

Several other investigators have shown an uncrossed thalamic projection from the fastigial nucleus but not from dentate or interpositus. Thus, Angaut & Guilbaud (119) stimulated the fastigial nucleus and recorded presynaptic fiber responses bilaterally widely in VL, VM, VA, centralis lateralis, and the medial part of VPL. In contrast, stimulation of interpositus (120) or dentate (121) evoked presynaptic spike activity only contralaterally. The observations of Stoupel (122), like those of Combs (116) and Combs & Saxon (117), also failed to demonstrate ipsilateral projections from the lateral, neocerebellar regions, but did show strong bilateral cerebral responses to stimulation of the vermian regions of the cerebellar cortex.

In attempting to understand these discrepancies as to laterality of distribution of cerebellocerebral evoked responses, it is important to recognize that in some electroanatomical experiments the condition of the preparation may be such as to allow appearance of only those evoked potentials mediated by the strongest cerebellocortical projections (relayed via the ventral thalamus), whereas other experimental preparations may allow the detection of weaker projections via the uncrossed BC, the reticular formation, or the diffusely projecting thalamic nuclei. The importance of anesthesia in the distribution of evoked cerebellocerebral activity is illustrated by the results of Li & Tew (111). Since anesthesia and the condition of the preparation are such critical determinants of results in studies of cerebellocerebral projections, it would be valuable to obtain electroanatomical data in chronic preparations with implanted electrodes; the study of Fanardjian & Donhoffer (123) has now provided this information. In cats with implanted electrodes, stimulation of cerebellar cortex and nuclei evoked responses in the sensorimotor cortex bilaterally, though the amplitude was considerably greater contralaterally.

In addition to the problem of anesthesia, there is the problem of whether a given cerebellar region projects to the cerebrum via the specific thalamic nuclei or via nonspecific systems. Widespread, bilateral evoked potentials of the type observed by Whiteside & Snider (118) may have been mediated by components of the reticular formation or the diffusely projecting thalamic nuclei, whereas cerebellocortical evoked potentials restricted to the contralateral sensorimotor cortex are presumably mediated by the link having the strongest monosynaptic cerebellar input, i.e., the ventral thalamus with topographically localized cortical projections; all investigators agree that this link is predominantly crossed. Indeed, Snider (124) concluded that the widespread bilateral cerebral activation evoked by cerebellar stimulation was mediated chiefly by cerebellar projections to centromedian, central medial, and central lateral thalamic nuclei—all of which have diffuse projections to the cortex.

The study of Cohen et al. (125) provided anatomical support for Snider's result—showing that *all three* cerebellar nuclei project to centromedian, and that fastigius projects to the central nuclei as well. This correlation led Cohen et al. (125) to suggest that the vermal-fastigial zone plays a role in the activation of the cerebral cortex by the cerebellum—a notion which was put forward earlier by Moruzzi and Magoun (126)—and which is also supported by the strong bilaterality of the fastigiothalamic projection (112).

Recent studies on the influence of the fastigial nucleus on the EEG provide additional evidence that fastigial efferents project diffusely to the cerebral cortex. Fadiga et al. (127) found in acute cat preparations that bilateral BC lesions did not affect the EEG, whereas bilateral inferior peduncle (IP) lesions were followed by widespread synchronization of the EEG. This effect of IP lesions could be reproduced by bilateral fastigial but not by vestibular nuclear lesions, which indicates that the "cerebellar efferents whose severance is critical are in all likelihood the fastigio-reticular fibers." Fadiga et al. (128, 129) have also stimulated the fastigial nuclei while recording the EEG and have found either synchronization or desynchronization, depending on the site of stimulation within the nucleus and/or the stimulus parameters. They also found that lesions in certain parts of the fastigial nuclei could lead to EEG activation rather than synchronization.

The role of the fastigial nucleus in EEG synchronization was further clarified by the results obtained in cats with chronically implanted electrodes, in which low frequency stimulation of the fastigial nucleus led to EEG synchronization and sleeplike effects (130). Additional work by Manzoni et al. (131) shows that though both arousal and synchronization of EEG can be elicited by fastigial stimulation, the synchronization effects predominate in the chronic preparation. Bava et al. (132) investigated the pathways which might mediate this synchronizing effect by recording fastigial-evoked unit activity in the following thalamic nuclei: centralis lateralis (CL), paracentralis (PC), centrum medianum (CM), ventralis anterior (VA), lateralis dorsalis (LD), medialis dorsalis (MD), lateralis posterior (LP), and reticularis thalami (RT). Units in three of these nuclei (LD, MD, and LP) were completely unaffected by fastigial stimulation, whereas 81 of 101 units in the remaining nuclei showed responses. It was found that for the midline nuclei (CL-PC and CM), unitary responses were equally well evoked for ipsi- or contralateral fastigial stimulation.

In general, the recent work is in harmony with the conclusion reached by Dow & Moruzzi (7, p. 325) who stated that, "Summing up the results which have been obtained so far, one remains with the impression that two different types of electrocortical responses can be obtained by stimulating the cerebellar cortex, namely (a) diffuse responses, characterized by an abolition of spindle bursts and flattening of the EEG record, elicited by stimulating vermal areas of the anterior lobe or the fastigial nuclei, and probably relayed by the ascending reticular system, and (b) responses mainly or exclusively confined to the sigmoid gyrus and to the neighboring cortical areas . . ."

Localization of cortical responses evoked by lateral cerebellar structures has also been seen by Fanardzhyan (133) in a study of cortical recruiting responses evoked by cerebellar stimulation. It was found that localized recruiting responses could be evoked in contralateral cerebral cortex by stimulation of the dentate or interpositus, but not by fastigial stimulation. These recruiting responses were mediated by nucleus reticularis and ventralis anterior. Not only were these recruiting responses restricted to the contralateral hemisphere, but they also showed shifts in cortical point of maximum amplitude as the location of the cerebellar stimulation was shifted. Thus, recruiting responses elicited by dentate or interpositus stimulation are both lateralized and localized within the hemisphere, whereas the cortical EEG synchronization or desynchronization, or a combination of these, resulting from fastigial stimulation is neither lateralized nor localized.

Granted that the fastigiocortical projection is diffuse and bilateral whereas the dentate and interpositus projections are localized and predominantly contralateral, there remains the question of the extent to which there is somatotopic localization of the dentate-interpositus projection *within* the contralateral sensorimotor area: Are there point-to-point projections from cerebellar cortex to cerebral cortex? All investigators who have studied responses of cerebral cortex to cerebellar cortex stimulation have agreed that the sensorimotor cortex shows the lowest threshold, highest amplitude responses, but beyond that point there are some discrepancies. One reason for the discrepancies seems to be the great sensitivity of the cerebellothalamocortical system to the state of the preparation (e.g., blood loss, level of anesthesia), a sensitivity which was emphasized by Henneman et al. (134) and commented on by most subsequent investigators. Nuclear stimulation is apparently less subject to these effects than is stimulation of the cerebellar cortex (134).

The study of Henneman et al. (134) in the cat showed that cerebellar areas defined as face, forepaw, and hindpaw sensory receiving areas of anterior lobe and simplex projected to the corresponding receiving areas of the contralateral sensorimotor cortex. These authors were unable to detect cerebral responses to stimulation of crura I and II of the ansiform lobe—a fact which was puzzling to them in view of the fact that these regions were known to project to the ventral thalamus. The absence of cerebral responses to stimulation of the ansiform lobe in the work of Henneman et al. (134) suggests that the type of preparation showing point-to-point projections from the "hand area" of the cerebellum onto the hand area of the cerebral cortex is one in which there is a depression of highly significant cerebello-cerebral pathways. The more recent electroanatomical studies of Combs & Saxon (117) and Stoupel (10) in the cat show that crura I and II project to the contralateral sensorimotor cortex without point-to-point localization. In exploring relations of other cerebellar zones to the cerebral cortex, Stoupel found that single-shock stimulation of vermal regions of anterior lobe and of culmen evoked only minor, unlocalized cortical responses, and that 400/sec stimulation of these areas evoked only a generalized desyn-chronization of cortical EEG activity. In contrast to Stoupel's results for midline cerebellar stimulation, Combs & Saxon (117) found that stimulation throughout the intermediate zone gave responses in the contralateral somato-sensory cortex, but without any precise localization within this area. Pro-jecting areas included IM-zone portions of culmen, ansiform, and para-median lobes, with the strongest projection from a medial portion of crus I. No projection was found from lateral parts of crus I and crus II. The results of Combs & Dennery (115) on the monkey showed that IM-zone portions of crura I and II, culmen, and simplex project to the contralateral precentral gyrus, with postcentral responses being almost as great as precentral. The strongest projection was from the simplex; L-zone portions of crus I, crus II, simplex, and culmen did not project. As to the question of point-to-point pro-jection, however, Combs & Dennery (115) stated that, "It should be empha-sized that at no time was any indication found of a somatotopic relationship between the cerebellar points stimulated and the various parts of the motor-sensory cortex."

Infantellina et al. (135, 136) have studied the cortical projections of the paraflocculus. Stimulation of the paraflocculus evoked bilateral (but predominantly contralateral) potentials in the anterior ectosylvian gyrus, with a minimum latency of 7 msec—approximately twice that of potentials evoked in sensorimotor cortex by cerebellar stimulation. No circumscribed projection fields for the different parafloccular folia were observed. The response was relayed through lateralis posterior of the thalamus. The medial geniculate showed no responses to stimulation of paraflocculus.

The observation of Infantellina et al. that cerebellar stimulation failed to elicit responses in the medial geniculate nucleus confirmed the earlier observation by Steriade & Stoupel (137) that stimulation of lobulus simplex evoked responses in the secondary auditory area (E.p.i.).

In a recent study (138) devoted to elucidating cerebellar influences on transmission in VPL, 65 of 505 VPL units responded to single-shock stimulation of the cerebellar nuclei. Mean latencies were 2.3, 3.9, and 4.4 msec for stimulation of dentate, interposed, and fastigial nuclei, respectively, and stimulation of the cerebellar cortex showed a slight trend toward greater responses from hemispheral as compared to vermal stimulation. Note that the VPL units receiving cerebellar inputs showed classical "lemniscal" responses to cutaneous or joint stimulation. Finally, it was shown that the response of VPL neurons to peripheral sensory inputs could be modified by cerebellar stimulation. Cerebellar stimulation has also been shown by Nakagoshi (139) to modify somatosensory cortex responses to peripheral nerve stimulation.

One aim of several of the studies just cited was to determine the role of cerebellocerebral connections in modulating sensory inputs. This problem—the role of the cerebellum in control of sensory inputs—might easily be the subject of a separate review and will not be dealt with here, both because of space considerations and because it has recently been covered by Snider (15) and by Fadiga & Pupilli (14).

Comment on pattern of nuclear projection.—It would seem that the phylogenetically old vermal-fastigial system has widespread connections to the cortex via both thalamus and reticular formation. In contrast, the neocerebellar-dentate-interpositus system has predominantly contralateral and topographically localized projections to ventral thalamus and thence to sensorimotor cortex. Cerebellar nuclear efferents (including fastigial) contact many but not all thalamic nuclei. Mehler et al. (140) made lesions in dentate and interpositus of the monkey and saw terminal degeneration in the CM-PF complex, para- and intralaminar nuclei, ZI, VPLo, VLo, VA, Area X, and most densely in VAmc, the last named nucleus being a structure which most authors include in VL. All of these nuclei except VL and VPL are components of the unspecific thalamocortical projection (cf. 141).

The thalamic nuclei with topographically organized projections to primary cortical visual and auditory areas are without a direct cerebellar input. Furthermore, the pulvinar (which projects to the parieto-temporo-occipital association cortex) does not receive fibers from the cerebellar nuclei. It would thus appear that the projection of the parieto-temporo-occipital association cortex to the cerebellum is stronger than the cerebellar return to these areas, and that while receiving inputs from sensorimotor *and* association cortex, the cerebellum focuses its direct nuclear output on the ventral thalamus and thence on the pre- and postcentral sensorimotor cortex. This lack of reciprocal connections between cerebrum and cerebellum deserves additional comment, because the strong reciprocal connection between motor cortex and cerebellum sometimes tends to obscure the lack of reciprocity between other cortical and cerebellar areas.

C. Connections from Cerebellum to Cerebrum Via the Red Nucleus

The role of the red nucleus (RN) as a relay between cerebellum and cerebral cortex has been reviewed by Massion (17). The cerebellar input to the RN arises entirely in the contralateral dentate and interpositus. Interpositus projects to the magnocellular portion of the RN, the site of origin of the rubrospinal tract, whereas dentate projects to the parvocellular part. In the cat, Courville (59) found that interpositus fibers were restricted to the posterior two thirds of RN. Combined, large lesions of interpositus and dentate caused preterminal degeneration throughout the entire RN, and thus (by exclusion) provided additional evidence that the anterior, parvocellular part of the RN receives a dentate but not an interpositus input. Angaut & Bowsher (58) made small stereotaxic lesions in individual cerebellar nuclei and found massive preterminal degeneration in the magnocellular part of the RN following interpositus lesions but not following lesions of dentate or fastigial nuclei. Thus, the magnocellular part of the RN has interconnections with interpositus but does not receive a dentate input. In man, the magnocellular part of the red nucleus is virtually absent, and cerebellorubral fibers arise entirely in the dentate (cf. 17). Thus, the parvocellular portion of RN provides a relay for output of the dentate but not for interposed or fastigial nuclei.

Granted that the parvocellular portion of the RN receives an input from the dentate, to what extent does it transmit this dentate output to the thalamus? Studies of the rubrothalamic projection are complicated by the fact that terminal degeneration in thalamus following RN lesions may be due either to destruction of RN neurons per se or to destruction of brachium conjunctivum (BC) fibers of passage. Indeed, not only does RN contain BC fibers of passage, but a single cerebellar nuclear fiber may give off synaptic branches which make contact with cells in RN and then pass on to terminate in ventralis lateralis. This was demonstrated by Tsukahara et al. (63) who showed that it was possible to produce synaptic activation of magnocellular neurons in RN by stimulation of interpositus terminals in ventralis lateralis. The VL stimulus caused antidromic activation of cerebellar nuclear fibers and the antidromic impulses passed backwards, invading collaterals in RN and thereby synaptically exciting cells in the magnocellular part of RN. Thus the notion of the existence of the rubrothalamic pathway has depended on findings of retrograde cell changes in RN following thalamic lesions. Such studies (cf. 17) have shown that, in subprimates, destruction of ventralis lateralis is followed by degeneration of some of the small and medium sized cells in the anterior third of the ipsilateral RN—i.e., the region of termination of the dentate input. The electrophysiological studies of Condé (142) in the cat provided additional information on the dentatorubrothalamic pathway. In these experiments dentate stimulation evoked numerous presynaptic but only rare postsynaptic responses in the caudal (magnocellular) part of RN, whereas anterior (parvocellular) RN gave both pre- and postsynaptic responses to dentate stimulation. Massion et al. (143) have shown additional differences between inputs to the magnocellular versus the parvocellular portions of the RN. Units in the parvocellular portion were found to have more heterosensory convergence than those in the magnocellular region. Further analysis of convergent inputs to the RN has been carried out by Steriade & Briot (144). Further analysis of the rubrothalamocortical pathway in the cat has been carried out by Stoupel (10), who observed that stimulation of the anterior RN caused modifications of activity in 83 of 166 motor cortex neurons.

The studies on the rubrothalamic pathway referred to above were carried out in subprimates, and a recent study by Poirier & Bouvier (145) indicates that in the monkey the rubrothalamic tract may not exist. Interruption of the central tegmental bundle (carrying fibers from RN to inferior olive) was followed by complete degeneration of cells in the parvocellular portion of RN. Poirier & Bouvier concluded that in the monkey the RN must discharge exclusively downwards. A similar conclusion as to the output of the parvocellular part of RN was reached by Verhaart (146) on the basis of studies of the relations of red nucleus, cerebellum, and inferior olive in man. Verhaart pointed out that in anthropoid apes and man the magnocellular part of RN is reduced to a very small number of scattered large cells and the rubrospinal tract cannot be identified. The material reported by Verhaart (his own work and that of previous investigators) showed that cells of the RN degenerate when the ipsilateral central tegmental tract is severed, which indicates that in man the large majority of red nucleus small cells project to the ipsilateral olive by way of the central tegmental tract. Thus, in man the red nucleus is part of a triangle involving dentate and inferior olive.

The observations of Verhaart (146) and of Poirier & Bouvier (145) thus indicate that in primates there is no rubrothalamic tract. Though the RN is a cerebellocerebral link in certain lower mammalian forms, it would appear not to have this function in monkey, ape, or man. The parvocellular part of the RN in monkey receives strong inputs from the cerebral cortex (cf. 52) and the dentate, but its output, rather than going to the thalamus, passes downward to the inferior olive which in turn projects back to the cerebellum.

Tsukahara & Kosaka (56) have shown that cells in magnocellular RN receive excitatory inputs both from the cerebral cortex and from the interposed nucleus. Toyama et al. (60) further found that stimulation of the cerebellar cortex elicited hyperpolarization of magnocellular RN cells but that this effect was due to disfacilitation of activity rather than to actual inhibition. Thus, increased activity of Purkinje cells following cerebellar cortex stimulation results in decreased activity of nuclear neurons in interpositus, which in turn results in a withdrawal of the tonic excitatory input to RN cells.

D. NUCLEUS VENTRALIS LATERALIS AND PROJECTION OF CEREBELLAR OUTPUT TO THE MOTOR CORTEX

The previously cited studies have shown that cerebellar nuclear efferents end in both the diffusely projecting midline thalamic nuclei and the specific relay nuclei (VL and VPL) of the ventral thalamus. It is to an understanding of the functional significance of the latter link, and especially ventralis lateralis, that much recent electrophysiological (as contrasted to electroanatomical work) has been directed. Attention will now be devoted to effects of cerebellar activity on ventralis lateralis, and thereby, on the neurons of the motor cortex. We should first point out that the cerebellum is but one of many sources of input to this nucleus: VL also receives inputs from the globus pallidus (cf. 147; 148), the midline thalamic nuclei (149), the motor and premotor cortex (150–153), other cortical areas (154, 155), and peripheral sensory receptors (cf. 156). In no sense, therefore, is VL a mere relay whose output to the cortex is a faithful duplicate of its input from the cerebellum. Rather, the neurons of VL appear to constitute a final common path upon which many components of motor and sensory systems converge. This view of the thalamus as an integrating center rather than as a relay is one which has been put forward and which has received much support from the work of the Fessards (cf. 157).

It has been pointed out that cerebellar nuclear fibers terminating in VL excite VL neurons. The role of noncerebellar inputs in controlling VL responses to these excitatory inputs via the brachium conjunctivum has been studied by Purpura and his colleagues (158–163). VL transmission of cerebellar inputs could be profoundly modified by concurrent activity in several other structures impinging on VL, these structures including the pallidum, medial thalamic nuclei, reticular formation, and cerebral cortex. Intracellular recordings revealed that a single VL neuron could be impinged upon by synaptic inputs from all of these structures. It should be recalled that both reticular formation and medial thalamus receive strong inputs from the fastigial nucleus. The findings of Purpura and his colleagues on the regulation of VL transmission by inputs from these two structures point to a mechanism whereby the cerebellar input to the brainstem reticular formation and the nonspecific thalamic nuclei may also regulate VL transmission, and hence control the motor cortex output.

Further information concerning the interaction of the various inputs to VL is provided by the work of Sakata et al. (164). In these studies VL neurons sending axons to the motor cortex were identified by their antidromic responses to motor cortex stimulation. About half the units responding to brachium conjunctivum (BC) stimulation were antidromically activated by cortical stimulation. About one tenth of the units were activated both synaptically and antidromically by cortical stimulation as well as by BC stimulation; VL units responded to stimulation of caudate, globus pallidus, centrum medianum, and centralis medialis as well as to cortical and BC inputs.

In addition to its numerous inputs from central structures, VL receives inputs from the periphery. Thus, Massion et al. (165) found that potentials (recorded with macroelectrodes) could be evoked in VL by auditory, visual, or somatic stimuli. A second study by Massion et al. (166) provided information on peripherally evoked unit activity in VL.

Even in the absence of stimulation, neurons of VL and a number of other thalamic nuclei exhibit rhythmic bursts of spikes separated by silent intervals of from 100–500 msec. These pauses of VL output occur in spite of a continuous high frequency input from cerebellar nuclear efferents: in both anesthetized (cf. 13) and intact unanesthetized (89, 90) preparations, the neurons in the cerebellar nuclei commonly have continuous high frequency discharges. The mechanisms responsible for the rhythmic VL activity are relevant to problems of cerebellocerebral connections because these mechanisms play a significant part in controlling the responsiveness of VL neurons to this constant bombardment of cerebellar excitation. Such mechanisms have been studied by several investigators. Purpura & Cohen (158) showed that stimulation of the medial thalamus evoked brief EPSPs followed by prolonged IPSPs in neurons of a number of thalamic nuclei, including VL. This sequence of synaptic events and the associated output patterns of the thalamic neurons (brief bursts followed by silence) explained the rhythmic bursts and pauses of thalamic neurons. The factors regulating rhythmic activity of thalamic neurons have also been studied by Andersen & Eccles (167). Their intracellular recordings of PSPs in thalamic neurons showed that the main cause of the rhythmic discharge pattern of the thalamic neuron is a large and prolonged IPSP. Additional studies have been carried out by Andersen and his colleagues (168–172). They and Eccles (171, 172) discuss the evidence that the rhythmic activity of thalamic neurons (both evoked and spontaneous) is based on IPSPs in thalamocortical relay cells, and that these IPSPs are caused by activation of interneurons via recurrent collaterals of the thalamic relay neurons.

The role of rhythmic VL activity in the relation between cerebellum and cortex has been dealt with extensively by Massion (18) in a recent study of regulation of VL transmission by sensory inputs. Massion proposed that the IPSPs responsible for rhythmicity of VL activity may be thought of as the closing of a gate. He suggested that IPSPs of VL neurons exhibiting rhythmic activity prevented then from relaying cerebellar and pallidal inputs. According to this theory, VL neurons would determine the properties of the movement "by subtraction". Massion's monograph summarizes the various pathways by which peripheral sensory inputs reach VL, and also gives evidence that nucleus reticularis of the thalamus is a major source of the rhythmic inhibitory input to VL.

Just as VL receives inputs from many structures in addition to the cerebellum, so too does the motor cortex receive inputs from many structures in addition to VL and VPL. A recent review by Phillips (105) has summarized these inputs which arise from the contralateral motor area via callosal fibers; other cortical areas within the ipsilateral hemisphere via corticocortical fibers; the diffusely projecting thalamic nuclei; the basal ganglia; and a number of peripheral sensory systems. Phillips comments that "it is interesting, as supporting the concept that the corticofugal neurons are common paths leading out of the cortex, that so many differentiated peripheral inputs are brought to bear on their surface membranes for integration. Such inputs may initiate movement by a cortical reflex, and also influence the course of the movements initiated and controlled by the intracerebral storage systems whose nature and location still elude us."

Space limitations prevent us from considering the synaptic processes underlying the influences of these several inputs on the pyramidal tract neurons (PTNs) and require that we focus on studies concerned primarily with the cerebellar input to PTNs. Detailed information on the peripheral sensory inputs to PTNs has been provided by Asanuma (174), Li (175), and Brooks and his associates (176, 177). Marchiafava (178) has reviewed the general topic of motor cortex inputs, Oscarsson (179) has reviewed the muscle afferent projection to motor cortex, while the projections to motor cortex from subcortical basal nuclei have been reviewed by Li & Davie (180). Stefanis & Jasper (181–183) deal with the topic of recurrent inhibition as it modifies the activity of PTNs, and Takahashi et al. (184) analyze recurrent facilitation in PTNs. Factors controlling motor cortex responses to electrical stimulation are covered by Schlag (185). Eccles (186) has reviewed cerebral synaptic mechanisms in general, relating current knowledge of cortical synaptic processes to knowledge of spinal cord synapses.

Amassian & Weiner (187) have analyzed the monosynaptic and polysynaptic activation of PTNs by thalamic stimulation, presenting evidence that PTNs may be excited monosynaptically by inputs from VA as well as from VL. Buser (188) has reviewed activation of PTNs by sensory impulses and in addition has dealt with the role of caudate and medial thalamic nuclei in control of motor cortex responses to sensory stimuli. Buser found that the pathway for sensory activation of motor cortex PTNs included CM, CL, VL, and the lateroventral part of VA—all of which receive strong cerebellar projections. He commented that VL and VA may be of particular importance in control of PTNs: neurons in these two nuclei receive cerebellar, peripheral sensory, caudate, and thalamic inputs, and their outputs exert strong monosynaptic excitatory effects on motor cortex PTNs.

Information directly related to PTN inputs from BC via VL has been reported by Yoshida et al. (189). They found that PTNs with high axonal conduction velocities showed short-latency (1.4–1.7 msec) monosynaptic EPSPs in response to VL stimulation, whereas PTNs with low axonal conduction velocities showed variable-latency (2.2–20 msec) polysynaptic EPSPs of variable amplitude. PTN responses to BC stimulation were also studied, and EPSPs evoked in fast PTNs were disynaptic (latencies 2.7–3.5 msec), with the first synaptic delay in VL and the second at the PTN. It was concluded that the cerebellothalamocortical excitatory action is exerted primarily upon the "fast" PTNs, there being only subsidiary influences on the "slow" PTNs.

Evidence that the VL input to PTNs is strong is provided by the studies of Akimoto & Saito (190), who showed that monosynaptic EPSPs in PTNs could follow VL stimulation up to frequencies of 200/sec. The augmenting response to VL stimulation (cf. 191–193) did not involve this monosynaptic EPSP, but instead involved augmentation of a polysynaptic EPSP with considerably longer latency. Recruiting responses evoked by stimulation of centre median involved a polysynaptic EPSP followed by a prolonged IPSP in PTNs; stimulation of the reticular formation led to an increase in PTN response to VL stimulation, together with increased and regularized discharges of PTN activity. In addition to its monosynaptic excitatory effects on PTNs, VL stimulation may exert a prolonged inhibitory effect on PTNs (194–197).

In addition to causing short-latency excitation of PTNs via a disynaptic pathway, the cerebellar output can modify the responsiveness of PTNs to sensory inputs. Casey & Towe (198) found that stimulation of the vermal-fastigial system (culmen, centralis, or simplex) yielded initial augmentation followed by delayed attenuation of the reflex pyramidal tract response to cutaneous stimulation. In contrast, stimulation of other portions of the cerebellum (crura I or II, paramedian lobules, tuber vermis) had no consistent effects on the reflex pyramidal tract response. Casey & Towe reviewed evidence for a diffuse vermal-fastigial projection to the cortex and pointed out that the observed effects could have been mediated via neural pathways which involve principally the reticular formation, the thalamus, and the pericruciate cortex.

In assessing the relative importance of thalamocortical versus cortico-cortical control of PTNs, it is useful to consider the functional capacity of sensorimotor cortex deprived of corticocortical inputs. Sperry (199) studied the function of an island of sensorimotor cortex in a hemisphere which had been deprived of all other neocortex and separated from the opposite hemisphere by section of the corpus callosum. Such an island allowed cats to perform somesthetic discriminations at high levels of accuracy, which shows that the island could elaborate motor outputs on the basis of somatosensory inputs without any apparent abnormality in the movement. Thus, thalamo-cortical and other subcortical inputs to the motor cortex are sufficient to allow the sensorimotor cortex to function under conditions requiring not only accurate volitional movements but complex somatosensory discriminations as well. This sufficiency of subcortical inputs in determining the outputs of the sensorimotor cortex might have been predicted from Sperry's (200) earlier finding in monkeys that motor coordination is preserved following multiple transection of sensorimotor cortex. The fact that subcortical inputs are capable of exerting powerful excitatory effects on PTNs, together with the capacity of these inputs to generate coordinated motor output in the absence of corticocortical connections, points to the importance of the role of subcortical and particularly thalamic pathways in the initiation and control of movement.

E. Reciprocal or Nonreciprocal Connections Between Cerebrum and Cerebellum?

A question of prime concern in discussing cerebrocerebellar interactions is the following: Does a cerebellar zone send to the same part of the cerebral cortex from which it receives, or does it send to a different part of the cortex? One point of view was expressed by Jansen & Brodal (2) in describing the input-output relations of the ansiform lobe with the cerebral cortex. They stated that both anatomical and electrophysiological studies show that the ansiform receives not only from the sensorimotor cortex but also from association areas in frontal, parietal, occipital, and temporal cortex—with a tendency for the association areas to be best represented laterally in the ansiform lobe. Anatomical evidence, on the other hand, suggests that the output of the ansiform lobe—and particularly of its lateral portions—is sent via VA and VL of the thalamus chiefly to the sensorimotor cortex. The connection between cerebrum and ansiform lobe would thus appear to be nonreciprocal, with the cerebral area projecting to the ansiform lobe being of greater extent than the cerebral area receiving from the cerebellum.

A different pattern of interconnection has been found for cerebrum and midline-intermediate cerebellar zones. Henneman et al. (134) showed that the same portions of the intermediate zone which receive from the sensorimotor cortex (and from somatosensory receptors at the periphery) send predominantly back to the somatosensory cortex. Similarly, the vestibular portion of the cerebellum, which receives from vestibular nuclei and even from primary vestibular afferents, sends largely to vestibular nuclei, and it has even been shown that vestibular zone Purkinje cells may return to inhibit primary vestibular afferents (200a).

One should not at the present time regard these two types of cerebellar operation as mutually exclusive, since *both* may in fact exist. But the problem for our present purpose of discussing the sequence of events in the elaboration of voluntary movement is to decide whether the lateral zone (lateral hemisphere-dentate) outputs generated by association cortex inputs return to the cortical association areas to modify activity there, or whether these outputs are sent to the sensorimotor cortex to trigger a motor output.

The anatomical and physiological evidence presented in Sections IA and ID agree in suggesting that the lateral zone receives mainly from association areas of the cerebral cortex and to a lesser extent from the sensorimotor cortex. The recent anatomical data discussed in Section II support Jansen & Brodal's conclusion that the lateral zone output is focused mainly on VA and VL, that VA and VL focus mainly on the sensorimotor cortex, that the L-zone projection to the association areas is only by diffuse and indirect pathways, and that the cerebellum does not project at all to those thalamic nuclei which project topically to the primary cortical sensory areas.

Physiological confirmation that the L zone projects chiefly to SM cortex is, nevertheless, lacking: stimulation of IM-zone cerebellar cortex has evoked potentials in the SM cerebral cortex, but stimulation of the lateral parts of the hemisphere has evoked no responses in the SM cerebral cortex (115, 117, 134). The failure of these studies to detect SM cortical potentials evoked by L-zone cerebellar stimulation is surprising (as the authors note) in view of the obvious pathway connecting the two. The explanation may lie in the peculiarities which are often encountered (cf. 7, 13) on stimulating the cerebellar cortex. Ito has shown that the Purkinje cell output to the nuclear cells is inhibitory. The only ways then for a brief cortical shock to influence the nuclear cell are (*a*) by the nuclear cell having a high maintained rate of firing which may be transiently stopped by the cortical shock, or (*b*) via an antidromic impulse down a mossy or climbing fiber commonly supplying both nucleus and cortex (cf. 13). If under experimental conditions the nuclear cell had no maintained discharge and if the conduction time down the Purkinje axon were shorter than that down the mossy or climbing fibers, then a cerebellar cortical shock could neither increase nor reduce the nuclear cell output, and thus could not evoke a response in the cerebrum even though connections exist which link the two. The demonstration that responses can be evoked in SM cortex by stimulation of the intermediate zone does not invalidate the argument, since the same conditions must apply there also for the shock to be effective, and in the experimental situation these conditions may be different for the lateral and the intermediate zones. Suffice it to say that physiological studies have not demonstrated a pathway from the lateral parts of the hemisphere to the sensorimotor cortex, but they have not ruled one out.

Several recent physiological studies have pointed to nonreciprocal interconnections between cerebrum and cerebellum. Thus, Fanardjian & Donhoffer (123) found that "in contradistinction to the reciprocal relationship between motor cortex and cerebellum, a definite one-way connection has been found between the hippocampus and the cerebellum." In these experiments, carried out in chronic cat preparations, hippocampal stimulation evoked widespread 2–15 msec latency response in cerebellar cortex, whereas "in no case could potentials be recorded in the hippocampus by stimulating the cerebellar cortex or the cerebellar subcortical nuclei . . ." A lack of reciprocity was also found by Infantellina et al. (135) for connections between cerebral cortex and paraflocculus, It was found that paraflocculus received no corticofugal impulses from the cortical area to which it projected.

In summary, from the anatomical and physiological studies of the cerebral cortical inputs to the cerebellar lateral zone, and from the anatomical and *some* physiological studies of the output of lateral zone to the cerebral cortex, it would appear quite possible that this part of the cerebellum has nonreciprocal connections with the cerebral cortex. Thus, rather than sending its output back to the association areas to modify their already initiated activity, it may send its output to the sensorimotor cortex and possibly *initiate* activity there. Choosing the correct alternative must await more detailed physiological studies of the distribution of the output of the lateral zone.

III. INITIATION OF MOVEMENT

Writing more than sixty years ago, Herrick (201) proposed two possible modes of cerebellar operation:

> One may picture the situation in one case as if a given contraction of a muscle and tension on its tendon were reported back to the cerebellum through the spinocerebellar tracts with resulting activity of the cerebellar cortex adapted to reinforce the contraction of the muscle and inhibit that of its antagonist so as to maintain the appropriate movement or posture, or to facilitate the motor process in some other way, thus stabilizing, prolonging, or readjusting the local intrinsic activity, posture or tone of the lower neuromotor unit. In the second case, one may say figuratively that activities of, say, the prefrontal cerebral cortex are discharged into the precentral gyrus, thus activating some particular system of motor neurons with resulting execution of a voluntary movement; and while this cerebral activity is in process the frontal cortex also activates the corticopontile path, sending this message into the cerebellum: 'I am about to leap forward, get set, and cooperate in the movement.' By the time the appropriate lower motor centers are activated through the pyramidal tract the cerebellar influence has become effective on these lower centers, with resultant improvement in the strength and efficiency of the movement.

To these two modes of cerebellar function may be added a third possibility—that the impulses from the cerebellum precede and in part initiate those of the motor cortex. According to this view the cerebellar cortex would compute certain aspects of the pattern of muscular contraction necessary for an impending movement, and the nuclear output would relay the results of this computation to the cerebral cortex via the thalamus. The hypothesis that the cerebellum plays a role in initiating motor cortex activity is by no means new: it was proposed by Holmes (202) on the basis of his finding that initiation of movement is delayed in patients with cerebellar lesions. Holmes found that when subjects with one-sided cerebellar lesions were asked to make prompt, simultaneous movements with both arms, the ipsilateral arm was slow to start and slow to relax. Conspicuous slowness of movement initiation following cerebellar lesions has also been described by Goldstein, by Bremer, by Russell, and by Fulton & Dow (cf. 202). Holmes believed that tardiness in initiation of movement following cerebellar damage could not be attributed to disturbances of muscle tone and concluded ". . . that they are due to disorder in the cerebral mechanisms of voluntary movement, as a result of which there is a delay in initiating cortico-spinal innervation . . ." It is of note that delays in movement onset following cerebellar lesions are especially prominent in man and chimpanzee (cf. 202)—the two species in which the great bulk of the cerebellar inputs and outputs are received from and directed toward the cerebral cortex.

The three hypotheses of Herrick and Holmes suggest cerebellar participation in three successive phases of movement: initiation of the corticospinal output; regulation of motoneuronal responses to this corticospinal discharge; and adjustment and correction of the motor output following its initiation. The three hypotheses are by no means mutually exclusive; on the contrary, it seems highly probable that the cerebellum participates at each of these three stages of movement. In the following discussion, however, we shall focus on the first of these hypotheses for two reasons: cerebrocerebellar interconnections would seem to be of particular importance in movement initiation; and the role of the cerebellum in the second and third phases of movement—regulation and correction—has been dealt with in several recent theoretical papers. Thus, Eccles (203) discusses the participation of the cerebellum both in the ongoing movement and in the correction of movements which are "off-target", while Houk & Henneman (204) go into the cerebellar contribution following emission of the cortical output. Other theoretical analyses of cerebellar function (205, 206) are likewise concerned in large part with the role of the cerebellum in the second and third of the above phases.

Holmes' ideas as to the role of the cerebellum in the initiation of movement were based largely on the observation that in patients with cerebellar lesions the initiation of movement is delayed. Walshe (207) has also suggested that in man the cerebellum finds its essential function in the synthesis of movement, and that cerebellar tremor actually results from disturbed corticospinal outputs consequent upon impaired cerebellocortical inputs. Rolando (cf. 7) may have originally proposed the idea that the cerebellum was responsible for the initiation of motor activity. Subsequent investigators rejected Rolando's proposal when it became apparent that impairment of movement initiation was more severe following motor cortex lesions than after removal of the cerebellum. However, the fact that movements can still be initiated after removal of the cerebellum does not rule out participation of the cerebellum (along with basal ganglia and other inputs to ventral thalamus) in the initiation of movement.

The hypothesis that the cerebellar projection is one of several pathways which initiate activity of PTNs does not imply that movement initiation should be more impaired following cerebellar than following motor cortex lesions. By analogy, pyramidal tract neurons of motor cortex certainly play a role in initiating motoneuronal discharge, yet one would not expect movement initiation to be more impaired by motor cortex lesions than by motoneuron lesions. Severity and permanence of motor impairment following a lesion depend on the proximity of the lesion to the final common pathway. Thus, the only set of neurons whose destruction can be guaranteed to eliminate movement initiation is the set of motoneurons. In primates, lesions of the pyramidal tract are next in their potency with respect to prevention of movement, and lesions of neuronal links which act via the discharges of pyramidal tract neurons must necessarily cause less impairment than destruction of the pyramidal tract itself.

We hasten to reiterate that the cerebellum is not the only structure which initiates thalamic and thence PTN activity, nor is VL the only thalamic nucleus which projects to the motor cortex (187, cf. 208, 209). Lesions of the striatum more obviously impair movement initiation (cf. 210), and it is likely that the cerebellum and pallidum act in parallel to set up the patterns of thalamocortical output necessary for the appropriate activation of corticospinal neurons.

Further evidence consistent with a role of the cerebellum in the initiation of movement has been provided by recent studies of the activity of ventralis lateralis neurons in relation to the tremor movements in both man (211–213) and monkey (214, 215). These recordings were stimulated by the discovery that the resting tremor of patients with Parkinsonism could be ameliorated by VL lesions (cf. 216). Jasper & Bertrand (213) observed that there are certain VL neurons ". . . which are activated by voluntary movements of a given limb but which we have failed to activate by passive movements of the same limb or palpation of the muscles or tendons. Such cells we have tentatively assumed must be involved in the initiation of movements rather than reflecting only the sensory response to movement." The activity of VL neurons prior to movement is consistent with but does not establish an even earlier cerebellar activity, since the VL discharges could have been initiated by one or more of the noncerebellar inputs to VL.

Direct evidence that cerebellar activity occurs prior to movement has been obtained from recordings of the activity of cerebellar Purkinje and nuclear cells in association with the performance of learned arm movements by monkeys (90), but the timing of the cerebellar discharges with respect to thalamic and PTN activity is not yet known.

Additional data consistent with the role of the VL input to motor cortex in movement initiation come from the extensive data on the strength of the excitatory synaptic connection between VL neurons and motor cortex pyramidal neurons: the VL input can drive PTNs monosynaptically and at higher frequencies than is the case for other inputs. In this respect, of course, the relation between VL and motor cortex is no different from the relation of any other thalamic relay nucleus and its cortical projection area. It is generally the case that the strongest excitatory inputs to a given cortical area arise from the specific thalamic relay to the area. Thalamic relay nuclei are often thought of as transmitting information from peripheral afferents and this has sometimes led to the view that the VL input to motor cortex is one which provides peripheral feedback information after the movement is underway, rather than information from other parts of the brain prior to the occurrence of movement. As pointed out by Hassler (209), however: "The viewpoint is obsolete that a supply by thalamic afferents is an evidence for a sensory or even somatosensory function of a cortical field. The thalamus is more than a somatosensory center; only one-eighth of the human thalamus serves as part of somatosensory systems; seven-eighths are relay stations of other functional systems—corticipetal or cortex independent."

If it be granted that the cerebellar output plays a role in initiating PTN activity prior to movement, then the question arises as to what parts of the cerebellum contribute to initiation of PTN activity and how they themselves are activated. VL, which relays the strongest and most direct cerebellar input to the cerebral motor cortex, receives mainly from the dentate, to a lesser extent from the interposed, and least from the fastigial nucleus. This would imply that the bulk of cerebellar input to the motor cortex comes from the more lateral portions of the cerebellar cortex—the lateral portions of anterior lobe and the ansiform lobe. These parts of the cerebellum themselves are activated from the cerebrum and especially from the NSM "association" cortex (Section IA, D). The implication is that certain parts of the cerebral "association" cortex discharge over the several different pathways open to them (principally the cerebropontine relay) into the lateral portions of the cerebellum which in turn activate the motor PTNs in the cerebrum.

This explanation would not take into account the smaller M_1 input into the lateral hemispheres: if the cerebellar hemispheres trigger M_1 activity, then the M_1 output must enter cerebellum after the cerebellar input into M_1, and long after the input to the cerebellum from the cerebral cortical association area. But information from the SM cortex (unlike that from NSM cortex) travels over several pathways other than the corticopontine (e.g., reticular, olivary) and may have an effect on these parts of the cerebellum quite different from the effect of the NSM-pontine input. The SM input may, for example, serve as feedback information on the results of cerebellar input into M_1 (which needn't slavishly follow cerebellar command since it has other inputs), and be used for an entirely different purpose. In summary, it would seem to be chiefly the lateral hemispheres and dentate nuclei that operate in relation to the cerebral motor cortex in the way that Holmes has proposed.

If we accept that the lateral (or corticospinal) portions of the cerebellum may in part initiate M_1 PTN activity, what might the intermediate portions do? It is again instructive to consider the output and input connections of this area. The output goes partly to VL, partly to reticular and vestibular nuclei, but mainly to the red nucleus (and especially the magnocellular part). The cerebellar endings in RN overlap with those from the cerebral cortex [mainly from M_1 in the monkey (52); and M_1 and S_1 in the cat (51, 53, 55, 56)]. The output of intermediate cerebellar areas would thus appear to converge with the SM output onto the part of the red nucleus which projects to the cord. One input to the intermediate (spinal) part of the cerebellum is, again, from the cerebrum, but in this case mostly from the SM area—with relatively less input from the NSM "association" cortex (2, 70, Tables I and III).

This would imply that the intermediate cerebellum is initially activated by its SM input. This input may be mediated over the large corticopontine path and over corticoreticular path inputs as well. A second input to the intermediate part of the cerebellar cortex is from the spinal cord itself, indirectly from somatosensory receptors. This could be a "feedback" input which informs the cerebellum of the effect of its output to the red nucleus and ultimately the cord. The intermediate zone output would act in parallel with the SM output to the red nucleus and would thus appear to operate in a fashion similar to that of Herrick's second mechanism.

Herrick's first hypothesis may describe in a very general way the function of the "vestibular" midline parts of the cerebellum. Since this part has no known cerebral cortical input (2), it would seem to be the part most likely to operate independently of the cerebral motor cortex. It is further distinguished in being the only part of the cerebellar cortex to receive primary afferent (vestibular nerve) fibers and it has the shortest path to spinal motoneurons (Purkinje cells directly to vestibular nuclei and thence to spinal inter-and motoneurons). In view of its intimate connections with the vestibular sensory and motor apparatus and its relative lack of other inputs, its activity must be relatively autonomous and relate to the automatic regulation of body position with respect to gravity.

So far we have considered only the simpler and more direct routes linking cerebrum and cerebellum, and have discussed only the simplest aspects of the function of these pathways. This discussion, in its attempt to dissect the sequence of activation of different parts of cerebellum and cerebral cortex purely from the known anatomy of their interconnections, has necessarily omitted some aspects of the problem (e.g., overlap between the pathways, the function of the olivocerebellar pathway in the initiation of movement, and the significance of the diffusely projecting cerebello-cerebral pathway). One cannot say at this point how important these omissions will prove to be.

LITERATURE CITED

1. Crosby, E. C., Humphrey, T., Lauer, E. W. *Correlative Anatomy of the Nervous System* (Macmillan, New York, 731 pp., 1962)
2. Jansen, J., Brodal, A. *Aspects of Cerebellar Anatomy* (J. Chr. Gundersen, Oslo, 1954)
3. Larsell, O. *The Comparative Anatomy and Histology of the Cerebellum from Myxinoids through Birds* (Univ. of Minnesota Press, Minneapolis, 291 pp., 1967)
4. Voogd, J. *The Cerebellum of the Cat; Structure and Fibre Connexions* (F. A. Davis Co., Philadelphia, 1964)
5. Bremer, F. Cerebral and cerebellar potentials. *Physiol. Rev.*, **38**, 357–88 (1958)
6. Brookhart, J. M. The cerebellum. *Handbook of Physiology. Sect. I: Neurophysiology*, **II**, 1245–80 (Am. Physiol. Soc., Washington, D.C., 1960)
7. Dow, R. S., Moruzzi, G. *The Physiology and Pathology of the Cerebellum* (Univ. of Minnesota Press, Minneapolis, 675 pp., 1958)
8. Jansen, J. Afferent impulses to the cerebellar hemispheres from the cerebral cortex and certain subcortical nuclei. *Acta Physiol. Scand.*, **41**, *Suppl. 143*, 1–99 (1957)
9. Kreindler, A., Steriade, M. *La Physiologie et la Physiopathologie du Cervelet* (Masson, Paris, 308 pp., 1958)
10. Stoupel, N. Contribution a l'étude du néocervelet. I. Étude électrophysiologique des relations cérébello-cérébrales. *Acta Neurol. Belgium*, **65**, 183–228 (1965)
11. Bell, C. C., Dow, R. S. Cerebellar circuitry. *Neurosci. Res. Program Bull.*, **5**, No. 2, 121–222 (1967)
12. Dow, R. S. The evolution and anatomy of the cerebellum. *Biol. Rev.*, **17**, 179–220 (1942)
13. Eccles, J. C., Ito, M., Szentagothai, J. *The Cerebellum as a Neuronal Machine* (Springer-Verlag, New York, 343 pp., 1967)
14. Fadiga, E., Pupilli, G. C. Teleceptive components of the cerebellar function. *Physiol. Rev.*, **44**, 432–86 (1964)
15. Snider, R. S. Functional alterations of cerebral sensory areas by the cerebellum. *Progr. Brain Res.*, **25**, 322–33 (1967)

16. Ajmone Marsan, C. The thalamus. Data on its functional anatomy and on some aspects of thalamo-cortical integration. *Arch. Ital. Biol.*, **103**, 847–82 (1965)
17. Massion, J. The mammalian red nucleus. *Phys. Rev.*, **47**, 383–436 (1967)
18. Massion, J. *Étude d'une Structure Motrice Thalamique, le Noyau Ventrolatéral et de sa Régulation par les Afférences Sensorielles* (Doctoral thesis, Fac. Sci. Paris, 1968)
19. Purpura, D. P., Yahr, M. D., Eds. *The Thalamus* Columbia Univ. Press, New York, 438 pp., 1966)
20. Yahr, M. D., Purpura, D. P., Eds. *Neurophysiological Basis of Normal and Abnormal Motor Activities* (Raven Press, Hewlett, N. Y., 500 pp., 1967)
21. Barker, D., Ed. *Symposium on Muscle Receptors* (Hong Kong Univ. Press, 292 pp., 1962)
22. Granit, R., Ed. *Muscular Afferents and Motor Control* (Wiley, New York, 1966)
23. Berry, C. M., Haft, J. S., Harman, P. J., Hovde, C. A. Significance of pharmacologic state in recording optic potentials from cat cerebellum. *Neurology*, **9**, 845–52 (1959)
24. Dow, R. S. Cerebellar action potentials in response to stimulation of the cerebral cortex in monkeys and cats. *J. Neurophysiol.*, **5**, 121–36 (1942)
25. Deura, S. Long-latency cerebellar responses in cerebellar pedunculi and cortex. *Neurology*, **11**, 940–49 (1961)
26. Provini, L., Redman, S., Strata, P. Mossy and climbing fibre organization on the anterior lobe of the cerebellum activated by forelimb and hindlimb areas of the sensorimotor cortex. *Exptl. Brain Res.* (1968) (In press)
27. Adrian, E. D. Afferent areas in the cerebellum connected with the limbs. *Brain*, **66**, 289–315 (1943)
28. Hampson, J. L. Relationship between cat cerebral and cerebellar cortices. *J. Neurophysiol.*, **12**, 37–50 (1949)
29. Snider, R. S., Eldred, E. Cerebral projections to the tactile auditory and visual areas of the cerebellum. *Anat. Record*, **100**, 714 (1948)
30. Snider, R. S., Eldred, E. Electro-

anatomical studies on cerebro-cerebellar connections in the cat. *J. Comp. Neurol.*, **95**, 1–16 (1951)

31. Snider, R. S., Eldred, E. Cerebro-cerebellar relationships in the monkey. *J. Neurophysiol.*, **15**, 27–40 (1952)

32. Jansen, J., Jr., Fangel, C. Observations on cerebro-cerebellar evoked potentials in the cat. *Exptl. Neurol.*, **3**, 160–73 (1961)

33. Provini, L., Redman, S., Strata, P. Somatotopic organization of mossy and climbing fibres to the anterior lobe of cerebellum activated by the sensorimotor cortex. *Brain Res.*, **6**, 378–81 (1967)

34. Snider, R. S., Stowell, A. Evidence of a representation of tactile sensibility in the cerebellum of the cat. *Fed. Proc.*, **1**, 82 (1942)

35. Snider, R. S., Stowell, A. Receiving areas of the tactile, auditory and visual systems in the cerebellum. *J. Neurophysiol.*, **7**, 331–57 (1944)

36. Chambers, W. W., Sprague, J. M. Functional localization in the cerebellum. I. Organization in longitudinal corticonuclear zones and their contribution to the control of posture, both extrapyramidal and pyramidal. *J. Comp. Neurol.*, **103**, 105–29 (1955)

37. Chambers, W. W., Sprague, J. M. Functional localization in the cerebellum. II. Somatotopic organization in cortex and nuclei. *Arch. Neurol. Psychiat.*, **74**, 653–80 (1955)

38. Szentagothai, J., Rajkovits, K. Über den Ursprung des Kletterfasern des Kleinhirns. *Z. Anat. Entwicklungsgeschichte*, **121**, 130–41 (1959)

39. Armstrong, D. M., Harvey, R. J. Responses in the inferior olive to stimulation of the cerebellar and cerebral cortices in the cat. *J. Physiol. (London)*, **187**, 553–74 (1966)

40. Eccles, J. C., Llinas, R., Sasaki, K. The excitatory synaptic action of climbing fibres on the Purkinje cells of the cerebellum. *J. Physiol. (London)*, **182**, 268–96 (1966)

41. Crill, W. E., Kennedy, T. T. Inferior olive of the cat: intracellular recording. *Science*, **157**, 716–18 (1967)

42. Bell, C. C., Grimm, R. J. Discharge properties of cerebellar Purkinje cells recorded with single and double microelectrodes (In preparation)

43. Ramon y Cajal, S. *Histologic du système nerveux de l'homme et des vertèbrés*, 1909–1911 French ed. (Azoulay, L., Transl., **2** vols., A. Maloine, Paris, 1955)

44. Granit, R., Phillips, C. G. Excitatory and inhibitory processes acting upon individual Purkinje cells of the cerebellum in cats. *J. Physiol. (London)*, **133**, 520–47 (1956)

45. Sedgwick, E. M., Williams, T. D. Responses of single units in the inferior olive to stimulation of the limb nerves, peripheral skin receptors, cerebellum, caudate nucleus and motor cortex. *J. Physiol. (London*, **189**, 261–79 1967)

46. Brodal, A. Experimentelle Untersuchungen über die olivo-cerebellare Lokalisation. *Z. Ges. Neurol. Psychiat.*, **169**, 1–153 (1940)

47. Walberg, F., Brodal, A. Spino-pontine fibers in the cat. *J. Comp. Neurol.*, **99**, 251–88 (1953)

48. Walberg, F. Descending connections to the inferior olive. *Aspects of Cerebellar Anatomy*, 249–63 (Johan Grundt Tanum Forlag, Oslo, 423 pp., 1954)

49. Walberg, F. Descending connections to the inferior olive. An experimental study in the cat. *J. Comp. Neurol.*, **104**, 77–172 (1956)

50. Walberg, F. Further studies on the descending connections to the inferior olive: reticulo-olivary fibers. An experimental study in the cat. *Ibid.*, **114**, 79–87 (1960)

51. Rinvik, E., Walberg, F. Demonstration of a somatotopically arranged cortico-rubral projection in the cat. *J Comp. Neurol.*, **120**, 393–407 (1963)

52. Kuypers, H. G., Lawrence, D. G. Cortical projections to the red nucleus and the brain stem in the Rhesus monkey. *Brain Res.*, **4**, 151–88 (1967)

53. Mabuchi, M. Corticofugal projections to the subthalamic nucleus, the red nucleus and the adjacent areas in the monkey. *Proc. Japan Soc.*, **43**, 818–21 (1967)

54. Mabuchi, M., Kusama, T. The cortico-rubral projection in the cat. *Brain Res.*, **2**, 254–73 (1966)

55. Tsukahara, N., Kosaka, K. The mode of cerebral activation of red nucleus neurones. *Experientia*, **22**, 193–94 (1966)

56. Tsukahara, N., Kosaka, K. The mode

of cerebral excitation of red nucleus neurons. *Exptl. Brain Res.*, **5**, 102–17 (1968)

57. Jansen, J., Jansen, J., Jr. On the efferent fibers of the cerebellar nuclei in the cat. *J. Comp. Neurol.*, **102**, 607–32 (1955)

58. Angaut, P., Bowsher, D. Cerebellorubral connexions in the cat. *Nature*, **208**, 1002–3 (1965)

59. Courville, J. Somatotopical organization of the projection from the nucleus interpositus anterior of the cerebellum to the red nucleus: an experimental study in the cat with silver impregnation methods. *Exptl. Brain Res.*, **2**, 191–215 (1966)

60. Toyama, K., Tsukahara, N., Udo, M. Nature of the cerebellar influences upon the red nucleus neurones. *Exptl. Brain Res.*, **4**, 292–309 (1968)

61. Tsukahara, N., Toyama, K., Kosaka, K. Intracellularly recorded responses of red nucleus neurons during antidromic and orthodromic activation. *Experientia*, **20**, 632–33 (1964)

62. Tsukahara, N., Toyama, K., Kosaka, K., Udo, M. 'Disfacilitation' of red nucleus neurones. *Ibid.*, **21**, 544–46 (1965)

63. Tsukahara, N., Toyama, K., Kosaka, K. Electrical activity of red nucleus neurones investigated with intracellular microelectrodes. *Exptl. Brain Res.*, **4**, 18–33 (1967)

64. Courville, J., Brodal, A. Rubrocerebellar connections in the cat: an experimental study with silver impregnation methods. *J. Comp. Neurol.*, **126**, 471–85 (1966)

65. Brodal, A., Grogstad, A. C. Rubrocerebellar connections. An experimental study in the cat. *Anat., Record*, **118**, 455–86 (1954)

66. Walberg, F. Descending connections to the lateral reticular nucleus. An experimental study in the cat. *J. Comp. Neurol.*, **109**, 363–89 (1958)

67. Courville, J. Rubro-bulbar fibers to the facial nucleus and the lateral reticular nucleus (nucleus of the lateral funiculus). An experimental study in the cat with silver impregnation methods. *Brain Res.*, **1**, 317–37 (1966)

68. Pompeiano, O., Brodal, A. Experimental demonstration of a somatotopical origin of rubrospinal fibers in the cat. *J. Comp. Neurol.*, **108**, 225–52 (1957)

69. Hinman, A., Carpenter, M. B. Efferent fiber projections of the red nucleus in the cat. *J. Comp. Neurol.*, **113**, 61–82 (1959)

70. Nyby, O., Jansen, J. An experimental investigation of the corticopontine projection in Macaca mulatta. *Norske Vid. Akad. Avh. I, Mat. Natur. Kl.*, **3**, 1–47 (1951)

71. DeVito, J. L., Smith, O. A., Jr. Projections from the mesial frontal cortex (supplementary motor area) to the cerebral hemispheres and brain stem of the Macaca mulatta. *J. Comp. Neurol.*, **111**, 261–67 (1959)

72. DeVito, J. L., Smith, O. A., Jr. Subcortical projections of the prefrontal lobes of the monkey. *Ibid.*, **123**, 413–19 (1964)

73. Whitlock, D. G., Nauta, W. J. H. Subcortical projections from the temporal neocortex in Macaca mulatta. *J. Comp. Neurol.*, **106**, 183–212 (1956)

74. Brodal, P. The corticopontine projection in the cat. I. Demonstration of a somatotopic organized projection from the primary sensorimotor cortex. *Exptl. Brain Res.*, **5**, 212–37 (1968)

75. Niemer, W. T., Jimenez-Castellanos, J. Cortico-thalamic connections in the cat as revealed by "physiological neuronography". *J. Comp. Neurol.*, **93**, 100–23 (1950)

76. Altman, J. Some fiber projections to the superior colliculus in the cat. *J. Comp. Neurol.*, **119**, 77–96 (1962)

77. Massopust, L. C., Jr., Ordy, J. M. Auditory organization of the inferior colliculi in the cat. *Exptl. Neurol.*, **6**, 465–77 (1962)

78. Jassik-Gerschenfeld, D., Ascher, P. Some responses of the superior colliculus of the cat and their control by the visual cortex. *Experientia*, **19**, 655–59 (1963)

79. Altman, J., Carpenter, M. Fiber projections of the superior colliculus in the cat. *J. Comp. Neurol.*, **116**, 157–77 (1961)

80. Snider, R. S. Electro-anatomical studies on a tecto-cerebellar pathway. *Anat. Record*, **91**, 299 (1945)

81. Batini, C., Castellanos, G., Buser, P. Study on cortico-cerebellar projections in the cat. *J. Physiol. (Paris)*, **56**, 286–87 (1964)

82. Brodal, A. The cerebellar connections of the nucleus reticularis lateralis

(nucleus funiculi lateralis) in rabbit and cat. Experimental investigations. *Acta Psychiat. Neurol.*, **18**, 171–233 (1943)

83. Kitai, S. T., Kennedy, D. T., Morin, F., Gardner, E. The lateral reticular nucleus of the medulla oblongata of the cat. *Exptl. Neurol.*, **17**, 65–73 (1967)

84. Walberg, F., Pompeiano, O. Fastigiofugal fibers to the lateral reticular nucleus: an experimental study in the cat. *Exptl. Neurol.*, **2**, 40–53 (1960)

85. Brodal, P., Marsala, J., Brodal, A. The cerebral cortical projection to the lateral reticular nucleus in the cat, with special reference to the sensorimotor cortical areas. *Brain Res.*, **6**, 252–74 (1967)

86. Crichlow, E. C., Kennedy, T. T. Functional characteristics of neurons in the lateral reticular nucleus with reference to localized cerebellar potentials. *Exptl. Neurol.*, **18**, 141–58 (1967)

87. Brodal, A., Torvik, A. Cerebellar projection of paramedian reticular nucleus of medulla oblongata in cat. *J. Neurophysiol.*, **17**, 485–95 (1954)

88. Brodal, A., Grogstad, A. C. Afferent connexions of the paramedian reticular nucleus of the medulla oblongata in the cat. An experimental study. *Acta Anat.*, **30**, 133–51 (1957)

89. Thach, W. T., Jr. Discharge of Purkinje and cerebellar nuclear neurons during rapidly alternating arm movements in the monkey. *J. Neurophysiol.* (1968) (In press)

90. Thach, W. T., Jr. The behavior of Purkinje and cerebellar nuclear cells during two types of voluntary arm movement in the monkey. *Dallas Neurol. Symp., March 1968* (Submitted for publication)

90a. Fujita, Y. Activity of dendrites of single Purkinje cells and its relationship to so-called inactivation response in rabbit cerebellum. *J. Neurophysiol.*, **31**, 131–41 (1968)

91. Crill, W. E. Delayed depolarization and repetitive firing in the cat inferior olive neurons. *XXIV Intern. Congr. Physiol. Sci., Aug. 25–31, 1968, Washington, D.C.* (In press)

92. Oshima, T., Provini, L., Tsukuhara, N., Kitai, S. T. Cerebro-cerebellar connections mediated by fast and slow conducting pyramidal tract fibers. *XXIV Intern. Congr. Physiol Sci., Aug. 25–31, 1968, Washington, D.C.* (In press)

93. Orioli, F. L., Mettler, F. A. Consequences of section of the simian olivary decussation. *J. Comp. Neurol.*, **106**, 319–38 (1956)

94. Evarts, E. V. Relation of discharge frequency to conduction velocity in pyramidal tract neurons. *J. Neurophysiol.*, **28**, 216–28 (1965)

95. Turner, R. S., German, W. J. Functional anatomy of the brachium pontis. *J. Neurophysiol.*, **4**, 196–206 (1941)

96. Brodal, A., Pompeiano, O., Walberg, F. The vestibular nuclei and their connections, anatomy, and functional correlations. *W. R. Henderson Trust Lectures* (Oliver & Boyd, Edinburgh, 1962)

97. Brodal, A., Hoivik, B. Site and mode of termination of primary vestibulo-cerebellar fibers in the cat. An experimental study with silver impregnation methods. *Arch. Ital. Biol.*, **102**, 1–21 (1964)

98. Ito, M., Kawai, N., Udo, M. The origin of cerebellar-induced inhibition and facilitation in the neurones of Deiters and intracerebellar nuclei. *XXIII Intern. Congr. Physiol. Sci. Abstr., Tokyo, 1965*, 997

99. Jansen, J., Brodal, A. Experimental studies on the intrinsic fibers of the cerebellum. II. The cortico-nuclear projection. *J. Comp. Neurol.*, **73**, 267–321 (1940)

100. Eager, R. P. Efferent cortico-nuclear pathways in the cerebellum of the cat. *J. Comp. Neurol.*, **120**, 81–104 (1963)

101. Walberg, F., Jansen, J. Cerebellar corticonuclear projection studied experimentally with silver impregnation methods. *J. Hirnforsch.*, **6**, 338–54 (1964)

102. Eager, R. P. Patterns and mode of termination of cerebellar corticonuclear pathways in the monkey (Macacamulatta). *J. Comp. Neurol.*, **126**, 551–65 (1966)

103. Goodman, D. C., Hallett, R. E., Welch, R. B. Patterns of localization in the cerebellar cortico-nuclear projections of the albino rat. *J. Comp. Neurol.*, **121**, 51–67 (1963)

104. Brodal, A. Anatomical studies of cerebellar fibre connections with special reference to problems of

functional localization. *Progr. Brain Res.*, **25**, 135–73 (1967)

105. Phillips, C. G., Changing concepts of the precentral motor area. *Brain and Conscious Experience*, 389–421 (Springer-Verlag, New York, 591 pp., 1966)

105a. Jansen, J., Larsell, O. *The Cerebellum from Birds to Man* (To be published)

106. Carrea, R. M. E., Mettler, F. A. The anatomy of the primate brachium conjunctivum and associated structures. *J. Comp. Neurol.*, **101**, 565–690 (1954)

107. Flood, S., Jansen, J. The efferent fibres of the cerebellar nuclei and their distribution on the cerebellar peduncles in the cat. *Acta Anat. (Basel)*, **63**, 137–66 (1966)

108. McMasters, R. E., Russell, G. V. Efferent pathways from the deep cerebellar nuclei of the cat. *J. Comp. Neurol.*, **110**, 205–19 (1958)

109. Niimi, K., Fujiwara, N., Takimoto, T., Matsugi, S. The course and termination of the ascending fibers of the brachium conjunctivum in the cat as studied by the Nauta method. *Tokushima J. Exptl. Med.*, **8**, 269–84 (1962)

110. McCance, I., Phillis, J. W., Westerman, R. A. Bilateral cerebellar projections to the feline thalamus. *Proc. Australian Soc. Med. Res.*, **1**, 168 (1965)

111. Li, C. L., Tew, J. M., Jr. The effect of cerebellar stimulation on neuronal activity in the motor cortex. *Exptl. Neurol.*, **14**, 317–27 (1966)

112. Thomas, D. M., Kaufman, R. P., Sprague, J. M., Chambers, W. W. Experimental studies of the vermal cerebellar projections in the brain stem of the cat (fastigiobulbar tract). *J. Anat.*, **90**, 371–85 (1956)

113. Bowsher, D., Angaut, P., Condé, H. Projections des noyaux cérébelleux sur le noyau ventro-latéral du thalamus: confrontation des résultats acquis par la technique anatomique et par la technique électrophysiologique. *J. Physiol. (Paris)*, **57**, 570 (1965)

114. Carpenter, M. B., Stevens, G. H. Structural and functional relationships between the deep cerebellar nuclei and brachium conjunctivum in Rhesus monkey. *J. Comp. Neurol.*, **107**, 109–63 (1957)

115. Combs, C. M., Dennery, J. M.

Cerebello-cerebral connections in the monkey as revealed by the evoked-potential method. *Exptl. Neurol.*, **2**, 613–22 (1960)

116. Combs, C. M. Course of fibers of brachium conjunctivum revealed by evoked potential method. *Exptl. Neurol.*, **1**, 13–27 (1959)

117. Combs, C. M., Saxon, S. V. Evoked potential evidence for connections from cerebellar hemispheres to sigmoid gyri. *Exptl. Neurol.*, **1**, 583–92 (1959)

118. Whiteside, J. A., Snider, R. S. The relation of the cerebellum to the upper brain stem. *J. Neurophysiol.*, **16**, 397–413 (1953)

119. Angaut, P., Guilbaud, G. Étude, chez le Chat anesthésié au chloralose, des projections du noyau fastigial du cervelet sur les structures diencéphaliques. *J. Physiol. (Paris)* **56**, 273–74 (1964)

120. Angaut, P., Reymond, M. C. Étude électrophysiologique des projections du noyau interposé du cervelet sur le diencéphale du Chat. *J. Physiol. (Paris.)*, **56**, 527–28 (1964)

121. Condé, H., Angaut, P. Electrophysiologic study of projections from the cerebellar dentate nucleus to the diencephalon in cats. *J. Physiol. (Paris)*, **57**, 235–36 (1965)

122. Stoupel, N. *Contribution Expérimentale à l'Étude des Relations Cérébello-Cérébrales* (Doctoral thesis, Fac. Med. Bruxelles, 1962)

123. Fanardjian, V. V., Donhoffer, H. An electrophysiological study of cerebello-hippocampal relationships in the unrestrained cat. *Acta Physiol. Acad. Sci. Hung.*, **24**, 321–33 (1964)

124. Snider, R. S. Further evidence for a cerebellar influence on the "reticular activating" system. *Anat. Record*, **124**, 441 (1956)

125. Cohen, D., Chambers, W. W., Sprague, J. M. Experimental study of the efferent projections from the cerebellar nuclei to the brain-stem of the cat. *J. Comp. Neurol.*, **109**, 233–59 (1958)

126. Moruzzi, G., Magoun, H. W. Brain stem reticular formation and activation of the EEG. *Electroenceph. Clin. Neurophysiol.*, **1**, 455–73 (1949)

127. Fadiga, E., Manzoni, T., Urbano, A. The tonic action of cerebellar efferents on the level of electrocortical activity, as appearing from

acute ablation experiments in the cat. *Arch. Sci. Biol.*, **51**, 24–40 (1967)

128. Fadiga, E., Manzoni, T., Sapienza, S., Urbano, A. Identification of synchronizing and desynchronizing structures within the rostral portions of nucleus fastigii. *Electroenceph. Clin. Neurophysiol.*, **21**, 518 (1966)

129. Fadiga, E., Manzoni, T., Sapienza, S., Urbano, A. Synchronizing and desynchronizing fastigial influences on the electrocortical activity of the cat, in acute experiments. *Ibid.*, **24**, 330–42 (1968)

130. Manzoni, T., Sapienza, S., Urbano, A. EEG and behavioural sleep-like effects induced by the fastigial nucleus in unrestrained, unanaesthetized cats. *Arch. Ital. Biol.*, **106**, 61–72 (1968)

131. Manzoni, T., Sapienza, S., Urbano, A. Electrocortical influences of the fastigial nucleus in chronically implanted unrestrained cats. *Brain Res.*, **4**, 375–77 (1967)

132. Bava, A., Manzoni, T., Urbano, A. Effects of fastigial stimulation on thalamic neurones belonging to the diffuse projection system. *Brain Res.*, **4**, 378–80 (1967)

133. Fanardzhyan, V. V. Recruiting reaction in cerebral cortex in relation to cerebellar stimulation. *Fed. Proc. (Transl. Suppl.)*, **23**, 1156–60 (1964)

134. Henneman, E., Cooke, P. M., Snider, R. S. Cerebellar projections to the cerebral cortex. *Res. Publ. Assoc. Res. Nervous Mental Disease*, **30**, 317–33 (1952)

135. Infantellina, F., Sanseverino, E. R., Sperti, L. Cerebello-cerebral relationships: projections of cerebellar paraflocculus on the cerebral cortex in the cat. *Arch. Sci. Biol. (Bologna)*, **49**, 97–122 (1965)

136. Infantellina, F., Sanseverino, E. R., Sperti, L. Pathway for impulses from the paraflocculus to the cerebral cortex in the cat. *Ibid.*, **50**, 1–19 (1966)

137. Steriade, M., Stoupel, N. Contribution a l'étude des relations entre l'aire auditive du cerevelet et l'écorce cérébrale chez le Chat. *Electroenceph. Clin. Neurophysiol.*, **12**, 119–36 (1960)

138. Bava, A., Manzoni, T., Urbano, A. Cerebellar influences on neuronal

elements of thalamic somatosensory relay-nuclei. *Arch. Sci. Biol. (Bologna)*, **50**, 181–204 (1966)

139. Nakagoshi, I. Certain influences of the cerebellum on impulses to and from the somato-sensory cortex in the cat. *J. Kyoto Prefect. Med. Univ.*, **75**, 1–14 (1966)

140. Mehler, W. R., Vernier, V. G., Nauta, W. J. H. Efferent projections from dentate and interpositus nuclei in primates. *Anat. Record*, **130**, 430–31 (1958)

141. Jasper, H. H. Unspecific thalamocortical relations. *Handbook of Physiology, Sect. I: Neurophysiology*, **II**, 1307–22 (Am. Physiol. Soc., Washington, D. C., 1960)

142. Condé, H. Analyse électrophysiologique de la voie dentato-rubrothalamique chez le Chat. *J. Physiol. (Paris)*, **58**, 218–19 (1966)

143. Massion, J., Albe-Fessard, D. Dualité des voies sensorielles afférentes controlant l'activité du noyau rouge. *Electroenceph. Clin. Neurophysiol.*, **15**, 435–54 (1963)

144. Steriade, M., Briot, R. Convergences inhibitrices d'influx cérébelleux et corticaux au niveau du noyau rouge et du noyau thalamique ventral latéral. *J. Physiol. (Paris)*, **59**, 298–99 (1967)

145. Poirier, L. J., Bouvier, G. The red nucleus and its efferent nervous pathways in the monkey. *J. Comp. Neurol.*, **128**, 223–44 (1966)

146. Verhaart, W. J. C. The red nucleus, the cerebellum and the inferior olive in man. *Acta Neurol. Scand.*, **38**, 67–78 (1962)

147. Johnson, T. N., Clemente, C. D. An experimental study of the fiber connections between the putamen, globus pallidus, ventral thalamus, and midbrain tegmentum in cat. *J. Comp. Neurol.*, **113**, 83–102 (1959)

148. Nauta, W. J. H., Mehler, W. R. A summary of projections from the lentiform nucleus in the monkey. *J. Neurosurg.*, **24** (Suppl.), 196–99 (1966)

149. Nauta, W. J. H., Whitlock, D. G. An anatomical analysis of the nonspecific thalamic projection system. *Brain Mechanisms and Consciousness*, 81–104 (Blackwell, Oxford, 556 pp., 1954)

150. Petras, J. M. Some fiber connections of the precentral cortex (areas 4

and 6) with the diencephalon in the monkey (Macaca mulatta). *Anat. Record*, **148**, 322 (1964)

151. Niimi, K., Kishi, S., Miki, M., Fujita, S. An experimental study of the course and termination of the projection fibers from cortical areas 4 and 6 in the cat. *Folia Psychiat. Neurol. Japon.*, **17**, 167–216 (1963)

152. Dormont, J. F., Massion, J. Study of the relations between the sensorimotor areas and the ventro-lateral nucleus of the thalamus in cats. *J. Physiol. (Paris)*, **57**, 603–4 (1965)

153. Torii, H. Reciprocal influences of impulses from specific and nonspecific thalamic nuclei on unit activities of the motor cortex in cat. *Psychiat. Neurol. Japon.*, **63**, 460–80 (1960)

154. Rinvik, E. The corticothalamic projection from the gyrus proreus and medial wall of the rostral hemisphere in the cat. An experimental study with silver impregnation methods. *Exptl. Brain Res.*, **5**, 129–52 (1968)

155. Rinvik, E. The corticothalamic projection from the second somatosensory cortical area in the cat. An experimental study with silver impregnation methods. *Ibid.*, 153–72

156. Albe-Fessard, D., Bowsher, D. Responses of monkey thalamus to somatic stimuli under chloralose anaesthesia. *Electroenceph. Clin. Neurophysiol.*, **19**, 1–15 (1965)

157. Albe-Fessard, D., Fessard, A. Thalamic integrations and their consequences at the telencephalic level. *Progr. Brain Res.*, **1**, 115–48 (1963)

158. Purpura, D. P., Cohen, B. Intracellular recording from thalamic neurons during recruiting responses. *J. Neurophysiol.*, **25**, 621–35 (1962)

159. Purpura, D. P., Frigyesi, T. L., McMurtry, J. G., Scarff, T. Synaptic mechanisms in thalamic regulation of cerebello-cortical projection activity. *The Thalamus* (See Ref. 19), 153–70

160. Purpura, D. P., Malliani, A. Intracellular studies of thalamo-caudate relations. *Trans. Am. Neurol. Assoc.*, **91**, 51–60 (1966)

161. Purpura, D. P., McMurtry, J. G., Maekawa, K. Synaptic events in ventrolateral thalamic neurons during suppression of recruiting responses by brain stem reticular

stimulation. *Brain Res.*, **1**, 63–76 (1966)

162. Purpura, D. P., Scarff, T., McMurtry, J. G. Intracellular study of internuclear inhibition in ventrolateral thalamic neurons. *J. Neurophysiol.*, **28**, 487–96 (1965)

163. Purpura, D. P., Shofer, R. Intracellular recording from thalamic neurons during reticulocortical activation. *J. Neurophysiol.*, **26**, 494–505 (1963)

164. Sakata, H., Ishijima, T., Toyoda, Y. Single unit studies on ventrolateral nucleus of the thalamus in cat: its relation to the cerebellum, motor cortex and basal ganglia. *Japan. J. Physiol.*, **16**, 42–60 (1966)

165. Massion, J., Angaut, P., Albe-Fessard, D. Activity evoked in the cat in the region of the nucleus ventralis lateralis by various sensory stimuli. I. Macro-physiological study. *Electroenceph. Clin. Neurophysiol.*, **19**, 433–51 (1965)

166. Massion, J., Angaut, P., Albe-Fessard, D. Activity evoked in the cat in the region of the nucleus ventralis lateralis by various sensory stimuli. II. Micro-physiological study. *Ibid.*, 452–69

167. Andersen, P., Eccles, J. C. Inhibitory phasing of neuronal discharge. *Nature*, **196**, 645–47 (1962)

168. Andersen, P. Rhythmic 10/sec activity in the thalamus. *The Thalamus* (See Ref. 19), 143–51

169. Andersen, P., Andersson, S. A., Lomo, T. Some factors involved in the thalamic control of spontaneous barbiturate spindles. *J. Physiol. (London)*, **192**, 257–81 (1967)

170. Andersen, P., Andersson, S. A., Lomo, T. Nature of thalamo-cortical relations during spontaneous barbiturate spindle activity. *Ibid.*, 283–307

171. Eccles, J. C. Inhibition in thalamic and cortical neurones and its role in phasing neuronal discharges. *Epilepsia*, **6**, 89–115 (1965)

172. Eccles, J. C. Properties and functional organization of cells in the ventrobassal complex of the thalamus. *The Thalamus* (See Ref. 19), 129–41

174. Asanuma, H. Microelectrode studies on the evoked activities of a single pyramidal tract cell in the somatosensory area in cats. *Japan. J. Physiol.*, **9**, 94–104 (1959)

175. Li, C. L. Some properties of pyramidal

neurones in motor cortex with particular reference to sensory stimulation. *J. Neurophysiol.*, **22**, 385–94 (1959)

176. Brooks, V. B., Rudomin, P., Slayman, C. L. Sensory activation or neurons in the cat's cerebral cortex. *J. Neurophysiol.*, **24**, 286–301 (1961)

177. Brooks, V. B., Rudomin, P., Slayman, C. L. Peripheral receptive fields of neurons in the cat's cerebral cortex. *Ibid.*, 301–25

178. Marchiafava, P. L. Activities of the central nervous system: motor. *Ann. Rev. Physiol.*, **30**, 359–400 (1968)

179. Oscarsson, O. The projection of group I muscle afferents to the cat cerebral cortex. *Muscular Afferents and Motor Control*, 307–16 (Wiley, New York, 1966)

180. Li, C. L., Davie, J. C. Evidence of afferent fibers in the motor cortex from subcortical basal nuclei. *J. Neurosurg.*, **24**, Part II, 221–26 (1966)

181. Stefanis, C., Jasper, H. Intracellular microelectrode studies of antidromic responses in cortical pyramidal tract neurons. *J. Neurophysiol.*, **27**, 828–54 (1964)

182. Stefanis, C., Jasper, H. Recurrent collateral inhibition in pyramidal tract neurons. *Ibid.*, 855–77

183. Stefanis, C., Jasper, H. Strychnine reversal in inhibitory potentials in pyramidal tract neurones. *Intern. J. Neuropharmacol.*, **4**, 125–38 (1965)

184. Takahashi, K., Kubota, K., Uno, M. Recurrent facilitation in cat pyramidal tract cells. *J. Neurophysiol.*, **30**, 22–34 (1967)

185. Schlag, J. Reactions and interactions to stimulation of the motor cortex of the cat. *J. Neurophysiol.*, **29**, 44–71 (1966)

186. Eccles, J. C. Cerebral synaptic mechanisms. *Brain and Conscious Experience*, 24–58 (Springer-Verlag, New York, 591 pp., 1966)

187. Amassian, V. E., Weiner, H. Monosynaptic and polysynaptic activation of pyramidal tract neurons by thalamic stimulation. *The Thalamus* (See Ref. 19), 255–86

188. Buser, P. Subcortical controls of pyramidal activity. *The Thalamus* (See Ref. 19), 323–47

189. Yoshida, M., Yajima, K., Uno, M. Different activation of the two types of the pyramidal tract neurones through the cerebello-thalamocortical pathway. *Experientia*, **22**, 331–32 (1966)

190. Akimoto, H., Saito, Y. Synchronizing influences and their interactions on cortical and thalamic neurons. *Progr. Brain Res.*, **21A**, 323–51 (1966)

191. Brookhart, J. M., Zanchetti, A. The relation between electrocortical waves and responsiveness of the corticospinal system. *Electroenceph. Clin. Neurophysiol.*, **8**, 427–44 (1956)

192. Brookhart, J. M., Arduini, A., Mancia, M., Moruzzi, G. Mutual facilitation of cortical responses to thalamic stimulation. *Arch. Ital. Biol.*, **95**, 139–46 (1957)

193. Spencer, W. A., Brookhart, J. M. Electrical patterns of augmenting and recruiting waves in the depths of sensorimotor cortex of cat. *J. Neurophysiol.*, **24**, 26–49 (1961)

194. Li, C. L. The inhibitory effect of stimulation of a thalamic nucleus on neuronal activity in the motor cortex. *J. Physiol. (London)*, **133**, 40–53 (1956)

195. Purpura, D. P., Shofer, R. J. Cortical intracellular potentials during augmenting and recruiting responses. I. Effects of injected hyperpolarizing currents on evoked membrane potential changes. *J. Neurophysiol.*, **27**, 117–32 (1964)

196. Purpura, D. P., Shofer, R. J., Musgrave, F. S. Cortical intracellular potentials during augmenting and recruiting responses. II. Patterns of synaptic activities in pyramidal and nonpyramidal tract neurons. *J. Neurophysiol.*, **27**, 133–51 (1964)

197. Branch, C. L., Martin, A. R. Inhibition of Betz cell activity by thalamic and cortical stimulation. *J. Neurophysiol.*, **21**, 380–90 (1958)

198. Casey, K. L., Towe, A. L. Cerebellar influence on pyramidal tract neurones. *J. Physiol. (London)*, **158**, 399–410 (1961)

199. Sperry, R. W. Preservation of high-order function in isolated somatic cortex in callosum-sectioned cat. *J. Neurophysiol.*, **22**, 78–87 (1959)

200. Sperry, R. W. Cerebral regulation of motor coordination in monkeys following multiple transection of sensorimotor cortex. *Ibid.*, **10**, 275–94 (1947)

200a. Llinás, R., Precht, W., Brachi, F., Huertas, J. The inhibitory cerebello-vestibular system in the frog. *XXIV Intern. Congr. Physiol. Sci., Aug. 25–31, 1968, Washington, D. C.* (In press)

201. Herrick, C. J. Origin and evolution of the cerebellum. *Arch. Neurol. Psychiat.*, **11**, 621–52 (1924)

202. Holmes, G. The cerebellum of man. *Brain*, **62**, 1–30 (1939)

203. Eccles, J. C. Circuits in the cerebellar control of movement. *Proc. Natl. Acad. Sci. U. S.*, **58**, 336–43 (1967)

204. Houk, J., Henneman, E. Feedback control of skeletal muscles. *Brain Res.*, **5**, 433–51 (1967)

205. Arbib, M. A., Franklin, G. F., Nilsson, N. Some ideas on information processing in the cerebellum. *Proc. Summer School on Math. Models of Neuronic Networks, Ravello, Italy, June 4-19, 1967* (In press)

206. Dow, R., Chmn. Information Processing in the Cerebellum. *Neurosci. Res. Program, Oregon, May 16-18, 1967* (In preparation)

207. Walshe. F. M. R. The significance of the voluntary element in the genesis of cerebellar ataxy. *Brain*, **50**, 377–85 (1927)

208. Hassler, R. Anatomy of the thalamus. *Introduction to Stereotaxis with an Atlas of the Human Brain*, 230–90 (Thieme, Stuttgart, 1959)

209. Hassler, R. Thalamic regulation of muscle tone and the speed of movements. *The Thalamus* (See Ref. 19), 419–38

210. Wilson, S. A. K. *Modern Problems in Neurology* (William Wood & Co., New York, 1929)

211. Jasper, H. H., Bertrand, G. Recording from microelectrodes in stereotactic surgery for Parkinson's disease. *J. Neurosurg.*, **24** (Suppl.), 219–21 (1966)

212. Jasper, H. H., Bertrand, G. Stereotaxic microelectrode studies of single thalamic cells and fibres in patients with dyskinesia. *Trans. Am. Neurol. Assoc.*, **89**, 79–82 (1964)

213. Jasper, H. H., Bertrand, G. Thalamic units involved in somatic sensation and voluntary and involuntary movements in Man. *The Thalamus* (See Ref. 19), 365–90

214. Cordeau, J. P. Further studies on patterns of central unit activity in relation with tremor. *J. Neurosurg.*, **24**, (Suppl.) 213–18 (1966)

215. Cordeau, J. P., Gybels, J., Jasper, H., Poirier, L. J. Microelectrode studies of unit discharge in the sensorimotor cortex: investigation in monkeys with experimental tremor. *Neurology*, **10**, 591–600 (1960)

216. Cooper, I. S. A cerebellar mechanism in resting tremor. *Neurology*, **16**, 1003–15 (1966)

NEUROPHYSIOLOGY OF VISION[1]

By Otto Creutzfeldt and Bert Sakmann

Department of Neurophysiology, Max-Planck-Institute of Psychiatry, Munich, Germany

Introduction

Writing a review on "central aspects" of the visual system and attempting to show the progress made from 1966–1968 is a thankless task. The number of papers published during this time is large and so is the variety of aspects and goals of the different groups of investigators. Having tried many ways of presenting the material, the reviewers humbly returned to the classical division into chapters as nature prescribes it, i.e. according to the different anatomical and functional levels, retina, lateral geniculate body, cortex, and tectum opticum, with subdivisions into anatomy and physiology, rather than dividing it into chapters according to function such as adaptation, color vision, and perception. Since the aim of our research is to find the mechanisms of these functions, it is appropriate to deal with them wherever they may be located. The purpose is, of course, to give a comprehensive survey which may enable the reader to see how far science in vision has developed and where the future ways may lead.

When dealing with central vision a thorough understanding of the function of the retina is absolutely necessary to appreciate what the more centrally located levels of the CNS actually "do" with the information offered to them. The precision with which the retina responds to light stimuli also makes it best suited for quantitative investigations of visual mechanisms, and the amount of quantitative research in this area has increased greatly during recent years. The chapter on the retina is therefore the biggest. The other important way of finding out how the nervous system handles information is a combined knowledge of structure and function. Therefore, great emphasis is placed on morphological papers, although we do not consider ourselves anatomists. However, in many aspects and on all levels of the visual system the gap between structure and function is still large and we still tend to fill this gap with wishful thinking when actual knowledge is lacking. An instructive example of the connection between structure and function was shown recently in the visual system of the fly (1, 2), but this work will not be reported here, since we decided to restrict ourselves to vertebrates.

The most tantalizing (240) task of research in the visual system is to find the mechanisms for perception and thus to build a bridge between

---

[1] This review is dedicated to R. Granit, H. K. Hartline, and G. Wald, who were awarded the Nobel prize 1967 for their work, which increased our knowledge and stimulated research in vision.

neurophysiology and psychology. Bishop in the preceding review (3) collected impressive pieces of material for this bridge. This task was further pursued during the last two years. A fine introduction into the physiology and psychology of vision was published by Gregory (4).

At the higher levels [superior colliculus, lateral geniculate nucleus (LGN) and cortex], inputs from the several retinal channels are combined and it is here that our knowledge as to how channels are combined at these levels has increased during the last few years.

Some principles of information transmission and synaptic transfer at the different levels of the visual system were recently discussed (176).

The final aim of science is to understand a matter well enough to build a theoretical or even a practical model which functions like the original. Blackbox modeling necessarily gives only a formal description of some aspects of the original. Cybernetic conclusions of this sort are frequently found, but as pragmatic physiologists we hesitated to include too much of this aspect. Some serious attempts in this direction will be mentioned and the readers' attention may be drawn to an intelligent though still premature attempt to present a general theory of vision (5).

THE RETINA

HISTOLOGICAL ORGANIZATION OF THE RETINA

The Cajal-Polyak concept of the neuronal organization of the retina has been further elaborated and corrected in some aspects. Quantitative data are now available on the size of dendritic fields of the different neuronal elements in the retina and the synaptology of the retina has been further analyzed. A vertical and a horizontal organization may be distinguished. The vertical channels extend from the receptors via the bipolars to the ganglion cells, while the horizontal and amacrine cells interact with the vertical channels peripherally (horizontal cells) and centrally (amacrine cells) from the bipolars. The synaptic contacts between the different elements in the primate retina have been analyzed extensively and a model of the synaptic organization of the retina has been presented (6). In the outer plexiform layer, synapses have been identified only on the base of the receptor cells, where they contact bipolar and horizontal cell processes. The synaptic nature of these contacts between receptor and horizontal cells is not quite evident, but is made probable by their strategic position. In the primate retina, no synaptic contacts have been shown between horizontal and bipolar cells, but are shown to exist in the cat's and rabbit's retina between the brushlike processes of the horizontal cells and the dendrites and somata of the bipolars (7).

Pre- and postsynaptic functions of the receptor-horizontal contacts have been discussed (6, 7). In the fish retina, the horizontal and amacrine cells were studied with light microscopy, and here the view is still maintained that they are glial cells (8). In the inner plexiform layer, synaptic contacts in both directions have been demonstrated between the processes of amacrine, bipolar, and ganglion cells and a feedback loop has been proposed between bipolar-amacrine-bipolar cells within the same synaptic formation (dyad) (6).

Tight synaptic contacts between the perikarya of the ganglion cells and large bipolar cell terminals, with fusion between the plasma membrane, have been shown in peripheral parts of the cat's retina; this suggests electrical axosomatic junctions. Rods connect only with rod (mop) bipolars, which make axodendritic and axosomatic contacts with the diffuse ganglion cells. Cones connect with midget as well as with flat bipolars. The ratio of cone to midget-bipolar cells is 1:1 (with several synapses), but the flat bipolars have contacts with several cones. The cone bipolars make only axodendritic synaptic contacts with the ganglion cells. In the plexiform layer the midget ganglion cells contact only with one midget bipolar with numerous synapses (6).

Several authors (6, 9–11) suggest that the vertical connection receptor-bipolar-ganglion cell dendrite is responsible for the center reaction of the receptive field, while the surround reaction is due to horizontal interference at the outer (horizontal cells) and inner (amacrine) plexiform layer. Brown (10) has pointed out that the centers of receptive fields in the rat have about the same diameter as the horizontal spread of the dendritic trees of the ganglion cells. In the cat, only the "diffuse" ganglion cells have dendritic trees of a diameter comparable to that of receptive-field centers ($400–700\,\mu$), while midget ganglion cells have smaller dendritic fields ($20–200\,\mu$). Leicester & Stone (12) found that the range in diameter of dendritic fields of retinal ganglion cells was $18–710\,\mu$ in the peripheral parts of the retina, i.e. smaller than the range of receptive fields [$85–880\,\mu$ (13, 14)]. In the central retina the differences may be even larger. A new type of ganglion cell with intraretinal axon and terminal branches has been described in the retina of dogs and humans (15).

No degeneration of retinal ganglion cells was seen 10 weeks after the optic tract of adult cats was cut, but it was complete after 2 years (16). This long delay must be kept in mind if the contribution of ganglion cell activity to the b-wave of the ERG is investigated by cutting the optic nerve and "waiting until retrograde degeneration of the ganglion cells is complete". Unexpectedly, only about 75 per cent of the ganglion cells of the temporal area of the retina ipsilateral to the tract section disappeared while 25 per cent remained unaffected; but 100 per cent disappeared in the nasal area. Since there is no evidence that remaining cells project into the contralateral lateral geniculate nucleus, a direct retinotectal projection of these cells is discussed. This was indeed described independently (17). Ganglion cells of the nasal and temporal half-fields overlap the midline up to 0.2 mm (0.9°).

FUNCTIONAL ORGANIZATION OF THE RETINA

In accordance with this anatomical concept we shall try to treat separately the vertical and the horizontal organization of the retina. It is clear that this separation is often too schematic, since a horizontal interaction between the different vertical channels seems to take place at all levels of the retina. Problems of adaptation and the discharge characteristics of retinal ganglion cells will then be treated. The early receptor potential will not be included in this review [for further information see (18–21)]. The electroretinogram literature will also be neglected and only some findings which are of interest for the problems treated in this review will be included. The review of Brown (22) may be consulted.

Vertical transfer from receptors to ganglion cells.—We still lack complete knowledge of the mechanisms by which light is transformed into slow membrane potentials of the receptors and of how the receptor potentials are transmitted to the ganglion cells via the bipolars. In the isolated vertebrate retina (*Rana esculanta*), Baumann (23) has recorded from outside the membrana limitans externa a slow and long-lasting extracellular positive potential after illumination. He concluded that it originated from the inner segments of the receptors. Its latency was in the same range as that of retinal ganglion cells and it was linearly related to the light intensity (over 3.1 log units from threshold). The amplitude-intensity plot was S-shaped with a linear relationship only at low intensities as in reticular cells of limulus (24). In the region of the outer segments, no light-evoked potential could be recorded.

In the isolated carp retina, polarizing generator potentials of single cones were recorded intracellularly (25). The recording place in the inner cell segments was shown with an electrode marking technique (26). Three types of cones were identified: red (74 per cent, peaking wavelength 611 ± 23 mμ); green (10 per cent, 529 ± 14 mμ); and blue (16 per cent, 462 ± 15 mμ). This spectral distribution is in close accord to the microspectrophotometrically determined absorption spectra of single cones of the goldfish (27).

In substantial agreement with Baumann's findings on the receptor are measurements of Maffei & Poppele (28), who also found a linear relationship between a sinusoidally modulated stimulus and the "late receptor potential" (LRP), recorded from the intact eye of the cat after occlusion of the retinal artery. The ganglion cell response (as measured by the discharge frequency during a sinusoidally modulated stimulus), on the other hand, was linear only at low modulation depth and low frequencies (29). At higher modulation depth and frequency the relation becomes nonlinear, as the mean discharge rate depends on modulation depth and frequency (29, 30) and as the phase angle between stimulus and response also depends on modulation depth (30). The frequency response curves of the late receptor potential (LRP), the retinal ganglion cells, and the total ERG differ: the LRP behaves like the output of a lowpass filter with strong attenuation above 1.5/sec (28), the ganglion cells show an increase between 5 and 10/sec (29, 31, 32), and the total ERG is in between the two (33).

The question is still open as to where and how the nonlinear transformation of stimulus intensity vs. neuronal reaction comes in. It must take place between the receptor output and the ganglion cell output. Since the total ERG response, which is assumed to represent the activity of receptors and bipolars (35), is a linear function of sinusoidal light modulation up to 50 per cent modulation depth and irrespective of background illumination (33, 28), it could be presumed that the transformation takes place centrally from the inner nuclear layer (bipolar cells). But equal response experiments on goldfish retinal ganglion cells (36) have shown that the nonlinearity is already present before the ganglion cell input. In this case, the transformation would have to be localized in the bipolar cells (36) or the bipolar-ganglion cell synapse. Easter's (36) experiments on the goldfish retina describe the stimulus-excitation transform by a power function with an exponent of 0.5–0.6. This intensity-excitation transformation was found to be the same for all parts of the receptive-field center of one ganglion cell. In the cat's retina, the response-intensity curve as tested with small spots of light shone into the receptive-field center and over an intensity range up to 2 log units above threshold was best fitted by a logarithmic function (296).

Of course, for a thorough discussion of the vertical transfer characteristics our knowledge of the receptor output is still too restricted. Only in limulus have the characteristics of the receptor response been sufficiently analyzed and described (37). The usefulness of the method of sinusoidal stimulation to answer the problem of vertical transfer has its limitations. The different frequency responses of the different components of retinal activity indicate a series of separate filter processes along the vertical transfer chain. Furthermore, adaptation at low frequencies, collateral inhibitory processes in the horizontal cell layers with low pass characteristics and increasing attenuation above 5/sec (34), different gain-control mechanisms at different levels, and different time constants of the different transducer elements in the chain (37) and the possibility of their independent variation with activity tend to invalidate a straightforward interpretation of the results. It must also be realized that turning off a light stimulus (be it a sine or square wave function) may not only be equal to a decrease of excitation, but may bring about an active excitatory or inhibitory off-process, which affects the ganglion cell discharge.

In this context a few words may be said about response-intensity relationships over a wider range of intensities, be it a retinal, geniculate, cortical, or psychophysical response. The question of whether these relationships can be drawn as straight lines in a simple or double log plot is often erroneously taken as evidence for or against the psychophysical laws of Fechner (38), Weber (39), or Stevens (40). It was pointed out (41, 42) that log and power functions with an exponent near 0.3 (0.2–0.4) have an almost identical course over several log units. Small deviations from both relationships are meaningless if no theory as to the underlying mechanism is tested. It seems more important that the simple log function appears to be valid only over a limited intensity range for most responses tested, but that over a wider intensity continuum the curves level off (S-shape); and this can be fitted neither by a log nor by a power function. This restricted intensity continuum of about 2 log units, which fits well to the log relationship, is independent of the state of adaptation over a wide range as shown for the ERG (43, 44) and retinal ganglion cell responses (own observations). Also the psychophysically determined relation ($\Delta I/I = K$) is valid only over a limited intensity range (45–47). All these observations indicate that at higher intensities and at large transient steps different processes are involved. In contrast, the response latencies of retinal ganglion cells are related by a simple log function to the stimulus intensity over a wider range (48). This may be brought into relation with the R·C-properties of excitable membranes.

Horizontal organization of the retina.—

Horizontal cells. In spite of the importance attached to the horizontal cells for gain control (adaptation) and inhibition of retinal ganglion cells, direct experimental evidence for this function is still lacking. All research done during the last two years was restricted to the fish retina. In contrast to the receptor cells which show no or only a small (26) area effect at different stimulus size, cells from which the different types of S-potentials originate (horizontal and amacrine cells?) show summation over a large stimulus area (up to 10°) (49–51). It has been suggested (50) that this spread might be due to tight contacts between horizontal cells demonstrated with the electron microscope (52, 53). Three different layers of horizontal cells with different S-potentials and no interaction between the layers were demonstrated (50). Biophysically, these horizontal cells behave differently from neurons and their responses are not related to ionic processes (50), in spite of the morphological criteria for neurons cited above.

Witkovsky (51), working on the carp, has found a different behavior of S-potentials and retinal ganglion cells to visual stimuli (spectral sensitivity, light and dark adaptation, threshold and increment threshold) and concluded "that ganglion cells respond independently of S-potentials for the stimulus parameters tested".

So, although the functional significance of the S-potential remains obscure, a series of experiments is worth mentioning because of the exemplary analysis of the chromatic responses of the color sensitive C-potentials (54, 55), the intensity responses of the L-potentials (56) and the adaptive behavior of the C-potentials (57). It was shown that cells responsible for the C-potential are in contact with two types of cones of opposite color sensitivity (green excitatory, blue inhibitory or red excitatory, blue inhibitory). The amplitude of S-potentials from L-cells was shown to be a hyperbolic function of light intensity and a membrane model was suggested in which a variable membrane conductance is changed proportional to the light intensity. In contrast to "real" light, "dark" light after bleaching had no effect on S-potentials, which indicates different mechanisms for dark and light adaptation.

Spatial integration in ganglion cells. A series of investigations attempted to give a quantitative description of the spatial integration of retinal gang-

lion cells across their receptive field. The superimposition model of reciprocally organized sensory receptive fields, suggested by Békésy (58, 59) and by
Wagner et al. (60) for the color-sensitive cells of the goldfish retina, was
applied to explain the receptive fields of retinal ganglion cells of the cat
(34, 61–64). In this model, it was assumed that a light stimulus within the
receptive field produced both inhibition and excitation, that the sensitivities
both of the excitatory and of the inhibitory area were maximal in the middle
of the receptive field, and that both fell off towards the periphery like a
Gaussian function. The center mechanism had a smaller σ and was much
stronger in the centrum; the periphery mechanism had a larger σ, was
weaker, and thus dominated only in the periphery (surround). A basic
assumption of this model is the linear summation of excitatory and inhibitory
mechanisms across the whole receptive field. This, however, is questioned
(34, 36, 64, 296).

Linearity of the processes which affected the activity of a ganglion cell
discharge was demonstrated in 20 per cent (X-cells) of the cat's retinal
ganglion cell, but not for the majority (80 per cent, Y-cells) (64). Even in
X-cells markedly nonlinear behavior was evident in the relation between
stimulus and response amplitude. Enroth & Robson (64) used for these
experiments a method (65) in which the stimulus consisted of a grating
pattern whose luminance perpendicular to the bars varied sinusoidally (or
rectangularly) about the mean level (up to a contrast of 0.45). Switching on
the grating thus led to an increase of light in one part, and a decrease in
another part of the receptive field. In this way, the summation of on- *and*
off-effects of different receptive-field compartments was tested. The receptive-field diameters of the X-cells were between 0.55 and 2.9° with a modal
value of 1–1.5°, and smaller fields towards the center of the visual field. This
was tested with the "contrast function": the contrasts were determined, by
which an equal response was elicited, if rectangularly modulated gratings of
different spatial frequencies were moved across the receptive fields. If spatial
summation is discussed in the context of these experiments, it should be
realized that light-"off" is not only a diminution of the excitation (or
inhibition) elicited by light. It is a stimulus in itself and thus initiates a new
set of active events.

In psychophysical experiments using the same method, the sensitivity
functions for sinusoidal and nonsinusoidal grating patterns were determined
(66). For threshold detection of different grating patterns, the amplitude of
the first Fourier component of a pattern was critical, whereas at discrimination between sinusoidal and nonsinusoidal patterns the next harmonic
reached threshold. It was concluded that the visual system does not behave
as a *single* detector mechanism preceded by a *single* broadband spatial filter
but as a number of independent detector mechanisms each preceded by a
relatively narrowband filter, "tuned" to a different frequency. Each filter
and detector would constitute a separate "channel" and each channel would
have its own contrast-sensitivity function. The functions of all the channels

would be the contrast-sensitivity function of the overall visual system. Since the spatial filter characteristics of the cat's retinal ganglion cells (64) are different from those postulated to explain the psychophysical experiments in humans, this explanation is hypothetical and a proof is possible only by neurophysiological demonstration of the corresponding "channels".

Linear spatial summation of only excitatory inputs is the basis of Ricco's law, which states that the product of area and intensity is constant. In the goldfish retina this was tested (36) by determining the threshold with concentric stimuli of different diameter. Confirming earlier results (67, 68), Ricco's law was shown to be valid under these conditions, but only up to a stimulus diameter of 0.8 mm in the central region of the receptive field. On the other hand, simultaneous suprathreshold illumination of two equisensitive parts of the receptive field had a stronger effect than illumination with double intensity of only one part. To evoke the same response with one spot, its intensity had to be about four times that of the intensity of each spot in the double spot stimulation. This led to the conclusion of a nonlinear intensity transformation from the receptor to the ganglion cell input, expressed by a power function with an exponent of 0.55 (average). It is assumed that the intensity at each point is transformed by such a power function into quantities of "excitation" which combine linearly to drive the ganglion cell. This "excitation process" is localized between the receptor output (if the receptors react linearly to intensity) and the ganglion cell input.

Büttner & Grüsser (34) did double spot experiments in a different way and thus came to a different interpretation of their findings. They compared the response produced by two spots given simultaneously [AB] with the algebraic sum of the responses produced by each spot given alone ([A]+[B]), and found that [AB] = 0.55 ([A]+[B])+C. The factor 0.55 is independent of stimulus intensity and the magnitude of the response, but dependent on the stimulus frequency of sinusoidal stimuli. It improved above a stimulus frequency of 5/sec and when the two stimuli were more separated. The findings were interpreted in the context of the superimposition model: a lateral interaction between the two stimuli was assumed. By application of theoretical models (69) it was tested whether the results could be explained by multiplicative or subtractive (forward) inhibition or by recurrent (backward) inhibition in the bipolar or ganglion cell layer. The question could not be answered by this formal treatment, as the results could be explained in both ways. The same summing properties of retinal ganglion cells were found by Stone & Fabian (296). In their experiments the summation quotients AB/(A+B) varied between 0.55 and 0.8. They suggest that this nonlinearity might be due to intrinsic properties of the retinal ganglion cells (e.g. refractoriness) rather than to lateral interaction of elements located before the ganglion cells. Inhibitory and excitatory responses also did not sum linearly.

A discussion of spatial summation in retinal ganglion cells of excitation must take into account the geometry of receptive fields. An attempt in this direction was made (70), on the basis of pictures of dendritic trees published by anatomists (11, 12). In a first approximation it was assumed that each receptor lying straight above a dendritic branch would get into contact with that branch via a bipolar cell. If these contacts were all excitatory and if horizontal interaction is disregarded, the amount of excitation elicited by a small light stimulus (correspondent to Rushton's excitation pool) would then be equal not to the illuminated area but to the number of illuminated receptors, which are actually in contact with a dendrite. Ricco's law would then only be valid if the density of dendritic branches is sufficient to make contacts with all receptors of that area. Even allowing for some lateral spread of receptor projection on dendrites due to branching of bipolars at the receptor and ganglion cell level, it was calculated that such a density is found only in the *central* parts of dendritic fields. This explains why Ricco's law could be confirmed on the cellular level only for the medial compartments of receptive-field centers (36, 67, 68, 297). The model was tested by comparing the responses of retinal on-neurons to discs of light of increasing diameter and to small spots shone into different parts of their receptive field (spatial-sensitivity curve) with the number of receptor-ganglion cell contacts covered by a simulated stimulus in the geometrical model. Both response curves had the same characteristics except that the surround effect was not simulated. But it was necessary to introduce in the model an attenuation of excitatory effects according to the dendritic length. This smoothed out the spatial-sensitivity curve of the model and gave it a Gaussian appearance like that of neurons. Differences in the average diameters of receptive-field centers between histology and experiment (around 1°) may be explained by lateral spread of bipolars. It may be remembered in this context that Kuffler (75) has already suggested that spatial-sensitivity variations within receptive fields may be due to differences in the density of receptors functionally connected to the ganglion cell.

"Specialized" receptive fields (comparative physiology of the retina). By scanning the receptive fields of *cat's* retinal ganglion cells with a moving stimulus and using automatic data analysis, Spinelli (71, 72) found that only slightly more than one third of the 145 neurons investigated showed the typical circular symmetrical center-surround arrangement first described by Kuffler (73). Another third showed asymmetrical surround areas, and one third exhibited different characteristics with bar- or edge-shaped receptive fields, on-activated cells with no inhibitory surround, and other unclassified irregularities. The author concludes that this indicates that in the cat's retina considerably more "data processing" is being performed than had been recognized. But he emphasizes that "the specificity of these 'detectors' [including also those described by other authors in the frog's retina (74) or the cat's visual cortex (75, 220)] is rather poor."

The stimulation with large contrasts in these experiments provoked strong criticism (76) when the first, rather unconventional results were published (71). Furthermore, the method of mapping the receptive fields and evaluating the data (by counting successive gating periods during the steady movement of the stimulus) is similar to the method used by Rodieck & Stone (13) and is open to the limitations mentioned earlier: simultaneous on- and off-effects due to the movement from one place to another and nonlinear summation of such effects, especially if large contrasts are used. The periphery effect (77, 78) may result in excessively large receptive fields. However, asymmetrical receptive fields in the cat's retina are not surprising in view of the structural-functional model reviewed above, and are indeed frequently observed. A new type of retinal ganglion cells was described, which were inhibited by contrasts, but could not be activated by any stimulus (79). These cells may correspond to those found earlier in the retina (298) and the geniculocortical radiation (80), which were inhibited at the beginning and the end of a diffuse light stimulus.

Some new types of ganglion cells in the *rabbit's* retina were described (81) in addition to the symmetrically organized on- and off-center units (about 40 per cent) and the movement-sensitive on- or off-center units (about 18 per cent) (82). In the visual streak, orientation-selective cells (about 12 per cent), local-edge detectors (20 per cent), and uniformity detectors (2.5 per cent) were classified. The orientation-selective cells had receptive fields which might be considered as elongated variations of concentric fields, oriented either horizontally or vertically. The local edge detectors had small on-off fields sensitive to movements of an edge not directionally selective. In contrast to the other neurons, the uniformity detectors had high on-going spontaneous activity and were inhibited by all forms of stimulation corresponding to the contrast-inhibited cells of the cat (79). An attempt was made to relate the different classes of retinal ganglion cells to the rabbit's visual behavior.

The preferred directions of the movement-sensitive neurons in the *rabbit's* retina were further investigated (83). All movement-sensitive neurons with on-off characteristics to stationary lights had preferred directions in the horizontal and vertical axes of the visual field, with a slight deviation of the mean from the true horizontal and vertical. These deviations corresponded to the directions of eye movements due to contraction of the anterior posterior and superior inferior rectus muscles respectively. This functional arrangement was interpreted as part of a servomechanism where "each group of cells could, without any further processing, provide the error signal thus minimizing retinal image motion." Movement-sensitive neurons with a pure on-center had three different preferred directions separated by about 120°. Without making a definite suggestion as to the possible function of these neurons, it was pointed out that three preferred directions were the minimum required to signal the full range of possible directions of motion.

The retinal ganglion cells of the diurnal *ground squirrel* (*Citellus mexicanus* with a pure cone retina) were extensively studied (84–86): 53 per cent of the 410 cells recorded showed concentrically organized center-surround fields with an on- or off-center and the usual characteristics of such fields (spatial summation, contrast sensitivity, better surround effect during center activation, and light adaptation). The cells had a maximal spectral sensitivity of center and surround at green (525 nm). Light-adaptation studies did not reveal a Purkinje shift, and the center diameters were between 0.5 and 5° (majority between 1.0–2.5°), were surrounded by annular antagonistic regions and were movement-sensitive in one preferred direction. No systematic distribution of these cells or of the preferred movements in the visual field was found. The model developed for the same type of cells in rabbits [i.e. unilateral inhibition from horizontal cells (87)] was adapted to explain the movement sensitivity. Also these cells had a maximum of spectral sensitivity at 525 nm. A third group of cells (24 per cent) had an opponent-color receptive-field organization. They were either green-on/blue-off (50 per cent) or green-off/blue-on units (50 per cent) with spectral maxima at 525 and 460 μ respectively. Some of these units had no center-surround organization (class I), others had a green (on- or off-center) and were blue-sensitive in the opposite direction throughout the whole (center-surround) field (class II), and others had only a green-sensitive center and a blue-sensitive surround without overlap of the two opponent systems (class III). Two populations of cones are assumed, green- and blue-sensitive, although only a green-sensitive cone pigment has so far been demonstrated spectroscopically (88).

In the perifoveal area of the red-cone retina of *Macacca mulatta*, evidence was presented for a convergence of rods and cones on the same ganglion cell (89). When stimulated at different adaptation states, it looked as if the cone responses were always earlier (by about 50 msec) than the rod responses. In contrast to the pure cone retina of *Citellus*, where the diameter of the receptive-field center of the color-sensitive neurons does not change during light adaptation (86), the field centers of the mixed ganglion cells of *Macaca mulatta* became smaller and only cone dependent during light adaptation. This suggested a smaller receptive field for cones than for rods. Also in the *plaice* (*Pleuronectes platessa*, L.) most ganglion cells received input both from cones and rods (90). However, when the receptive fields of color-sensitive neurons in the lateral geniculate nucleus of the macaque were analyzed with small spots of monochromatic light, cells with pure cone and mixed rod-cone inputs were found (193). Further experiments on the neuronal organization of color mechanisms in the primate are reported on page 520.

In the *frog*, an attempt was made (91) to relate some inborn visual releasing mechanisms (92) (catching and flight response) to facts already known about this animal's retina. The quantitative relation between ganglion cell response and stimulus parameters (93, 94) was studied systematically and compared with the stimulus parameters used to release the behavior patterns. The result was that visual stimulus patterns which elicited a certain behavioral reaction were not optimal for any one class of neurons, but were such that they would activate different classes. Stimuli optimal for only one class of neurons had little effect on behavior.

It was concluded that an additional neuronal network (in the optic tectum) combines the activities of the four different retinal classes of neurons, in order to differentiate the behaviorally relevant key stimuli.

Adaptation.—Rushton's analysis of adaptation (95) will certainly guide investigation and lesser confusion in this field. His model of an adaptation pool, which receives its input from the receptors and which serves as a further control for the receptor output, and his distinction between "field" and "bleaching" adaptation may serve as guidelines for further investigation. But whether dark and real light affect the control system in different ways (101) or by the same mechanism (102, 103) is not yet settled. Further work may help to decide between these hypotheses. The experiments on S-potentials (57) are not conclusive because of their ambiguous functional role.

There is general agreement that photochemical processes only play a role for slow dark adaptation after bleaching. These photochemical processes in the receptor were extensively investigated in the isolated frog retina (96–100). The scotopic dark adaptation of the ERG-threshold is not related to the regeneration of bleached rhodopsin (100), but goes parallel with the amount of metarhodopsin which slowly diminishes following bleaching (96, 97). But even for the slow adaptation processes an additional "neural" mechanism is not excluded (100).

Further evidence was presented for a localization of the fast adaptive process in the bipolar layer (104, 105). The suggestion was based on the observation that the b-wave of the ERG, which supposedly originates in the bipolar layer, shows adaptation properties (decrease of sensitivity with increasing background luminance, decreased intensity-response curves at higher background intensities), while the a-wave (probably originating at the receptor or horizontal cell layer) shows only little adaptation and saturates at high background level. A synaptic mechanism based on ultrastructural features of amacrine-bipolar contacts was suggested, by which the amacrines feed back to the same bipolars from which they receive excitation, and thus control the gain of the bipolars in proportion to the amount of excitation received from them (105).

Adaptation of neuronal firing during continuous illumination of the retina is still a complicated and controversial matter. Do retinal ganglion cells signal continuously the amount of light falling on the retina or are they connected through an $R \cdot C$ coupling of relatively short time constant to the light-sensitive parts of the retina? The perception of brightness without contrast as well as the homolateral and consensual pupillary reactions [also during dark adaptation (106)] suggest that, at least in humans, continuous brightness information must reach the brain. The following investigations have been done on cats.

It is general knowledge that the initial reaction of on-center neurons, which over a wide range of intensities is linearly related to the log of intensity of the stimulus (48, 296), decays quickly within a few 100 msec up to several sec to a steady-state discharge rate. This is reported not to be significantly different from the dark discharge rate in most neurons (48), to be different from the dark discharge but unsystematically related to the light intensity (107), or to be systematically related to the light intensity [increase of on-center neuron discharge rate during illumination, decrease of off-center activity (108, 109)].

On-center neurons seem to show larger variability, some of them being activated, some inhibited during continuous illumination, while most off-center neurons show a decrease during illumination (109–111). Complete discharge silence was reported in many off-center neurons during long-lasting illumination up to several minutes (110, 112, 113). But near threshold and within the scotopic range (with dilated pupils) a gradual increase of the maintained firing rate of on-center neurons and a gradual decrease of off-neurons during steady illumination were found (113). Beyond this range, full adaptation of firing was seen in most on-center, but strong depression or complete cessation of firing in most off-center units. The decrease of off-center neuron activity during steady illumination probably explains the decrease of overall activity of the optic nerve (114) and the lateral geniculate body (114, 115) during steady illumination reported earlier. This complete suppression of off-center neuron activity led Jung (116) to underline the importance of the off-center system for perception of dark objects during light adaptation, since introducing a dark contrast leads to a strong activation of off-center neurons. At different adaptation levels the response-intensity curves of on-center neurons are parallel even if the maintained firing rate changed little. But the incremental threshold $\Delta I/I$ decreases with stronger background (113). The response-intensity plots at different adaptation states are similar to those shown for the ERG of the isolated frog's retina (43); this indicates a mechanism located before the ganglion cell level. Similar observations were recently reported by Barlow (117). These findings on adaptation of maintained discharge during continuous illumination, and especially the differences between the on- and off-system, are not easily explained by the current adaptation theories.

"*Field adaptation*" with electrophysiological methods has been investigated in the isolated goldfish (118) and in the cat's retina (119). If only one part of the receptive field of the retina is illuminated, the sensitivity of the remainder of the receptive field is about equally diminished. In the cat's retina, this adapting effect is stronger if the center of the receptive field is illuminated. The adaption field shows spatial summation and is roughly concentric with the excitatory receptive field. The diameter of this adaptation pool may be as large as 5°, if tested with small points or rings. But if tested with discs of increasing diameter, most of the effect is reached at a diameter of up to 2° and a further increase of the spot has little further effect. This is similar to the "inhibition" of Pirenne (121), who had demonstrated in psychophysical experiments an increase of threshold in an area whose surround was continuously illuminated. Bleaching adaptation after illumination of one part of the receptive field [corresponding to the psychophysiological experiment of Rushton & Westheimer (122) and the neurophysiological experiment in the frog's retina by Lipetz (120)] is less effective and has a much smaller lateral extend than "field adaptation". Lipetz' findings could not be confirmed in the goldfish retina, where desensitization after focal bleaching was essentially restricted to the bleached area (118). This difference between field and bleaching adaptation gives further support to the hypothesis of two distinct mechanisms. But it may still be argued that the difference in the effectiveness is only due to the poorer contrast of real light than of "dark light" and that only one mechanism is responsible (117).

The discussion on the lateral extent of the psychophysically determined "adaptation pool" (or area) continues (85, 123). In any case, the lateral spread of light adaptation as determined psychophysically is much smaller than that of "field adaptation" in the cat, about 5–6 min at 10° eccentricity (123), i.e. even smaller than originally measured by Rushton (95). When the retina was illuminated with discs of increasing diameter, the threshold in the center of the adapting disc increased only up to a diameter of 45 min, but decreased at larger diameters (124). This disinhibition effect was not seen in the cat's retinal ganglion cells (119). The question arises as to whether these differences between neurophysiological and psychophysical experiments are due to species differences (different diameters of receptive fields) or to the fact that perception is not just a mononeuronal event, but the result of combined activation of a large number of antagonistically organized and spatially arranged neurons, a "sensation pool".

Characteristics of spontaneous activity and transfer characteristics of retinal ganglion cells.—From scattered information contained in some papers and from our own experience, it seems as if the maintained high spontaneous dark activity of retinal ganglion cells seen in cats and higher animals is not common to all vertebrates. In the retinas of lower animals which have a greater variety of more "complex" receptive fields, most cells show only little spontaneous activity, while in the cat and higher animals, a relatively high spontaneous discharge rate comparable to a carrier frequency is modulated in both directions by spatial and temporal intensity gradients of light. The retinal cells of lower animals with little or no spontaneous activity seem to give predominantly "yes" or" no" answers to stimuli with certain spatial and temporal characteristics. It would be interesting to discover more about this.

The origin of maintained activity of the cat's retinal ganglion cells is still obscure. Two recent hypotheses may be mentioned. It is believed (125) that the dark discharge is not due to the activity of receptors, but should be regarded as the expression of "autochtonous" activity of the functionally disconnected neural part of the retina. This assumption is based on the finding that the time courses of adaptation of discharge frequency (2–3 min) and threshold adaptation (up to 1 hr) are different after a strong bleach of the receptor pigment, and that nearby ganglion cells discharge independently (126). However, loss of maintained activity of retinal ganglion cells was found after chemical destruction of the photoreceptors, and slight statistical dependence of maintained dark discharges of nearby ganglion cells was described by Rodieck (107). He concluded that maintained activity of the ganglion cells is dependent on the receptors.

Whatever the generating mechanism, the type of discharge which is revealed by spike interval histograms (127–129) suggests a random driving process modulated by some well known membrane processes following a spike discharge, such as refractory period, or polarizing and depolarizing afterpotentials (130). Apart from the occasionally observed split of the first peak following the "dead time" in the interval histograms, other multimodal peaks due to rhythmic discharging (48, 107, 109, 131) have now been shown to be due to low temperature (129) or to pharmacological effects (130). There is no need to postulate neuronal feedback loops (132, 133) in order to explain the temporal characteristics of spontaneous retinal neuron activity. During complete darkness slow rhythmical changes of the spontaneous discharge rates (ranging from 2/min to 2/hr) have been observed, whose mechanism and physiological significance are as yet unknown (134). The statistical properties of spontaneous and evoked activities of retinal ganglion cells of the cat were investigated with reference to information theory (126, 135). Distribution of interspike intervals and the functional relation between standard deviation and discharge frequency were invariant under different stimulus conditions (135).

The distribution of *conduction velocities* of optic nerve fibers was investigated again with macro- (136) and with microelectrodes (137). Single units showed conduction velocities between 10 and 50 m/sec with two peaks at 15 and 30 m/sec (137), while the compound evoked potential gave conduction velocities between 3.5 and 70 m/sec with a maximum at 15–25 m/sec (136) in agreement with earlier measurements (137). New anatomical data on the distribution of fiber diameters (with light microscopy) showed a range between 1.0 and 10.5 μ which is in satisfactory agreement with the conduction velocity measurements, but with only one single-sized grouping at 2.5 μ (138). In the human optic nerve, the existence of nonmyelinated fibers could not be confirmed (139); occasional unmyelinated axons were interpreted as myelinated axons cut within the node of Ranvier.

No relation of conduction velocities to the type of neuron (on- or off-center fiber) was found, but the conduction velocity was positively related to the flicker fusion frequency and to the spontaneous dark activity (137). Efferent effects on retinal ganglion cells have again been described (140–142), though not convincingly and thus without clarifying satisfactorily this question of centrifugal fibers in the optic nerve. No centrifugal myelinated fibers were found in the cat's optic nerve (143). After reviewing the literature, Ogden (144) concludes that the bird is the only vertebrate in which conclusive evidence of an efferent retinal projection can be found. Data on the topographical projection of these centrifugal fibers in the pigeon are now available (145).

The absolute *threshold of retinal ganglion cells* to light has been reinvestigated with averaging methods and was found between 1.1×10^{-7} and 6.8×10^{-6} cd/m² (146), lower than has yet been assumed (127). It corresponds to psychophysical determinations of the feline threshold. Slight statistical differences between on- and off-center fibers were noted. The behaviorally determined incremental brightness threshold of sqirrel monkeys is identical to the incremental light intensity which elicits a just perceivable phasic response in the integrated neuronal activity of the lateral geniculate nucleus at on and off (110). Maintained activity during continuous illumination and phasic responses of on- and off-center neurons are considered significant for threshold perception. In cats, the ability to recognize simultaneous contrasts was related to the different phasic response components of on-center neurons (147, 148). At contrast intensities which were just recognized at a 90 per cent level in behavioral experiments, the reactions of on-center units were significantly different only during the first 50–100 msec of their response. Since the activity of off-center neurons was completely suppressed at the background intensities used, it was assumed that the information was carried only by on-center neurons.

Several studies were done on the effects of *drugs* on spontaneous and evoked retinal ganglion cell activity. The question of which are the synaptic transmitters in the retina is still open. But there is general agreement that strychnine does not abolish the light-on or -off induced inhibition of off- and on-center neurons (111, 149–151). After intracarotidal injection (149), strychnine, L-glutamate, and physostigmine have an activating effect on all neurons; GABA, serotonin, and ergometrine have a depressant effect; acetylcholine, norepinephrine, and *d*-amphetamine activated or depressed different neurons. Desipramine given intravenously strongly suppresses the spontaneous activity, but does not significantly influence the phasic response to light stimuli (152). The basic feature of spatial organization of retinal receptive fields is not changed by barbiturate anesthesia, but considerable changes were observed in the temporal organization of retinal responses to light stimuli and this must be taken into account if the functional organization of more centrally located units is investigated under barbiturate anesthesia (130).

Conclusions.—The principles of transformation of visual stimuli into nervous messages in the retina are now understood. But there are still large gaps in our knowledge of receptor mechanisms, of the mechanisms of vertical transfer within retinal channels, and of horizontal interaction of these channels. Many questions can still be asked and many hypotheses and speculations can be made. Are receptor potential changes transmitted to the ganglion cells by spikes or by slow potentials of the bipolar cells? In which way do neighboring bipolars interact with each other? Are there specialized excitatory and inhibitory bipolars? Or do on- and off-center cells react differentially to the same input? Are the horizontal cells responsible for adaptation and the amacrine cells for lateral inhibition? What is the mechanism of gain control?

At least it is known approximately where to localize the mechanisms of intensity transformation, spatial integration, and adaptation (gain control) within the different levels of the retina. It also seems that these mechanisms are principally the same in all vertebrates. But the spatial organization of receptive fields of retinal ganglion cells shows considerable differences in different groups of vertebrates. There is a large variability in the shape and diameter of receptive fields and in the optimal stimulus parameters. The combination of different types of neurons in one retina also varies in different species. The structural basis of these differences is not precisely known. Variable dendritic fields of the ganglion cells, asymmetrical connections of bipolars with ganglion cells and with each other, and asymmetrical connections of inhibitory horizontal cells with bipolars or ganglion cells are possible. It can be assumed that there is a close correlation between the functional organization of an animal's retina and the organization of its whole central nervous system and therefore its behavior. But only few scattered data are available for a serious discussion of this aspect. Careful experiments are necessary to avoid premature speculations.

THE LATERAL GENICULATE NUCLEUS (LGN)

HISTOLOGICAL ORGANIZATION OF INTRAGENICULATE SYNAPSES AND FIBERS

Functionally the discovery and further analysis of the synaptic glomeruli (153–157) is of great importance. These peculiar synaptic structures, situated on the grapelike dendritic appendages at the first branchings of dendrites close to the soma and surrounded by a dense glial layer, are composed of several synapses derived from different afferents: terminals of optic tract fibers, corticofugal fibers, and probably also axons from intergeniculate Golgi II neurons. Optic tract fibers terminate exclusively in the glomeruli, and there is good evidence that one optic tract fiber supplies several glomeruli of one ganglion cell, but is in contact with more than one geniculate cell. However, how many optic tract fibers have direct contact with one geniculate cell has not yet been conclusively answered by the anatomists, although some estimates have been made (158–160). Within the glomeruli, one optic tract terminal has several axodendritic synapses, but axo-axonal synapses between the terminals of different origin are also seen (154, 155, 161). Ultrastructural evidence shows that the optic tract fibers are exclusively presynaptic to the nonretinal terminals (156, 157, 162).

Optic tract terminals do not cross the laminar borders (161) although dendrites of some geniculate cells may (158). Degenerating terminals after small retinal lesions show considerable overlap within one lamina (159). But this does not imply a functional overlap on as many cells as covered by the volume of overlap, since electrophysiologically a distinct retinotopical projection with little or no overlap was found (163). A separate laminar projection from both eyes has been described in all further animals investigated during the last years and a number of comparative anatomical features have been described [tree shrew (164), marsupial phalanger (165), owl monkey (166), galago (167), squirrel monkey (168)]. Further evidence was presented for a triple representation of each part of the retina: in the main laminae, in the central and medial interlaminar nuclei (170). The distribution of retrograde changes of lateral geniculate nucleus neurons after localized lesion of the different visual cortical areas in the cat suggests that the medium and small cells project into area 17 and the large cells into areas 17 and 18, supposedly with branching axons (169). Ablation of any one area only leads to slight (area 18) or no (area 17) retrograde changes, but ablation of both areas produces complete retrograde degeneration of the large cells. Observations after small cortical lesions suggest that geniculate columns project into cortical columns (169).

Further evidence has been presented for corticofugal efferents into the geniculate (161, 170). These cortifugal fibers build fine terminals, which cross the laminar borders (161) and terminate mainly on individual, distal dendritic synapses (162). A retinotopical projection seems to be preserved (169). Degenerating fibers could be traced back into the peristriate area (154). Axons of intrageniculate origin terminate close to their parent cells (158). A three-dimensional reconstruction of some geniculate cells of the rat from a serial electronmicroscopic analysis (171) shows only few synapses on the soma, but numerous ones on the proximal dendrites. Spines have now also been demonstrated on more distal dendrites of the adult cat's geniculate cells (158).

NEUROPHYSIOLOGY

Synaptic organization and transfer of retinal input.—In spite of the challenging picture of the synaptic organization of LGN cells which emerges from the anatomical studies, a straightforward intracellular analysis of the synaptic transmission has proved to be difficult, simply because LGN cells are extremely difficult to impale by a microelectrode. This may be due to the dense glial sheet which surrounds at least some parts of these cells (160). But from extracellular analysis, from a few intracellular records, and from "quasi-intracellular" records of geniculate cells a relatively clear, though still incomplete picture emerges (172–180).

The discharge of an optic tract fiber leads to a large, all-or-nothing type EPSP with a rise time of 1–2 msec and a decay time of 10-40 msec. The depolarization elicited by one EPSP is one to two times smaller than the threshold depolarization, so that temporal summation of several EPSPs (or depolarization from other sources) is necessary to fire a cell. EPSPs near threshold may induce a local response (delayed depolarization) which leads to a short cluster of spikes (174). The spontaneous and the response frequency, the amplitude distribution, and the receptive fields of the EPSPs make it possible to identify EPSPs originating from single optic nerve fibers. There is good evidence that, at least in some cells in which an appropriate analysis was possible, the main specific excitatory drive can be attributed to only one optic tract fiber, which may be an on- or an off-center fiber (175). Bishop (172) came to a similar conclusion after the analysis of extracellular responses to electrical stimulation of the optic tract. The fact that large EPSPs are not found in all "quasi-intracellular" records may be due to variable locations of the electrode relative to a synaptic glomerulus. Besides the major EPSPs a fine synaptic noise is recorded, whose analysis is difficult.

Electrical stimulation of the optic nerves elicits an EPSP only from one side, but an IPSP from both sides (180). The latency of the IPSP elicited from the dominant optic nerve (the one producing the EPSP) is about 1 msec longer than that of the EPSP (173, 176, 180), whereas after stimulation of the nondominant nerve the IPSP latency is several msec longer (180). Large IPSPs can also be elicited by diffuse light (173) or by small light stimuli shone into an inhibitory area of a neuron's receptive field (174). Such a light-induced postsynaptic polarization starts 20–40 msec later than the cessation of EPSP activity elicited by the same light stimulus (174). Pure lack of excitation without postsynaptic inhibition is possible, but was only rarely observed. Whether this reflects differences between cells or just between some parts of a neuron's receptive field is not yet clear, since complete receptive-field analysis during intracellular recordings has not yet been reported. On-center as well as off-center fibers from the dominant eye can lead to a primary EPSP. From these results it can be concluded that on- and off-center optic nerve fibers have a powerful direct excitatory contact with the LGN relay cells and that inhibition is relayed through recurrent collaterals, inhibitory interneurons, or both (176).

In the rat's LGN, two types of cells can be distinguished according to their latency and firing pattern after optic nerve and cortical stimulation (177–179). The longer-latency cells (difference about 1 msec) were interpreted as inhibitory interneurons (I-cells), the shorter-latency cells as principal relay cells (P-cells), although proof for such an interpretation is still lacking. In the cat also, some cells with repetitive discharge and long latency after optic nerve stimulation have been recorded extracellularly (180, 181), but the latencies here were too long to explain the IPSP after stimulation of the dominant eyes. The synaptic transmitter of the optic fibers is not yet known. ACh and related drugs applied iontophoretically have a strong excitatory action on LGN cells, but there is no evidence that ACh is the transmitter released by the optic nerve terminals. It may be the transmitter of nonspecific (reticular) afferents to the LGN (182).

A short word may be said with respect to *presynaptic inhibition in the LGN:* As mentioned in the above discussion of LGN histology, there is good anatomical evidence in the LGN for axo-axonal synapses, the assumed morphological equivalent for presynaptic inhibition. But the anatomists clearly state that optic tract terminals are presynaptic to nonretinal terminals. On the other hand, a slow intrageniculate negative wave and corresponding threshold decrease or amplitude increase of the antidromic optic tract potential after intrageniculate stimulation was observed by a number of authors after reticular and cortical stimulation (183–190). During rapid eye movements the antidromic response in the optic tract and the presynaptic component in the LGN after optic nerve stimulation were also diminished (191). The interpretation of these effects still remains obscure, since no direct proof for presynaptic inhibition is yet available. The whole question of presynaptic inhibition in the LGN needs further investigation, if possible with intracellular methods, before its functional significance can be seriously discussed.

At the present state of our knowledge, we can conclude that because of its synaptic organization, the dorsal LGN is mainly a relay station in which little spatial reorganization of the optic nerve input takes place. The active inhibition elicited by stimulating inhibitory zones of a receptive field (surround of on-center neurons and center of off-center neurons) results in a diminution of the effect of diffuse light (192), but it is doubtful whether it serves to sharpen the spatial contrast and to reorganize in a major degree the spatial organization of the retina, since receptive-field characteristics of LGN cells [even if tested with color stimuli in the monkey (193)] do not seem to be very different from optic nerve fibers so far known (75, 175). One role of postsynaptic inhibition in the LGN may also be the complete suppression of nonspecific excitatory inputs during stimulation of an inhibitory area.

The transfer characteristics of LGN cells tested for steady (194) or sinusoidally modulated light (195) are very similar to those of retinal ganglion cells except for some filter characteristics revealed by sinusoidal stimulation. The observation that the signal: noise ratio of LGN cells increases more if a sinusoidally modulated stimulus is distributed over a larger area of the excitatory receptive field than if the same amount of light is concentrated on one small spot was taken as evidence (196) that spatial summation of several retinal ganglion cells takes place in LGN cells. But whether this "spatial averaging" already takes place at the retinal level, as suggested by the two-point stimulation experiments of Easter (36) or whether it is a geniculate performance needs experimental testing. Also Grüsser & Snigula (148) suggested a spatial summation in the LGN in order to improve signal detection. However, it should be realized that temporal summation of EPSPs coming from one single optic tract fiber may be sufficient for transfer in the LGN because of the long EPSPs (10–40 msec), and the high spontaneous discharge (around 30/sec) and response frequencies (up to 300/sec) of optic tract fibers. In fact, the transfer function should be nonlinear with improvement of the input-output relation at shorter intervals (higher frequencies) because of the slow decay of the EPSPs. Since one single EPSP usually does not reach the threshold, temporal summation of two or more EPSPs may be necessary to fire an LGN cell. The Poisson-type interval distribution of optic nerve fiber activity is therefore favorable for transmission, because short intervals capable of suprathreshold temporal summation can appear also at suprathreshold low discharge frequencies (176).

Nonretinal input into the LGN.—One main function of the LGN may be seen in the fact that here the specific retinocortical activity comes under the influence of activity of other brain structures (194, 197–199, 291), mainly from the reticular formation. Nonretinal inputs have a clear influence on geniculate activity as shown by a decrease of unit activity and change in discharge pattern during synchronized sleep (192, 202, 203) and by the maintenance of a reduced spontaneous discharge rate after block of the retinal output (198) or after enucleation of the eyes (202). The sleep-induced changes of LGN activity are even more marked after enucleation, with a decrease of activity during light and an increase above the level of wakefulness during deep sleep (202). In the freely moving cat the sleep-induced changes appeared simultaneously in several simultaneously recorded units (204). The transfer of geniculate cells as tested by their response to sinusoidally modulated light stimuli is impaired during synchronized sleep (203). Also the electrically induced postsynaptic response of the geniculate evoked potential after optic tract stimulation is diminished during synchronized but increased during desynchronized sleep (190). The possible role of presynaptic inhibitory mechanisms is discussed in relation to all these effects.

Nonretinal input more directly related to vision was discovered during eye movements in REM sleep (191). About two thirds of the cells showed an increase, about 10 per cent a decrease, in firing rate during the rapid eye movements, which were accompanied also by slow waves in the LGN. This activation was seen in complete darkness and during the slow waves even in enucleated cats, and it was not necessarily accompanied by actual eye movements. It therefore must be of extraretinal origin and is thus different from the slow wave seen in the optic tract, LGN, and visual cortex (λ-waves) during eye movements of the awake animal, which is of retinal origin and disappears during darkness (205). Richards (206) reports on preliminary experiments which indicate different activity of LGN neurons during convergence and divergence. It is thought that this might be a neurophysiological basis for spatial remapping of the LGN at different states of divergence and convergence. This is supposed to be one important function of the LGN in depth perception. Also, a depolarization of optic terminals and presynaptic inhibition during eye movements is discussed (207, 208).

Binocular interaction.—Binocular interaction in the lateral geniculate nucleus was a matter of argument for many years. The demonstration of binocular inhibitory and monocular excitatory retinal input in the cat by intracellular recording (180) has now provided a firm basis for this argument. From these findings a mainly inhibitory binocular interaction must be expected. But the functional significance of this interaction is still unclear, and it is hoped that more will become known about the spatial organization of the inhibitory input from the nondominant eye.

In accordance with expectation, a response diminution in two thirds of

LGN neurons was found during binocular stimulation as compared to stimulation of the dominant eye alone (201). Lindsley et al. (200) saw in 20 per cent of the units a larger variety of interocular ("dichoptic") effects (change of latency and alteration of discharge pattern). Very few cells with clearly defined responses to stimulation of each eye were mentioned again (200).

Color-sensitive cells in the primate lateral geniculate nucleus (LGN).— Color-sensitive neurons of the monkey were investigated at the geniculate level (193, 209–211). There is as yet no indication that the organization of the different types of color-sensitive neurons is different in retinal and LGN neurons (193), so that from this point of view the experiments do not add to the problem of specific geniculate functions. However, an important geniculate aspect is the distribution of different color-sensitive cells in the different layers of the LGN, especially in the context of some older anatomical theories [trichromatic layer theory (212), photopic-scotopic theory (213)]. Opponent- and non-opponent-color units were found nearly equally distributed in the four dorsal layers (layer 6-3 of the anatomists) without clearly defined response differences (193). But in the ventral layers (layers 1 and 2) only non-opponent-color cells were found (193, 209). It was concluded that in the ventral layers the importance of color is reduced (193).

The neurons were differently classified according to the method of investigation [stimulation with small spots of monochromatic light (193) or stimulation with diffuse monochromatic light (209, 211)]. Wiesel & Hubel (193) were mainly interested in the spatial organization of color receptive fields. Four types of neurons with some subtypes were found: opponent-color units with different spectral sensitivities of the center and surround (type I), opponent-color units without any center-surround differentiation (type II), and units with an on-center off-surround arrangment of equal (type III) or almost equal (type IV) spectral sensitivities of the center and surround mechanism. Diffuse light of any wavelength suppressed the activity of type III and IV cells because of the strong surround inhibition. This may explain why Jones (270) found only "off-cells" in the ventral layers of the owl monkey if they were tested with diffuse light. The type I cells were of five varieties with either red-green opponent-color sensitivity (green or red on- or off-center) or with a blue on-center/green off-surround. Type II cells could be of either the green-on/blue-off or the green-off/blue-on subtype. Receptive-field centers were all below 1° (modal value of type I cells around 10 min); the smallest centers of some type I cells were about 2 min, not larger than a few cones. It is assumed that type I cells were connected to one type of cones in the center and to the opponent-color type in the surround, type II cells to two opponent types throughout the whole receptive field (with different action of any one type), and type III cells to all three types of cones in the center and the surround. It is remarkable that this color organization seems to get partially lost in area 17 (214).

De Valois et al. (209, 211) continued earlier studies and distinguished between spectrally opponent and non-opponent cells. The first class (similar to type I, 193) were either red-green (R+/G− or G+/R−) or yellow-blue opponent-color units (blue or yellow excitatory). The opponent-color cells were thought to be mainly concerned with color coding, while the second class [non-opponent, corresponding to class III and IV (193)] seemed primarily concerned with brightness, since the mean spectral sensitivity of all cells closely matched the human photopic luminosity function (211). The averaged wavelength discrimination of all the opponent-color cells closely matched the behavioral color discrimination ability of the monkey (209). Only broadband off- or on-cells were found in the LGN of the owl monkey (*Actes*), which has only one apparent photoreceptor type (210).

CORTEX

ANATOMY

Afferent connections of the visual cortex.—The distribution of geniculate fibers in the cat's cortex is more widespread than has yet been assumed and there is good evidence that the LGN projects differentially upon the three architectonic and functional subdivisions of the visual cortex (169, 215, 216). Dense terminal degenerations after LGN lesions were found in area 17 and 18 [according to the architectonic classification of Otsuka & Hassler (214)]; medium or dense degeneration on both banks of the suprasylvian fissure and light degeneration widely distributed in area 19 and on the suprasylvian and posterior ectosylvian gyri (169, 215, 216). As mentioned earlier the large LGN cells probably project into area 17 and 18 with branching axons, while the middle and small cells are supposed to project only into 17 (169). These findings explain the short-latency responses found in area 18 (218). Area 19 receives afferents mainly from the central and medial intralaminar nuclei (169, 216). The finding of crossed geniculocortical degeneration and the conclusion that a crossed geniculocortical pathway existed (215) were not confirmed (216).

In all visual areas, the anteroposterior projection of the LGN is the same (anterior parts of the LGN anteriorly on the cortex), but mediolateral projection is reversed in area 17/18 [medial parts of the LGN project laterally on 17 and medially on 18 (169)]. This is in good agreement with the electrophysiologically determined topographical projection of the visual field on the visual cortex, the mirrorlike reversal of this projection in areas 17 and 18, and the projection of the vertical meridian into the 17/18 border (219–221). Also, the wide distribution of visually evoked potentials (222, 223) has now some anatomical basis, and the wide cortical distribution of geniculate fibers, even after minute lesions in the LGN, may account for the smaller impairment of visual acuity after circumscribed lesions in area 17 as compared to the effect of correspondent retinal lesions (217). In the light of these recent anatomical demonstrations of primary geniculate projection into area 17, 18, and even 19, the finding of only complex and hypercomplex cells in 18 and 19 of the cat (220) in contrast to area 17 is of special interest, and may indicate different functional connections of the geniculate afferents with the pyramidal cells of area 17 and 18, unless further research does reveal more "simple field" neurons in 18 also.

Intracortical connections between the different visual areas were further investigated (224): area 17 sends association fibers to areas 18 and 19 and to the lateral suprasylvian cortex, while area 18 projects to areas 17, 19 and to the lateral suprasylvian gyrus. But it is not known whether all areas are reciprocally connected.

Area 6 was the only nonvisual area to which 17 and 19 projected. [It may be mentioned in this context that unit discharges during and after saccadic and following eye movements were observed in the frontal eye field of the monkey (225)]. Callosal projections were found in the extreme lateral part of area 17, the medial part of 18, and the lateral part of 19, but more in the rest of area 17 (224).

Synaptic organization of the visual cortex.—The actual distribution of afferent fibers on single cortical neurons is becoming of increasing interest to physiologists. While degenerating fibers were seen mainly in layer 4, some in layer 3, and none in 2 [monkey (216)], a more widespread dendritic spine diminution was found in the rabbit following enucleation or geniculate lesions immediately after birth (226). The changes in spine distribution after appropriate lesions suggest that (in the rabbit) the geniculocortical fibers terminate mainly on the central three quartiles of layer II-V pyramidal cells (226) and transcallosal afferents on the oblique shafts of apical dendrites (227). Recurrent collaterals are presumed to terminate on basilar dendrites. It was assumed that there were direct contacts of geniculate afferents with the cortical pyramidal cells, as the short-axoned stellate cells (type II) appeared normal after enucleation. In the mouse, spine diminution was reported to be specifically localized in layers IV and III after enucleation (228), but distributed all over the apical dendrites in animals reared in the dark (229). In contrast, rabbits which were visually deprived during the first week of their lives showed only slight changes of the apical spines but showed changes of the stellate cells (230).

Some interesting comparative aspects of the functional development of the visual cortex resulted from a quantitative electronmicroscopic study of the visual and motor cortex of different species (231). In the mouse and the monkey, the density of synapses was $6-9 \times 10^{11}/cm^3$. However, the density of neurons decreased with increasing brain weight (mouse $95 \times 10^6/cm^3$, cat about $40 \times 10^6/cm^3$), but was relatively high again in primates ($110 \times 10^6/cm^3$ in *Macaca mulatta*, about $40 \times 10^6/cm^3$ in man) in contrast to the further decrease of neuronal density in the motor cortex of primates. The number of synapses per neuron in the visual cortex were 7000 (mouse) to 5600 (monkey), in the motor cortex 13,000 (mouse) to 60,000 (monkey). It is clear that these figures are much higher than the number of intra- and extracortical fibers per neuron, which may be at least two orders of magnitudes smaller. Further evidence for a distinction between two types of synapses (symmetrical and asymmetrical, roughly corresponding to Gray's type I and II) was collected, but no clear functional significance emerges from this classification (232).

Two structural models of the cortical columns, which may account for the columnar arrangement of functionally different neurons (233, 234), were suggested by Colonnier (235–237) and Globus & Scheibel (241). The vertical connections between pyramidal cells lying above each other is, in the view of Colonnier (235–237), mainly due to vertical spread of cortical interneurons (mainly the *cellules à double bouquet dendritique* of Cajal), whose variable and often elongated dendritic fields are supposed to determine their receptive fields. "Specific thalamic afferents synapse in layer IV and III with stellate cells of the fusiform and basket types. The radially arborizing axons of the fusiform cells excite pyramidal cells above and below, transmitting the specific modulations received from the specific fibers, to a radial column of cells. The pericellular endings of the basked cell are considered as inhibiting pyramidal cells to each side of the column" (237). This view is based on a somewhat different idea of afferent connections with cortical neurons. Szentagothai (162) rejects strongly the general statement that afferents primarily come into contact with Golgi II neurons of layer IV. From the neurophysiological point of view, it should be pointed out that cortical neurons may have inhibitory areas (238–240), but rarely a regular inhibitory surround.

Globus & Scheibel (241) see the basis of the vertical organization of the rabbit's cortex in the vertical spread of afferent fibers, which make contacts with the apical dendritic shafts of pyramidal cells lying above each other (thus proposing that monosynaptic geniculocortical contacts are not solely confined to layer IV). According to their different shaft lengths, pyramidal cells have different amounts of exposure to afferents rising vertically through the cortex. Since the oblique branches and the basilar dendrites are believed to receive mainly transcallosal or intracortical afferents respectively, "each pyramidal cell would then combine its own unique sample of extracortical synaptic drive (specific afferents), a function of the length of the apical dendrite, with a fixed level of intracortical (and transcallosal) synaptic drive, a function of the width of the dendritic skirt and apical arch. The axonal distribution of class II neurons (with intracortical axons) would impress upon class I cells a spatial pattern distinct from the vertical and modular organization dictated by the specific afferents from the LGN and the alignment of pyramids." Following the original suggestion of Cajal, the functional importance of an increasing number of interneurons in higher animals is underlined. This second model agrees relatively well with the analysis of Szentagothai whose drawing of a cortical receptive unit (162) is not very different in its basic features. He underlines the horsetail-like assembly of terminal branches, which suggests that one vertically arising afferent fiber establishes several contacts with one pyramidal cell. Taking all this evidence together, the horizontal distribution of dendritic trees (235) can be considered of minor importance for the determination of cortical receptive fields. Instead, the combination of different single afferents on each individual neuron should determine its main afferent drive. [Since this review was written, Szentagothai has reported that horsetail synapses between geniculocortical fibers and cortical pyramidal cells are found mainly on the basilar dendrites of pyramidal cells in the III and IV layer, but only few on the apical dendrites. On these the synapses are mainly derived from cortical interneurons. (To be published: Jasper, H. H., et al., Eds., *Basic Mechanisms of the Epilepsies*, Little, Brown, Boston, 1969).]

Physiology

The synaptic organization of the visual cortex.—This latter suggestion is supported by recent results of an intracellular study of primary visual cortex neurons by Creutzfeldt & Ito (238). Under resting conditions the membrane potential fluctuated, as in the rabbit's visual cortex (173), 3–10 mV below the firing level as a result of continuous bombardment with EPSPs and IPSPs, and only rarely reached the threshold. Consequently, the spontaneous discharge rate of cortical neurons is low. After visual stimulation, temporal summation of several EPSPs was necessary to fire a cell. This resulted in a long input-output delay (15–60 msec depending on the frequency of the EPSPs), the well known decrease of discharge frequency at the cortical level, and the more sluggish responses of cortical cells. The frequencies of isolated PSPs were similar to those of single geniculate fibers under comparable stimulus conditions, and postsynaptic effects of one type of input (major EPSPs or IPSPs) had receptive fields in shape, size, and functional organization like individual geniculate fibers. In each cortical receptive field, different input fields from the dominant eye could be identified with a separation of receptive-field centers of the different inputs by about 1–3° and a corresponding overlap. It was concluded that these separate input fields represented the activity of individual LGN fibers. On- as well as off-center fibers could have excitatory or inhibitory action on different cortical cells. The large variety of functional combinations and of spatial overlap of such few inputs could explain a great variety of simple or even of some "complex" cortical cells. The possible combinations were practically at random. As was suggested earlier (239) with diffuse light, inhibitory and excitatory inputs often canceled each other. Movement-sensitive neurons (about half of the sample) usually had an excitatory off-center input in or besides the movement-sensitive area. The main features of the receptive fields investigated could be simulated by a simple computer model assuming direct afferent input, whose number, type, and receptive field were experimentally determined. Some cells with large and apparently less clearly organized receptive fields were found mainly in the superficial layers. The findings may be considered to complement the analysis of neuronal output in the cat's area striata (239) by showing the input organization.

The question is not yet settled as to whether EPSPs and IPSPs can both be elicited monosynaptically from geniculate afferents or whether IPSPs have always an intracortical relay. After electrical stimulation of the optic tract or radiation, IPSPs always have a longer latency (about 1 msec) than EPSPs (242) and receptive fields of inhibitory inputs to cortical cells seem often to be different from geniculate receptive fields (238). In contrast, after diffuse electronic flashes the differences of latencies of EPSPs and IPSPs elicited in different cells were much smaller than could be accounted for by the input-output latency of the cells primarily excited by the flash (243). Direct inhibitory actions of geniculocortical fibers cannot therefore be excluded. A comparison between extracellularly recorded responses after electrical radiation stimulation and receptive-field properties of cortical neurons showed long excitatory latencies (above 10 msec) or only inhibition in complex cells, and latencies between 1.5 and 5 msec in simple cells (244). These long latencies of complex cells after electrical stimulation suggest a primary, possibly direct (i.e. monosynaptic) inhibitory input in these cells which has to be overcome by the synaptic excitation.

Cortical receptive fields and organizational principles in different animals.— In addition to earlier work on cats (220, 234, 239), receptive fields and the functional arrangement of cortical neurons were investigated in rabbits (245), in monkeys (240), and in humans (246). In cats the spatial distribution of binocular effects was further elaborated with respect to the problem of depth perception and cortical disparities (247–250).

In the *cat's visual cortex*, the optimal parameters for moving stimuli were determined (249). Optimal stimulus speeds varied widely from unit to unit (mean 4°/sec) without correlation between receptive-field size and optimal stimulus speed. Simple units with directional selectivity and only one peak of activation during passage of a stimulus through the receptive field had the most specific stimulus requirements and had nearly always zero background activity. Horizontally and vertically oriented stimuli were preferred. Complex units usually had a high level of background activity.

Receptive fields in the visual cortex of the *rabbit* (245) also showed a columnar topographical organization like those in the cat, but there was a larger variability in field size and response in cells of one column. The simplest fields were round or oval, some cells within a column seemed to have more general ("complex") stimulus properties, all were much more sensitive to moving than to stationary stimuli (with clearly circumscribed movement-sensitive areas), and the receptive fields ranged from 5°–75°. Direction specificity of movement-sensitive neurons as seen in the rabbit's retina was not seen in cortical neurons, which indicates that some of the specific information extracted from the environment by the retina may get lost in the cortex. This may be compared to the loss of color specificity in most cortical neurons of the monkey (240).

Cells in area 17 of the *macaque and spider monkey* could also be classified into simple, complex, or hypercomplex cells (240). Only a small proportion of them were color-coded, which might seem strange in view of the color organization of geniculate cells of the monkey (139), but not if the combinations of different inputs on cortical cells are considered. Also in the human visual cortex, no color sensitivity was found in the few cells so far investigated (246). The receptive fields of the monkey's striate area were smaller (simple cells, 0.25×0.25–$0.5 \times 0.75°$) than in the cat. Two different organizational principles were demonstrated: a vertical and a horizontal. At least two vertical column systems are suggested which mutually overlap, one according to receptive-field orientation, the other to eye preference (homo- or contralateral). A third vertical system may represent direction of movement sensitivity. In the different horizontal layers, cells were segregated by "hierarchical" orders: the upper layer (II and upper thirds of III) contain complex and hypercomplex cells (mostly binocularly driven) and virtually no simple cells. Simple cells, mostly monocularly driven, were found deep in layer III, and in IV A and B, the main level of termination of geniculate fibers (216). Cells without orientation specificity in these layers were difficult to distinguish from geniculate fibers. Layers V and VI contained mostly complex and hypercomplex cells, binocularly driven. The function of the visual cortex is seen in this elaboration of simple cortical fields from geniculate concentric fields, complex from simple, and hypercomplex from complex. No preference for any single field orientation was found. In psychophysical experiments in humans, certain preferred directions for the perception of lines were described (251–253), but in view of findings in animals it is premature to relate these experiments to cortical receptive fields.

A few single units were recently recorded in the *human* visual cortex (area 17 and para- and peristriate cortex) during a stereotactic operation (246). Concentric and bar-shaped excitatory receptive fields without inhibitory areas were described. Visual imagery of the objects seen previously and which had influenced the units did not influence the activity. "These cells seem to have no role in mental visual imagery." Eye closure decreased the spontaneous discharge rate of the units recorded.

In the *cat's* visual cortex, the vertical and horizontal disparities of the paired retinal images that yielded the maximum response in binocularly driven units had a horizontal range of 6.6°, and a vertical range of 2.2° (247). It was assumed that with fixed convergence different units will be optimally excited by objects lying at different distances, and that this may be a basic mechanism underlying depth discrimination in the cat. A rather smaller range of disparities ($\pm 1.2° \pm 0.6$) was found by Pettigrew et al. (248), and also Hubel & Wiesel (254) confirmed their earlier finding (239) that the receptive fields of binocular units occupied corresponding positions in the two retinas, at least to within a degree or so. It may be difficult to define exactly the center of a cortical receptive field because of the variable disparities of afferent fibers converging on one cortical cell from one eye (238). In any case, if tested with stationary stimuli (247) or with moving slits (250), facilitation or summation of binocular responses was only seen within a very narrow range of binocular superposition. When the binocular stimuli were only slightly displaced relative to each other, binocular occlusion could be demonstrated in all units (250). Also some "complex" units showed binocular specificity with a very narrow range of facilitation like simple units, while other complex units showed binocular facilitation over a wide range of prism settings.

Interhemispheric connections of the visual fields.—The connection of the visual areas of both hemispheres across the corpus callosum is restricted to the projection area of the vertical meridian at the 17/18 border (254–256). In the posterior corpus callosum, most units could be driven by visual stimuli and had simple, complex, or hypercomplex fields near the midline (254, 256). Overlap of receptive fields across the midline of bilaterally recorded cortical neurons in the 17/18 border was 0.5–1° (257) or 1–2° (254) and was still present after section of the corpus callosum (257, 259). This overlap can still be explained by the midline overlap of ganglion cells in the retina (16) and of their receptive-field size. Transcallosal visual activation of cortical units was reported after section of one optic tract (258), and disappeared after cooling of the contralateral 17/18 region (255). The findings extend anatomical observations (170, 260) and support the view (170, 255, 261) that an important function of the corpus callosum in the sensory and motor areas is to serve as a functional connection of the midline parts of the body representation.

Outside the visual area, unit responses to light were investigated in the monkey's temporal cortex (262). About one quarter of the units recorded in the middle temporal gyrus (area TE) responded to light, but no clearly defined receptive fields were found and the reactions were weak. In the superior temporal gyrus (area TA) virtually no units could be driven by visual stimuli, but about one half by auditory stimuli. These findings correspond to the effect of isolated destructions of these areas reported by other authors, which impair the performance of visual or auditory discriminations respectively. Temporal ablations do not lead to impairment of visual acuity in the monkey (263).

Conclusions.—In spite of the increasing knowledge about the anatomical and functional connections of the visual cortex, about the way in which the geniculate inputs combine on single cortical cells with the result of asymmetrical receptive fields of all possible shapes, and about the input-output organization of cortical cells, the "cortical code" is not yet understood. The frequency code of stimulus intensities is less clear, the spatial organization becomes less exact, and other retinogeniculate codes like color (240) or direction selectivity of movements at least in rabbits (250) seem to be less important for single cortical cells. The functional characteristics of complex and hypercomplex field neurons rather tend to obscure retinal organization. The hierarchical sequence of neurons of increasing complexity (240) may be one principle of cortical organization, and it suggests that more general stimulus aspects are extracted at each level. But no convincing correlations have yet been found between certain optimal stimuli of higher-order neurons and correspondent "units of perception". Therefore, the question arises as to whether the hypothesis is correct that different stimulus aspects ("invariaants") are processed in separate neuronal channels, i.e. whether different sets of neurons are made to recognize different stimulus properties like a pattern-recognizing computer. This hypothesis is often not clearly stated and only implicit in the methods of investigation and the presentation of data, but it has strongly influenced biocybernetic thinking about the nervous system. Doubts about this hypothesis have been pronounced (238), and a review of the recent literature only reinforces them.

THE SUPERIOR COLLICULI

(prepared by M. Straschill)

A short review of the tectum opticum will be included since this area is the main structure responsible for visually guided behavior in lower vertebrates and still seems to play a role for spatial orientation of higher animals. The way it processes information arising from the retina is now better understood because of extensive studies during the last years. Deficits of visual attention, pursuit-movements, and visually guided orientation following destruction of the tectum opticum (t.o.) in the cat (264) and hamster (265) demonstrate that, despite the increasing functional importance of the retinocortical system in higher vertebrates, some segments of visually guided behavior remain dependent on retinotectal mechanisms. The transformation of visual input, as performed by neurons of the tectum opticum, is an important component of these mechanisms and has been studied by several authors (266–275) in different species.

Tectal neurons of all species investigated were reported to respond optimally to luminous or dark objects moving within a limited range of speed (movement detectors). Speeds of 5–10°/sec were optimal in the rat and monkey (268). In the cat, where much higher velocities evoke a response (270), discharge rate of some units is related to velocity by a power function with exponents of 0.7 (275). In the rat, some units continued discharging when a dark object stopped moving in the receptive field (268). In the cat (269, 270, 275, 276), ground squirrel (271), and rabbit (273) many neurons responded selectively to movements in one particular direction. This preferred direction points towards the center of the visual field in the rabbit (273) and away from it in the cat (277). In the rat, directional selectivity occurs in the pretectum, but not in the tectum (268, 274). Two spot experiments (275) and other observations (270) suggest a selective unilateral inhibition to be responsible for directional selectivity. Orientation of a slit-shaped stimulus, as well as its direction of movement, was found to be critical for units of the ground squirrel (271). Response decrement with repeated stimulation was frequently observed (268, 270) and quantitatively studied (275, 278).

The frog's threshold intensity has been studied in single neurons and was found to vary within limits of 5 log units (272). Color sensitivity of the squirrel monkey's tectum opticum seemed to be indicated by differences in latency and amplitude of potentials evoked by red and green stimuli (279). The receptive-field position remained constant within one vertical penetration column (270, 277, 299) and corresponded to retinotopic projection, whose general principle of organization was found to be the same in the rat

(274), rabbit (273), and cat (242, 270, 277, 280, 299). The horizontal meridian of the visual field of the contralateral eye (or contralateral half-field) projects upon a longitudinal division line of the tectum opticum. The projection of the vertical meridian traverses the tectal surface from medial to lateral. Within the projection of the visual field, the degree of magnification varies according to retinal histology (242, 274). Receptive-field sizes were in the range of 2–15° and 30–90° in the rat (278), 4–80° in the rabbit (267, 273), 4–80° in the cat (275, 269), and 2–90° in the monkey (268).

Distribution of feline field sizes into distinct size ranges of 6–12° and 30–45° was reported (269), but not confirmed (275, 299). Receptive fields were described as uniformly organized with no systematic segregation of on- and off-areas (267, 268, 270, 275). Off- and on-off-fields predominate.

Only in the ground squirrel did some units have a central activating orientation-sensitive area flanked by antagonistic areas. They were described as resembling hypercomplex cells of nonstriate cortex (271). In the cat, inhibition can be elicited by movements from regions surrounding the receptive field (270). In addition to analysis of characteristics of the receptive fields and quality of stimuli detected, the relationship between localization and functional properties of tectal units is dealt with in a few reports.

In pigeons (281, 282) and ducks (283) a good correlation was observed between the laminar structure of the tectum opticum, the field potential profiles, and the unitary activity elicited by the electrical stimulation of the optic nerve. In the cat, directionally selective neurons with preference for upward-directed movements were located medial to the projection of the horizontal meridian of the visual field. Downward-oriented preferred direction was correlated with recording sites in the lateral half of the tectum opticum. Horizontal preferred directions pointed to the contralateral side (277).

Field size increased discontinuously [rat (268)] or continuously (cat, monkey) with increasing recording depth (268, 277, 280, 299). In the cat and rabbit, incidence of spontaneously active, directionally unselective, and monocularly driven units was high in layers near the surface and low in the depth (str.gris med. or str. gris. prof.). Below the str. opticum, most neurons were directionally selective. quickly adapting, responsive to stimulation of either eye (273, 277, 299), and activated by tactile or acoustic stimuli (277, 278). Tactile input reaches the cat's tectum opticum after relay in the visual cortex or by direct spinotectal pathways (284). In the rabbit, multimodal responses were observed even in surface layers (278). In the rabbit, movements of the visual field induced by passive or active rotation of head and body were readily signaled by neurons of the superficial layers. Neurons of str. prof. responded only when the animal was passively moved in front of a strongly patterned background, but were inhibited during active movements and arousal (285).

In addition to its retinal input, the tectum opticum receives a retinotopically organized projection from the visual cortex (242, 286). The function of these descending pathways was investigated by several authors (268, 269, 287–290), but still remains obscure and a matter of disagreement. In the cat, depression of tectal responses evoked by light or optic nerve stimulation after ablation or temporary inactivation of the visual cortex (288, 291) was interpreted as due to loss of cortical facilitatory influence. The enhancement of tectal responses after cortical strychninization (288, 291) seems to be in line with this interpretation. But in another group of experiments, ablation did not affect responses evoked in or mediated by the tectum opticum (289, 290). Since tectal responses could be depressed by cortical seizure discharges induced by cooling, an inhibitory effect of corticotectal pathways was assumed (290). Functional properties of single tectal units were not altered by neocortical ablation in the rabbit (287) and rat (268). In the cat, no change of function of single units occurred after acute neocortical ablation (269), while loss of directional selectivity and of responsiveness to either eye was observed 1–3 weeks after ablation of the visual cortex (275). The functional importance of corticotectal interactions in visually guided behavior of cats was also suggested by the effects of combined lesions of the visual cortex and the tectum opticum (292).

Despite some species differences, considerable uniformity of the results reviewed permits the following *general characterization of tectal neurons.* Tectal neurons are mainly concerned with the detection of movements in restricted parts of the visual field. Some of them signal movements of a particular direction. Novelty and speed of the moving object influence the response. Spatial information is preserved by a retinotopic projection, but lost to some extent in units of deeper layers, where pooling from large areas occurs. To a certain degree, functionally different neuronal populations are spatially separated in the tectum. In the ascending vertebrate phylogenetical scale, the main functional characteristics of the tectum opticum seem to show little alteration. But its functional significance for behavior changes considerably, the more the cortex takes over. Some of its functions may become apparent even in higher animals after the visual cortex is removed. Monkeys deprived of their visual cortex (area 17) can be trained to detect and accurately reach out for objects, especially if moving, and it is suggested that these reactions may be mediated by the tectum opticum (293). Unfortunately, nothing is known about the functional organization of units in posterior thalamic nuclei, which are known to receive a sizable input from the tectum opticum.

CONCLUSIONS

How the visual world is transformed into nervous signals, how these signals are transmitted, and how the different channels are combined at the higher levels of the central nervous system is known in principle and our knowledge has greatly increased during the last years. But since a discovery does not finish scientific search, but rather opens the way to ask more appropriate, more exact, and more exciting questions, we may expect an even more ardent scientific activity in visual physiology.

Some basic mechanisms of vision are common to all vertebrates. This explains the good correspondence between certain psychophysical observations in humans and neurophysiological data in lower animals: brightness perception, contrast phenomena, adaptation, spatial integration within the retina, and a long list of other phenomena (294) known to sensory physiologists for a long time and supplemented during the last years. But knowledge of the mechanisms of these phenomena (many of which may be only disturbing side effects or artificially produced phenomena of the visual apparatus) does not yet lead us to a real understanding of perception. This ignorance is not due to the continuing gaps in our exact knowledge of retinal mechanisms or of geniculate and cortical synaptic connections. It is rather due to the fact that the higher we go in the ascending nervous system the more obscure the "language" of the nervous system becomes.

Retinal data analysis of higher animals is easy to understand with some common sense, since it is in principle not much more than a transformation of the visual world, i.e. the spatial brightness distribution into a spatio-temporally distributed matrix of electrical signals in a large number of channels. This matrix is not a faithful replica of the physical reality, since spatial or temporal energy differences may be differentially amplified and equal energy distributions are underrated. But this transformation only enhances certain stimulus aspects, and the original picture can still be reconstructed from resulting data. However, the combination of the messages of the single retinal channels in the higher centers results in a spatio-temporal code which seems very remote from the original input. Although we already know a great deal about the synaptic mechanisms, the complexity, and even the actual wiring arrangement of such central combinations, this code is still far from being understood.

The general statement that at higher levels of the central nervous system more general aspects are extracted from the information sent by the retina is of little help, as long as we do not know the semantics of such generalizations. No correlations between any such general stimulus aspects and "units of perception" have yet been discovered. It is difficult to conceive of experiments which could demonstrate these correlations. Our method of analyzing the higher visual centers is therefore still similar to the deciphering procedure of an archeologist who finds a document written with letters which he has never seen, in a language which he does not know, and on a subject of which he has only some vague idea. He can describe the signs in terms of geometry or statistics, and can find out some formal principles. But only if he compares the document to other related findings and tries to put it into the context of its historical and cultural environment may he one day succeed in deciphering the document. Although the visual scientist may be justified in assuming that the content of his "document" is somehow related to the visual perception of physical reality, he would be naive to search for a literal correspondence between the unknown text and his own subjective perception of the outer world.

To recognize not only similarities but also dissimilarities of the visual systems of different animals will contribute much to the solution of our problem. Relating each visual system to its use by the respective animal may be an important tool in learning more about the language of the nervous system. Owing simply to different connections between receptors and ganglion cells, the frog, rat, cat, and primate retinae probably "see" differently. In lower animals, a great amount of the optical environment is already filtered out by the retina because it is irrelevant to them. Only aspects which are important (e.g. moving objects, colors, or any other single aspect of a visual stimulus) are transmitted. In primates who in their foveal visual field receive a discrete message from almost every single receptor of their retina and thus from almost every minute of arc of their optical environment, a much larger mass of information enters the brain, is available for further analysis and finally for decision making. The number of possible combinations and the degrees of freedom available for decisions at the highest level of the central nervous system offered by the frog's retina are certainly smaller than by that of the cats or the primates.

Another comparative aspect is the development of higher, more complex structures in the brain. The optic tectum, in lower animals the only nervous structure available to coordinate the behavior with the visual environment, is still present and functions in a similar manner in higher animals with a well developed cortex. But here the cortical visual areas take over most of the visual control mechanisms. Thereby the imperative power on behavior which the older system has in the lower animals is reduced. In the cortex itself, the principles of convergence of retinal channels seem to be the same in rabbits, cats, and monkeys; however, not only do larger areas of cortex develop to deal with visual information, but in addition a horizontal "hierarchy" appears to develop within each volume of cortex with more complex data convergence in the "upper" horizontal layers of the primate visual cortex. The role played by the posterior thalamus in this phylogenetic development of forebrain preponderance has not yet been investigated.

The meaning of those organizational principles is still obscure. But it is hoped that with further experience we may learn from the nervous system itself to ask the right questions to investigate it. The question should not be: "How does an animal perceive?" but rather: "Which information from the environment enters the brain? How is this information transformed into which patterns? And how do these patterns result in a coordinated output, i.e. behavior?" In this sense, a less psychological, less anthromorphic, and less digital-computer-minded way of abstract thinking may be needed in dealing with the neurophysiology of vision. And in this sense, too, we may conclude this article with a quotation from J. von Kries (295) who was a strong supporter of the idea of a *parallelism* between physiological mechanisms and psychological phenomena:

Man wird also im Auge behalten müssen, daß die Physiologie des Sehorgans und die Psychologie der Gesichtsempfindungen zwei sehr verschiedene Dinge sind, selbstverständlich nicht ohne mannigfaltige Beziehungen zueinander, aber dennoch keineswegs sich so vollständig deckend, wie man es vielfach geglaubt hat annehmen zu dürfen, und daß es daher im gegenwärtigen Stadium der Forschung unerläßlich ist, die Probleme und Tatsachen, die dem einen oder dem anderen Gebiet angehören, sorgfältig auseinanderzuhalten.

LITERATURE CITED

1. Kirschfeld, K. Die Projektion der optischen Umwelt auf das Raster der Rhabdomere im Komplexauge von Musca. *Exptl. Brain Res.*, **3**, 248–70 (1967)
2. Braitenberg, V. Patterns of projection in the visual system on the fly. I. Retina lamina projections. *Exptl. Brain Res.*, **3**, 271–98 (1967)
3. Bishop, P. O. Central nervous system: afferent mechanisms and perception. *Ann. Rev. Physiol.*, **29**, 427–84 (1967)
4. Gregory, R. L. *Eye and Brain. The Psychology of Seeing* (World Univ. Library. Weidenfeld & Nicolson, London, 1966)
5. Kabrisky, M. *A proposed model for visual information processing in the human brain* (Univ. Illinois Press, Urbana and London, 104 pp., 1966)
6. Dowling, J. E., Boycott, B. B. Organization of the primate retina: electron microscopy. *Proc. Roy. Soc. B*, **166**, 80–111 (1966)
7. Dowling, J. E., Brown, J. E. Synapses of horizontal cells in rabbit and cat retinas. *Science*, **153**, 1639–41 (1966)
8. De Testa, A. S. Morphological studies on the horizontal and amacrine cells of the teleost retina. *Vision Res.*, **6**, 51–59 (1966)
9. Gallego, A., Cruz, J. Mammalian retina: Associational nerve cells in ganglion cell layer. *Science*, **150**, 1313–14 (1965)
10. Brown, J. E. Dendritic fields of retinal ganglion cells of the rat. *J. Neurophysiol.*, **28**, 1091–1100 (1965)
11. Brown, J. E., Major, D. Cat retinal ganglion cell dendritic fields. *Exptl. Neurol.*, **15**, 70–78 (1966)
12. Leicester, J., Stone, J. Ganglion, amacrine and horizontal cells of the cat's retina. *Vision Res.*, **7**, 695–705 (1967)
13. Rodieck, R. W., Stone, J. Response of cat retinal ganglion cells to moving visual patterns. *J. Neurophysiol.*, **28**, 819–32 (1965)
14. Stone, J., Fabian, M. Specialized receptive fields of the cat's retina. *Science*, **152**, 1277–79 (1966)
15. Gallego, A., Cruz, J. Mammalian retina: associated nerve cells in ganglion cell layer. *Science*, **150**, 1313–14 (1965)
16. Stone, J. A quantitative analysis of the distribution of ganglion cells in the cat's retina. *J. Comp. Neurol.*, **124**, 337–52 (1966)
17. Laties, A. M., Sprague, J. M. The projection of optic tract fibers to the visual centers in the cat. *J. Comp. Neurol.*, **127**, 35–70 (1966)
18. Arden, G. B., Ikeda, H., Siegel, I. M. New components of the mammalian receptor potential and their relation to visual photochemistry. *Vision Res.*, **6**, 373–84 (1966)
19. Brown, K. T., Crawford, M. J. Intracellular recording of rapid light evoked responses for pigment epithelium cells in the frog eye. *Vision Res.*, **7**, 149–64 (1967)
20. Brown, K. T., Crawford, M. J. Melanin and the rapid light evoked responses from pigment epithelium cells in the frog eye. *Ibid.*, 165–78
21. Brown, K. T., Murakami, M. Delayed decay of the late receptor potential of monkey cones as a function of stimulus intensity. *Vision Res.*, **7**, 179–89 (1967)
22. Brown, K. T. The electroretinogram: its components and their origins. *Vision Res.*, **8**, 633–78 (1968)
23. Baumann, Ch. Rezeptorpotentiale der Wirbeltiernetzhaut. *Pflügers Arch.*, **282**, 92–101 (1965)

24. Fuortes, M. G. F., Yeandle, S. Probability of occurrence of discrete potential waves in the eye of Limulus. *J. Gen. Physiol.*, **47**, 443–63 (1964)

25. Tomita, T., Kaneko, A., Murakami, M., Pantler, E. L. Spectral response curves of single cones in the carp. *Vision Res.*, **7**, 519–31 (1967)

26. Kaneko, A., Hashimoto, H. Recording site of the single cone response determined by an electrode marking technique. *Vision Res.*, **7**, 847–51 (1967)

27. Marks, W. B., MacNichol, E. F., Jr. Difference spectra of single goldfish cones. *Fed. Proc.*, **22**, *Abstr. 2143* (1963)

28. Maffei, L., Poppele, R. E. Frequency analysis of the late receptor potential. *J. Neurophysiol.*, **30**, 993–99 (1967)

29. Hughes, G. W., Maffei, L. Retinal ganglion cell response to sinusoidal "light stimulation". *J. Neurophysiol.*, **29**, 333–52 (1966)

30. Cleland, B., Enroth-Cugell, C. Cat retinal ganglion cell responses to changing light intensities: sinusoidal modulation in the time domain. *Acta Physiol. Scand.*, **68**, 365–81 (1966)

31. Rackensperger, W., Grüsser, O.-J. Sinuslichtreizung der rezeptiven Felder einzelner Retinaneurone. *Experientia*, **22**, 192 (1966)

32. Reidemeister, Ch., Grüsser, O.-J. Flimmerlichtuntersuchungen an der Katzenretina. I. On-Neurone. *Z. Biol.*, **111**, 241–43 (1959)

33. Poppele, R. E., Maffei, L. Frequency analysis of the electroretinogram. *J. Neurophysiol.*, **30**, 982–92 (1967)

34. Büttner, U., Grüsser, O.-J. Quantitative Untersuchungen der räumlichen Erregungssummation im rezeptiven Feld retinaler Neurone der Katze. *Kybernetik*, **4**, 81–94 (1968)

35. Arden, G. B., Brown, K. T. Some properties of components of the cat electroretinogram revealed by local recording under oil. *J. Physiol.* (*London*), **176**, 429–61 (1965)

36. Easter, S. S. Excitation in the goldfish retina: evidence for a non-linear intensity code. *J. Physiol.* (*London*), **195**, 253–71 (1968)

37. Fuortes, M. G. F., Hodgkin, A. L. Changes in time scale and sensitivity in the ammatidia of Limulus.

J. Physiol. (*London*), **172**, 239–63 (1964)

38. Fechner, G. T. *Elemente der Psychophysik* (Breitkopf & Härtel, Leipzig, 1860)

39. Weber, E. H. *Tastsinn und Gemeingefühl* (F. Vieweg, Braunschweig, 49 pp., 1851)

40. Stevens, S. S. On the psychophysical law. *Psychol. Rev.*, **64**, 153–81 (1957)

41. Creutzfeldt, O. D., Kuhnt, U. The visual evoked potential: Physiological, developmental and clinical aspects. *Electroenceph. Clin. Neurophysiol.*, *Suppl. 26*, 29–41 (1967)

42. Kuhnt, U. Visuelle Reaktionspotentiale an Menschen und Katzen in Abhängigkeit von der Intensität. *Pflügers Arch.*, **298**, 82–104 (1967)

43. Sickel, W. Stoffwechsel und Funktion desisolierter Netzhaut. In *The Visual System: Neurophysiology and Psychophysics*, 80–94 (Jung, R., Kornhuber, H., Eds., Springer-Verlag, Berlin-Göttingen-Heidelberg, 1961)

44. Dowling, J. E. Neural and photochemical mechanisms of visual adaptation in the rat. *J. Gen. Physiol.*, **46**, 1287–1301 (1963)

45. König, A. Experimentelle Untersuchungen über die psychophysische Fundamentalformel in Bezug auf den Gesichtssinn. In *Sitzungsber. Preuss. Akad. Wiss. Berlin*, **27**, 641–44 (1889)

46. Steinhardt, J. Intensity discrimination in the human eye. *J. Gen. Physiol.*, **20**, 185–208 (1936)

47. Blackwell, H. R. Contrast thresholds of the human eye. *J. Opt. Soc. Am.*, **36**, 624–34 (1946)

48. Ogawa, T., Bishop, P. O., Levick, W. R. Temporal characteristics of responses to photic stimulation by single ganglion cells in the unopened eye of the cat. *J. Neurophysiol.*, **29**, 1–30 (1966)

49. Norton, A. L., Spekreijsje, H., Wolbarsht, M. L., Wagner, H. G. Receptive field organization of the S-potential. *Science* (In press) (1968)

50. Negishi, K. Excitation spread along horizontal and amacrine cell layers in the teleost retina. *Nature*, **218**, 39–69 (1968)

51. Witkovsky, P. A comparison of ganglion cell and S-potential response properties in carp retina. *J. Neurophysiol.*, **30**, 546–61 (1967)

52. O'Daly, J. A. ATP-ase activity of the

functional contacts between retinal cells which produce S-potential. *Nature*, **216**, 1329–31 (1967)

53. Yamanaga, E., Ishikawa, T. The fine structure of the horizontal cells in some vertebrate retina. *Cold Spring Harbor Symp. Quant. Biol.*, **30**, 383–92 (1965)

54. Naka, K. I., Rushton, W. A. H. S-potentials from colour units in the retina of fish (Cyprinidol). *J. Physiol. (London)*, **185**, 536–55 (1966)

55. Naka, K. I., Rushton, W. A. H. An attempt to analyse colour reception by electrophysiology. *Ibid.*, 556–86

56. Naka, K. I., Rushton, W. A. H. The generation and spread of S-potentials in fish. *Ibid.*, **192**, 437–61 (1967)

57. Naka, K. I., Rushton, W. A. H. S-potential and dark-adaptation in fish. *Ibid.*, **194**, 249–69 (1968)

58. Békésy, G. von, Neural inhibitory units of the eye and skin. Quantitative description of contrast phenomena. *J. Opt. Soc. Am.*, **50**, 1060–70 (1960)

59. Békésy, G. von, Machband type lateral inhibition in different sense organs. *J. Gen. Physiol.*, **50**, 510–32 (1967)

60. Wagner, H. G., MacNichol, E. F., Jr., Wolbarsht, M. L. Functional basis for "on"-center and "off"-center receptive fields in the retina. *J. Opt. Soc. Am.*, **53**, 66–70 (1963)

61. Rodieck, R. W., Stone, J. Analysis of receptive fields of cat retinal ganglion cells. *J. Neurophysiol.*, **28**, 833–49 (1965)

62. Rodieck, R. W. Quantitative analysis of cat retinal ganglion cell response to visual stimuli. *Vision Res.*, **5**, 583–601 (1965)

63. Wuttke, W., Grüsser, O.-J. Die funktionelle Organisation der rezeptiven Felder von on-Zentrum-Neuronen der Katzenretina. *Pflügers Arch.*, **289**, R83 (1966)

64. Enroth-Cugell, C., Robson, J. G. The contrast sensitivity of retinal ganglion cells of the cat. *J. Physiol.*, *(London)*, **187**, 517–52 (1966)

65. Schadé, O. H., Sr. Optical and photoelectric analog of the eye. *J. Opt. Soc. Am.*, **46**, 721–39 (1956)

66. Campbell, F. W., Robson, J. G. Application of Fourier analysis to the visibility of gratings. *J. Physiol. (London)* (In press) (1968)

67. Barlow, H. B. Summation and inhibition in the frog's retina. *J. Physiol. (London)*, **119**, 69–88 (1953)

68. Wagner, H. G., Wolbarsht, M. L. Studies on the functional organization of the vertebrate retina. *Am. J. Ophthal.*, **46**, 46–55 (1958)

69. Fuhrman, G. G. Comparison of models for subtractive and shunting lateral inhibition in receptorneuron fields. *Kybernetik*, **2**, 257–74 (1965)

70. Creutzfeldt, O. D., Sakmann, B., Scheich, H. Zusammenhang zwischen Struktur und Funktion der Retina. In *Kybernetik* (Oldenbourg, München, 1968) (In press)

71. Spinelli, D. N. Visual receptive fields in the cat's retina. "Complications". *Science*, **152**, 1768, 1769 (1966)

72. Spinelli, D. N. Receptive field organization of ganglion cells in the cat's retina. *Exptl. Neurol.*, **19**, 291–315 (1967)

73. Kuffler, S. W. Discharge patterns and functional organization of mammalian retina. *J. Neurophysiol.*, **16**, 37–68 (1953)

74. Lettvin. J. Y., Maturana, M. D., McCulloch, W. S., Pitts, W. H. What the frog's eye tells the frog's brain. *Proc. Radio Engrs. N.Y.*, **47**, 1940–51 (1959)

75. Hubel, D. H. Integrative processes in central visual pathways of the cat. *J. Opt. Soc. Am.*, **53**, 58–66 (1963)

76. Barlow, H. B., Levick, W. R., Westheimer, G. Computer-plotted receptive fields. *Science*, **154**, 920 (1966)

77. McIlwain, J. T. Receptive fields of optic tract axons and lateral geniculate cells peripheral extent and barbiturate sensitivity. *J. Neurophysiol.*, **27**, 1154–73 (1964)

78. McIlwain, J. T. Some evidence concerning the physiological basis of the periphery effect in the cat's retina. *Exptl. Brain Res.*, **1**, 265–71 (1966)

79. Rodieck, R. W. Receptive fields in the cat retina: A new type. *Science*, **157**, 90–91 (1967)

80. Jung, R., Creutzfeldt, O., Grüsser, O.-J. Die Mikrophysiologie corticaler Neurone und ihre Bedeutung

für die Sinnes- und Hirnfunktionen. *Deut. Med. Wochschr.*, **82**, 1050–59 (1957)

81. Levick, W. R. Receptive fields and trigger features of ganglion cells in the visual streak of the rabbit's retina. *J. Physiol. (London)*, **188**, 285–307 (1967)

82. Barlow, H. B., Hill, R. M., Levick, W. R. Retinal ganglion cells responding selectively to direction and speed of image motion in the rabbit. *J. Physiol. (London)*, **173**, 377–430 (1964)

83. Oyster, C. W., Barlow, H. B. Direction-selective units in rabbit retina: Distribution of preferred directions. *Science*, **155**, 841–42 (1967)

84. Michael, C. Receptive fields of single optic nerve fibres in a mammal with an all cone retina I: Contrast sensitive units. *J. Neurophysiol.*, **31**, 249–56 (1968)

85. Michael, C. Receptive fields of single optic nerve fibres in a mammal with an all cone retina II. Directionally sensitive units. *Ibid.*, 257–67

86. Michael, C. Receptive fields of single optic nerve fibres in a mammal with an all cone retina III: Opponent colour units. *Ibid.*, 283–82

87. Barlow, H. B., Levick, W. R. The mechanism of directionally selective units in rabbits retina. *J. Physiol. (London)*, **178**, 477–504 (1965)

88. Dowling, J. E. Structure and function in the all-cone retina of the ground squirrel. *The Physiological Basis for Form Discrimination Symp. Brown Univ., Providence, R.I., 1964*, 17–23

89. Gouras, P. The effects of light-adaptation on rod and cone receptive field organization of monkey ganglion cells. *J. Physiol. (London)*, **192**, 747–60 (1967)

90. Hammond, P. Spectral properties of dark-adapted retinal ganglion cells in the plaice (*Pleuronectes platessa*, L.). *J. Physiol. (London)*, **195**, 535–56 (1968)

91. Grüsser, O.-J., Grüsser-Cornehls, U. The neurophysiological basis of visual innate releasing mechanisms in frogs. *Z. Vergleich. Physiol.*, **59**, 1–24 (1968)

92. Lorenz, K. Der Kumpan in der Umwelt des Vogels. *J. Ornithol.*, **83**, 137–213, 289–413 (1935)

93. Grüsser, O.-J., Finkelstein, D., Henn, V. A quantitative analysis of movement detecting neurones in the frog's retina. *Pflüger's Arch.*, **293**, 100–6 (1967)

94. Butenandt, E., Grüsser, O.-J. The effect of stimulus area on the response of movement detecting neurones in the frogs retina. *Pflüger's Arch.*, **298**, 283–93 (1968)

95. Rushton, W. A. H. The Ferrier Lecture: Visual adaptation. *Proc. Roy. Soc. B*, **162**, 20–46 (1965)

96. Donner, K. O., Reuter, T. The effect of metarhodopsin on the sensitivity of the rhodopsin rods in the frog during dark adaptation. *Acta Physiol. Scand.*, **68**, *Suppl.277*, 40 (1966)

97. Donner, K. O., Reuter, T. Dark adaptation processes in the rhodopsin rods of the frog's retina. *Vision Res.*, **7**, 17–41 (1967)

98. Baumann, Ch. Sehpurpurbleichung und Stäbchenfunktion in der isolierten Froschnetzhaut. I. Die Sehpurpurbleichung. *Pflügers Arch.*, **298**, 44–60 (1967)

99. Baumann, Ch. Sehpurpurbleichung und Stäbchenfunktion in der isolierten Froschnetzhaut. II. Begrenzung der Stäbchenfunktion durch Helladaptation. *Ibid.*, 61–69

100. Baumann, Ch. Sehpurpurbleichung und Stäbchenfunktion in der isolierten Froschnetzhaut. III. Die Dunkeladaptation des skotopischen Systems nach partieller Sehpurpurbleichung. *Ibid.*, 70–81

101. Rushton, W. A. H. Bleached rhodopsin and visual adaptation. *J. Physiol. (London)*, **181**, 645–55 (1965)

102. Barlow, H. B. Dark adaptation: a new hypothesis. *Vision Res.*, **4**, 47–58 (1964)

103. Barlow, H. B., Sparrock, J. M. B. The role of afterimages in dark adaptation. *Science*, **144**, 1309–14 (1964)

104. Brown, K. T., Watanabe, K. Neural stage of adaptation between the receptors and inner nuclear layer of the monkey retina. *Science*, **148**, 1113–15 (1965)

105. Dowling, J. E. The site of visual adaptation. *Science*, **155**, 273–78 (1967)

106. Alpern, M., Campbell, F. W. The behaviour of the pupil during dark adaptation. *J. Physiol. (London)*, **165**, 5–6P (1962)

107. Rodieck, R. W. Maintained activity

of cat retinal ganglion cells. *J. Neurophysiol.*, **30**, 1043–71 (1967)

108. Straschill, M. Aktivität von Neuronen des Tractus opticus und corpus geniculatum laterale. *Kybernetik*, **3**, 1–8 (1966)

109. Heiss, W. D., Bornschein, H. Die Impulsverteilung der Daueraktivität von Einzelfasern des N. opticus. *Pflügers Arch.*, **286**, 1–18 (1965)

110. Brooks, B. A. Neurophysiological correlates of brightness discrimination in the lateral geniculate nucleus of the squirrel monkey. *Exptl. Brain Res.*, **2**, 1–17 (1966)

111. Heiss, W.-D. Daueraktivität retinaler Neurone unter Einwirkung von Strychnin und Pikrotoxin. *Vision Res.*, **7**, 583–98 (1967)

112. Schulz, A. Neuronale Entladungen retinaler Ganglienzellen der Katze im Dunkeln und bei diffusem Dauerlicht. *Pflügers Arch.*, **283**, R29 (1965)

113. Sakmann, B. *Daueraktivität, Inkrementalschwelle und Reiz-Reaktionskennlinien retinaler Neurone im skotopischen und mesopischen Bereich* (Inaugural dissertation, Med. Fak., München, 1968)

114. Arduini, A., Pinneo, L. R. Properties of the retina in response to steady illumination. *Arch. Ital. Biol.*, **100**, 425–48 (1962)

115. Brooks, B. A. (Personal communication); *Vision Res.* (In preparation) (1969)

116. Jung, R. Neuronale Grundlagen des Hell-Dunkelsehens und der Farbwahrnehmung. *Ber. Deut. Ophthal. Ges.*, **66**, 69–111 (1964)

117. Barlow, H. B. Coding of light intensity by the cat retina. *Proc. Intern. School of Phys. "Enrico Fermi"*, XLIII Course. Processing of optical data by organisms and by machines (1968)

118. Easter, S. S. Adaptation in the goldfish retina. *J. Physiol. (London)*, **195**, 273–81 (1968)

119. Sakmann, B., Creutzfeldt, O., Scheich, H. An experimental comparison between the ganglion cell receptive field and the receptive field of the adaptation pool in the cat retina. *Pflügers Arch.* (In press) (1968)

120. Lipetz, L. E. A mechanism of light adaptation. *Science*, **133**, 639–40 (1960)

121. Pirenne, M. H. Some aspects of the sensitivity of the eye. *Ann. N.Y. Acad. Sci.*, **74**, 377–84 (1958)

122. Rushton, W. A. H., Westheimer, G. The effect upon the rod threshold of bleaching neighbouring rods. *J. Physiol. (London)*, **164**, 318–29 (1962)

123. Barlow, H. B., Andrews, D. P. Sensitivity of receptors and receptor "pools". *J. Opt. Soc. Am.*, **57**, 837–38 (1967)

124. Westheimer, G. Spatial interaction in the human retina during scotopic vision. *J. Physiol. (London)*, **181**, 881–94 (1965)

125. Hughes, G. W., Maffei, L. On the origin of the dark discharge of retinal ganglion cells. *Arch. Ital. Biol.*, **103**, 45–59 (1965)

126. Gestri, G., Maffei, L., Petracchi, D. Spatial and temporal organization in retinal units. *Kybernetik*, **3**, 196–202 (1966)

127. Kuffler, S. W., Fitzhugh, R., Barlow, H. B. Maintained activity in the cat's retina in light and darkness. *J. Gen. Physiol.*, **40**, 683–702 (1957)

128. Herz, A., Creutzfeldt, O., Fuster, J. Statistische Eigenschaften der Neuronaktivität im ascendierenden visuellen System. *Kybernetik*, **2**, 61–71 (1964)

129. Heiss, W. D., Heilig, P., Hoyer, J. Die Aktivität von Einzelfasern des Nervus opticus bei verschiedenen Temperaturen. *Exptl. Brain Res.*, **4**, 321–29 (1968)

130. Schmidt, R., Creutzfeldt, O. Veränderungen von Spontanaktivität und Reizantwort retinaler und geniculärer Neurone der Katze bei fraktonierter Injektion von Pentobarbital-Na. *Pflügers Arch.*, **300**, 129–47 (1968)

131. Laufer, M., Verceano, M. Periodic activity in the visual system of the cat. *Vision Res.*, **7**, 215–29 (1967)

132. Gestri, G. Functional significance of the statistical properties of the retinal discharge. *Kybernetik*, **3**, 265–67 (1967)

133. ten Hoopen, M. Multimodal interval distributions. *Kybernetik*, **3**, 17–24 (1966)

134. Rodieck, R. W., Smith, P. S. Slow dark discharge rhythms of cat retinal ganglion cells. *J. Neurophysiol.*, **29**, 942–53 (1966)

135. Färber, G. Berechnung und Messung des Informationsflusses der Nervenfaser. *Kybernetik*, **5**, 17–29 (1968)

136. Spehlmann, R. Compound action potentials of cat optic nerve produced by stimulation of optic tracts and optic nerves. *Exptl. Neurol.*, **19**, 156–65 (1967)

137. Fukada, Y., Motokawa, K., Norton, A. C., Tasaki, K. Functional significance of conduction velocity in the transfer of flicker information in the optic nerve of the cat. *J. Neurophysiol.*, **29**, 698–714 (1966)

138. Donovan, A. The nerve fibre composition of the cat optic nerve. *J. Anat.*, **101**, 1–11 (1967)

139. Cohen, A. I. Ultrastructural aspects of the human optic nerve. *Invest. Ophthal.*, **6**, 294–308 (1967)

140. Spinelli, D. N., Weingarten, M. Afferent and efferent activity in single units of the cat's optic nerve. *Exptl. Neurol.*, **15**, 347–62 (1966)

141. Weingarten, M., Spinelli, D. N. Retinal receptive field changes produced by auditory and somatic stimulation. *Ibid.*, 363–76

142. Vatter, V. Das photisch evozierte Rindenpotential und die optische Sensitivität des Plataneneichhörnchens (*Sciurus notatus*). *Vision Res.*, **6**, 61–81 (1966)

143. Brindley, G. S., Hamasaki, D. I. Histological evidence against the view that the cat's optic nerve contains centrifugal fibres. *J. Physiol.*, (*London*), **184**, 444–49 (1966)

144. Ogden, T. E. On the function of efferent retinal fibres. In *Structure and function of inhibitory neuronal mechanisms*, 89–109 (Euler, C. von, Skoglund, S., Söderberg, K., Eds, Pergamon, Oxford, 1968)

145. McGill, J. I., Powell, T. P. S., Cowan, W. M. The organization of the projection of the centrifugal fibres to the retina in the pigeon. *J. Anat.*, **100**, 35–49 (1966)

146. Heiss, W. D., Milne, D. C. Single fibres of cat optic nerve: "Thresholds" to light. *Science*, **155**, 1571–72 (1967)

147. Snigula, F., Grüsser, O.-J. Vergleichende verhaltensphysiologische und neurophysiologische Untersuchungen am visuellen System von Katzen. I. Die simultane Helligkeitsschwelle. *Psychol. Forsch.*, **32**, 14–42 (1968)

148. Grüsser, O.-J., Snigula, F. Vergleichende verhaltensphysiologische und neurophysiologische Untersuchungen am visuellen System von Katzen. II. Simultankontrast. *Ibid.*, 43–63

149. Straschill, M. Action of drugs on single neurons in the cat's retina. *Vision Res.*, **8**, 35–48 (1968)

150. Bornschein, H., Heiss, W. D. Strychnine resistant inhibition in the retina. *Experientia*, **22**, 49 (1966)

151. Creutzfeldt, O. Contribution to the discussion. In *Structure and function of inhibitory neuronal mechanisms*, 213–14 (Euler, C. von, Skoglund, S., Söderberg, K., Eds., Pergamon, Oxford, 1968)

152. Heiss, W. D., Heilig, P., Hoyer, J. Retinale Impulsaktivität und Elektroretinogramm unter dem Einfluss von Desipramin. *Experientia*, **23**, 728 (1967)

153. Szentagothai, J. The structure of the synapse in the lateral geniculate body. *Acta Anat.*, **55**, 166–85 (1963)

154. Szentagothai, J., Hamori, J., Tömböl, T. Degeneration and electron microscope analysis of the synaptic glomeruli in the geniculate body. *Exptl. Brain Res.*, **2**, 283–301 (1966)

155. Peters, A., Palay, S. L. The morphology of lamina A and A_1 of the dorsal nucleus of the lateral geniculate body of the cat. *J. Anat.*, **100**, 451–86 (1966)

156. Hamori, J. Presynaptic-to-presynaptic axon contacts under experimental conditions giving rise to rearrangement of synaptic structures. *Structure and function of inhibitory neuronal mechanisms* (Euler, C. von, et al., Eds., Pergamon, Oxford, 1968)

157. Szentagothai, J. Synaptic structure and concept of presynaptic inhibition. In *Structure and function of inhibitory neuronal mechanisms*, 15–31 (Euler, C. von, Skoglund, S., Söderberg, K., Eds., Pergamon, Oxford, 1968)

158. Guillery, R. W. A study of Golgi preparations from the dorsal lateral geniculate nucleus of the adult cat. *J. Comp. Neurol.*, **128**, 21–50 (1966)

159. Stone, J., Hansen, S. M. The projection of the cat's retina on the lateral geniculate nucleus. *J. Comp. Neurol.*, **126**, 601–24 (1966)

160. Colonnier, M., Guillery, R. W. Synaptic organization in the lateral geniculate nucleus of the monkey. *Z. Zellforsch.*, **62**, 333–55 (1964)

161. Guillery, R. W. Patterns of fibre degeneration in the dorsal lateral

geniculate nucleus of the cat following lesions in the visual cortex. *J. Comp. Neurol.*, **130**, 197–222 (1967)

162. Szentagothai, J. The anatomy of complex integrative units in the nervous system. In *Results in Neuroanatomy, Neurochemistry, Neuropharmacology and Neurophysiology* (Lissak, K., Ed., Akad. Kaido, Budapest, 1967)

163. Bishop, P. O., Kozak, W., Levick, W. R., Vakkur, G. J. The determination of the projection of the visual field onto the lateral geniculate nucleus in the cat. *J. Physiol. (London)*, **163**, 503–39 (1962)

164. Glickstein, M. Laminar structure of the dorsal lateral geniculate nucleus in the tree shrew (*Tuysaia glis*). *J. Comp. Neurol.*, **131**, 93–102 (1967)

165. Hayhow, W. R. The lateral geniculate nucleus of the marsupial phalanger, *Trichosurus vulpecula*. *J. Comp. Neurol.*, **131**, 571–604 (1961)

166. Jones, A. E. The lateral geniculate complex of the owl monkey *Aotes trivirgatus*. *J. Comp. Neurol.*, **126**, 171–180 (1966)

167. Campos-Ortega, J. A., Glees, P. The termination of ipsilateral and contralateral optic fibres in the lateral geniculate body of *Galago crassicaudatus*. *J. Comp. Neurol.*, **129**, 279–84 (1967)

168. Doty, R. W., Glickstein, M., Calvin, W. H. Lamination of the lateral geniculate nucleus in the squirrel monkey, *Saimiri sciureus*. *J. Comp. Neurol.*, **127**, 335–40 (1966)

169. Garey, L. J., Powell, T. P. S. The projection of the lateral geniculate nucleus upon the cortex in the cat. *Proc. Roy. Soc. B*, **169**, 107–26 (1968)

170. Garey, L. J., Jones, E. G., Powell, T. P. S. Interrelationships of striate and extrastriate cortex with the primary relay sites of the visual pathway. *J. Neurol. Neurosurg. Psychiat.*, **31**, 135–57 (1968)

171. Karlsson, U. Three dimensional studies of neurons in the lateral geniculate nucleus of the rat. II. Environment of perikarya and proximal parts of their branches. *J. Ultrastruct. Res.*, **16**, 482–504 (1966)

172. Bishop, P. O. The neural organization of the visual pathways in the cat. *Progr. Neurobiol.*, **6**, 149–84 (1964)

173. Fuster, J. M., Creutzfeldt, O., Straschill, M. Intracellular recording of neuronal activity in the visual system. *Z. Vergleich. Physiol.*, **49**, 605–22 (1965)

174. McIlwain, J. T., Creutzfeldt, O. Microelectrode study of synaptic excitation and inhibition in the lateral geniculate nucleus of the cat. *J. Neurophysiol.*, **30**, 1–22 (1967)

175. Creutzfeldt, O. Functional synaptic organization in the lateral geniculate body and its implication for information transmission. In *Structure and function of inhibitory neuronal mechanisms*, 117–22 (Euler, C. von, Skoglund, S., Söderberg, V., Eds., Pergamon, Oxford, 1968)

176. Creutzfeldt, O., Fuster, J. M., Herz, A., Straschill, M. Some problems of information transmission in the visual system. In *Brain and Conscious Experience*, 138–64 (Eccles, J. C., Ed., Springer Verlag, New York, 1964)

177. Burke, W., Sefton, A. J. Discharge patterns of principal cells and interneurones in lateral geniculate nucleus of rat. *J. Physiol. (London)*, **187**, 201–12 (1966)

178. Burke, W., Sefton, A. J., Recovery of responsiveness of cells of lateral geniculate nucleus of rat. *Ibid.*, 213–29

179. Burke, W., Sefton, A. J., Inhibitory mechanisms in lateral geniculate nucleus of rat. *Ibid.*, 231–46

180. Suzuki, H., Kato, E. Binocular interaction at cat's lateral geniculate body. *J. Neurophysiol.*, **29**, 909–20 (1966)

181. Bishop, P. O., Burke, W., Davis, R. The identification of single units in central visual pathways. *J. Physiol. (London)*, **162**, 409–31 (1962)

182. Phillis, J. W., Tebécis, A. K., York, D. H. A study of cholinoceptive cells in the lateral geniculate nucleus. *J. Physiol. (London)*, **192**, 695–713 (1967)

183. Kahn, N., Magni, F., Pillari, R. V. Depolarization of optic fibre endings in the lateral geniculate body. *Arch. Ital. Biol.*, **105**, 573–82 (1967)

184. Angel, A., Magni, F., Strata, P. Evidence for presynaptic inhibition in the lateral geniculate body. *Nature*, **208**, 495–96 (1965)

185. Iwama, K., Sakakura, H., Kasamatsu, T. Presynaptic inhibition in pri-

mate lateral geniculate body induced by stimulation of the cerebral cortex. *Japan. J. Physiol.*, **15**,
310–22 (1965)

186. Suzuki, H., Kato, E. Cortically induced presynaptic inhibition in
cat's geniculate body. *Tohoku J.
Exptl. Med.*, **86**, 277–89 (1965)

187. Pecci-Saevedra, J., Wilson, P. Presynaptic inhibition in the lateral
geniculate body induced by stimulation of the cerebral cortex. *Nature*, **210**, 740–42 (1965)

188. Angel, A., Magni, F., Strata, P. Excitability of intrageniculate optic
tract fibres after reticular stimulation in the mid-pontine pretrige-
minal cat. *Arch. Ital. Biol.*. **103**,
668–93 (1965)

189. Angel, A., Magni, F., Strata, P. The
excitability of optic nerve terminals
in the lateral geniculate nucleus
after stimulation of visual cortex.
Ibid., **105**, 104–17 (1967)

190. Iwama, K., Kawamoto, T., Sakakura,
H., Kasamatsu, T. Responsiveness
of cat lateral geniculate at pre- and
postsynaptic levels during natural
sleep. *Physiol. Behav.*, **1**, 45–53
(1966)

191. Bizzi, E. Discharge patterns of single
geniculate neurones during the
rapid eye movements of sleep. *J.
Neurophysiol.*, **29**, 1087–95 (1966)

192. Hubel, D. H. Single unit activity in
lateral geniculate body and optic
tract of unrestrained cats. *J.
Physiol. (London)*, **155**, 383–98
(1961)

193. Wiesel, T. N., Hubel, D. H. Spatial
and chromatic interactions in the
lateral geniculate body of the
Rhesus monkey. *J. Neurophysiol.*,
29, 1115–56 (1966)

194. Arduini, A., Cavaggioni, A. Tranmis-
sion of tonic activity through lateral geniculate body and visual
cortex. *Arch. Ital. Biol.*, **103**, 652–67
(1965)

195. Maffei, L., Rizzolatti, G. Transfer
properties of the lateral geniculate
body. *J. Neurophysiol.*, **30**, 333–40
(1967)

196. Maffei, L. Spatial and temporal
averages in retinal channels. *J.
Neurophysiol.*, **31**, 283–87 (1968)

197. Arden, G. B., Söderberg, U. The
transfer of optic information through
the lateral geniculate body of the
rabbit. In *Sensory Communication*,

521–44 (M.I.T. Press, Cambridge,
Mass, 1961)

198. Arduini, A. Specific and non-specific
activities in the central visual pathways. *Ateneo Parmense Acta Bio-
med.*, **39**, 1–16 (1968)

199. Widén, L., Ajmone-Marsan, C. Effects of corticopetal and corticofugal impulses upon single elements of the dorsolateral geniculate nucleus. *Exptl. Neurol.*, **2**,
468–502 (1960)

200. Lindsley, D., Chow, K. L., Gollender,
M. Dichoptic interactions of lateral
geniculate neurones of cats to contralateral and ipsilateral eye stimulation. *J. Neurophysiol.*, **30**, 629–
44 (1967)

201. Freund, H. D., Lauff, D., Grüne-
wald, G. Binoculare Interaktion im
geniculatum laterale der Katze.
Pflügers Arch., **297**, R85

202. Sakakura, H., Iwama, K. Effects of
bilateral eye enucleation upon
single unit activity of the lateral
geniculate body in free behaving
cats. *Brain Res.*, **6**, 667–78 (1967)

203. Maffei, L., Moruzzi, G., Rizzolatti, G.
Influence of sleep and wakefulness
on the response of lateral geniculate
units to sinewave photic stimulation. *Arch. Ital. Biol.*, **103**, 596–
608 (1965)

204. Thomas, J., Groves, P., Verzeano, M.
The activity of neurons in the
lateral geniculate body during
wakefulness and sleep. *Experientia*,
24, 360–62 (1968)

205. Naquet, R., Lanoir, J., Bach-y-Rita,
P., Saier, J., Rhodes, J. M. Induction par les mouvements ocu-
laires de réponses evoquées dans les
voies visuelles. In *Mechanism of
orienting reaction in man*, 101–14
(Ruttkay-Edecky, I. and colleagues, Eds., Publ. House Slovak
Acad. Scie., Bratislava, 1967)

206. Richards, W. Spatial remapping in
the primate vusual system. *Kybernetik*, **4**, 146–56 (1968)

207. Bizzi, E. Changes in the orthodromic
and antidromic response of optic
tract during the eye movements of
sleep. *J. Neurophysiol.*, **29**, 861–70
(1966)

208. Kawamura, H., Marchiafava, P. L.
Modulation of transmission of optic
nerve impulses in the alert cat.
Brain Res., **2**, 213–15 (1966)

209. De Valois, R. L., Abramov, I., Mead,
W. R. Single cell analysis of wave-

length discrimination at the lateral geniculate nucleus in the macaque. *J. Neurophysiol.*, **30**, 415–33 (1967)

210. Jones, A. E. Wavelength and intensity effects on the response of single lateral geniculate nucleus units in the owl monkey. *J. Neurophysiol.*, 125–38 (1966)

211. De Valois, R. L., Abramov, I., Jacobs, G. H. Analysis of response patterns of LGN cells. *J. Opt. Soc. Am.*, **56**, 966–77 (1966)

212. Clark, W. E. L. Anatomical basis of colour vision. *Nature*, **146**, 558–59 (1940)

213. Walls, G. L. The lateral geniculate nucleus and visual histophysiology. *Univ. Calif. Publ. Physiol.*, **9**, 1–100 (1953)

214. Otsuka, R., Hassler, R. Ueber Aufbau und Gliederung der corticalen Sehsphäre bei der Katze. *Arch. Psychiat. Nervenkr.*, **203**, 212–34 (1962)

215. Glickstein, M., King, R. A., Miller, J., Berkley, M. Cortical projections from the dorsal lateral geniculate nucleus of cats. *J. Comp. Neurol.*, **130**, 55–76 (1967)

216. Wilson, M. E., Cragg, B. G. Projections from the lateral geniculate nucleus in the cat and monkey. *J. Anat.*, **101**, 677–92 (1967)

217. Weiskrantz, L., Cowey, A. Striate cortex lesions and visual acuity of the Rhesus monkey. *J. Comp. Physiol. Psychol.*, **56**, 225–21 (1963)

218. Doty, R. W. Potentials evoked in cat cerebral cortex by diffuse and by punctiform photic stimuli. *J. Neurophysiol.*, **21**, 437–64 (1958)

219. Talbot, S. A., Marshall, W. H. Physiological studies on neural mechanisms of visual localization and discrimination. *Am. J. Ophthal.*, **24**, 1255–63 (1941)

220. Hubel, D. H., Wiesel, T. N. Receptive fields and functional architecture in two nonstriate visual areas (18 and 19) of the cat. *J. Neurophysiol.*, **28**, 229–89 (1965)

221. Bilge, M., Bingle, A., Seneviratne, K. N., Whitteridge, D. A map of the visual cortex in the cat. *J. Physiol. (London)*, **191**, 116–18 (1967)

222. Buser, P., Borenstein, P., Brunner, J. Étude des systèmes associatifs visuels et auditifs chez le chat anésthesié en chloralose. *Electro-*

enceph. Clin. Neurophysiol., **11**, 305–24 (1959)

223. Bignall, K. E. M., Imbert, M., Buser, P. Optic projections to non-visual cortex of the cat. *J. Neurophysiol.*, **29**, 396–409 (1966)

224. Garey, L. J., Jones, E. G. Powell, T. P. S. Interrelationships of striate and extrastriate cortex with the primary relay sites of the visual pathway. *J. Neurol. Neurosurg. Psychiat.*, **31**, 135–57 (1968)

225. Bizzi, E. Discharge of frontal eye field neurones during saccadic and following eye movements in unanesthetized monkeys. *Exptl. Brain Res.*, **6**, 69–80 (1968)

226. Globus, A., Scheibel, A. B. Synaptic loci on visual cortical neurones of the rabbit: the specific afferent radiation. *Exptl. Neurol.*, **18**, 116–31 (1967)

227. Globus, A., Scheibel, A. B. Synaptic loci on parietal cortical neurones. Terminations of corpus callosum fibres. *Science*, **156**, 1127–29 (1967b)

228. Valverde, F. Structural changes in the area striata of the mouse after enucleation. *Exptl. Brain Res.*, **5**, 274–93 (1968)

229. Valverde, F. Apical dendritic spines of the visual cortex and light deprivation in the mouse. *Ibid.*, **3**, 337–52 (1967)

230. Globus, A., Scheibel, A. B. The effect of visual deprivation on cortical neurones: A Golgi study. *Exptl. Neurol.*, **19**, 331–45 (1967)

231. Cragg, B. G. The density of synapses and neurones in the motor and visual areas of the cerebral cortex. *J. Anat.*, **101**, 639–54 1967)

232. Colonnier, M. Synaptic patterns on different cell types in the different laminae of the cat visual cortex. An electron microscope study. *Brain Res.*, **9**, 268–87 (1968)

233. Mountcastle, V. B. Modalities and topographic properties of single neurones of the cat's sensory cortex. *J. Neurophysiol.*, **20**, 408–35 (1957)

234. Hubel, D. H., Wiesel, T. N. Shape and arrangement of columns in the cat's striate cortex. *J. Physiol. (London)*, **165**, 559–68 1963)

235. Colonnier, M. The tangential organization of the visual cortex. *J. Anat.*, **98**, 327–44 (1964)

236. Colonnier, M. The structural design after neocortex. In *Brain and con-*

scious experience, 1–33 (Eccles, J. C., Ed., Springer-Verlag, New York, 1966)

237. Colonnier, M. The fine structural arrangement of the cortex. *Arch. Neurol.*, 16, 651–57 (1967)

238. Creutzfeldt, O., Ito, M., Functional synaptic organization of primary visual cortex neurones in the cat. *Exptl. Brain Res.*, 6, 324–52 (1968)

239. Hubel, D. H., Wiesel, T. N. Receptive fields, binocular interaction and functional architecture in the cat's visual cortex. *J. Physiol. (London)*, 160, 106–54 (1962)

240. Hubel, D. H., Wiesel, T. N. Receptive fields and functional architecture of monkey striate cortex. *Ibid.*, 195, 215–44 (1968)

241. Globus, A., Scheibel, A. B. Pattern and field in cortical structure: The rabbit. *J. Comp. Neurol.*, 131, 155–72 (1967)

242. Watanabe, S., Konishi, M., Creutzfeldt, O. Postsynaptic potentials in the cat's visual cortex following electrical stimulation of afferent pathways. *Exptl. Brain Res.*, 1, 272–83 (1966)

243. Creutzfeldt, O., Rosina, A., Ito, M., Probst, W. The visual evoked response of single cells and the EEG in the primary visual area of the cat. *J. Neurophysiol.*, 32, (In press) (1969)

244. Denney, D., Baumgartner, G., Adorjani, C. Response of cortical neurones to stimulation of the visual afferent radiations. *Exptl. Brain Res.*, 6 (In press) (1968)

245. Arden, G. B., Ikeda, H., Hill, R. M. Rabbit visual cortex: Reaction of cells to movement and contrast. *Nature*, 214, 909–12 (1967)

246. Marg, E., Adams, J. E. Rutkin, B. Receptive fields of cells in the human visual cortex. *Experientia*, 24, 348–50 (1968)

247. Barlow, H. B., Blakemore, C., Pettigrew, I. D. The neural mechanism of binocular depth discrimination. *J. Physiol. (London)*, 193, 327–42 (1967)

248. Nikara, T., Bishop, P. O., Pettigrew, I. D. Analysis of retinal correspondence by studying receptive fields of binocular single units in cat striate cortex. *Exptl. Brain Res.*, 6, 353–72 (1968)

249. Pettigrew, I. D., Nikara, T., Bishop, P. O. Responses to moving slits by single units in cat striate cortex. *Ibid.*, 373–90

250. Pettigrew, I. D., Nikara, T., Bishop, P. O. Binocular interaction on single units in cat striate cortex: simultaneous stimulation by single moving slit with receptive fields in correspondence. *Ibid.*, 391–410

251. Campbell, F. W., Kulikowski, J. J. Orientational selectivity of the human visual system. *J. Physiol. (London)*, 187, 437–45 (1966)

252. Andrews, D. P. Perception of contour orientation in the central fovea. Part I: Short lines. *Vision Res.*, 7, 975–97 (1967)

253. Andrews, D. P. Perception of contour orientation in the central fovea. Part II: Spatial integration. *Ibid.*, 999–1013

254. Hubel, D. H., Wiesel, T. W. Cortical and callosal connections concerned with the vertical meridian of visual field in the cat. *J. Neurophysiol.*, 30, 1561–73 (1967)

255. Choudhury, B. P., Whitteridge, D., Wilson, M. E. The function of the callosal connections of the visual cortex. *Quart. J. Exptl. Physiol.*, 50, 214–19 (1965)

256. Berlucchi, G., Gazzaniga, M. S., Rizzolatti, G. Microelectrode analysis of transfer of visual information by the corpus callosum. *Arch. Ital. Biol.*, 105, 583–96 (1967)

257. Leicester, J. Projection of the visual vertical meridian to cerebral cortex of the cat. *J. Neurophysiol.*, 31, 371–82 (1968)

258. Vesbaesya, C., Whitteridge, D., Wilson, M. E. Callosal connexions of the cortex representing the area centralis. *J. Physiol. (London)*, 191, 79–80P (1967)

259. Berlucchi, G., Rizzolatti, G. Binocularly driven neurones in visual cortex of split-chiasm cats. *Science*, 159, 308–10 (1968)

260. Ebner, F. F., Myers, R. E. Distribution of corpus callosum and anterior commissure in cat and raccoon. *J. Comp. Neurol.*, 124, 353–66 (1965)

261. Jones, E. G. Pattern of cortical and thalamic connections of the somatic sensory cortex. *Nature*, 216, 704–5 (1967)

262. Gross, C. G., Schiller, P. H., Wells, C., Gerstein, G. L. Single unit activity in temporal association cortex of

the monkey. *J. Neurophysiol.*, **30**, 833–43 (1967)

263. Cowey, A., Weiskrantz, L. A comparison of the effects of inferotemporal and striate cortex lesions on the visual behaviour of Rhesus monkeys. *Quart. J. Exptl. Psychol.*, **19**, 246–53 (1967)

264. Sprague, J. M., Meikle, T. H. The role of the superior colliculus in visually guided behaviour. *Exptl. Neurol.*, **11**, 115–46 (1965)

265. Schneider, G. E. Contrasting visuomotor functions of tectum and cortex in the golden hamster. *Psychol. Forsch.*, **31**, 52–62 (1967)

266. Gaze, R. M., Keating, M. J. Visual responses from ipsilateral tectal units in the frog. *J. Physiol. (London)*, **190**, 52P (1966)

267. Hill, R. M. Receptive field properties of the superior colliculus of the rabbit. *Nature*, **211**, 1407–9 (1966)

268. Humphrey, N. K. Responses to visual stimuli of units in the superior colliculus of rats and monkeys. *Exptl. Neurol.*, **20**, 312–40 (1968)

269. Marchiafava, P. L., Pepeu, G. The responses of units in the superior colliculus of the cat to a moving visual stimulus. *Experientia*, **22**, 51–53 (1966)

270. McIlwain, J. T., Buser, P. Receptive fields of single cells in the cat's superior colliculus. *Exptl. Brain Res.*, **5**, Fasc. 4 (1968)

271. Michael, C. R. Integration of visual information in the superior colliculus. *J. Gen. Physiol.*, **50**, 2584–86 (1967)

272. Mkrticheva, L. I., Samsonova, V. G. Sensitivity of neurones of the frog's tectum to changes in the intensity of light stimulus. *Vision Res.*, **6**, 419–26 (1966)

273. Schaefer, K. P. Mikroableitungen im Tectum opticum des frei beweglichen Kaninchens. *Arch. Psychiat. Nervenkr.*, **208**, 120–46 (1966)

274. Siminoff, R., Schwassmann, H. O., Krüger, L. An electrophysiological study of the visual projection to the superior colliculus of the rat. *J. Comp. Neurol.*, **127**, 435–44 (1966)

275. Straschill, M., Taghavy, A. Neuronale Reaktionen im tectum opticum der Katze auf bewegte und stationäre Lichtreize. *Exptl. Brain Res.*, **3**, 353–67 (1967)

276. Wickelgren, B., Sterling, P. Receptive fields in cat superior colliculus. *Physiologist*, **10**, 244 (1967)

277. Straschill, M., Hoffmann, K. P. Relationship between localization and functional properties of movement-sensitive neurones of the cat's tectum opticum. *Brain Res.*, **8**, 382–85 (1968)

278. Horn, G., Hill, R. M. Responsiveness to sensory stimulation of units in the superior colliculus and subjacent tectotegmental regions of the rabbit. *Exptl. Neurol.*, **14**, 199–223 (1966)

279. Wolin, L. R., Massopust, P., Jr., Meder, J. Differential color responses from the superior colliculi of squirrel monkeys. *Vision Res.*, **6**, 637–44 (1966)

280. Hoffmann, K.-P. *Position und Struktur der rezeptiven Felder im Tectum opticum der Katze* (Inaugural dissertation, Naturwiss. Fak., München, 1969)

281. Holden, A. L. The field potential profile during activation of the avian optic tectum. *J. Physiol. (London)*, **194**, 75–90 (1968)

282. Holden, A. L. Types of unitary response and correlation with the field potential profile during activation of the avian optic tectum. *Ibid.*, 91–104

283. O'Flaherty, J. J. The optic tectum of the duck (*Anas platyrhynchos* and *Cairina moschata*). I. A descriptive and experimental anatomical study. II. An analysis of responses to stimulation of the contralateral optic nerve and stratum album centrale. *J. Exptl. Neurol.* (In press) (1969)

284. Jassik-Gerschenfeld, D. Activity of somatic origin evoked in the superior colliculus of the cat. *Exptl. Neurol.*, **16**, 104–18 (1966)

285. Schaefer, K. P. Neuronale Entladungsmuster im Tectum opticum des Kaninchens bei passiven und aktiven Eigenbewegungen. *Arch. Psychiat. Nervenkr.*, **209**, 101–26 (1967)

286. Giolli, R. A., Guthrie, M. B. Organization of projection of visual areas I and II upon the superior colliculus and pretectal nuclei in the rabbit. *Brain Res.*, **6**, 388–90 (1967)

287. Horn, G., Hill, R. M. Effect of removing the neocortex on the response to repeated sensory stimula-

tion of neurones in the midbrain. *Nature*, **211**, 754–55 (1966)

288. Jassik-Gerschenfeld, D., Ascher, P., Guevara, J. A. Influence of the geniculo-cortical system on visual responses of the superior colliculus. *Arch. Ital. Biol.*, **114**, 30–49 (1966)

289. Marchiafava, P. L., Pepeu, G. C. Electrophysiological study of tectal response to optic nerve volley. *Arch. Ital. Biol.*, **104**, 406–20 (1966)

290. Marchiafava, P. L., Rizzolatti, G., Sprague, J. M. Studies on cortico-tectal activity in the unanesthetized mid-pontine cat. *Arch. Ital. Biol.*, **106**, 21–41 (1968)

291. Meulders, M., Colle, J. Influence du cortex visuel sur l'activité évoquée dans les voies optiques souscorticales. *Electroenceph. Clin. Neurophysiol.*, **20**, 475–84 (1966)

292. Sprague, J. M. Interaction of cortex and superior colliculus in mediation of visually guided behaviour in the cat. *Science*, **152**, 1544–47 (1966)

293. Humphrey, N. K., Weiskrantz, L. Vision in monkeys after removal of the striate cortex. *Nature*, **215**, 595–97 (1967)

294. Jung, R. Neurophysiologie und Psychiatrie. In Gruhle, H. W., Jung, R., Mayer-Gross, W., Müller, M., Eds. *Psychiatrie der Gegenwart*, I/1A, 325–928 (Springer-Verlag, Berlin-Göttingen-Heidelberg, 1967)

295. von Kries, J. Die Gesichtsempfindungen. In Nagel, W., Ed. *Handbuch der Physiologie des Menschen*, **III**, 109–282 (Physiologie der Sinne. Friedrich Vieweg & Sohn, Braunschweig, 1904)

296. Stone, J., Fabian, M. Summing properties of the cat's retinal ganglion cell. *Vision Res.*, **8**, 1023–40 (1968)

297. Cleland, B. G., Enroth-Cugell, C. Quantitative aspects of sensitivity and summation in the cat retina. *J. Physiol. (London)*, **198**, 17–38 (1968)

298. Brown, K. T., Wiesel, T. N. Intraretinal recording with micropipette electrodes in the intact cat eye. *J. Physiol. (London)*, **149**, 537–62 (1959)

299. Straschill, M., Hoffmann, K. P. Functional aspects of localization in the cat's tectum opticum. *Brain Res.* (In press) (1969)

COMPARATIVE PHYSIOLOGY OF HEARING[1]

By Alan D. Grinnell

Department of Zoology, University of California, Los Angeles
Los Angeles, California

The aim of comparative auditory physiology is an understanding both of basic mechanisms and their evolution and of the adaptations of particular animals for special uses of sound. This review will, I hope, reflect both interests. In most instances, I have concentrated on studies of the past three years, building upon the excellent reviews of Katsuki (110), Wever (232), and Schwartzkopff (194). The current literature in the field is immense. I have purposely neglected large areas of research, including all references to studies of human audition, and no doubt accidentally neglected many others. The result perforce reflects the bias of my own interest.

Peripheral Structure and Function

External ear.—Little is known about the role of external ear structures. In many animals, especially nocturnal ones, the external ears are relatively immense and freely movable to be directed toward a point of interest. The pinnae clearly function as sound collectors, increasing absolute sensitivity by as much as 10–15 dB in cats (54). By creating turbulence in the airflow around the ear, they also prevent "closed-pipe" resonance in the external meatus (40). The importance of the external ears to normal behavior is best seen, however, in animals with highly developed capabilities for acoustic localization. Normal external ear structure and position are critical to obstacle avoidance by the long-eared bat *Plecotus* (73). Another genus, *Rhinolophus*, has been shown to move one pinna forward, the other backward, in synchrony with emitted orientation pulses, presumably to better utilize the information (perhaps Doppler shift) in returning echoes (75, 169).

Further study of the role of external ear structures in bats has shown that the pinna and tragus impose a complicated and sharply directional pattern of sensitivity on each ear, which shifts in position when these structures are moved (83). Although the pinna does increase sensitivity by 10–15 dB to sounds coming from most effective angles, a more important function of the pinna and tragus is the reduction of sensitivity at other angles, sharpening directional reception, especially at high frequencies, in a way that is postulated to aid importantly in target localization.

An interesting problem arises in aquatic mammals, which have good hearing but whose external ears, being of no function in a medium of essentially

[1] The survey of literature for this review was concluded in May 1968.

the same refractive index as flesh, have been lost. Recent experiments on dolphins (7) appear to confirm the hypothesis of Norris (151, 152) that sound energy is picked up principally in the lower jaws and transmitted through fat bodies inside the jaw to the bulla on each side, against which the fat body abuts. Air spaces surrounding the bulla elsewhere isolate it from sound arriving through other pathways.

Middle ear.—A voluminous literature is devoted to middle ear function, particularly the impedance-matching properties of the middle ear ossicles of mammals. Transformation ratios, but very little more, are known for the simple one or two ossicle couplings of submammalian vertebrates. As Gaudin (64) has shown for the pigeon columella, however, the simpler structures need not be less effective. The pigeon ossicle rotates around a point on its attachment at the round window, achieving an unexpectedly high degree of leverage.

Tonndorf & Khanna (217), using a stimulus of known displacement and recording microphonics at the round window, conclude that at a cat's threshold of hearing, displacement of the malleus is 10^{-10} cm at 1 kc, 10^{-11} cm at 5 kc. The annular ligament of the stapes acts as a low-frequency attenuator, filtering out frequencies lower than 600 cycles at a slope of 12 dB/octave. Guinan & Peake (86), measuring ossicular movement with stroboscopic illumination, found that at frequencies below 3 kc/sec at sound pressure levels up to 140–150 dB, the ossicular chain moves as a rigid body. At higher frequencies, however, the stapes and incus lag behind the malleus, by 180° at 5 kc. Apparently there is flexion at the joint between malleus and incus. The amplitude of ossicular movement is a linear function of intensity to 130 dB or higher.

The quality of the impedance match achieved by the middle ear is a function also of the size of the air-filled cavity and the nature of the gas inside. Replacing the air of a cat's middle ear with xenon shifts downward the resonant frequency of the system, while replacement with helium has the opposite effect (218). Webster (226) has postulated that the extraordinary volume of the auditory bulla of kangaroo rats may serve to decrease the damping of movement of the tympanic membranes and ossicles, thereby increasing the sensitivity at low frequencies. Kangaroo rats also have an unusually large tympanic membrane and malleus, and an unusually small stapes, however. The resulting transformation ratio (approximately 100:1) is perhaps a more important adaptation for achieving high absolute sensitivity.

The role of the middle ear muscles in normal function has been a subject of increasing attention. In addition to protective reflex contraction to loud sounds, especially at low frequencies, contraction accompanies vocalization and a wide spectrum of body movements (15, 187). Moreover, even low-intensity stimuli can initiate the "reflex", and prior experience and states of sleep and wakefulness can strongly affect the magnitude or sensitivity of the response, which indicates that there are important central controls

(15, 196). Simmons (196), in particular, has emphasized the potential of the middle ear muscles beyond simple protection: for example, the avoidance of resonance in the middle ear, or the maintenance of attention and sensitivity. The contractions coinciding with vocalization and body movement are of obvious value in reducing sensitivity to sounds generated internally. The latter function is most beautifully illustrated in certain bats, where Henson (92) has shown that contraction of the middle ear muscles normally begins a few milliseconds before emission of an orientation cry, and ends just at the end of the pulse, effectively reducing sensitivity by up to 20 dB during the emitted sound but not during the period after each pulse when the bat must be sensitive to returning echoes.

COCHLEAR FUNCTION

Structure.—Phase microscopy, histochemical techniques, and electron microscopy have greatly increased our understanding of structure-function relationships in the cochlea. Four recent books by notable contributors in the field summarize many of these recent findings and their implications (35, 101, 171, 200). Most obviously important is the elucidation of the fine-structural organization and polarization of kinocilium and stereocilia on each hair cell, a feature common to all vertebrate hair cells except those in the cochlea, which lose the kinocilium during development but retain a basal body in the same polarized position (see 49–51, 53, 101, 229 and their bibliographies). In a given sensory organ the hair cells are oriented either all in one direction (ampullae of the semicircular canals, cochlea) or half in one direction, half in the opposite direction (lateral line organs, saccular and utricular maculae). Other noteworthy morphological studies have been concerned with the contacts between the stereocilia and the tectorial membrane (100, 101, 119), the fine structure of afferent and efferent synapses on hair cells (101, 229), and the morphological interrelationship of the cochlear nerve fibers as they converge into the cochlear nerve (188). The relevance of these investigations will be discussed in the context of physiological findings.

Cochlear mechanics.—A wide variety of techniques have been used to firmly establish the traveling-wave nature of vibration of the cochlear partition. To these can now be added an application of the Mössbauer technique by at least two laboratories. Gilad et al. (66) find no phase difference between stapes vibration and movement of the umbo of the basilar membrane. Vibration amplitude increases logarithmically with change in intensity at all frequencies, and vibration amplitude of the basilar membrane at 60–90 dB was 2–100 Å. Johnstone & Boyle (107) found vibration amplitudes of 400–500 Å to 90 dB tones at the place on the guinea pig basilar membrane most affected by 18–21 kc. Stapes vibration was 1/10 to 1/100 that large. At the point on the basilar membrane maximally vibrated by 18–21 kc, vibration produced by frequencies lower than this was reduced at a rate of approximately 13 dB/octave, by 70 dB/octave at higher frequencies.

Electrical potentials in the cochlea.—Wever (232) has recently reviewed the extensive literature on this subject, but a number of interesting recent reports and stimulating problems deserve mention. There are three clear-cut types of cochlear electrical potentials: the AC cochlear microphonic (CM), recordable anywhere in the cochlea; the "summating potentials" (SP) seen as a positive or negative DC bias of the CM, depending on recording location, frequency, and intensity of stimulation; and the endolymph potential (EP), a strongly positive potential, approximately 80 mV positive with respect to the perilymph of the sc. vestibuli and sc. tympani in mammals. In other vertebrates, the EP tends to be much smaller or absent [Schmidt & Fernandez (189)].

It is assumed that the hair cells have typical cytoplasm and a normal negative intracellular potential. One of the greatest puzzles of cochlear physiology, however, is the apparent presence of an extracellular negative potential of up to -90 mV in the organ of Corti, recorded with electrodes of 15–30 μ tip diameter (10, 41, 214). This suggests that the organ of Corti is a separate chamber, between the sc. media and sc. tympani, filled with "cortilymph". The problem of the cortilymph potential will be discussed below.

Origin of the endolymphatic potential.—The EP is highly dependent on metabolism and independent of the hair cells, which can be experimentally eliminated (23) or naturally lacking (214) without affecting the EP. Present evidence favors the view that the potential is a secretory potential, probably arising in the stria vascularis (22, 214). It is not dependent upon ionic environment in any obvious way. Replacement of endolymph with perilymph or Ringer's solution causes no immediate change in the EP (122).

The high K^+ content of the endolymph is maintained by active processes. K^{42} is rapidly secreted from the blood into the endolymph, while it enters the perilymph more slowly (16), and labeled K^+ is transferred quickly from the sc. vestibuli into the sc. media (172). When Diamox (acetazolamide) is used to inhibit carbonic anhydrase activity, the K^+ level in the endolymph falls; this fall coincides with a reduction in numbers of pinocytotic vesicles in the stria vascularis (105).

Perhaps the best evidence that the positive endolymph potential ($+EP$) is a secretory potential rather than a diffusion potential is its fast disappearance and reversal to a large negative potential ($-EP$), almost immediately after onset of anoxia. The $-EP$ then gradually falls to zero in the totally anoxic animal [Butler (10)]. There is no change in the conductance of the endolymph during the polarity reversal, but a gradual decrease in resistance parallels the decline of the $-EP$, until endolymph and perilymph are of equal conductance when the EP reaches zero. [There is a concurrent drop in the K/Na ratio in the endolymph (106).] These observations strongly suggest that the $-EP$ reflects the K^+ diffusion potential across the membranes separating endolymph from perilymph or blood, and that the decay of the $-EP$ is caused by diffusion of K^+ down its concentration gradient. The view that the EP is normally balanced between positive secretion potential and negative diffusion potential is consistent with findings (120,

127) that an increase in K^+ concentration in the sc. tympani reduces the cochlear microphonic (CM) and causes a temporary increase in the $+EP$. If the K^+ concentration around the hair cells increases, it would be expected both to depolarize the hair cells, decreasing the CM, and to decrease the K^+ gradient between endolymph and cortilymph, thereby reducing the endolymph-negative diffusion potential and enhancing the effect of the positive secretion potential. On the other hand, if the cortilymph has nearly the same K^+ concentration as the endolymph, such a K^+ diffusion potential across the reticular lamina would not exist and another explanation for these phenomena must be sought.

It has been generally assumed that the organ of Corti is filled with perilymph. The presence of a negative "cortilymph potential", if in fact it is extracellular, forces one to question this assumption. Certainly the basilar membrane is a less effective permeability barrier than the reticular lamina, since changes in Na^+ or K^+ concentration in the sc. tympani but not the sc. media quickly affect the CM and nerve action potentials (120, 127, 134). Tetrodotoxin can penetrate the basilar membrane but not the reticular lamina (121). Since both afferent and efferent nerves pass through the cortilymph, it seems most unlikely that it could have a K^+ concentration much higher than that of perilymph. On the other hand, the cortilymph is reported (130) to stain more like endolymph than perilymph.

More puzzling, its negative polarization is sharply reduced by increasing the K^+ concentration in the sc. tympani (10, 120), the reduction approximating a 58 mV/10-fold concentration increase, consistent with a transmembrane K^+ diffusion potential perhaps located at the basilar membrane. This would require a high K^+ concentration in the cortilymph, however, which is probably not the case. It seems improbable that electrode penetration of the organ of Corti could cause sufficient K^+ leakage to create a stable, strongly negative diffusion potential. An attractive explanation would be the existence of an ionic pump, perhaps pumping K^+ back into the endolymph as it leaks in through the hair cells. Ouabain blocks the microphonic when applied near the base of the hair cells but not into the endolymph of the fish sacculus (134). Such a pump, if it existed, would appear to have properties different from those of the pump responsible for the EP, since the EP is reduced by a slight temperature drop, while the cortilymph potential remains unchanged with rather large temperature changes (10).

Earlier experiments with perfusion of the sc. vestibuli (97) led to the conclusion that anoxia acted not by blocking active processes but by allowing toxins to accumulate. These experiments have been repeated (123) with the conclusion that perfusion does not wash out toxins, but rather maintains a hydrostatic pressure in the sc. vestibuli which, in normal or anoxic cochleas, partially increases the EP. Increase of hydrostatic pressure in the sc. tympani has the opposite effect.

Experiments with anoxic cochleas have produced some surprising results that appear to be inconsistent with much of what has been concluded above.

Konishi et al. (123) report that in kanamycin-treated guinea pigs, in which the stria vascularis is apparently left intact but most of the hair cells are destroyed, anoxia causes a much slower drop in +EP than in normal cochleas (10–30 min as opposed to 1 min), and the −EP is small, only about −10 to −15 mV, as opposed to −80 mV in anoxic cochleas of normal guinea pigs. The more severe the lack of hair cells, the smaller the −EP. Such a slow drop in the +EP is unexpected, if anoxia suddenly stops the secretion potential, as it appears to do in normal cochleas. Moreover, if the composition of the endolymph is the same in normal and kanamycin-treated cochleas, one would expect a negative K^+ diffusion potential to be as large as usual. Konishi et al. argue unconvincingly that the negative potential is a reflection of the negative hair cell intracellular potential, revealed when anoxia eliminates the positive secretory potential. There appears to be no information about possible effects of kanamycin on the ionic composition of the endolymph or on any of the membranes involved. If the K^+ concentration of the endolymph were reduced, the negative diffusion potential would also be reduced, and perhaps the rate of its development altered. The unexplained "cortilymph potential" (see previous section) might also play some role in this result, although in what way is unknown.

Origin of cochlear microphonics.—Cochlear microphonics are seen only when hair cells are present (232) and their polarity reverses with penetration of a recording electrode through the region of the reticular lamina (41, 213), hence it is generally accepted that they represent current flow across the hair-bearing surface of the hair cells as the transmembrane resistance changes with displacement of the stereocilia (21, 22). The current is supposed to be driven by both the negative hair cell intracellular potential and the positive EP, the sum of which in mammals can be as much as 160 mV. In birds, lizards, and snakes, the EP may contribute a small fraction of the driving force; in other reptiles, amphibians, and fish only the intracellular potential is present (189), and the microphonics are relatively minute.

When current is passed between the sc. media and the sc. tympani in an anoxic guinea pig cochlea in such a way that the EP is made more positive, the cochlear microphonic (CM) is increased. When the EP is reduced, so is the CM (123). Kurokawa (127) has measured directly the resistance of the cochlear partition and shown that this resistance, most of which can be localized with microelectrodes to the reticular lamina, falls to 80 per cent of the normal value within 4 min after onset of anoxia. Displacement of the cochlear partition toward the sc. tympani (which increases the +EP and hyperpolarizes the hair cells) causes an increase in resistance proportional to the displacement. Displacement toward the sc. vestibuli causes a proportional decrease in resistance and a decrease in the +EP. Sound stimulation that causes a change in the EP (e.g., during a summating potential) was also paralleled by a proportional change in resistance, and the time course of recovery of the EP was the same as the recovery of resistance after termination of the acoustic stimulus. Displacement had no influence on the electrical resistance of Reissner's membrane. Johnstone, Johnstone & Pugsley (108) arrive at similar conclusions with a more complicated resistance-measuring arrangement. Quite possibly the observed changes in resistance represent changes in conductance at the hair cell surface.

The molecular mechanism of conductance change is unknown for any receptor, or, indeed, any excitable cell. At least five different theories have been put forward to explain transduction of sound energy into microphonics in the inner ear, but none appears to offer any advantages over the generally accepted explanation that mechanical bending of the hairs somehow causes molecular changes in the membrane that increase or decrease the membrane permeability, permitting a corresponding change in flow of ionic current through the membrane.

Experiments with lateral-line canal organs lead to the conclusion that deflection of the hairs toward the kinocilium or basal body causes depolarization, while displacement in the opposite direction causes hyperpolarization (49, 50, 53). Such functional directionality explains the well-known presence of microphonics at twice the stimulus frequency in the lateral line where there are two, oppositely oriented, hair cell populations.

With two oppositely oriented receptor populations of approximately equal size, it would be predicted that no recordable microphonic should result if the hair cells respond linearly with displacement in either direction. The fact that a doubled microphonic is seen is evidence that the potential produced by a given hair cell is not perfectly symmetrical. This has been demonstrated directly in fish lateral-line receptors by Flock (49, 50) and in the goldfish saccular macula by Furukawa & Ishii (60). In the lateral-line organs, Flock displaced an oscillating mechanical lever and found that the contribution of one population of hair cells was much reduced, that of the other enhanced. Pressure applied to the swimbladder of the ostariophysian goldfish had the same effect on the saccular hair cells. In both organs, the hair cells can produce much larger depolarizations than hyperpolarizations. Furukawa & Ishii (60) found that no microphonic could be recorded below a sound pressure level of 75 dB in their preparation, which indicates that it is at approximately this intensity, in the normal goldfish macula, that the hyperpolarizing current becomes nonlinear. Trinkner (219) found a similar nonlinearity of response in the ampullary organs of the semicircular canals of guinea pigs, suggesting that this is a feature common to all hair cells.

The nature of the ionic current flow is of interest. Since endolymph is similar in composition to cytoplasm, there are probably no significant ionic concentration gradients across the hair cell surface. Yet there is a large separation of charge across the membrane, on the order of 150 mV in mammals. Thus there must be a constant flow of K^+ into the cell and Cl^- out, down their electrochemical gradients, at rates governed by membrane permeability. The net exchange must be replaced either by the stria vascularis pump maintaining the high K^+ in the endolymph or perhaps by a pump located in the organ of Corti, pumping K^+ out and Cl^- back in. (Such a pump might explain the apparent negative cortilymph potential.) An increase in permeability at the hair-bearing surface might be specific to a given ion (such as K^+) or nonspecific, causing flow of all permeant ions down their electrochemical gradients.

Katsuki et al. (114) have shown that while tetrodotoxin injected electrophoretically into the organ of Corti affects only the nerve action potentials, tetraethylammonium depresses the cochlear microphonic, possibly implicating a K^+ channel similar to that responsible for delayed rectification in excitable nerve and muscle membrane. It can be speculated that a major evolutionary advantage in having essentially symmetrical solutions on both sides of the polarized hairbearing surface is that changes in permeability, either increases or decreases, will cause roughly equivalent changes in ion flow in either direction. Probably the larger the intracellular potential change in the hair cells, the more effective will be excitation of the afferent nerves. If the extracellular solution (endolymph) were Na^+-rich, one might expect the membrane to be strongly rectifying. More primitive vertebrates, in which the endolymphatic K^+ is less, might be expected to have less linear microphonics than mammals.

The generation of microphonics poses some serious problems. The resistance of the hair cell surface in contact with endolymph is apparently sufficiently high compared with the rest of the cell membrane that the endolymphatic K^+ does not significantly depolarize the hair cell. High K^+ applied in the region of the hair cell bodies in the fish saccular macula eliminates the microphonic, presumably by depolarizing the hair cells, while K^+ added to the saccular endolymph has no effect (134). Yet a microphonic that depends on ionic currents charging and discharging the hair cell membrane requires that the resistance and capacitance of the polarized membrane be such that AC currents can be produced even at frequencies as high as 100–150 kc. The required time constant is on the order of 10 μsec, nearly 100 times as short as that of resting squid axon membrane, but close to the value for the active squid axon. Perhaps the mechanism of conductance change is qualitatively different when cilia are involved. Any scheme, however sensitive, still faces the problem of explaining resolution of signal from noise at threshold displacements of 10^{-10} to 10^{-11} cm.

These considerations become largely irrelevant if one is to believe the recent report by Lawrence (128) that the tectorial membrane (potential zero) is actually separating the $+EP$ from the negative potential previously thought to occur only beneath the reticular lamina. Lawrence (128, 129) and others [see Naftalin (141)] feel that the cochlear microphonic is caused by some type of solid state transduction or ion shuttling within the tectorial membrane. The evidence for this appears to be minimal.

Origin of the summating potentials.—Summating potentials (SP) are generated at the same place as the CM, i.e., across the reticular lamina, reversing polarity when a recording electrode penetrates the lamina (124, 213). Current passed between the sc. tympani and sc. vestibuli in such a way that the polarization across the lamina is increased enhances the SP. When the polarization is reduced, so is the SP (124).

Such potentials are not exclusively a mammalian cochlear phenomenon, however. A negative SP accompanies the AC microphonic produced in lateral-line receptors (126) and in the cochleas of birds, where there are no rods of Corti and no distinction between inner and outer hair cells (203). Whitfield & Ross [(236); see also Flock (49)] have calculated that one can explain most or all of the observed SP phenomena on the basis of nonlinear vibration of the cochlear partition or nonlinearity of the potential produced by displacement in opposite directions. The latter nonlinearity exists at high intensities. While the AC potential changes are largely canceled out by vector addition of components of all different phases, a DC bias caused by larger negative than positive half-periods will summate. Nieder & Nieder (147) have recently provided experimental evidence that this is the case. The DC bias will exist intracellularly as well as extracellarly, and could affect transmitter release at high intensities.

Earlier speculation that the negative SP arises from the inner hair cells, the positive from the outer hair cells, cannot yet be discounted although it is far from compelling (see 22). Johnstone & Johnstone (109) have proposed an interesting model incorporating nonlinear generators and reasonable assumptions about hair angles in inner and outer rows. Their model can explain essentially everything, but requires much larger movements of the cochlear partition than actually occur, and attributes the $-$SP to the outer hair cells and the $+$SP to the inner hair cells, whereas streptomycin is known to destroy the outer hair cells and greatly reduce the CM, without greatly depressing the $-$SP.

Uses of cochlear microphonic (CM) recording.—For nearly forty years cochlear microphonics have been providing useful information about the audible range and sensitivity of a wide variety of animals. However, it has recently become clear that there are dangers inherent in the interpretation of CM data. The range of frequencies producing CMs, for example, is usually greater than that eliciting behavioral responses or cochlear nerve action potentials (232). Since the CMs are produced throughout the length of the cochlea, results can be expected to differ with recording site and size of cochlea. In general, the microphonics, which have no threshold, cannot be discriminated in the amplifier noise at stimulus intensities less than 40 dB above threshold (232). Knowing that CMs vary linearly with intensity at intensities below 100–110 dB, experimenters usually select a criterion amplitude, such as 1 μV, to gauge sensitivity at different frequencies; but 1 μV at one frequency may be quite different, in terms of behavioral level, from 1 μV at another. As Wever (230) has shown, the CMs vary much less with frequency than does the behavioral audiogram, and the range of maximum sensitivity is much broader. In some animals the CM is a quite good reflection of actual sensitivity. In others, it is very poor. A good example of misleading CM data is that obtained in bats. Dalland et al. (19) have shown that in the big brown bat the behavioral threshold at 2.5 kc corresponds to a microphonic of 28 μV; at 20 kc, 0.002 μV; at 40 kc, 0.02 μV; at 60 kc, 0.008 μV; and at 100 kc, 0.036 μV. At the low-frequency extreme (below 10 kc) the CM decreased by approximately 7 dB/octave, compared with 42 dB/octave for the behavioral threshold. Either the recording technique is subject to discrepancies of this magnitude in accurately detecting the CM, or, more likely, the coupling between CM and neural processes is not a constant function of CM amplitude throughout the frequency range analyzed by the cochlea.

It has also been recognized only recently that, because the CM varies with temperature, judgments of sensitivity based upon measurements of CMs in animals that do not maintain a constant body temperature are subject to error on that account. This can be especially serious in view of the observation that cooling depresses the CMs (like the neural responses) more at high frequencies than at low (91, 221).

Excitation of afferent nerve terminals.—Electron microscopic studies of the synapses between hair cells and afferent nerve terminals have led to general preference for a chemical mode of transmission. Furukawa & Ishii (61) have now demonstrated electrophysiologically that transmission is chemically mediated. Recording intracellularly from the afferent nerves innervating the saccular macula of goldfish, they found generator potentials up to 20 mV in amplitude, largest in the nerve terminals, that accurately reflected the waves of the stimulating sound and microphonic (or at twice that frequency). The latency was 0.6 to 0.8 msec. This generator potential, unlike the microphonic, adapted readily in one class of fibers, not in another. Above 2 kc, the generator potential took the form of a smooth depolarization. By hyperpolarizing the nerve, the generator potentials could be increased to 60 mV or more. In certain cases, quantal increases in the size of the generator potentials were seen—perhaps analogous to the miniature postsynaptic potentials of other chemical synapses studied.

Little is known about the pharmacology of these synapses. Katsuki and his associates (113, 212) could not affect either the cochlear microphonic (CM) or neural responses with electrophoretic injection of Na^+, K^+, Ca^{++}, or Cl^- into the organ of Corti at currents of 10^{-5} or less for 20 min. GABA and strychnine likewise had no effect on CMs or afferent sensitivity, nor did epinephrine or atropine applied locally. On the other hand, acetylcholine (ACh) had an abrupt depressing influence on the CM, as did prostigmine. Afferent nerves stopped firing as the CM fell, although the presumed reason is the drop in receptor potential rather than block of synaptic transmission. ACh also reduces the EP, but this by itself does not fully account for the drop in CM, since dTC blocks the effect of ACh on the CM but not on the EP.

NEURAL PROCESSING OF INFORMATION

Auditory neural processing appears much more complicated than visual processing. Part of the explanation no doubt lies in the greater anatomical complexity of the auditory pathway, with more subcortical nuclei and more complex mixing of bilateral inputs. In most cases, it is still impossible to say what operations necessary to behavior are performed at which level. The literature is filled with seeming inconsistencies and friendly controversies. This is doubtless a reflection of restricted sampling, but even more a product of the wide diversity of experimental techniques used—in depth of anesthesia, method of stimulation, complexity of stimulus, and type of data analysis. One of the curses of the field, in fact, is the existence of too many alternative mechanisms of information processing. The task is not so much to find mechanisms that might explain the ability of an animal to perform a given discrimation, but rather to decide which of the many known mechanisms are operative most importantly at each level. Probably one of the most productive approaches to this problem will be the careful correlation of neurophysiological findings with behavior in animals that perform given auditory tasks more or less well than monkeys, cats, or guinea pigs.

Auditory Nerve

Most first-order auditory afferents are spontaneously active, firing irregularly at rates from under 10 to over 200/sec (112, 117, 149). The spontaneous rate is normally not related to the frequency of greatest sensitivity of the unit ["best frequency" (BF), also termed "characteristic frequency" by many authors]. The typical response is an increase in firing rate, sustained throughout the stimulus and monotonically related to stimulus intensity. At relatively low frequencies the unit fires once or several times in synchrony with the same phase of each wave of the stimulus (95, 112, 178, 182). Spikes are generated by the rarefactory phase of a sound wave (224), known from other experiments to cause depolarization of the hair cells. In units with high spontaneous firing rates, the stimulus often causes no increase, or even a decrease, in the absolute number of spikes per unit time; it merely synchronizes them (182).

Phase-locked responses to frequencies as high as 5 kc/sec by units having tuning curves with BFs unrelated to the frequency they are following have led to the suggestion (95, 178) that at frequencies where such following occurs, pitch discrimination is accomplished by a period-time code rather than a place code. This is possibly the case in lower vertebrates and invertebrates, where frequency discrimination is poor and following can be seen to 2000 cps or higher (61). On the other hand (see 192), localized damage on the apical portion of the basilar membrane of guinea pigs or cats can cause restricted deficits of hearing at frequencies well below 5 kc, where surviving hair cells and nerves are presumably still "following" the frequency of an ineffective stimulus. Place analysis of frequency remains an adequate explanation, with obvious advantages for analysis of complex sounds.

Most first-order units [80 per cent of which are said to innervate the inner hair cells (200)] respond to test tone pips in a way consistent with known vibration patterns of the cochlear partition, that is, with a steep drop in sensitivity on the high-frequency side of the best frequency and a much more gradual drop on the low-frequency side (107, 112, 115, 117, 118, 178, 182, 186). Units sensitive to high frequencies tend to fire at shorter latency than those responding at low frequencies (111) and there is distinct tonotopic localization of fibers in the cochlear nerve (62, 112, 117). A few units, however, have nearly symmetrical "tuning curves", with a gradual drop in sensitivity at frequencies above the best frequency (112, 118, 182). These units may be the radial fibers which innervate hundreds of outer hair cells over considerable lengths of the basilar membrane.

More interesting for their implications are units showing unusually narrow or irregularly shaped response areas (56, 59, 115, 149, 182). Although short-latency (less than 2 msec) inhibition of spontaneous activity has been reported in monkeys (149), most workers, studying cats, have been unable to demonstrate this. With two-tone stimulation, however, inhibitory supression is obvious (56, 118, 149). Sachs & Kiang (186) report that all primary units show inhibitory interaction (defined as 20 per cent suppression) from simultaneous tones somewhat higher or lower than the excitatory signal, sharpening their response area much as neural interaction does at higher neural levels. The effect may be primarily mechanical since comparable interactions can be seen in the cochlear microphonic (147). The inhibition appears not to last beyond the inhibitory tone. The presence of such interaction, sharpening response areas when two or more frequencies are presented, has important implications for the role of neural interaction at higher neural levels.

Fibers having a given best frequency may differ in threshold by as much as 60–70 dB. Katsuki et al. (112) and Nomoto et al. (149) have reported a bimodal distribution of sensitivities and response patterns in monkey units tuned to 6 kc and below, with the less numerous population being 40 dB less sensitive. These populations behaved differently with increasing intensity. It is tempting to correlate these populations, as they did, with units excited by inner and outer hair cells, the inner hair cells having the higher threshold. However, Kiang et al. (118) could find no such orderly grouping of thresholds in the cat, and there is no obvious reason why such a dichotomy should be found only below 6 kc, in animals that can hear to 20 or 30 kc. It should be noted, however, that there is more ambiguity about the identity of first-order neurons in cats than in monkeys.

Higher Neural Pathways

Firing patterns and the role of inhibition.—Firing patterns change dramatically from peripheral to central nuclei. Although spontaneous activity is found in higher-order neurons, it becomes progressively less common and lower in frequency, from rates of 20–300/sec in the cochlear nucleus (116, 204) to under 40/sec in the medial geniculate body (2) and cortex (69). Many units in the cochlear nuclei and superior olive fire with sustained discharges similar to those of primary units (67). This is uncommon at higher levels (1, 2, 80, 96, 131, 180, 204). In general, the fewer the spontaneously active units, the greater is the proportion of phasically responding units, firing only a short burst at the onset (or occasionally the "off") of the stimulus. Especially in cochlear nucleus neurons, but also, commonly, in the inferior colliculus, the ensuing silence is brief, followed by irregular sustained discharge throughout the rest of the stimulus (68, 116, 234).

Phasic discharges, at levels above the auditory nerve, are the result of inhibitory interaction between afferents. This inhibition may vary in strength and duration as a function of frequency, intensity, and binaural cues in ways that are clearly important to frequency discrimination, sound localization, and pattern recognition. For our knowledge of intracellular mechanisms of inhibition, we still rely on the experiments of Katsuki et al. (112) on cat cortical neurons and Nelson & Erulkar (144) on collicular and geniculate neurons. Typical excitatory and inhibitory postsynaptic potentials were seen interacting to produce all varieties of "on" and "off" responses, and explaining changes in response with slight changes in frequency or intensity.

Medial geniculate neurons, which have been intensively studied only recently, behave much like collicular neurons. In cats, approximately 80 per cent (131) are "onset" units; the rest respond throughout a stimulus but usually with no relation to the stimulus frequency (1, 2). Of the onset units, nearly 10 per cent have latencies as long as 100–200 msec.

Cortical neurons show much more complex response behavior. In unanesthetized cats virtually all auditory cortical units respond to sound (69), unlike those of anesthetized cats (65, 69). The response may be "on", "off", "on-off", or sustained, or any combination of these, with "off" units relatively uncommon or missing (69, 112, 158). The response characteristics may change completely with changes in frequency or intensity, or in changing from tone burst to click stimulation. A significant number of units will not fire to any pure tone, requiring instead a more complex sound: clicks in some cases or frequency or amplitude modulated sounds (37). Important influences of mood, attention, or experience are seen in unanesthetized animals.

Coupled with the shift from spontaneous to nonspontaneous behavior, from phasic-tonic to purely phasic response, and with the increasing complexity of analysis, there is an increase in the necessary time between signals before a given unit or population can respond a second time or "follow" a train of stimuli. When cat evoked potentials are used as a criterion, auditory nerve responsiveness is largely recovered in 10–20 msec (162); collicular responsiveness in approximately 20–50 msec (237). Medial geniculate and cortical recovery requires 100 msec or longer (2, 5, 158).

Binaural interaction.—Binaural interaction is seen first in the superior olivary complex. Destruction of the S-shaped nucleus and more lateral nuclei reportedly results in virtually total loss of frequency discrimination in cats, while destruction of the trapezoid body and medial olivary nuclei does not (48). Instead, their destruction leads to an inability to localize sounds in space (133). Several workers have confirmed and extended the initial findings of Galambos et al. (63) that in medial superior olivary neurons there can be remarkably precisely timed inhibition of one input by another, at intervals of only a few tens of microseconds between stimulation of the two ears. Binaural time differences on the order of 0.3 msec are maintained at this nucleus, and evoked potentials reflect the precise timing of inputs from the two ears. Units are usually excited contralaterally, inhibited ipsilaterally, but a few are excited by both ears at the same frequencies, or both excited and inhibited by input from one ear. Responses are commonly almost all-or-none, going from threshold to maximum firing in an average of 8 dB (88). The inhibition can cause suppression of response or change in latency of firing, and can be seen either with changes in dichotic stimuli or in angle of incidence of a remote stimulus (88, 140, 183). The inhibition is sometimes present for only 0.5–1 msec, an unusually short time for a normal IPSP, suggesting that this may be a form of electrical inhibition.

As predicted from human psychophysical experiments, time differences can be overcome by intensity differences. Hall (88) found the time-intensity trading relation to vary with intensity, from 100 μsec/dB near threshold to 20 μsec/dB at 60 dB greater intensity.

Boudreau & Tsuchitani (6) have recently analyzed binaural interaction in the cat S-shaped nucleus. Approximately 85 per cent of the cells are tonically excited ipsilaterally and tonically inhibited contralaterally, with both effects having approximately the same latency, the same tuning curves, comparable thresholds, and equivalent potency of effect. Thus for a sound on the midline, the excitation from one ear only slightly exceeds inhibition from the other. An intensity increase to one ear can be balanced by an equal increase to the other. As a signal is moved laterally, however, the effect of one input increases while the other decreases, exaggerating the effect of angular change on response.

Cells of the inferior colliculus may be driven by either ear. More often, one ear (usually the contralateral) causes excitation, the other, inhibition that may last as long as 100–200 msec (36, 144) and depends critically on small binaural time or intensity differences, much as at the superior olive (181). In certain cases, a unit that is excited by one ear and unaffected by stimulation of the other alone, shows a reduced response when both ears are stimulated simultaneously (96). Such binaural interaction increases the directionality of sensitivity in echolocating bats (80, 204). Single units change in sensitivity or response by as much as 9 dB with a 1 degree change in signal angle (80).

Binaural interaction continues to be important in the medial geniculate body. Aitkin & Dunlop (1) report that units may be excited monaurally or binaurally, with the predominant influence again being contralateral. When one ear did not excite, it usually inhibited, but for a shorter time than the postexcitatory inhibition following monaural excitation in the same units. At the level of the primary auditory cortex, binaural influences are so mixed and responses so complicated that it is difficult to recognize any qualitative refinements in interaction (89).

Tuning curves, tonotopic localization, frequency resolution, and pattern recognition.—The tuning curves of single units, while highly variable within any nucleus, tend to become sharper and sharper from the auditory nerve to the inferior colliculus or medial geniculate body, then become broader again at the cortex. Usually the broadest response ranges are found in low-frequency units. Each nucleus has a few such broadly tuned units, while the cortex has a significant proportion that fire throughout most of the audible range (69, 115, 180). The broadest cortical units are also prone to be the most labile in their response characteristics (112). Especially at the cortex, one finds units having two or more peaks of sensitivity separated by as much as 50 per cent of the audible range (69, 112).

Broadening of response areas may easily be explained by excitatory convergence. Much more attention has been devoted to the mechanism of sharpening the response areas of units. This is accomplished by convergence on a given cell of excitatory input at one frequency, and inhibitory inputs at frequencies just higher or just lower than this, or both. Such interactions have been studied intensively at the level of the cochlear nuclei (72, 135, 139, 204), the inferior colliculi (144, 204, 205, 209), and the auditory cortex (69, 206, 207). In the bat colliculus, such sharpening results in units having a dynamic range of 60 dB or more and restricted to as little as 2–4 per cent of the range of audible frequencies (80, 204). With units such as these, having cutoffs of tens of dBs per 1 per cent change in frequency, it is not difficult to explain accurate frequency resolution.

Such innervation can also result in responses highly specific for intensity and pattern of frequency change. When the best frequencies for the excitatory and inhibitory inputs are close together, the response areas of the inputs tend to overlap at high intensities. In these cases, if the inhibitory input is strong enough, it can greatly suppress or inhibit altogether the response to the excitatory input. The result is a highly nonmonotonic relationship between stimulus intensity and response. In the cochlear nuclei, most units respond monotonically, but approximately 20 per cent show a decrease in firing rate above a certain intensity, or go through a dip in firing rate at moderately high intensities (68, 72, 80, 206). In the inferior colliculus, a much larger proportion are nonmonotonic, with a significant fraction being totally suppressed at only moderately high intensities (36, 80, 180, 204).

Studies of responses to frequency-modulated (FM) sounds, in the cochlear nuclei and colliculi (84, 205, 206, 209) and cortex of bats (207) and in the colliculi (145) and cortex of cats (233), have shown that neurons with excitatory response areas sharply bounded by inhibitory areas may respond only to highly specific stimuli. Inhibitory inputs of differing threshold or efficacy on either side of the excitatory areas can result in response only to a sweep in one direction within a certain intensity range. If the latencies of the excitatory and inhibitory inputs are different, the response may be absent or a phasic discharge of corresponding duration. It can also depend on the rate of sweep. All such specific response patterns have been found at collicular and cortical levels, as well as units that respond only to FM or particular complex sounds and not to any constant-wavelength sound, or that have a lower threshold (by 10 dB or more) to an FM sound of certain characteristics than to any constant-wavelength stimulus. The latter phenomenon may represent a case of disinhibition such as is seen in the *Limulus* eye. Such specificity of response is equivalent to that of many units in the visual cortex, e.g., those requiring movement in one direction of a line oriented at a given angle.

Interaction between elements responding in the same approximate frequency range is facilitated by the maintenance of tonotopic localization throughout the auditory nervous system. It is prominently present in several discrete maps in the cochlear nuclei (179), difficult to show but apparently present in at least some of the nuclei of the superior olivary complex (220), and conspicuous again in the inferior colliculi (80, 180). In the auditory cortex there is a consistently repeated vertical, columnar organization, such that a given microelectrode penetration perpendicular to the surface finds units sensitive to the same restricted frequency range (65, 157, 207). There is no such uniformity in firing patterns. This vertical organization is reminiscent of the columnar organization found in the somatic or visual sensory cortex.

EFFERENT REGULATION

Major emphasis has been devoted in the past ten years to the feedback loops that help govern afferent pathways. Efferent innervation of the cochlea has now been demonstrated, with minor variations of morphology or physiology, in frogs (52, 174), pigeons, and alligators (197), as well as in mammals. Although the total number of cochlear efferents is miniscule compared with the number of afferents (500–600 compared with 50,000 in cats), there are more efferent than afferent terminals on the outer hair cells. Relatively few efferent endings are found on the inner hair cells (210). The cochlear efferents originate in the area of the contralateral S-shaped nucleus or preolivary nuclei (crossed olivocochlear bundle, OCB), and in the S-shaped nucleus on the ipsilateral side (uncrossed OCB). Approximately one fifth of the efferents are uncrossed (43).

Workers continue to take advantage of the fact that the efferents contain relatively high concentrations of acetylcholine (ACH) esterase, and can be selectively stained (99). It is possible that ACh is an inhibitory transmitter. Katsuki and his co-workers found that electrophoretically applied curare did not block efferent suppression (113, 212). On the other hand, Russell (185) has shown that curare blocks comparable efferent inhibition of *Xenopus* lateral-line activity, and Fex (46) has reported a blocking action of curare on efferent effects in cats. The efferent synapses are blocked by strychnine and brucine, while physostigmine, dihydro-β-erythroidine, NH_4Cl, and picrotoxin have no effect (26, 45).

The effect of stimulation of the crossed olivocochlear bundle is well known (44, 45, 199, 236). At a latency of 12–40 msec, it causes a decrease in N_1 amplitude (corresponding at maximum effect to about 25 dB attenuation) and an enhancement of the cochlear microphonic (CM) (by about 4 dB) and EP, particularly with low-intensity, low-frequency stimuli (42, 44, 45, 99, 236). No facilitation or rebound occurs after the inhibition (42). The same effects are seen in the pigeon cochlea, although the neural inhibition is less pronounced, the CM potentiation somewhat greater. Strychnine again blocks the effect (24). The uncrossed efferents also suppress N_1, somewhat less strongly, but they do not affect the CM (25, 43). Their latency can be as short as 3 msec to an ipsilateral electrical stimulus, although the range is large (usually 8–40 msec) and highly variable with intensity change (43). Both crossed and uncrossed fibers show regular spontaneous firing, but the uncrossed appear to have a lower rate (around 10/sec vs. 20–40/sec) and to achieve maximal effect with a slower firing rate (120/sec vs. 400/sec). In some cases, sound causes a decrease in the spontaneous firing rate (184).

Fex (45) has studied efferent-induced DC potentials in the cochlea, presumably representing postsynaptic potentials in the hair cells. These potentials can outlast a stimulus by 200 msec or more. They are positive in the organ of Corti and sc. tympani, changing to negative (and 4–10 times larger, reaching 3 mV) with penetration through the reticular lamina into the sc. media. These polarities suggest that they represent hyperpolarization of the hair cells, arising through an increase in conductance of the hair cell membrane, which reduces the potential change across the synaptic membranes and the amount of transmitter released. Fex (45) postulates that the decrease in hair cell resistance increases the shunt between sc. media and sc. vestibuli, increasing current flow and potentiating the cochlear microphonic. It seems more likely that the hyperpolarization of the hair cells simply increases the polarization across the hair-bearing surface, and hence the amount of current flow for a given mechanically induced change in membrane permeability. Fex (45) suggests that the uncrossed fibers affect the neural responses selectively because they end on the afferent terminals instead of the hair cells. The inhibition mediated by crossed fibers is associated with an increase in N_1 latency, while that by the uncrossed efferents is not (199).

The normal function of the cochlear efferents is still unknown, but they have restricted response areas bordered by inhibitory areas, as in afferent fibers, and "high-frequency" efferents end on hair cells in the basal turn of the cochlea (43, 44). Despite the small number of efferents, they probably exert a specific feedback inhibitory influence. Dewson (26) has proposed that the cochlear efferents aid in overcoming the masking effects of noise by inhibiting primarily the hair cells having lowest threshold, leaving higher-threshold receptors for which the signal-to-noise ratio is larger. Unless there is convergence of high- and low-sensitivity receptors on single neurons, however, it is not obvious how signal discrimination can be improved. On the other hand, Dewson (27) has demonstrated that the efferents do help monkeys discriminate speech sounds in the presence of noise.

Feedback also affects higher auditory nuclei, probably all of them. The cochlear nuclei receive efferents from the superior olivary complex [claimed to be excitatory by Comis & Whitfield (17)], the inferior colliculi, the cerebellum (47, 170) and, perhaps indirectly, from the insulotemporal cortex [Dewson, Nobel & Pribram (28)]. Both the colliculus and the medial geniculate receive feedback efferents from the cortex (132, 148, 225). Watanabe et al. (225) have shown that the effects may be either inhibitory (generally from the AI cortex) or facilitatory (AII). Collicular units could be activated by efferents from either ipsilateral or contralateral cortex, while medial geniculate units were affected at shorter latency (8.3–30 msec) only by ipsilateral cortical efferents. The efferent fibers are tonotopically related to the units they innervate, which suggests that they might function as a "gating" device for passing or excluding particular signal components.

COMPARATIVE ASPECTS

The remainder of this review is concerned with studies of "nonlaboratory" animals and the findings relevant to problems of the evolution of hearing, basic principles of auditory function, and behavior.

INVERTEBRATES

Although all animals show sensitivity to mechanical stimuli, hearing, as opposed to sensitivity to substrate vibration, is restricted to a few groups of invertebrates and to the vertebrates. Among the invertebrates, hearing is evident only in terrestrial arthropods. [See Katsuki (110) for a thorough discussion of vibration sensitivity in molluscs and aquatic arthropods.] Certain arachnids have leg joint receptors (lyriform organs) capable of responding to a wide range of airborne frequencies (20–45,000 cps) at low intensities. Frequency discrimination appears to be restricted to the bottom of this frequency range (below 1000 cps, this fact probably indicating discrimination on the basis of frequency-of-firing), and to airborne as opposed to web-borne vibrations (223). The spiders will attack sources of vibration at 400–700 cps.

Hearing in some insects is well developed and much studied [see Katsuki (110) for earlier references]. Insect phonoreceptors are predominantly of two types: chordotonal organs consisting of sensory nerve terminals surrounded by supporting cells and connected by an attachment cell to a tympanic membrane; and sensory hairs, widely distributed, each with—in most cases—a single innervating nerve. As Gray (71) has shown, the sensory dendrites of the chordotonal organs terminate in a cilium with the characteristic nine peripheral fibrils but no axial fibrils, and without the basal body typical of vertebrate cilia. The nerve terminals of the hair sensillae also show ciliary ultrastructure (216). There is good reason to believe that, in either type of ending, distortion of the nerve terminal causes a change in membrane conductance, leading to depolarization and spike generation possibly central to the bipolar cell body. Sensitivity can be highly directional (146). The insect phonoreceptor generator potentials are smooth monophasic depolarizations unlike the vertebrate microphonics (110). Although the stimulus frequencies in insects are normally several kilocycles, clear microphonics are seen in vertebrate hair cells at this frequency [unlike the afferent nerve generator potentials in vertebrates (61)]. Perhaps this represents a difference between the membrane resistance of hair cells and the insect sensory dendrite, across which the current is presumed to flow. In general, the chordotonal organs are most sensitive at high frequencies (1 or 2 to 50 or 100 kc/sec), the hair sensillae to lower frequencies (below 1–2 kc/sec).

While several insect orders stridulate, usually with interesting behavioral correlations, the organs of hearing or vibration sensitivity have been studied principally in two orders: Orthoptera and Lepidoptera. Interest has centered on two facets of analysis: frequency discrimination and sound localization. In orthopterans, there are many neurons in each chordotonal organ [(70) in *Locusta* (71)]. Single nerves are spontaneously active at a slow rate, and respond with a slowly adapting discharge (up to 300/sec) throughout an effective stimulus. Most results indicate that all neurons attached to a given lympanic membrane have the same tuning curve, although they may have very different thresholds. On the other hand, second-order neurons—the single large "T-fibers" (and unknown numbers of smaller ones) in each thoracic connective that are phasically excited ipsilaterally and inhibited contralaterally—have somewhat restricted response areas, mainly in the form of loss of low-frequency sensitivity. It has recently been shown (239) that this shaping disappears if nerves other than the tympanic nerves are cut, eliminating input from other receptors (e.g., subgenual or cercal hair sensillae). It is concluded that these low-frequency-sensitive receptors provide input that inhibits second-order response to the tympanic nerve input. In the range of frequencies where this inhibition is effective, frequency discrimination is probably possible. The contralateral inhibition is important in exaggerating bilateral differences in response, facilitating localization.

Pharmacological studies (see 110) have shown that picrotoxin causes a sharp increase in firing rate of the large T-fibers, interpreted as resulting from inhibition of the synapse between contralateral tympanic nerve fibers and the T-fiber. Physostigmine, butyryocholine and ACh have a less potent excitatory effect, interpreted as due to general excitation of the T-fibers. GABA, γ-amino-butyryocholine, and d-tubocurarine inhibit T-fiber activity, presumably by blocking the excitatory input.

Limited studies of firing patterns of cells in the optic lobes and brain of locusts (98) have found few units responding only to auditory input. Most are audiovisual units responding with a phasic "on" discharge and showing no evidence of frequency discrimination. They are activated by the tympanic organ, but commonly prefer complex sounds to pure tones. Occasional units showed strong prolonged firing throughout a stimulus, or even suppression of spontaneous activity at the onset of a sound. There were a variety of complicated interactions with visual inputs. Clearly a good deal of further auditory processing is taking place.

The noctuid tympanic organ is particularly fascinating because of its simplicity and its importance to the normal behavior of the moths (177). There are a total of four primary neurons, two in each tympanic organ. These have the same tuning curves (range 2–100 kc/sec, best at 25–60 kc/sec), but differ in threshold by approximately 20 dB, with the more sensitive one firing spontaneously and responding tonically at rates as high as 500–900/sec. The less sensitive cell fires phasically, a condition reminiscent of the crayfish stretch receptor. There is no evidence of frequency discrimination at any level; but it has been demonstrated that moths can detect and evade bats on the basis of this sensory input. Roeder (175) has shown that the minimum effective intensity at the best frequency is approximately 0.2–0.3 dyne/cm^2, at which point there is a clearly detectable burst of spikes superimposed on the spontaneous firing of the sensitive cell. This sensitivity is sufficient for detection of an echolocating bat at 32–40 m, about ten times greater distance than that at which the bat could detect the moth.

Second-order neural processing is apparently done predominantly by one of two types of interneurons (176). "Relay" neurons are excited ipsilaterally and fire with a pattern nearly identical to that of the incoming tympanic nerves, differing only in that they are not phase-locked and adapt somewhat more quickly. Unlike the tympanic neurons, relay units send axons both ipsilaterally and contralaterally. The other common interneurons are "pulse-marker" neurons, so called because they respond with a single spike to each input train of 3–4 spikes at intervals of 2 msec or less. They signal the repetition rate of a sound, following with great sensitivity to 40/sec or more. The importance of this transformation of information is seen in the fact that long-sustained ultrasonic pulses have no effect on moth behavior, while rapid short pulses do.

The behavioral responses range in an adaptive way from simply flying away from a sound source to evasive flight and finally a steep dive to the ground. Each behavior pattern can be correlated with differing activity of peripheral receptors. Of utmost importance to the moth is the necessity to localize the sound source. A careful study (161) of the directional sensitivity of the noctuid ear, taking into consideration the large changes in sensitivity with alteration in wing angle, suggests that it is possible to explain accurate localization and behavior on the basis of measurements of variations in relative intensity at the two ears for different pulses, and of wing position at the time of reception. The latter information is probably provided by the nonauditory "B-fiber" present in each tympanic organ.

VERTEBRATES

Fish.—Although no fishes hear particularly well, many use sound in a large variety of biologically significant ways (215). Since the vertebrate organ of hearing effectively evolved in the fish, it is of great interest to examine the diversity of structures used, and the various mechanisms of hearing found.

Lateral-line receptors have been intensively studied in recent years, with a recent symposium volume documenting many of the advances (11). Lateral-line receptors have been repeatedly shown to be responsive to low-frequency (100 cps and under) vibrations. Harris & van Bergeijk (90) pointed out, however, that the effective stimuli in these cases are the near-field water displacements from the sound source rather than far-field pressure waves in the water. It is concluded that the lateral-line organs can be considered organs of hearing only for low frequencies produced near the animal.

Fishes that differ in hearing capacity differ principally in "middle ear" devices for converting pressure waves in water into displacements of the fluid around the hair cells of the inner ear maculae. Elasmobranchs have no swimbladder and are probably restricted to the sensitivity of the lateral-line receptors and inner ear maculae to near-field low-frequency (below 120 cps) vibrations (3). There are other reports (125, 143), however, that sharks can utlize frequencies up to 1500 cps and localize far-field sounds. Underwater stimulation is so difficult to control that this discrepancy is not surprising.

The swimbladder of teleost fishes is an important aid to hearing, transforming pressure waves from far-field sounds into displacement waves that can strongly affect the nearby inner ears (4). Many teleosts have further specializations that improve the coupling between the swimbladder and the inner ear: the Weberian ossicles of ostariophysian species, and air ducts or sacs extending into the region of the labyrinth in Anabastidae, Mormyridae, and Clapeidae (33, 110). Fish without specialized couplings are usually restricted to frequencies below 1200 cps (215), while those with air cavity coupling respond to 3000–5000 cps, and the ostariophysi respond with considerably greater sensitivity in a range extending up to 4–13 kc/sec (33). Goldfish, a well-known ostariophysian species, are said to be able to discriminate frequencies approximately one tenth as accurately as man (102). Most reports, particularly of behavioral responses, must be examined carefully in view of the important distinction between near-field and far-field stimulation, only recently recognized and shown by Enger (32) and Enger & Andersen (34) to be important in experimentally determining audiograms.

Electrophysiological studies of hearing in fish have been done principally by Enger (31, 33, 34), Furukawa & Ishii (60, 61), and Grözinger (85). In important papers, Furukawa & Ishii (60, 61) studied microphonics and nerve responses from the trunk innervating the saccular and lagenar maculae of goldfish. They found that the nerve fibers could be differentiated into three types: large fibers innervating the anterior part of the saccular macula (S_1-fibers), small fibers innervating the posterior part of the saccular macula

(S$_2$), and lagenar fibers (L). S$_1$-fibers showed no spontaneous activity while S$_2$-fibers and L-fibers were spontaneously active at rates from 10 to more than 200/sec, often in bursts. S$_1$-fibers fired either (a) to each compressional wave, (b) to each rarefactional wave, or (c) with the same minimum latency to either phase of sound, hence with twice the frequency of the sound.

The latter behavior is interpreted as resulting from innervation by a single fiber of hair cells oriented in opposite directions. S$_1$-fibers could respond with two or more spikes/cycle at frequencies below about 500 cps, and followed reliably to about 2200 cps, frequently "missing" at higher frequencies, but continuing to follow to 2500-3200 cps. Maximum sensitivity (threshold ca. +80 dB re 0.0002 dyne/cm^2) was at 700–800 cps. S$_2$-fibers were maximally responsive at 200–400 cps (threshold +56 dB), seldom responded much above 500 or 600 cps. One-to-one following was seen to either compressional or rarefactional phases of the sound, but there was no frequency doubling. Where S$_1$-fibers adapted rapidly to a sustained sound, S$_2$-fibers adapted very slowly. Lagenar fibers were much like S$_2$-fibers, differing principally in that the latency was considerably larger and the response was narrowly tuned. Experiments showed that the effective stimulus was resonant vibration within the saccular chamber, and not the incident sound waves.

Enger (31) had earlier found comparable populations, differing in detail, in the acoustic nerve of sculpin (including branches from the utriculus, sacculus, and lagena). Populations differed in pattern of spontaneous activity, in rate of adaptation, and in range of effective frequencies. Such differently tuned populations, like those found in goldfish, may be used to explain frequency discrimination either by volley-type period measurement, or by interaction between populations at a higher neural level.

Enger (33) has found clear evidence of interaction between populations responding to different frequencies in auditory areas of the medulla of the herring. Units responding only up to 500 cps (approximately 65 per cent of the total) showed only excitation; units responding to higher frequencies as well were about equally divided into those excited by high frequencies and inhibited by low, and those inhibited by high frequencies and excited by low. Even at one frequency, the response might change from excitation to inhibition or vice versa during the course of a long stimulus. Best frequencies for individual units were widely distributed through the frequency range below 1200 cps. Interaction between differently tuned populations appears to be a likely mechanism of frequency discrimination.

As van Bergeijk (4) has pointed out, most fish, having a single swimbladder, should be incapable of far-field sound localization. Those with paired air sacs around the inner ears may well be able to localize, but otherwise this is probably accomplished only in the near-field.

Amphibians.—It is well known that sound plays a major role in the behavior of many amphibians, and there is good evidence that hearing is well developed, at least in anurans. Little has been done with urodeles, although a recent study by Smith (198) indicates that the inner ear is well developed for vibration sensitivity between 50 and 400 cps.

Behavioral tests and measurements of galvanic skin responses or saccular michrophonics have shown that frogs hear well between 20 cps and 3–4 kc/sec, perhaps up to 10 kc/sec, with minimum threshold around 0.1 dyne/cm² in the range 200–1500 cps (110). This sensitivity appears to be seasonal, however, which necessitates caution in considering experimental results (228). Peripheral structures and neural responses have been well studied [see Frishkopf & Geisler (58) for earlier references]. The sensitive maculae appear to be the amphibian and basilar papillae of the sacculus, separated by a thin membrane from the perilymphatic duct. The amphibian papilla is larger and more complexly innervated, with 3 times as many neurons, and 10 times as many hair cells, having their kinocilia oriented in complicated ways (52). There is both afferent and efferent innervation and, in the middle of the nerve plexus below the macula, a few instances of tight junctions between axons, probably afferents. With few if any exceptions, efferents go only to the amphibian papilla (52, 174). As would be expected from the orientation of the hair cells, the microphonic response to sound is doubled (13).

Frishkopf & Geisler (58) analyzed the two types of peripheral afferent units in bullfrogs. "Simple" units were spontaneously active, responsive in the range 1000–1500 cps, could not be inhibited by acoustic stimuli, and followed stimuli repeated at rates up to 100/sec (not 200/sec). "Complex" units were mostly not spontaneously active, responded best between 200 and 700 cps, and were frequently (but not always, as originally reported) inhibited by frequencies just higher than the excitatory frequency. This inhibition was found even after deep anesthesia and after sectioning of the auditory nerve, so it is not mediated by efferents. On the contrary, such inhibition is seen even in the microphonic (13), so it is very likely a result of mechanical rather than neural interaction. Both simple and complex units show minimum thresholds of about 25 dB re 0.0002 dyne/cm²—comparable to the thresholds of the experimenters. These populations seem well suited for analysis of a bullfrog's vocal repertoire. On the basis of the localization of responses in the auditory nerve, Frishkopf & Geisler (58) feel confident that simple units come from the basilar papilla, complex units from the amphibian papilla.

Frishkopf, Capranica & Goldstein (57) found bullfrog medullary units to be similar in many respects to peripheral units. There are again two populations, one responding to low frequencies and inhibitable, the other responding to high frequencies and not inhibitable. However, several new response properties were seen. Low frequencies could often facilitate response of high-frequency units; and many low-frequency units gave phasic responses and could not follow as high repetition rates as peripheral units. High-frequency units tended to respond with gradual adaptation throughout the stimulus, and followed at repetition rates as high as their peripheral counterparts.

In a comparable study of medullary neurons of cricket frogs, Capranica & Frishkopf (14) found two populations of units, with different tuning and thresholds. A few were sensitive to vibration. The effective frequency ranges coincided well with the range of emitted frequencies. There was no evidence of interaction between populations, and in both there were units ranging from strict "onset" responders to those that fired without adaptation throughout a stimulus.

Potter (163) investigated single units in the bullfrog mesencephalon. Most (97 per cent) were "onset" units, in contrast to most peripheral units. The response range was from under 100 cps to 4 or 5 kc/sec, with greatest sensitivity between 200 and 1500 cps, as at the periphery. Response areas were sharpened by inhibitory interaction, which manifested itself in many other ways as well: in highly nonmonotonic relationships between intensity and response magnitude, in high-intensity "thresholds", and in units (as many as 10 per cent of those studied) preferring certain specified stimulus durations, not more, not less. As at peripheral levels, there was a sprinkling of units sensitive to substrate vibration.

Reptiles.—The structure of the reptilian inner ear varies greatly. Except for snakes, all have seemingly effective middle ear structures and a highly developed basilar membrane that constitutes a first step in the evolution of a cochlea. In crocodilians it is prolonged in an endolymph duct surrounded by perilymph chambers, much as in the bird cochlea. Wever and his colleagues have recorded microphonics from a large number of species, normally judging sensitivity by a criterion amplitude of 0.1 μV. While the presence of microphonics is obviously meaningful, it is dangerous to conclude a great deal about the limits of hearing on the basis of such studies, for reasons discussed above. Wever et al. (233) have shown that the size of the microphonic is closely correlated with the number of hair cells, while sensitivity is not. Choice of the criterion microphonic can strongly influence results. Whatever the limitations of the technique, this is the source of most of our knowledge of reptilian hearing.

Wever's group found certain colubrid snakes to be unexpectedly sensitive to low-frequency (under 700 cps) vibrations of both air and substrate. Turtles have proved to be among the most sensitive of reptiles, judging by microphonics (thresholds down to +30 dB re 0.0002 dyne/cm²) (159); but they respond only in a very restricted frequency range (20–1000 cps).

Lizards have been more broadly studied, especially the geckos, which are known to communicate by sound. These studies have been reviewed by Wever (231). The microphonic is generally best between 400 and 2000 cps, with no response above 8–10 kc/sec. Geckos differ not so much in microphonic behavior (although they do show somewhat greater sensitivity) as in morphology and complexity of the basilar papillae. This structure can vary in length and width, size of fundus on the basilar membrane, and number of hair cells per unit area of membrane. Nongekkonid lizards have relatively small, uniform papillae with few hair cells. Gekkonid lizards have a much enlarged, elongated basilar membrane, changing in width by about 3 times and by a much larger factor in number of hair cells.

In a more recent study of microphonics in *Gekko gecko*, Hepp-Reymond & Palen (94) report that the response waveform is often doubled at high intensities, which might result from two populations of hair cells attached differently to the tectorial membrane, for which they see evidence, or to the existence of oppositely oriented hair cell populations. They cite a personal communication from M. Mulroy to the effect that the latter is the case in *Gerronotus multicarinatus*. Since this is not seen in the basilar membranes of higher vertebrates, the report is of some interest.

Suga & Campbell (210) have studied higher-order medullary neurons in the gekkonid *Coleonyx variegatus*, among which they found units responding between 100 and 17,000 cps, with lowest thresholds at about 27 dB re 0.0002 dyne/cm² at 800–2000 cps. Individual response areas were quite broad, with best frequencies between 110 and 400 cps. Most neurons increased their firing rates monotonically with increases in intensity, but others were inhibited at intensities only a few decibels above threshold by inputs commonly having the same best frequency as the excitatory input. The effect was to depress response at high intensities rather than sharpen the response area.

Birds.—Hearing in birds is of great interest, yet it has been almost totally neglected to date. The interest lies mainly in the fact that the bird cochlea is very much like that of certain reptiles, especially crocodilians, yet hearing appears, from the few studies that exist, to be essentially as useful and accurate as that of mammals. The morphological differences between the ears of birds and mammals are striking: (*a*) the bird middle ear consists of one ossicle (the columella) instead of three; (*b*) the bird cochlea is much shorter, and straight rather than coiled; (*c*) the blood supply is located in a bulky tegmentum vasculosum located between the sc. vestibuli and sc. media, where the thin Reissner's membrane is found in mammals; (*d*) there is no distinction between inner and outer hair cells in birds, but instead a uniform row of 30–50 hair cells in a given transverse plane across the membrane; (*e*) where in a mammal the basilar membrane changes fourfold in width, the increase in width from base to apex in birds is only about 25 per cent; (*f*) there are 10 times more hair cells in mammals than in most birds; (*g*) the lagenar macula remains at the tip of the cochlear duct in birds, while it is missing in all but the monotreme mammals; and (*h*) the helicotrema is absent in birds. Of all the birds studied, owls have by far the largest, most highly developed cochlea, and the most hair cells, and the most highly developed central auditory tracts.

Despite the differences between bird and mammal cochleas, Békésy has shown that the point of maximum displacement of the bird basilar membrane changes with frequency just as the mammal's does, and early studies [see

Schwartzkopff (195)] of responses in birds indicate sensitivity equivalent to that of mammals at frequencies up to 4–5 kc/sec with behavioral response to 10–15 kc/sec (20). This is a lower frequency range than that expected of a mammal of comparable size, but in the range of best frequencies, frequency resolution is said to be 0.3–0.7 per cent—nearly as accurate as that of man. [A recent behavioral study of frequency discrimination in pigeons (165), on the other hand, arrived at difference limens nearly 10 times this large.] Temporal resolution is extremely accurate. As in mammals, second- or third-order neurons respond with restricted tuning areas and "best frequencies" are found throughout the range of effective frequencies (202).

Owls are well known both for their ability to locate targets acoustically and in certain genera for the marked asymmetry of their skulls and external ear openings. Payne (160) and more recently Norberg (150) have measured the directionality of receptivity of each ear in different species of owls, using microphonics or physical measurements on owl heads. They propose that such owls can locate prey accurately on the basis of "built-in" asymmetrical directional sensitivity, especially at frequencies above 12,000 cps, simply by turning the head until it is aimed in the direction in which minimal interaural intensity differences exist. It would be reassuring to have neural recordings showing that owls can utilize frequencies this high (195).

ECHOLOCATION

The general discussion of cochlear and auditory pathway physiology that began this review was based almost entirely on experiments with mammals, especially cats, guinea pigs, monkeys, and bats. A further detailed consideration of mammalian hearing would add little. Instead, attention will be directed toward a problem of intense interest in comparative auditory physiology, the mechanisms of sound analysis in echolocating animals. Echolocation occurs in all bats of the suborder Microchiroptera that have been studied, in at least one genus of the suborder Megachiroptera (*Rousettus*), in two genera of birds (*Steatornis* and *Colocallia*), in a large number of odontocete cetaceans, and probably in shrews and tenrecs. It would be most surprising if other small mammals and birds are not found to use echolocation. The ability to echolocate has been claimed for seals and sea lions (164), but most evidence does not favor this view (193). Their vocal repertoire, on the other hand, is extensive; and their hearing is of special interest because of the necessity for hearing both in air and water. Møhl (136, 137) has shown with behavioral experiments that the ear of the seal *Phoca vitulina* is primarily adapted for hearing underwater, with a range up to 160 kc/sec and greatest sensitivity at 32 kc/sec (compared with a high-frequency limit of just over 20 kc/sec in air). Frequency discrimination is limited to frequencies below 60 kc, however.

Uses of echolocation.—Capabilities for echolocation differ. In microchiropteran bats, hearing is the predominant source of information about the environment, although vision may not be as inadequate as originally thought (211). Sounds are produced in the larynx and are highly structured (73). Cetaceans also have highly evolved echolocation skills, but they have good vision and use it preferentially when sufficient light is available. Emitted sounds are normally short-duration clicks, probably produced in the air sacs of the melon (151, 152), although there is still controversy on this matter (166). *Rousettus* likewise uses echolocation facultatively when there is insufficient light for vision. Their orientation sounds are clicks produced by tongue movement and their echolocation skills are distinctly inferior to those of other bats (73). Echolocating birds (73) and shrews and tenrecs (70) also produce sounds by tongue clicking, and probably have rather primitive capabilities. Much of the recent work on echolocation, especially in cetaceans, is summarized in a symposium volume (8).

Microchiropteran bats probably represent the highest degree of adaptation for echolocation. Most are insectivorous or frugivorous, but others feed on nectar, blood, fish, or small birds and mammals. The species-specific orientation sounds vary from brief (1–2 msec) frequency-modulated (FM) pulses or pulses containing a constant-wavelength fundamental and several harmonics, to long (30–100 msec or longer), mostly constant-wavelength pulses with only a slight FM sweep at beginning and end. In bats using constant-wavelength pulses, the specific frequency may be critical. Schnitzler (191) has shown that *Rhinolophus*, which emit constant-wavelength pulses of 83 or 104 kc/sec, depending on the species studied, compensate for changes in returning echo frequency due to Doppler shift by altering the emitted frequency just enough so that the returning frequency is 83 or 104 kc/sec. Probably the ear is adapted for specific forms of analysis at these frequencies only. Whatever the type of pulse structure used, all bats tested appear to be approximately equally skillful in obstacle avoidance, detecting and avoiding an array of wires down to approximately 0.1 mm diameter (82, 138, 156, 190). Bats using brief pulses emit them at rates up to 100–200/sec during pursuit or obstacle avoidance, and have been seen to capture insects at rates up to 2/sec (78). Detection and wire avoidance have been demonstrated in the presence of broadband noise sufficiently loud that the ratio of signal energy/noise power per cycle bandwidth is around −5 dB, below the theoretical minimum for a single receiver (77). Target discrimination has been studied in little brown bats, *Myotis lucifugus*, which can be trained to discriminate mealworms tossed into the air from any decoy not having the same dimensions, probably by the pattern of changes in echo strength at different frequencies with changing target orientation in space (74, 76).

A bat must be able to detect a faint ultrasonic echo, recognize it as being an echo of its own outgoing cry, determine the distance and direction of the object returning the echo in both horizontal and vertical axes, determine what kind of a target it is and whether it is moving and, if so, in what direction. Detection is immensely complicated by several forms of interference, foremost among them the loud emitted cry immediately preceding the returning echoes (travel time of sound in air is 34.4 cm/msec) and, even more serious, the presence of echoes at nearly the same time from a large number of targets, all of potential interest to a bat.

Adaptations of bats for echolocation.—The adaptation of bats for their sophisticated use of sound is evident morphologically. The external ears are often huge and complicated; the middle ear ossicles are specialized; the middle ear muscles are relatively huge and heavily innervated; the cochlea is large and clearly adapted for high-frequency analysis (73, 168, 176). The auditory centers, at least in the level of the midbrain, are vastly hypertrophied compared with other sensory pathways (79).

Recent electrophysiological studies of audition in bats have concentrated on cochlear microphonics (19, 92, 93, 221, 222), or on evoked potentials and single-unit responses at neural levels from the auditory nerve to auditory cortex, with greatest emphasis on the cochlear nuclei and inferior colliculi (55, 79–81, 83, 84, 204–209). A number of response characteristics appear to represent adaptation suited to the requirements of echolocation. The use of ultrasonic frequencies, a necessity in obtaining information about objects of the dimensions of interest to bats, is matched by sensitivity throughout the range of emitted frequencies. Indeed, there is a pronounced tendency for greatest sensitivity (thresholds approximately 0.0002 dyne/cm^2) to occur consistently in the specific range of frequencies used in the orientation sounds, especially in bats employing largely constant-wavelength pulses (81). Cochlear microphonics provide a rather poor estimate of sensitivity at different frequencies in bats (18, 19, 91, 221).

The effect of inhibitory interaction in restricting the response area of single units appears more extreme in bats than in other mammals studied in comparable ways. At the level of the inferior colliculus, almost all responses are highly phasic and most are narrowly tuned, with cutoffs as high as 20 dB per 1 per cent change in frequency at both high and low frequency borders (80, 204). In many such units, inhibition predominates at high intensities, even at the unit's best frequency, so that high-intensity thresholds are common, 20–50 dB above the low-intensity threshold (80, 206, 207). With both evoked potentials and unit responses, change in response is often seen to changes of only 0.5 dB, or even 0.1–0.2 dB in certain instances (80).

The importance of inhibitory interaction becomes especially evident when complex or frequency-modulated signals are used (81, 84, 205–209). Collicular units are found that will respond only to constant-wavelength pulses, not to FM, or vice versa, or in ways that depend on the direction, rate, and intensity of the frequency swept pulse. It is easy to explain this in terms of the relative thresholds of excitatory and inhibitory inputs, their response areas, and the strength, duration, and latencies of the inputs. Clearly the neural machinery is available to discriminate frequencies accurately, and compare intensities and sweep patterns of outgoing pulses and returning echoes. Such comparison is necessary for recognition of an echo and judgment of the nature of a target.

Even more conspicuous adaptations exist that help overcome the interference of the outgoing pulse and many returning echoes. Contraction of the middle ear muscles in synchrony with emission of orientation pulses helps reduce their masking effect (92, 93). Except at highest pulse repetition rates, sensitivity during the outgoing cry is reduced by 10–15 dB compared with the period when returning echoes must be analyzed. There may be neural mechanisms for accomplishing the same effects in the cochlea or at higher neural levels, but they have so far not been demonstrated.

Even more important is the remarkable temporal precision of the bat auditory system. Frequency can apparently be discriminated on the basis of as few as 2–3 cycles of a tonal stimulus (80, 81). Recovery of responsiveness, as judged by the amplitude of the evoked potential representing input to the colliculus, is complete and even supranormal at 2 msec interval between stimuli (80). This is more than an order of magnitude faster than in cats (238). Single units show recovery cycles consistent with these observations (80, 205). Of particular interest is the fact that full recovery is faster at this level than at the cochlear nuclei, and faster there than at the auditory nerve. N_1 is only 50 per cent recovered in 2 msec. There appears to be a mechanism for selectivity emphasizing information about second or subsequent signals in a series at cochlear nucleus and third-order neural levels. Such facilitation is not seen in other mammals, even echolocating cetaceans (7). Facilitation is also obvious in the observation that at 2 msec intervals between a pair of tone pips, the first of which is louder, a threshold auditory nerve potential to the second is seen when it is approximately 45 dB fainter than the first; a collicular evoked potential is seen, however, down to an intensity 60 dB fainter than the first. The information at −60 dB is obviously present in the auditory nerve in this case, even though it is grossly undetectable.

Single units in both the cochlear nucleus and colliculus respond to both signals down to intervals of 0.6–1 msec, although most do not resolve below 2–5 msec. Other units respond only to the second of two pulses of the same frequency, or show as much as 20 dB facilitation that decays over a period of 10–20 msec (55, 80, 205). The existence of "tuned" populations, facilitated briefly by a signal of specific frequency (and perhaps rate of frequency sweep, duration, and other stimulus parameters), provides firm theoretical basis for echo detection and analysis, as long as the cochlea and auditory nerve can handle the information. High rates of spontaneous activity in primary neurons probably ensure a significant population responsive to any signal following another by as much as 100–200 μsec (81).

Distance determination by echolocating bats can be explained most simply by measurements of the intervals between responses of neurons firing to both emitted sound and returning echo and by the recognition of which populations, having different recovery rates at a given intensity, are firing and which are not. It would be surprising if these mechanisms were not used. Bats employing longer pulses with long constant-wavelength segments, however, must analyze echoes that return while the pulse is still being emitted. In certain species, pulse length appears to be regulated so that there is always a certain amount of overlap (155). These pulses end in an FM sweep that could provide an exact interval measurement, but it is also possible that distance is determined by some form of difference tone measurement, as was originally proposed by Pye and Kay for FM-emitting bats (see 168).

Determination of target direction by bats can apparently be accomplished with only one echo, or at most two or three (79, 82, 227). Because the ears are so close together, binaural arrival time differences are probably too small for accurate angular resolution, and could not provide information about vertical angle from a single echo in any case. Hence it is most likely that localization is done by highly sensitive comparison of binaural intensity differences at several frequencies (80, 83). Binaural interaction increasing the angular sensitivity of collicular potentials in bats has already been described. The pinnae and tragus impose a high degree of directionality on each ear, in both the horizontal and vertical planes, with changes of approximately 0.5 dB/degree angular change being characteristic. The pattern changes with frequency. By comparing the binaural intensities of a given signal at three or more different frequencies, preferably well separated in the audible spectrum, it is theoretically possible for a bat to determine the one point in space from which all frequencies sampled could have the observed binaural intensity differences (83).

Echolocation in cetaceans.—Cetaceans are known to use a large repertoire of sounds for communication (12, 29). It is also well known that odontocete cetaceans echolocate, with most study devoted to the bottle-nosed dolphin *Tursiops*. Dolphins use brief (2 msec or shorter) clicks for echolocation, emitted at rates up to 400–600/sec during difficult discrimination tasks. Each contains the whole spectrum of frequencies up to 150 or 200 kc/sec, although most of the energy is below 30 kc/sec. The pulses are directionally beamed forward and slightly above the horizontal plane of the animals (39, 153).

Trained *Tursiops* can discriminate acoustically between spheres differing in diameter by 10 per cent (154), and between metal plates of equal exposed surface area when they are of different thickness (38). These results suggest the use of rather complicated phase-related or "double-echo" cues. The porpoise *Phocaena phocaena* can detect threads of 0.8–1 mm diameter, or metal wires of 0.2 mm diameter, in obstacle-avoidance tests comparable to those done with bats (9). The difference between threads and wires may lie in some form of resonance by the wire. As in bats, there is a sharp increase in pulse repetition rate as a target is approached.

The behavioral studies of Johnson (103, 104) have resolved earlier controversy about the range of hearing in dolphins. Using a trained *Tursiops*, Johnson found maximum sensitivity between 20 and 70 kc/sec, where the threshold is approximately −55 dB re 1 μbar. Sensitivity falls off sharply above 120 kc, and gradually below 15 kc, with a lower limit of 200–300 cps. No near-field sensitivity to sound, such as is seen in fish, was found. Near threshold, intensity changes as small as 1 dB could be distinguished.

The cetacean auditory system, like that of bats, is greatly hypertrophied (87). The development of anesthesia techniques (142, 173) led to an electrophysiological study of auditory evoked potentials in the dolphins *Stenella* and *Tursiops* (7). This study showed that sound reaches the cochlea primarily via the lower jaws, although areas of the melon are also effective as sound pathways to the ears. Sensitivity is maximal between 20 and 70 kc/sec in both species, and responses are seen to 140 kc/sec. Frequency and intensity discrimination are comparable to that seen in bats, and FM signals affect evoked potentials in ways that indicate highly specific pattern recognition by auditory units. Recovery of responsiveness following stimulation is extremely fast, with full recovery within 2–5 msec at the level of the input to the colliculus. There is no evidence of facilitation of response to second stimuli, however, as is seen in bats. Directionality of sensitivity underwater is sharp and frequency dependent near the midline, and target localization can be explained by the animal's maximizing intensities at the two ears.

LITERATURE CITED

1. Aitkin, L. M., Dunlop, C. W. *J. Neurophysiol.*, **31**, 44–61 (1968)
2. Aitkin, L. M., Dunlop, C. W., Webster, W. R. *J. Neurophysiol.*, **29**, 109–23 (1966)
3. Banner, A. In *Lateral Line Detectors* (Cahn, P. H., Ed., 1967)
4. van Bergeijk, W. A. In *Marine Bio-Acoustics*, 281–329 (Tavolga, W. N., Ed., 1964)
5. Borsanyi, S. F. *Ann. Otolaryngol.*, **73**, 312–26 (1964)
6. Boudreau, J. C., Tsuchitani, C. *J. Neurophysiol.*, **31**, 442–54 (1968)
7. Bullock, T. H., Grinnell, A. D., Ikezona, E., Kameda, K., Katsuki, Y., Nomoto, M., Sato, O., Suga, N., Yanagisawa, K. *Z. Vergleich. Physiol.*, **59**, 117–56 (1968)
8. Busnel, R. G., Ed. *Animal Sonar Systems* (INRA-CNRZ Jouy-en-Josas 78, France, 1967)
9. Busnel, R. G., Dziedzic, A. In *Animal Sonar Systems*, 307–35 (1967)
10. Butler, R. A. *J. Acoust. Soc. Am.*, **37**, 429–33 (1965)
11. Cahn, Phyllis H., Ed. *Lateral Line Organs* (Indiana Univ. Press, 1967)
12. Caldwell, M. C., Caldwell, K. D. In *Animal Sonar Systems*, 879–936 (Busnel, R. G., Ed., 1967)
13. Capranica, R. R., Flock, Å., Frishkopf, L. S. *J. Acoust. Soc. Am.*, **40**, 1262 (1966)
14. Capranica, R. R., Frishkopf, L. S. *J. Acoust. Soc. Am.*, **40** 1263 (1966)
15. Carmel, P. W., Starr, A. *J. Neurophysiol.*, **26**, 598–617 (1963)
16. Choo, Y. B., Tabowitz, D. *Ann. Otolaryngol.*, **740** 140–45 (1965)
17. Comis, S. D., Whitfield, I. C. *J. Neurophysiol.*, **31**, 62–68 (1968)
18. Dalland, J. I. *J. Aud. Res.*, **5**, 95–108 (1965)
19. Dalland, J. I., Vernon, J. A., Peterson, E. A. *J. Neurophysiol.*, **30**, 697–709 (1967)
20. Dalton, L. W. *J. Aud. Res.*, **7**, 25–29 (1967)
21. Davis, H. *Physiol. Rev.*, **41**, 391–416 (1961)
22. Davis, H. *Sensory Receptors. Cold Spring Harbor Symp. Quant. Biol*, **30**, 181–90 (1965)
23. Davis, H., Deatherage, B. H., Rosenblüt, B., Fernandez, C., Kimura, R., Smith, C. A. *Laryngoscope*, **68**, 596–627 (1958)
24. Desmedt, J. E., Delwaide, P. J. *Exptl. Neurol.*, **11**, 1–26 (1965)
25. Desmedt, J. E., Lagrutta, V. *Nature*, **200**, 472–74 (1963)
26. Dewson, J. H. III. *J. Neurophysiol.*, **30**, 817–33 (1967)
27. Dewson, J. H. III *Ibid.*, **31**, 122–30 (1968)
28. Dewson, J. H. III, Nobel, K. W., Pribram, K. H. *Brain Res.*, **2**, 151–59 (1966)
29. Dreher, J. J., Evans, W. E. In *Marine Bio-acoustics* (See Ref. 4), 373–93
30. Duvall, A., Rhodes, V. T. *Arch. Otolaryngol.*, **86**, 143–51 (1967)
31. Enger, P. S. *Acta Physiol. Scand.*, **59**, *Suppl. 210* (1963)
32. Enger, P. S. *Comp. Biochem. Physiol.*, **18**, 859–68 (1966)
33. Enger, P. S. *Ibid.*, **22**, 527–38 (1967)
34. Enger, P. S., Andersen, R. *Ibid.*, 517–25
35. Engström, H., Ades, H. W., Andersson, A. *Structural Pattern of the Organ of Corti* (Williams & Wilkins, Baltimore, 1966)
36. Erulkar, S. D. *Proc. Roy. Soc. B*, **150**, 336–55 (1960)
37. Evans, E. F., Ross, H. F., Whitfield, I. C. *J. Physiol.*, **179**, 238–47 (1965)
38. Evans, W. E., Powell, B. A. In *Animal Sonar Systems* (See Ref. 8), 363–82
39. Evans, W. E., Sutherland, W. W., Beil, R. G. In *Marine Bio-Acoustics* (See Ref. 4), 353–70
40. Feldman, H., Steimann, G. *Arch. Klin. Exptl. Ohren-, Nasen-Kehlkopfheilk.*, **190**, 69–85 (1964)
41. Fernández, C., Butler, R., Konishi, T., Honrubia, V., Tasaki, I. *J. Acoust. Soc. Am.*, **34**, 1411–17 (1962)
42. Fex, J. *Acta Phys. Scand. Suppl 189* (1962)
43. Fex, J. *Ibid.*, **64**, 43–57 (1965)
44. Fex, J. *Sensorineural Hearing Processes and Disorders*, 77–86 (Graham, A. B., Ed., Henry Ford Hosp. Intern. Symp., 1967)
45. Fex, J. *J. Acoust. Soc. Am.*, **41**, Part 1: 666–76 (1967)
46. Fex, J. In *Hearing Mechanisms in Vertebrates*, 169–81 (de Rensk, A. V. S., Knight, J., Eds., Ciba Found., Churchill, London, 1968)
47. Filogamo, G., Candilollo, L., Rossi, G. In *Relazione 23rd Raduno Gruppo Otorinolaringol. Alta Italia, Torino, 1965*
48. Fisher, G. L., Harrison, J. M. *J.*

Comp. Neurol., **119**, 269–79 (1962)
49. Flock, Å. *Acta Otolaryngol. Suppl. 199*, 1–90 (1965)
50. Flock, Å. In *Sensory Receptors Cold Spring Harbor Symp. Quant. Biol.*, **40**, 133–45 (1965)
51. Flock, Å, Duvall, A. J. *J. Cell Biol.*, **25**, 1–8 (1965)
52. Flock, Å., Flock, Britta, *J. Acoust. Soc. Am.*, **40**, 1262 (1966)
53. Flock, Å., Wersall, J. *J. Cell Biol.*, **15**, 19–27 (1962)
54. Flynn, W. E., Elliott, D. N. *J. Acoust. Soc. Am.*, **38**, 104–5 (1965)
55. Friend, J. H., Suga, N., Suthers, R. A. *J. Cellular Physiol.*, **67**, 319–32 (1966)
56. Frishkopf, L. S. *J. Acoust. Soc. Am.*, **36**, 1016 (A) (1964)
57. Frishkopf, L. S., Capranica, R. R., Goldstein, M. H., Jr. *Proc. IEEE*, **56**, 969–80 (1968)
58. Frishkopf, L. S., Geisler, C. D. *J. Acoust. Soc. Am.*, **40**, 469–72 (1966)
59. Furman, G., Frishkopf, L. S. *J. Acoust. Soc. Am.*, **36**, Part 3: 2194–2202 (1964)
60. Furukawa, T., Ishii, Y. *Japan. J. Physiol.*, **17**, 572–88 (1967)
61. Furukawa, T., Ishii, Y. *J. Neurophysiol.*, **30**, 1377–1403 (1967)
62. Gacek, R. R. *Sensorineural Hearing Processes and Disorders* (See Ref. 44), 49–59
63. Galambos, R., Schwartzkopff, J., Rupert A. *Am. J. Physiol.*, **197**, 527–36 (1959)
64. Gaudin, E. P. *Acta Otolaryngol.*, **65**, 316–26 (1968)
65. Gerstein, G. L., Kiang, N. Y. S. *Exptl. Neurol.*, **10**, 1–18 (1964)
66. Gilad, P., Shtrikman, S., Hillman, P., Rubinstein, M., Eviatar, A. *J. Acoust. Soc. Am.*, **41**, 1232–36 (1967)
67. Goldberg, J. M., Adrian, H. O., Smith, F. D. *J. Neurophysiol.*, **27**, 706–49 (1964)
68. Goldberg, J. M., Greenwood, D. D. *J. Neurophysiol.*, **29**, 72–93 (1966)
69. Goldstein, M. H., Jr., Hall, J. L. II, Butterfield, B. O. *J. Acoust. Soc. Am.*, **43**, 444–55 (1968)
70. Gould, E. *Proc. Am. Phil. Soc.*, **109**, 352–60 (1965)
71. Gray, E. G. *Phil. Trans. Roy Soc.*, **243**, 75–94 (1960)
72. Greenwood, D. D., Maruyama, N. *J. Neurophysiol.*, **28**, 863–92 (1965)
73. Griffin, D. R. *Listening in the Dark* (Yale Univ. Press, New Haven, Conn., 1958)
74. Griffin, D. R. In *Animal Sonar Systems* (See Ref. 8), 273–300
75. Griffin, D. R., Dunning, D. C., Cahlender, D. A., Webster, F. A. *Nature*, **196**, 1185–88 (1962)
76. Griffin, D. R., Friend, J. H., Webster, F. A. *J. Exptl. Zool.*, **158**, 155–68 (1965)
77. Griffin, D. R., McCue, J. J. G., Grinnell, A. D. *J. Exptl. Zool.*, **152**, 229–50 (1963)
78. Griffin, D. R., Webster, F. A., Michael, C. R. *Animal Behav.*, **8**, 141–54 (1960)
79. Grinnell, A. D., *Neural Correlates of Echolocation in Bats* (Ph.D. thesis, Harvard Univ., Cambridge, Mass., 1962)
80. Grinnell, A. D. *J. Physiol.*, **167**, 38–127 (1963)
81. Grinnell, A. D. In *Animal Sonar Systems* (See Ref. 8), 451–81
82. Grinnell, A. D., Griffin, D. R. *Biol. Bull.*, **114**, 10–22 (1958)
83. Grinnell, A. D., Grinnell, V. S. *J. Physiol.*, **181**, 830–51 (1965)
84. Grinnell, A. D., McCue, J. J. G. *Nature*, **198**, 433–35 (1963)
85. Grözinger, B. *Z. Vergleich. Physiol.*, **57**, 44–76 (1967)
86. Guinan, J. J., Peake, W. T. *J. Acoust. Soc. Am.*, **41**, 1237–61 (1967)
87. Hall, J. G., *Acta Otolaryntol. Suppl. 224*, 244–50 (1966)
88. Hall, J. L. II, *J. Acoust. Soc. Am.*, **37**, Part 2: 814–24 (1965)
89. Hall, J. L. II, Goldstein, M. H., Jr. *J. Acoust. Soc. Am.*, **43**, 456–61 (1968)
90. Harris, G. G., von Bergeijk. W. A. *J. Acoust. Soc. Am.*, **34**, 1831–41 (1962)
91. Harrison, J. B. *Physiol. Zool.*, **38**, 34–48 (1965)
92. Henson, O. W., Jr. *J. Physiol.*, **180**, 871–87 (1965)
93. Henson, O. W., Jr. In *Animal Sonar Systems* (See Ref. 8), 949–1003
94. Hepp-Reymond, M. C., Palen, J. *Acta Otolaryngol.*, **65**, 270–92 (1968)
95. Hind, J. E., Anderson, D. J., Brugge, J. F., Rose, J. E. *J. Neurophysiol.*, **30**, 794–817 (1967)
96. Hind, J. E., Goldberg, J. M., Greenwood, D. D., Rose, J. E. *J. Neurophysiol.*, **26**, 321–41 (1963)
97. Honrubia, V. H., Johnstone, B. M., Butler, R. A. *Acta Otolaryngol.*, **60**, 105–12 (1965)
98. Horridge, G. A., Scholes, J. H., Shaw,

S., Tunstall, J. In *The Physiology of the Insect Central Nervous System* (Treherne, J. E., Beament, J. W. L., Eds., Academic Press, New York, 1965)

99. Ishii, T., Murakami, Y., Gacek, R. R. *Acta Otolaryngol.*, **64**, 267–79 (1967)

100. Iurato, S. *J. Acoust. Soc. Am.*, **34**, 1381–95 (1962)

101. Iurato, Salvatore et al. *Submicroscopic Structure of the Inner Ear* (Pergamon, London, 1967)

102. Jacobs, D. W., Tavolga, W. N. *Animal Behav.*, **16**, 67–71 (1968)

103. Johnson, C. S. In *Marine Bio-Acoustics*, **2**, 247–55 (1967)

104. Johnson, C. S. *J. Acoust. Soc. Am.*, **43**, 751–63 (1968)

105. Johnson, R. L., Spoendlin, H. H. *Ann. Otolaryngol.*, **75**, 127–37 (1966)

106. Johnstone, B. M. *Acta Otolaryngol.*, **60**, 113–20 (1965)

107. Johnstone, B. M., Boyle, A. J. F. *Science*, **158**, 389–90 (1967)

108. Johnstone, B. M., Johnstone, J. R., Pugsley, I. D. *J. Acoust. Soc. Am.*, **40**, Part 2: 1398–1404 (1966)

109. Johnstone, J. R., Johnstone, B. M. *J. Acoust. Soc. Am.*, **40**, 1405–13 (1966)

110. Katsuki, Y. *Physiol. Rev.*, **45**, 380–423 (1965)

111. Katsuki, Y. *Progr. Brain Res.*, **21A**, 71–97 (1966)

112. Katsuki, Y., Suga, N., Kanno, Y. *J. Acoust. Soc. Am.*, **34**, 1396–1410 (1962)

113. Katsuki, Y., Tanaka, Y., Miyoshi, T. *Nature*, **207**, 32–34 (1965)

114. Katsuki, Y., Yanagisawa, K., Kanzaki, J. *Science*, **151**, 1544–45 (1966)

115. Kiang, N. Y. *Acta Otolaryngol.*, **59**, 186–200 (1965)

116. Kiang, N. Y. S., Pfeiffer, R. R., Warr, W. B., Backus, S. N. *Ann. Otolaryngol.*, **74**, 463–85 (1965)

117. Kiang, N. Y., Watanabe, T., Thomas, E., Clark, L. F. *Ann. Otolaryngol.*, **71**, 1008–26 (1962)

118. Kiang, N. Y. S., Wantanabe, T., Thomas, E. C., Clark, L. F. *Discharge Patterns of Single Fibers in the Cat's Auditory Nerve* (MIT Press, Cambridge, Mass., 1965)

119. Kimura, R. S. *Acta Otolaryngol.*, **61**, 55–72 (1966)

120. Konishi, T., Kelsey, E. *J. Acoust. Soc. Am.*, **43**, 462–70 (1968)

121. Konishi, T., Kelsey, E. *Ibid.*, 471–80

122. Konishi, T., Kelsey, E., Singleton, G. T. *Acta Otolaryngol.*, **62**, 393–404 (1966)

123. Konishi, T., Kelsey, E., Singleton, G. T. *Ibid.*, **64**, 107–18 (1967)

124. Konishi, T., Yasuno, T. *J. Acoust. Soc. Am.*, **35**, Part 2: 1448–52 (1963)

125. Kritzler, H., Wood, L. *Science*, **133**, 1480–82 (1964)

126. Kuijper, J. W. *The microphonic effect of the lateral line organs* (Thesis, Groningen, 1956)

127. Kurokawa, S. *Japan. J. Oto-Rhino-Laryngol.*, **68**, 1177–95 (1965)

128. Lawrence, M. *Ann. Otolaryngol.*, **76**, 287–312 (1967)

129. Lawrence, M. In *Sensorineural Hearing Processes and Disorders* (See Ref. 44), 21–36

130. Lawrence, M., Clapper, M. *Stain Technol.*, **36**, 305–8 (1961)

131. Maruyama, N., Kawasaki, T., Abe, J., Katoh, I., Yamazaki, H. *Intern. Audiology*, V 184–88 (1966)

132. Massopust, L. C., Jr., Ordy, J. M. *Exptl. Neurol.*, **6**, 465–77 (1962)

133. Masterton, R. B., Jane, J. A., Diamond, I. T. *J. Neurophysiol.*, **20** 341–60 (1967)

134. Matsuura, S., Ikeda, K. Furukawa, T. *Science*, **169**, 1117–19 (1968)

135. Mikaelian, D. O. *Acta Otolaryngol.*, **62**, 545–56 (1966)

136. Møhl, B. *Videnskab. Medd. Dansk Naturh. Foren.*, **127**, 283–94 (1964)

137. Mohl, B. *Science*, **157**, 99 (1967)

138. Möhres, F. P. In *Animal Sonar Systems* (See Ref. 8), 115–27

139. Moushegian, G., Rupert, A., Galambos, R. *J. Neurophysiol.*, **25**, 515–30 (1962)

140. Moushegian G., Rupert, A., Whitcomb, M. *J. Neurophysiol.*, **27**, 1174–91 (1964)

141. Naftalin, L. In *Sensory Receptors, Cold Spring Harbor Symp. Quant. Biol.*, **30**, 169–80 (1965)

142. Nagel, E. L., Morgane, P. J., McFarland, W. L. *Science*, **146**, 1591–93 (1964)

143. Nelson, D. R., Gruber, S. H. *Science*, **142**, 975–77 (1963)

144. Nelson, P. G., Erulkar, S. D. *J. Neurophysiol.*, **26**, 908–23 (1963)

145. Nelson, P. G., Erulkar, S. D., Bryan, J. S. *J. Neurophysiol.*, **29**, 834–60 (1966)

146. Nicklaus, J. Z. *Vergleich. Physiol.*, **50**, 331–62 (1965)

147. Nieder, P., Nieder, I. *J. Acoust. Soc. Am.*, **43**, 1092–1106 (1968)

148. Nobel, K. W., Dewson, J. H. III, *J. Aud. Res.*, **6**, 67–75 (1966)
149. Nomoto, M., Suga, N., Katsuki, Y. *J. Neurophysiol.*, **27**, 768–87 (1964)
150. Norberg, Å. *Arkiv Zool.*, **20**, 181–204 (1968)
151. Norris, K. S. In *Marine Bio-Acoustics* (See Ref. 4), 317–36 (1964)
152. Norris, K. S. In *The Biology of Marine Mammals* (Andersen, H. T., Ed., Academic Press, New York, 1968)
153. Norris, K. S., Evans, W. E. (In press)
154. Norris, K. S., Evans, W. E., Turner, R. N. In *Animal Sonar Systems* (See Ref. 8), 409–37
155. Novick, A. *Ergebn. Biol.*, **26**, 21–26 (1963)
156. Novick, A., Vaisnys, J. R. *Biol. Bull.*, **127**, 478–88 (1964)
157. Parker, D. E. *J. Aud. Res.*, **2**, 99–124 (1962)
158. Parker, D. E., Mundie, J. R. *J. Aud. Res.*, **7**, 287–301 (1967)
159. Patterson, W. C. *J. Aud. Res.*, **6**, 453–64 (1966)
160. Payne, R. *Tech. Rept. No. 1* (ONR Contr. 3225(00) Harvard Univ., Cambridge, Mass, 1961)
161. Payne, R. S., Roeder, K. D., Wallman, J. *J. Exptl. Biol.* **44**, 17–31 (1966)
162. Peake, W. T. *An analytical study of electric responses at the periphery of the auditory system. Tech. Rept. 365* (MIT Res. Lab. Electron., Cambridge, Mass, 1960)
163. Potter, H. D. *J. Neurophysiol.*, **28**, 1155–84 (1965)
164. Poulter, T. In *Animal Sonar System* (See Ref. 8), 157–86
165. Price, L. L. *J. Aud. Res.*, **7**, 229–39 (1967)
166. Purves, D. E. In *Animal Sonar Systems* (See Ref. 8), 197–270
167. Pye, Ade. *J. Morphol.*, **118**, 495–510; **119**, 101–20 (1966) and **121**, 241–54 (1967)
168. Pye, J. D. In *Hearing Mechanisms in Vertebrates* (See Ref. 46), 66–84
169. Pye, J. D., Flinn, M., Pye, A. *Nature*, **196**, 1185–88 (1962)
170. Rasmussen, G. L. In *Sensorineural Hearing Processes and Disorders* (See Ref. 44), 61–75
171. Rauch, S. *Biochemie des Hörorgans.* Georg Thieme Verlag, Stuttgart, 469 pp., 1964)
172. Rauch, S., Kostlin, A., Schneider, E., Schindler, K. *Laryngoscope*, **73**, 135–47 (1963)
173. Ridgeway, S. H., McCormick, J. G. *Science*, **158**, 511–12 (1967)
174. Robbins, Ruth G., Bauknight, R. S., Honrubia, V. *Acta Otolaryngol.*, **64**, 436–48 (1967)
175. Roeder, K. D. *J. Insect Physiol.*, **12**, 843–59 (1966)
176. Roeder, K. D. *Ibid.*, 1227–44
177. Roeder, K. D. *Science*, **154**, 1515–21 (1966)
178. Rose, J. E., Brugge, J. F., Anderson, D. J., Hind, J. E. *J. Neurophysiol.*, **30**, 769–93 (1967)
179. Rose, J., Galamos, R., Hughes, J. In *Neural Mechanisms of the Auditory and Vestibular Systems* (Rasmussen, G. L., Windle, W. F., Eds., 1960)
180. Rose, J. E., Greenwood, D. D., Goldberg, J. M., Hind, J. E. *J. Neurophysiol.* **26**, 294–321 (1963)
181. Rose, J. E., Gross, N. B., Geisler, C. D., Hind, J. E. *J. Neurophysiol.*, **29**, 288–314 (1966)
182. Rupert, A. Moushegian, G., Galambos, R. *J. Neurophysiol.*, **26**, 449–65 (1963)
183. Rupert, A., Moushegian, G., Whitcomb, M. A. *J. Acoust. Soc. Am.*, **39**, 1069–76 (1966)
184. Rupert, A. L., Moushegian, G., Whitcomb, M. A. *Exptl. Neurol.*, **20**, 575–84 (1968)
185. Russell, I. J. *Nature*, **219**, 177–78 (1968)
186. Sachs, M. B., Kiang, N. *J. Acoust. Soc. Am.*, **43**, 1120–28 (1968)
187. Salomon, G. *Acta Otolaryngol. Suppl.* **244**, 218–19 (1966)
188. Sando, I. *Acta Otolaryngol.*, **59**, 417–36 (1965)
189. Schmidt, R. S., Fernandez, C. *J. Cellular Comp. Physiol.*, **59**, 311–22 (1962)
190. Schnitzler, H.-U. In *Animal Sonar Systems* (See Ref. 8), 69–87
191. Schnitzler, H.-U. *Z. Vergleich. Physiol.*, **57**, 376–408 (1968)
192. Schuknecht, H. F. In *Neural Mechanisms of the Auditory and Vestibular Systems* (See Ref. 179), 76–90
193. Schusterman, R. J. In *Animal Sonar Systems* (See Ref. 8), 535–617
194. Schwartzkopff, J. *Ann. Rev. Physiol.*, **29**, 485–512 (1967)
195. Schwartzkopff, J. In *Hearing Mechanisms in Vertebrates* (See Ref. 46), 41–59
196. Simmons, F. B. *Ann. Otolaryngol.*, **73**, 724–40 (1964)
197. Smith, C. A., Rasmussen, G. L. *Ann. Otolaryngol.*, **72**, 489–506 (1963)

198. Smith, J. J. B. *J. Exptl. Biol.*, **48**, 191–205 (1968)
199. Sohmer, H. *Acta Otolaryngol.*, **62**, 74–88 (1966)
200. Spoendlin, H. H. *The organization of the cochlear receptor* (Karger, Basel, Advan. Oto-Rhino-Laryngol., **13**, 1966)
201. Spoendlin, H. H., Gacek, R. R. *Ann. Otolaryngol.*, **72**, 660–86 (1963)
202. Stopp, P. E., Whitfield, I. C. *J. Physiol.*, **158**, 165–77 (1961)
203. Stopp, P. E., Whitfield, I. C. *Ibid.*, **175**, 45–46P (1964)
204. Suga, N. *J. Physiol.*, **172**, 449–74 (1964)
205. Suga, N. *Ibid.*, **175**, 50–80
206. Suga, N. *Ibid.*, **179**, 26–53 (1965)
207. Suga, N. *Ibid.*, **181**, 671–700
208. Suga, N. *Nature*, **206**, 890–91 (1965)
209. Suga, N. *J. Physiol.* (In press) (1968)
210. Suga, N., Campbell, H. W. *Science*, **157**, 88–90 (1967)
211. Suthers, R. *Science*, **152**, 1102–4 (1966)
212. Tanaka, Y., Katsuki, Y. *J. Neurophysiol.*, **29**, 94–108 (1966)
213. Tasaki, I., Davis, H., Eldredge, D. H. *J. Acoust. Soc. Am.*, **26**, 765–73 (1954)
214. Tasaki, I., Spyropoulos, C. S. *J. Neurophysiol.*, **15**, 497–512 (1959)
215. Tavolga, W. N., Ed. *Marine Bio-Acoustics* (See Ref. 4)
216. Thurm, U. In *Sensory Receptors. Cold Spring Harbor Symp. Quant. Biol.*, **30**, 75–94 (1965)
217. Tonndorf, J., Khanna, S. M. *J. Acoust. Soc. Am.*, **41**, 513–21 (1967)
218. Tonndorf, J., Khanna, S. *Ann. Otolaryngol.*, **77**, 154–63 (1968)
219. Trinkner, D. *Pflügers Arch.*, **264**, 351–82 (1957)
220. Tsuchitani, C., Boudreau, J. C. *J. Neurophysiol.*, **27**, 814–27 (1964)
221. Vernon, J. A., Dalland, J. I., Wever, E. G. *J. Aud. Res.*, **6**, 153–63 (1966)
222. Vernon, J., Peterson, E. *J. Aud. Res.*, **6**, 181–87 (1966)
223. Walcott, E. *J. Exptl. Biol.*, **40**, 595–611 (1963)
224. Watanabe, T. *Japan. J. Physiol.*, **15**, 92–100 (1965)
225. Watanabe, T., Yanagisawa, K., Kanzaki, J., Katsuki, Y. *Exptl. Brain. Res.*, **2**, 302–17 (1966)
226. Webster, D. B. *Natural History*, 27–33 (Feb. 1965)
227. Webster, F. A. In *Animal Sonar Systems* (See Ref. 8), 673–713
228. Weiss, B. A., Strother, W. F. *J. Aud. Res.*, **5**, 297–305 (1965)
229. Wersäll, J., Flock, Å., Lundquist P. G. In *Sensory Receptors. Cold Spring Harbor Symp. Quant. Biol.*, **30**, 115–32 (1965)
230. Wever, E. G. *Ann. Otol. Rhinol. Laryngol.*, **68**, 975–89 (1959)
231. Wever, E. G. *J. Aud. Res.*, **5**, 331–71 (1965)
232. Wever, E. G. *Physiol. Rev.*, **46**, 102–27 (1966)
233. Wever, E. G., Vernon, J. A., Crowley, D. E., Peterson, E. A. *Science*, **150**, 1172–74 (1965)
234. Whitfield, I. C. *The Auditory Pathway* (Edward Arnold Ltd., London, 1967)
235. Whitfield, I. C., Evans, E. F. *J. Neurophysiol.*, **28**, 655–72 (1965)
236. Whitfield, I. C., Ross, H. F. *J. Acoust. Soc. Am.*, **38**, 126–31 (1965)
237. Wiederhold, M. C., Peake, W. T. *J. Acoust. Soc. Am.*, **40**, Part 2: 1427–30 (1966)
238. Wigand, M. E. *Pflügers Arch.*, **271**, 296–315 (1960)
239. Yanagisawa, K., Hashimoto, T., Katsuki, Y. *J. Insect Physiol.*, **13**, 635–43 (1967)

BIOLOGICAL MEMBRANES: THE PHYSICAL BASIS OF ION AND NONELECTROLYTE SELECTIVITY[1]

By Jared M. Diamond and Ernest M. Wright

Department of Physiology, University of California Medical Center
Los Angeles, California

Contents

[1] The survey of literature for this review was concluded in August 1968.

Basic to the function of cell membranes is the ability to select between closely similar ions and molecules, such as potassium and sodium, calcium and magnesium, alcohols and aldehydes, and esters and acids. An understanding of the principles underlying selectivity is relevant to the study of neurophysiology, active transport, passive permeation, enzyme activation, and membrane structure. The present chapter has a twofold purpose: to summarize experimental evidence concerning the distinctive and consistent selectivity patterns exhibited by biological membranes; and to review recent developments that have made it possible to account in large part for the main features of these patterns in terms of intermolecular and interatomic forces. Analyses of selectivity must begin by trying to explain as many phenomena as possible in terms of elementary physical concepts such as free energy, and in terms of the simplest principles governing the interactions of ions, such as Coulomb's law, or the simplest principles governing the interactions of nonelectrolytes, such as hydrogen bonding and van der Waals forces. While consideration of additional forces may prove necessary to interpret some more complex phenomena, explanations that do not take account even of the simplest forces cannot provide an adequate starting-point. The first half of this chapter is devoted to ion selectivity, while the second half deals with nonelectrolyte selectivity.

PART I. ION SELECTIVITY
INTRODUCTION

Potassium and sodium exhibit marked quantitative differences in their abilities to penetrate cell membranes at rest and during excitation, in their affinities for active transport mechanisms, and in their potency in activating enzymes. For example, resting nerve membrane is about 30 times more permeable to K^+ than to Na^+, while active nerve membrane is 10 times more permeable to Na^+ than to K^+. These differences form the basis for much of neurophysiology and for the maintenance of cell volume. However, K^+ and Na^+ are quite similar in their physical and chemical properties to each other and to the three other alkali cations in group I of the periodic table, lithium (Li^+), cesium (Cs^+), and rubidium (Rb^+). As far as their interactions with water and with simple anions are concerned, the five alkali cations can be well approximated as rigid, nonpolarizable, monopolar spheres differing only in radius. The mechanism of alkali-cation discrimination is therefore not only one of the central problems of cell physiology but also a question of basic physical interest. Analogous problems of biological importance and of equal physical interest are posed by discrimination among the alkaline-earth cations (Ca^{++}, Mg^{++}, Sr^{++}, Ba^{++}) and among the halide anions (Cl^-, Br^-, I^-, F^-).

Nonbiological systems, such as soils, minerals, ion exchange resins, and glass electrodes, also discriminate among the alkali cations and among ions of other groups. The ranges of selectivity patterns observed (the so-called "transition sequences" discussed below) show such striking and detailed similarities in nonbiological and in biological systems as to make it likely that the underlying physical mechanism of discrimination is the same in both cases. As a result of theoretical studies stemming from Jenny in the late 1920s, further advanced by Bungenberg de Jong, recently stimulated by the development of the ion-specific glass electrodes and by accumulated measurements of biological sequences, but most of all as a result of the work of Eisenman (1–3), physical chemists interested in ion selectivity are now in general agreement concerning the theoretical framework for interpretation (see 4–6 for discussions).

We shall therefore begin by summarizing the alkali-cation selectivity patterns observed in nonliving systems and by tabulating recently determined patterns in biological systems for comparison. The basic physical principles governing alkali-cation equilibrium selectivity are then discussed in broad outline. The patterns and the physical basis of halide anion selectivity and of divalent-cation selectivity are similarly summarized. Finally, some physical determinants of ion selectivity, and some common misconceptions in the physiological literature, are re-examined in more detail.

Alkali-Cation Selectivity in Nonliving Systems

Historically, the problem of alkali-cation selectivity in nonliving systems first received systematic attention in studies conducted by geologists and chemists early in this century on ion exchange by soils. The ability of soils to bind different alkali cations with different strengths was found to be due to the presence of naturally occurring aluminosilicate minerals which were isolated, studied as ion exchangers, and compared with artificial aluminosilicates. For example, Jaeger (7) found that the mineral ultramarine at 160° C bound Li^+ the most strongly of the five alkali cations and Cs^+ the least strongly, the whole sequence being $Li^+ > Na^+ > K^+ > Rb^+ > Cs^+$. The measured ionic (nonhydrated) radii of the alkali cations increase in this order, Li^+ being smallest and Cs^+ largest [Li^+ 0.60Å, Na^+ 0.95Å, K^+ 1.33Å, Rb^+ 1.48Å, Cs^+ 1.69Å, from Pauling (8)]. It was therefore natural to interpret the ion exchange selectivity of ultramarine in terms of the closeness with which nonhydrated positive ions of different sizes could approach the negatively charged aluminosilicate site:[2] the center of charge of the small Li^+ would be closest to the negative site, Li^+ would experience the greatest electrostatic attractive force, and would therefore be the most strongly bound.

On the other hand, many other aluminosilicates, such as a permutit studied by Jenny (9), exhibited the reverse sequence of binding strength, $Cs^+ > Rb^+ > K^+ > Na^+ > Li^+$. In aqueous solution the measured mobilities

[2] In the language of ion exchange a site is defined as a group fixed in the membrane and bearing a net ionic charge (e.g., $AlOSi^-$, COO^-, etc.) which is balanced electrically by oppositely charged mobile ions. In this chapter we shall also use the word site loosely (e.g., in the expression, ion:site interactions) to mean whatever membrane group is the nearest neighbor of a mobile permeating ion, whether the membrane group bears a net charge or not (see p. 607 and footnote 3, p. 592, for discussion).

decrease, and hence the calculated Stokes-law hydrated radii increase, in the same order (the so-called lyotropic series): Li^+ has the smallest ionic radius but also the smallest free-solution mobility and thus the largest apparent hydrated size. The reason is that the smaller the ion, the nearer to water molecules its center of charge lies, and hence the more strongly it is hydrated. Jenny therefore postulated that the different selectivity patterns of ultramarine and of permutit arose because the ions were present in the non-hydrated form in the former case, in the hydrated form in the latter case; and that Cs^+ was most strongly bound in permutit because it had the smallest hydrated size and could now approach closest to the negative charge of the aluminosilicate site.

Unfortunately for this simple interpretation, it soon became apparent that still other selectivity patterns than these two were exhibited by some other minerals. For example, Barrer, Rees & Ward (10) found that a synthetic aluminosilicate called Linde A, which belongs to the class of aluminosilicates called zeolites, binds alkali cations in the sequence $Na^+ > K^+ > Rb^+ > Li^+ > Cs^+$. The patterns $Cs^+ > K^+ > Rb^+ > Na^+ > Li^+$, $K^+ > Cs^+ > Rb^+ > Na^+ > Li^+$, $Na^+ > K^+ > Rb^+ > Cs^+ > Li^+$, $Na^+ > K^+ > Li^+ > Rb^+ > Cs^+$, or $Na^+ > Li^+ > K^+ > Rb^+ > Cs^+$ were found in other zeolites. These puzzling patterns corresponded neither to the order of the nonhydrated radii nor to the order of the apparent hydrated radii, and Jenny (9, p. 2252) referred to them as "irregularities in the lyotropic series".

A second class of objects besides soil minerals marked by "irregularities" in alkali-cation selectivity was provided by the development of the commercial ion exchange resins (4). Most of these consisted of a polystyrene matrix crosslinked to varying extents with divinylbenzene and bearing negatively charged groups, such as sulfonate or carboxyl, which acted as sites for exchange of cations. In some resins the alkali cations were bound in the order of their apparent hydrated radii (the lyotropic series), as in Jenny's permutit. However, sequences other than the lyotropic series or the sequence of the ionic radii were also obtained. For instance, Reichenberg (4) found that the affinity sequence for a resin with sulfonate groups and with moderate crosslinking (10–15 per cent divinylbenzene) was $K^+ > Cs^+ > Na^+ > Li^+$ (Rb^+ not tested), which differs from the lyotropic series in that the order of K^+ and Cs^+ is reversed.

A third source of "irregularities" came from electrical measurements on permselective collodion membranes, which are permeable to cations but not to anions by virtue of containing negatively charged carboxyl groups. Ling & Kushnir (see 1) estimated the relative permeabilities of different alkali cations from the electrical potential difference developed when the membrane separated solutions of two different alkali cations. Depending upon how the membranes were prepared, the relative permeabilities were in one of three sequences: $Cs^+ > Rb^+ > K^+ > Na^+ > Li^+$, $Cs^+ > K^+ > Rb^+ > Na^+ > Li^+$, or $K^+ > Cs^+ > Rb^+ > Na^+ > Li^+$. The first of these is the lyotropic series, but the other two sequences are neither in the order of nonhydrated size nor of apparent hydrated size.

At this point one might wonder whether systematic study would show the number of alkali-cation selectivity sequences to be so large as to be essentially random and chaotic and to defy generalization, since permutation of the five alkali cations (5!) would yield 120 possible selectivity sequences. However, certain sequences were found repeatedly in these studies of minerals, resins, and collodion membranes, while other permutations were never observed. For instance, systems preferring Na^+ to Cs^+ generally preferred K^+ to Rb^+ and Rb^+ to Cs^+, though they might or might not prefer Na^+ to K^+, while systems preferring Li^+ to Na^+ generally did prefer Na^+ to K^+.

The systematic search for regularities in cation selectivity sequences was greatly facilitated by the development of the cation-selective glass electrodes. Glass electrodes which were made of SiO_2 and the oxide of an alkali metal and whose electrical potential differences were governed almost solely by the hydrogen ion (activity) gradient had been known since the time of Cremer (1906). Hughes (11) and others showed that these pH electrodes exhibited an "alkaline error", i.e., a sensitivity to alkali metal ions as well as to $[H^+]$, which introduced an error into pH determinations at high pH (low H^+ concentration) and whose magnitude was correlated with the amounts of Al_2O_3 or B_2O_3 present in the glass. In 1957 Eisenman, Rudin & Casby (12) exploited this finding by preparing three-component glasses of $SiO_2 + Al_2O_3 + Na_2O$ mixed in varying proportions and found that varying the glass composition produced systematic variations in selectivity among the alkali cations and other ions; they thereby obtained practical electrodes responding preferentially to different alkali cations. In addition to the SiO_2-Al_2O_3-Na_2O glasses, these authors also studied glasses in which Na_2O had been replaced by Li_2O or K_2O, Al^{+++} had been replaced by B^{+++} or Sc^{+++}, and SiO_2 had been replaced by GeO_2. Later the effects of numerous other components added to SiO_2 plus the alkali oxide were tested (13). The particular alkali cation to which a given glass was most sensitive did not need to be a component of the glass. The selectivity preferences of most of these glasses for the five alkali cations fell into one of 11 sequences, the other 109 possible permutations not being observed in practice. The selectivities of most soil minerals and synthetic aluminosilicate ion exchangers, resins, and collodion membranes were noted in retrospect to belong to the same 11 sequences (1). They are:

$$\text{I} \quad Cs^+ > Rb^+ > K^+ > Na^+ > Li^+$$
$$\text{II} \quad Rb^+ > Cs^+ > K^+ > Na^+ > Li^+$$
$$\text{III} \quad Rb^+ > K^+ > Cs^+ > Na^+ > Li^+$$
$$\text{IV} \quad K^+ > Rb^+ > Cs^+ > Na^+ > Li^+$$
$$\text{V} \quad K^+ > Rb^+ > Na^+ > Cs^+ > Li^+$$
$$\text{VI} \quad K^+ > Na^+ > Rb^+ > Cs^+ > Li^+$$
$$\text{VII} \quad Na^+ > K^+ > Rb^+ > Cs^+ > Li^+$$
$$\text{VIII} \quad Na^+ > K^+ > Rb^+ > Li^+ > Cs^+$$
$$\text{IX} \quad Na^+ > K^+ > Li^+ > Rb^+ > Cs^+$$
$$\text{X} \quad Na^+ > Li^+ > K^+ > Rb^+ > Cs^+$$
$$\text{XI} \quad Li^+ > Na^+ > K^+ > Rb^+ > Cs^+$$

Each sequence differs from the preceding and following sequence only in inversion of the positions of one pair of cations; the sequences II through X constitute "transition sequences" linking sequence I, the lyotropic series defined by increasing apparent hydrated size, to sequence XI, defined by increasing nonhydrated size. That this sequential arrangement of the transition series corresponds to some underlying reality is shown by the fact that as one increases the Al_2O_3/Na_2O ratio in the electrode glass, or raises the pH from an acid value, one proceeds through the sequences in the direction I through XI. Beginning with sequence I, the first inversions encountered (sequences I–IV) involve Cs^+, Rb^+, and K^+, the three largest and hence least strongly hydrated cations; then (sequences IV–VII) the position of Na^+, which is more strongly hydrated, inverts with respect to each of these three cations in turn; and finally (sequences VII–XI) Li^+, the smallest and most strongly hydrated cation, inverts with respect to the other four to yield sequence XI, in which affinity decreases with increasing nonhydrated size. The underlying reason why the inversions start with the largest and end with the smallest ion is discussed on p. 606.

In addition to the regular qualitative pattern defined by these 11 sequences actually observed out of 120 possible permutations, quantitative regularities were also observed in the magnitudes of selectivity encountered in glass electrodes, aluminosilicate ion exchangers, and collodion membranes: a given sequence also implied a given range of selectivity ratios. For instance, sequence IX ($Na^+ > K^+ > Li^+ > Rb^+ > Cs^+$) implied approximately the ranges of selectivity ratios $Na^+/K^+ = 5$ to 80, $Li^+/K^+ = 0.2$ to 1, $Rb^+/K^+ = 0.1$ to 0.2, $Cs^+/K^+ = 0.006$ to 0.01. The existence of these quantitative patterns became clear in the course of attempts to find glass electrodes with higher or differing selectivities by varying glass components or their proportions: such attempts only yielded more electrodes with the same range of selectivity magnitudes (1, 13). When the selectivity ratios for many systems are plotted on the same graph as a function of, say, the Na^+/K^+ selectivity ratio, one obtains a set of five intersecting curves (the so-called selectivity isotherms) for the five alkali cations, the intersections determining transitions from one sequence to the next. In the vicinity of sequence II the Cs^+, Rb^+, and K^+ isotherms lie close to each other, and the exact sequence of intersections varies somewhat among different systems, so that $Cs^+ > K^+ > Rb^+ > Na^+ > Li^+$ (sequence IIa) and $K^+ > Cs^+ > Rb^+ > Na^+ > Li^+$ (sequence IIIa) are obtained in some systems as minor quantitative variants of sequences II and III. Since these selectivity isotherms for the alkali cations have been published previously [e.g., Figure 8 of (1), Figure 8 of (2), Figure 7 of (3)], they are not reproduced here but are similar in principle to the halide isotherms and alkaline-earth isotherms derived in Figures 1 and 2 of this chapter. Detailed discussion of selectivity isotherms and their construction will therefore be postponed until we consider Figures 1 and 2; the meaning of the present paragraph should then become clearer.

ALKALI-CATION SELECTIVITY IN BIOLOGICAL SYSTEMS

Relative potencies of the alkali cations have been determined by varied methods for many different kinds of effects in a wide variety of biological systems. These effects include: the ability to mimic potassium in controlling the resting potential of cell membranes; the ability to mimic sodium in controlling the height of the action potential in nerve, muscle, and other excitable tissues; contributions to membrane conductance; passive one-way tracer fluxes across membranes; affinities for active transport mechanisms; ability to activate Na^+- or K^+-requiring enzymes; the permeability induced in thin lipid membranes by peptide and polyene antibiotics such as valinomycin; and miscellaneous effects such as stimulation of respiration in yeast and stimulation of the salt receptor in blowflies.

This large and diverse body of experimental results may be briefly summarized by saying that the alkali-cation selectivity patterns determined in most biological systems belong to the same 11 selectivity patterns (and are characterized by similar ranges of selectivity and permeability ratios) as those found in nonliving systems. Since earlier evidence for these statements has been reviewed in detail elsewhere (3, 14), we shall mention only some of the more recent studies of selectivity patterns:

Berridge (15) found that the rate of urine flow in Malpighian tubules of the blowfly *Calliphora erythrocephala* was stimulated in the order $K^+ > Rb^+ > Cs^+ > Na^+ > Li^+$ (sequence IV).

The permeability sequence in rabbit gallbladder epithelium was determined by Wright & Diamond (16) as $K^+ > Na^+ > Cs^+$ (sequence V or VI) at pH 7, and as $K^+ > Cs^+ > Na^+$ (sequence III or IV) at pH 2.4.

The potency order for replacing Na^+ in the "sodium channel" of squid axon was given by Chandler & Meves (17) as $Li^+ > Na^+ > K^+ > Rb^+ > Cs^+$ (sequence XI), extending the familiar observation that Li^+ can replace Na^+ in generating spikes but that the action potential selects sodium over potassium.

Salt receptors of blowflies (18) are stimulated in the order $K^+ > Na^+ > Rb^+ > Cs^+ > Li^+$ (sequence VI).

Much recent interest has been attracted by the selective cation permeability induced in thin lipid membranes by small quantities of large-ring compounds, such as the cyclic polypeptide antibiotics related to valinomycin, the macrolide actins, the carboxyl antibiotics related to nigericin, and the cyclic "crown" polyethers. Selectivity patterns determined by Pressman (19) for six of these compounds, based on cation migration from an aqueous phase to a butanol-toluene phase containing the antibiotic, are: nigericin, $K^+ > Rb^+ > Na^+ > Cs^+ > Li^+$ (sequence V); dianemycin, $Na^+ > K^+ > Rb^+$, $Cs^+ > Li^+$ (sequence VII); X-206, $K^+ > Rb^+ > Na^+ > Cs^+ > Li^+$ (sequence V); X-537, $Cs^+ > K^+ > Rb^+ > Na^+ > Li^+$ (sequence IIa); valinomycin, $Rb^+ > K^+ > Cs^+ > Na^+ > Li^+$ (sequence III); monensin, $Na^+ > K^+ > Rb^+ > Cs^+$ (sequence VII or higher). $Rb^+ > K^+ > Cs^+ > Na^+ > Li^+$ (sequence III) was obtained by Mueller & Rudin (20) for thin lipid membranes containing valinomycin, enniatin B, gramicidin A, or dinactin, by Lev & Buzhinsky (21) for thin lipid membranes containing valinomycin, and by Andreoli, Tieffenberg & Tosteson (22) for thin membranes made from sheep erythrocyte lipids after addition of valinomycin. Eisenman, Ciani & Szabo (23) found $K^+ > Rb^+ > Cs^+ > Na^+ > Li^+$ (sequence IV) for permeabilities of lipid bilayers containing monactin or the cyclic polyether XXXI [names of these ethers follow Pedersen's (24) terminology], for the conductance of bilayers containing monactin, for cation migration from an aqueous phase into a hexane or methylene chloride phase containing monactin, and for migration into a methylene chloride phase containing the polyether XXXI; $Cs^+ > Rb^+ > K^+ > Na^+ \sim Li^+$ (sequence I) for the conductance of bilayers containing polyether XXXI; and $K^+ > Rb^+ > Na^+ > Cs^+ > Li^+$ (sequence V) for migration into a hexane phase containing polyether XXXI. Studying migration into a methylene chloride phase containing a polyether, Pedersen (25) obtained sequence IV for polyethers V', VI', and X'; sequence VII for polyether IV'; and sequence XI for polyether II'.

Effectiveness in maintaining the potential difference across the isolated beef cornea (26) (presumably reflecting affinities for an active transport mechanism) is in the order $Li^+ > Na^+ > K^+$, Rb^+ (sequence XI).

The enzyme microsomal phosphatase from gastric mucosa (27) is stimulated in the order $K^+ > Rb^+ > Cs^+ > Na^+$, Li^+ (sequence IV).

From changes in electrophoretic velocity Bungenberg de Jong (28) estimated binding affinities to the colloids pectinate, pectate, and agar to decrease in the order $Cs^+ > Rb^+ > K^+ > Na^+ > Li^+$ (sequence I).

DNA from calf thymus and RNA from yeast (29) bind cations in the order $Li^+ > Na^+ > K^+ > Rb^+ > Cs^+$ (sequence XI).

Relative affinities for the cation transport system in yeast (30) are $K^+ > Rb^+ > Cs^+ > Na^+ > Li^+$ (sequence IV).

The order of equilibrium distribution ratios for muscle cells (31) is $K^+ > Rb^+ > Cs^+ > Na^+$ (sequence IV).

Myosin ATPase (32) is inhibited by alkali cations in the order $Li^+ > Na^+ > K^+ > Rb^+ > Cs^+$ (sequence XI).

The sequence for stimulation of sodium extrusion in squid axons was determined as $K^+ > Rb^+ > Cs^+$ (sequence IV or higher) by Sjodin & Beaugé (33) from efflux rate constants of radioactive sodium. Baker & Connelly (34) obtained the same sequence by a different method, measurement of oxygen consumption, for stimulation of sodium extrusion in crab nerve.

As deduced by Lindley & Hoshiko (35) from measurements of changes in the potential difference across frog skin, the permeability order is $Na^+ > Li > Rb^+$, K^+, Cs^+ (approximately sequence X) at the outer surface of the skin, but $K^+ > Rb^+ > Cs^+ > Li^+ > Na^+$ (differs from sequence IV only in the higher potency of Li^+) at the inner surface.

Maizels (36) found that the effect on Na^+ efflux from red cells of a second alkali cation, present in the bathing solution and inside the cells, depended upon the sodium concentration: $K^+ > Cs^+ > Rb^+ > Li^+$ (sequence IIIa) at high [Na^+], $Cs^+ > K^+ > Rb^+ > Li^+$ (sequence IIa) at lower [Na^+], and $Cs^+ > K^+ > Li^+ > Rb^+$ and $Cs^+ > Li > K^+ > Rb^+$ (deviant sequences due to anomalous position of Li^+) at still lower [Na^+].

There are three other instances similar to the last two sequences reported by Maizels and the pattern for frog skin inner surface, which differ from the usual patterns in that transitions involving the smallest cation Li^+ apparently occur before rather than after other transitions.

Actomyosin ATPase is inhibited by alkali cations (37) in the order $Cs^+ > Li^+ > Rb^+$, $K^+ > Na^+$ (differs from sequence I in Li^+ inversions but no other inversions).

Relative effects on electrophoretic velocities of phosphate colloids are $Li^+ > Cs^+ > Rb^+ > Na^+ > K^+$ for egg lecithin and $Li^+ > Cs^+ > Na^+ > Rb^+ > K^+$ for the alcohol-soluble fraction of soya bean phosphatide (28). These two colloid cases reverse completely the usual order of transitions, in that Li^+ inversions are being followed by inversions for the next smallest cation Na^+, which must in turn be followed by inversions among the three largest cations Cs^+, Rb^+, and K^+.

Selectivity isotherms may be constructed from these biological data as already mentioned in connection with the data from nonliving systems (p. 586) and as will be explained in more detail when we come to the halide and alkaline-earth isotherms (Figures 1 and 2 of this chapter). The resulting biological isotherms and the glass electrode isotherms differ principally in a shift in the Li^+ curve, such that biological systems discriminate against Li^+ less sharply than do glasses even when Li^+ stands qualitatively in one of the usual "glass" sequences, as is generally the case. This point may be appreciated by comparing Figure 9 of (3) with the upper half of Figure 7 of the same reference. The significance of this quantitative Li^+ shift and of the more marked sequence anomalies just cited involving Li^+ is discussed on p. 607. A further feature of both the biological and the glass isotherms to be discussed later is the indication provided by a few systems that the Rb^+ and Cs^+ isotherms re-intersect the other isotherms after sequence XI to commence a new set of sequences. This is illustrated by one recent example: the sequence $Li^+ > Na^+ > Rb^+ > K^+ > Cs^+$ for affinities to DNA (38), differing from sequence XI in the Rb^+-K^+ reversal.

The Origin of Alkali-Cation Equilibrium Selectivity

Early attempts to explain the origin of alkali-cation equilibrium selectivity and to predict the observed transition sequences were put forward by Jenny (9, 39) in 1927, by Bungenberg de Jong (28, 40) in 1939, by Gregor (41) in 1948, and by Ling (42) in 1952. Jenny (9, p. 2252 and p. 2257) reasoned: "The observed irregularities [i.e., the transition sequences] in the lyotropic series of natural aluminum silicates can be interpreted as various stages in the reversal of the normal hydration order of the exchanging cations. . . . Obviously the most hydrated ion will be first affected by dehydration processes. . . . It appears that these 'hydrodynamic radii' [=hydrated ion radii] vary accordingly to the nature of the colloidal system." Jenny did not discuss what factors might be responsible for this progessive dehydration of ions. His assumption that the most hydrated ion should be first to become dehydrated leads to the prediction that inversions involving Li^+ should occur first, those involving Na^+ next, and those involving K^+, Rb^+, and Cs^+ last as one proceeds from sequence I to XI, whereas the actual order in most cases is the opposite of this prediction, as already discussed (p. 586).

Bungenberg de Jong (40; 28, pp. 287–88) attributed selectivity to the relative polarizabilities of the negatively charged ion exchange site and of water. Polarization either of the site or of water by a cation would increase site:cation or water:cation electrostatic attraction and would be stronger for smaller cations. A site much more polarizable than water would yield sequence XI, the order of nonhydrated radii; a site much less polarizable than water would yield sequence I, the order of apparent hydrated size; and intermediate degrees of polarizability would yield transition sequences. However, the predicted transition sequences are the reverse of most of those actually observed, since Bungenberg de Jong's postulate predicts, as did Jenny's, that reversals involving Li^+ should occur first as one proceeds from sequence I to XI. Gregor (41) related the ion exchange equilibrium constant to the different hydrated volumes of different cations, the elastic counterpressure built up within the exchanger, and the stripping of water molecules from hydrated ions. His theory was criticized for its failure to explain the apparent differential stripping of hydration water that had to be postulated to account for transitions, and for the arbitrariness inherent in using apparent hydrated sizes as the reference point. Ling (42) calculated electrostatic forces between hydrated cations and anionic sites, but was unable (43) to account on this basis for sequences inverted from those of apparent hydrated sizes, such as $Na^+ > K^+$, and was also criticized, as was Gregor, for using apparent hydrated sizes as his reference point. Thus, these earlier theories of ion selectivity all broke down over their failure to solve the problem of the transition sequences.

The interpretation of alkali-cation equilibrium selectivity which is now generally accepted by physical chemists (4–6), and which correctly predicts the transition sequences, was put forward by Eisenman (1–3, 13, 14) in 1961. Eisenman's theory attributes selectivity to the different attractive forces, mainly Coulombic, exerted on different cations by water on the one hand and by membrane negative charges on the other. Before discussing in detail how the strength of membrane negative charges controls selectivity, let us consider first some simple observations indicating that such is actually the case, from glass electrode studies and from a recent study on a biological membrane.

The glass electrodes specific for alkali cations are ion exchangers in which the negatively charged site for cation exchange is $(AlOSi)^-$. Protons can screen the negative charge on the site, reducing the effective negative charge strength experienced by a positive counterion. It is found experimentally [cf. Figure 3 of (1)] that the selectivity pattern of a given glass electrode shows some pH dependence, shifting in the direction from sequence XI (order of nonhydrated size) towards sequence I (order of free-solution mobilities) with decreasing pH (increasing H^+ concentration). For example, a glass with the composition 18.3 per cent Na_2O–7.1 per cent Al_2O_3–74.6 per cent SiO_2 exhibits selectivity sequence IX above pH 7, sequence VIII between pH 7 and 5, sequence VII between pH 5 and 3.5, and sequences VI, V, IV, and III in turn as one goes from pH 3.5 to pH 2. A second way of screening the negative $(AlOSi)^-$ sites in a Na_2O–Al_2O_3–SiO_2 electrode is with the Na^+ of the glass itself, by increasing the proportion of Na_2O to Al_2O_3 in the glass. An increased Na^+/Al^{+++} ratio of the glass shifts selectivity in the direction from sequence XI to sequence I (1). For example, if the Si content of a glass is held constant at 50 atoms per cent, an increase in the ratio Na^+/Al^{+++} from 1 to 5 progressively shifts selectivity from sequence X to sequence II. Glasses in which the alkali oxide is Li_2O or K_2O rather than Na_2O show qualitatively the same dependence of selectivity on the Li^+/Al^{+++} or K^+/Al^{+++} ratio. In summary, the empirical observations concerning the systematic dependence of glass electrode selectivity on pH and glass composition suggest that selectivity is controlled by the strength of the negative sites, weaker (more screened) sites yielding sequences nearer the free-solution mobility sequence.

Similar observations suggesting the control of selectivity by negative charge strength have been reported for a biological membrane by Wright & Diamond (16, 44). They estimated relative ionic permeability coefficients in rabbit gallbladder epithelium from measurements of the transepithelial diffusion potentials resulting from ion concentration gradients. At pH 7 the epithelium was more permeable to cations than to anions (e.g., a dilute solution of KCl went electrically positive to a concentrated solution), which suggests that the epithelial cell membranes bore a net negative charge (possibly carboxyl or phosphate groups). At pH 2.4, which the epithelium withstood well providing the exposure was brief, the dilute solution of KCl went electrically negative rather than positive, which indicates that permeability to anions was now higher than to cations and suggests that the membrane bore a net positive charge (possibly amino groups). Variation of pH in the range 2.4 to 10 yielded a graph of KCl diffusion potentials against pH [see Figures 1 and 3 (16)] similar to a pH titration curve for an amphoteric substance with an isoelectric point around pH 3. Low pH both reduced cation conductance and increased anion conductance, as one would expect for a membrane with ionizable negative as well as positive groups.

This picture of the gall bladder as an amphoteric membrane was reinforced by two other kinds of observations: calcium reduced cation conductance and increased anion conductance, presumably by binding membrane negative charges and by acting as a positive site for anion exchange; and exposure to 1,5-difluoro-2,4-dinitrobenzene, which removes positive charge by reacting with amino and other groups, decreased the ratio P_{Cl^-}/P_{Na^+} at low pH. Thus, the strength of the membrane charges responsible for ion selectivity could be monitored by measurements of KCl diffusion potentials and manipulated by changes in pH. Measurement of alkali-cation permeability ratios as a function of pH, based on bi-ionic potentials, yielded two conclusions: 1. The permeability sequence for alkali cations was $K^+ > Na^+ > Cs^+$ (sequence V or VI) at pH 7 but was $K^+ > Cs^+ > Na^+$ (sequence III or IV) at pH 2.4. Thus, a Na^+–Cs^+ inversion occurs between pH 2.4 and 7. 2. The ratio P_{K^+}/P_{Na^+}, while it did not invert, was considerably greater than the free-solution mobility ratio at pH 7 and decreased towards the free-solution value with decreasing pH. This shift of alkali-cation selectivity in a simple biological membrane towards free-solution sequences and values when membrane negative charges are screened by protons is analogous to the behavior of the glass electrodes. It happens that the inversions observed in the gallbladder are duplicated in detail by a glass electrode with the composition 28.3 per cent Na_2O–9.7 per cent Al_2O_3–62.0 per cent SiO_2. Undoubtedly the same phenomenon underlies the observation (45) that the relative potencies of Li^+, Na^+, and K^+, measured electrophoretically, in blocking the negative charges of colloidal trioxystearate and hexaoxystearate shift from sequence X or XI to sequence VI or lower as pH is decreased from 10 to 6.

Thus, these observations on the glass electrodes, on a biological membrane, and on colloids suggest that variation in negative charge strength is what primarily controls alkali-cation selectivity. How does this control operate? Eisenman's reconstruction (1, 2) is based on three facts: 1. Equilibrium cation specificity depends, by definition, upon the free energy difference between ion:membrane and ion:water interactions. 2. Free energies of interactions involving the alkali cations depend largely upon electrostatic forces. 3. The observed selectivity patterns imply that the principal electrostatic forces involved in most systems studied are Coulomb forces (i.e., the forces between two nonpolarizable point charges, varying as the inverse square of the distance). The first two of these statements are self-evident truisms, while the third is an empirical observation which need not apply to all systems.

Consider a material with negative charges,[3] in contact with an aqueous solution containing different alkali cations. The cation preferred by the

[3] The material need not have *net* negative charge: for energetic reasons the nearest neighbor of an alkali cation in biological and many nonbiological systems is at most times certain to be some negatively charged oxygen atom, either in a water molecule, or else in a carboxyl, phosphate, aluminosilicate, or other group. The principles of equilibrium selectivity are the same whether the negative charge is on a biological membrane, an enzyme, an active transport "carrier", a glass electrode or other ion exchange membrane, or a clay or mineral. Relations between nonequilibrium selectivity (e.g., mobility differences) and equilibrium selectivity are discussed on p. 610.

negative site as its nearest neighbor will be that cation which experiences the greatest decrease in free energy when its nearest neighbor becomes the site rather than water. In general, the relative affinities of the site for two different cations a and b will be governed by the free energy difference

$$\Delta F_{a,\,\text{site}} - \Delta F_{b,\,\text{site}} - \Delta F_{a,\,\text{water}} + \Delta F_{b,\,\text{water}} \qquad\qquad 1.$$

where $\Delta F_{a,\text{water}}$ and $\Delta F_{b,\text{water}}$ are the free energies of hydration and $\Delta F_{a,\text{site}}$ and $\Delta F_{b,\text{site}}$ are free energies of interaction between the cation and the negative site. Consider now two extreme cases. Suppose that the site has a very high electric field strength, so that cation:site attractive forces and ΔF's, and their differences, are much higher than the hydration energies and their differences. Then affinities will be controlled by $\Delta F_{a,\text{site}} - \Delta F_{b,\text{site}}$. The smallest cation will have its center of charge nearest the site and will experience the largest attractive force, which for a strong site outweighs its also having the highest free energy of hydration, so that affinity will decrease with increasing ionic radius and sequence XI ($Li^+ > Na^+ > K^+ > Rb^+ > Cs^+$) is obtained. Suppose on the other hand that the site has a very low electric field strength, so that ion:site attractions are much weaker than hydration energies. Then expression 1 is dominated by $\Delta F_{a,\text{water}} - \Delta F_{b,\text{water}}$, the difference in free energies of hydration. In this case the smallest cation, which has the highest free energy of hydration, will have the most unfavorable value of $\Delta F_{\text{ion, site}} - \Delta F_{\text{ion, water}}$ so that affinity will decrease with decreasing ionic radius (increasing apparent hydrated size) and sequence I ($Cs^+ > Rb^+ > K^+ > Na^+ > Li^+$), the lyotropic series, is obtained. These two extreme cases would correspond to glasses with low or high alkali oxide content, or to glasses or membranes at high or low pH.

As site strength is varied continuously from a very low to a very high value, one expects selectivity to proceed through transition sequences which must be calculated from the ΔF's of expression 1. Differences between ΔF's of hydration are accurately known experimentally (46, 47). Eisenman (1, 2) employed two methods of obtaining $\Delta F_{\text{ion, site}}$ for sites of different strengths. Both methods used the alkali halides as examples of anionic sites with different field strengths: the four halide anions (F^-, Cl^-, Br^-, I^-) differ from each other to a first approximation only in size, so that the strongest electrostatic attractive forces for a cation would be exerted by the small F^-, which consequently behaves as a site with high effective field strength; while the weakest attraction would be exerted by the large I^-, whose effective field strength is consequently low. The first method of estimating $\Delta F_{\text{ion,site}}$ for halide-type sites of different field strengths was therefore to equate these ΔF's with the experimentally determined free energies of formation of the alkali halides (NaF, RbCl, KBr, etc.), either as the diatomic gases, or as the crystals, or in aqueous solution (from activity coefficients and osmotic coefficients). This thermochemical method thus used empirical quantities without making assumptions about the forces responsible for these ΔF's. The second method was to apply Coulomb's law to a system consisting of a negatively charged sphere of variable radius and a positively charged sphere of radius equal to the ionic radius of one of the alkali cations. This method assumes that non-Coulombic forces make only a minor contribution to the free energy, an approximation that is valid for alkali cations and halide sites. The Coulomb calculation was carried out both for a system with widely separated sites (such as a diatomic gas) and for a system with sites at the minimum possible distance (such as an alkali halide crystal), in the latter case taking account of the Madelung constant derived from crystal geometry (see p. 609 for the effect of site spacing). Both the thermochemical and the Coulomb methods yield curves of $(\Delta F_{\text{ion, site}} - \Delta F_{\text{ion, water}})$, as a function of the site field strength or the radius of the halide ion, for each of the five alkali cations. These curves repeatedly intersect each other, the intersections determining transitions from one selectivity sequence to another. Both the thermodynamic method and the Coulomb approximation yield essentially the same nine transition sequences (see 1, Figures 16, 17, 18, 20), which are found to be the same as those consistently observed in biological and nonliving systems and listed on p. 585. The intuitive explanation why these particular transition sequences are obtained is discussed on p. 606.

While these model calculations varied the radius of a halide-type site to produce different field strengths and hence different selectivity sequences, the sites in most biological systems will be either carboxyl or phosphoric acid groups, so that only two different values of actual site radius should occur biologically despite the wide range of biological selectivity sequences. However, the field strength (hence the selectivity pattern) of carboxyl and phosphate groups will vary greatly, depending upon whether inductive effects exerted by the site's immediate molecular environment increase or decrease electron density on the site. This influence of the environment upon the field strength of a given chemical grouping is reflected not only in counterion selectivity patterns but also in the much more familiar variation in the acid dissociation constant or pK_a of the site. The pK_a depends upon field strength because an anionic site with high field strength binds protons more firmly than one with low field strength, hence the protons dissociate less readily and the stronger site has a lower dissociation constant and higher pK_a (is a "weaker" acid). As is well known, the pK_a of a given grouping is intimately dependent upon the chemical environment: for instance, the pK_a of the carboxyl group in acetic acid is 4.75 but is 0.70 in trichloroacetic acid because of the electron-withdrawing effect of the chlorines on the carboxyl oxygens. Further examples are provided by the frequently large differences between the pK_a's of free amino acids and their values in proteins.

This relation between pK_a and field strength is important in that it offers the possibility of predicting the pK_a of membrane sites controlling ion selectivity from the observed selectivity pattern, and vice versa. Eisenman set out from the known pK_a's of HCl and HF, the known crystal radii of Cl^- and F^-, and the known alkali-cation selectivity patterns of Cl^- and F^-

(from ΔF's of formation of alkali chlorides and fluorides, combined with hydration free energies of the alkali cations). If one assumes a linear relation between pK_a and equivalent site radius, then the two points for Cl^- and F^- determine a straight line from which pK_a's corresponding to other values of equivalent site radius (hence other selectivity patterns) can be read off [cf. Figure 7, ref. (2)]. Tests of these predictions can be made from experiments on the gallbladder and on glass electrodes. The graph of KCl diffusion potentials against pH in the gallbladder [Figure 3, ref. (16)] implies that the sites for cation exchange in gallbladder cell membranes have a pK_a near 3. From the relation determined by Cl^- and F^-, a pK_a of 3 for widely spaced sites implies cation selectivity sequence VII approaching sequence VI. The actual sequence obtained from bi-ionic potentials in the gallbladder (16) is $K^+ > Na^+ > Cs^+$, which implies either selectivity sequence VI or else V, in satisfactory agreement with the prediction. The observed selectivity patterns of glass electrodes also agree well with predictions based on pK_a's of their ion exchange sites and on the $Cl^- - F^-$ relation (1). Correlations between ion selectivity patterns and pK_a's had already been noticed empirically, though not understood theoretically, by Jenny (9) in 1932 when he studied different soil minerals and by Bregman (48) in 1953 when he investigated different organic ion exchange resins. If one applies the same considerations to the selectivity change underlying action potentials in nerve, this change can be interpreted in two ways: cations may cross nerve membranes via the same channels in the active as in the resting state, but a change in the molecular environment during the rising phase of the action potential inductively modifies the charges in the channels so that they acquire a higher field strength and higher pK_a; or else (perhaps more likely), during the rising phase of the action potential a new set of channels is opened, whose charges have a higher pK_a than those controlling ion permeation in the resting state.

Anion Selectivity

Considerations identical to those outlined above for discrimination among the five alkali cations can be extended to the four halide anions (F^-, Br^-, Cl^-, I^-), except that one must consider interactions of negative mobile ions with positive sites instead of positive mobile ions with negative sites. From experimental ΔF's of formation of alkali halides as crystals and in aqueous solution, using the different alkali cations as models of positive sites with different field strengths, Eisenman (3) predicted seven selectivity sequences out of the 24 possible permutations of the four halide anions. We find that application of Coulomb's law to infinitely separated positive sites, or of Coulomb's law times the Madelung constant to closely spaced positive sites, yields the same seven sequences as Eisenman's thermochemical predictions:

$$I \quad I^- > Br^- > Cl^- > F^-$$
$$II \quad Br^- > I^- > Cl^- > F^-$$
$$III \quad Br^- > Cl^- > I^- > F^-$$

IV $Cl^- > Br^- > I^- > F^-$

V $Cl^- > Br^- > F^- > I^-$

VI $Cl^- > F^- > Br^- > I^-$

VII $F^- > Cl^- > Br^- > I^-$

Sequence I, the order of the free-solution mobilities, is associated with weak sites, while sequence VII, in which the ion with the smallest non-hydrated radius is preferred, arises at strong sites. Five transition sequences link I to VII. As one proceeds from I to VII, the first inversion involves the weakly hydrated I^- and Br^-, which have the largest ionic size; the next inversions (II→III, III→IV) involve the more strongly hydrated Cl^-; and the remaining inversions involve F^-, the smallest and most strongly hydrated anion.

For comparison with these predictions, 17 instances have come to our attention in which halide selectivity patterns were recently determined in biological systems. The positive sites in biological systems are most likely amino groups, though there are other possibilities. Wherever quantitative information was provided in these publications, we have extracted estimates of relative potencies (taking Cl^- as 1.00) and list these estimated potencies in parentheses next to each ion in the following survey. In all 17 cases the observed pattern is one of the predicted seven sequences:

From effects on the membrane potential of *Ascaris* muscle (49) the order of permeability was deduced to be $I^- > Br^- > Cl^-$ (sequence I).

The anion potency sequence for stimulation of the olfactory receptor in frogs, as judged by surface electrode recording, was determined (50) as $Cl^- > Br^-$, $F^- > I^-$ (sequence V or VI).

Alkali salts of different halides (18) stimulated the salt receptor of the blowfly with the relative potency I^- (1.5) $> Br^-$ (1.2) $> Cl^-$ (1.0) $> F^-$ (0.4) (sequence I).

The conductances induced by γ-aminobutyric acid in the inhibitory post-synaptic membrane of the crayfish neuromuscular junction (51) were reported as Br^- (1.28) $> Cl^-$ (1.00) $> I^-$ (0.87) (sequence III).

The permeability order of the outer surface of bullfrog skin (35) is Br^- (1.06) $> Cl^-$ (1.00) $> I^-$ (0.25) (sequence III).

Efflux rate constants from red blood cells were observed (52) to be in the order Cl^- (1.0) $> Br^-$ (0.2) $> F^-$ (0.1) $> I^-$ (0.02) (sequence V), and equilibrium concentration ratios in the order I^- (1.82) $> Br^-$ (1.09) $> Cl^-$ (1.00) $> F^-$ (0.86) (sequence I).

From permeabilities determined for the nonsynaptic membrane of cat motoneurons from recovery of the inhibitory postsynaptic potentials after intracellular injection of various salts (53), one obtains the permeability order Br^- (1.26) $> Cl^-$ (1.00) $> I^-$ (0.67) (sequence III).

The order $I^- > Br^- > Cl^-$ (sequence I) is obtained for abilites to diminish the electrophoretic velocity of three positively charged proteins discussed by Bungenberg de Jong (28): casein (2.96, 1.7, 1.0), gelatin (2.24, 1.59, 1.0), and clupein.

The order of anion conductances in cardiac muscle is $I^- > Br^- > Cl^-$ (sequence I) (54). The reverse order, Cl^- (1.00) $> Br^-$ (0.67) $> I^-$ (0.44) (sequence IV or higher), holds for the anion conductances of frog skeletal muscle (55).

The bi-ionic potentials reported (56) for thin lipid membranes treated with the polyene antibiotic nystatin imply the permeability order Cl^- (1.00) $> I^-$ (0.80) $> F^-$ (0.38) (sequence III or IV).

Observations (57) on the abilities of internally perfused halide ions to block conduction in squid axons lead to the permeability order I^- (5.55) $>$ Br^- (1.61) $> Cl^-$ (1.00) $> F^-$ (0.23) (sequence I).

Anions potentiate the contracture of vascular smooth muscle (58) in the order I^- (1.75) $> Br^-$ (1.25) $> Cl^-$ (1.00) (sequence I).

The enzyme carbonic anhydrase is inhibited by halides (59) in the order of decreasing inhibition I^- (22.2) $> Br^-$ (2.5) $> Cl^-$ (1.0) $> F^-$ (0.8) (sequence I).

From these experimental values for relative potencies, the halide selectivity isotherms of Figure 1 have been constructed by plotting the relative potency of each halide ion on the ordinate scaled according to the I^-/Cl^- potency ratio on the abscissa. It is apparent that the experimental numbers determine four curves, intersections between which correspond to transitions from one sequence to another. The fact that a regular pattern is observed means simply that once one knows the I^-/Cl^- selectivity ratio, one not only can predict qualitatively the whole halide sequence but also quantitatively the approximate relative potencies for F^- and for Br^-. For instance, in the nonsynaptic membrane of cat motoneurons and in the GABA-treated inhibitory postsynaptic membrane of crayfish neuromuscular junction, where the F^- was not tested in the published studies, F^- should prove to be less potent than the other three halogens and roughly 30 per cent as potent as Cl^-.

It will be recalled that the alkali-cation selectivity pattern of an anionic site can be predicted from its acid dissociation constant, since both selectivity pattern and pK_a are related to field strength (p. 594). Similarly, the halide selectivity pattern of a positively charged site should be predictable from its pK_b, a strong site (e.g., halide sequence VII) being associated with a high pK_b. Two kinds of positive sites must be distinguished, which may be written as M^+ and MH^+. In biological systems quaternary ammonium groups provide examples of M^+ sites, and the alkali cations serve as inorganic models. For the MH^+ site the biological representatives would be primary, secondary, and tertiary amino groups, and NH_4^+ ($pK_b = 4.75$) serves as an inorganic model. Calculations similar to those published by Eisenman (2) for anionic sites lead us to the conclusion that an M^+ site exhibits a much higher halide selectivity sequence than an MH^+ site with the same pK_b and site spacing; and that only sequence VII should result from any M^+ site with $pK_b > 0.7$ ($pK_a < 13.3$), even at infinite spacing. Thus, the fact that erythrocyte anion permeability is sequence V (52) and that the positive charges controlling the permselectivity of erythrocytes appear to

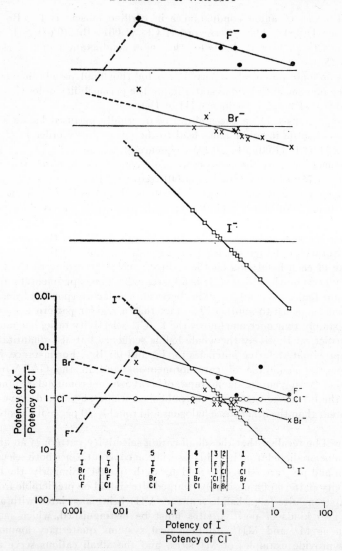

FIG. 1. Below, selectivity isotherms for the halide anions in biological systems. Each set of four points arranged vertically above each other is one of the relative potency sequences experimentally measured in a biological system and listed on pp. 595–96 (●F⁻, ○Cl, ✕Br⁻, □I⁻). The potencies relative to Cl⁻=1 are plotted logarithmically on the ordinate. They are arranged according to the relative I⁻ potency, plotted logarithmically on the abscissa. [For instance, halides inhibit the enzyme carbonic anhydrase (59) with the relative potencies I⁻=22.2, Br⁻=2.5, Cl⁻=1.0, F⁻=0.8. These points have therefore been arranged on an imaginary vertical line intersect-

have $pK_b = 5$ means that these charges are not quaternary ammonium groups but belong to the MH^+ type.

DIVALENT-CATION SELECTIVITY

The divalent cation calcium is important in many biological systems in controlling permeability to monovalent ions, and plays a direct role in generating action potentials in some crustacean nerves and muscles. Of the four alkaline-earth cations (magnesium, calcium, strontium, and barium), all of which are rather similar in their physical and chemical properties, one other, magnesium, occurs naturally in biological systems and is generally found to be very different from calcium in its biological effects. The problem of alkaline-earth selectivity is therefore one whose physical interest and biological importance is second only to that posed by the alkali ions.

A simplified theory of alkaline-earth equilibrium selectivity has been developed independently by Sherry (5), by Truesdell (6, 60), and by Eisenman (3). As in Eisenman's treatment for monovalent cations, specificity in these models is controlled by the field strength of membrane negative charges with which the cations interact. The driving force underlying selectivity is the difference between the free energy of cation:site interaction and the cation's free energy of hydration, and contributions of non-Coulomb forces to cation:site interactions are neglected. Two principal kinds of conclusions emerge from these treatments:

1. The relative affinities of a site for monovalent and for divalent cations depend critically upon intersite spacing: widely spaced sites prefer monovalent to divalent cations, while closely spaced sites prefer divalent cations. Previously, physical chemists had anticipated that the more highly charged

---

ing the horizontal axis at 22.2, and constitute the set of points lying furthest to the right. Since the ordinate gives potency relative to Cl^- as a function of the relative I^- potency on the abscissa, the Cl^- value of 1.0 automatically falls on a horizontal line intersecting the ordinate at 1.0, and the I^- value of 22.2 automatically falls on the line of $45°$ slope. The Br^- value of 2.5 and the F^- value of 0.8 have been used in constructing the empirical isotherms for these two ions, drawn by eye through all the Br^- or F^- points.] The intersections of these four experimental isotherms represent transitions among seven sequences predicted theoretically by Eisenman and listed below the pattern and numbered 1 through 7 (the most potent ion is written on the bottom in each case). Above, the F^-, Br^-, and I^- isotherms are replotted separately for clarity. In the absence of experimental data for sequences higher than sequence 5, the isotherms have been extrapolated towards the left to show the theoretical predictions that F^- will cross the Br^- and then the Cl^- isotherm. The meaning of the regular pattern is that once the relative potencies of two halides are known, the whole sequence and the approximate potencies of the other two halides can be predicted. For instance, reading vertically upwards from 0.1 on the abscissa, a system in which I^- is one tenth as potent as Cl^- should be in sequence 5 ($Cl^- > Br^- > F^- > I^-$) and should have a F^- potency of about 0.2 and a Br^- potency of about 0.6 relative to Cl^-.

ion should always be preferred and had been surprised to find monovalent ions actually preferred over divalents in some zeolites (61). The zeolites preferring monovalent cations have low site densities (widely spaced sites), while those preferring divalent cations have closely spaced sites, in accord with the theoretical prediction. In principle this fact opens the possibility of estimating site spacings for those biological membranes in which calcium and its analogues are known to displace sodium and potassium.

2. Sherry predicted for closely spaced sites that out of the 24 possible permutations of the four alkaline-earth cations, only seven should be observed as selectivity sequences.[4] These are:

$$\text{I} \quad Ba^{++} > Sr^{++} > Ca^{++} > Mg^{++}$$
$$\text{II} \quad Ba^{++} > Ca^{++} > Sr^{++} > Mg^{++}$$
$$\text{III} \quad Ca^{++} > Ba^{++} > Sr^{++} > Mg^{++}$$
$$\text{IV} \quad Ca^{++} > Ba^{++} > Mg^{++} > Sr^{++}$$
$$\text{V} \quad Ca^{++} > Mg^{++} > Ba^{++} > Sr^{++}$$
$$\text{VI} \quad Ca^{++} > Mg^{++} > Sr^{++} > Ba^{++}$$
$$\text{VII} \quad Mg^{++} > Ca^{++} > Sr^{++} > Ba^{++}$$

Sequence I, the order of the free-solution mobilities, arises at weak sites, where the free energy of hydration dominates exchange; but sequence VIII, in which the ion with the smallest ionic radius is preferred, arises at strong

---

[4] The sequences predicted by Truesdell and by Eisenman differ from those of Sherry and disagree with those observed experimentally in biological systems. We have repeated the calculations, and find that the predictions differ because Truesdell neglected entropy changes, equating free energy with enthalpy, while Sherry took estimated entropies of hydration into account; and that Sherry used the Goldschmidt radii for the alkaline-earth ions, while Truesdell used Green-Evans radii and Eisenman used Pauling radii. The Goldschmidt radii are the more appropriate ones, since they were derived from oxide crystals and the biological sites are oxygen sites. Sequences obtained from a number of minerals, resins, and glasses [summarized in Table 11-3, (6)] do conform to Truesdell's predictions and differ from the experimental biological sequences. However, almost all of the biological studies cited on pp. 601-2 involve measurements of equilbrium selectivity without a mobility component (cf. p. 610), whereas the mineral and glass patterns for divalent cations may be controlled by mobility differences rather than reflecting equilibrium selectivity, since mobilities of divalent cations in glasses and minerals are far below those of monovalent cations (6). For his calculations Sherry extracted free energies of hydration of the four alkaline-earth ions from the thermal data of Rossini et al. (46) by assuming that the entropy of ionization in the gas phase is the same for all four ions. The resulting free energies of hydration are very close to those estimated recently by Rosseinsky (47); Rosseinsky's values lead to prediction of the same specificity patterns. Sherry suggested that infinitely spaced anionic sites yielded only the lyotropic series, but he did not carry his calculation below an equivalent site radius of 0.8 Å. For infinitely spaced sites with smaller radii (higher field strengths) we find that the predicted selectivity pattern is virtually the same as for closely spaced sites, except that sequence III becomes $Ba^{++} > Ca^{++} > Mg^{++} > Sr^{++}$.

sites, where ion : site interactions are stronger than free energies of hydration. In addition, a selectivity shift in the direction VII to I occurs with increasing site spacing at constant field strength, as also found for alkali-cation selectivity (see p. 609).

The agreement between Sherry's predicted sequences and those recently observed experimentally in biological systems is substantial. Wherever quantitative information was available, the potencies relative to $Ca^{++} = 1.0$ which we extracted are given in parentheses:

Bungenberg de Jong (28) summarized the results obtained by himself and by several other authors in so-called reversal-of-charge experiments on the electrophoretic mobility of proteins and of phosphate, carboxyl, and sulfate colloids of biological origin. The underlying principle is that the relative potencies of different cations in blocking negative charges on amphoteric colloids are determined by finding the concentration of cation necessary to reverse the charge of the colloid (the more potent the cation, the lower this concentration). Of the 19 systems discussed by Bungenberg de Jong, 18 yielded sequences predicted by Sherry, and five of the seven Sherry sequences are represented. The details are: $Ba^{++} > Sr^{++} > Ca^{++} > Mg^{++}$ (sequence I), the carboxyl colloids arabinate (1.64, 1.38, 1.00, 0.85), pectinate (2.90, 1.25, 1.00, 0.79), and pectate (2.08, 1.18, 1.00, 0.80), the sulfate colloids chondroitin sulfate (1.37, 1.16, 1.00, 0.85), agar (6.67, 2.17, 1.00, 0.74), and carrageen (1.59, 1.35, 1.00, 0.93), the colloids SiO_2 (1.56, 1.06, 1.00, 0.93) and TiO_2 (4.0, 1.2, 1.0, 0.7); $Ba^{++} > Ca^{++} > Sr^{++} > Mg^{++}$ (sequence II), the carboxyl colloid hexaoxystearate at pH 6 and the phosphate colloid nucleate (1.23, 1.00, 0.91, 0.81); $Ca^{++} > Ba^{++} > Sr^{++} > Mg^{++}$ (sequence III), the phosphate colloid soya bean phosphatide II (1.00, 0.90, 0.74, 0.59); $Ca^{++} > Mg^{++} > Ba^{++} > Sr^{++}$ (sequence V), the protein gelatin and the phosphate colloid egg lecithin+50 per cent cholesterol (1.00, 0.66, 0.30, 0.26); $Ca^{++} > Mg^{++} > Sr^{++} > Ba^{++}$ (sequence VI), the protein casein, the carboxyl colloid trioxystearate at pH6, and the phosphate colloids egg lecithin (three different preparations: 1.00, 0.52, 0.14, 0.12; 1.00, 0.49, 0.13, 0.11; 1.00, 0.70, 0.29, 0.22), sphingomyelin (1.00, 0.27, 0.08, 0.055), and soya bean phosphatide I (1.00, 0.73, 0.35, 0.26); and $Mg^{++} > Ca^{++} > Sr^{++} > Ba^{++}$ (sequence VII), the carboxyl colloids oleate (1.85, 1.00, 0.93, 0.81) and trioxystearate at pH10. Hexaoxystearate at high pH yielded $Mg^{++} > Ca^{++} > Ba^{++} > Sr^{++}$, which differs from sequence VII in that Ba^{++} has recrossed Sr^{++} (see discussion of "post-Coulomb sequences", pp. 603 and 607). More recently, Bangham, Pethica & Seaman (62) have confirmed Ca^{++} (1.00) $> Sr^{++}$ (0.36) $> Ba^{++}$ (0.14) (VI or VII; Mg^{++} not tested) for egg lecithin.

Bungenberg de Jong's results are also important in showing that the selectivity pattern for divalent cations shifts with decreasing pH (decreasing field strength) in the direction from the strong-field sequence VII to the weak-field sequence I, as discussed for the effects of pH on monovalent-cation selectivity (pp. 591–92). This is seen in the effect of pH on the charge reversal patterns of oleate and trioxystearate.

Wright & Diamond (16) compared the potencies of the alkaline earths in blocking membrane negative charges in the gallbladder, as measured by the decrease in NaCl diffusion potentials and hence in P_{Na}/P_{Cl} caused by the addition of a divalent cation at $5mM$. The potency order was Ba^{++} (1.13) > Ca^{++} (1.00) > Sr^{++} (0.61) > Mg^{++} ($\sim$0) (sequence II) in three gallbladders, Ca^{++} (1.00) > Ba^{++} (0.84) > Sr^{++} (0.57) > Mg^{++} ($\sim$0) (sequence III) in nine other gallbladders. Presumably the sites were stronger or more closely spaced in the latter preparations.

Goldner, Cassidy & Tidball (63) compared the alkaline earths in their ability to restore the normal permeability properties of the intestine after treatment with EDTA and obtained Mg^{++} (1.25) > Ca^{++} (1.00) > Sr^{++} (0.50) > Ba^{++} (0.29) (sequence VII).

Effects on the rate of rise of the spike in barnacle muscle were shown by Hagiwara & Takahashi (64) to be in the order Ca^{++} > Mg^{++} > Sr^{++} (Ba^{++} not tested; sequence IV, V, or VI).

Peak transient membrane currents in the alga *Chara australis* (65) are stimulated in the sequence Ca^{++} (1.00) > Sr^{++} (0.8) > Mg^{++} ($\sim$0), Ba^{++} ($\sim$0). This is not a Sherry sequence but is nearest VI, differing in the low potency of Mg^{++}.

Ability to replace calcium in reactivating the enzyme Taka amylase A (66) is in the order Mg^{++} (1.17) > Sr^{++} (1.04) > Ca^{++} (1.00) > Ba^{++} (0.95). This order is also not a Sherry sequence but is nearest VII, differing in the reversed positions of Sr^{++} and Ca^{++} (see discussion of post-Coulomb sequences, pp. 603 and 607).

Ponder (67) noted that red cells incubated in solutions of the alkaline-earth chlorides at 4° C lost K^+ in exchange for divalent cations. The extent of K^+ loss is a measure of the divalent-cation permeability and yields the sequence Ca^{++} > Ba^{++} > Mg^{++} > Sr^{++} (sequence IV).

The order of the apparent binding constants of the alkaline earths with the protein G-actin (68) is Ca^{++} (1.00) > Mg^{++} (0.25) > Sr^{++} (0.03), Ba^{++} (0.01) (sequence V or VI).

The amounts of divalent cations bound to reconstituted collagen (69) are in the order Mg^{++} (1.68) > Ca^{++} (1.00) > Sr^{++} (0.79) (sequence VII).

Stimulating effects of alkaline earths on peak sodium and potassium conductance of squid axon (70) follow the sequence Ba^{++} > Ca^{++} > Mg^{++} (sequence I or II).

Thus, all of the Sherry sequences have been observed in biological systems, and 27 of the 30 reported experimental sequences fit the Sherry patterns.

From these experimental values for relative potencies, the alkaline-earth selectivity isotherms of Figure 2 have been constructed by plotting the relative potency of each ion on the ordinate scaled according to the Ba^{++}/Ca^{++} potency ratio on the abscissa. The experimental potencies cluster closely about four curves, intersections between which correspond to transitions from one sequence to another. The fact that a regular pattern is observed means simply that once one knows the relative potencies for two ions, one not only can predict qualitatively the whole alkaline-earth sequence but also quantitatively the approximate relative potencies of the other two ions. For example, as regards binding to reconstituted collagen, where the published study did not test Ba^{++}, Ba^{++} should prove to be bound less strongly than the other three alkaline-earth ions and roughly 60 per cent as strongly as Ca^{++}.

The experimental isotherms of Figure 2 have maxima, so that a given value of Ba^{++}/Ca^{++} may correspond to either of two sequences and sets of selectivity ratios. It is obvious that if the isotherms are extrapolated in the high-field-strength direction (towards the left) beyond sequence VII, the isotherms for the two largest ions Ba^{++} and Sr^{++} will recross the Ca^{++} isotherm, giving rise to a new set of sequences not predicted by the Coulomb model. Two out of the three non-Sherry sequences from the recent experimental literature (hexaoxystearate at high pH, and Taka amylase A) in fact belong to this new series. An analogy is encountered in alkali-cation selectivity, where the isotherms also have maxima (3, Figure 7) and a new set of sequences not predicted by the Coulomb model appears at very high field strengths, beginning with recrossings by Rb^+ and Cs^+, the two largest ions. The same may prove true of the halide isotherms, but the available experimental data have not yet included high-field-strength sequences (halide sequences VI and VII) where the maxima would become apparent. This appearance of post-Coulomb sequences at high field strengths is to be expected from simple electrostatic considerations involving non-Coulomb forces, as will be discussed on pp. 606–7.

OTHER IONS

Polyvalent cations other than the alkaline earths, such as La^{+++}, the transition-metal ions (Mn^{++}, Fe^{++}, Co^{++}, Ni^{++}, Cu^{++}, etc.), Al^{+++}, and the actinides (UO_2)$^{++}$ and Th^{++++}, mimic the effects of calcium to varying extents in several biological systems. Apparent potency sequences have been determined for polyvalent cation effects on the calcium spike of barnacle muscle (64), on reducing sodium conductance and increasing chloride conductance in gallbladder (16), on the electrophoretic mobility of colloids (28), and on Na^+ and K^+ conductances in squid axon (70). Some biological potency sequences for monovalent inorganic ions other than the alkali metals and halogens (e.g., Ag^+, Tl^+, NH_4^+, NO_3^-) and for monovalent organic ions have also been obtained.

Whereas analyses based solely on Coulomb forces usually predict successfully the behavior of the alkali cations, the halides, and the alkaline earths, non-Coulomb forces cannot be disregarded for other ions, which have received little theoretical attention because of the resulting complexities [see (13), Figures 51 and 52 for theoretical Ag^+, Tl^+, and NH_4^+ isotherms]. In addition, it is frequently not appreciated that many polyvalent cations undergo transformation reactions (hydrolysis, oxidation, and complex

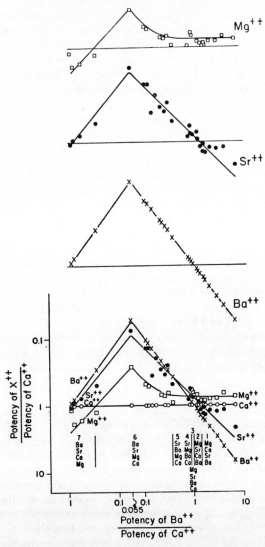

FIG. 2. Below selectivity isotherms for the alkaline-earth cations in biological systems. Each set of four points arranged vertically above each other is one of the relative potency sequences experimentally measured in a biological system and listed on p. 600 ($\square$Mg++, $\bigcirc$Ca++, $\bullet$Sr++, $\times$Ba++). The potencies relative to Ca++=1 are plotted logarithmically on the ordinate. They are arranged according to the relative Ba++ potency, plotted logarithmically on the abscissa. [For instance, alkaline-earth cations reverse the charge of colloidal agar (28) with the relative potencies Ba++ =6.67, Sr++=2.17, Ca++=1.00, Mg++=0.74. These points have therefore been ar- ranged on an imaginary vertical line intersecting the horizontal axis at 6.67, and con-

formation) in aqueous solution, some of which cause large shifts in pH (cf.16). Thus, biological effects reported for such ions as Cu^{++} and Al^{+++} are not due to these ions themselves but to their transformation products, and must even be suspected of resulting from pH changes in cases where these were not specifically ruled out. For instance, the apparent effect of Cu^{++} on anion permeability in frog skin (71) and other epithelia is probably actually due to interaction of the anion $(CuCl_4)^{--}$, the most stable form of copper in $CuCl_2$ solutions (72), with membrane positive charges.

Non-Coulomb Forces, and the Meaning of the Transition Sequences

Having considered in broad outline the basis of equilibrium ion selectivity, we now examine in more detail the effects of some variables related to selectivity, beginning with non-Coulomb forces (forces other than those between two point charges or monopoles).

The thermochemical method of calculating ion selectivity sequences makes no assumptions about the relative contributions of enthalpy and entropy terms, nor about the relative contributions of Coulomb and non-Coulomb forces, to the free energy of ion-site interaction. Alkali cations and halide anions interacting with each other can in fact be well approximated as monopolar charges on spherical, nonpolarizable particles, and it is therefore not surprising that the thermochemical method and the calculations based solely on Coulomb forces have yielded the same alkali-cation selectivity sequences when applied to halide-type sites.

What is the reason for the particular pattern of transition sequences predicted by the Coulomb model? As discussed on p. 586, the pattern was that inversions involving the large Cs^+, Rb^+, and K^+ occurred first, those involv-

---

stitute the set of points lying furthest to the right. Since the ordinate gives potency relative to Ca^{++} as a function of the relative Ba^{++} potency on the abscissa, the Ca^{++} potency of 1.00 automatically falls on a horizontal line intersecting the ordinate at 1.00, and the Ba^{++} value of 6.67 automatically falls on the line of 45° slope. The Sr^{++} value of 2.17 and the Mg^{++} value of 0.74 have been used in constructing the empirical isotherms for these two ions, drawn by eye through all the Sr^{++} or Mg^{++} points.] The significance of the observed regularity is that once one knows the relative Ba^{++} potency, one not only can predict qualitatively the whole alkaline-earth sequence but also quantitatively the approximate relative potencies. For instance, reading vertically upwards from 2 on the abscissa, a system in which Ba^{++} is twice as potent as Ca^{++} should be in sequence 1 ($Ba^{++}>Sr^{++}>Ca^{++}>Mg^{++}$) and should have a Sr^{++} potency of about 1.3 and a Mg^{++} potency of about 0.7 relative to Ca^{++}. The degeneracy of the abscissa and the maxima in the isotherms mean that a given Ba^{++} potency may correspond to either of two sequences and relative potencies. The intersections of these four experimental isotherms determine seven sequences predicted theoretically by Sherry and listed below the pattern (the most potent ion is written on the bottom in each case). Above, the Mg^{++}, Sr^{++}, and Ba^{++} isotherms are replotted separately for clarity.

ing the smaller Na^+ next, and those involving the smallest ion Li^+ last, as one proceeded from the case (sequence I) where ion-site attractions were much weaker than hydration energies to the case (sequence XI) where they were much stronger. The same pattern is observed in the seven selectivity sequences for halide anions (pp. 595–96).

The underlying reason for these patterns is that cation: halide-site forces decrease more slowly with increasing distance than do cation: water forces. The forces between an alkali cation and a halide anion are largely Coulomb or monopole-monopole forces, which decrease as the inverse square of the distance. The forces between an alkali cation and a multipolar water molecule are largely dipolar and quadrupolar forces, which vary as r^{-3} and r^{-4}, respectively. The difference between the attraction for a small ion (e.g., Li^+) minus the attraction for a large ion (e.g., Cs^+) is therefore less marked for a monopolar site than for a water molecule. As site strength is increased so that ion-site attraction gradually begins to increase in strength relative to ion-water attraction, the expression ($\Delta F_{ion,site} - \Delta F_{ion,water}$) goes negative most rapidly for Cs^+ and most slowly for Li^+, hence inversions affecting the largest ions occur first.

The opposite extreme is the case in which ion-site forces decrease more rapidly with increasing distance than do ion-water forces. This would be true, for instance, in the case of a highly polarizable site for which ion: induced-dipole forces (varying as r^{-5}) were more important than for the ion-water case. This greater contribution of polarization energy to $\Delta F_{ion,site}$ than to $\Delta F_{ion,water}$ would be largest for the smallest ion Li^+, whose center of charge would be nearest the site (or water) and which would therefore be the most effective ion at polarizing. Hence inversions affecting Li^+ would occur first as one proceeded from sequence I to XI. This case corresponds to the assumption of Bungenberg de Jong (see p. 590) that the relative polarizabilities of the site and water control cation selectivity.

A more general analysis of alkali-cation selectivity encompassing both these extreme cases was made by Ling (43), who calculated site-cation and water-cation interactions for a linear model, taking into account all non-exchange forces, including such non-Coulomb effects as polarization of the ion by the site, polarization of the site by the ion, and Born repulsion forces. Over a range of values for the site polarizability up to 2 Å these detailed calculations yielded the same alkali-cation sequences as those predicted from Coulomb forces alone, while high polarizabilities yielded different sequences (4, 43).

Whether ion-site interactions will be dominated by Coulomb or non-Coulomb forces, and whether ion-site forces will fall off more rapidly or more slowly with distance than ion-water forces, are questions that can be answered for a membrane only if its structure is known. From the properties of aluminosilicate sites it is physically reasonable that a Coulomb model should successfully predict the selectivity sequences observed in minerals and glass electrodes. Different sequences, in which Li^+ inversions occur first and are followed by Na^+ inversions, have been observed in systems with more polarizable sites, such as carboxylate ion exchange resins (4) and two of the phosphate colloids studied by Bungenberg de Jong (28). In biological membranes the identity of the groups controlling ion permeation is unknown. The fact that most biological sequences fit the Coulomb pattern implies that the groups are either ionic (acidic groups) or else relatively nonpolarizable permanent dipoles. However, the shift in the biological Li^+ isotherm, and the sequences in which the position of Li^+ is qualitatively anomalous, discussed on p. 589, suggest that non-Coulomb forces related to site polarization by counterions are more important for the permeability-controlling groups in biological systems than for the aluminosilicate sites of zeolites and glass electrodes. Non-Coulomb forces appear to be responsible for the maxima in the alkaline-earth isotherms (Figure 2) and alkali-cation isotherms and for the resulting post-Coulomb sequences. At very high site field strengths, polarization of the counterion by the site can no longer be considered negligible in comparison with Coulomb forces. The largest ions would be the most polarizable, so that a new set of transitions is expected in which the largest ions (Rb^+ and Cs^+, Ba^{++} and Sr^{++}) again become more potent than the smallest ions. The post-Coulomb sequences appearing at high field strengths and cited earlier (p. 589 and p. 603) are in fact of this expected type. For more polarizable ions such as Ag^+, polarization by the site contributes significantly to the interaction energy even at low field strength and results in glass electrodes being much more permeable to Ag^+ than one would predict from a Coulomb model (13).

In brief, then, most observed sequences are those predicted from consideration of Coulomb forces alone; and the occasional deviations from these patterns are those expected from considering in addition the most important non-Coulomb forces.

"Uncharged" Membranes

Much of the experimental work on ion selectivity has been done on ion exchange membranes, and it has been convenient to develop the theory of ion selectivity using the language of ion exchange. By definition an ion exchange membrane is one containing fixed ionic charges to which mobile, oppositely charged ions from the solution serve as counterions. It would be a serious misunderstanding, however, to assume that there must be some totally different explanation for specificity in systems lacking fixed ionic charges: specificity will still be controlled by electrostatic forces, as generalized in the preceding section (i.e., not necessarily just Coulomb forces), whether the negative charge nearest the cation is ionic, on a permanent dipole (or multipole), or on an induced dipole (or multipole), and whether the site is fixed or located on a mobile carrier. For example, in a molecule with carbonyl groups or ether linkages but no carboxyl groups, the carbon–oxygen bonds will in general have permanent (and induced) dipole moments in which the oxygen is negative. The interactions of a cation with such an oxygen will still depend upon the oxygen's field strength and the distance between the cation's and oxygen's centers of charge, just as if the oxygen had been in a carboxyl group from which a proton had dissociated. If the electric field of the carbonyl or ether group falls off more slowly with distance than does the field of a water molecule, then the same selectivity sequences as predicted by the Coulomb model may be obtained, for the reasons discussed in the preceding section. Recent calculations by Eisenman (73) on a permanent dipolar model yield Coulomb sequence patterns over a considerable range of charge values and spacings. In general, one expects that the Coulomb model will be most successful for those dipoles with the lowest polarizabilities and the largest separation between the positive and negative ends.

These facts are reflected in the recent experience with the classes of macrocyclic compounds that produce spectacular selective increases in the cation permeability of mitochondrial, erythrocyte, and thin lipid membranes (see p. 587). Incorporation of these compounds into high-resistance membranes may increase alkali-cation permeability by several orders of magnitude, the effect being much more marked for some cations than for others. While the class including nigericin and monensin does contain one carboxyl group (in addition to numerous ether and hydroxyl oxygens), the other classes, such as the cyclic polypeptide antibiotics (e.g., valinomycin and the enniatins), the macrolide actins, and the cyclic "crown" polyethers, lack ionizing groups and contain oxygen only in ether, ester, and hydroxyl groups. Nevertheless, both the selectivity patterns and the magnitudes of selectivity observed with these various classes of macrocyclic compounds agree well with the previously established patterns for nonliving and other biological systems, as discussed on p. 587. Although the *permeation mechanism* induced by these compounds is proving of great interest, the above-mentioned agreement provides no reason to believe, and ample reason not to believe, that their mechanism of *selectivity* involves fundamentally new principles. From this point of view it is misleading to think of these molecules as uncharged or neutral: they lack ionic charges but do have dipoles whose negative oxygen end gives rise to the usual patterns of inter-cation selectivity in the usual way.

The same considerations also mean that discussions of ion selectivity which explicitly or implicitly (e.g., 74, 75) neglect electrostatic forces, for example, because the ion is supposed to cross the membrane via an uncharged pore, are based on a physically impossible fiction. Even if ions crossed biological membranes via pores consisting of pure hydrocarbon with no oxygen groups and with only the small (but not nonexistent) permanent dipoles of carbon–hydrogen bonds—a hypothesis that is highly unlikely but not utterly impossible—the ion:induced-dipole forces between the ion and the surrounding hydrocarbon, together with the free energies of hydration, would still control equilibrium selectivity according to expression 1, p. 593.

DEGREE OF HYDRATION

An increase in the amount of water in the vicinity of the mobile ion and a site of opposite sign reduces the magnitude of selectivity ratios without altering the selectivity sequence [compare Figures 6A, B, C, and D of (2)].

Only those ions in immediate contact with membrane charges without intervening water molecules contribute significantly to selectivity patterns differing from those of free solution, so that "we may, to a first approximation, regard the effect of additional water as merely to 'dilute' the processes giving rise to selectivity" (4, p. 268). This expectation is in accord with the finding that the magnitudes of selectivity in ion exchangers decrease with increased swelling (hydration) of the exchanger. Since the magnitudes as well as the patterns of alkali-cation selectivity observed in biological membranes are comparable to those observed in zeolites, glasses, and collodion membranes, the implication is that both kinds of systems are in comparable hydration states, i.e., that the association between water and charged groups in biological membranes is comparable to that in a crystalline hydrate.

EFFECT OF SITE SPACING OR ION COORDINATION NUMBER

For ions of the same charge, variation in site spacing or in ion coordination number (the number of sites which the ion nearly touches) does not affect the pattern of transition sequences: closer site spacing or higher coordination number merely yields a sequence corresponding to higher field strength [e.g., compare Figures 3C and 3D of (2)]. The intuitive explanation is that one high-strength site exerts the same force as several low-strength sites.

As discussed previously (pp. 599–600), intersite spacing is critical in governing selectivity between a monovalent and divalent ion.

With nondeformable site-bearing molecules, different ions may have different coordination numbers: for instance, alkali cations of different sizes may be in contact with different numbers of carbonyl or ether oxygens in a macrocyclic polypeptide antibiotic or polyether. In the case of deformable macrocyclic compounds the deformation energy required for a compound to achieve the configuration of minimum energy and maximum coordination number with a given ion may contribute significantly to the free energy balance of expression 1, p. 593.

ENTROPY EFFECTS

In a membrane in which the replacement of one permeating ion by another leads to no change in the structure or hydration state of the membrane, the entropy change in ion exchange should be given by the difference in entropies of hydration, and $\Delta S_{ion,site}$ should be the same for all ions. Sherry (5) has pointed out that entropy changes in the membrane or exchanger phase are sometimes significant in zeolites with high water content. This is due in part to water transfer in or out of the membrane (hence a change in entropy of the transferred water), associated with the exchange of one ion for another.

NONEQUILIBRIUM SELECTIVITY

Up to this point we have discussed the application of physical principles only to the problem of equilibrium selectivity. That is, we have asked the question: given a material (a membrane, enzyme, mineral, etc.) in contact with an aqueous solution containing several similarly charged ions, in what order will these ions be preferred by the material as its nearest neighbor at equilibrium? Some of the effects whose ionic selectivity we wish to explain involve this kind of purely equilibrium problem: for example, the binding constants of an ion exchanger or of DNA or of proteins, the affinities for active transport mechanisms, the ability to stimulate or inhibit an enzyme, and the reversal-of-charge concentration in electrophoresis of colloids. However, other effects whose specificity has been cited actually contain a nonequilibrium component (as a mobility or an interfacial activation energy) in addition to the equilibrium affinity: for example, the permeability of a glass electrode or of a biological membrane or of a thin lipid membrane, as judged from electrical potential differences under concentration gradients, from electrical conductances, or from tracer fluxes. For an ion exchange membrane, for instance, one may write the permeability ratio P_1/P_2 for two ions as $P_1/P_2 = K(u_1/u_2)$, where K is the ion exchange equilibrium constant for the two ions and u_1/u_2, the mobility ratio, is a nonequilibrium parameter (3). What can be said about selectivity involving nonequilibrium parameters?

The empirical fact is that the selectivity sequences we have cited for effects with nonequilibrium components are essentially the same as the selectivity patterns cited for purely equilibrium effects, and are also the same as those predicted from a theoretical consideration of equilibrium selectivity alone. There are two possible explanations: either the nonequilibrium parameters (e.g., mobilities) in a given system differ much less among the various ions than do the equilibrium parameters; or else the nonequilibrium parameters are dependent functions of the equilibrium parameters. In the glass electrodes it has been shown experimentally that both explanations apply (3): a potassium-selective electrode ($P_{K^+}/P_{Na^+} = 10.3$) was found to have $K = 34$ for K^+-Na^+ exchange (K^+ bound 34 times more strongly than Na^+) but $u_K/u_{Na} = 0.3$. Thus, the mobility ratio is in the opposite direction from the binding-constant ratio (the most strongly bound ion is the least mobile, as one might expect) but is much closer to 1, so that it is the equilibrium sequence which determines the permeability sequence. This quantitative comparison between the binding-constant ratio and the mobility ratio provides the answer to the common misconception, "Shouldn't the most strongly bound ion be the least permeable rather than the most permeable?" In the case of lipid bilayers containing uncharged carriers such as macrocyclic antibiotics it has been suggested (23) that the expression $P_1/P_2 = (u_{1s}K_1)/(u_{2s}K_2) \doteq K_1/K_2$ holds where K is an association constant between the ion and carrier and u_{1s} or u_{2s} is the mobility of the ion-carrier complex; i.e., that the permeability ratio and equilibrium selectivity ratio are nearly the same because all ion-carrier complexes have approximately the same mobility.

To a large extent the forces governing nonequilibrium selectivity are the same as those governing equilibrium selectivity, acting in the opposite direction. However, Born repulsion forces ("steric effects") may assume additional importance: in sufficiently rigid and close frameworks, steric effects may reduce the mobility of larger ions, giving rise to ion sieving. Two clear and typical examples of the extent of this effect, which should neither be neglected nor overstressed, may be drawn from ion exchange studies on the class of aluminosilicates called zeolites [summarized by Sherry in (5)]. The channels and cavities in the relatively rigid zeolite frameworks are often of atomic dimensions, and their sizes can be accurately and independently determined by crystallographic methods for comparison with their experimentally observed sieving properties.

1. The channels in basic sodalite have a free radius of 1.3 Å. The following monovalent ions, all of which have ionic (nonhydrated) radii comparable to or less than 1.3 Å, are found to exchange rapidly (but with different equilibrium affinities) into and out of basic sodalite cages: Li^+ (Pauling crystal radius 0.60 Å), Na^+ (0.95 Å), Ag^+ (1.26 Å), K^+ (1.33 Å). The following ions with larger crystal radii exchange with great difficulty into and out of basic sodalite cages: NH_4^+ (1.40 Å), Tl^+ (1.40 Å), Rb^+ (1.48 Å), Cs^+ (1.69 Å). The *hydrated* radii estimated from a modified form of Stokes' law are about 3.3 Å for Na^+ and 3.7 Å for Li^+ (76, p. 126), i.e. much greater than the basic sodalite channel. The good exchangeability of these ions with small ionic radii but large hydrated radii shows that water of hydration has been readily stripped off these monovalent cations, and that sieving of alkali cations is primarily related to nonhydrated size.

2. Free energies of hydration for divalent cations such as the alkaline earths, and trivalent cations such as La^{+++}, are about 3 to 6 times those of the monovalent alkali cations, respectively. When a polyvalent cation has an ionic radius less than the channel radius but a hydrated radius greater than the channel radius, the cation may be unable to enter the channel, unlike the just-cited result for monovalent cations. For instance, Tl^+ (ionic radius 1.40 Å) diffuses into the sodalite cages of Linde X at 25° C, whereas Ba^{++} (ionic radius 1.35 Å) does not, despite its smaller ionic size. Again, the ionic radius of La^{+++} (1.15 Å) is significantly less than the radius of the sodalite channels in Linde Y (1.25 Å); La^{+++} exchanges completely at 100° C but not at all at 25° C. The hydration energy of these polyvalent cations is evidently too large, and the sodalite framework too rigid, to permit enough stripping of water of hydration and enough vibrational fluctuation in channel size for passage through the sodalite channels to occur at room temperature.

Nonequilibrium steric effects with the strongly hydrated polyvalent cations presumably explain why the glass electrodes are much less permeable to Ca^{++} than to the alkali cations, despite high binding constants for Ca^{++}. For example, the mineral montmorillonite binds Ca^{++} twice as strongly as Na^+, but montomorillonite membranes are 40 times more permeable to Na^+ than to Ca^{++}, because the mobility of Ca^{++} is 80 times lower than that of Na^+ (6). It seems likely that low mobility may similarly explain the low permeability of most biological membranes to Ca^{++}, despite the high equilibrium affinity for Ca^{++} suggested by the ability of small concentrations of

Ca^{++} to suppress permeability of monovalent cations present in much higher concentrations (e.g., 16).

For the alkali cations, however, the available experience indicates that steric effects will be much more closely related to the nonhydrated sizes than to apparent hydrated sizes. Since the "equivalent pore radii" measured for nerve, erythrocyte, and other biological membranes are about 4 to 6 Å (77) and since the largest alkali cation, Cs^+, has a radius of only 1.69 Å, ion-sieving effects in permeation of alkali cations through biological membranes are probably of only secondary importance.

PORE RADIUS AND ALKALI-CATION SELECTIVITY

As the final topic in ion selectivity, mention must now be made of attempts to explain all of alkali-cation selectivity in terms of sieving of naked or hydrated ions, attempts which should be of purely historical interest but which are unfortunately still invoked in much current physiological literature.

The experimental facts that have often led physiologists to attribute selectivity to ion sieving and pore radius are that most cells are more permeable to K^+ than to Na^+, K^+ having the smaller apparent (e.g., Stokes' law) hydrated size; and that some biological specificity sequences for cations or anions happen to be in the order of the apparent hydrated sizes (the lyotropic series) or else of the measured nonhydrated sizes. This point of view is similar to that adopted by physical chemists before about 1920. Physiologists still adopting this point of view have apparently not been aware of the large and detailed body of information on ion selectivity, summarized in the preceding pages, that had already necessitated the abandonment of this interpretation by Jenny in 1927: that these two kinds of sequences which do apparently correlate with size are only two out of a class of observed sequences, the others of which correlate neither with nonhydrated nor with apparent hydrated size; that the transitions between these sequences can be produced experimentally by changes in electrostatic forces in nonliving systems, biological colloids, and at least one biological membrane (the gallbladder); that calculations of electrostatic forces correctly reconstruct these sequences; and that the sieving effects on alkali cations demonstrable in narrow-pore systems are primarily related to ionic size. The apparent correlation of the lyotropic series with calculated hydrated sizes is now recognized by physical chemists concerned with ion selectivity to be "a misleading accident" (4, p. 269), since hydration affects ion selectivity through energy balance and not through size considerations: if ion:membrane interactions are energetically weak, they are outweighed by ion:water interactions, and the ion with the lowest hydration energy experiences the largest free energy decrease (or smallest increase) on passing from water to the membrane, yielding the lyotropic series.

The same general objections plus further specific objections are relevant to two recent misapplications of pore and sieving concepts to ion selectivity. First, some authors (e.g., 78, 79), working with the ion-selective cyclic antibiotics, initially interpreted their selectivity in terms of the ring size of the antibiotic sterically determining the size of the permeating ion (e.g., the hole in the antibiotic's ring might provide a pore through which only certain ions would fit). However, evaluation of the accumulated evidence from macrocyclic compounds of varying ring size shows that there is no simple relation between the ring size and the observed selectivity patterns, which are the same as those observed in other biological and nonbiological systems and predicted from the Coulomb model.

Second, Mullins (74) has argued that a pore might select a partially hydrated ion, with a certain number of hydration shells, of an optimal size and might discriminate against both larger and smaller ions:

> If an ion at a specified level of hydration closely approximates the size and shape of a pore, it may exchange all its hydration, beyond the specified level, for the solvation afforded by the walls of the membrane pore. . . . If K^+ approaches a pore that is precisely the same size as this ion with its first hydration shell (denoted $(K^+)_1$), it may, as indicated previously, exchange hydration, for water shells from 2 to infinity, for *a similar attraction* with the structure lining the pore. If the pore is somewhat smaller than $(K^+)_1$, penetration cannot occur for steric reasons, while if the pore is somewhat too large, penetration likewise cannot occur because the attraction of the ion for water shells of 2 and greater is not compensated by a solvation of *similar magnitude* in the pore.

[(74, pp. 125–126); italics added by the reviewers]. The erroneous assumption implicit in the italicized expressions "similar attraction" and "similar magnitude" is that any nearest neighbor at a given distance, whether water or membrane substance, will exert similar attractive forces upon the ion. In fact, the attractive force exerted by the membrane may be much more or much less than that exerted by water, depending upon whether its field strength is much more or much less than that of water, and it is this variation in electrostatic forces which determines selectivity. In addition, one of the earliest reasons why physical chemists (e.g., 80) discarded Gregor's selectivity theory and Ling's 1952 theory, which were founded on the concept of hydrated size, was the ambiguity of this concept, and Mullins' discussion of the precise fit of a pore to specific hydration shells of an ion is even less defensible physically. Calculated "hydrated ion sizes", whether extracted from Stokes' law, from Debye-Hückel theory, or from other measurements, depend upon what the ion interacts with and what property one is measuring. For instance, the sequence of hydrated sizes obtained from Debye-Hückel theory for Cs^+, Rb^+, and K^+ inverts, depending upon whether F^- (OH^-, acetate) or Cl^- (Br^-,I^-) is the counterion; and the sequence for I^-, Br^-, and Cl^- inverts, depending upon whether Li^+ (Na^+, K^+) or Rb^+ (Cs^+) is the counterion. The use of "hydrated sizes" to explain data other than the data from which they were calculated has virtually disappeared from texts of physical chemistry, since hydration effects can be consistently explained only if the fundamental criterion is energy (as in Eisenman's theory), not size.

SUMMARY OF ION SELECTIVITY

The problem of Na^+-K^+ discrimination by biological membranes is part of the general problem of discrimination among the five alkali cations (Li^+, Na^+, K^+, Rb^+, Cs^+). Although these five ions can be permuted 120 different ways, only 11 of these permutations are consistently observed as selectivity sequences in nonliving systems such as minerals, ion exchange resins, and glass electrodes. It is a striking fact that the selectivity orders observed in most biological systems fit the same pattern of 11 sequences, which suggests that the physical basis of discrimination is the same in nonliving and in living systems. The principal factor controlling cation equilibrium specificity is the field strength of membrane negative charges. A simplified model which estimates the energies of ion:site interaction thermochemically or by Coulomb's law and compares these with free energies of hydration correctly predicts the observed pattern of 11 sequences. The selectivity patterns for halide anions and for divalent cations are constructed; these are also successfully predicted by a Coulomb model. Predictions, which have received some experimental confirmation, can be made relating the expected ion selectivity pattern to the pK_a of the membrane sites with which the ions interact. The contributions to ion selectivity from non-Coulomb forces, hydration, site spacing, entropy effects, and nonequilibrium effects such as ion sieving are summarized.

PART II. NONELECTROLYTE SELECTIVITY

INTRODUCTION

If one makes a comparison of pairs of nonelectrolytes with approximately the same sizes, molecular weights, free-solution diffusion coefficients, and empirical formulae, one finds that permeability coefficients measured in the same biological membrane may differ by a factor of up to 10^8 between members of a pair. This selectivity is of interest not only because of its physiological importance, but also because it arises directly from the structure of much of the cell membrane and thus provides evidence concerning membrane structure.

Nonelectrolytes vary enormously in size, shape, structure, intramolecular interactions between substituent groups, and interactions with other molecules, as well as in permeating power. Thus, studies which attempt to draw conclusions about the general patterns of selectivity but are based on permeability determinations for a few molecules run the risk of yielding misleading results, although such studies may be useful in the further analysis of specific problems once the general patterns have been established. Most of the discussion will therefore center on two comprehensive investigations of nonelectrolyte permeation: the studies of Collander (81–96) on giant algal cells of the family Characeae and on model systems; and the permeability determinations by Wright & Diamond (97–99) in rabbit gallbladder epithelium. Fortunately, although no two biological objects could be more dissimilar than giant algae and rabbit gallbladders, the qualitative patterns that emerge from these two studies are in detailed agreement, and studies on other tissues appear to provide merely quantitative variants of these same patterns. We shall begin by describing the algal and gallbladder experiments and presenting the permeability patterns that were obtained. It will be shown that the main pattern of nonelectrolyte selectivity is similar to that in simple model systems, and that the three classes of deviations from this main pattern are related to the specific structure of biological membranes. Finally, the origin of main-pattern selectivity will be discussed on the basis, first, of a thermodynamic analysis using incremental partial molar quantities associated with specific residues, and then on the basis of intermolecular forces. Discussion will be confined to selectivity associated with passive, noncarrier-mediated permeation, since the nonelectrolyte selectivity patterns associated with permeases and active transport mechanisms are quite different, in contrast to the situation for ions.

Giant Algae and Rabbit Gallbladders

The Characeae or stoneworts are a family of green algae whose cells may be up to several inches long, 1 mm or more thick, and nearly cylindrical in shape. Most of the volume of the cell is the vacuole, separated by a typical plasma membrane (the tonoplast) from a layer of protoplasm, which is separated in turn by another typical plasma membrane (the plasmalemma) from an external cellulose wall up to 10 μ thick. The most extensive quantitative study of permeation in the Characeae was Collander's determination of permeability coefficients for 70 nonelectrolytes in cells of the alga *Nitella mucronata* by direct chemical analysis (81). In most cases the efflux rate of a substance from a cell which had previously equilibrated with a solution of the substance was measured, while influx rates were determined for the least permeable substances. Numerous different nonelectrolytes were often compared directly on the same cell. Collander measured the permeability of heat-killed cells and subtracted the resulting resistance (the reciprocal of the permeability coefficient) from the resistance of the live cell to obtain a resistance corrected approximately for unstirred layers. A similar, earlier study (82) by Collander & Bärlund yielded permeability coefficients for 45 nonelectrolytes in the related alga *Chara ceratophylla*. In scope, care, and value these two studies offer by far the best measurements of permeability coefficients to date.

Some other studies by Collander which are of equal importance and quality but which have unfortunately tended to be overlooked by animal physiologists deserve to have specific attention drawn to them here: permeability to rapidly penetrating nonelectrolytes, measured by an osmotic method (83); permeability to small molecules (84, 85); permeability to branched molecules (86); permeability to very large molecules (87); permeability of other plant, fungal, bacterial, and yeast cells (88–91); partition between bulk lipid solvents and water (92–95); the chemical interpretation of partition phenomena (95); and a general review of nonelectrolyte permeation and partition phenomena by Wartiovaara & Collander (96).

Rabbit gallbladder is a sac consisting of a single layer of uninterrupted epithelial cells fused to each other around the whole circumference by continuous tight junctions, and supported on the outside by connective tissue. Wright & Diamond (97–99) measured the permeability of this epithelium to 206 nonelectrolytes. The parameter determined was not the permeability coefficient but the reflection coefficient or Staverman coefficient σ (100), which is the ratio of the osmotic flow caused by a gradient of a test molecule to the flow caused by the same gradient of a molecule known to be impermeant. This ratio is 1 for an impermeant molecule and decreases progressively below 1 for increasingly permeant molecules until $\sigma = 0$ is reached for a solute as permeant as water. This relation between osmotic flow rates (effective "osmotic pressure") and the permeability of the solute responsible for the osmotic gradient is due to two facts: the osmotic flow rate from dilute to concentrated solution is reduced below the volume flow rate of solvent in this direction by the volume flow rate of solute diffusing down its concentration gradient from concentrated to dilute solution; and the diffusing solute may drag some solvent from concentrated to dilute solution, if and only if solute and solvent interact while crossing the membrane. Thus, the following expression holds (101):

$$\sigma = 1 - \omega v_s / L_p - K f_{sw} / (f_{sw} + f_{sm}) \qquad 2.$$

where ω is the solute permeability coefficient and v_s its partial molar volume, L_p is the hydraulic conductivity, K a partition coefficient, and the f's are frictional coefficients between solute and water (f_{sw}) or solute and membrane (f_{sm}). In addition, measured σ's for permeant molecules are reduced still further below 1 in proportion to their permeability, as a result of dissipation of the solute concentration gradient in unstirred layers adjacent to the membrane.

Flow rates can be measured in rabbit gallbladder in a fraction of a minute by means of streaming potentials, so that in practice Wright & Diamond took σ as the ratio of the streaming potential produced by 0.1 molal of the test substance to the streaming potential, measured immediately before and afterwards, produced by 0.1 molal of the impermeant solute sucrose. Smyth & Wright (102) had previously found close agreement in the intestine between σ's measured by this electrical method and σ's obtained from a gravimetric procedure for measuring flow rates, as expected from the observed direct proportionality between streaming potentials and flow rates (103); and Collander had previously found that a similar osmotic procedure yielded virtually the same permeability sequences in *Nitella mucronata* as did direct chemical analysis (81, 83). The advantages resulting from the rapidity of

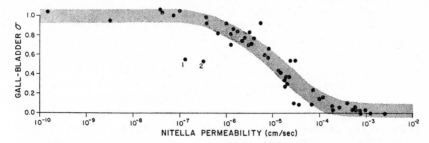

FIG. 3. Ordinate, reflection coefficients (σ's) of nonelectrolytes measured in rabbit gallbladder epithelium by Wright & Diamond (98). Abscissa, permeability coefficients of the same nonelectrolytes measured in the alga *Nitella mucronata* by Collander (81). The two deviant points are urea (1) and methyl urea (2). Except for these two solutes, gallbladder σ's decrease closely in parallel with increasing permeability in *Nitella*, showing that the two systems have essentially the same permeability pattern. The shaded band is drawn to indicate the general trend of the points and has no theoretical significance.

this electrical method were that several dozen σ's could be determined in a single experiment, facilitating comparison of closely similar molecules in the same preparation; and that σ's could be obtained for unstable molecules which undergo rapid chemical transformation on being dissolved in water and which therefore yield erroneous permeability values by slower methods. Of the three papers reporting these experiments, the first (97) presented the method, the second (98) analyzed the patterns of permeation and the effects of pH and temperature, and the third (99) analyzed the molecular forces responsible for nonelectrolyte selectivity.

Figure 3 plots σ's in the gallbladder against P's or permeability coefficients ($P = \omega RT$) in *Nitella mucronata* for 52 solutes of varying sizes, shapes, and solubility properties studied in both preparations. Except for urea and methylurea, the results correlate closely: gallbladder σ's decrease from 1 to 0 with increasing permeability in *Nitella mucronata*. Two conclusions follow from this correlation: that in either preparation σ's measured by streaming potentials would be closely correlated with permeability coefficients measured by direct chemical analysis; and that nonelectrolyte permeation is governed by the same selectivity principles in rabbit gallbladder epithelium as in the alga *Nitella mucronata*.

Three general questions concerning active transport, complex membranes, and unstirred layers apply to the interpretation of these results or of any other study of nonelectrolyte permeation. First, no mechanism for active transport or facilitated diffusion of a nonelectrolyte has been discovered in *Nitella* or the gallbladder, although the transport properties of both have been the subject of much work; solutes whose transport is carrier-mediated in other tissues (glycerol, sugars, amino acids) show permeability properties in *Nitella* and the gallbladder expected for simple diffusion; and on teleological grounds neither preparation would be expected to have active transport mechanisms for nonelectrolytes. The measurements may therefore be safely interpreted in terms of passive permeation. Second, both *Nitella* and the gallbladder are complex membranes, consisting of two membranes in series. The relative resistances of the tonoplast and the plasmalemma to nonelectrolytes in *Nitella mucronata* are unknown. In the gallbladder, it is likely, though not certain, that the electrical method measures σ's for the membranes at the luminal faces of the epithelial cells; but the membranes at the luminal and serosal faces appear in any case to have the same relative permeability properties (97). Finally, measured "membrane resistances" (reciprocals of permeabilities) are the sum of the true cell membrane resistance plus the resistance of adjacent unstirred layers. The more permeant the solute, the greater is therefore the unstirred-layer effect, which causes measured P's and σ's to be lower than real ones. Since the unstirred-layer effect is itself proportional to real permeability, it is of minor importance if one analyzes empirical relations between measured permeabilities and other properties (solubilities, chemical structure, etc.), but is of critical importance when one requires absolute values of σ's or P's or their ratios to insert into kinetic or thermodynamic equations tacitly assuming perfect stirring. The gallbladder results were not corrected for unstirred-layer effects, which may have been considerable for the more permeant solutes. Collander (81) attempted to correct for unstirred-layer effects by measuring and subtracting the resistance of the dead cell; this procedure has not escaped criticism (104, p. 302) but should nevertheless hold approximately, and the correction is in any case significant only for Collander's most permeant solutes. Further discussion of this important unstirred-layer problem will be found in (97, 104–106).

Patterns of Nonelectrolyte Permeability

The main pattern.—Seventy years ago Overton (107) suggested on the basis of extensive but largely qualitative studies that nonelectrolyte permeability correlated well with the lipid solubility of the test solute relative to its water solubility. This concept, which provided the earliest evidence for the key role of lipids in cell membranes, has been quantitatively confirmed by the *Nitella* and gallbladder studies.

If the mechanism of nonelectrolyte permeation were the same through cell membranes as through a bulk lipid phase, the following expression should hold:

$$P_i = K_i D_i / d \qquad\qquad 3.$$

where d is the membrane thickness, $P_i = \omega RT$ is the permeability coefficient of the ith solute, D_i is its diffusion coefficient in the membrane interior, and K_i is its lipid:water or membrane:water partition coefficient (the equilibrium ratio of the test solute's concentration in a lipid phase to its concentration in water, the two phases being in contact and mutually immiscible).

The tacit assumption behind this equation is that permeation is limited by diffusion in the membrane interior and not by the two phase-boundary transitions (from water to membrane and from membrane to water). While one would ideally like to have K's for membrane lipids themselves, these are unavailable, but many K's have been measured for other lipid solvents, particularly for ether and olive oil (81, 95). As demonstrated experimentally and discussed by Collander (92, 96), K sequences in different lipid solvents are closely correlated, the quantitative differences in K ratios between different solvents reflecting mainly the balance between their hydrogen-bonding and hydrocarbon portions rather than their specific chemical properties. For diffusion coefficients in bulk solvents the relation $DM^{1/2} = $ constant, where M is the molecular weight, holds approximately for small molecules and $DM^{1/3} = $ constant for very large molecules (108; 109, Figure 3.2). Thus, P and σ should correlate closely with $KM^{-1/2}$ in a homogeneous, bulk, lipid membrane.

Wright & Diamond (98) plotted gallbladder σ's against K_{oil}, K_{ether}, $M^{-1/2}K_{oil}$, and $M^{-1/2}K_{ether}$. All four graphs looked much the same, because K_{ether}'s and K_{oil}'s are closely correlated, and because K varied over a 63,000,000-fold range but M only over a 7-fold range for the molecules graphed, so that the presence or absence of the $M^{-1/2}$ term made little difference. Figure 4 is the graph of σ against $M^{-1/2}K_{ether}$. It is apparent that σ decreases from 1.0 to 0 with increasing $M^{-1/2}K_{ether}$, i.e. that permeability increases in close correlation with increasing partition coefficient for the overwhelming majority of the solutes tested. All the conspicuously deviant points belong to two classes of exceptions: small molecules with low K's, whose σ's are much lower than the main pattern (points 1 through 9, Figure 4); and highly branched molecules, whose σ's are much higher than the main pattern (points 10 through 13, Figure 4).

Collander (81) plotted *Nitella* P's against various functions of M and K_{oil} or K_{ether}. Since M varied over a 25-fold range among the solutes tested, the *Nitella* results are a more sensitive test of the size dependence of permeation than the gallbladder results. P increased conspicuously with increasing K, but also increased somewhat with decreasing M at constant K. Collander concluded that the best empirical fit of P was to $M^{-1.5}(K_{oil})^{1.32}$: the expression $PM^{1.5}/K^{1.32}$ was roughly constant and independent of M above $M = 70$. However, the expression increased progressively with decreasing M below about $M = 70$ (81, Figure 4). Thus, in *Nitella* as in the gallbladder, permeability increases with the partition coefficient, but the smallest molecules are more permeant than expected from the main pattern. Analysis of P's measured by Collander & Bärlund in *Chara ceratophylla* yielded the same conclusion (82).

The pattern of nonelectrolyte permeability may therefore be tentatively summarized as a main pattern with three classes of exceptions: sequences and ratios of permeability coefficients in biological membranes are similar to those for permeation through a bulk lipid phase, except that: the size

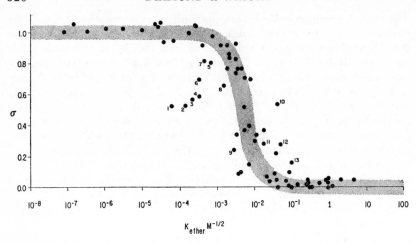

FIG. 4. Ordinate, reflection coefficients (σ's) of nonelectrolytes measured in rabbit gall bladder by Wright & Diamond (98); abscissa, the ether:water partition coefficient (K) times the reciprocal square root of molecular weight (M) for each nonelectrolyte. Points referring to small solutes and branched solutes are numbered: small solutes, 1 = urea, 2 = methyl urea, 3 = formamide, 4 = acetamide, 5 = ethylene glycol, 6 = dimethyl urea, 7 = ethyl urea, 8 = propionamide, 9 = dimethyl formamide; branched solutes, 10 = pinacol, 11 = isovaleramide, 12 = 2-methyl-2,4-pentanediol, 13 = triacetin. The shaded band is drawn to indicate the general pattern of the other points and has no theoretical significance. (From 98.)

dependence is steeper (ca. $M^{-1.5}$ rather than $M^{-0.5}$); small molecules permeate relatively more rapidly; and branched molecules permeate relatively more slowly. Further evidence for the reality of these three exceptions, and discussion of their significance, will be postponed until after discussion of the main pattern.

The significance of the main pattern.—The main pattern (i.e., the close correlation between P's or σ's and K's for most molecules) means that the intermolecular forces governing selective nonelectrolyte permeation through cell membranes are the same as the forces governing nonelectrolyte partition between a bulk lipid phase and water.

This tautology is consistent with either of two different permeation mechanisms: (*i*) The rate-limiting step is diffusion through the membrane interior, as implicit in the equation $P = KD/d$; the achievement of partition equilibrium at the two membrane: water interfaces is very rapid; differences in P's for different solutes are due principally to variation in K's, which is much greater than variation in D's (this is true for bulk solvents); and K's for membrane lipids correlate closely with K's for various bulk lipid solvents, which correlate closely with each other. Two or all of the three observed classes of deviations from the main pattern would find a ready explanation in expected limitations upon the validity of bulk-phase extrapolations to very thin membranes. (*ii*) Diffusion through the membrane interior is relatively rapid, and the rate-limiting step is passage through the water:membrane interface. The activation energy for crossing this interface will be determined by essentially the same intermolecular forces which govern lipid:water partition coefficients, namely, the forces between solute and water which must be broken and the forces between solute and lipids (or membrane) which are gained. Solute:water forces are generally considerably stronger than solute:lipid forces (p. 633) and dominate both partition coefficients and, presumably, activation energies. These two mechanisms represent opposite extremes in a spectrum of possibilities: the resistance of the membrane interior and of the water-to-membrane interface might be comparable, or the balance might differ for different solutes in the same membrane.

The dilemma in clarifying this unresolved problem of the rate-limiting step in permeation is that the governing intermolecular forces and the expected selectivity patterns are the same in either case, so that discussions in terms of one mechanism can be reworded in terms of the other mechanism with equal validity. This ambiguity is illustrated by the fact that Stein (109), who assumed the second mechanism to hold for most molecules, and Diamond & Wright (99), who assumed the first mechanism to hold, invoked essentially the same kinds of chemical arguments and selectivity principles as each other and as Collander (95) had invoked in explaining bulk lipid:water partition coefficients. Three attempts based on the transition-state theory of activated diffusion have been made to resolve this question, but all three appear to us to be invalidated by this equivocal nature of the arguments:

(*a*) The application of activated-diffusion theory to membrane permeation was pioneered by Danielli (110), who assumed that the chief resistance to slowly permeating solutes is at the water-to-membrane interface but is in the membrane interior for rapidly permeating solutes. As Zwolinski et al. (111) point out, this assumption is groundless: the magnitude of the permeability coefficient gives no indication about the locus of the resistance.

(*b*) Zwolinski, Eyring & Reese (111) assumed that the increase in permeability associated with a $-CH_2-$ group (i.e., the increase in P and decrease in σ in a homologous series with increasing hydrocarbon chain length) arose mainly from an increase in K due to a decrease in the rate constant for crossing the membrane-to-solution interface (k_{ms} in their terminology), and that the rate constants for diffusion within the membrane (their k_m) and for crossing the solution-to-membrane interface (their k_{sm}) were little changed. Their tacit assumption was that the $-CH_2-$ group primarily increases solute:lipid forces without changing solute:water forces. On this basis they calculated relative resistance loci for various solutes in various cells. However, it is now clear (pp. 635, 641) that much of the increase in permeability brought about by a $-CH_2-$ group represents a decrease in solute:water forces due to an entropy effect.

(c) Stein (109) has published a valuable analysis of P's measured by Collander and others on the basis of the equations of Zwolinski et al. (111), but tacitly made the same unjustified starting assumption as did Danielli. Reasoning correctly that the water-to-membrane interfacial resistance will depend largely on the number of solute-to-water hydrogen bonds, he extrapolated a graph of log $PM^{1/2}$ against estimated number of hydrogen bonds for various solutes to obtain the limiting maximal $PM^{1/2}$ for a non-hydrogen-bonding solute (109, Figures 3.6 and 3.11). He interpreted the ΔF, ΔH, and ΔS calculated from the slope of this graph as thermodynamic parameters of the transition state for interfacial passage, interpreted the intercept P as the D/d of a non-hydrogen-bonding solute such as a pure hydrocarbon, and thus attempted to estimate diffusion coefficients in the membrane interior. However, one can equally well interpret Stein's ΔF, ΔH, and ΔS as the equilibrium parameters of partition between solute and membrane (cf. Equation 4, p. 630), if one assumes at the opposite extreme [as we have elsewhere (99)] that the membrane interior is rate limiting for most solutes. Stein's assumption that pure hydrocarbons would be limited by the membrane interior is also not necessarily valid because of the same underlying ambiguity: the same arguments which predict low interfacial resistance to a hydrocarbon explain its high partition coefficient (hence low membrane-interior resistance). Finally, even if Stein's assumptions about resistance loci were correct, his intercept would equal KD/d, not D/d, and hence would not yield D without knowledge of K.

The exceptions to the main pattern.—The three respects in which permeation patterns through cell membranes differ from those through a bulk lipid phase provide important clues to the structure of cell membranes.

The effect of branching.—In bulk lipid solvents, branched molecules have lower K's than straight-chain homologues, for reasons discussed on p. 624. However, quantitative comparisons of P's or σ's in several cells with bulk-solvent K's show that cell membranes discriminate even more sharply against branched solutes than does a bulk lipid phase:

(a) From the gallbladder results, the most markedly deviant point on the right-hand side of Figure 4 is number 10, pinacol $\begin{bmatrix} H_3C & OH & OH\,CH_3 \\ & \diagdown\; | & |\;\diagup \\ & C\!\!-\!\!C \\ & \diagup & \diagdown \\ H_3C & & CH_3 \end{bmatrix}$, the

only solute tested with two tertiary-carbon branch-points. The main pattern predicts that it should be freely permeant ($\sigma \sim 0$), but its σ is actually 0.54. Three other solutes with too high σ's (too low permeabilities) in Figure 4 each have one tertiary-carbon branch-point: number 11, isovaleramide $\begin{pmatrix} H_3C \\ \diagdown \\ \qquad CH-CH_2-\overset{\overset{\textstyle O}{\|}}{C}-NH_2 \\ \diagup \\ H_3C \end{pmatrix}$; number 12, 2-methyl-2,4-pentanediol

$\begin{pmatrix} \quad CH_3 \\ \quad | \\ H_3C-C-CH_2-CH-CH_3 \\ \quad | \qquad | \\ \quad OH \quad\; OH \end{pmatrix}$; and number 13, triacetin $\begin{pmatrix} \qquad \overset{\overset{\textstyle O}{\|}}{} \\ H_3C-C-O-CH_2- \end{pmatrix}$

$\begin{pmatrix} \overset{\overset{\textstyle O}{\|}}{O}-C-CH_3 \quad O \\ | \qquad\qquad\; \| \\ CH-CH_2-O-C-CH_3 \end{pmatrix}$. Comparison of the four isomeric butanols is also in-

structive (98, Table 3): the branched isobutanol $\begin{pmatrix} \qquad CH_3 \\ \qquad | \\ H_3C-CH-CH_2-OH \end{pmatrix}$ has

higher ether and olive oil K's than the straight-chain *sec*-butanol

$\begin{pmatrix} \quad OH \\ \quad | \\ H_3C-CH-CH_2-CH_3 \end{pmatrix}$ but is less permeant (has a higher σ); and the most

highly branched isomer *tert*.-butanol $\begin{pmatrix} \quad CH_3 \\ \quad | \\ H_3C-C-OH \\ \quad | \\ \quad CH_3 \end{pmatrix}$ has a much higher σ than

the other three isomers, quite out of proportion to the modest difference in K's.

(b) In *Nitella mucronata* Collander (81) showed that four solutes with a tertiary-carbon branch-point (*tert*.-butanol, triacetin, trimethyl citrate, and triethyl citrate) had lower P's than expected from the main pattern of *Nitella*.

(c) Oura, Suomalainen & Collander (91, Figure 2) showed for three kinds of yeast that the branched isovaleric acid and isobutyric acid were not only less permeant than the straight-chain *n*-valeric acid and *n*-butyric acid but also less permeant than expected from the main pattern in each yeast.

(d) Collander (90, Figure 1) indirectly measured permeability of *Elodea*

leaves and found that dimethyl malonic acid $\begin{pmatrix} H_3C \diagdown \qquad \diagup COOH \\ \qquad C \\ H_3C \diagup \qquad \diagdown COOH \end{pmatrix}$ and two

acids with tertiary-carbon branch-points (tricarballylic and aconitic acids) were less permeant than expected from the main pattern.

(e) Collander (86) showed that the highly branched pentaerythritol

$$\begin{bmatrix} & \text{CH}_2\text{-OH} & \\ & | & \\ \text{HO-CH}_2\text{-C-CH}_2\text{-OH} & \\ & | & \\ & \text{CH}_2\text{-OH} & \end{bmatrix}$$

has a higher K_{ether} than the straight-chain erythritol

$$\begin{bmatrix} \text{HO-CH}_2\text{-CH-CH-CH}_2\text{-OH} \\ \qquad | \quad | \\ \qquad \text{OH} \;\; \text{OH} \end{bmatrix}$$

but permeates more slowly in three plant cells and a luminous bacterium.

The fact that cell membranes discriminate more sharply against branched solutes than do bulk lipid solvents is probably attributable (96, 98, 112) to the fact that lipid molecules possess a more highly ordered configuration in cell membranes than in bulk solvents and may even have the hydrocarbon tails of the fatty acid residues aligned in parallel (110). Lipid: lipid forces are largely very short-range van der Waals forces, which are effectively proportional to surface contact area. A branched molecule has less area of close contact with surrounding molecules than does a nonbranched molecule, so that the latter should experience stronger van der Waals forces. This difference will be amplified in an environment where the solvent molecules are rigidly oriented and less free to bend around a solute molecule. The distortion in an oriented solvent structure caused by a branched molecule would also locally reduce the intermolecular forces between the solvent molecules themselves. One therefore expects the enthalpy change for transfer from water to lipid to be less negative, and the lipid-to-water partition coefficient to be lower, for a branched solute, and this difference to be exaggerated in the less flexible molecular arrangement of the membrane interior as compared to the situation in bulk lipid solvents. In addition, membrane lipid structure may act like a molecular sieve in preferentially depressing the diffusion coefficient of a branched solute relative to free solution.

The effect of size.—To determine the effect of size per se as distinct from other molecular properties requires permeability determinations for a very large number of solutes covering a wide range of molecular weights, since size effects are otherwise obscured by the huge range (10^8-fold) in K's among nonelectrolytes. The only adequate test is provided by the *Nitella* results, where Collander initially (81) concluded that P varied as $M^{-1.5}$ between molecular weights $M = 70$ and $M = 480$. Later (87) Collander tested two polypropylene glycols with $M = 425$ and $M = 1025$ and obtained lower permeabilities than predicted from an $M^{-1.5}$ dependence. On recalculation we find that a dependence between $M^{-2.5}$ and M^{-3} is required to explain the polypropylene glycol results and is compatible with the earlier *Nitella* results. This inverse dependence on size is far steeper than the $M^{-1/2}$ or $M^{-1/3}$ dependence observed for diffusion in free solution, and may have the same explanation as the discrimination against branched molecules: the distortion introduced by a large solute molecule into the oriented hydrocarbon interior of a membrane would reduce the solute's partition coefficient, and might also reduce its diffusion coefficient because of a molecular-sieve effect.

Permeation of the smallest solutes.—In *Chara ceratophylla* (82) and *Nitella mucronata* (81) the smallest solutes (water, methanol, formamide, acetamide, etc.) permeate more rapidly than expected from the main pattern. In the gallbladder all solutes tested that are both small ($M < 75$) and have low partition coefficients ($K_{ether} < 0.1$, $K_{oil} < 0.007$) have σ's far below the main pattern (points 1 through 9, Figure 4). Most of these deviant small solutes are relatively polar molecules (ureas or amides). For example, urea (point 1, Figure 4) should be impermeant ($\sigma = 1.0$) according to the main pattern but actually has $\sigma = 0.53$, a value expected only for a molecule 100 times more lipid-soluble than urea actually is. These deviations persist even if the size dependence of the main pattern is taken as M^{-3} or M^{-4}. It is possible that nonzero values of the water-drag component of σ, $K f_{sw}/(f_{sw} + f_{sm})$ in Equation 2 (p. 616), contribute to these low σ's in the gallbladder, but it seems safe to assume that in addition permeability is much higher than normal, by analogy with the *Nitella-Chara* results in which P's rather than σ's were measured.

Two possible explanations for the anomalously high permeability of the smallest and most polar solutes must be considered: First, these solutes may follow the same route through membrane lipids as do other solutes, and their enhanced permeation may be another expression of the sieve properties of oriented membrane lipids. Detailed statements of this interpretation have been presented [Wartiovaara (112), Wartiovaara & Collander (96)]. Second, these solutes may follow a separate route through the cell membrane, interacting with membrane polar groups rather than with the hydrocarbon tails of lipids. The latter interpretation, according to which the membrane behaves as a mosaic towards permeating solutes, appears to us more probable for the following five reasons:

(a) For molecules fitting the main pattern of permeation, the relations between chemical structure and permeability are summarized in a set of rules which were first formulated empirically by Overton, which also apply to lipid:water partition coefficients, and which are readily explained in terms of differences between solute:water forces and solute:lipid forces. However, there are many instances in the gallbladder and other tissues where a change in structure of a small molecule produces a change in permeability that violates Overton's rules and is apparently related primarily to size. Typical examples are the cases in which the second compound in a homologous series is less permeant than the first, although the addition of each subsequent $-CH_2-$ group increases permeability [e.g., the order of σ's in the gallbladder is formamide < acetamide > propionamide > butyramide > valeramide > hexanamide, and methanol < ethanol > propanol > butanol; the order of P's in mitochondria (113) is formamide > acetamide = propionamide < butyramide < valeramide. See (98, Tables 4 and 5) for many other examples.] Correspondingly, the magnitude of the deviation of gallbladder σ's of small solutes from the main pattern shows no correlation with partition coefficients or Overton's rules. This suggests that these solutes interact with hydrocarbon tails of membrane lipids minimally or not at all.

(b) If the explanation were the same sieving effect in the lipid phase responsible for $M^{-1.5}$ dependence, one might expect this effect to restrict permeation continuously and increasingly from the smallest to the largest solute. In fact, both in *Nitella* and in the gallbladder a single empirical relation describes P's or σ's of all solutes above about $M = 70$ to 90 and the enhanced permeation of polar solutes appears only below this size. The *Nitella* results, incidentally, suggest that the "extra" permeability of water is simply that expected from extrapolation of the "extra" permeability of other small solutes to the size of the water molecule (81, Figure 4).

(c) In the gallbladder, σ's for solutes fitting the main pattern increase markedly at low pH, possibly because of altered charge and packing of membrane lipids. On the other hand, σ's for the deviant small solutes remain virtually unchanged (98, Table 9), again suggesting that they bypass membrane lipids. The same interpretation may underlie the observation in toad urinary bladder (114) that permeabilities to non-ionic forms of fatty acids decrease at low pH, the effect becoming more marked with increasing chain length (increasing lipid solubility) (see 98 for further discussion).

(d) In the gallbladder, σ's for solutes fitting the main pattern decrease greatly with increasing temperature, while the effect of temperature is much less marked on σ's of the deviant small solutes (98, Tables 6, 7, and 8). This means that the temperature coefficient of permeation is higher in the lipid pathway than in the polar pathway, perhaps because more energy is required for solute transfer from water to lipid than from water to another polar environment. Wright & Diamond (98) showed that the formerly confusing patterns obtained by Wartiovaara (115–117) for Q_{10}'s of nonelectrolyte permeation in six kinds of plants can be easily rationalized if there is a separate polar pathway with low Q_{10}'s. Even if one considers only those solutes fitting the main pattern and following the lipid route, Danielli's prediction that "$PM^{1/2}$ and (Q_{10}) are negatively correlated for a homogeneous membrane" (110, p. 332) is unlikely to be confirmed. This prediction would be valid only if ΔF for permeation or partition could be equated with ΔH and if entropy changes were negligible. In fact, entropies of permeation are large (109, 111) and in many cases (pp. 635, 641) outweigh enthalpies.

(e) Sequences of permeation rates of larger nonelectrolytes are very similar in different cells, but sequences involving smaller nonelectrolytes show much variation. For instance, a survey of erythrocytes of 39 vertebrate species by Jacobs, Glassman & Parpart (118) revealed that 22 were more permeable to thiourea than to urea, 17 vice versa; Höber & Ørskov (119) surveyed erythrocytes of nine vertebrate species and found urea more permeant than methylurea in five species, vice versa in four, and acetamide more permeant than propionamide in four species, vice versa in four, equally permeant in one; Collander & Wikström (85) studied protoplasts of 36 plants and found 31 more permeable to methylurea than to urea, vice versa in five. There is a voluminous literature, particularly by botanists, on these reversals, which have been used to define "permeability types" ("urea-permeable," "methylurea-permeable") and for which diverse explanations specific to particular molecules have been advanced. Most of this variation between different tissues, different species, or different individuals is of the kind one would expect if there were separate lipid and polar pathways whose relative contributions to nonelectrolyte permeation varied in different cases, and if in addition the upper size limit for permeating solutes in the polar pathway varied.

The following two cases suggest variation in the lipid pathway with little variation in the polar pathway: (i) σ's for four nonelectrolytes were measured in axons of the Chilean squid *Dosidicus gigas* (120) and the Venezuelan squid *Doryteuthis plei* (121). Values for the two least lipid-soluble solutes, urea and glycerol, showed little species difference, but σ's for the more lipid-soluble formamide and ethylene glycol were much lower in *Dosidicus* than in *Doryteuthis*. (ii) In *Doryteuthis* σ's decrease during electrical stimulation. This decrease is marked for the solutes with the highest K's and is slight for the solutes with the lowest K's (121, Table 3 and Figure 5), which suggests some reorganization of membrane lipids during the action potential.

The following three cases imply variation in the polar pathway with little variation in the lipid pathway: (i) Collander (81) found two *Nitella mucronata* cells which were up to three times more permeable to small polar solutes than most other cells but whose permeabilities to larger solutes with higher K's were normal. (ii) The bacterium *Beggiatoa mirabilis* became a frequently cited extreme case on the basis of Ruhland's & Hoffmann's claim (122) that permeability was correlated solely with size and not at all with lipid:water K's. Examination of Schönfelder's more detailed study (123) shows that P does increase with K at constant M, and that *Beggiatoa* is unusual only in that the polar route passes molecules up to the size of disaccharides (diameters ca. 10 Å), rather than cutting off around 3-carbon compounds (diameters ca. 5 or 6 Å), as in *Nitella* and the gallbladder. Some diatoms behave similarly to *Beggiatoa* in this respect (88). (iii) The opposite extreme from *Beggiatoa* is the alga *Valonia ventricosa*, which, by several criteria discussed on p. 628, behaves as if it lacked a polar pathway, although its permeability to nonpolar solutes is similar to that of the Characeae. Gutknecht (124) showed that σ's for four small polar solutes in *Valonia* (urea, formamide, acetamide, ethylene glycol) were near 1, and that P for water was so low that σ for methanol was actually negative.

If one accepts this evidence of an additional permeation pathway for small polar solutes, how can it be interpreted in terms of the molecular structure of cell membranes? Whatever polar groups (proteins, or the polar ends of lipid molecules) are present in the membrane interior will interact more strongly with each other than with hydrocarbon tails of membrane lipids, so that in the most stable configuration these groups would be aggregated into polar regions instead of being dispersed among the hydrocarbon tails. Associated with the polar groups will be water molecules in a more or less "frozen" state, as in crystalline hydrates. These polar regions may be few, as in the Davson-Danielli model, or numerous, as in some more recent membrane models (e.g., 125), and may be permanent or constantly re-arranging. Since solute molecules following these polar routes would not contact hydrocarbon tails of membrane lipids or pass out of a polar environment, no correlation between the permeability of these regions and lipid: water K's or Overton's rules is expected, and steric factors in the polar framework would set an upper limit to the size of permeating solutes. The total permeability to a given solute would be the sum of its permeabilities in the two pathways.

The polar route is also probably responsible for several other distinctive permeability properties which are present in most (but not all: cf. *Valonia*) cell membranes and absent in membranes composed purely of lipids: (*a*) There has been a long debate over whether the osmotic permeability to water P_f is greater than the diffusional permeability P_d, with much of the earlier evidence invalidated by neglect of unstirred-layer effects. Careful recent studies by Sha'afi et al. (126), Gutknecht (124), Finkelstein & Cass (56), and Dainty & House (105) show conclusively that P_f is greater than P_d in erythrocytes and probably in frog skin but that P_f equals P_d in the alga *Valonia* and in artificial membranes of pure lipids. $P_f > P_d$ implies interactions (e.g., frictional) between permeating water molecules as would arise in a polar route, while $P_f = P_d$ implies singly diffusing, noninteracting water molecules, as expected and found in the thin lipid membranes. (*b*) Solvent-drag effects of water on permeating small nonelectrolytes have been demonstrated in frog skin (127) but are absent in *Valonia* (124). As implied by electrokinetic phenomena, drag effects between water and permeating ions have been demonstrated in the algae *Chara australis* and *Chaetomorpha darwinii* by Barry (128) and in squid axon by Vargas (120). (*c*) As implied by values of σ less than $1 - \omega v_s/L_p$ (see Equation 2, p. 616), drag effects of permeating solutes on water exist in erythrocytes (129) and in *Nitella* (130) but are absent in *Valonia* (124). The inference that high permeability to water and small polar solutes is correlated with $P_f > P_d$, solvent drag, electrokinetic phenomena, and solute drag, and that all these effects arise at the same membrane structures, which are distinct from hydrocarbon tails of membrane lipids, is supported by the fact that none of these phenomena has been demonstrated in thin lipid membranes or in the alga *Valonia*, but that some or all have been demonstrated in erythrocytes, frog skin, squid axon, gallbladder, intestine, and the Characeae.

In regard to the upper size limit for solutes using the polar route, equations derived from macroscopic sieving theory have been applied to σ's and P's by Solomon (77) and others and used to calculate "equivalent pore radii" for biological membranes. The appropriate parameters to use in such calculations are not σ's and P's themselves, but instead the deviations of σ's and P's from the main pattern, i.e. the permeability associated with the polar route alone. Most published calculations of this type have assumed without proof that the solutes in question are "lipid-insoluble" and permeate only via pores, not via lipid. Actually there is no small solute, not even urea, with a K so low that this assumption would in general be justified, since permeation of any given one of the small solutes commonly used for pore-radius determinations occurs primarily through lipid in some cells and primarily via the polar route in other cells. Thus, either the separate determination of σ and P and use of Equation 2, or else the measurement of enough σ's or P's to reconstruct the main pattern in the particular cell under study, would be a desirable adjunct of pore-radius determinations. Deviations from the basic assumption of macroscopic sieving theory, that an object's passage is determined solely by its geometrical properties, are inevitable for nonelectrolytes in molecular-sized pores because of the same types of membrane:solute interaction that control ion selectivity. For instance, among the amino acids histidine, phenylalanine, alanine, and glycine Eisenman found that glass electrodes exhibited five different selectivity sequences which were correlated with field strength and interpretable in terms of solute polarization by charged groups of the glass (13). The biological colloids which Bungenberg de Jong studied for alkali-cation, halide-anion, and alkaline-earth selectivity also yielded examples of selectivity patterns among organic acids, amines, esters, and alkaloids (28). In the gallbladder there are at least four cases or groups of cases in which the deviations of measured σ's of small polar solutes from the main pattern are not explicable on the basis of size, presumably because of these inevitable membrane:solute interactions (98).

THE MOLECULAR BASIS OF MAIN-PATTERN SELECTIVITY

The correlations ("Overton's rules") between molecular structure and permeating power for solutes fitting the main pattern are the same as those describing partition coefficients between a bulk lipid solvent and water. The origin of these selectivity principles lies in the differences between water: nonelectrolyte and lipid:nonelectrolyte intermolecular forces. In the remainder of this chapter we shall analyze these forces from two points of view. First, we shall adopt a thermodynamic approach and calculate the changes which the principal substituent groups produce in the partial molar free energies (and, where possible, enthalpies and entropies separately) of interaction between nonelectrolytes and either water or lipids. These incremental thermodynamic quantities indicate to what extent the nonelectrolyte selectivity of a given membrane is due to differences between various solutes in their solute:water forces, and to what extent it is due to differences in solute:membrane forces. The separation of enthalpy and entropy contributions is also instructive. The conclusions which follow from this thermodynamic analysis are summarized on pp. 633–35. Secondly, we shall attempt to identify what the controlling intermolecular forces actually are.

Incremental thermodynamic quantities.—The following expression relates lipid:water partition coefficients (K's) to thermodynamic properties:

$$K = e^{-\Delta F_{w\to l}/RT} = e^{-(\Delta H_{w\to l} - T\Delta S_{w\to l})/RT} \qquad\qquad 4.$$

where $\Delta F_{w\to l}$ is the free energy change in transferring 1 mole of solute from water to lipid solvent (or cell membrane), $\Delta H_{w\to l}$ and $\Delta S_{w\to l}$ are the corresponding partial molar enthalpy and entropy changes, R is the gas constant, and T the absolute temperature ($RT = 592$ cal/mole at 25° C). If nonelectrolyte permeation through cell membranes is limited by diffusion through the membrane interior so that $P = KD/d$ (Equation 3) holds, Equation 4 reads: $Pd/D = e^{-\Delta F_{w\to l}/RT}$. Assuming that variation in P's is due largely to variation in K's and not to variation in D's,[5] one may substitute into Equation 4 the ratio of the permeability coefficients for two solutes differing in a single functional group and obtain the incremental quantities $\delta\Delta F_{w\to l}$, $\delta\Delta H_{w\to l}$, and $\delta\Delta S_{w\to l}$ by which the group alters the partition equilibrium between membrane lipids and water. If nonelectrolyte permeation is limited by the membrane:water interface, these incremental quantities have the significance of activation parameters for the transition state, as assumed by Stein (109). As already discussed (pp. 621–22), present evidence is inadequate to decide which of these interpretations of the parameters of Equation 4 is correct.

Values of $\delta\Delta F_{w\to l}$ associated with various substituent groups (e.g., –OH, –NH₂) for transfer from water to isobutanol, water to ether, water to olive oil, or water to *Nitella mucronata* membrane were calculated as follows. Tables of partition coefficients show that in a given solvent system introduction of a given substituent group into a variety of molecules reduces all their K's by a roughly constant factor, characteristic for that particular substituent group and solvent system. The same is true for effects of substituent groups on P's in biological membranes. For instance, an –OH group on the average reduces values of $K_{isobutanol}$ by 5 times, K_{ether} by 32 times, K_{oil} by 110 times, and P's in *Nitella mucronata* by 450 times. The K or P ratio is substituted into Equation 4 to yield $\delta\Delta F_{w\to l}$ for the given group. To obtain the necessary K or P ratios, we used values of $K_{isobutanol}$ from (93), K_{ether} from (95), K_{oil} from (81), and P's in *Nitella mucronata* (81), for pairs of compounds differing in the presence or absence of a single substituent group. Thus, in *Nitella*, P is 177×10^{-7} cm/sec for CH₂(OH)·CH₂·CH₂·CH₂·CH₂· CH₂OH, 0.42×10^{-7} cm/sec for CH₂(OH)·CH(OH)·CH₂·CH₂·CH₂·CH₂OH,

[5] This assumption seems reasonable because at constant molecular weight, K's for a given solvent vary over a 10^{10}-fold range but D's vary over less than a 2-fold range; and because substituents such as –CH₂– groups and halogens, which are known to increase lipid:solute intermolecular forces and to increase K's and presumably to decrease D's slightly, are observed to increase rather than to decrease permeating power.

so that the additional –OH reduces P by $177/0.42 = 420$ times in this case. We also utilized pairs of compounds differing in that an –OH on one was replaced by some other group on another, and obtained $\delta\Delta F_{w \to l}(X)$ by adding $\delta\Delta F_{w \to l}(OH)$ to $\delta\Delta F_{w \to l}(X\text{-}OH)$. For example, K_{ether} is 7.7 for $CH_3 \cdot CH_2 \cdot CH_2 \cdot CH_2OH$, 0.058 for $CH_3 \cdot CH_2 \cdot CH_2 \cdot CONH_2$, so –$CONH_2$ reduces K by $7.7/0.058 = 133$ times more than does –OH in this case; but the average reduction in K_{ether} caused by –OH is 32 times; so that the effect of –$CONH_2$ is a reduction by $(133)(32) = 4200$ in this case. P's for small solutes likely to penetrate via the polar route were excluded for consideration. In the cases of

$$\overset{O}{\underset{\|}{-C-}}, \quad \overset{O}{\underset{\|}{-C\text{-}OH}}, \quad \overset{O}{\underset{\|}{-C\text{-}O\text{-}R}}, \quad \overset{O}{\underset{\|}{-C\text{-}NH_2}}, \text{ and } \overset{O}{\underset{\|}{-NH\text{-}C\text{-}NH_2}} \text{ but not } -C\equiv N \text{ the}$$

comparisons were chosen so that the introductions occurred by replacement of –CH_2– groups and the total number of carbon atoms in the molecule remained unchanged. Table I lists the average values of $\delta\Delta F_{w \to l}$ obtained in this manner.

To resolve $\delta\Delta F_{w \to l}$ into components associated with solute:water and with solute:lipid interactions, let us imagine that transfer from water to lipid solvent (or membrane) is broken down into two stages: vaporization of solute from an aqueous solution at infinite dilution into vacuum, followed by condensation and solution of solute from vacuum into lipid solvent. Then one write: $\Delta F_{w \to l} = -\Delta F_w + \Delta F_l$ where ΔF_w and ΔF_l are the partial molar free energy of solution at infinite dilution in water and in lipid solvent, respectively (ΔF's of solution equal ΔF's of vaporization with a negative sign). The incremental quantities associated with individual substituent groups may be written $\delta\Delta F_w$ and $\delta\Delta F_l$. Similarly, $\Delta H_{w \to l}$ or $\Delta S_{w \to l}$ can be equated with the difference between two heats or entropies of solution. At infinite dilution the solute:solute forces in the vapor phase responsible for the nonideal behavior of real gases, and solute:solute forces in the aqueous phase, may be neglected, and ΔF_w is a direct measure of the solute:water intermolecular forces (plus the change in water:water forces caused by intrusion of the solute). Similarly, ΔF_l measures solute:lipid or solute:membrane intermolecular forces. (An alternative cycle would be two-stage transfer of solute from water to lipid via a liquid or solid phase of pure solute. This has the disadvantage that solute:solute forces in the solute phase contribute significantly to the resulting ΔF's of solution, which are no longer a measure solely of solute:water or solute:membrane forces. Thus, comparison of solubilities in water may yield misleading conclusions about solute:water forces: e.g., tertiary butanol is more water-soluble than n-butanol because in the former case solute:solute forces are weaker, not because solute:water forces are stronger.)

We have calculated values of $\delta\Delta F_w$ and $\delta\Delta F_l$ for each substituent group as follows: Butler (131, Tables 1 and 2), Frank & Evans (132, Table 4), and Franks (133, Table 1) have given tables of ΔF's of solution or vaporization at infinite dilution in water for 41 simple nonelectrolytes, mostly aliphatic hydrocarbons with a single functional group. Inspection of their results

TABLE I

INCREMENTAL FREE ENERGIES OF SOLUTION (calories/mole)

	$\delta\Delta F_{w\to l}$ $(=-\delta\Delta F_w+\delta\Delta F_l)$				$\delta\Delta F_w$	$\delta\Delta F_l$			
	iso-butanol	ether	olive oil	*Nitella*		iso-butanol	ether	olive oil	*Nitella*
–OH	1000	2100	2800	3600	−7000	−6000	−4900	−4200	−3400
–O–	600	1400	1400	800	−4000	−3400	−2600	−2600	−3200
$\overset{O}{\overset{\|}{-C-}}$	—	2100	2200	2500	−6100	—	−4000	−3900	−3600
$\overset{O}{\overset{\|}{-C-OH}}$	1100	1700	2800	—	−8600	−7500	−6900	−5800	—
$\overset{O}{\overset{\|}{-C-O-R}}$	1200	1200	1400	1400	−5400	−4200	−4200	−4000	−4000
$\overset{O}{\overset{\|}{-C-NH_2}}$	1700	4900	4800	6200	—	—	—	—	—
$\overset{O}{\overset{\|}{-NH-C-NH_2}}$	1900	5500	5300	7300	—	—	—	—	—
$-C\equiv N$	—	1100	—	—	−5800	—	−4700	—	—
$-NH_2$	1100	3500	—	—	−6600	−5500	−3100	—	—
$-CH_2-$	−530	−670	−660	−610	160	−370	−510	−500	−450

The second through fifth columns give for each group listed in the first column the average values of $\delta\Delta F_{w\to l}$, the amount by which the group changes the difference between a nonelectrolyte's partial molar free energy of solution in water and its partial molar free energy of solution in isobutanol, ether, olive oil, or *Nitella* membrane. These $\delta\Delta F_{w\to l}$'s were calculated by substituting into Equation 4 the factor by which the group reduced isobutanol : water, ether : water, or olive oil : water partition coefficients or else permeability coefficients in *Nitella*. Each 1000 cal/mole corresponds to a 5.4-fold reduction in partition or permeability coefficients. The sixth column is $\delta\Delta F_w$, the amount by which the group changes a nonelectrolyte's partial molar free energy of solution (out of vacuum) in water. The amounts in the sixth column were added to the amounts in the second through fifth columns to obtain the $\delta\Delta F_l$'s in the seventh through tenth columns, the amount by which the group changes a nonelectrolyte's partial molar free energy of solution (out of vacuum) in isobutanol, ether, olive oil, or *Nitella* membrane. The more positive the value of $\delta\Delta F_{w\to l}$, the more effective is the group at reducing partition coefficients or permeability coefficients; the more negative the value of $\delta\Delta F_w$ or $\delta\Delta F_l$, the more the group promotes solubility in the given solvent.

shows that the difference $\delta\Delta F_w$ between ΔF_w for a hydrocarbon and ΔF_w for the corresponding monosubstituted hydrocarbon (e.g., $CH_3 \cdot CH_2 \cdot CH_3$ versus $CH_3 \cdot CH_2 \cdot CH_2OH$) is a nearly constant quantity for a given functional group, independent of hydrocarbon chain length. For instance, from Butler (131), ΔF_w is $+3090$ cal/mole for CH_3OH, $+10,080$ for CH_4, yielding

$\delta\Delta F_w = 6990$ cal/mole for the alcoholic $-OH$ group; ΔF_w is $+3490$ for $n-$ C_4H_9OH, $+10,460$ for $n-C_4H_{10}$, yielding $\delta\Delta F_w = 6970$ cal/mole for the $-OH$ group. Similarly, inspection of these published ΔF_w's shows that the difference between ΔF_w's for two hydrocarbons with different chain lengths but the same functional group is also a nearly constant quantity independent of functional group. Thus, one can also meaningfully define a $\delta\Delta F_w$ associated with the methylene group $-CH_2-$. Table I gives the average values of $\delta\Delta F_w$ we have extracted in this fashion. For each substituent group this $\delta\Delta F_w$ was then added to the value of $\delta\Delta F_{w\to l} = -\delta\Delta F_w + \delta\Delta F_l$ for each lipid solvent to obtain the values of $\delta\Delta F_l$ listed in Table I.

There are two principal sources of uncertainty in the quantities of Table I. First, although values of $\delta\Delta F_{w\to l}$ are relatively constant, and values of $\delta\Delta F_w$ constant to better than 1 per cent, when calculated from monosubstituted hydrocarbons, there is more scatter in $\delta\Delta F$ values deduced from polyfunctional hydrocarbons because of the so-called secondary effects discussed on pp. 639–40. Secondly, when the power of the molecular weight M describing the size dependence of main-pattern selectivity (see pp. 624–25) is better established, values derived from P's should be corrected on this basis, as Stein (109, Tables 3.5 and 3.6) has tentatively done. Since the changes in K produced by substituents are generally much larger than the changes in M, the correction will generally be small, and it does not apply to $\delta\Delta F$'s estimated from K's.

The following conclusions may be drawn from Table I and these thermodynamic considerations:

1. Values of $\delta\Delta F_{w\to l}$ are positive for all substituents in all four systems (isobutanol:water, ether:water, olive oil:water, Nitella:water) except for $-CH_2-$. That is, every substituent was found to reduce permeability and partition coefficients except for $-CH_2-$, which increased them.

2. Virtually every substituent group has a negative value of $\delta\Delta F_l$ or $\delta\Delta F_w$ in all five solvents (water, isobutanol, ether, olive oil, and Nitella), i.e., is associated with net attractive intermolecular forces. The sole exception is $-CH_2-$ in water, which has a positive $\delta\Delta F_w$ and actually decreases "water solubility".

3. For every substituent (except $-CH_2-$) and for all four systems the value of $(-\delta\Delta F_w)$ is considerably greater than $(-\delta\Delta F_l)$, as follows necessarily from the previous two conclusions. Expressed pictorially, solute:water forces are much stronger than solute:lipid-solvent (or solute:membrane) forces for nonelectrolyte substituent groups, and the differences in these strong solute:water forces largely swamp the differences among the weaker forces in the lipid phase. In this sense the common tendency to view permeability as controlled by "lipid solubility" represents a basic misinterpretation of the observed fact that permeability correlates with lipid:water partition coefficients. Most substituents decrease permeating power because they increase the energy required to tear the solute loose from water, and despite the fact that they also increase solute:lipid attraction. Thus, explanations

for the qualitative selectivity patterns of biological membranes must be sought largely in terms of the physical chemistry of aqueous solutions. This is the reason why the main-pattern selectivity sequences of biological objects as dissimilar as rabbit gallbladders and giant algae are essentially the same.

4. For $-CH_2-$, $\delta\Delta F_w$ is positive but $\delta\Delta F_l$ is negative, i.e., increasing hydrocarbon chain length causes a solute to be "pushed out of" the aqueous phase as well as to be "pulled into" the membrane or lipid phase.

5. Comparison of Butler's (131) ΔF_w's for branched solutes with ΔF_w's for their straight-chain isomers shows that one branch-point in a carbon chain makes ΔF_w on the average 80 cal/mole more positive, which by substitution in Equation 4 would *increase* K's or P's by 14 per cent. This very small effect is opposite to that actually observed, so that the explanation for the large *decrease* in K's or P's associated with branching must be sought in the lipid or membrane phase. As discussed previously (p. 624), the explanation is that the van der Waals forces experienced in a lipid solvent are smaller for a branched molecule than for a straight-chain isomer.

6. While selectivity patterns qualitatively are largely determined by differences in $\delta\Delta F_w$ between different substituent groups, the quantitative differences between different systems must be due to differences in $\delta\Delta F_l$ for a given group. Of the four "lipid solvents" compared, *Nitella* provides the greatest selectivity, in the sense that it has the largest range (6500 cal/mole) of $(-\delta\Delta F_w + \delta\Delta F_l)$ among substituents other than $-CH_2-$, hence the largest spread in P's or K's. For instance, the ratio of P for methyl acetate to P for glycerol is 780,000 in *Nitella*, while the K ratio in olive oil is only 6100, in ether only 4100, and in isobutanol only 26. This is due to the fact that *Nitella* is the weakest "solvent": it has both the smallest range (800 cal/mole) and the lowest absolute values of $\delta\Delta F_l$'s (for substituents other than $-CH_2-$). The most marked differences among $\delta\Delta F_l$'s in the four lipid solvents involve the isobutanol values (higher than in the other three solvents) and the disproportionately high values for $-OH$ and $-COOH$ in ether (higher than in olive oil or *Nitella*, although ether is comparable to olive oil and *Nitella* in $\delta\Delta F_l$'s for other groups). The molecular basis of these variations in $\delta\Delta F_l$'s is discussed on p. 641.

7. Some resolution of these free energy changes into enthalpy and entropy terms is possible and illuminating. In 20 cases Butler (131) obtained values not only for ΔF_w but also for ΔH_w and ΔS_w, so that incremental heats and entropies of solution in water $\delta\Delta H_w$ and $\delta\Delta S_w$ may be obtained. These values show that the effects of the $-OH$, $-NH_2$, $-\overset{\text{O}}{\overset{\|}{C}}-$, $-\overset{\text{O}}{\overset{\|}{C}}-O-R$, and $-O-\overset{\text{O}}{\overset{\|}{}}$ groups (and by analogy, probably, the $-C\equiv N$ and $-\overset{\text{O}}{\overset{\|}{C}}-OH$ groups, for which data necessary to obtain $\delta\Delta H_w$ and $\delta\Delta S_w$ are lacking) in increasing water solubility are enthalpy-controlled. For instance, comparison of $CH_3 \cdot CH_3$ and $CH_3 \cdot CH_2OH$ yields $\delta\Delta F_w = -6860$ cal/mole, $\delta\Delta H_w = -8450$ cal/

mole, $\delta\Delta S_w = -5.4$ cal/mole/degree, $T\delta\Delta S_w = -1610$ cal/mole for the $-OH$ group, which promotes water solubility ($\delta\Delta F_w < 0$) because of the enthalpy term ($\delta\Delta H_w < 0$) and despite the entropy term ($\delta\Delta S_w < 0$). One can describe this result by saying that $-OH$ and most other substituents increase water solubility because they strengthen solute:water intermolecular forces, even though this automatically [as implicit in the Barclay-Butler rule (132, 134) relating entropies of solution to heats of solution] reduces the system's degrees of freedom and causes a small loss of entropy. On the other hand, the effect of the $-CH_2-$ group in reducing water solubility and "pushing" the solute out of water proves to be entropy-controlled. For instance, comparison of $CH_3 \cdot CH_2OH$ and $CH_3 \cdot CH_2 \cdot CH_2OH$ yields $\delta\Delta F_w = +160$ cal/mole, $\delta\Delta H_w = -1540$ cal/mole, $\delta\Delta S_w = -5.7$ cal/mole/degree, $T\delta\Delta S_w = -1700$ cal/mole for the $-CH_2-$ group, which reduces solubility ($\delta\Delta F_w > 0$) because of an entropy effect ($\delta\Delta S_w < 0$) and despite the enthalpy term ($\delta\Delta H_w < 0$). Regarding the origin of $\delta\Delta F_l$'s in bulk lipid phases, thermal measurements of Butler & Harrower (135) prove that $\delta\Delta F_l$ for the $-CH_2-$ group in benzene is enthalpy-controlled, and the general validity of the Barclay–Butler rule in nonpolar solvents implies that $\delta\Delta F_l$'s for other groups are also enthalpy-controlled. $\delta\Delta F_{w\to l}$ for the $-CH_2-$ group and $\Delta F_{w\to l}$ for hydrocarbons and the higher alcohols prove to be entropy-controlled, $\Delta F_{w\to l}$ for the lower alcohols enthalpy-controlled, in the benzene:water system and presumably in other bulk lipid:water systems. The molecular interpretation of these large entropy effects associated with nonpolar residues in the aqueous phase is considered on p. 641.

Intermolecular forces.—The principal forces between nonelectrolytes and water depend upon hydrogen bonds, whereas the principal forces between nonelectrolytes and lipids are short-range van der Waals forces (forces between permanent dipoles, forces between a permanent dipole and an induced dipole, and London dispersion forces). The preceding thermodynamic analysis showed that selectivity in nonelectrolyte partition and permeation is dominated by interactions in the aqueous phase, and that these aqueous-phase interactions are enthalpy- rather than entropy-controlled except in the case of the $-CH_2-$ group. Thus, most of nonelectrolyte selectivity should be explicable in terms of hydrogen bonds. In fact, as recognized initially by Collander (95), the reduction in permeating power caused by a substituent can be predicted from the number and strength of hydrogen bonds it forms. As background to the following discussion it may be recalled that a hydrogen bond is a bridge formed by hydrogen between two electro-negative atoms acting as proton acceptor and proton donor, respectively; that the strongest bridges involve O as the donor and O or N as the acceptor (e.g., $CH_3-O-H\cdots NH(CH_3)_2$); and that dipole-dipole forces, resonance stabilization, and dispersion forces all contribute to the bridge strength. Spectroscopic studies (e.g., 136, 137) have shown that $-COOH > -CONH_2 > OH$ are the most effective donor groups, $-NH_2$ being considerably weaker; and that the approximate potency sequence for acceptors is

$$-NH_2 > -\overset{\overset{\text{O}}{\|}}{C}-OH > -\overset{\overset{\text{O}}{\|}}{C}-NH_2 > -OH > -O- > -\overset{\overset{\text{O}}{\|}}{C}H > \overset{}{\underset{}{C=O}}, \quad -\overset{\overset{\text{O}}{\|}}{C}-O-R$$

$$> -C\equiv N > -NO_2.$$

We shall consider in turn the primary hydrogen-bonding effects, secondary effects (intramolecular bonding and inductive effects), and the effect of the $-CH_2-$ group. More detailed discussion and examples will be found in the analysis by Diamond & Wright (99).

Primary effects.—

1. *Hydroxyl.* Of the six simple oxygen functions

$$\left(-OH, -O-, -\overset{\overset{\text{O}}{\|}}{C}-, -\overset{\overset{\text{O}}{\|}}{C}H, -\overset{\overset{\text{O}}{\|}}{C}-O-R, -\overset{\overset{\text{O}}{\|}}{C}-OH\right), \text{ the } -OH \text{ group is the most po-}$$

tent $\left(\text{with the possible exception of } -\overset{\overset{\text{O}}{\|}}{C}-OH\right)$: it reduces P's in *Nitella mucronata* by 450 times, P's in *Chara ceratophylla* by 23 times, $K_{\text{isobutanol}}$ by 5 times, K_{ether} by 32 times, K_{oil} by 110 times, and is associated with the largest value of $\delta\Delta F_w$ after $-COOH$. This potency is due to the fact that $-OH$ acts

both as a proton donor $(-O-H\cdots\cdots X-)$ and as a proton acceptor

$(H-\overset{|}{O}\cdots\cdots H-X-)$, whereas $-O-$, $-\overset{\overset{\text{O}}{\|}}{C}-$, $-\overset{\overset{\text{O}}{\|}}{C}-H$, and $-\overset{\overset{\text{O}}{\|}}{C}-OR$ have no protons to donate and act only as acceptors. In addition, spectroscopic evidence shows that $-OH$ is a more effective acceptor than $-O-$, $-\overset{\overset{\text{O}}{\|}}{C}-$, $-\overset{\overset{\text{O}}{\|}}{C}-H$, or $-\overset{\overset{\text{O}}{\|}}{C}-OR$. Although an oxygen in a water molecule can accept two protons by using both of its unshared electron pairs, oxygen in most alcohols and other organic molecules can probably accept no more than one proton, so that the total number of H bonds formed by the alcoholic $-OH$ group is estimated as two. Table I shows that $-OH$ is relatively less potent $(-\delta\Delta F_w + \delta\Delta F_l$ is smaller) in reducing K_{ether} than K_{oil} or P_{Nitella}. This is because the $-O-$ in ether acts as an acceptor for the hydroxyl proton, so that $-OH$ shifts partition equilibrium by little more than one H bond in the ether:water system but by two bonds in the other systems.

2. *Ether.* The $-O-$ link reduces K's and P's because it acts as a proton acceptor (but not donor). One's first expectation would be that, given a lipid phase devoid of H-bonding sites, two $-O-$'s should be as potent as one $-OH$ in reducing K and P since $-O-$ would form approximately one H bond, $-OH$ two. Actually, the numerous comparisons provided by the gallbladder results (99, Table 3) show that two $-O-$'s are slightly less potent than one $-OH$. This is in agreement with the spectroscopic evidence that $-O-$ is a somewhat less effective acceptor than $-OH$, presumably because of greater

steric hindrance to H bonding at the ether oxygen, which is flanked by two rather than one alkyl groups.

3, 4. *Aldehydes and ketones.* Earlier workers found that $-\overset{\overset{\displaystyle H}{|}}{C}=O$ and $\diagdown C=O$ were as potent as $-OH$ in reducing P's, whereas one would have expected them to be only half as potent because they cannot act as proton donors. However, in aqueous solution many carbonyl compounds actually become rapidly transformed into hydroxy compounds, either through addition of water to the double bond $\left[\diagdown C=O \xrightarrow{H_2O} \begin{matrix} OH \\ \diagup \\ C \\ \diagdown \\ OH \end{matrix} \right]$ or through intramolecular hydrogen migration forming an enolic tautomer $\left[-\overset{\overset{\displaystyle O}{||}}{C}-CH_2 \rightarrow -\overset{\overset{\displaystyle OH}{|}}{C}=CH- \right]$. By repeated measurements of σ's beginning 1 min after first contact of aliphatic aldehydes with water, Wright & Diamond (97, Figure 4) showed that permeating power in the gallbladder decreased from an initially high value towards the value expected for a hydroxylated compound with a half-time of 150–300 sec, in agreement with rate constants for the aldehyde hydration reaction measured by purely physical techniques. Extrapolated zero-time σ's for aliphatic aldehydes, and σ's of two carbonyl compounds which are known neither to hydrate nor to enolize, show that the native carbonyl group does reduce permeability but by much less than the $-OH$ group, as predicted from H-bond considerations (99).

5. *Esters.* The $-\overset{\overset{\displaystyle O}{||}}{C}-OR$ group is less potent than $-OH$ at reducing P's and K's, as expected from its possessing acceptor but not donor properties. Table I shows that its potency is of the same order as that of the ether oxygen, but the available evidence is inadequate to make a finer comparison between these two acceptor groups.

6. *Carboxyl.* Collander's evidence (95, Table 8) suggests that $-\overset{\overset{\displaystyle O}{||}}{C}-OH$ and $-OH$ have roughly comparable potencies in reducing K_{ether}, and this is also true for K_{oil} and $K_{isobutanol}$. Like $-OH$, $-COOH$ is both a proton donor and a proton acceptor, and is more potent than oxygen functions lacking donor properties $\left[-O-, -\overset{\overset{\displaystyle O}{||}}{C}-, -\overset{\overset{\displaystyle O}{||}}{C}-H, -\overset{\overset{\displaystyle O}{||}}{C}-OR \right]$ at reducing K_{oil} but only equally potent in its effect on K_{ether}, since ether itself is an acceptor.

7. *Amines.* $\left[-NH_2, \diagdown NH, -N \overset{\diagup R}{\diagdown R} \right]$. The amino group has nearly as high

a $\delta\Delta F_w$ as –OH, and is as potent or more so at depressing P's and K's. Primary amines (–NH$_2$) and secondary amines $\left[\ \diagdown\!\!\diagup\!\! NH\ \right]$ have both donor $\left[\ \diagdown\!\!\diagup\! N\text{–H}\cdots\cdots X\text{–}\ \right]$ and acceptor $\left[\ H\text{–}N\cdots\cdots H\text{–}X\text{–}\ \right]$ properties, while tertiary amines $\left[\ \text{–}N\diagup^{R}_{\diagdown R}\ \right]$ have only acceptor properties. However, inspection of Collander's K_{ether} and $K_{\text{isobutanol}}$ values shows that tertiary amino groups are somewhat more potent than secondary, and secondary more potent than primary, at depressing K's, which suggests that the effect of amino groups is mainly due to the acceptor properties of N's single unshared electron pair.

This is in agreement with spectroscopic evidence that $\diagdown\!\!\diagup N\cdots\cdots H\text{–}X\text{–}$ bridges are stronger than $\diagdown\!\!\diagup O\cdots\cdots H\text{–}X\text{–}$ bridges, because of greater resonance stabilization, but that $\diagdown\!\!\diagup N\text{–}H\cdots\cdots X\text{–}$ bridges are much weaker than either or than –O–H$\cdots\cdots$X–. The loss of the weak $\diagdown\!\!\diagup N\text{–}H\cdots\cdots X\text{–}$ bridges as one proceeds from –NH$_2$ to $\diagdown\!\!\diagup NH$ to $\diagdown\!\!\diagup N$– is more than compensated by a strengthening of the $\text{–}\diagdown\!\!\diagup N\cdots\cdots H\text{–}X\text{–}$ bridge due to inductive effects of alkyl groups. In the ether:water system, where the acceptor properties of ether largely cancel effects of the solute's donor properties on partition and only the solute's acceptor properties are effective, amines are more potent than hydroxyls (Table I).

    8. *Amides.* In the gallbladder, *Nitella*, isobutanol, and olive oil, the $\overset{\text{O}}{\overset{\|}{-\text{C}}}\text{–NH}_2$ group is more potent than one –OH but less potent than two –OH's in depressing P's and K's, while it is slightly more potent than two –OH's in its effect on K_{ether} (because –OH is less potent, not because $\overset{\text{O}}{\overset{\|}{-\text{C}}}\text{–NH}_2$ is more potent). This is as expected from the facts that $\overset{\text{O}}{\overset{\|}{-\text{C}}}\text{–NH}_2$ has two proton-ac-

cepting sites (O and N) as well as two protons to donate, and from the experimental finding (137) that $-\overset{\overset{\textstyle O}{\|}}{C}-NH_2$ exceeds $-OH$ both in acceptor and in donor abilities.

9. *Ureas*. In the gallbladder, *Nitella*, and olive oil derivatives of urea $\left(R-NH-\overset{\overset{\textstyle O}{\|}}{C}-NH_2 \right)$ have approximately the same K or P as dihydroxy alcohols with the same number of carbon atoms, because of the numerous proton donor and acceptor sites on the urea residue (nominally three each). As in the case of amines, the urea effect should be due mainly to its acceptor properties, and this is consistent with the fact that urea affects K_{oil} and K_{ether} equally, while $-OH$ (for which donor and acceptor properties are equally important) affects K_{ether} less than K_{oil}.

10. *Nitriles*. In the gallbladder, $-C \equiv N$ reduces P by more than $-O-$ but by less than $-OH$ because of proton acceptance by the nitrogen and possibly by the π electrons of the triple bond as well. The difference between the permeabilities of aromatic compounds and homologous saturated compounds, and the complex effect of unsaturation in nonaromatic compounds $\left(\overset{\diagup}{\underset{\diagdown}{C}}=\overset{\diagup}{\underset{\diagdown}{C}} \text{ and } -C \equiv C- \right)$, also arise in part from H bonding to π electrons (see 99 for details).

11. *Sulfur*. Sulfur compounds are more permeant and have higher K's than their oxygen analogues because of the much weaker H-bonding ability of sulfur. In the gallbladder and presumably in those other tissues where thiourea $\left(H_2N-\overset{\overset{\textstyle S}{\|}}{C}-NH_2 \right)$ is less permeant than urea $\left(H_2N-\overset{\overset{\textstyle O}{\|}}{C}-NH_2 \right)$, this arises from preferential permeation of urea via the polar route, not via lipid.

Secondary effects.—Stein (109), had the courage to try to predict permeability ratios for different nonelectrolytes by attributing a certain number of H bonds to each group regardless of its molecular environment and by counting up the number of each kind of group in a given molecule. His Figure 3.11 does succeed in predicting, within a factor of 5 for all solutes except water, the values of $PM^{1/2}$ which Collander (82) obtained for 48 nonelectrolytes in *Chara ceratophylla*. Since the P's spanned a range of 30,000, Stein's graph constitutes a good fit, which strikingly illustrates the controlling role and predictive power of H bonds in nonelectrolyte permeation.

The residual scatter in Stein's graph, and the scatter we encountered in experimental values of K ratios and P ratios for different pairs of compounds used to calculate the average $\delta \Delta F$ values in Table I, are due mainly to the fact that the molecular environment does affect somewhat the H-bonding ability of a given group in two ways: intramolecular H bonding and inductive effects.

1. *Intramolecular H bonding.* If two groups on the same molecule, one a proton acceptor and the other a proton donor, are sufficiently close, an intramolecular H bond may be formed, reducing by up to two the number of H bonds that can be formed with water and therefore increasing P's or K's. A typical example is the decrease in gallbladder σ's (increase in permeability) among the isomeric dihydroxy cyclohexanes as the two $-OH$'s are moved

successively closer: HO—⬡—OH $\sigma = 1.02$, HO—⬡ with OH $\sigma = 0.94$,

HO, HO—⬡ $\sigma = 0.54$. Evidently much of the latter molecule is in the form

H—O, H—O—⬡ . Intramolecular H bonding must be considered in interpreting the permeation or distribution of almost any polyfunctional solute, and is the explanation of Overton's empirical rule that two substituents on a molecule are more potent the further apart they are. For the same reason, comparison of Butler's (131) ΔF_w's for hydrocarbons and their mono- and polyhydroxy derivatives yields smaller values of $\delta \Delta F_w$ for the $-OH$ group when it is introduced next to another $-OH$ group than when it is introduced into a pure hydrocarbon.

2. *Inductive effects.* As already mentioned in the discussion of ion permeation (p. 594), the electron density on a group (hence the group's proton-donating or -accepting ability) is modified by neighboring groups. Alkyl groups are electron-releasing, but most other groups, notably $-NO_2$ and halogens, are electron-withdrawing, this inductive effect decreasing with increasing distance between the modifying group and the affected group. Simple examples of inductive effects are provided by the gallbladder σ's of halogenated amides (99, Tables 8 and 9), which show that halogenation increases the permeating power of amides due to electron withdrawal from the amide N and O and hence reduction in proton-accepting abilities.

Hydrocarbon chain length and entropy effects.—The introduction of each $-CH_2-$ group into a molecule increases K_{oil}, K_{ether}, P in *Nitella*, and K's in many other lipid solvents by a factor of about 3, and increases narcotizing potency in tadpoles and other test objects by the same factor ("Ferguson's rule"). The thermodynamic analysis of pp. 630–35 showed that this is due partly to an enthalpy-dominated negative $\delta \Delta F_l$ "pulling" the solute into the lipid phase and readily attributable to increased van der Waals forces with lipids, but is also due to an entropy-dominated positive $\delta \Delta F_w$ which "pushes" the solute out of the aqueous phase and whose origin is less obvious. Diamond

& Wright (99) showed that the high partition coefficients of pure hydro-carbons, and, by implication, the high permeability coefficients of any solute with a large nonpolar residue, are primarily an entropy effect in the aqueous phase: i.e., $\Delta F_{w \to l}$ is dominated by the large negative value of the entropy of solution in water. Thus, as first recognized in a classic study by Frank & Evans (132), hydrocarbons and hydrocarbon residues, because of their weak force fields, behave in aqueous solution as if they permitted increased order-ing of surrounding water molecules and stabilized adjacent H-bonded water clusters, a phenomenon which Frank & Evans pictorially described as "icebergs". Solutes with long hydrocarbon chains are driven into the lipid phase by the gain in entropy resulting from "melting" of the "iceberg" [see (99, 132, 133, 138, 139) for further discussion of these entropy effects]. Similarly, halogens exercise a direct effect in increasing K's and P's analogous to that of $-CH_2-$ and distinct from their inductive effects (99). Calculation of K's for chloroform ($CHCl_3$), which is highly permeant in the gallbladder, from the thermal data of Frank & Evans (132) shows that this direct effect of halogens is also an entropy effect in the aqueous phase.

CONTROLLING VARIABLES IN MAIN-PATTERN SELECTIVITY

The most conspicuous differences between the nonelectrolyte permeability patterns of different cells concern small polar solutes and are apparently due to differences in the importance of the polar route. Otherwise the selectivity patterns of all cells are quite similar. What differences do exist between main-pattern selectivities (i.e., selectivities associated with permeation via membrane lipids) appear to be of two sorts:

1. *Selectivity magnitudes.* Although main-pattern selectivity sequences differ little from cell to cell, there are significant quantitative differences in the ranges of selectivity. For instance, comparison of three related algae shows that "in *Nitella* the permeability to methanol is 180,000 times, in *Nitellopsis* 21,000 times, and in *Chara* only 2600 times greater than that of glycerol" (81, p. 443). P's are proportional to $(K_{oil})^{1.32}$ in *Nitella*, to $(K_{oil})^{1.15}$ in *Nitellopsis*, and to $(K_{oil})^{1.0}$ in *Chara*. The $-OH$ group reduces P's on the average by 450 times in *Nitella*, by only 23 times in *Chara*.

Collander's studies (92–96) on K's of bulk lipid solvents suggest that the molecular parameter governing these quantitative differences is the ratio of hydrogen-bonding groups to $-CH_2-$ groups in the membrane interior: the lower this ratio, the lower are the values of ΔF_l, the larger is $(-\Delta F_w + \Delta F_l)$, and hence the higher are the magnitudes of selectivity. The reason is that hydrogen-bond energies are considerably stronger than van der Waals attractions to hydrocarbons, so that solvent hydrogen-bonding groups in a predominantly lipid phase markedly increase solute:lipid forces and ΔF_l's. For instance, analysis of Collander's studies of monohydroxy alcohols of varying chain length as solvents shows that the $-OH$ group decreases K's on the average by 5.2 times in C_4H_9OH, by 7.2 times in $C_5H_{11}OH$, by 8.5 times in $C_8H_{17}OH$, by 14.7 times in $C_{15}H_{35}OH$, by 107 times in olive oil, by

1300 times in benzene, and P's by 450 times in *Nitella*. From these values one can calculate that the incremental free energy of solution $\delta\Delta F$ associated with the –OH group decreases from -6970 cal/mole in water, to -6000 cal/mole in C_4H_9OH (isobutanol), to -5400 cal/mole in $C_{18}H_{35}OH$, to -3300 cal/mole in *Nitella*, to -2700 cal/mole in benzene. K's measured separately between two different lipid solvents a or b and water are related by an equation of the form $K_a = x(K_b)^y$ in which, for a given solvent b, the exponent y, which measures the magnitude of selectivity, increases with increasing chain length of solvent a if a is an aliphatic alcohol. As another example, Table I shows that isobutanol, which has a higher ratio of H-bonding sites to –CH$_2$– groups than does ether or olive oil, has the highest values of $\delta\Delta F_l$ (nearly comparable to $\delta\Delta F_w$, the values in water) and the lowest range of selectivity $(-\delta\Delta F_w + \delta\Delta F_l)$ of the lipid solvents studied. Thus, a very few hydrogen-bonding groups in the membrane interior, by increasing lipid:solute forces from the low values typical of a pure hydrocarbon towards the high values prevailing in water, could markedly depress selectivity ratios. The facts that *Nitella* P's are proportional to $(K_{oil})^{1.32}$, and that the –OH group depresses *Nitella* P's by a larger factor than K's for olive oil or $C_{18}H_{35}OH$, suggest that the interior of a *Nitella* cell membrane is much closer to a pure hydrocarbon than even an 18-carbon monohydroxy alcohol. The same conclusion follows from the fact that one –OH group offsets the change in P or σ produced by six –CH$_2$– groups in *Nitella* or the gallbladder (99), but offsets the effect of only 5.3 –CH$_2$– groups on K's in benzene, 4.3 in olive oil, 2.15 in $C_{18}H_{35}OH$, and 1.86 in C_4H_9OH.

2. *Membrane "acidity"*. The extensive botanical literature on permeability shows that some cells, while normal in other respects, are unusually permeable to basic solutes like amides (88). This has been interpreted to mean that such cells have unusually "acidic" cell membranes, by analogy with the fact that addition of small quantities of acids to an organic phase increases K's for bases in that phase. Expressed in more general terms, a few proton-donor groups in the membrane might selectively improve permeability to proton acceptors due to H-bond formation (hence higher ΔF_l's) in the membrane. An illustration of the opposite effect (preferential permeability to proton donors) is that the –OH and –COOH groups are less effective at reducing K's in ether than in olive oil (Table I), so that a membrane composed of an ether phase would be more permeable to alcohols and acids. Ether and olive oil are otherwise similar in their solubility properties, but the –O– of ether is a proton acceptor, increasing $\delta\Delta F_l$'s and K's for proton-donating solutes.

SUMMARY OF NONELECTROLYTE SELECTIVITY

For the overwhelming majority of nonelectrolytes the selectivity patterns of biological membranes are very similar to the selectivity patterns of a bulk lipid phase, so that the explanation for nonelectrolyte selectivity must be sought largely in the differences between solute:water and solute:lipid intermolecular forces. Exceptions to this main pattern are that branched molecules are less permeant, and the inverse relation between permeating power and molecular size is apparently steeper, than that found for permeation through a bulk lipid phase; these differences are attributed to the more organized structure of lipids in cell membranes. In addition, small polar solutes permeate more rapidly than they would through a bulk lipid phase; the interpretation supported by several lines of evidence is that some predominantly polar regions in the membrane provide a parallel permeation pathway that bypasses membrane lipids. Analysis of incremental free energies of solution in water, bulk lipids, or membranes, associated with specific functional groups, shows that the main pattern of selectivity is largely due to differences in water:solute intermolecular forces: the stronger these forces, the lower the solute's permeating power. The most important contributing forces are hydrogen bonds, modification of hydrogen bonding by inductive effects and intramolecular bonds, van der Waals forces in membrane lipids, and entropy effects in hydrocarbon:water interactions. Main-pattern permeability differences between different biological membranes are principally determined by the ratio of hydrogen-bonding groups to $-CH_2-$ groups in the membrane interior, and by whether these hydrogen-bonding groups are proton donors or proton acceptors.

ACKNOWLEDGMENTS

It is a pleasure to record our debt to Dr. George Eisenman for valuable and generous advice on ion selectivity and for his criticism of the first half of this chapter; to Drs. P. H. Barry, R. S. Eisenberg, and A. D. Grinnell for critical readings of the manuscript; and to Dr. H. S. Sherry for discussion of divalent cation selectivity.

LITERATURE CITED

1. Eisenman, G. Biophys. J., 2, Part 2, 259–323 (1962)
2. Eisenman, G. In Symposium on Membrane Transport and Metabolism, 163–79 (Kleinzeller, A., Kotyk, A., Eds., Academic Press, New York, 608 pp., 1961)
3. Eisenman, G. Proc. 23rd Intern. Congr. Physiol. Sci., Tokyo, 489–506 (Excerpta Med. Found., Amsterdam, 644 pp., 1965)
4. Reichenberg, D. In Ion Exchange, I 227–76 (Dekker, New York, 424 pp., 1966)
5. Sherry, H. S. In Ion Exchange, II (Dekker, New York, in press, 1968)
6. Truesdell, A. H., Christ, C. L. In Glass Electrodes for Hydrogen and Other Cations, 293–321 (Dekker, New York, 582 pp., 1967)
7. Jaeger, F. M. Trans. Faraday Soc., 25, 320–45 (1929)
8. Pauling, L. The Nature of the Chemical Bond (Cornell Univ. Press, Ithaca, N. Y., 450 pp., 2nd ed., 1948)
9. Jenny, H. J. Phys. Chem., 36, 2217–58 (1932)
10. Barrer, R. M., Rees, L. V. C., Ward, D. J. Proc. Roy. Soc. A, 273, 180–97 (1963)
11. Hughes, W. S. J. Am. Chem. Soc., 44, 2860–67 (1922)
12. Eisenman, G., Rudin, D. O., Casby, J. U. Science, 126, 831–34 (1957)
13. Eisenman, G. Advan. Anal. Chem. Instr., 4, 213–369 (1965)
14. Eisenman, G. Bol. Inst. Estud. Méd. Biol. 21, 155–83 (1963)
15. Berridge, M. J. J. Exptl. Biol., 48, 159–74 (1968)
16. Wright, E. M., Diamond, J. M. Biochim. Biophys. Acta, 163, 57–74 (1968)
17. Chandler, W. K., Meves, H. J. Phys-

iol. (*London*), **180,** 788–820 (1965)

18. Gillary, H. L. *J. Gen. Physiol.*, **50,** 359–68 (1966)

19. Pressman, B. C. *Ann. N.Y. Acad. Sci.* (In press) (1968)

20. Mueller, P., Rudin, D. O. *Biochem. Biophys. Res. Commun.*, **26,** 398–404 (1967)

21. Lev, A. A., Buzhinsky, E. P. *Tsitologiia*, **9,** 102–6 (1967)

22. Andreoli, T. E., Tieffenberg, M., Tosteson, D. C. *J. Gen. Physiol.*, **50,** 2527–34 (1967)

23. Eisenman, G., Ciani, S., Szabo, G. *Fed. Proc.* (In press) (1968)

24. Pedersen, C. J. *J. Am. Chem. Soc.*, **89,** 7017–36 (1967)

25. Pedersen, C. J. *Fed. Proc.* (In press) (1968)

26. Lindeman, B. *Exptl. Eye Res.*, **7,** 62–69 (1968)

27. Forte, J. G., Forte, G. M., Saltman, P. *J. Cell Physiol.*, **69,** 293–304 (1967)

28. Bungenberg de Jong, H. G. In *Colloid Science*, **II,** 259–334 (Kruyt, H. R., Ed., Elsevier, New York, 753 pp., 1949)

29. Barber, R., Noble, M. *Biochim. Biophys. Acta*, **123,** 205–206 (1966)

30. Armstrong, W. McD., Rothstein, A. *J. Gen. Physiol.*, **50,** 967–88 (1967)

31. Ling, G. N., Ochsenfeld, M. M. *J. Gen. Physiol.*, **49,** 819–43 (1966)

32. Warren, J. C., Stowring, L., Morales, M. F. *J. Biol. Chem.*, **241,** 309–16 (1966)

33. Sjodin, R. A., Beaugé, L. A. *J. Gen. Physiol.* **51,** No. 5, Part 2, 152s–161s (1968)

34. Baker, P. F., Connelly, C. M. *J. Physiol.* (*London*), **185,** 270–97 (1966)

35. Lindley, B. D., Hoshiko, T. *J. Gen. Physiol.*, **47,** 749–71 (1964)

36. Maizels, M. *J. Physiol.* (*London*), **195,** 657–79 (1968)

37. Katz, A. M. *Biochim. Biophys. Acta*, **162,** 79–85 (1968)

38. Kuznetsov, I. A., Mezentsev, A. N., Moshkovskii, Y. S., Lukanin, A. S. *Biophysics*, **12,** 425–30 (1967)

39. Wiegner, G., Jenny, H. *Kolloid Z.*, **42,** 268–74 (1927)

40. Teunissen, P. H., Bungenberg de Jong, H. G. *Kolloid-Beiheft*, **48,** 33–57 (1939)

41. Gregor, H. P., Bregman, J. I. *J. Colloid Sci.*, **6,** 323–47 (1951)

42. Ling, G. N. In *Phosphorus Metabolism*, **II,** 748–97 (McElroy, W. D., Glass, B., Eds., Johns Hopkins Press, Baltimore, 930 pp., 1952)

43. Ling, G. N. *A physical theory of the living state: the association-induction hypothesis* (Blaisdell, New York, 680 pp., 1962)

44. Diamond, J. M., Wright, E. M. *Fed. Proc.*, **27,** 748 (1968)

45. Teunissen, P. H. Rosenthal, S., Zaaijer, W. H. *Rec. Trav. Chim. Pays Bas*, **57,** 929–40 (1938)

46. Rossini, F. D., Wagman, D. D., Evans W. H., Levine, S., Jaffe, I. *Selected Values of Chemical Thermodynamic Properties* (U.S. Govt. Printing Office, Washington, 1952)

47. Rosseinsky, D. R. *Chem. Rev.*, **65,** 467–90 (1965)

48. Bregman, J. I. *Ann. N.Y. Acad. Sci.*, **57,** 125–43 (1953)

49. Castillo, J. del, Mello, W. C. de, Morales, T. *J. Gen. Physiol.*, **48,** 129–40 (1964)

50. Takagi, S. F., Wyse, G. A., Yajima, T. *J. Gen. Physiol.*, **50,** 473–89 (1966)

51. Takeuchi, A., Takeuchi, N. *J. Physiol.* (*London*), **191,** 575–90 (1967)

52. Tosteson, D. C. *Acta Physiol. Scand.*, **46,** 19–41 (1959)

53. Araki, T., Ito, M., Oscarsson, O. *J. Physiol.* (*London*), **159,** 410–35 (1961)

54. Hutter, O. F., Hoble, D. *J. Physiol.* (*London*), **157,** 335–50 (1961)

55. Hutter, O. F., Padsha, S. M. *J. Physiol.* (*London*), **146,** 117–32 (1959)

56. Finkelstein, A., Cass, A. *J. Gen. Physiol.*, **52,** No. 5, Part 2, 145s–172s (1968)

57. Tasaki, I., Singer, I., Takenaka, T. *J. Gen. Physiol.*, **48,** 1095–1123 (1965)

58. Jhamandas, K. H., Nash, C. W. *Can. J. Physiol. Biochem.*, **45,** 675–82 (1967)

59. Lindskog, S. *Biochemistry*, **5,** 2641–46 (1966)

60. Truesdell, A. H. *Study of natural glasses through their behavior as membrane electrodes* (Ph.D. thesis, Harvard Univ., Cambridge, Mass., 1962)

61. Ames, L. L. *Am. Mineralogist*, **49,** 1099–1110 (1964)

62. Bangham, A. D., Pethica, B. A., Seaman, G. V. F. *Biochem. J.*, **69,** 12–19 (1958)

63. Goldner, A. M., Cassidy, M. M., Tidball, C. S. *Proc. Soc. Exptl. Biol. Med.*, **124,** 884–87 (1967)

64. Hagiwara, S., Takahashi, K. *J. Gen. Physiol.*, **50,** 583–601 (1967)

65. Findlay, G. P., Hope, A. B. *Australian J. Biol. Sci.*, **17**, 400–11 (1964)
66. Toda, H., Narita, K. *J. Biochem.*, **62**, 767–68 (1967)
67. Ponder, E. *J. Gen. Physiol.*, **36**, 767–75 (1953)
68. Kasai, M., Oosawa, F. *Biochim. Biophys. Acta*, **154**, 520–28 (1968)
69. Weinstock, A., King, P. C., Wuthier, R. E. *Biochem. J.*, **102**, 983–88 (1967)
70. Blaustein, M. P., Goldman, D. E. *J. Gen. Physiol.*, **51**, No. 5, Part 2, 279–91 (1968)
71. Koefoed-Johnsen, V., Ussing, H. H. *Acta Physiol. Scand.*, **42**, 298–308 (1958)
72. Moeller, T. *Inorganic Chemistry* (Wiley, New York, 966 pp., 1957)
73. Eisenman, G. *Neurosciences Research* (In preparation)
74. Mullins L. J. In *Molecular Structure and Functional Activity of Nerve Cells*, 123–66 (Grenell, R. G., Mullins, L. J., Eds., AIBS, Washington, 169 pp., 1956)
75. Lindley, B. D. *J. Theoret. Biol.*, **17**, 213–28 (1967)
76. Robinson, R. A., Stokes, R. H. *Electrolyte Solutions* (Butterworths, London, 2nd ed. revised, 571 pp., 1965)
77. Solomon, A. K. *J. Gen. Physiol.*, **51**, No. 5, Part 2, 335s–364s (1968)
78. Tosteson, D. C., Cook, P., Andreoli, T., Tieffenberg, M. *J. Gen. Physiol.*, **50**, 2513–25 (1967)
79. Lardy, H. A., Graven, S. N., Estrada-O., S. *Fed. Proc.*, **26**, 1355–60 (1967)
80. Glueckauf, E. *Proc. Roy. Soc. A*, **214**, 207–25 (1952)
81. Collander, R. *Physiol. Plantarum*, **7**, 420–45 (1954)
82. Collander, R., Bärlund, H. *Acta Botan. Fennica*, **11**, 1–114 (1933)
83. Collander, R. *Physiol. Plantarum*, **3**, 45–57 (1950)
84. Collander, R. *Ibid.*, **2**, 300–11 (1949)
85. Collander, R., Wikström, B. *Physiol. Plantarum*, **2**, 235–46 (1949)
86. Collander, R. *Physiol. Plantarum*, **12**, 139–44 (1959)
87. Collander, R. *Ibid.*, **13**, 179–85 (1960)
88. Collander, R. *Trans. Faraday Soc.*, **33**, 985–90 (1937)
89. Collander, R. *Protoplasma*, **46**, 123–42 (1956)
90. Collander, R. *Physiol. Plantarum*, **10**, 397–405 (1957)
91. Oura, E., Suomalainen, H., Collander, R. *Physiol. Plantarum*, **12**, 534–44 (1959)
92. Collander, R. *Acta Physiol. Scand.*, **13**, 363–81 (1947)
93. Collander, R. *Acta Chem. Scand.*, **4**, 1085–98 (1950)
94. Collander, R. *Ibid.*, **5**, 774–80 (1951)
95. Collander, R. *Ibid.*, **3**, 717–47 (1949)
96. Wartiovaara, V., Collander, R. *Protoplasmatologia*, **2C8d**, 1–98 (1960)
97. Wright, E. M., Diamond, J. M. *Proc. Roy. Soc. B* (In press) (1968)
98. Wright, E. M., Diamond, J. M. *Ibid.*
99. Diamond, J. M., Wright, E. M. *Ibid.*
100. Kedem, O., Katchalsky, A. *Biochim. Biophys. Acta*, **27**, 229–46 (1958)
101. Dainty, J., Ginzburg, B. Z. *J. Theoret. Biol.*, **5**, 256–65 (1963)
102. Smyth, D. H., Wright, E. M. *J. Physiol. (London)*, **182**, 591–602 (1966)
103. Diamond, J. M., Harrison, S. C. *J. Physiol. (London)*, **183**, 37–57 (1966)
104. Dainty, J. *Advan. Botan. Res.*, **1**, 279–326 (1963)
105. Dainty, J., House, C. R., *J. Physiol. (London)*, **185**, 172–84 (1966)
106. Dainty, J., Ginzburg, B. Z. *Biochim. Biophys. Acta*, **79**, 122–28 (1964)
107. Overton, E. *Vjschr. Naturforsch. Ges. Zürich*, **44**, 88–135 (1899)
108. Spandau, H. *Ber. Deut. Chem. Ges.*, **74**, 1028–30 (1941)
109. Stein, W. D. *The Movement of Molecules across Cell Membranes* (Academic Press, New York, 369 pp., 1967)
110. Davson, H., Danielli, J. F. *The Permeability of Natural Membranes* (Cambridge Univ. Press, Cambridge, 365 pp., 1952)
111. Zwolinski, B. J., Eyring, H., Reese, C. E. *J. Phys. Colloid Chem.*, **53**, 1426–53 (1949).
112. Wartiovaara, V. *Physiol. Plantarum*, **3**, 462–78 (1950)
113. Tedeschi, H., Harris, D. L. *Arch. Biochem. Biophys.*, **58**, 52–67 (1955)
114. Rosen, H., Leaf, A., Schwartz, W. B. *J. Gen. Physiol.*, **48**, 379–89 (1964)
115. Wartiovaara, V. *Ann. Botan. Soc. Zool. Botan. Fennicae Vanamo*, **16**, 1–111 (1942)
116. Wartiovaara, V. *Physiol. Plantarum*, **2**, 184–96 (1949)
117. Wartiovaara, V. In *Handbuch der Pflanzenphysiologie*, **2**, 369–80 (Ruhland, W., Ed., Springer, Berlin, 1072 pp., 1956)
118. Jacobs, M. H., Glassman, H. N., Parpart, A. K. *J. Cellular Comp. Physiol.*, **7**, 197–225 (1935)
119. Höber, R., Ørskov, S. L. *Pflügers Arch.*, **231**, 599–615 (1933)

120. Vargas, F. *J. Gen. Physiol.*, **51**, No. 5, Part 2, 123s–130s (1968)

121. Villegas, R., Bruzual, I. B., Villegas, G. M. *J. Gen. Physiol.*, **51**, No. 5, Part 2, 81s–92s (1968)

122. Ruhland, W., Hoffmann, C. *Planta*, **1**, 1–83 (1925)

123. Schönfelder, S. *Planta*, **12**, 414–504 (1930)

124. Gutknecht, J. *Biochim. Biophys. Acta*, **163**, 20–29 (1968)

125. Kavanau, J. L. *Structure and Function in Biological Membranes*, **1** (Holden-Day, San Francisco, 321 pp., 1965)

126. Sha'afi, R. I., Rich, G. T., Sidel, V. W., Bossert, W. H., Solomon, A. K. *J. Gen. Physiol.*, **50**, 1377–99 (1967)

127. Andersen, B., Ussing, H. H. *Acta Physiol. Scand.*, **28**, 60–76 (1953)

128. Barry, P. H., Hope, A. B. *Biophys. J.* (In press) (1969)

129. Rich, G. T., Sha'afi, R. I., Barton, T. C. Solomon, A. K. *J. Gen. Physiol.*, **50**, 2391–2405 (1967)

130. Dainty, J., Ginzburg, B. Z. *Biochim. Biophys. Acta*, **79**, 129–37 (1964)

131. Butler, J. A. V. *Trans. Faraday Soc.*, **33**, 229–36 (1937)

132. Frank, H. S., Evans, M. W. *J. Chem. Phys.*, **13**, 507–32 (1945)

133. Franks, F. *Ann N.Y. Acad. Sci.*, **125**, 277–89 (1965)

134. Barclay, I. M., Butler, J. A. V. *Trans. Faraday Soc.*, **34**, 1445–54 (1938)

135. Butler, J. A. V., Harrower, P. *Trans. Faraday Soc.*, **33**, 171–78 (1937)

136. Gordy, W., Stanford, X. C. *J. Chem. Phys.*, **8**, 170–77 (1940)

137. Mizushima, S. *Structure of Molecules and Internal Rotation* (Academic Press, New York, 244 pp., 1954)

138. Aranow, R. H., Witten, L. *J. Phys. Chem.*, **64**, 1643–48 (1960)

139. Miller, K. W., Hildebrand, J. H. *J. Am. Chem. Soc.*, **90**, 3001–4 (1968)

CARDIAC MUSCLE: ACTIVATION
AND CONTRACTION[1,2]

By Edmund H. Sonnenblick and Allan C. Stam, Jr.

*Department of Medicine, Peter Bent Brigham Hospital
and Harvard Medical School, Boston, Massachusetts*

We shall not attempt an exhaustive or encyclopedic review, but will restrict our remarks to areas of cardiac physiology where either new or challenging information has become available, controversy has developed, or necessary data have accumulated to permit some meaningful generalizations. Several pertinent symposia (1–8), monographs (9–12), and reviews (13–14), published over the past 18 months, help to summarize much recent data on cardiac muscle. These include the extensive proceedings of the 1966 Gordon Conference on Myocardial Contractility (2), two symposia on the actions of catecholamines (6–7), and several books of current interest in cardiac physiology (1–4, 10–12). These publications provide substantive reviews of much current work in cardiac physiology.

A point of departure for current studies of function in the intact heart rests on the application to heart muscle of the tools and concepts originally applied to skeletal muscle and reflects an appreciation of the fact that the heart is a muscle prior to being a pump. Nevertheless, it is also appreciated that the heart is not merely an elusive skeletal muscle but, with its variable contractility and complex structure, cardiac muscle presents unique problems relative to its control systems and mechanical operation.

CARDIAC STRUCTURE

Older studies have claimed that the wall of the ventricle is composed of discrete muscle layers which are readily identified on gross dissection. In contrast, Streeter (15) has restudied the arrangement of fibers in the left ventricle of the pig and has demonstrated that fibers do not form discrete layers, but rather a continuum as one passes through the wall of the heart. Thus, epicardial fibers are directed nearly vertically from the base to apex and change progressively through the wall like a Chinese fan, so that they are circumferential in the midwall and nearly vertical again at the endocardium. Quantitative measurements of fiber orientation in the wall of the ventricle should be of aid in the critical analysis of force generation in the heart.

James & Sherf (16, 17) have studied the atrioventricular node and its

---

[1] This review covers the period from July 1966 to June 1968.

[2] Supported in part by USPHS grant No. HE 11306-02, American Heart Association grant No. 67782, and National Science Foundation grant No. GB-7201.

blood supply. The sinus and atrioventricular nodes appear similar in a number of species (16, 17) and are characterized by their autonomic innervation (18). Four separate cell types have been described in the atrioventricular node but their functional significance if any is not known (16). The ultrastructure of the Purkinje system has also been studied but unlike the atrioventricular node would appear to differ between species in cell size, fiber content of myofibrils, glycogen content, and fiber packing (18, 19). Some of these differences reflect the different areas of the conduction system which have been selected for study, namely the common bundle of His versus the distal branches of the conduction system which pervade the trabeculae carnae (18, 19). Aside from differences in the specific site of the conduction system studied, tighter packing of fibers in the Purkinje system of larger mammals has been noted and its contribution to more rapid conduction velocity has been suggested (19). Other physiological implications of species variation in structure await definition.

Sommer & Johnson (19) have also claimed that Purkinje (P) fibers may be distinguished from true ventricular (V) fibers by the absence of a transverse tubular (T) system in the Purkinje cells. This lack has been supported by the failure of the peroxidase reaction product to enter Purkinje fibers (20). These authors have suggested that the more rapid conduction velocity in the conduction system may be explained at least in part by the lowering of membrane capacitance due to the absence of T-tubules.

The structural organization of the T-system and the sarcoplasmic reticulum of heart muscle has received further clarification. The physiological significance and structural characterization of these tubular membrane systems which are of prime importance in excitation and relaxation have been reviewed recently (21). Using a "freeze-etching" technique and electron microscopy, Rayns, Simpson & Bertaud (22) have shown that the external apertures of the T-tubules at the surface sarcolemma are arranged in rows corresponding transversely to the spacing between myofibrils and longitudinally to the Z-lines of the sarcomeres along the myofibrils. By use of ferritin or the products of the peroxides reaction in the manner utilized for skeletal muscle, the direct continuity of the T-system of ventricular fibers with the extracellular fluid has clearly been demonstrated (20, 23). However, such a T-system by which the extracellular fluids penetrate the cell is absent in Purkinje fibers, much of the mammalian atria (23), and the amphibian ventricle (24).

It is now concluded that no open communication exists between the T-system tubules and the intracellular sarcoplasmic reticulum (19), although prior studies suggested that such connections might exist (23). Part of this difficulty in interpretation is explained by the recent findings of Girardier & Forssmann (25) that with a peroxidase marker T-tubules are shown to branch laterally throughout the cell, decreasing to the size of tubules of the sarcoplasmic reticulum while losing the basement membrane. From these and other studies it is clear that the T-system or its extensive lateral ramifications cannot be identified with assurance without the use of extra-cellular fluid markers such as the peroxidase reaction product.

Thus the T-system is continuous with the cell surface membrane (sarco-lemma) and forms a deeply ramifying extension of this membrane into the cell by which the extracellular environment is distributed throughout the fiber. The attachment of the intracellular sarcoplasmic reticulum to the extracellular membranes or their extension into the cell, i.e. the T-system, have been closely studied, since these junctions may be of vital importance to the transfer of superficial electrical activity to intracellular activation, as reviewed by Page (26). The sarcoplasmic reticulum is a continuous network of small tubules which in heart muscle are continuous from sarcomere to sarcomere (19, 23). This spread of the sarcoplasmic reticulum from sarco-mere to sarcomere, as well as the lateral ramifications of the T-system in heart muscle, may help to explain why Mueller (27) was unable to obtain localized contractions of single sarcomeres by applying a microelectrode to the surface of the sarcolemma in the region of the Z-line, as had been done in skeletal muscle by Huxley and Taylor in 1958.

The sarcoplasmic reticulum of heart muscle, which is more profuse than generally noted, forms couplings (or junctions) along the T-tubules in the general region of the Z-line of the sarcomere. However, these couplings are formed without the prominent dilatations or cisternae noted in skeletal muscle. Further, in heart muscle, couplings of the sarcoplasmic reticulum are readily noted along the sarcolemma and the close junctions of the inter-calated disc (20, 26, 28). These couplings of the sarcoplasmic reticulum at the T-system or along the sarcolemma characteristically contain granular inclusions similar to that found in the terminal cisternae of skeletal muscle (29), and have been shown to contain calcium (30). The finding of acid mucopolysaccharides in the sarcoplasmic reticulum (31) has led to the chal-lenging hypothesis that chondroitin sulfate may provide a reversible binding site for calcium in the couplings of the sarcoplasmic reticulum. The question then remains as to the role of portions of the sarcoplasmic reticulum which do not contain these inclusions. Whether there are discrete loci for release, reaccumulation, and storage of calcium in the sarcoplasmic reticulum awaits definition.

The effects of altering ionic milieu on the morphology of the T-system and sarcoplasmic reticulum have been studied in the perfused papillary muscle preparation of the dog (32). Perfusion with low sodium chloride pro-duced dilatation of T-system and sarcoplasmic reticulum, while perfusion with low sodium or high calcium and normal chloride resulted in dilatation of the sarcoplasmic reticulum alone. The dilatation of the T-system following perfusion with low chloride-containing solutions is difficult to explain unless fixed charges exist along the tubule or the character of the lining basement membrane is altered. The authors (32) suggest that the dilatation of the sarcoplasmic reticulum which accompanies high calcium or low sodium per-fusion reflects the excessive sequestering of calcium within these tubules and is correlated with increased contractility and contracture. Unexplained is the fact that the observed changes occurred only 50 per cent of the time. However, these views are consonant with the thesis that the sarcoplasmic reticulum is a major site of variable calcium release and uptake in excitation-contraction coupling in heart muscle (21, 26, 33). Nevertheless, detailed explanations of such changes in the sarcoplasmic reticulum will require further assessment of the effects of fixatives themselves on membrane and tubule dimensions as Krames & Page have noted (34).

Muir (35) has extended his studies of the intercalated disc by exploring the effects of calcium deprivation on cardiac structure. Brief *in vitro* perfusion of the rat heart with salt solutions lacking calcium led to the reversible uncoupling of excitation from contraction but did not alter the sarcoplasmic reticulum, myofibrils, or intercalated disc. However, prolonged perfusion of the heart without calcium led to an irreversible loss of both the mechanical activity and the surface recorded electrocardiogram. On electron microscopy, the cells of the heart were separated at the intercalated disc with only the tight junctions (or nexi) of the disc remaining intact. The remainder of the cell structure was well maintained. Other divalent ions, namely Se^{++} or Ba^{++}, could not be substituted for Ca^{++} in order to maintain intercellular adhesion.

The failure of the electrocardiogram to persist following low Ca^{++} perfusion led Muir (35) to question the role of the "tight junction" in intercellular conduction. However, using two impaled microelectrodes Kawamura & Konishi (36) have shown that the form of the action potential and the velocity of intercellular electrical conduction were essentially unchanged following perfusion of the rabbit myocardium with low calcium- or EDTA-containing salt solutions which led to the separation of the intercalated discs except for the "tight" junctions. Alternatively, perfusion of the myocardium with hyperosmolar solutions has led to separation of the intercalated disc at the tight junctions with preservation of the desmosome connections (37). In this situation, electrical continuity between cells was lost (37). Taken together, these findings support the widely held view that the tight junctions of the intercalated disc provide a site of low resistance between myocardial cells for electrical conduction.

Revel & Karnovsky (38) have studied the so-called "tight" junctions of the intercalated disc, utilizing lanthanum hydroxide as an extracellular fluid marker. Lanthanum hydroxide was shown to permeate the tight junctions of the disc; and on cross section, a hexagonal pattern was noted with center to center spacings of 90 Å. This pattern resembles the structure of electrical synapses of the central nervous system. While this study demonstrates that the tight junctions of the disc, by which electrical transmission between cells is mediated, are not completely fused, patterned areas of fusion across the hexagonal array apparently exist, leaving the "tight" junction as a site of low resistance.

The relations between sarcomere length and tension development in heart muscle have received further study. Grimm & Whitehorn (39) have determined the relation between actively developed isometric tension and initial muscle length of the rat papillary muscle. Muscles were fixed in formalin at known lengths relative to the length-tension curve and imbedded in paraffin. Average sarcomere length was then determined from sections viewed under the light microscope. As in previous studies of the cat papillary muscle, the average sarcomere length was proportional to muscle length along the major portion of the ascending limb of the length-active tension curve, with maximum tension being generated at a sarcomere length of 2.1 μ. Although undetermined extent of shrinkage due to paraffin imbedding has limited discussion of myofilament disposition relative to these findings, this study lends support to the view that tension development in heart muscle can be correlated with average sarcomere length and is in general agreement with the "sliding filament" hypothesis for muscle.

Sarcomere dimensions have also been studied in the left ventricular wall both at rest (39, 40) and following contraction (41, 42). The left ventricles of dogs and cats arrested in diastole have been fixed at various filling pressures by perfusion of their coronary system with glutaraldehyde, and average sarcomere length within the wall has been measured by electron microscopy (40). At the upper limit of normal ventricular filling pressure for both the dog and cat (12 mm of mercury), average sarcomere length in the midwall approaches 2.2 μ, which corresponds to the apex of the sarcomere length-tension curve. Left ventricles of normal dogs have also been fixed acutely by rapid perfusion of the cannulated coronary artery system in either diastole or systole (41), and sarcomere dimensions in the ventricular wall determined (42). Sarcomere length in the mid-wall of the left ventricle averaged 2.07 μ at end diastole and 1.81 μ at end systole. This difference in sarcomere length adequately accounts for a 50 per cent ejection fraction observed. When ventricles were acutely distended beyond the physiological filling pressures, two phenomena were noted (40): thin filaments were pulled from the center of elongated sarcomeres ($>2.2 \mu$) with the formation of H-zones; and fibers tended to slip, one relative to the other. These studies imply that the normal left ventricle functions with sarcomere lengths near the optimal length for myofilament overlap and hence optimal force generation. Further, although some variation in sarcomere length occurs within the wall of the myocardium, average sarcomere length is predictably altered by ventricular filling pressure (39, 40, 42), and changes in sarcomere length help to explain Starling's law of the heart.

In contrast to the above studies, Gay & Johnson (43) have reported a lack of any consistent relation between sarcomere length and overall muscle length in small trabeculae carnae of the rabbit ventricle. However, neither resting nor developed tensions were measured, and while reference is made to length-tension curves from the papillary muscle, no data are presented. Because trabeculae carnae from the right ventricle cavity have very substantial sheaths of connective tissue which are not present in the ventricular wall itself, and because of the presence of Purkinje fibers in this tissue which are specialized for conduction (21), it is difficult to attribute physiological importance to these findings. Rather, it would appear that these authors are studying fibers at short lengths due to their large amounts of connective tissue, and the folding of muscle fibers is appropriate for these short lengths. This is clearly not the case at physiological filling pressures and fiber lengths in the ventricular wall itself (39, 40).

EXCITATION-CONTRACTION COUPLING

Sandow (33 and unpublished observations) has suggested that excitation-contraction coupling be considered in terms of two components: electrochemical and chemical-mechanical. To this we will add a third component, mechanical-chemical uncoupling.

ELECTROCHEMICAL COUPLING

The action potential and ionic currents.—Electrochemical coupling begins with the action potential, and includes its propagation and the subsequent release of an activator substance. There has been considerable recent progress in delineating the various ionic currents involved in this process along with their mutual interdependency and specific generation in various cell types and species.

The ascending phase of the myocardial action potential continues to be regarded as secondary to an increase in sarcolemmal sodium permeability (P_{Na}). This has been supported by the observation that tetrodotoxin, which decreases P_{Na}, abolished the negative inward excitatory current in Purkinje fibers, rat ventricular fibers and less strikingly in guinea pig ventricular fibers, as shown by Coraboeauf & Vassort (45). The latter authors implicate an inward calcium current (I_{Ca}) in the terminal portion of the upstroke of the action potential in the guinea pig heart through the depression of this phase by manganese, a known inhibitor of calcium conductance (G_{Ca}).

Involvement of I_{Ca} in the overshoot of the spike of the action potential was shown by Niedergerke & Orkand using frog ventricular strips (46). With increasing calcium the overshoot of the action potential was increased initially but decreased subsequently as high extracellular calcium was maintained. Similar results occurred with decreased extracellular sodium or with increased rate of contraction. It was concluded that the overshoot of the action potential resulted from an inward calcium current through the excitable sarcolemma while depression of the overshoot was secondary to progressive accumulation of calcium in some undefined intracellular store.

Recently Reuter (47) presented data concerning the inactivation of the initial outward current (probably I_{Cl}) which occurs at the junction of the spike and the plateau of the action potential. He concluded that a change in the driving force did not account for this current and theorized that a decreased membrane conductance for chloride ions underlies the inactivation.

Sleator & de Gubareff (48) have studied the action potential spikes and plateaus of human atrial muscle. Increased calcium in the bathing media shortened the duration of the spike while caffeine or a short spike interval prolonged the spike duration. They propose that spike duration, which they equate with an open sodium channel, is inversely related to the amount of calcium bound to a specific membrane site, presumably on the sarcolemma. This concept appears relevant to myocardial cells with a limited T-system, such as the atria, but application to mammalian ventricular cells which have an extensive T-system would require further direct support. The measurement of calcium which is bound to an isolated sarcolemma preparation might provide a direct test of their proposal.

Analysis of the ionic currents responsible for the plateau has proven to be complex. Delayed disappearance of increased P_{Na}, delayed appearance of increased P_K (49), and anomalous rectification, i.e. decreased P_K associated with the delayed disappearance of increased P_{Na} (50–53), have all been implicated in the generation of the plateau of the action potential. Noble & Tsien (54) have analyzed in detail the unmodified current voltage relationships in Purkinje fibers and have suggested that the slow outward current in Purkinje fibers is carried by potassium ion. Further, they have presented data supporting a modification of their equivalent circuit model to include an inward-going rectification in G_{K_2} and reduction of the exponent on the kinetic variable to one. The activation of the slow potassium current by potentials sufficiently negative to avoid the fast sodium conductance allowed the potassium current to be studied over the entire range of pacemaker potentials. This has allowed a demonstration of the importance of the negative slope in the current voltage relationships in generating the last phase of the pacemaker depolarization.

The general relevance of the two-component model for potassium conductance to Purkinje fibers which have a positive plateau and to the various non-Purkinje fibers of various species is yet to be determined. Thus broader generalizations on this point are not possible at present.

The contribution of calcium currents (I_{Ca}) to the action potential is receiving much current interest. Reuter & Scholz (55) have studied I_{Ca} in sheep ventricular trabeculae bathed in sodium-free solutions using voltage-clamp techniques. In the absence of calcium no tension was developed despite reversal of the membrane potential. In calcium-containing solutions a regenerative portion of deplorization began at −60 mV, as did tension development. The threshold for both I_{Ca} and tension was independent of external calcium concentration. However, increasing calcium did increase the rate of depolarization and the amplitude of the second current, both changes being linearly related to tension developed at different calcium concentrations. The authors hypothesized that during depolarization, calcium ions carry charge across the cardiac sarcolemma in a sodium-free solution and that this flux of calcium reflects a process operative in physiologic excitation-contraction coupling. The possibility of calcium ions contributing to the plateau of the action potential is difficult to evaluate because of the effect of calcium ions on permeability of the membrane to all other ions. However, this data is most suggestive.

Further support of an increased calcium conductance (G_{Ca}) during the plateau is derived from the finding of Coraboeuf & Vassort (45) that manganese, known to decrease G_{Ca}, decreases the height and duration of the plateau in rat ventricle but not the duration in the guinea pig ventricle. Postsystolic potentiation, presumably related to an increased G_{Ca}, produced the opposite effect of manganese in rat and guinea pig ventricles (45).

The overall complexity of the ionic currents involved in the generation of the action potential has been underlined by several studies of Trautwein and his colleagues (56–58). Dudel et al. (56) studied the excitatory membrane currents in Purkinje fibers and confirmed the large inward negative sodium current during rapid depolarization, but also found a nonsodium, negative, inward current component specific for cardiac muscle. Calcium had the required equilibrium potential for this second current. However, this current could still be observed in the absence of extracellular calcium and was not increased by a fortyfold increase in calcium. Further, the effects of changing the extracellular concentrations of one ion on the currents carried by other ions have been emphasized (57). In a sodium-free solution, the positive potassium current in the region of the negative potential is increased, while the negative nonsodium current is decreased. The time dependence of the potassium current near resting potentials is also altered (57). With decreasing extracellular potassium, the inward, excitatory current of sodium increases initially and then decreases. Relevant to Noble & Tsien's studies (52), these authors found the potassium system to be virtually independent of time when studied with partial inactivation of the sodium system.

Dudel, Peper, Rudel & Trautwein (58) studied the effects of tetrodotoxin on the membrane currents in Purkinje fibers and found that the negative inward excitatory current attributed to sodium was abolished. They concluded that the increase in positive current observed following the removal of sodium was not due to the lack of a negative sodium current, but rather to the depression of a nonsodium negative current. The ionic nature of this current was not defined. An additional increase in a positive potassium current could not be excluded.

The effect of sodium and calcium on the excitation of the *Mytilus* (bivalve) heart muscle is quite distinctive (59). The *Mytilus* heart was excitable and contracted spontaneously for more than 3 hours in a sodium-free solution. When calcium was increased in a sodium-free solution, the amplitude and rate of rise of the action potential spike increased. On the other hand, the administration of manganese chloride led to a decrease of the amplitude of the spike potential while the duration of the spike potential increased substantially. Since tetrodotoxin was without effect on this ventricle (59), it was concluded that in the *Mytilus* heart, a calcium rather than a sodium current forms the basis of the action potential.

Most of these studies of ionic currents responsible for the action potential depend on voltage-clamp techniques originally developed for the squid axon. While modifications such as the sucrose-gap technique have improved these methods, their complete validity remains in question. The complex morphology of cardiac tissue has made uniform voltage clamping of the myocardium at best very difficult and further studies are required before there can be full acceptance of the conclusions derived from such methods. Further, some of the variation in results may reflect differences in the tissue studied, namely atria, ventricle, or conduction system, or the species employed. The membrane structures, as noted previously, vary considerably in these instances and the details of the electrical activity and its specific ionic basis would also appear to vary (45).

Trans sarcolemmal ionic fluxes.—Sodium exchange has been studied in the arterially perfused papillary muscle of the dog (60). Langer found three kinetically defined phases or compartments for sodium which could account for all the myocardial sodium. Phase 2, characterized as an intracellular sodium rate of exchange, was proportional to the frequency of contraction. Further, changes in the exchange rate of intracellular sodium were proportional to changes in the tension development of the positive rate staircase. Accordingly, it was concluded that alterations in sodium exchange form a primary determinant of calcium movement and that a lag in the sodium pump was indirectly responsible for the changes in tension seen in the positive rate staircase. However, this proposal must explain the observed net gain in tissue calcium, not simply a redistribution of intracellular calcium. Sodium competition with calcium efflux might explain this phenomenon. Alternatively, calcium efflux, like sodium efflux, requires an active process (61). The arguments supporting the association of a lag in the sodium pump with increased frequency of contraction apply equally well to a lag in a calcium pump, and the requirement for dependency on sodium for the rise in intracellular calcium is not necessary.

The kinetics of calcium exchange in relation to alterations in length, tension, and work have also been examined in the perfused dog papillary muscle (62). Neither the total tissue calcium nor the rate of calcium exchange was affected by alterations in length-tension relations, muscle shortening, or work performed. However, interpretation of these results is limited by the ± 5 per cent error in the determination of total tissue calcium, since the calcium required for full activation of the contractile apparatus represents at most 6 to 7 per cent of the total calcium in the myocardium. Shelburne et al. (63) studied the rate staircase in relation to calcium exchange in the arterially perfused rabbit ventricular septum and found that when a fall in temperature was accompanied by positive inotropism, there was an associated increased content of phase 2 calcium. Again these phenomena were attributed to a lag in the sodium pump which in turn controls subsequent calcium movements and, thus, tension development. However, a lag in the calcium pump due to lowered temperature might also explain these findings.

Naylor (64) has reported that the net influx of calcium into the myo-

cardium is augmented by an increase in the rate of contraction or extracellular calcium concentration in guinea pig atria and dog papillary muscles.
Epinephrine also increased the uptake of calcium to a small but significant
amount, while this response was blocked by propranolol. Further, propranolol decreased the calcium uptake in the absence of epinephrine (64).
Since propranolol cannot block the positive inotropic effect of increased
calcium, there is doubt regarding the relevance of these observations to
epinephrine's inotropic effects, as noted by the author.

BIOCHEMICAL BASIS FOR ACTIVE SARCOLEMMAL TRANSPORT

Controversy exists as to whether sodium-potassium-stimulated ouabain-
inhibited ATPase (Na^+-K^+ ATPase) of the myocardium is an enzymatic
constituent of the surface sarcolemma or the intracellular sarcoplasmic
reticulum (65, 66). Sarcolemma has been prepared from the dog ventricle by
extraction with 1 M KI and shown to contain a Na^+-K^+ ATPase which is
inhibited by small amounts of ouabain ($5 \times 10^{-7} M$) (67). Paired microsome
and mitochondrial preparations showed little or none of this activity (67).

A highly active and specific Na^+-K^+ ATPase has been obtained from
calf heart by successive treatments with deoxycholate and sodium iodide
(68). The high activity found with this preparation may reflect the inclusion
of sodium ions on the inner side of the sarcolemmal sacs which may be the
locus of the sodium-sensitive portion of this transport enzyme complex.

Matsui & Schwartz (69) have more recently reported specific digoxin
binding to the same calf heart Na^+-K^+ ATPase. This binding of digoxin,
which required ATP and Mg^{++}, was stimulated by sodium, depressed by K^+,
and persisted when acetyl phosphate substituted for ATP. From considerations of the similarity of changes in digoxin binding and the phosphorylated
intermediate of the ATPase under various conditions, it was suggested that
digoxin binds to phosphorylated enzyme. Thus, digoxin's inhibition of the
Na^+-K^+ ATPase was attributed to the stability of the digoxin-phosphory-
lated intermediate complex.

Weber (61) has presented the data supporting a requirement for an active
transport process for calcium efflux from skeletal muscle and the same arguments apply for the heart. The same conclusion was drawn by Lahrtz et al.
(70) from studying calcium transport in isolated guinea pig atria during
hypothermia. The demonstration of a calcium-activated ATPase of red cell
membranes (71) suggests that a similar enzyme should be sought in heart
muscle sarcolemma. Currently it is not known whether the active transport
systems in heart muscle for calcium and sodium represent separate or shared
channels. Further, the extent and nature of calcium binding, release, and
competition with sodium in cardiac sarcolemma is completely unknown.
These questions are central to our understanding of excitation-contraction
coupling since the control of ionic movements across the external membranes
is intimately involved.

The identity of the intracellular site for release of calcium which activates the contractile system can only be inferred from studies of calcium uptake since there is at present no adequate method to release calcium *in vitro* by electrical currents (72). Nevertheless, on the basis of the data to be presented under the heading Mechanical-Chemical Uncoupling, it is accepted that this site of release for activator calcium in the mammalian myocardium is the sarcoplasmic reticulum.

Data bearing on the timing of activator calcium release from the sarcoplasmic reticulum are provided by a recent study of Morad & Trautwein (73). Tension development was recorded with action potentials abolished by voltage clamp after a variable duration. The earliest commitment to some tension was found with an action potential duration of 2 msec. The associated tension development increased rapidly over the first 50 msec of the action potential and the processes involved in time-dependent commitment to tension were complete by 150 msec, in an action potential lasting 500 msec. Increasing extracellular calcium markedly increased the tension development due to changes in the very early portion of the action potential. These observations could be explained by release of calcium from an internal store which contains more calcium to be released or by an increased flux of calcium from another site.

Orkand (74) studied the frog heart with low stimulation rates and recorded dP/dt as well as tension. Facilitated contraction following previous stimulation was summated linearly with that remaining from previous responses. The decay of facilitation had two components characterized by half-times of 3 and 50 sec. This finding lends support to the suggestion that there are two distinct release sites for activator calcium.

Langer (75) has estimated that, with low sodium perfusion, total tissue calcium rose from 3 to 8 mM/liter heart water while his phase 2 calcium, thought to represent that contained within the sarcoplasmic reticulum, rose from 1.5 to 2.7 mM/liter heart water. However, these total calcium values are far in excess of what could be contained within the sarcoplasmic reticulum as currently known, and one must thus suggest that a secondary store must be operative. Since contracture develops at these calcium levels, the efficiency of this secondary store must be limited. Under these conditions the mitochondria have been suggested as this secondary store (32).

In the crayfish, a model of activation which contains a channeled current with selective anion permeability in the distal portions of the transverse tubular system has been presented (76). A chloride current is thought to control the calcium release in this system. The relevance of this provocative suggestion to activation of the mammalian myocardium warrants study.

The central role of the calcium ion in the activation of the contractile mechanism is clear. The pertinent and extensive studies in skeletal muscle in this regard have been reviewed recently (33, 61). We will deal first with the role of the calcium ion in activating the contractile machinery (chemical-mechanical coupling) and then the process involved in calcium removal, i.e. deactivation or mechanical-chemical uncoupling.

CHEMICAL-MECHANICAL COUPLING

The calcium ion plays an essential role in the activation of cardiac contraction-coupled actomyosin ATPase activity (77–79). Summarizing this relationship, Katz (80) demonstrated that the ATPase activity of cardiac myosin in the presence of actin was a function of calcium concentration (pCa). In the absence of actin, myosin ATPase was inactive and uninfluenced by pCa (78, 80) while in the presence of either skeletal or cardiac actin, myosin ATPase activity rose as a function of increasing free calcium ion concentration (80). The analogue of relaxation, inactivation of actomyosin ATPase activity, occurred when the pCa was raised to 7 or 8, while full activation was reached with a pCa of 5 to 6.

Ebashi and colleagues (81, 82) have recently clarified the relationship of calcium to actomyosin activity. The interaction of actin with myosin was shown to occur spontaneously in the presence of ATP and Mg^{++} but with the total absence of Ca^{++}. However, in the presence of another structural protein, troponin, this interaction did not occur but could be induced by adding Ca^{++}. Through immunofluorescent techniques, troponin has been localized to the thin filaments composed primarily of actin with a periodicity approximating 375 Å. From these important observations, it may be concluded that the activating role of calcium is to bind to troponin and thus remove the troponin inhibition of the actin-myosin interaction which the troponin provides in the resting state. The troponin-dependent inhibition of the interaction of actin and myosin is specifically removed by calcium on an equimolar basis (81). Since there are about 70 μmoles of troponin per kg of heart, 70 μmoles of calcium/kg of heart would be required to activate fully the actomyosin of the myocardium. These values establish the stoichiometric requirements that must be met in the handling of calcium transport in the process of excitation-contraction coupling in the heart (81, 82).

Whether the interaction of calcium with troponin is the only system concerned with the control of actin and myosin interactions is not clear. An actomyosin-inhibiting substance has been reported (83) that imparts epinephrine responsiveness to well-glycerinated cardiac myofibrils in terms of ATPase activity. The myofibrillar ATPase depression by the actomyosin-inhibiting substance and its removal by catecholamines was found to be independent of calcium. Weber et al. (84) were unable to demonstrate the inhibitory effects of this substance. However, in these studies fresh skeletal muscle fibrils, rather than glycerinated cardiac fibers, were used and the direct pertinence to cardiac muscle must be questioned.

More recently, Honig (85, 86) has reported a direct stimulation of the contraction-coupled ATPase activity of fresh cardiac fibers by catecholamines. Further, beta-blocking agents depressed the ATPase activity of both myofibrils and myosin B. However, catecholamines had no effect on the superprecipitation and ATPase activity of myosin B; this last finding was initially shown by Katz (87). Thus, the problem remains as to whether there are nontroponin attenuator systems which can modify responses to calcium stimulation.

MECHANICAL-CHEMICAL UNCOUPLING

At the beginning of the period covered by this review it was established that myocardial subcellular particles could take up calcium and cause relaxation *in vitro* (88–90) and that a component of microsomal calcium uptake was distinct from mitochondrial calcium uptake as judged by response to inhibitors (90). More recently, Katz & Repke (91) have demonstrated a calcium uptake by microsomes prepared from the dog ventricle of 29 μmoles/g microsomal protein in the absence of oxalate.

Fairhurst et al. (92) have studied calcium uptake by slices of rabbit ventricle glycerinated for 24 hours and identified a reticular uptake of calcium by responses to inhibitors. A half-maximal value of 15 to 20 μmoles of calcium/gram of protein was found at a pCa of 7, which suggests that the active portion of the slice preparation was capable of taking up calcium in physiological amounts and at a physiologic pCa.

Recently rapid mixing techniques and the murexide method for calcium measurement have been applied to the problem of uptake rates of calcium by microsomes from the canine heart (93). An uptake of at least 50 μmoles calcium/g microsomal protein was demonstrated in less than 90 msec. This value readily satisfies the rate requirements for physiological relaxation. Further, through the use of zonal centrifugation, the uptake of calcium at a pCa of 8 was shown to be due entirely to the reticular component of the cardiac microsomes (94).

The interaction of sodium ions with the uptake of calcium by cardiac microsomes has been studied. Carsten (95) has found that the rate of calcium accumulation by a partially purified fraction of microsomes in the presence of ATP, Mg^{++}, Ca^{45}, and oxalate was not affected by changes in K^+ or Na^+ or by the substitution of isosmotic amounts of sucrose for 75 per cent of the Na^+. Katz & Repke (96) have also studied the effects of sodium and potassium on the uptake of calcium by cardiac microsomes, in the presence and absence of oxalate. In the presence of oxalate, under conditions where it was difficult to evaluate the relevance of the solubility product of Ca oxalate, calcium uptake was augmented by KCl and NaCl at concentrations less than 1.0 M while higher concentrations of these salts decreased calcium uptake. At lower concentrations of microsomes, where uptake of calcium was maximal, replacement of KCl by equimolar amounts of NaCl decreased both the rate and extent of calcium uptake. However, in the absence of oxalate, ATP-dependent uptake of calcium was not altered by replacing K^+ with Na^+.

In contrast to the work of Carsten (95) and Katz & Repke (96), Palmer & Posey (97) found that Na^+ and to a lesser extent Li^+, but not K^+, reduced the amount of calcium taken up by microsomes in the absence of oxalate. The apparent reduction produced by Na^+ was not attributed to an inhibition of calcium uptake but rather to a rapid release of bound calcium. This con-

clusion is not strongly supported, and the specificity of the preparation requires further clarification. Indeed, this is an important consideration for
all microsome preparations. Further study is needed to clarify this relation
of sodium to calcium uptake by cardiac microsomal, mitochondrial, and
sarcolemmal preparations.

The interaction of cardiac glycosides with cardiac actomysin ATPase
activity and superprecipitation remains unsettled, since stimulation (98),
depression (99), and no effect (100) have been reported. Similarly, variable
responses have been reported for the effects of glycosides on calcium uptake
of cardiac microsomes (95, 101, 102). Thus, while it is clear that glycosides
inhibit the Na^+-K^+ ATPase of the sarcolemma, other effects, if any, remain
to be defined, especially in relation to pharmacological concentrations of the
drug. The recent study demonstrating a relation between the inotropic
effect of ouabain and a protein moiety in the heart which is apparently lost
when isolated cat hearts are perfused with Krebs-Ringer solution warrants
further evaluation (103).

Morad & Kavaler (104) studied the effects of epinephrine on electrical
and mechanical events and observed biphasic mechanical responses during a
given depolarization. Mechanical relaxation often preceded sarcolemmal
repolarization. These observations suggest that onset of calcium uptake by
the reticulum is independent of and may precede repolarization. Further
support for this view has been provided by Reuter (105) who demonstrated
a slow current for myocardial calcium. This calcium current was associated
with potentiated tension of the subsequent beat but not of the beat in which
the increased I_{Ca} occurred. This suggests that the increased influx of the
calcium was picked up by an activated calcium pump in the reticulum and
thus became available for release in the next beat.

Muscle Mechanics

The mechanical analogues in cardiac muscle have received continued
interest with the application to heart muscle of the principles and methods
initially utilized for the study of skeletal muscle. Several unique features of
cardiac muscle relative to skeletal muscle are now well recognized: (a) heart
muscle cannot be tetanized and phenomena of contractile activity must be
considered in relation to time; (b) at muscle lengths where developed tension
is maximal, substantial resting tension exists in heart muscle; and (c) the
active state in heart muscle, a mechanical measure of the force generating
reactions at contractile sites, is *slow* to develop maximally, *prolonged* in duration, and *variable* in its maximum intensity (106–111).

These latter observations have centered about the application of A. V.
Hill's three-component model to cardiac muscle, with careful consideration
of the properties of the model components (Figure 1). The characterization
of the model components is central both to the definition of cardiac contractility and to the extension of the principles of muscle mechanics to analysis of the intact heart.

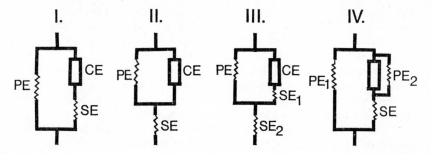

FIG. 1. Mechanical analogues of muscle. PE = parallel elastic element; SE = series elastic element and CE = contractile element.

The contractile element (CE), which at rest is thought to be freely extensible but with activation develops force and shortens, has been characterized by the inverse relation between its velocity of shortening and the load, i.e. the force-velocity relation, and the course of active state (44, 45). Prior studies have shown that the contractile state or contractility of heart muscle is variable under the influence of many inotropic interventions but can be characterized by the relation between force, velocity of shortening, instantaneous muscle length, and time (106, 109, 110). Thus a given state of contractility of cardiac muscle has been defined as a surface created by the related variables, force, velocity, and length (106). The activated muscle, or rather its contractile elements, move across this surface, depending on the load that is borne and the length the muscle starts from.

For the given state of contractility, then, there is a unique velocity of shortening for any muscle length and load. However, as Brady has emphasized (107), the muscle requires time to reach this surface and has a limited time to move across it. In this sense, the surface is time-limited. Further, sudden perturbations such as quick releases or quick stretches of the muscle may alter these relations by disrupting the active state (107, 109). Changes in contractility are characterized by a change in the force-velocity-length relation such that both maximum velocity of shortening (V_{max}) and maximum force development are altered. Again the newly created surface describes the course for velocity related to force and instantaneous length, working within limits of the time that the muscle is active (106).

The character of the active state in heart muscle has received intensive study. With quick release methods, the active state was shown to be slow in onset, reaching a peak in 150 to 200 msec in an isometric contraction which reaches maximum tension in 400 to 500 msec (106–111). The active state is close to its maximum intensity for most of the second half of the rising phase of the isometric contraction (109, 110). With inotropic influences which alter contractility, the course of the active state may be altered (106, 108–

110). For example, norepinephrine accelerates the onset of maximum active state, increases its maximum intensity, decreases its duration, and accelerates its dissipation (110). Strophanthidin acts similarly but with lesser decrements in the duration of the maximum intensity of active state (108, 110). It should be noted that the changes in the maximum intensity of active state have their direct manifestation in changes in the force-velocity relation, while the changes in the time course of the active state are directly correlated with the isometric contraction (109, 110).

The observation that the onset of active state is delayed and the twitch tension development possibly limited by time has led to the suggestion that caution be used in the interpretation of force-velocity measurements in heart muscle (109). Certainly, it has been recognized that a delay exists in attaining maximum velocity of shortening in the individual, afterloaded, isotonic contraction from which the force-velocity curve is generally derived (112). Thus, measured slopes of the shortening trace of the muscle reflect this delayed maximal velocity as seen by electrical differentiation, and derived force-velocity curves actually reflect contractile element velocity during the latter half of the rising tension trace where the intensity of active state is virtually maximal and relatively in a steady state (112). Further, the twitch of cardiac muscle resembles a short tetanus of skeletal muscle. Support for this view is found in the observation that prolongation of the isometric contraction by voltage-clamp techniques does not augment tension further (73). Rapid stretches throughout contraction also fail to increase the tension significantly beyond that of the peak isometric contraction (107, 109).

When force-velocity relations of heart muscle are determined, an inverse curvilinear relation is generally observed. However, except in a few instances the curve is not a true displaced hyperbola as described by the Hill equation in that the velocity declines and force falls off at high loads so that the maximum isometric tension (P_0) is less than predicted. Nevertheless, much of this discrepancy disappears if proper corrections are made for the shortening of the contractile elements as the series elastic elements are stretched, and a true hyperbolic relation is approached (Brutsaert and Sonnenblick, unpublished observations).

In the model for muscle of A. V. Hill, developed tension is manifest externally when the contractile element (CE) shortens and stretches the series-elastic element (SE). Thus, the properties of the SE which is a passive elastic structure and its arrangement relative to the CE and parallel elastic element (PE) are of central importance. Using quick release methods, Parmley & Sonnenblick (112) have demonstrated that the length-extension curve of the SE of cat papillary muscle is exponential in form with an extension of 4–5 per cent of initial muscle length for full isometric tension development. Further, the modulus of elasticity of the SE was shown to be a linear function of developed tension (112), a finding supported by Brady (113) and Edman & Nilsson (111).

A pertinent question raised by these studies is how these components of the Hill model are arranged (Figure 1) (112, 113–115). The models for muscle are of help in studying contractile mechanisms and in planning further studies, and are not meant to imply structural reality.

In model I of Figure 1, the PE spans the CE and the SE so that resting tension is supported by the PE alone and for all intents and purposes the length of the SE at rest cannot be altered by changing muscle length. Were the CE not to be very compliant at rest, the SE length could be altered. However, this would convert model I to model II for analogue purposes. In model II, the PE spans only the CE, and resting tension is the sum of the PE plus the SE. Increasing initial muscle length in model II will permit the SE to be prestretched by elongating the muscle prior to activation. In model III, the potential of models I and II are combined by splitting the location of the SE. From the present body of experimental data (112, 113–115) it would appear that none of these simple models can explain all of the findings.

Clearly the stiffness of the series elastic element is increased by increasing initial muscle length (112, 114). When initial muscle length is increased, isometric tension is augmented but the extent to which the SE is stretched to produce this increased tension is not changed (114). Except with very high preloads, the length-extension curves for the SE may be readily correctible back to a single length-extension curve but with a different starting point which is directly dependent on the preload (112). These results could occur by having all or a substantial portion of the SE in series with both the SE and PE as occurs in model II. However, these results would not exclude models III or IV which are more complex variants of model II. Were the SE to be stretched after the onset of activity, the SE could be placed on a stiffer portion of its curve as a function of muscle length and model I might be operative. However, present data are not readily explained in this simple model (73, 112, 113). With this in mind, the simplified views of muscle models recently presented would not appear warranted (13). Further, it remains possible to alter the stiffness of the SE were one to have a number of model I structures arranged in parallel but with unequal stress and length. In view of the dispersion of sarcomere lengths within the myocardial wall, such a possibility remains (42).

While the analogue models do not denote a structural counterpart, it is generally acknowledged that the CE is located in the sarcomere, most likely at the cross bridges between actin and myosin. Although such bridges have been demonstrated by electron microscopy in skeletal muscle, their presence in heart muscle awaits definition. The localization of the SE is even more obscure. Some of the SE must exist in the elastic attachments of the muscle and in the arrangement of the fibers. It has also been suggested that some of the SE exists in the contractile proteins and in the bridges of the CE.

Hoffman et al. (116) have presented the challenging proposition that the diastolic compliance or extensibility of cardiac muscle is variable under the influence of paired-pulse stimulation (sustained postextrasystolic potentiation) and inotropic drugs. From these experiments, the authors suggest that some residual interactions (or active state) may remain during diastole in heart muscle.

However, the interpretation and physiological significance of these findings has been questioned. Feigl (117) examined isometric and isotonic contractions of the isolated cat papillary muscles and observed apparent changes in diastolic extensibility (compliance) with paired stimulation; these changes were only seen in muscles with spontaneous aftercontractions between driven beats. In isotonic contractions (constant preload without afterload) end diastolic length depended on frequency of contraction since the muscle "crept" to a longer length when diastole was prolonged. Feigl (117) interpreted these results to indicate that no true change in extensibility had occurred but rather a change in the timing between beats and the onset of the aftercontraction. This would readily produce an apparent decrease in extensibility.

Further, Sonnenblick et al. (118) studied the effects of paired stimulation and other inotropic drugs on the resting length-tension relations of the cat papillary muscle and isovolumic dog ventricle. In freely isotonic or afterloaded muscles, or where developed force remained constant, these inotropic interventions did not alter diastolic compliance as long as time for complete relaxation was allowed. However, under isometric conditions, paired stimulation did induce a small fall in diastolic tension but only while systolic force rose. Similar decrements in diastolic tension were observed when force of contraction was augmented simply by increasing afterload alone.

It was thus concluded that inotropic interventions do not alter the resting length-tension relations (compliance or extensibility) per se. However, resting length does increase slightly upon augmentation of systolic force alone. From these findings it was postulated that a series viscous component may exist in heart muscle. Together with Feigl's (117) observations on aftercontractions which are only observed at lower than physiological temperatures or very high calcium levels, a series viscous component explains the observations of Hoffman et al. (116). Evidence for a persistent active state during normal or physiological diastole has yet to be adduced.

Recently Grimm & Whitehorn (119) have sought to localize the site of resting tension in heart muscle. Extensibility of the rat papillary muscle has been studied before and after treatment with proteolytic enzymes and various solutions to extract proteins. They found that proteolytic enzymes reduced both resting and active tension while extraction of myosin with salt solutions of moderate ionic strength did not alter extensibility. However, extraction of actomyosin by salt solutions of high ionic strength greatly increased extensibility, which implied that a significant portion of the resting elasticity of the heart must reside in intracellular elements and not just within collagen fibers and superficial membranes such as sarcolemma. These views warrant further study. The study of muscle extensibility in the presence of hypertonic solutions which disrupt the mechanical connections of cells across the intercalated disc might shed further light on this question.

Brecher et al. (120) have further emphasized the presence of elastic forces which help to restore initial volume of the ventricle and thus may facilitate filling of the ventricle following contraction. Of interest in this regard is the demonstration in skeletal muscle fibers from the chick embryo of intrafibrillar restoring forces during relaxation which help to elongate the sarcomeres (121). The exact nature of these forces awaits definition but in the heart where time for ventricular filling is limited they may have important physiological implications.

Active work has continued in the application of the principles of muscle mechanics derived from isolated muscle preparations to the analysis of function in the intact heart (122–127). Taylor et al. (124) have utilized force (tension)-velocity relations to evaluate myocardial function in the left ventricle of sedated dogs with closed chests. Instantaneous contractile element velocity (V_{ce}) was calculated from left ventricular pressure and its first derivative, during a single isovolumic left ventricular contraction produced by sudden balloon occlusion of the ascending aorta during diastole. Wall tension (T) was derived from ventricular volume and wall thickness. During isovolumic contractions, an inverse relation between V_{ce} and T existed except during the first 40 msec of systole and near peak tension. Increasing diastolic volume (preload) shifted the tension-velocity to the right with an increase in isovolumic tension, but without a change in the maximum velocity of shortening (V_{max}). Glycosides increased both V_{max} and isovolumic tension. These findings are entirely analogous to those obtained in isolated muscle preparations.

Covell et al. (125) have determined tension-velocity relations in the left ventricle of the intact dog by the same method and compared the results with the classical ventricular function curve: the tension-velocity curve was more sensitive in detecting small changes in contractile state. These methods have also been useful in demonstrating the positive inotropic influence of increasing heart rate (126), and provide a sensitive method by which contractility of the heart may be evaluated without disruption of the circulation.

Levine (123) has reviewed this work on the muscle mechanics in the intact heart of the dog and further applied these principles to the intact human heart with examples of their potential usefulness in evaluating the failing myocardium. Further, Forwand et al. (127) have determined the modulus of elasticity of the SE in the intact heart, albeit by indirect methods, and have shown that is not greatly different from that obtained from isolated cardiac muscle preparations. However, it should be emphasized that the application of such a modulus to the derivation of CE activity requires relatively synchronous ventricular contractions.

Myocardial mechanics have been useful in evaluating ventricular function in acute (128) and chronic (123, 129, 130) heart failure; all of these studies of myocardial depression have demonstrated a depression of the intrinsic CE velocity (V_{max}), within the failing myocardium. These observations are consistent with the findings of Spann et al. (131) who studied the contractile state of papillary muscles from cat right ventricles which were either hypertrophied or failing, secondary to pulmonary artery constriction, and observed that the maximum velocity of shortening (V_{max}), active length-tension curves, and maximum rate of tension development were all depressed.

Taylor et al. (132) demonstrated that ventricular contractile state is usually normal in the dog with a large aortocaval fistula despite the presence of circulatory congestion, elevated ventricular filling pressures, and fluid retention, all of which were attributed to the large hemodynamic flow load. It is thus apparent that the contractile state of the left ventricle can and must be evaluated apart from the impact of the peripheral circulation. The application of muscle mechanics to this analysis permits such an evaluation.

The effects of alterations of aortic pressure on the mechanics of ventricular contraction have received further study. Monroe et al. (133), utilizing an isolated dog heart where pressure and volume could be monitored continuously, observed that a sudden increase in impedance to ventricular emptying was attended by a positive inotropic effect, previously termed homeometric autoregulation. Part but not all of this effect could be attributed to a local pressure-dependent release of catecholamines (134) since beta-adrenergic (133) blockade attenuated, but did not abolish, the response. Clancy et al. (135) have assessed the mechanics of left ventricular contraction following aortic pressure induced homeometric autoregulation, defined by a fall in left ventricular end-diastolic pressure following a sudden increase in aortic pressure. The relative contributions of a change in initial fiber length and an altered contractility were measured from force-velocity relations. It was concluded that the increase in left ventricular performance during the steady state following pressure-induced homeometric autoregulation is associated with a very small augmentation of left ventricular contractility. The major effects observed resulted from an increase in ventricular fiber length accompanied by viscous changes which yield a decrease in ventricular filling pressure below that anticipated from the increase in volume.

Central to the application of muscle mechanics to the intact heart is the accurate measurement of ventricular volumes, shape, and wall thickness, both at rest and during the course of systole. Using measurements of external length and two cross-sectional areas of the dog left ventricle, Sanmarco and associates (136–139) obtained an estimate of diastolic ventricular volume which could be correlated with left ventricular volumes obtained by biplane or single-plane angiocardiography. In agreement with others, calculated end systolic volumes were smaller than measured, and end systolic volumes were generally obtained by subtracting the stroke volume from the end diastolic volume. Support was gained for the view that the ventricle is a thick-walled ellipse with a length to diameter ratio of 2:1 to 3:1 and a ratio of wall thickness to internal radius of 0.5 to 1.75. These latter findings are of importance in formulating equations for force distribution within the ventricular wall. Present formulations provide only gross approximations.

Urschel et al. (140) studied the effects of experimental aortic and mitral regurgitation on myocardial performance in the dog ventricle and showed how the lowered impedance to ventricular emptying in both circumstances leads to more rapid emptying of the heart. This unloading due to decreased impedance, and hence increased speed and extent of muscle shortening, helps to compensate for the increase load and illustrates the primary importance of impedance to ventricular performance despite unchanged myocardial contractility.

The effects on left ventricular performance of experimentally decreased aortic compliance, which serves to increase impedance during ejection, have been studied in the dog (141). The results serve to emphasize the view that with a given state of contractility as expressed by tension-velocity relations and fiber length, the instantaneous fiber shortening, and hence ventricular performance, depends on the instantaneous impedance to ventricular ejection. The importance of the impedance matching of the periphery to central ventricular function has thus been emphasized.

CARDIAC ENERGETICS

Recent studies have helped to relate the energy utilization of heart muscle to the mechanics of contraction. Three general methods have been employed including the measurement of oxygen consumption, the determination of high energy phosphate utilization following blockade of net synthesis, and the measurement of heat production. In general, these different methods have provided similar conclusions and have substantiated the recent viewpoint that the energy utilization of the myocardium is determined in a complex manner and is not simply dependent on tension development alone.

Graham et al. (142) have studied the relative influence on myocardial oxygen consumption (MV_{O_2}) of tension development and the contractile or inotropic state as reflected in V_{max}, the maximum velocity of shortening of unloaded contractile elements. The isovolumically contracting ventricle was studied under conditions where wall tension and V_{max} could be varied separately. MV_{O_2} was shown to be increased by increases in both developed tension and V_{max}. Support was found for the view that the oxygen cost of augmentation of contractility is substantial, can be independent of changes in fiber shortening, and is similar in order of magnitude to the effect of alterations in tension development.

MV_{O_2} has also been studied in the dog during drug-induced cardiac depression (143). Changes in the tension-time index, contractile-element work, or contractile-element power did not correlate invariably with changes in MV_{O_2} while reductions in contractile element velocity at similar tension development and left ventricular rate of pressure development were always associated with reductions in MV_{O_2}. The observations that negative inotropic influences are associated with a reduction in myocardial energy utilization, when considered in light of the earlier observations showing that positive inotropic influences induce an augmentation of MV_{O_2}, provide evidence that the inotropic state and its mechanical correlates are coupled with myocardial energy utilization by a mechanism independent of tension development (162).

Extension of these findings has helped to resolve the dispute concerning the effects of digitalis on MV_{O_2} (143). In the nonfailing canine right-bypass preparation in which the major hemodynamic variables were controlled, acetylstrophanthidin always increased MV_{O_2} while calculated cardiac efficiency fell. This occurred despite the fact that the tension-time index fell somewhat although the contractile state rose considerably. In contrast, in the failing heart MV_{O_2} did not rise. However, in these experiments a large fall in ventricular volume, and hence wall tension, occurred. It was thus concluded that digitalis glycosides tend to increase MV_{O_2} as a result of their positive inotropic action; however, this positive inotropic effect frequently results in a fall in wall tension which tends to oppose and possibly mask this former effect. In support of this view is the study of Coleman (145) in which the effects of acetylstrophanthidin on the oxygen consumption of the isolated cat papillary muscle were determined. Acetylstrophanthidin shifted the force-velocity relation to the right with increments in MV_{O_2} associated with these increments in contractility, despite constant tension development.

Two approaches to the study of energetics in skeletal muscle have now been applied to cardiac muscle: the measurement of the utilization of high energy phosphates (146–148) and the determination of heat production (149–151) in relation to contraction.

The utilization of creatine phosphate (CP) and adenosine triphosphate (ATP) relative to mechanical activity has been studied in the cat papillary muscle following blockade of their net production with nitrogen and iodoacetate (146–148). The net utilization of ATP, reflected in a fall in CP concentration, was shown to be a function of initial tension in the resting muscle. In the isometrically contracting muscle, net utilization of high energy phosphates was proportional to the number of activations and the summated tension development with a mechanochemical coupling efficiency of 33 per cent (146). Under afterloaded isotonic conditions, an additional amount of energy was utilized in association with external work performed, over and above that related to the development of tension (147). With the same methods it has also been possible to define the effects of norepinephrine on the utilization of high energy phosphates (148). Norepinephrine did not alter the initial energy stores or the basal rate of energy utilization. However, norepinephrine-treated muscles used greater amounts of high energy phosphates for the same tension development. Thus the increase in contractility induced by norepinephrine results in an increase in the chemical energy utilized that is disproportionate to the work performed.

Gibbs, Mommaerts & Ricchiuti (149) have designed a thermopile for measuring heat production by the cat papillary muscle in relation to mechanical activity. The agreement between these myothermic measurements and those obtained from the measurement of high energy phosphate utilization (146–148) is excellent. A fast phase of heat production, associated with contractile events, was followed by slower phase. Resting heat production was increased when resting tension and muscle length were augmented (149). In the isometric contraction, heat produced was directly related to actively developed tension, while in the isotonic contraction, more heat was liberated than that related to tension development alone. This extra heat production (149) or, alternatively, energy utilization (147) was load dependent, and corresponds to the previously described Fenn effect of skeletal muscle. These results, showing that the total energy utilization is determined by both the tension developed and the external work, help to explain why the relation between oxygen consumption in the afterloaded isotonic papillary muscle is curvilinear with a maximum at a load which is only about 50 per cent of the maximum tension developed (152).

Gibbs (150, 151) has also studied the effects of epinephrine on the heat production of the rabbit papillary muscle. Epinephrine increased the resting heat production and augmented the heat production at any tension development. This effect was attributed to an increase in the magnitude of the tension-independent heat obtained by shortening initial length. This heat, which is measured at that muscle length where developed tension is minimal, has been termed an "activation" heat. However, such measurements do not exclude the energy utilized in overcoming internal restoring forces at short muscle lengths and thus may not be truly tension independent. Increasing calcium did not alter the relation between total active heat production and developed tension.

Thus multiple techniques support the view that several factors contribute to the determination of energy utilization and thus oxygen consumption in heart muscle. While a small contribution to the MV_{O_2} comes from external work, the major determinants of MV_{O_2} are the product of tension development and heart rate, and the contractile state of the myocardium.

Myocardial Failure

The basis of myocardial failure has received further study utilizing more recently available methods. Spann et al. (131) studied the mechanical properties of the right ventricular papillary muscles from cats with right ventricular hypertrophy and failure secondary to pulmonary artery banding. Both maximum velocity of muscle shortening (V_{max}) and maximum force of contraction were depressed in the presence of hypertrophy as well as failure. A similar depression of muscle contractility has been observed in the hypertrophied soleus muscle of the rat (153).

In line with R. Olson's original suggestions, energy production, storage, and utilization in myocardial failure have been further studied. Mitochondrial function as characterized by P:O ratios and respiratory control has now been shown to be normal in the dog with chronic hypertrophy (154) and the cat with right ventricular hypertrophy and failure (155). Although mitochondria are increased in number, their structure is unaltered (154). The stores of high energy phosphates have also been determined. Stores of ATP were normal in both ventricular muscle and papillary muscles from cats with right ventricular hypertrophy and failure (156). Stores of creatine phosphate (CP) were somewhat depressed but were readily restored to normal *in vitro* (156). Similarly CP and ATP were not depressed in hearts from dogs with heart failure induced by hyperthyroidism (157). It has thus been concluded that the depressed contractility observed in heart failure is not due to reductions in energy stores. However, *in vivo* depressions in CP stores may be secondary to an unbalance between energy production and utilization in the overloaded, hypertrophied, and failing heart (156).

Previous studies have suggested a depression of myofibrillar ATPase activity in the presence of myocardial failure. These findings have now been confirmed and extended to largely exclude the ATPase of mitochondrial contaminants (158). Further, the degree of myofibrillar depression was correlated with the extent of depression of the myocardial contractility expressed as the maximum rate of force development (158). This finding is of interest in view of the correlation of the ATPase activity of myosin from several different striated muscles with speed of muscle shortening (159). The basis of the depression of myofibrillar ATPase activity in the presence of myocardial failure is not known.

While previous studies have shown that cardiac norepinephrine stores are in general markedly reduced in congestive heart failure, the mechanism responsible for this depletion is poorly understood. In experimental congestive heart failure, Pool et al. (160) have demonstrated a reduction in the activity of cardiac tyrosine hydroxylase, the rate-limiting enzyme in the biosynthesis of norepinephrine. Despite the reduction of norepinephrine stores and a reduction in the cardiac response to postganglionic sympathetic nerve stimulation in experimental heart failure (161), the depression of contractile activity is not the result of the norepinephrine depletion per se. Thus, the intrinsic contractile state of heart muscle is not altered by the depletion of norepinephrine stores from normal heart muscle, either by cardiac denervation or with reserpine administration (162). Further, normal cardiac function is remarkably well preserved in dogs whose sympathetic responses have been eliminated either by sympathetic neural denervation or beta-adrenergic blockade (163, 164).

LITERATURE CITED

1. Briller, S. A., Conn, H. L., Eds. *The Myocardial Cell: Structures, Function and Modification* (Univ. Pennsylvania Press, Philadelphia, 374 pp., 1966)
2. Tanz, R. D., Kavaler, F., Roberts, J., Eds. *Factors Influencing Myocardial Contractility* (Academic Press, New York, 693 pp., 1967)
3. *The Contractile Process.* Proc. New York Heart Assoc. Symp. (Little, Brown, Boston, 299 pp., 1967)
4. Reeve, E. B., Guyton, A. C., Eds. *Physical Bases of Circulatory Transport: Regulation and Exchange* (Saunders Co., Philadelphia, 381 pp., 1967)
5. Marchetti, G., Taccardi, B., Eds. *Coronary Circulation and Energetics of the Myocardium* (Karger, New York, 320 pp., 1967)
6. Reader, R., Ed. *Catecholamines in Cardiovascular Physiology and Disease* (*Circ. Res. Suppl. 111*, XXI, 247 pp., 1967)
7. Moran, N. C., Ed. *New Adrenergic Blocking Drugs: Their Pharmacological, Biochemical and Clinical Actions* (Ann. N.Y. Acad. Sci., 1967)
8. Sano, T., Mizuhira, V., Matsuda, K., Eds. *Electrophysiology and Ultrastructure of the Heart* (Bunkodo Co. Ltd., Tokyo, 267 pp., 1967)
9. Thorp, R. H., Cobbin, L. B. *Cardiac Stimulant Substances* (Academic Press, New York, 288 pp., 1967)
10. Braunwald, E., Ross, J., Jr., Sonnenblick, E. H., *Mechanisms of Contraction of the Normal and Failing Heart* (Little, Brown, Boston, 205 pp., 1968)
11. Marshall, R. J., Shepherd, J. T., *Cardiac Function in Health and Disease* (Saunders, Philadelphia, 409 pp., 1968)
12. Berne, R. M., Levy, M. N. *Cardiovascular Physiology* (Mosby Co., St. Louis, 243 pp., 1967)
13. Jewell, B., Blinks, J. *Ann. Rev. Pharmacol.*, **8**, 113–30 (1968)
14. Mason, D. T., Braunwald, E. Mechanisms of action and therapeutic uses of cardiac drugs. *Modern Trends in Pharmacology and Therapeutics*, 112–66 (Fulton, W. F. M., Ed., Butterworths, London, 1967)
15. Streeter, D. D., Jr., Bassett, D. L. *Anat. Record*, **155**, 503 1966)
16. James, T. N. *Circ. Res.*, **20**, 638–48 (1967)

17. James, T. N., Sherf, L. *Circulation*, **37**, 1049–70 (1968)
18. Maekawa, M., Nohara, Y., Kawamura, K., Hayashi, K. *Circulation*, **8**, 41–54 (1968)
19. Sommer, J. R., Johnson, E. A. *J. Cell Biol.*, **36**, 497–526 (1968)
20. Sommer, J. R., Johnson, E. A. *Ibid.*, **37**, 570–74
21. Peachey, L. D. *Ann. Rev. Physiol.*, **30**, 401–40 (1968)
22. Rayns, D. G., Simpson, F. O., Bertaud, W. S. *Science*, **156**, 656–57 (1967)
23. Forssmann, W. G., Girardier, L. *Z. Zellforsch.*, **72**, 249–75 (1966)
24. Girardier, L., Dreifuss, J. J., Forssmann, W. G. *Acta Anat.*, **68**, 251–57 (1967)
25. Girardier, L., Forssmann, W. G. (Personal communication)
26. Page, E. *J. Gen. Physiol.*, **51**, 211S–220S (1968)
27. Müller, P. *Helv. Physiol. Acta*, **24**, C106 (1966)
28. Page, E. *J. Ultrastruct. Res.*, **17**, 72–83 (1967)
29. Peachey, L. D. *J. Cell Biol.*, **25**, 209–31 (1965)
30. Heumann, H. G., Zebe, E. *Z. Zellforsch. Mikroskop. Anat.*, **78**, 131–50 (1967)
31. Philpott, C. W., Goldstein, M. A. *Science*, **155**, 1019 (1967)
32. Legato, M. J., Spiro, D., Langer, G. A. *J. Cell Biol.*, **37**, 1–12 (1968)
33. Sandow, A. *Pharm. Rev.*, **17**, 265–320 (1965)
34. Krames, B., Page, E. *Biochim. Biophys. Acta*, **150**, 24 (1968)
35. Muir, A. R. *J. Anat. (London)*, **101**, 239–61 (1967)
36. Kawamura, K., Konishi, T. *Japan. Circ. J.*, **31**, 1533–43 (1967)
37. Berger, W., Dewey, M., Barr, L. *Proc. Intern. Union Physiol. Sci.*, **7**, 38 (1968)
38. Revel, J. P., Karnovsky, M. J. *J. Cell Biol.*, **33**, C7–C12 (1967)
39. Grimm, A. F., Whitehorn, W. V. *Am. J. Physiol.*, **214**, 1378–87 (1968)
40. Spotnitz, H. M., Sonnenblick, E. H., Spiro, D. *Circ. Res.*, **18**, 49–66 (1966)
41. Ross, J., Jr., Sonnenblick, E. H., Covell, J. W., Kaiser, G. A., Spiro, D. *Circ. Res.*, **21**, 409–21 (1967)
42. Sonnenblick, E. H., Ross, J., Jr., Covell, J. W., Spotnitz, H. M., Spiro, D. *Circ. Res.*, **21**, 423–31 (1967)

43. Gay, W. A., Jr., Johnson, E. A. *Circ. Res.*, **21**, 33–43 (1967)
44. Dudel, J., Peper, K., Rüdel, R., Trautwein, W. *Pflügers Arch.*, **295**, 213–26 (1967)
45. Coraboeuf, E., Vassort, G. *J. Electrocardiol.*, **1**, 19–30 (1968)
46. Niedergerke, R., Orkand, R. *J. Physiol.* (*London*), **184**, 291–311 (1966)
47. Reuter, H. *Proc. Intern. Union Physiol. Sci.*, **7**, 364 (1968)
48. Sleator, W. W., de Gubareff, T. *Proc. Intern. Union Physiol. Sci.*, **7**, 404 (1968)
49. Weidmann, S. *J. Physiol.* (*London*), **115**, 227–36 (1951)
50. Brady, A., Woodbury, J. *J. Physiol.* (*London*), **154**, 385–407 1960)
51. Coraboeuf, E., Zacouta, F., Gargouil, Y., Laplaud, J. *Compt. Rend. Acad. Sci.*, **246**, 2934–37 (1958)
52. Noble, D. *Nature*, **188**, 495–97 (1960)
53. Peck, K. A., Trautwein, W. *Pflügers Arch.*, **280**, 63–80 (1964)
54. Noble, D., Tsien, R. *J. Physiol.* (*London*), **195**, 185–214 (1968)
55. Reuter, H., Scholz, H. *Pflügers Arch.*, **300**, 87–107 (1968)
56. Dudel, J., Peper, K., Rüdel, R., Trautwein, W. *Pflügers Arch.*, **292**, 255–73 (1966)
57. Dudel, J., Peper, K., Rüdel, R., Trautwein, W. *Ibid.*, **296**, 308–327 (1967)
58. Dudel, J., Peper, K., Rüdel, R., Trautwein, W. *Ibid.*, **295**, 213–26 (1967)
59. Irisawa, H., Shigeto, M., Otani, M. *Comp. Biochem. Psychol.*, **23**, 199–212 (1967)
60. Langer, G. A. *J. Gen. Physiol.*, **50**, 1221–39 (1967)
61. Weber, A. M. *Current Topics Bioenerg.*, **1**, 203–54 (1966)
62. Langer, G. A., Serena, S. D. *Am. J. Physiol.*, **213**, 1125–30 (1967)
63. Shelburne, J. C., Serena, S. D., Langer, G. A. *Am. J. Physiol.*, **213**, 1115–24 (1967)
64. Nayler, W. G. *Circ. Res.*, **20 & 21**, *Suppl. III*, 213–21 (1967)
65. Schwartz, A., Laseter, A. H. *Biochem. Pharmacol.*, **13**, 337–48 (1964)
66. Wollenberger, A., Schulze, W. *Naturwissenschaften*, **53**, 134 (1966)
67. Stam, A. C., Jr., Sonnenblick, E. H. *Proc. Intern. Union Physiol. Sci.*, **6**, 239–40 (1968)
68. Matsui, H., Schwartz, A. *Biochim. Biophys. Acta*, **128**, 380–90 (1966)
69. Matsui, H., Schwartz, A. *Ibid.*, **151**, 655–63 (1968)
70. Lahrtz, H. G., Lüllmann, H., Van Zwieten, P. A. *Biochim. Biophys. Acta*, **135/4**, 701–9 (1967)
71. Vincenzi, F. F., Schatzmann, H. J. *Helv. Physiol. Pharmacol. Acta*, **25**, CR233–CR234 (1967)
72. Lee, K. S. In *Factors Influencing Myocardial Contractility* (See Ref. 2), 519–31
73. Morad, M., Trautwein, W., *Pflügers Arch.*, **299**, 66–82 (1968)
74. Orkand, R. K. *J. Physiol.* (*London*), 196, 311–25 (1968)
75. Langer, G. A. In *Factors Influencing Myocardial Contractility* (See Ref. 2), 351–61
76. Grundfest, H. *Am. Zool.*, **7**, 623 (1967)
77. Weber, A. M., Herz, R., Reiss, I. *J. Gen. Physiol.*, **46**, 679–702 (1963)
78. Otsuka, M., Ebashi, S., Shoichi, I. *J. Biochem.* (*Japan*), **55**, 192 (1964)
79. Fanburg, B., Finkel, R. M., Martonosi, A. *J. Biol. Chem.*, **239**, 2298–2306 (1964)
80. Katz, A. M., Repke, D. I., Cohen, B. R. *Circ. Res.*, **19**, 1062–70 (1966)
81. Ebashi, S. *Proc. Intern. Union Physiol. Sci.*, **6**, 17–18 (1968)
82. Ebashi, S. *Progr. Biophys.*, **18**, 123 (1968)
83. Stam, A. C., Jr., Honig, C. R. *Am. J. Physiol.*, **209**, 8–16 (1965)
84. Weber, A., Herz, R., Reiss, I. *Biochem. Biophys. Acta*, **131**, 188–94 (1967)
85. Honig, C. R. In *Factors Influencing Myocardial Contractility* (See Ref. 2), 373–83
86. Honig, C. R. *Am. J. Physiol.*, **214**, 357–64 (1968)
87. Katz, A. M. *Am. J. Physiol.*, **212**, 39–42 (1967)
88. Weber, A. M., Herz, R., Reiss, I. *J. Gen. Physiol.*, **46**, 679–702 (1963)
89. Otsuka, M., Ebashi, S., Imai, I. *J. Biochem.* (*Japan*), **55**, 196 (1964)
90. Fanburg, B., Finkel, R., Martonosi, A. *J. Biol. Chem.*, **239**, 2298–2306 (1964)
91. Katz, A. M., Repke, D. I. *Circ. Res.*, **21**, 153–62 (1967)
92. Fairhurst, A. A., Palus, D. A., Jenden, D. J. *Circ. Res.*, **21**, 433–38 (1967)
93. Stam, A. C., Jr., Sonnenblick, E. H. (Submitted for publication)
94. Stam, A. C., Jr., Sonnenblick, E. H. (Submitted for publication)
95. Carsten, M. E. *Circ. Res.*, **20**, 599–605 (1967)
96. Katz, A. M., Repke, D. *Circ. Res.*, **21**, 767–75 (1967)

97. Palmer, R. F., Posey, V. A. *J. Gen. Physiol.*, **50**, 2085–95 (1967)

98. Stowring, L., Bowen, W. J., Mattingly, P., Morales, M. *Circ. Res.*, **19**, 496–506 (1966)

99. Jacobson, A. L. *Circ. Res.*, **22**, 625–32 (1968)

100. Katz, A. M. *J. Pharmacol. Exptl. Therap.*, **154**, 558–65 (1966)

101. Lee, K. S., Choi, S. J., *J. Pharmacol. Exptl. Therap.*, **154**, 114–20 (1966)

102. Gertz, E. W., Hess, M. L., Lain, R. F., Briggs, F. N. *Circ. Res.*, **20**, 477–84 (1967)

103. Gabel, L. P., Bihler, I., Dresel, P. E. *Circ. Res.*, **21**, 263–69 (1967)

104. Morad, M., Kavaler, F. *Circ. Res.*, **18**, 492–501 (1966)

105. Reuter, H. *Inward Currents in Myocardial Fibers and Activation of Contraction* (Presented Gordon Res. Conf. Cellular Control of Cardiac Contraction, Holderness, N. H., Aug. 12–16, 1968)

106. Sonnenblick, E. H. *Fed. Proc.*, **24**, 1396–1409 (1965)

107. Brady, A. J. *Fed. Proc.*, **24**, 1410–20 (1965)

108. Edman, K. A. P., Grieve, D. W., Nilsson, E. *Pflügers Arch.*, **290**, 320 (1966)

109. Brady, A. J. *J. Physiol. (London)*, **184**, 560–80 (1966)

110. Sonnenblick, E. H. *J. Gen. Physiol.*, **50**, 661–76 (1967)

111. Edman, K. A. P., Nilsson, E. *Acta Physiol. Scand.*, **72**, 205–19 (1968)

112. Parmley, W. W., Sonnenblick, E. H. *Circ. Res.*, **20**, 112–23 (1967)

113. Brady, A. J. *Physiologist*, **10**, 75–86 (1967)

114. Sonnenblick, E. H. *Am. J. Physiol.*, **207**, 1330–38 (1964)

115. Hefner, L. L., Bowen, T. E., Jr. *Am. J. Physiol.*, **212**, 1221–27 (1967)

116. Hoffman, B. F., Bartelstone, H. J., Bassett, A. L. In *Factors Influencing Myocardial Contractility* (See Ref. 2), 17–36

117. Feigl, E. O. *Circ. Res.*, **20**, 447–58 (1967)

118. Sonnenblick, E. H., Ross, J., Jr., Covell, J. W., Braunwald, E. *Circ. Res.*, **19**, 980–88 (1966)

119. Grimm, A. F., Whitehorn, W. V. *Am. J. Physiol.*, **210**, 1362–67 (1966)

120. Brecher, G. A., Kolder, H., Horres, A. D. *Circ. Res.*, **19**, 1080–87 (1966)

121. Parsons, C., Porter, K. R. *Science*, **153**, 426–27 (1966)

122. Ross, J., Jr., Covell, J. W., Sonnenblick, E. H., Braunwald, E. *Circ. Res.*, **18**, 149–63 (1966)

123. Levine, H. J. In *Factors Influencing Myocardial Contractility* (See Ref. 2), 93–112

124. Taylor, R. R., Ross, J., Jr., Covell, J. W., Sonnenblick, E. H. *Circ. Res.*, **21**, 99–115 (1967)

125. Covell, J. W., Ross, J., Jr., Sonnenblick, E. H., Braunwald, E. *Circ. Res.*, **19**, 364–72 (1966)

126. Covell, J. W., Ross, J., Jr., Taylor, R., Sonnenblick, E. H., Braunwald, E. *Cardiovasc. Res.*, **1**, 2–8 (1967)

127. Forwand, S. A., McIntyre, K. M., Lipana, J. G., Levine, H. J. *Circ. Res.*, **19**, 970–79 (1966)

128. Ross, J., Jr., Covell, J. W., Sonnenblick, E. H. *J. Clin. Invest.*, **46**, 299–312 (1967)

129. Gault, J. H., Ross, J., Jr., Sonnenblick, E. H., Braunwald, E. *Circulation*, **34** (*Suppl. 111*), 108 (1966)

130. Gault, J. H., Ross, J., Jr., Braunwald, E. *Circ. Res.*, **22**, 451–63 (1968)

131. Spann, J. F., Jr., Buccino, R. A., Sonnenblick, E. H., Braunwald, E. *Circ. Res.*, **21**, 341–54 (1967)

132. Taylor, R. R., Covell, J. W., Ross, J., Jr. *J. Clin. Invest.*, **47**, 1333–42 (1968)

133. Monroe, R. G., La Farge, C. G., Gamble, W. J., Rosenthal, A., Honda, S. *Circ. Res.*, **22**, 333–44 (1968)

134. Monroe, R. G., La Farge, C. G., Gamble, W. J., Hammond, R. P., Morgan, C. L. *Circ. Res.*, **19**, 774–90 (1966)

135. Clancy, R. L., Graham, T. P., Jr., Ross, J., Jr., Sonnenblick, E. H., Braunwald, E. *Am. J. Physiol.*, **214**, 1186–92 (1968)

136. Sanmarco, M. E., Fronek, K., Philips, C. M., Davila, J. C. *Am. J. Cardiol.*, **18**, 584–93 (1966)

137. Sanmarco, M. E., Bartle, S. H. *Circ. Res.*, **19**, 11–17 (1966)

138. Bartle, S. H., Sanmarco, M. E. *Ibid.*, 295–306

139. Sanmarco, M. E., Davila, J. C. In *Factors Influencing Myocardial Contractility* (See Ref. 2), 199–214

140. Urschel, C. W., Covell, J. W., Sonnenblick, E. H., Ross, J., Jr., Braunwald, E. *J. Clin. Invest.*, **47**, 867–83 (1968)

141. Urschel, C. W., Covell, J. W., Sonnenblick, E. H., Ross, J., Jr., Braunwald, E. *Am. J. Physiol.*, **214**, 298–304 (1968)

142. Graham, T. P., Jr., Covell, J. W.,

Sonnenblick, E. H., Ross, J., Jr., Braunwald, E. *J. Clin. Invest.*, **47**, 375–85 (1968)

143. Graham, T. P., Jr., Ross, J., Jr., Covell, J. W., Sonnenblick, E. H., Clancy, R. L. *Circ. Res.*, **21**, 123–38 (1967)

144. Covell, J. W., Braunwald, E., Ross, J., Jr., Sonnenblick, E. H. *J. Clin. Invest.*, **45**, 1535–42 (1966)

145. Coleman, H. N. *Circ. Res.*, **21**, 487–95 (1967)

146. Pool. P. E., Sonnenblick, E. H. *J. Gen. Physiol.*, **50/4**, 951–65 (1967)

147. Pool, P. E., Chandler, B. M., Seagren, S. C., Sonnenblick, E. H. *Circ. Res.*, **22**, 465–72 (1968)

148. Chandler, B M. Sonnenblick, E. H., Pool, P. E. *Circ. Res.*, **22**, 729–35 (1968)

149. Gibbs, C. L., Mommaerts, W. F. H. M Ricchiuti, N. V. *J. Physiol. (London)*, **191/1**, 25–46 (1967)

150. Gibbs, C. L. *Australian J. Exptl. Biol. Med. Sci.*, **45/4**, 379–92 (1967)

151. Gibbs, C. L. *Circ. Res.*, **21** (*Suppl. III*), 223–30 (1967)

152. Coleman, H. N. *Am. J. Physiol.*, **214**, 100–6 (1968)

153. Lesch, M., Parmley, W. W., Hamosh. M., Kaufman, S., Sonnenblick, E. H. *Am. J. Physiol.*, **214**, 685–90 (1968)

154. Wollenberger, A., Kleitke, B., Schulze, W. *Acta Biol. Med. Germ.*, **17/3**, 334–42 (1966)

155. Sobel, B. E., Spann, J. F., Jr., Pool, P. E., Sonnenblick, E. H., Braunwald, E. *Circ. Res.*, **21/3**, 355–63 (1967)

156. Pool, P. E., Spann, J. F., Jr., Buccino, R. A., Sonnenblick, E. H., Braunwald, E. *Circ. Res.*, **21**, 365–73 (1967)

157. Piatnek-Leunissen, D., Olson, R. E. *Circ. Res.*, **20**, 242–52 (1967)

158. Chandler, B. M., Sonnenblick, E. H., Spann, J. F., Jr., Pool, P. E. *Circ. Res.*, **21**, 717–25 (1967)

159. Bárány, M. *J. Gen. Physiol.*, **50/6**, 197–218 (1967)

160. Pool, P. E., Covell, J. W., Levitt, M., Gibb, J, Braunwald, E. *Circ. Res.*, **20**, 349–53 (1967)

161. Covell, J. W., Chidsey, C. A., Braunwald, E. *Circ. Res.*, **19**, 51–56 (1966)

162. Spann, J. F., Jr., Sonnenblick, E. H., Cooper, T., Chidsey, C. A., Willman, V. L., Braunwald, E. *Circ. Res.*, **19**, 317–25 (1966)

163. Donald, D. E., Ferguson, D. A., Milburn, S. E. *Circ. Res.*, **22**, 127–34 (1968)

164. Stone, H. L., Bishop, V. S., Dong, E., Jr. *Circ. Res.*, **20**, 587–93 (1967)

165. Embry, R., Briggs, A. H. *Am. J. Physiol.*, **210/4**, 826–30 (1966)

CHRONOBIOLOGY[1,2]

By Franz Halberg

Periodicity Analysis Laboratories, Department of Pathology
University of Minnesota, Minneapolis

Introduction

The study of physiologic rhythms, overlapping a number of traditional disciplines in biology and medicine, depends also on progress in engineering— benefitting, as it does, from modern technology for the sensing and tele-metering of body functions and from advances in electronic computer science. Computers already process data much more efficiently and quickly than was heretofore possible; their contribution to the study of biologic rhythms, however, is yet more important. Precisely because of their high speed and efficiency, they enable us not only to do the "old" kinds of tasks better, but also to resolve new dimensions, e.g., to detect rhythms that could not possibly have been uncovered otherwise by all too laborious hand computations (1). By virtue of this fact, the electronic computer yields for the student of biologic time structure what the microscope or the electron microscope resolves for the student of spatial structure (2).

One purpose of this review will be to illustrate developments in the display of objective quantitative estimates of rhythm parameters in terms of their level, amplitude and various phase relations at each of several frequencies. This is done with a view toward the future of a field which may become a domain of quantitative biology, even though the major part of work thus far, including that published during the last few years, has been done primarily by naturalists who relied on the visual inspection of data. Endpoints from quantitative rhythmometry here reviewed will bear upon healthy human beings and a few laboratory animals, notably nonhuman primates and rodents, included as illustrative examples for comparative physiologic purposes.

Problems relating to the phase shifting of rhythms, again with the principal focus upon primates, will be alluded to with special reference to long-distance, transmeridian travel.

Alterations of rhythms, notably as a function of drug administration or disease, will not be discussed, since they have been dealt with at a number of recent symposia (10–14). The information here reviewed represents the background for the as yet unanswered questions: 1. whether rhythm alteration might represent an early etiologically determinant stage in disease, or at least a sign of threatening, even if as yet not established, illness and, if so, 2. whether correction of rhythm alteration will prevent or alleviate

[1] The survey of literature for this review was concluded on September 1, 1968.

[2] Work supported by the United States Public Health Service (5-K6-GM-13,981) and by NASA (NGR 24-005-006 and NAS 2-2738).

certain diseases. Answers to these questions may eventually be provided by means of developments such as (a) sensors for nuisance-free collection of time series on biophysical, biochemical, and more broadly behavioral variables; (b) means for automatic data transfer to a medium and into a format directly amenable to analysis (e.g., on magnetic tape); and (c) means for a so-called microscopic evaluation of rhythms (e.g., by electronic computer programs). Such technical developments, prompted largely by plans for extraterrestrial research, embody a worthwhile bonus to life on this planet.

Some definitions will be necessary in order to introduce rhythms as an aspect of the broader field of chronobiology.

Most of the work based exclusively upon the viewing of data plotted as a function of time—in chronograms—and interpreted as representing a physiologically unqualified "clock", will not be evaluated here. The use of chronograms to evaluate the variability contributed by factors such as an unqualified time of day has been discussed elsewhere (3); it also remains beyond our scope herein.

For the aforementioned kinds of contributions, as well as for more rigorous approaches to rhythms, the interested reader can be referred to a number of symposia (4–16, 292), books (17–27), recent review articles (28–30, 286), a handbook on biologic data (31), and a bibliography on time series (32).

COMMENTS ON TERMS USED

Rhythms, synchronizers, and biorhythms.—Whether they are viewed "macroscopically" or "microscopically" (see below), rhythms can be defined as statistically validated physiologic changes recurring with a reproducible waveform. *Rhythm* in "macroscopic" terms denotes a reliably periodic aspect of data displayed as a function of time. A "microscopically" defined rhythm constitutes a periodic component of biologic time series with an objectively quantified (average) period, τ, and/or (average) acrophase (crest time) ϕ, and an (average) amplitude C demonstrated to be different from zero by inferential statistical means (1, 2; cf. Figure 1 and Tables 1–3).

Endpoint and confidence interval estimates for these rhythm parameters, and also for the level C_0, are obtained by the use of approximating functions [*inter alia*, by functions of the form: $f(t) = C_0 + C \cos(\omega t + \phi)$, where ω is the angular frequency and $t = $ time] as sketched in Figure 1.

Synchronizers, time-givers or entraining agents, clues or cues (4, 5, 17, 18, 21) are environmental factors determining the temporal placement of a given rhythm along an appropriate time scale (e.g., uniformly demarcated "local time" and, preferably, also the separately coded Greenwich Mean Time). The adjectives "primary" and "secondary" describe the relative roles played by different environmental synchronizers; in several strains of inbred mice, fed *ad libitum*, the lighting regimen is the primary synchronizer of the blood eosinophil rhythm; the lighting effect overrides any secondary effect of feeding time, under usual laboratory conditions. The adjectives "dominant" and "modifying" also can be used to describe the effect of a given environmental factor in relation to a given rhythm. Under unusual circumstances a secondary synchronizer may become dominant. Thus in

C$_3$H (Minnesota) mice subjected to a 50 per cent restriction in dietary calories, the feeding time may be dominant over the lighting regimen. Moreover, a rhythm can be influenced by secondary synchronizers and other modifying factors—modulators or, more generally, influencers.

A *biorhythm* is a rhythm which, if it be amenable to frequency synchronization and thus to phase-shifting by a known synchronizer, persists after elimination of the synchronizer effect. For a biorhythm the minimal number of persisting periods (which depends upon the system) and any damping noted during the persistence test also should be indicated, with the test conditions, such as blinding or constancy of light (or darkness), environmental temperature, *ad libitum* feeding. For instance, in our hands the cirdadian rhythm in intraperitoneal temperature telemetered at 10′ intervals from 6 blinded mature, inbred Minnesota Sprague-Dawley rats, kept singly housed with food freely available at 24 ± .5° C environmental temperature in light and darkness alternating at 12-hr intervals persisted with a 24.3 ± .03 hr period during an entire 116-day test span, with a circadian amplitude of .57 ± .03° C corresponding roughly to that of .61 ± .02° C in 5 concomitantly evaluated intact rats with a 24 ± .00 hr period.

Chronobiology and its subspecialties.—"Chronobiology" is the study of the temporal characteristics of biologic phenomena, leading to an objective description of biologic time structure.

Biologic time structure, in turn, can be defined as the sum total of nonrandom and thus predictable temporal aspects of organismic behavior—including bioperiodicity, developmental changes, and age trends. Biologic time structure characterizes individuals as well as groups of organisms or of their subdivisions: organ systems, organs, tissues, cells, and intracellular elements (including electronmicroscopic ultrastructure).

Chronobiology includes, among other "subspecialties":

1. "chronophysiology"—investigation of temporal features in physiologic behavior and of physiologic factors underlying biologic temporal characteristics;

2. "chronotoxicology"—investigation of undesired or harmful effects from chemical, physical, or other agents including poisons, pollutants, and overdoses of drugs upon biologic temporal characteristics and as a function of biologic timing;

3. "chronopathology"—investigation of alterations in biologic temporal characteristics as a function of disease and as determinants of disease;

4. "chronopharmacology"—investigation of drug effects upon biologic temporal characteristics and as a function of biologic timing.

Considerable information is available in fields 1. and 2. above (29, 30, 33); fields 3. and 4. are no longer utopian concepts but they will have to be amplified on the basis of further work.

All subspecialties of chronobiology usually involve the collection of observations, measurements, or counts recorded as a function of time, i.e., of time series. However, occasionally chronobiologic observations may describe an apparently unique phenomenon, rather than a recurring one; for example, birth (34, 35) or death (36, 37) in populations of humans or rodents (38).

Macroscopic versus microscopic approach (*2, 39*).—Chronobiology (also chronophysiology, chronopathology, etc.) can be considered to be "macroscopic" when it evaluates biologic temporal characteristics:

1. with time as the sole reference frame for the raw (or averaged) data;
2. by the procedures of classical biometry, such as analyses of variance, computations of correlation or of regressions (or of both) among others;
3. *without* the explicit endeavor not only to separate the biologic temporal characteristic under study (a "desired" signal, e.g., a rhythm) from the effect of other unidentified or unevaluated factors (biologic noise) but also, and in any event, to evaluate parameters by inferential statistical point and interval estimations.

Biologic noise for a student of rhythms is the sum total of variability stemming from unidentified or unevaluated sources and interfering with the signal to be evaluated, i.e., with one or several rhythms. Different kinds of errors in measurement, in counting or in other observations—errors that may be random, systematic or even "blundering"—are part of the noise term. In a given time series or time function transformed into a frequency spectrum, variance or energy corresponding to biologic noise is spread more or less uniformly through the entire spectral domain amenable to such a transformation. By contrast, variance accumulated in a more or less sharply defined spectral region, e.g., a narrow spectral band or line, may correspond to a rhythm.

The temporal characteristic studied in such macroscopic periodicity analysis is a bioperiodicity, which can be defined as a rhythm plus noise.

"Microscopic" chronobiology, on the other hand, evaluates biologic temporal components, preferably in edited data (174, 175):

1. after isolation from biologic noise;
2. on the basis of inferential-statistical summaries in terms of a prominent frequency f or period τ (i.e., reciprocal f), Table I, and/or phase, ϕ, Table II, of some appropriate approximating function, as indicated in Figure 1 (40), as well as with further assessment of waveform, where indicated and practical (62, 63, 336);
3. with the estimation of objective, numerical and relativized endpoints (41) and of confidence intervals for each biologic temporal endpoint (42, 43);
4. when indicated, in terms of displays of such results in the domains of f, τ, and ϕ as well as time t.

For instance, a biologic temporal component such as a rhythm with a given frequency can be evaluated not only in terms of a correlation function (44–46) and variance as a function of frequency in a variance spectrum (47–53, 64) but also in terms of quotients derived, e.g., from variance spectra, such as the circadian quotient CQ (53, 58); in terms of amplitude as a function of frequency in a periodogram (46, 59–61); in a periodic regression (62) or in the least squares spectrum (1); in terms of amplitude-weighted phase in

TABLE I

ILLUSTRATIVE SPECTRUM OF RHYTHMS

DOMAIN: *	HIGH FREQUENCY $\tau < 0.5h$		MEDIAL FREQUENCY $0.5h < \tau \leq 6d$		LOW FREQUENCY $\tau > 6d$
REGIONS:	$\tau \sim 0.1$ s $\tau \sim 1$ s et cetera		ULTRADIAN $(0.5 < \tau < 20h)$ CIRCADIAN $(20 \leq \tau \leq 28h)$ INFRADIAN $(28 < \tau \leq 6d)$		CIRCASEPTAN $(\tau \sim 7d)$ CIRCAVIGINTAN $(\tau \sim 20d)$ CIRCATRIGINTAN $(\tau \sim 30d)$ CIRCANNUAL $(\tau \sim 1$ yr)
RHYTHMS in:	Electroencephalogram Electrocardiogram Respiration		Rest-Activity Sleep-wakefulness Responses to drugs Blood constituents Urinary variables Metabolic processes, generally		Menstruation 17-Ketosteroid excretion with spectral components in all regions indicated above and in other domains

*Domains and regions [named according to frequency (f) criteria] delineated according to reciprocal f, i.e., period (τ) of function approximating rhythm. ♡ s=second, h=hour, d=day.

Several variables examined thus far exhibit statistically significant components in several spectral domains.

Fossil circadian, circatrigintan (about 30-day) and circannual rhythms have gained interest for possible use in paleo-bio-geochronometry (207–216, cf. also 217, 218). Assuming that the length of the year has been reasonably constant, changes in length of the day and month considered on the basis of astronomical evidence (217, 218) have been aligned, *inter alia*, with possible about-monthly and about-annual groupings of presumed circadian growth lines in fossil organisms—as compared to corresponding groupings in currently living marine invertebrates (207, 216).

TABLE II

SYMBOLS AND TERMS FOR DIFFERENT ACROPHASES*

SYMBOL	TERM	PHASE REFERENCE	[ILLUSTRATIVE PHASE REFERENCE]
∅	COMPUTATIVE ACROPHASE	arbitrary date and clock hour	00^{00} on Day 1 of study
φ	EXTERNAL ACROPHASE	point on synchronizing environmental cycle	mid-dark span for man, mid-light span for rodents
Φ	INTERNAL ACROPHASE	acrophase of another rhythm with same frequency	body core temperature acrophase

*As estimates of a rhythm's timing in relation to different phase references.

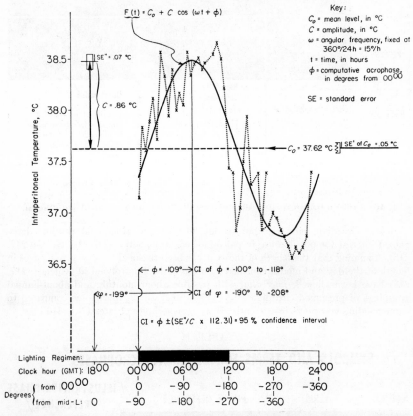

Least Squares Fit of 24-Hour Cosine Function (Continuous Line)
to Intraperitoneal Temperatures (×) of an Adult Female MSD Rat.

Telemetry at ~30' intervals for 24 hours

FIG. 1. Imputation of level, amplitude, and acrophase by a least-squares fit as a first step in the cosinor procedure; such imputations are intermediate computations rather than being endpoints in themselves (42). Note in any event two of the several kinds of acrophases, computative and external (cf. Table II). (Internal acrophase not shown.)

the cosinor (1, 42; cf also 63); in terms of a phase not weighted by the amplitude (43) under certain conditions only (42, 43); or in terms of a rhythm-adjusted level. Table III indicates how some of these procedures yielding distinct displays are related in terms of computational procedure.

   The biologic temporal component isolated from noise, evaluated by such microscopic rhythmometry as a mathematical function fitting the data, is the quantified rhythm.

   It is realized that the meaning of the terms "microscopic" and "macro-

TABLE III

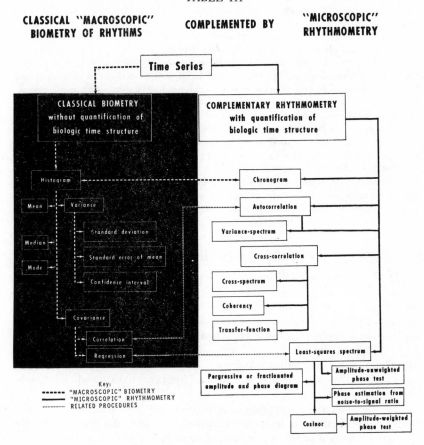

CLASSICAL "MACROSCOPIC"
BIOMETRY OF RHYTHMS

COMPLEMENTED BY

"MICROSCOPIC"
RHYTHMOMETRY

This table ignores the problems associated with data collection, editing and filtering—specialized tasks that are greatly facilitated by electronic computer methods (cf. e.g., 42, 43, 47–50, 53–57, 59–64).

scopic" is changed when they are used to denote methods for the resolution of rhythms. The term macroscopic then refers to findings from classical biometry displayed in the time domain only. By contrast, the word "microscopic" used in the context of certain techniques for rhythmometry indicates the higher level of resolution of rhythms by such methods, i.e., their "isolation" from noise, and the feasibility of estimating the parameters of each "isolated" rhythm.

Electronic computers serve for preparing most rapidly and efficiently the macroscopic display of rhythms as well as for the isolation of a rhythm and for the subsequent estimation of its parameters. Rhythmometry thus depends rather heavily yet not critically upon electronic computers. For certain limited rhythmometric purposes, mechanical or optical analyzers may be used in conjunction with a desk calculator, in lieu of an electronic computer. In any event, and in contrast to a microscopic analysis of tissues, a "microscopic" analysis of time series, like the study of so-called microscopic aspects of physics, does not necessarily depend upon the use of a microscope.

Transient misunderstandings arising from the use of terms such as microscopic seem to be a lesser disadvantage than the probable confusion that can be anticipated from the coining of completely new words. Understanding of words such as microscopic, when used in the context of rhythmometry elsewhere, may be facilitated by placing them under quotation marks at the outset.

In contrast to widespread practice, reference to terms such as clocks, oscillators, or other physical analogies or models will be avoided so far as possible, notably in defining the endpoints of biologic rhythms. Analogies, e.g., to light microscopy, can indicate the level of resolution achieved by certain approaches; they must not bias the objectivity of the measurements and the interpretation of what has been measured. Consequently, reference will be made to those measurable aspects of a rhythm that can be approximated by a mathematical function—e.g., in Figure 1. The endpoints of rhythms are to represent objective, numerical, and inferential-statistical aspects of physiologic variables.

Units of Rhythmometry

In the service of medicine, it is particularly worthwhile to attempt to quantify objectively a statistical and microscopic chronobiology, by analogy to statistical and microscopic physics. As such ambitious aims may be realized, the new definitions of the endpoints of a rhythm lead to new units—such as the acrophase in Table II. When the endpoints and units are meaningfully defined, one can more readily satisfy the condition that certain characteristics of a bioperiodicity under study be invariably expressed numerically and that such numbers be comparable from case to case and biologically meaningful as well.

In the microscopic approach, a precise and reproducible inferential statistical procedure can be made available in the form of a given electronic computer program or set of routines, after ascertaining the predictive value of the results obtained with the program in various biomedical test situations.

For this purpose, the selection of reference standards for endpoints of rhythms, like the selection of the analytical procedure, must be standardized. To the extent that pertinent international agreements can be made on a broader basis toward such steps of standardization, the results on endpoints of rhythms obtained at different times and in different localities will be more directly and more reliably comparable. Tables IV to XIII demonstrate halting first steps in this direction. The acrophases of certain circadian rhythms summarized objectively in these tables agree remarkably well in studies on healthy subjects carried out by different investigators and methods many years and time zones apart. These acrophases thus may serve as reference standards for possible chronopathology such as that reported for certain emotional disorders (95, 274–277) or cancer (285).

Tables IV to XIII serve as illustrative examples of endpoints from

TABLE IV

CIRCADIAN RHYTHM OF HUMAN PLASMA 17-HYDROXYCORTICOSTEROID IN SAMPLES OF TIME SERIES FROM DIFFERENT GEOGRAPHIC LOCATIONS (cf. 105)

N of subjects* [Δt, h]	Level, C_0 $C_0 \pm SE'$	Noise-to-signal or Rhythm detection (SE''/C)	P	Circadian amplitude C	Circadian acrophase Φ or ϕ†	Author(s), Year, Ref.
				(.95 confidence limits)	(.95 confidence limits)	
11 [3–6]	9.7±1.0		<.04	2.6 (.2 to 5.0)	−124° (− 34 to −181)†	Bliss et al. 1953 (91)
12 [1–12]	10.7±1.2		<.001	5.1 (2.7 to 7.5)	− 99° (− 37 to −137)	Migeon et al. 1956 (92)
13 [3]	13.5±.9		.005	4.1 (2.3 to 6.0)	−100° (− 63 to −137)	Halberg et al. 1961 (93)
8 [3]	7.4±.9		<.002	5.3 (2.7 to 7.9)	−113° (− 61 to −151)	Doe 1966 (94)
10 [8]	9.8±.8		<.002	4.6 (2.3 to 6.9)	− 71° (− 41 to −111)	Curtis et al. 1966 (95)
7 [5, 10]	10.4±.7		<.003	7.2 (3.6 to 10.8)	−105° (− 81 to −126)†	McClure 1966 (96)
21 [4, 6]	14.5±1.6		<.001	6.2 (5.2 to 7.3)	− 89° (− 72 to −107)	Krieger et al. 1966 (97)
13 [4, 8]	20.6±.6		<.001	2.0 (1.0 to 3.1)	−103° (− 64 to −144)	Bridges et al. 1966 (98)
7 [4]	11.9±.9		<.005	4.9 (2.7 to 7.1)	−112° (− 83 to −169)	Knapp et al. 1967 (99)
26 [2–8]	10.0±1.5	.6₇‡		3.4	−124°†	Linquette et al. 1967 (100)
5 [3–8]	12.2±1.2	.16₈		8.7 (5.8 to 11.5)	− 76° (− 57 to − 95)	Cade et al. 1967 (101)
8 [3]	8.6±.9		<.05	2.1 (.04 to 4.2)	− 92° (−312 to −120)	Gordon et al. (102)

* Total span of study 24 h for all subjects. C_0 and C in $\mu g/100$ ml.

† $\tau = 24$ h $= 360°$; 1 h $= 15°$. Φ reference $= 15°$. Φ reference = middle of habitual sleep span; ϕ reference = local midnight. Acrophases with latter reference indicated with (†) sign.

‡ Decimals shown as subscripts indicate doubtful significance.

TABLE V

CIRCADIAN RHYTHM OF HUMAN 17-HYDROXYCORTICOSTEROID EXCRETION IN SAMPLES
OF TIME SERIES FROM DIFFERENT GEOGRAPHIC LOCATIONS (cf. 105)

Site of study	N of subjects (N of days)	Circadian amplitude C (mg/hr)	Circadian acrophase Φ*	Author(s), Ref.
		(.95 confidence limits)		
USA				
(Minnesota)	4 (5)	.15 (.04 to .26)	$-129°$ ($-$ 83 to -200)	Halberg & Haus (unpubl.)
(Minnesota)	8 (1)	.12 (.06 to .17)	$-153°$ (-128 to -177)	Doe (94)
(Maryland)	7 (2)	.11 (.06 to .16)	$-154°$ (-123 to -181)	Bartter et al. (103)
(Pennsylvania)	9 (1)	.09 (.04 to .14)	$-144°$ (-104 to -183)	Curtis et al. (95)
(Minnesota)	1 (34)	.17 (.13 to .20)	$-130°$ (-117 to -144)	Haus & Halberg (104)
Mexico	1 (20)	.05 (.04 to .06)	$-159°$ (-145 to -173)	Peña (105)
	1 (12)	.03 (.01 to .05)	$-133°$ (-103 to -163)	
	1 (8)	.10 (.08 to .12)	$-112°$ ($-$ 77 to -130)	
	1 (9)	.09 (.07 to .11)	$-110°$ ($-$ 87 to -132)	
	1 (12)	.07 (.05 to .09)	$-118°$ (-109 to -139)	
	1 (6)	.04 (.02 to .06)	$-115°$ (-105 to -142)	
South Dutch Guiana	10 (2)	.08 (.05 to .11)	$-169°$ (-143 to -192)	Halberg & Simpson (106)
	10 (2)	.11 (.07 to .15)	$-164°$ (-134 to -202)	
Scotland	10 (2)	.18 (.06 to .23)	$-165°$ (-152 to -175)	Halberg & Simpson (106)
	10 (2)	.19 (.11 to .28)	$-157°$ (-133 to -182)	
France	12 (1)	.07 (.05 to .09)	$-138°$ (-121 to -155)	Reinberg (105)
	6 (2)	.08 (.04 to .12)	$-146°$ (-115 to -176)	Reinberg et al. (107)
	6 (2)	.06 (.01 to .11)	$-135°$ ($-$ 77 to -191)	
Germany	9 (2)	.15 (.08 to .22)	$-143°$ (-127 to -195)	Hofmann, Halhuber et al.
	9 (2)	.18 (.07 to .29)	$-142°$ (-121 to -178)	(105)
Austria	10 (3)	.9 (.1 to 1.6)	$-166°$ ($-$ 89 to -223)	Günther et al. (108)
	10 (25)	3.6 (2.4 to 4.7)	$-173°$ (-150 to -194)	
	10 (25)	3.7 (2.1 to 5.3)	$-188°$ (-165 to -206)	
	10 (25)	4.5 (2.8 to 6.2)	$-176°$ (-154 to -195)	
	10 (3)	2.8 (1.3 to 4.4)	$-169°$ (-139 to -196)	
Italy	31 (1)	.17 (.15 to .19)	$-134°$ (-124 to -143)	Ceresa (109)
Thailand	13 (1)	.06 (.02 to .10)	$-150°$ (-106 to -194)	Marotta & Linwong (110)
Australia (tetrahydro-F)	8 (1)	.06 (.03 to .09)	$-103°$ ($-$ 85 to -133)	Gordon et al. (102)

* $\tau = 24$ h $= 360°$; 1 h $= 15°$. Φ reference $=$ middle of habitual sleep span.

rhythmometry. The reader can consult the original references for information
on the kind of subjects providing the samples analyzed, their age, sex, genetic background, nutritional state, and other characteristics. Such details, as
well as references to the biophysical or biochemical methods employed and
to the standardization for data collection, also must be specified before such
endpoints can more generally be used.

TABLE VI

CIRCADIAN RHYTHM OF HUMAN POTASSIUM EXCRETION IN SAMPLES OF TIME SERIES FROM DIFFERENT GEOGRAPHIC LOCATIONS (cf. 105)

Site of study	N of subjects (N of days) [Δt, h]	Noise-to-signal (SE''/C)	P or Rhythm detection	Circadian		Author(s). Ref.
				amplitude C†	acrophase Φ*	
				(.95 confidence limits)		
USA						
(Minnesota)	5 (5) [4, 8]		<.005	1.3 (.7 to 1.9)	−161° (− 98 to −202)	Halberg (105)
(Minnesota)	8 (1) [3]		<.001	2.1 (1.4 to 2.8)	−157° (−130 to −181)	Doe (94)
(New York)	8 (1) [4, 9]		<.001	1.4 (.9 to 1.9)	−117° (− 95 to −171)	Krieger (111)
France	1 (21) [2–7]	.11		1.2 (.9 to 1.4)	−159° (−146 to −172)	Reinberg (105)
	4 (1) [4]		<.025	3.2 (1.4 to 4.9)	−151° (− 87 to −189)	Reinberg et al. (112)
Germany	9 (2) [3–15]		<.002	1.0 (.5 to 1.5)	−149° (−125 to −215)	Halhuber, Hofmann, et al. (105)
	9 (2) [3–15]		<.02	1.6 (.4 to 2.8)	−156° (−126 to −189)	
Australia	10 (3) [1.5, 10]		<.01	1.6 (.8 to 2.3)	−158° (−132 to −177)	Günther et al. (108)
	10 (25) [1.5, 10]		<.01	1.8 (1.2 to 2.4)	−155° (−139 to −174)	
	10 (25) [1.5, 10]		<.01	1.5 (1.0 to 2.1)	−150° (−137 to −174)	
	10 (25) [1.5, 10]		<.01	1.5 (.8 to 2.2)	−140° (−123 to −167)	
	10 (3) [1.5, 10]		<.01	1.3 (.6 to 1.9)	−150° (−117 to −187)	
Australia	8 (1) [~3]		<.001	2.6 (1.6 to 3.3)	−123° (− 92 to −143)	Gordon et al. (102)

* $\tau = 24$ h $= 360°$; 1 h $= 15°$. $\Phi =$ middle of habitual sleep span.
† Amplitude expressed in meq/hr.

TABLE VII

CIRCADIAN RHYTHM OF HUMAN HEART RATE (BEATS/MIN)IN SAMPLES OF
TIME SERIES FROM DIFFERENT GEOGRAPHIC LOCATIONS (cf. 105)

N of subjects (N of days) [Δt, h]	Noise-to-signal or (SE''/C)	P Rhythm detection	Circadian		Author(s), Ref.
			amplitude C	acrophase Φ*	
			(.95 confidence limits)		
			Minnesota		
1 (516) [~8]	.08₈		6.6 (5.4 to 7.7)	−282° (−272 to −292)	Halberg (105)
5 (5) [4,8]		<.01	8.5 (3.1 to 13.8)	−210° (−187 to −273)	Halberg (105)
			France		
1 (21) [2-10]	.11₃		9.3 (7.2 to 11.4)	−219° (−203 to −236)	Reinberg (105)
			Austria		
10 (25) [1.5, 10]		<.01	2.7 (1.7 to 3.7)	−206° (−160 to −236)	Günther et al.
10 (25) [1.5, 10]		<.01	2.6 (1.1 to 4.1)	−228° (−198 to −263)	(108)
10 (25) [1.5, 10]		<.01	2.5 (.7 to 4.3)	−225° (−195 to −291)	
10 (3) [1.5, 10]		<.05	3.9 (1.1 to 6.6)	−196° (−169 to −277)	

* τ =24 h=360°; 1 h =15°. Φ reference =middle of habitual sleep span.

Moreover, most of the information summarized in Tables IV to XIII is obtained transversely, i.e., in studies covering only one or a few periods of the rhythm investigated, on groups of subjects. Because of this limitation in length of time series, the average period of the rhythm is not estimated, beyond stating at a certain level of statistical confidence that a rhythm with the frequency fitted or with a frequency close to that fitted characterizes the data (42). Thus, in several estimations of circadian acrophase and amplitude there remains some uncertainty as to period, whether the period fitted is precisely 24 hr in length (Tables IV–XIII) or is different from the exact 24-hr length (some of the analyses summarized in Figure 6).

ENDPOINTS OF RHYTHMS—CRITERIA TO BE MET AND PITFALLS TO BE AVOIDED

Let us assume, first, that observations covering many cycles of a rhythm under study are available longitudinally on each of a number of individuals. We may assume, next, that in such series certain physiologic rhythms exhibit changes from one cycle to the next—changes that cannot readily be assessed by inspection of data plotted as a function of time, i.e., in a chronogram. Since in such plots of data along the 24-hr scale, one may not consistently find any rhythm markers comparable, say, to the P, Q, or T of an electrocardiogram, reproducible features of certain waveforms in the chronogram can be described more meaningfully by endpoints derived from certain (ordinary and/or generalized) harmonic analyses complemented by inferential statistical methods.

TABLE VIII

CIRCADIAN RHYTHM IN TIME ESTIMATION (COUNT FROM 1 TO 120) IN SAMPLES
OF TIME SERIES FROM DIFFERENT GEOGRAPHIC LOCATIONS (cf. 105)

N of subjects (N of days) [Δt, h]	Noise-to-signal or (SE''/C)	P Rhythm detection	Circadian amplitude C	Circadian acrophase Φ*	Author(s) Ref.
			(.95 confidence limits)		
			Minnesota		
1 (516) [~8]	.19₃		2.7 (1.7 to 3.7)	− 2° (−341 to −24)	Halberg (105)
5 (5) [4, 8]		<.001	5.2 (4.7 to 5.8)	− 7° (−344 to −98)	Halberg (105)
			Austria		
10 (25) [1.5, 10]		<.01	3.6 (.8 to 6.4)	−18° (−355 to −64)	Günther et al.
10 (25) [1.5, 10]		<.01	4.5 (1.7 to 7.2)	−34° (− 19 to −42)	(108)
10 (25) [1.5, 10]		<.01	5.3 (2.7 to 7.9)	−20° (− 14 to −72)	

* τ =24 h=360°, 1 h=15°. Φ reference =middle of habitual sleep span.

TABLE IX

CIRCADIAN RHYTHM IN 17-KETOSTEROID EXCRETION BY HEALTHY
ADULTS IN DIFFERENT GEOGRAPHIC LOCATIONS* (cf. 277)

Site of study	N of subjects (age range) [N of days]	Circadian amplitude C	Circadian acrophase Φ	Author(s) Ref.
		(.95 confidence limits)		
		Males		
USA (Minnesota)	1 (37) [34]	.17 (.13 to .20)	− 99° (− 78 to −126)	Haus & Halberg (104)
USA (Minnesota)	4 (19–49) [10]	.11 (.01 to .22)	−133° (−355 to −171)	Halberg & Haus (unpubl.)
Japan	3 (28–33) [1]	.11 (.01 to .22)	−107° (−354 to −168)	Sakai (113)
Denmark	1 (44) [1]	.08 (.05 to .11)	−131° (−110 to −152)	Halberg et al. (1)
	1 (52) [5]	.05 (.02 to .07)	−124° (− 96 to −153)	
USA (New York)	11 (20–43) [10]	.07 (.04 to .11)	−124° (− 91 to −158)	Vestergaard & Leverett (114)
Thailand	13 (19–23) [1]	.07 (.04 to .09)	−108° (− 89 to −127)	Marotta & Linwong (110)
		Females		
USA (Maryland)	7 (yg. adult) [2]	.04 (.01 to .08)	−136° (−123 to −181)	Bartter et al. (103)
USA (New York)	11 (20–43) [10]	.07 (.03 to .11)	−124° (− 88 to −158)	Vestergaard & Leverett (114)

* C in mg/hr; Φ in degrees, with 360°=24 hr. Φ reference=middle of habitual sleep span.

A microscopic alteration of the circadian acrophase in urinary 17-ketosteroid of depressed patients is recorded (277; cf. 113); a possibly broader multivariable chronopathology of this illness deserves scrutiny (274–276, 287–290).

TABLE X

CIRCADIAN RHYTHMS IN NONHUMAN PRIMATES, PRESUMABLY UNDER CONDITIONS OF SYNCHRONIZATION WITH A 24-HOUR SOCIAL (AND/OR LIGHTING) ROUTINE

Species* N of subjects N of days [Δt, h]	Physiologic variable	Level $C_0 \pm SE'$	Circadian amplitude C (.95 confidence int.)	Noise-to-signal ($SE_?^2/C$) or P value	Circadian acrophase φ^+ or ϕ^{++} (.95 confidence arc)	Author(s) Ref.
			Blood Constituents			
7 Mm, 1 [3]	Polymorphonuclears, (1000/mm³)	10±1	3 (0 to 7)	.68$_7$	−132°+	Migeon et al. (116)
	Lymphocytes (1000/mm³)	6±.5	2 (.6 to 3)	.42$_4$	−301°+	
	Eosinophils (/mm³)	374±29	205 (121 to 289)	.20$_9$	−359° (−338 to −22)+	
	17-hydroxycorti-costeroids (µg/100 ml)	35±2	16 (10 to 22)	.16$_8$	−85° (−63 to −107)+	
10 Mm, 1 [2, 4]	17-hydroxycorti-costeroids (µg/100 ml)	48±3	69 (26 to 112)	.005	−177° (−173 to −181)++	Mason et al. (117)
			Heart Rate			
1 Cebus albifrons, 1 [.5]	Heart rate (beats per min)	99±1	29 (25 to 33)	.07$_3$	−156° (−148 to −164)+	Winget et al. (118)
			Temperature (°C)			
1 Cebus albifrons, 1 [.5]	Deep body	37.7±.04	1.9 (1.8 to 2.0)	.04$_3$	−174° (−169 to −179)+	Winget et al. (118)
1 Mm, 4 [25]	Brain	38.7±.16	1.5 (1.4 to 1.6)	.02$_3$	−211° (−208 to −213)+	Stroebel (119)
32 M irus, 1 [6]	Rectal	38.1±.05	.7 (.6 to .9)	.09$_4$	−226° (−216 to −237)+	Honjo et al. (120)
2 Mm, 1 M cyano-molgus; 1 Papio hamadryas; 1 Cercopithecus patas, 7 [2]	Axillary	38.0±.04	.8 (.7 to .8)	.001	−197° (−183 to −211)+	Simpson et al. (121)

* M = Macaca, m = mulatta. φ reference = middle of daily dark span; φ reference = local midnight. 360° = 24 hr; 15° = 1 hr.

TABLE XI

CIRCADIAN RHYTHMS IN SUSCEPTIBILITY TO POTENTIALLY HARMFUL AGENTS*
Dilute Brown (D_8) and Bagg-Albino (C) Mice

Inbred strain	Agent tested, dosage (endpoint recorded)	Circadian	
		amplitude C (% of mean)	acrophase φ from mid-L
D_8	Ouabain; .5 mg/.2 cc/20 g b.wt.; % mortality	62 (57–67)	−315° (−305 to −324)
	Librium; 5.4 mg/20 g b.wt.; survival time	19 (6–24)	−220° (−184 to −263)
	White noise; 104 db; % with convulsion	67 (31–103)	−128° (− 98 to −159)
	Dimethylbenzanthracene; .05 ml .5%; % w/tumor	24 (13–35)	− 56° (− 27 to − 85)
C	Ouabain; .15 mg/.2 cc; % mortality	31 (26–36)	−283° (−164 to −302)
	Ethanol; .8 cc 25%; % mortality	41 (23–59)	−107° (− 80 to −134)
	Methopyrapone; 325–400 mg/kg b.wt.; % mortality	23 (11–35)	−105° (− 82 to −128)
	Endotoxin; 100 μg/.2 cc/20 g b.wt.; % mortality	71 (47–95)	− 37° (− 18 to − 57)

* Animals maintained on regularly alternating light/dark cycle [L (06⁰⁰–18⁰⁰)/D (18⁰⁰–06⁰⁰)] (see reference 122).

In principle, all curves can be accounted for by harmonic analysis, and the indications for this method at first seem universal. In practice, the fewer the data points available on a variable and the more nonsinusoidal the "shape" of a rhythm, the more difficult it is to describe this rhythm with the fit of a few sines and cosines. A more or less sinusoidal form becomes an essential requirement for a meaningful harmonic analysis whenever the number of available data points is so restricted that only a single cosine function can be fitted. In such instances, the dangers of uncritical curve fitting indeed are great. To drive this point to the absurd, a single cosine function fitted to a single cardiac cycle in an electrocardiographic tracing would do no more than obscure the information on P, QRS, and T—so

TABLE XII

CIRCADIAN PARAMETER ESTIMATIONS ON VARIABLES
INFLUENCED BY CORTICOSTEROID

Physiologic variable	Circadian amplitude C^*	Circadian acrophase φ
	(.95 confidence limits)	
Gross motor activity	65 (23 to 107)	$-160°$ (-123 to -198)
Liver phospholipid labeling	13 (9 to 17)	$-164°$ (-146 to -182)
Colonic temperature		$-161°$ (-125 to -196)
Depression of blood eosinophil count	98 (62 to 134)	$-181°$ (-160 to -202)
Depression of pinnal mitoses	44 (26 to 62)	$-201°$ (-179 to -223)
Liver glycogen	92 (89 to 111)	$-294°$ (-288 to -300)

* C given as % of mean. φ from mid-L. Mice maintained on regularly alternating light:dark cycle $[L(06^{00}-18^{00}) : D(18^{00}-06^{00})]$ τ fitted $= 24$ h $= 360°$; 1 h $= 15°$ (see 65 and 123).

readily and usefully available when the original tracing in time is viewed by the naked eye. Nonetheless, when such rather obvious pitfalls are kept in mind, the fitting of certain harmonic functions to longitudinal data can be carried out in order to procure reproducible endpoints of circadian or other rhythms, and in the process, other equally vexing and common pitfalls that stem from the exclusively macroscopic viewing of a chronogram may be avoided. In any event, rhythm characteristics—whether evaluated macroscopically or microscopically—must meet several requirements:

TABLE XIII

ACROPHASES OF 24-HOUR SYNCHRONIZED CIRCADIAN ADRENAL CYCLE
AND ITS NEUROENDOCRINE INTERACTIONS. MOUSE

Physiologic variable	Circadian acrophase (.95 confidence arc)	
	Φ^*	Φ
	from mid-L	from serum corticosterone φ
Serum corticosterone	$- 66°$ ($- 42$ to $- 89$)	
Adrenal corticosterone	$- 79°$ ($- 47$ to -112)	
Hypothalamic CRF	$- 88°$ ($- 11$ to -147)	
Adrenal reactivity to ACTH (in vitro)	$-235°$ (-210 to -258)	$-169°$ (-144 to -192)
Pituitary ACTH	$-339°$ (-319 to -359)	$+ 87°$ ($+107$ to $+ 67$)

* $L(06^{00}-18^{00})$: $D(18^{00}-06^{00})$; τ fitted $= 24$ hr $= 360°$; 1 hr $= 15°$ (see 123–126, also 127–128).

1. The average period length τ of the rhythm and/or its acrophase ϕ should be determined objectively. In this context, objectivity requires that:

(a) The method used for determining the τ or ϕ of an individual's rhythm be applicable throughout an entire sampling span, whatever its length T, when $T \gg \tau$.

(b) It be applicable to time series from any and all available subjects in a sample.

(c) When a given procedure is applied to the same time series by different investigators, their inferences as to a τ or a ϕ be similar or preferably the same.

2. Endpoints other than τ or ϕ, such as the extent of rhythmic change— i.e., the amplitude C and the level around which rhythmic changes recur C_0—should also be objectively evaluted, in keeping with (a) to (c) above.

3. All endpoints should be expressed in numerical form.

4. Statistical dispersion indices should be sought for each endpoint.

Even in longitudinal studies on a given individual, some approximation of their statistical confidence limits should be given with numerical endpoints such as the ϕ and the C or the τ of a rhythm.

Given the test of the same hypotheses and other things being comparable, work meeting the above four requirements promises to lead to a more complete and more reliable description of biologic phenomena than studies ignoring these same methodologic desiderata. Furthermore, any biologic research aimed at interpreting the factors underlying a given physiologic change will be particularly useful if it enables one to make reliably predictive statements. From this pragmatic viewpoint, we are led to yet another methodologic point:

5. Whenever possible, the results of any method of analysis should be checked by additional sampling aimed at validating the predicted temporal behavior of a rhythm.

For instance, if a τ of 23.5 hr is detected for the circadian rhythm of a given variable in one individual or group, whereas a τ of 24 hr is found for the same variable in another individual or group, and if the rhythms' phases in the two individuals or groups also are known, a large difference in the temporal placement along the 24-hr scale of the crests of the two rhythms can be predicted to occur on certain days. The presence or absence of this difference can be readily and economically checked by additional sampling at a few appropriately chosen time points during single 24-hr spans, as will become apparent from the study of Figures 2 and 3 (29, 65, 66).

Of course, similar considerations apply to differences in the circadian period of two or more variables in the same organism. One variable may exhibit a component with $\tau = 24.5$ hr, whereas another variable in the same organism conceivably maintains a $\tau = 24$ hr: accordingly, large deviations from the usual phase relation of the circadian components of these two variables can be anticipated at certain predictable times. Furthermore, such alterations of internal timing may result in undesirable or even deleterious

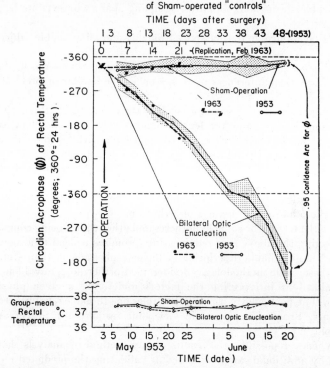

**Phase-drift of Desynchronized Circadian Rhythm
in Body Temperature of Blinded Mature CBC mice**
Compared with 24-h-synchronized Circadian Rhythm
of Sham-operated "controls"

FIG. 2. Reproducibility of circadian desynchronization following blinding in studies on CBC mice and C mice done 10 years apart with different sampling techniques. A study on CBC's in 1953 is summarized by open circles connected with continuous lines. Note that results on ϕ obtained in 1963 are within the 95 per cent confidence interval computed for results on ϕ obtained a decade earlier. The confidence interval is referred to as confidence arc on the graph simply to indicate the particular method used for computing it, i.e., the cosinor (42). Note also from the bottom of the graph that average levels of body temperature (1953 data only are shown) are roughly the same in both blinded animals and controls. Thus, rhythmometry detects a clear, quantifiable, and reproducible alteration of rhythm after blinding, whereas the more classical study of levels fails to detect an effect. In all studies, light daily from 06^{00} to 18^{00} alternated with darkness.

effects at certain predictable times. This possiblility of a predictably recurring chronopathology then becomes amenable to testing at appropriate times, i.e., when the largest deviation from the usual internal timing can be anticipated from the very rhythmometry yielding the two initially considered values of τ. Rigorous data supporting this line of thought are as yet unavailable.

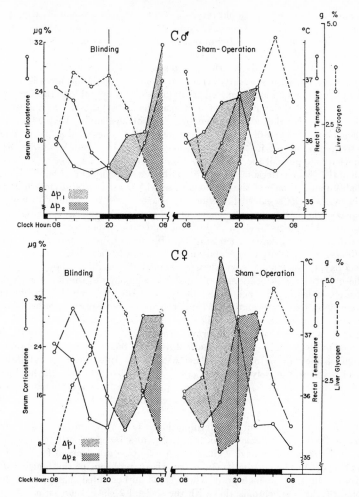

FIG. 3. Time relations of circadian rhythms in liver glycogen, serum corticosterone, and rectal temperature in C mice at 21 days after surgery. The "transient antiphase" seen macroscopically from this plot was predicted on the basis of microscopic results shown in Figure 2.

Condition 1(a) stated above requires that there should be no "good" and "bad" fractions of a time series, such that some can be interpreted and others cannot. Rhythmometry must be applicable even to sections of a time series so noisy that investigators rightly refrain from drawing inferences solely from the inspection of their chronograms—otherwise the "microscopic" method can hardly prove its usefulness in clinical or experimental medicine or in biology. One must not end up in the difficult situation of suggesting to a patient that his record is "not good enough" for the time being and that perhaps he should return at some other time when his record *might* be amenable to evaluation. This status quo prevails in more than one contemporary approach to rhythms; it not only limits a priori any application of rhythmometry in medicine but invalidates many an inference in biology as well.

Condition 1(b) stated above attempts to ascertain that the results of longitudinal group studies will be more nearly representative of a population investigated since the data from all individuals sampled are required to be amenable to the same analyses. Unless this condition is met, one may again be embarrassed by having to advise certain patients that they are not amenable to rhythm evaluation. By the same token, the choice by a biologist of "good" animals over "bad" ones from a specified sample impresses one as a most questionable endeavor. Indeed, condition (a) above comes to mind: what is to prevent the "good" one from turning "bad"?

All of the above criteria of objectivity, although self-evident and minimal, are not invariably met by some of the methods most widely used for studying rhythms. A case in point is the so-called behavior day chart—a display familiar to child psychologists—where, for example, spans of sleep and wakefulness are displayed as black and white areas along a 24-hr scale and strips from consecutive days are mounted one under another. One can then observe, for instance, onsets of sleep or wakefulness on consecutive days and can readily see whether these recur at the same times of day, or consistently somewhat earlier or later. For this purpose—rather than for the objective quantification of the multiple endpoints of rhythms—such charts often are satisfactory in themselves; many biologists, too, rely largely if not exclusively upon the interpretation of similar strip charts displaying 24-hr records of motor activity mounted one below the other in the order in which they are obtained. Historically such approaches have provided most interesting information and their continued use for certain purposes of orientation can be recommended; yet one must not confuse the viewing of such a chart with a quantitative inferential statistical study of rhythms, precisely because one may thus fail to meet even the minimal objectivity criteria (a) to (c) stated above—quite apart from the circumstance that quantitative information on certain parameters such as level or amplitude is almost irretrievably lost.

Difficulties resulting from the interpretation of *some* charts can be illustrated by a specific example. Two senior clinical investigators independently commented in print on the same behavior day chart of an infant on self-demand feeding. In the original report displaying the behavior day chart, problems of rhythmicity were a side issue alluded to in small print. The original author noted that prior to the developing rhythm's synchronization with the societal 24-hr cyclic routine, sleep and wakefulness in this infant recurred with a period of 23 hr. Another author, finding the graphic record and reproducing it, apparently did not read the small print, presumably since he did not read the language of the original text; he reports from viewing the same behavior day chart that the "period" of the sleep-wakefulness rhythm in this infant was initially *longer* than 24 hr, rather than shorter.

Nothing is gained when the "interpretation" of a rhythm's period can drastically differ from one investigator to the next. Rather, much harm will be done if similar procedures should continue in exclusive or even primary use in studies on human beings directed at clinical applications, among others. Let us assume that the two clinical investigators alluded to above arrive at their discrepant interpretations in the (as yet) hypothetical situation of studying a period alteration in disease with the endeavor to correct it—rather than being concerned, as they were, with physiologic aspects of the infant's development on a schedule of self-demand feeding. In the former situation, one clinical investigator might attempt to slow down a rhythm interpreted by him as being pathologically too fast. The other, on the basis of the same evidence, would aim at speeding up the rhythm—interpreted by him as being too slow. Such actions should justly be questioned: the field of chronobiology as well as that of a fledgling chronopathology can gain only discredit from confusion that could be avoided (for applicable methods see lower half of Table 2 in Ref. 39).

SINGLE FREQUENCY VERSUS SPECTRAL APPROACHES

Rhythms can be studied at different levels of complexity, determined by the number of (a) spectral components with distinct frequencies—one frequency = one rhythm; (b) physiologic variables investigated (58); and (c) study conditions.

Single-frequency approaches.—

(a) *One frequency—one physiologic variable—one condition.* Surveys of rhythms under one condition in field or laboratory abound but are mainly macroscopic, except for some first halting microscopic steps on human data, Tables IV–IX, on nonhuman primates, Table X, and on rodents, Tables XI–XIII.

(b) *One frequency—one physiologic variable—several conditions.* This approach, widely practiced, has been a preferred one in limited studies on a given rhythm; thus one may focus upon a circadian rhythm, a circannual one, or any other frequency in the given time series. In evaluating a single rhythm under varying conditions, one may follow, for instance, the synchronization of the rhythm with a societal routine and its desynchronization from that routine—as suggested for the case of a circadian rhythm in Figures 2 (3, 66) and 4 (67) and for the case of a circaseptan rhythm in Figure 5 (1).

(c) *One frequency—several physiologic variables—one or several conditions.* An illustrative example at this level of complexity is a macroscopic map of the time relations among circadian rhythms in body core temperature, blood cortiocosterone and liver glycogen levels, Figure 3 (cf. also corresponding microscopic summary in 65). Among very many others, macroscopic circadian chronograms also are available for the rhythms in flashing, luminescence glow, cell division, and photosynthetic capacity in *Gonyaulax polyedra* (cf. Figure 1 in 68). In many cases the chronogram does not allow for a quantification of a rhythm, as may be seen from the chronograms of circaseptan rhythms in Figure 5. Figure 6 (78–80), in turn, explores microscopically the phase relation of two circadian rhythms in (a) blinded mice ($\tau = 23.5$ or 23.4 hr) as well as in sham-operated controls and in (b) human beings, each isolated in a separate cave, and following their subsequent resynchronization with a societal routine [cf. Figure 4 (67)].

The macroscopic phase relations of circadian rhythms during human isolation in a bunker for spans of several weeks have been discussed by Aschoff & Wever (69–77). Series of observations covering 9 days of isolation

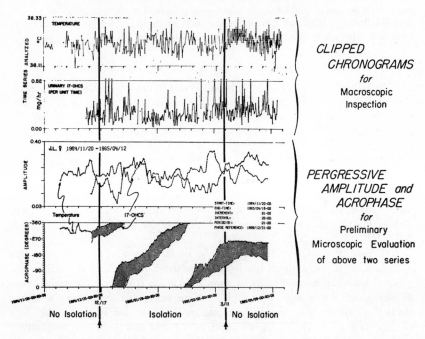

RESOLUTION OF CIRCADIAN RHYTHMS IN UNEQUALLY SPACED NOISY DATA ON RECTAL TEMPERATURE
AND URINARY 17-HYDROXYCORTICOSTEROID EXCRETION OF A HEALTHY FEMALE SUBJECT
a) during isolation in a cave for about 3 months, and
b) during synchronization with a 24-hr societal routine for another month.

Fig. 4. Phase relations of circadian rhythms in the urinary excretion of 17-hy-droxycorticosteroids and in rectal temperature of a woman during isolation in a cave and following resynchronization with a 24-hr cyclic societal routine. Clipped chronogram of the time series shown on top. (For clipping, values above or below the mean ±3 standard deviations were repeatedly equated to the nearer of these limits until the result of this iterative procedure was no longer associated with a change in mean and standard deviation to the nearest four decimal places. Extreme values thus "clipped" are indicated by a dot on top of the corresponding chronogram.)

A macroscopic inspection of these time plots is barely contributory: long-period changes of some regularity—corresponding presumably to the menstrual cycle (79)—are apparent for rectal temperature in particular and changes with shorter periods also are suggested by the record, yet it seems unjustified on the basis of inspection alone even to attempt to ascribe a precise period to a circadian rhythm or to discuss the phase relations of circadian components in the two time series.

By contrast, the display of acrophase in the bottom row—part of the microscopic approach—indicates first that the rhythms of both functions changed their period during isolation—only to be resynchronized with a 24-hr cyclic routine thereafter; second, that the rectal temperature acrophase lagged behind that for 17-hydroxycorticosteroid excretion during isolation, as well as following resynchronization; and third, that resynchronization of body temperature occurred considerably faster than that of 17-hydroxycorticosteroid excretion. The latter finding may be related at least in part to the circumstance that on the day of emergence from the cave the φ of rectal have been reported by Schaefer et al. (81, 82) with special reference to the respiratory subsystem.

When the results from different studies, each limited to a single rhythm, i.e., to a single spectral component in one or several physiologic variables, are viewed *in toto*, they reveal a broad spectrum of physiologic rhythms extending from periods of a millisecond or so to periods measured in years. Such a spectrum of rhythms (with different frequencies) for a number of different variables was conceived and depicted by Golenhofen & Hildebrandt (83, 84) and by Aschoff (85, cf. 88–90). Their abstract spectrum, along with a reference to more recent work by Pye & Chance (86), is displayed at the top of Figure 7. Aschoff emphasizes two theoretical points: 1. that a broad spectrum of rhythms constitutes a physiologic entity, and 2. that—like rhythms with frequencies much higher than one cycle per day— circadian rhythms or rhythms with lower frequency also have endogenous features. Two more important steps lead to the abstract scheme shown at the bottom of Figure 7 and have already been documented (1) by concrete spectral work involving the concomitant estimation of several rhythms (with different frequencies) in the same time series. One step is a conceptual one derived from concrete work, i.e., that distinct spectral regions characterize not only different physiologic time series, as suggested earlier, but one and the same variable as well. The second step was the actual concomitant objective estimation of the several spectral components as endpoints satisfying the criteria 1. to 5. on page 691 (cf., e.g., Figure 8) (1).

Multi-frequency approaches.—

(*a*) *Several frequencies—one physiologic variable—one condition.* Variance spectra have been used to assess concomitantly several rhythms with different frequencies—circadian to circannual—in rectal temperatures measured on individuals synchronized with an institutional routine (49, 50, 53, 87).

(*b*) *Several frequencies—one physiologic variable—several conditions.* Least squares spectra, as well as variance spectra, have demonstrated concomitantly circadian and circatrigintan (menstrual) (29, 53, 79) components in body core temperature of healthy women subjected to a 24-hr cyclic social

---

temperature was nearer its usual temporal placement in relation to the synchronizer than was the ϕ of 17-OHCS.

From the pergressive amplitude diagram—third row from top—it can be seen that the amplitude, notably that of the rhythm in 17-OHCS excretion during isolation, showed no indication of damping, as a conditioned reflex phenomenon might be expected to do. If there was a difference between the amplitude at the end of isolation and that upon resynchronization, this measure of the extent of circadian periodic change in 17-OHCS excretion indicated a more marked rhythm at the end of isolation than following resynchronization.

Adding confidence limits to each C and ϕ estimate makes such a preliminary evaluation more definitive; these limits can now be routinely and automatically plotted by fast computer-directed plotters.

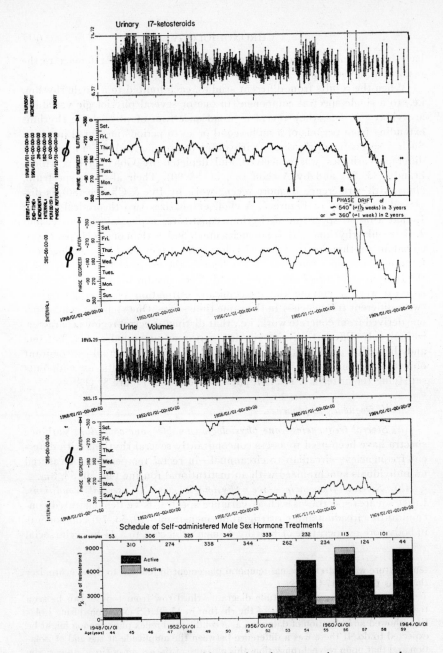

Fig. 5. Human urinary 17-ketosteroid excretion chronogram in top row and pergressive acrophase (ϕ) diagrams computed with half-year intervals for analysis in the second row, and with 1-year intervals in the third row. Substantial amounts of androgen were repeatedly self-administered by the subject at "A" and after "B" for the last 3 years of study, but not before "A" (1). Note after "B" in the pergressive acrophase diagrams the desynchronization of circaseptan rhythms in 17-KS, a phenomenon not detected for urine volumes in the row next to the bottom.

INTERNAL TIMING OF RHYTHMS
IN RECTAL TEMPERATURE AND ADRENOCORTICAL FUNCTION
IN SYNCHRONIZED AND DESYNCHRONIZED CIRCADIAN SYSTEMS

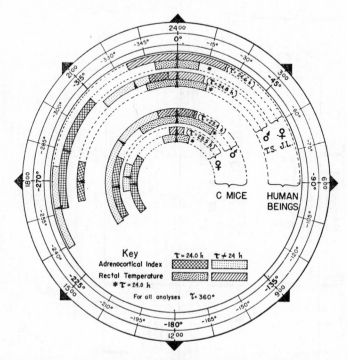

FIG. 6. Adrenocortical acrophase—gauged by urinary 17-OHCS in human beings (67) *or* by serum corticosterone in inbred C mice (65)—leads body core temperature acrophase within ~1/4 circadian period. Internal timing is similar in mice and man in these cases: ϕ is comparable when the circadian periods are of 24-hr average length in mice and men subjected to a 24-hr cyclic synchronizer effect and after the blinding of the mouse (65, 66) or under conditions of human isolation in a cave (67, 78–80) when the rhythms are desynchronized from the 24-hr day.

synchronization; alterations in period length of these two spectral components have been recorded in a woman in the absence of a societal synchronization, with the menstrual component shortening as the circadian one lengthened during 3 months' isolation in a cave—on "self-demand" lighting of low intensity (79).

Infradian spectral components have been recorded in disease and are of particular chronopathologic interest when their prominence in the spectrum is associated with a marked reduction in the prominence of circadian rhythms (49).

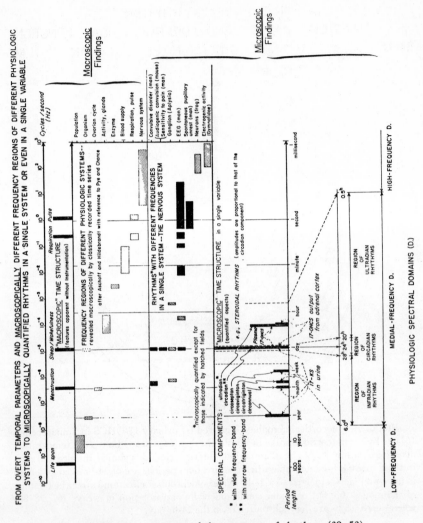

FIG. 7. Changing concepts of the spectrum of rhythms (39, 52).

For human urinary 17-ketosteroid excretion, circadian, circaseptan (about 7-day), circavigintan (about 20-day), circatrigintan (about 30-day), and circannual (about a year) rhythms have been concomitantly demonstrated during spans with and without androgen administration, Figures 5 and 8 (1).

(c) *Several frequencies—several physiologic variables—one or several conditions.* Spectral components with several different frequencies were also evaluated in the urine volume of the healthy man whose 17-ketosteroid

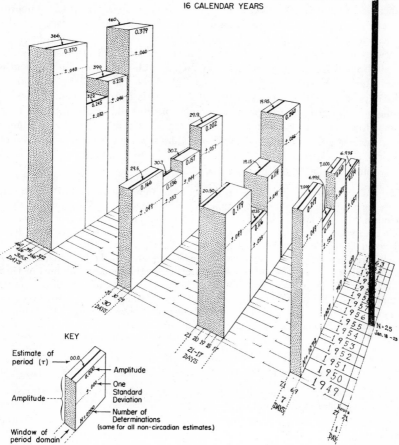

PERIOD ESTIMATES, AMPLITUDES AND STANDARD DEVIATIONS IN FOUR DOMAINS ANALYZED BY WINDOWS OF LEAST SQUARES SPECTRA OF HUMAN 17-KETOSTEROID EXCRETION OVER 16 CALENDAR YEARS

FIG. 8. Reproducibility, from one data section to the next, of certain rhythms with a relatively low frequency in the urinary 17-ketosteroid excreted by a healthy man. Arrow in heavy print visualizes certain comparable estimates for the much more prominent circadian rhythm of urinary 17-ketosteroid excretion (1). Such components may contribute to the intermittency of certain diseases (25–26, 115, 176–187, 287–290) believed to be more or less cyclic. Apart from medical problems, the circannual component continues to be of particular interest to avian physiologists (85, 188–203), among others (325, 330).

excretion rhythms are summarized in Figures 5 and 8 (1). This self-study by a scientist spanned a decade and a half: the circannual rhythms of this subject as well as components with higher frequency thus could be concomitantly examined. The circannual rhythm in 17-ketosteroid excretion was prominent but apparently not synchronized with the calendar year, whereas the circannual rhythm in urine volume was clearly 1-year synchronized. When in this case of circannual rhythms the analyses suggest the occurrence of different prominent periods in a given spectral region for each of two variables, a comparison of the phase relations among these variables at slightly different frequencies is not meaningful. This same inference also holds during the last 3 years of this study (1) when the non-7-day (6.93-day) circaseptan 17-KS component differed with statistical significance from the 7-day-synchronized circaseptan component of urine volume in the same subject. However, for the first 10 years of the same study (1) the prominent frequencies in these two physiologic variables were the same; comparison of their phase relations does then become of interest and reveals a phase-difference, demonstrated in Figure 9.

The student of circannual rhythms can record longitudinally but 60 to 70 individual cycles in a lifetime; for the same number of cycles the student of circadian rhythms requires "only" 2 months or so; students of high frequency rhythms, of course, obtain a very large number of cycles within a fraction of the span covered by a single circannual or even circadian cycle. For this reason, perhaps, the multifrequency, multivariable approach continues to be applied primarily in the high frequency domain of rhythms (cf. 279–283, for studies of interactions among rhythms in CNS function and respiration), where, of course, the total study duration requirements are more modest. The multifrequency approach already can be extended to cover concomitantly the domains of high and medial frequency; thus circadian components of the human electroencephalogram have been quantified (41).

HUMAN RHYTHMS, LONG-DISTANCE TRANSMERIDIAN TRAVEL AND ODD ENVIRONMENTS; PHASE-SHIFTS AND PHASE-DRIFTS

This problem area, notably that of post-travel adaptation, comprises a number of related, yet distinct topics.

Relatively early, several authors report on rhythms during sea travel (129–131).

Second, physiologic observations, or quite often impressions, from transmeridian flights are numerous (132–152). Any effects of relatively short-distance transmeridian flights involving the crossing of no more than a single time zone or two, although pertinent in the same connection, apparently have been ignored as a field of study. Discussion continues on problems revolving around the adaptation to a new schedule of living after a flight (333, 334); attention also has been paid to rhythms and physiologic performance during flight (148). In preparation for the transmeridian travel, an attempt at preadaptation to the new routine of living anticipated upon arrival has been recommended (140–142).

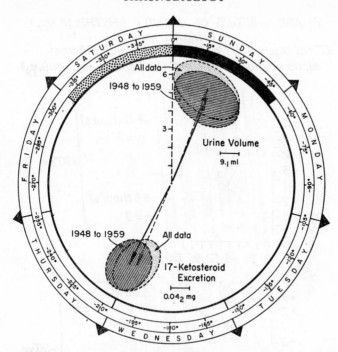

FIG. 9. Cosinor summary of the circaseptan rhythms in 17-ketosteroid excretion and urine volume of a healthy man. Rhythms in both variables are synchronized with societal 7-day routine during all of the time span analyzed (urine volume) or during most of that span (17-ketosteroid); cf. Figure 5 (1).

Third, reports abound on the phase shifting of rhythms in a fixed geographic setting by the manipulation of environmental cycles such as the regimen of light and darkness and/or the daily routine of activity and rest (153–160, 271–72; cf. 19). Pittendrigh had suggested earlier that for many species (164) the adaptation of a circadian rhythm to an altered synchronizer schedule is faster following a synchronizer delay than after a synchronizer advance. But for chaffinches kept in 12-hr light (250 lux) alternating with 12-hr darkness (.5 lux), Aschoff & Wever (165) found a faster adaptation when a single span of light or darkness was shortened by 6 hr rather than lengthened by the same amount. From a macroscopic study of chronograms, they conclude that resynchronization following a lengthening by 6 hr of either the light or the dark span lasts 4 to 5 days, whereas only half that time is needed for resynchronization following an advance of rhythm by 90°, Figure 10. The opposite behavior was found for rats (40, 166), Figure 11, as well as for humans (40, 167), Figure 12, and even for monkeys (168)—from the microscopic analysis of data in the classical study by Simpson & Gal-

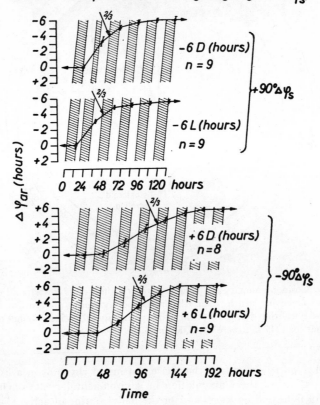

PHASE SHIFTING OF ACTIVITY RHYTHM (△φar)
in Fringilla coelebs L.
(From Aschoff a. Wever 1963) following different
kinds of manipulation of the lighting regimen(△φs)

FIG. 10. Rhythm adaptation in chaffinches following a change in synchronizing regimen of alternating light (250 lux) and darkness (.5 lux). Macroscopic interpretation of data: adaptation following advance of synchronizer faster than following delay (165).

braith (121). This problem deserves further scrutiny under controlled conditions; special attention should be paid to individual differences in various aspects of circadian rhythm adaptation following changes in synchronizer or adherence to unusual routines. Such studies pertain to work hygiene—even to the performance of healthy subjects on odd routines—quite apart from bearing upon adaptation following transmeridian flights. Since such flights result in a shift of the synchronizer as well as in a geographic dis-

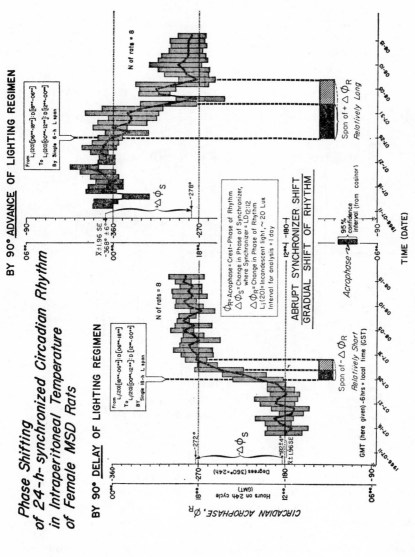

Fig. 11. Rhythm adaptation in inbred female Minnesota Sprague-Dawley rats is faster following a delay of synchronizing lighting regimen than following an advance (40, 166).

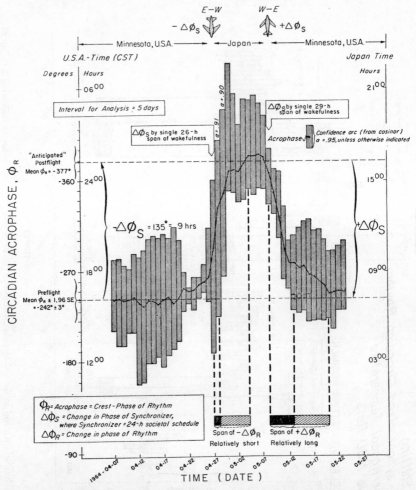

FIG. 12. Rhythm adaptation following a flight from east to west, involving social synchronizer delay, seems to be faster than that following a flight from west to east involving synchronizer advance—despite the circumstance that rhythm advance is associated with return to familiar home setting (40, 167).

placement, one should control each of these two factors, preferably on separate groups of subjects studied concomitantly.

Rhythms also continue to be studied in unusual environments, such as the Arctic (161–162), caves (29, 67, 78–80, 163, 171–173, cf. 28), or extraterrestrial space (170). The question remains open whether on unusual work routines there is rhythm alteration and decrement in performance. Holmquest, Retiene & Lipscomb (169) studied male rats living on a regimen in which light and dark were randomly presented over a span of 40 days. Body weight, endocrine organ weight, adrenal function, and gross motor activity were recorded. In comparison with control animals living on a regular LD regimen, the group rhythms in motor activity and adrenal steroid level were apparently altered, but no effects of the random regimen on the animals' health were noted.

No untoward effects had been reported earlier by Holmgren & Swensson (335) who subjected rats to repeated inversions of a 24-hr LD regimen at intervals of 4 days over the course of 16 weeks (cf. 19, 284).

Plasma corticosteroids in subjects on unusual schedules have been macroscopically studied by Orth, Island & Liddle (204). In discussing their results they indicate that a "single day (on an abnormal schedule) does not disrupt the 17-OHCS (rhythm) for that day" and also that "several individuals on 19 and 33-hour sleep-wakefulness schedules appeared to exhibit two 17-OHCS (cycles) per sleep-wake cycle" (204), yet they conclude that the pituitary-adrenal cycle is a function of the duration of the subject's sleep-wakefulness cycle. This inference must be qualified, since the prominent rhythm in urinary 17-OHCS excretion and in certain other variables of human subjects isolated in a cave for a span of 3 to 4 months continues to exhibit a circadian frequency desynchronized from the 24-hr local time, even though spectra of sleep-wakefulness data from the same subjects exhibit frequencies lower than one cycle in 28 hr (29, 67, 78–80). Furthermore, microscopic studies (206) reveal prominent circadian components with a period near 24 hr persisting in the urinary corticosteroid excretion of subjects living on a 21-hr day in the Arctic (161).

Such studies are the more interesting since it will be important to determine the extent to which the societal 24-hr schedule should be altered in the artificial environments of certain cities of the future—now actually on drafting boards—in vehicles for extraterrestrial space, or in underwater environments. In several such milieus, alterations of schedule may be logistically desirable yet they also should be physiologically acceptable; one should ascertain whether prolonged life on non-24-hr routines might lead to a detriment in performance or health, notably to deficits in resistance to potentially noxious agents. It also has been suggested that certain acute concomitants of phase shifting, such as insomnia, may be prevented if shift workers would adopt a 25-hr day—the daily working span being prolonged from 8 hr to 8 hr and 20 min in this case and the resting span accordingly to 16 hr and 40 min. With such a system, Eränkö, who has studied shift work problems with Kihlberg (205), wished to achieve a schedule whereby work for a given individual began 1 hr later each calendar day—day work thus changing only gradually (rather than abruptly) into night work and vice versa, with a full cycle being completed in 25 days. The implications of rhythms are of obvious interest also to those involved in the global movement of personnel on various schedules (337, 338).

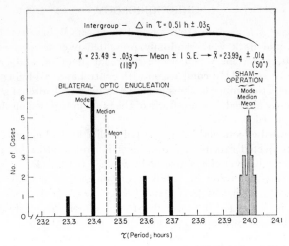

FIG. 13. Circadian period of rectal temperature in 14 blinded and 18 sham-operated CBC mice (1953-Series), determined by least-square spectrum. "Circadian" denotes periods of blinded and sham-operated animals (see Appendix A). Circadian synchronization requires objective validation of a period dispersion < ±.1 hr. Sham-operated controls exhibit a 24-hr-synchronized circadian rhythm. Period of blinded mice deviates from 24 ±.1 hr length—we are dealing with a presumably free-running circadian rhythm desynchronized from 24-hr "solar" and 24.8-hr "lunar" day. In many cases such a fine resolution is a priori not practicable *inter alia* because of insufficient length of available time series. [Summary of data collected every 4 hr from mice kept in light from 06⁰⁰ to 18⁰⁰ alternating with darkness, originally described at the 4th Conference of the International Society for the Study of Biological Rhythms in Basle, Switzerland, Sept. 18–19, 1953. Pergressive analyses in Figure 2. Amplitude-damping of ∼31% in blinded mice during observation span of 48 days—May–June 1963 (14).]

RHYTHMS IN EXPERIMENTAL ORGANISMS

Models of rhythms with various frequencies continue to attract interest (219–246), partly as a follow-up of some older models (247–252). A number of these papers, but by no means all of them, at least refer to biologic data, and in a few instances a model in the form of an oscillating circuit (219) or an oscillator (220) is actually formulated with reference to biologic data. At the other extreme, purely mathematical and statistical papers also are available (245). Winget et al., apart from contributing a series of studies on deep body temperature and heart rate among other rhythms of nonhuman primates and chickens (118, 253–255), also address themselves to the important task of evaluating the waveform of a rhythm by "microscopic" procedures.

Stroebel applies variance spectra to the study of circadian rhythms in behavioral parameters of experimental animals. He studies features of conditioned emotional responses as a function of circadian system phase (119) and explores learning rates of rats in various circadian system phases, advocating a controlled biologic rhythm approach to psychiatric problems (256). Controlled studies on rhythms and behavior presented by Randall

APPENDIX A

Terms for Rhythms in a Domain of Medial Frequencies[a]

[Adjectives and by zero change nouns for the tentative designation of the frequency or period of certain biologic rhythms (cf. 1)]

Term	Derivations all from Latin	Pronunciation		Physiologic spectral region	
		spoken accent[b]	phonetic notation[c]	description	limits[d]
Ultradian	*ultra*, beyond *dies*, day *-anus*[e]	ul*tra*dian	ul trä′ dē ən	Certain frequencies higher than circadian	From 1 cycle/1 hr to 1 in 19.9 hr/1–21 horan[f]
Circadian	*circa*, about *dies*, day *-anus*	cir*ca*dian	sûr kā′ dē ən	1 cycle in about 24 hr *or* 1 cycle in precisely 24 hr	From 1 cycle/20 hr to 1 in 27.9 hr/20–28 horan
Infradian (cf. Fig. 13)	*infra*, below *dies*, day *-anus*	in*fra*dian	in frä′ dē ən	Certain frequencies lower than circadian	From 1 cycle/1.166 d to 1 in 5.999 d/29 horan to 5 dian

[a] As compared to 1. the much higher frequencies exhibited, among others, by rhythms that are more specific for the nervous, circulatory and respiratory system, e.g., by action potentials of brain or heart; or to 2. much lower frequencies, e.g., of menstrual and circannual cycles.

[b] Italicized syllable indicates spoken accent.

[c] Spoken accent is indicated by the symbol of the written accent (′) placed at the end of the syllable intended to be the prominent one. Separations indicate syllables. Phonetic notation is used according to *Webster's New International Dictionary*, Springfield, Mass., 1961. Thus, one should pronounce "a" as in *add*; "ä" as in *arm*; "ā" as in *arm*; "ā" as in *ace*; "e" as in *end*; "ē" as in *even*; "i" as in *it*; "u" as in *up*; "ū" as in *fuse*; "ə" as in silent. Limits of spectral regions are tentative and subject to revision.

[d] hr = hour or hours; d = day or days; yr = year or years.

[e] Adjective-forming suffix.

[f] From *hora*, hour, and *-anus*.

(257–258) also stand out by virtue of the experimental approach employed. In contrast to others publishing on "clocks" after experimental manipulation, Randall & Littschwager (257) include control animals in their work; they explore circannual changes and higher frequencies by a combination of Fourier analysis and analyses of variance (257). The adrenal gland continues to be studied by investigators of intrinsic aspects of rhythms (259, 260), as is the pineal gland (261–264, 273, 291, 304, 312); reports on extrinsic factors continue to be contributed by Brown (265, 266). The synchronization of biologic rhythms (267) and the role of automation in biologic rhythms (268) are discussed by Sollberger. Menaker (278) reports on rhythm synchronization in the sparrow by extraretinal light perception.

The amenability to phase shifting of mitotic rhythms in the epithelium of rodent skin (3) is confirmed by Alov (293) and extended to rhythms in the epithelia of cornea, tongue, and esophagus (293); variations in mitotic counts after thyroidectomy and adrenalectomy in the rat are given apparently without ascertaining the extent of adrenal insufficiency by determinations of corticosterone or by other means (cf. 294).

Cherkovich (295) subjects three monkeys (*Papio hamaeryas*) to variations in lighting regimen ranging from (*a*) illumination by day, over (*b*) illumination by night and rest and darkness by day, (*c*) 6-hourly alternations of light and darkness followed by (*d*) such 6-hr "days" and "nights" displaced along the 24-hr scale by 6 hr, to (*e*) continuous illumination for 24 hr, (*f*) continuous darkness for 24 hr, "and so on". After 2 months of such "systematic interference" with illumination and feeding, all three monkeys reportedly developed a neurosis with severely deranged conditioned reflex activity and the appearance of somatic pathology, including coronary insufficiency and micronecroses in the heart of one monkey.

Ulcer production in monkeys subjected to 12-hr cycles involving 6 hr of forced activity alternating with 6 hr of rest is under continued study by Brady (296, 297); his findings are extended to the rat by Rice (298). The chronopathology of gastric ulcers is a subject of experimental (305) and clinical interest (306), as remains the mapping of rhythms in a variety of variables (299–304, 322–332, 340, 341) including the so-called hours of changing resistance (33, 107, 307–310, 313). Suggestions on statistical design and analysis also are available (42, 43, 47, 48, 52, 61–63, 311, 314, 315).

The time relation between the development of rhythmicity on the one hand and its synchronization with environmental factors on the other hand is a topic of continuing interest (316–318), as are problems more generally related to the development of circadian rhythms (316–321). In a moth *Pectinophora gossypiella*, rhythmicity of a population is elegantly induced by Minis & Pittendrigh with a single stimulus, the manipulation of environmental temperature or lighting (316). Conceivably the time at which a circadian rhythm can be induced in the moth may be "microscopically" found to precede by a few hours if not by a day the time at which the rhythms can be coupled to environmental stimuli, unless, as is equally possible, there be an important difference in this connection between the moth and human beings. For several human infants fed on self-demand, the occurrence of a desynchronized circadian period for considerable spans of time—weeks or months—prior to the actual societal synchronization of the circadian system has been macroscopically ascertained (317, 318).

CONCLUSION

In an attempt to determine whether a given value is "normal" or "abnormal", clinicians as well as biologists customarily study many rhythmic variables on the basis of single samples—without qualifying such values in terms of the phases of the various rhythms contributing to the variable sampled, even though it has been pointed out that a single datum can meaningfully be qualified as to circadian system phase if the conditions of study are standardized (269). This review indicates that from relatively few samples—some of variables extensively utilized by biologists and clinicians—reasonably reliable new and potentially useful endpoints of rhythms can be obtained by rhythmometry.

This "chronobiologic" endeavor to acquire new endpoints from the study of rhythms as yet relates to investigative biology and medicine rather than to clinical practice.

It is pertinent that, as shown in the Tables included with this review: (a) the acrophases (crest-phases) of certain circadian rhythms in blood, in urine, and in systemic functions of healthy human beings, as well as in certain experimental animals, can be objectively and readily determined by electronic computation—as will be the rhythm-adjusted level, the amplitude, and the waveform of a rhythm—and that (b) these acrophases agree remarkably well in studies carried out by different investigators working many years and miles apart with differing biophysical, biochemical, or behavioral methodology, under dissimilar standardization of the conditions chosen for observation and of the kind and extent of sampling. Such agreement among endpoints allows me to conclude this review with the suggestion that the time is ripe for the planning, at the international level, of conditions and techniques that may be adopted generally for obtaining standardized time series on rhythmic variables and for checking these out in different laboratories around the world, with a view toward a subsequent, broader-scale study of rhythm modifications in biology and medicine (105.)

In concluding his review of a related problem—annual reproductive cycles—A. C. Giese in 1959 wrote that "a tremendous amount (of work) is still undone which can provide a lifetime of problems for those who are challenged by them" (270). In 1968 there still remains a lifetime of work for students of rhythmometry; they face the challenges of obtaining new biologic characteristics from the study of rhythms and of applying these endpoints toward an understanding of underlying factors, in different forms of life (339).

LITERATURE CITED

1. Halberg, F., Engeli, M., Hamburger, C., Hillman, D. Spectral resolution of low-frequency, small-amplitude rhythms in excreted ketosteroid; probable androgen-induced circaseptan desynchronization. *Acta Endocrinol. Suppl. 103*, 54 pp. (1965)

2. Halberg, F. Resolving power of electronic computers in chronopathology—an analogy to microscopy. *Scientia, 101*, 412–19 (1966)

3. Halberg, F. Physiologic 24-hour periodicity; general and procedural considerations with reference to the adrenal cycle. *Z. Vitamin- Hormon-Fermentforsch.*, 10, 225–96 (1959)

4. *Circadian Clocks, Proc. Feldafing Summer School* (Aschoff, J., Ed., North-Holland, Amsterdam, 479 pp., 1965)

5. *Biological Clocks, Cold Spring Harbor Symp. Quant. Biol.* (Long Island Biol. Assoc., New York, 524 pp., 1960)

6. *Circadian Systems, Rept. 39th Ross Conf. Pediat. Res.* (Fomon, S. F., Ed., Ross Labs. Columbus, Ohio, 93 pp., 1961)

7. *Rhythmic Functions in the Living System, Ann. N. Y. Acad. Sci.* (Wolf, W., Ed., New York, 1326 pp., 1962)

8. *Photo-Neuro-Endocrine Effects in Circadian Systems, with Particular Reference to the Eye, Ann. N. Y. Acad. Sci.* (Hague, E. B., Ed., New York, 645 pp., 1964)

9. *Interdisciplinary Perspectives of Time, Ann. N. Y. Acad. Sci.* (Fischer, R., Ed., New York, 915 pp., 1967)

10. *Symposium on Rhythms*, in *Verhandl. Deut. Ges. Inn. Med. 33rd Kongr.*, 886–994, 1116–17 (Bergmann, München, 1967)

11. *Proc. 1st Intern. Symp. Biorhythms in Exptl. Clin. Endocrinol., Florence, May 30-31, 1966. Rass. Neurol. Veget.*

12. *Symposium on Rhythms*, in *Proc. 4th Panam. Symp. Pharmacol. Therapy, Mexico City* (Excerpta Med. Found., Amsterdam, 1968) (In press)

13. *La Photoregulation de la Reproduction chez les Oiseaux et les Mammiferes, Colloq. Intern. CNRS, Montpellier, 1967* (Benoit, J., Assenmacher, I., Eds., CNRS, Paris, in press)

14. *Biological Cycles and Psychiatry, 3eme Symp. Bel-Air* (Dick, R., Ed.)

15. *Biologische Rhythmen, Nachr. Akad. Wiss. Göttingen* (Birukow, G., Rensing, L., Eds., Vandenhoeck & Ruprecht, Göttingen, 1967)

16. *Photoperiodism and Related Phenomena in Plants and Animals* (Withrow, R. B., Ed., Publ. #55 AAAS, Washington, D. C., 903 pp., 1959)

17. Reinberg, A., Ghata, J. *Biological Rhythms* (Walker, New York, 138 pp., 1964)

18. Bünning, E. *The Physiological Clock* (Springer-Verlag, Berlin, 145 pp., 1964)

19. Menzel, W. *Menschliche Tag-Nacht-Rhythmik und Schichtarbeit* (Benno Schwabe, Basel/Stuttgart, 189 pp., 1962)

20. Sollberger, A. *Biological Rhythm Research* (Elsevier, New York, 461 pp., 1965)

21. Cloudsley-Thompson, J. L. *Rhythmic Activity in Animal Physiology and Behavior* (Academic Press, New York, 236 pp., 1961)

22. Harker, J. E. *The Physiology of Diurnal Rhythms* (Cambridge Univ. Press, London, 114 pp., 1964)

23. Goodwin, B. C. *Temporal Organization in Cells* (Academic Press, New York, 163 pp., 1963)

24. Danilevskii, A. S. *Photoperiodism and Seasonal Development of Insects* (Oliver & Boyd, Edinburgh, 283 pp., 1965)

25. Richter, C. P. *Biological Clocks in Medicine and Psychiatry* (Thomas, Springfield, Ill., 109 pp., 1965)

26. Lunedei, A., Cagnoni, M., Fantini, F., Tarquini, B., Morace, G., Maiello, M., Panerai, A., Scarpelli, P. T., Toccafondi, R. *Sindromi Diencefaliche (Problemi in discussione)* (L. Pozzi, Roma, 413 pp., 1967)

27. Kleitman, N. *Sleep and Wakefulness* (Univ. Chicago Press, Chicago, 552 pp., 1965)

28. Mills, J. N. Human circadian rhythms. *Phys. Rev.*, 46, 128–71 (1966)

29. Halberg, F., Reinberg, A. Rythmes circadiens et rythmes de basses fréquences en physiologie humaine. *J. Physiol. (Paris)*, 59, 117–200 (1967)

30. Kayser, C., Heusner, A. A. Le rythme nycthéméral de la dépense d'énergie. Etude de physiologie comparée. *J. Physiol. (Paris)*, 59, 3–117 (1967)

31. Biological Rhythms. *Environmental Biology*, 565–607 (Altman, P. L., Dittmer, D. S., Eds., Fed. Am. Soc. Exptl. Biol., Bethesda, Md., 694 pp., 1966)

32. *Bibliography on Time Series and Stochastic Processes* (Wold, H., Ed., Oliver & Boyd, Edinburgh, 516 pp., 1965)

33. Reinberg, A. The hours of changing responsiveness or susceptibility. *Perspect. Biol. Med.*, **11**, 111–26 (1967)

34. Malek, J., Gleich, J., Maly, V. Characteristics of the daily rhythm of menstruation and labor. *Ann. N.Y. Acad. Sci.*, **98**, 1042–55 (1962)

35. Kaiser, I. H., Halberg, F. Circadian aspects of birth. *Ann. N.Y. Acad. Sci.*, **98**, 1056–68 (1962)

36. Frey, S. Der Tod des Menschen in seinen Beziehungen zu den Tages und Jahreszeiten. *Deut. Z. Chir.*, **218**, 366–69 (1929)

37. McFarland, R. A. *Human Factors in Air Transportation; Occupational Health and Safety* (McGraw-Hill, New York, 830 pp., 1953)

38. Halberg, F. Physiologic 24-hour rhythms: a determinant of response to environmental agents. In *Man's Dependence on the Earthly Atmosphere*, 48–89 (Schaefer, K. E., Ed. Macmillan, New York, 1962)

39. Halberg, F., Künkel, H. Ansätze zu einer "mikroskopischen" Rhythmometrie in der Neurologie. *Fortschr. Med.*, **86**, 85–90 (1967)

40. Halberg, F., Nelson, W., Runge, W., Schmitt, O., Pitts, G., Reynolds, O., Tremor, J. Tests of circadian rhythm characteristics—design evaluation by results on rodents and men. *Space Sci.*

41. Halberg, F. Rhythmic interactions of steroidal and neural functions. In *Hormonal Steroids*, 966–79 (Martini, L. et al. Eds., Excerpta Med. Found., Amsterdam, 1967)

42. Halberg, F., Tong, Y. L., Johnson, E. A. Circadian system phase—an aspect of temporal morphology; procedures and illustrative examples. In *The Cellular Aspects of Biorhythms*, 20–48 (Mayersbach, H. v., Ed., Springer, Berlin, 198 pp., 1967)

43. Batschelet, E. *Statistical methods for the analysis of problems in animal orientation and certain biological rhythms* (AIBS, Washington, D.C., 1965)

44. Brazier, M. A. B., Casby, J. U. Cross-correlation and autocorrelation studies of EEG potentials. *Electroenceph. Clin. Neurophysiol.*, **4**, 201–11 (1952)

45. Brazier, M. A. B., Barlow, J. S. Some applications of correlation analysis to clinical problems in electroencephalography. *Electroenceph. Clin. Neurophysiol.*, **8**, 325–31 (1956)

46. Halberg, F. Temporal coordination of physiologic function. *Cold Spring Harbor Symp. Quant Biol.*, 289–310 (1960)

47. Blackman, R. B., Tukey, J. W. *The Measurement of Power Spectra* (Dover, New York, 190 pp., 1958)

48. Mercer, D.M.A. Analytical methods for the study of periodical phenomena obscured by random fluctuations. *Cold Spring Harbor Symp. Quant. Biol.*, 73–86 (1960)

49. Halberg, F., Panofsky, H. I. Thermovariance spectra; method and clinical illustrations. *Exptl. Med. Surg.*, **19**, 284–309 (1961)

50. Panofsky, H., Halberg, F. II. Thermovariance spectra; simplified computational example and other methodology. *Ibid.*, 323–38

51. Sato, K., et al. On the physiological significance of the average time- and frequency-patterns of the electroencephalogram. *Electroenceph. Clin. Neurophysiol.*, **8**, 325–31 (1956)

52. Künkel, H. *Die Periodik der paroxysmalen Dysrhythmie im Elektroenzephalogramm* (Habilitationsschrift, Freie Univ. Berlin, 1966)

53. Halberg, F., Stein, M., Diffley, M., Panofsky, H., Adkins, G. Computer techniques in the study of biologic rhythms. *Ann. N. Y. Acad. Sci.*, **115**, 695–720 (1964)

54. Adey, W. R., Walter, D. O. Analysis of brain-wave generators as multiple statistical time series. *IEEE Trans.*, **BME-12**, 8–13 (1965)

55. Walter, D. O., Adey, W. R. Spectral analysis of electroencephalograms recorded during learning in the cat, before and after subthalamic lesions. *Exptl. Neurol.*, **7**, 481–501 (1963)

56. Walter, D. O., Adey, W. R. Spectral analysis for electroencephalograms: mathematical determination of neurophysiological relationships from records of limited duration. *Ibid.*, **8**, 155–81

57. Adey, W. R., Walter, D. O. Applica-

tion of phase detection and averaging techniques in computer analysis of EEG records in the cat. *Ibid.*, **7**, 186–209

58. Halberg, F. Periodicity analysis—a potential tool for biometeorologists. *Intern. J. Biometeorol.*, **7**, 167–91 (1963)

59. Schuster, A. On the investigation of hidden periodicities with application to a supposed 26-day period of meteorological phenomena. *Terrestr. Mag.*, **3**, 13–41 1898)

60. Koehler, F., Okano, F. K., Elveback, L. R., Halberg, F., Bittner, J. J. Periodograms for the study of physiologic daily periodicity in mice and in man. *Exptl. Med Surg.*, **14**, 3–30 (1956)

61. Enright, J. T. Accurate geophysical rhythms and frequency analysis. In *Circadian Clocks* (See Ref. 4), 31–42

62. Bliss, C. I. Periodic regression in biology and climatology. *Conn. Agr. Exptl. Sta. Bull. 615* (1958)

63. Chapman, S., Bartels, J. *Geomagnetism*, 2 vols. (Clarendon, Oxford, 1049 p., 1940)

64. Künkel, H. Moderne Analysen periodischer Vorgänge in der Neurologie. *Deut. Med. J.*, **9**, 320–27 (1968)

65. Haus, E., Lakatua, D., Halberg, F. The internal timing of several circadian rhythms in the blinded mouse. *Exptl. Med. Surg.*, **25**, 7–45 (1967)

66. Halberg, F. Body temperature, circadian rhythms and the eye. *Colloq. Intern CNRS, Montpellier, July 11–22, 1967* (In press)

67. Ghata, J., Halberg, F., Reinberg, A., Siffre, M. Rythmes circadiens desynchronisés (17-hydroxycorticosteroïdes, température rectale, veille-sommeil) chez deux sujets adultes sains. *Ann. Endocrinol.*, **29**, 269–70 (1968)

68. Hastings, J. W., Keynan, A. Molecular aspects of circadian systems. In *Circadian Clocks* (See Ref. 4), 167–82

69. Aschoff, J., Gerecke, U., Wever, R. Desynchronization of human circadian rhythms. *Japan. J. Physiol.*, **17**, 450–57 (1967)

70. Aschoff, J., Wever, R. Spontanperiodik des Menschen bei Ausschluss aller Zeitgeber. *Naturwissenschaften*, **15**, 337–42 (1962)

71. Aschoff, J. Tagesrhythmus des Menschen bei völliger Isolation. *Umschau Wiss. Tech.*, **12**, 378–83 (1966)

72. Aschoff, J. Human circadian rhythms in activity, body temperature and other functions. *Life Sci. Space Res.*, **5**, 159–73 (Brown, A. H., Favorite, F. G., Eds., North-Holland, Amsterdam, 1967)

73. Aschoff, J. Significance of circadian rhythms for space flight. In *Bioastronautics and the Exploration of Space*, 465–84 (Bedwell, T. C., Jr., Strughold, H., Eds., San Antonio, Texas, 1964)

74. Aschoff, J., Gerecke, U., Wever, R. Phasenbeziehungen zwischen den circadianen Perioden der Aktivität und der Kerntemperatur beim Menschen. *Pflügers Arch.*, **295**, 173–83 (1967)

75. Aschoff, J. Die minimale Wärmedurchgangszahl des Menschen am Tage und in der Nacht. *Pflügers Arch.*, **295**, 184–96 (1967)

76. Aschoff, J. Exogenous and endogenous components in circadian rhythms. *Cold Spring Harbor Symp. Quant. Biol.*, **25**, 11–27 (1960)

77. Aschoff, J. Physiologie biologischer Rhythmen. *Ärztl. Praxis*, **18**, 1569–93 (1966)

78. Halberg, F., Siffre, M., Engeli, M., Hillman, D., Reinberg, A. Etude en libre-cours des rythmes circadiens du pouls, de l'alternance veille-sommeil et de l'estimation du temps pendant les deux mois de séjour souterrain d'un homme adulte jeune. *Compt. Rend. Acad. Sci.*, **260**, 1259–62 (1965)

79. Reinberg, A., Halberg, F., Ghata, J., Siffre, M. Spectre thermique (rythmes de la température rectale) d'une femme adulte avant, pendant et après son isolement souterrain de trois mois. *Comp. Rend. Acad. Sci.*, **262**, 782–85 (1966)

80. Siffre, M., Reinberg, A., Halberg, F., Ghata, J., Perdriel, G., Slind, R. L'isolement souterrain prolongé. Etude de deux sujets adultes sains avant, pendant et après cet isolement. *Presse Med.*, **74**, 915–19 (1966)

81. Schaefer, K. E., Dougherty, J. H. Variability of respiratory functions based on circadian cycles. *Rept. 486 NASA* (Naval Submarine Base, New London, Conn., 1966)

82. Schaefer, K. E., Clegg, B. R., Carey, C. R. Dougherty, J. H., Weybrew,

B. B. Effect of isolation in a constant environment on periodicity of physiological functions and performance levels. *Aerospace Med.*, **38**, 1002–18 (1967)

83. Hildebrandt, G. Rhythmus und Regulation. *Med. Welt*, Nr. 2, 73–81 (1961)

84. Golenhofen, K., Hildebrandt, G. Die Beziehungen des Blutdruckrhythmus zu Atmung und peripherer Durchblutung. *Pflügers Arch.*, **267**, 27–45 (1958)

85. Aschoff, J. Jahresperiodik der Fortpflanzung bei Warmblutern. *Stud. Gen.*, **8**, 742–76 (1955)

86. Pye, K., Chance, B. Sustained sinusoidal oscillations of reduced pyridine nucleotide in a cell-free extract of saccharomyces carlsbergensis. *Proc. Natl. Acad. Sci.*, **55**, 888–94 (1966)

87. Halberg, F. Physiological rhythms. In *Physiological Problems in Space Travel*, 298–322 (Hardy, J. D., Ed., Thomas, Springfield, Ill., 1964)

88. Aschoff, J. Adaptive cycles: their significance for defining environmental hazards. *Intern. J. Biometerol.*, **11**, 255–78 (1967)

89. Aschoff, J. Circadian rhythms in birds. In *Proc. XIV Intern. Ornithol. Congr.*, 81–105 (Snow, D. W., Ed., Blackwell, Oxford, 1967)

90. Aschoff, J., Saint Paul, U. v., Wever, R. Circadiane Periodik von Finkenvögeln unter dem Einfluss eines selbstgewählten Licht-Dunkel-Wechsels. *Z. Vergleich. Physiol.*, **58**, 304–21 (1968)

91. Bliss, E. L., Sandberg, A. A., Nelson, D. H., Eik-Nes, K. The normal levels of 17-hydroxycorticosteroids in the peripheral blood of man. *J. Clin. Invest.*, **32/3**, 818–23 (1953)

92. Migeon, C. J., Tyler, F. H., Mahoney, J. P., Florentin, A. A., Castle, H., Bliss, E., Samuels, L. T. The diurnal variation of plasma levels and urinary excretion of 17–OHCS in normal subjects, night workers and blind subjects. *J. Clin. Endocrinol.*, **16**, 622–33 (1956)

93. Halberg, F., Frank, G., Harner, R., Matthews, J., Aaker, H., Graven, H., Melby, J. The adrenal cycle in men on different schedules of motor and mental activity. *Experientia*, **17**, 282 (1961)

94. Doe, R. P. *A study of the circadian variation in adrenal function and related rhythms* (Ph.D. thesis, Univ. of Minnesota, June 1966)

95. Curtis, G. C., Fogel, M., Zarate, C. The effect of sustained affect on the diurnal rhythm of adrenal cortical activity. *Psychosomat. Med.*, **28**, 696–713 (1966)

96. McClure, D. J. The diurnal variation of plasma cortisol levels in depression. *J. Psychosomat. Res.*, **10**, 189–95 (1966)

97. Krieger, D. T., Krieger, H. P. Circadian variation of the plasma 17-hydroxycorticosteroids in central nervous system disease. *J. Clin. Endocrinol. Metab.*, **26**, 929–40 (1966)

98. Bridges, P. K., Jones, M. T. The diurnal rhythm of plasma cortisol concentration in depression. *Brit. J. Psychiat.*, **112**, 1257–61 (1966)

99. Knapp, M. S., Keane, P. M., Wright, J. G. Circadian rhythm of plasma 11-hydroxycorticosteroids in depressive illness, congestive heart failure and Cushing's syndrome. *Brit. Med. J.*, **2**, 27–30 (1967)

100. Linquette, M., Fossati, P., Racadot, A., Hubschman, B., Decoulx, M. Les variations circadiennes de la cortisolemie dans la maladie de Cushing et les états frontières. *Ann. Endocrinol.*, **29**, 69–76 (1967)

101. Cade, R., Shires, D. L., Barrow, M., Thomas, W. C. Jr. Abnormal duirnal variation of plasma cortisol in patients with renovascular hypertension. *J. Clin. Endocrinol. Metab.*, **27**, 800–6 (1967)

102. Gordon, R., Spinks, J., Dulmanis, A., Hudson, B., Halberg, F., Bartter, F. Phase relations of several circadian rhythms in human plasma and urine resolved by cosinor. *Clin. Sci.* (In press)

103. Bartter, F., Delea, C. S., Halberg, F. A map of blood and urinary changes related to circadian variations in adrenal cortical function in normal subjects. *Ann. N. Y. Acad. Sci.*, **98**, 969–83 (1962)

104. Haus, E., Halberg, F. Circadian phase diagrams of oral temperature and urinary functions in a healthy man studied "longitudinally". *Acta Endocrinol.*, **51**, 215–23 (1966)

105. Halberg, F., Reinhardt, J. Bartter, F., Delea, C., Gordon, R., Wolff, S., Reinberg, A., Ghata, J., Hofmann, H., Halhuber, M., Günther, R., Knapp, E., Peña, J. C., Garcia Sainz, M. Agreement in endpoints

from circadian rhythmometry on healthy human beings living on different continents. *Experientia* (In press)

106. Halberg, F., Simpson, H. Circadian acrophases of human 17-hydroxy-corticosteroid excretion referred to midsleep rather than midnight. *Human Biol.*, **39**, 405–13 (1967)

107. Reinberg, A., Zagula-Mally, Z. W., Ghata, J., Halberg, F. Circadian rhythms in duration of salicylate excretion referred to phase of excretory rhythms and routine. *Proc. Soc. Exptl. Med. Biol.*, **124**, 826–32 (1967)

108. Günther, R., Knapp, E., Halberg, F. Circadiane Rhythmometrie mittels elektronischer Rechner zur Beurteilung von Kurwirkungen. In *Kurverlaufs- und Kurerfolgsbeurteilung*, 106–11 (Teichmann, W., Ed., Sanitas-Verlag, Bad Wörishofen, 1968)

109. Ceresa, F., Angeli, A., Gaidano, G. P., Boccuzzi, G., Molino, G. P., Perotti, L. Aspetti della regolazione della secrezione corticotropa nell' obesita. *Atti XII° Congr. Soc. Ital. Endocrinol.* (1968)

110. Marotta, S. F., Linwong, M. Excretion of urinary 17-ketosteroids and 17-ketogenic steroids. 1. Effects of age, time of day and season. *Chiengmai Med. Bull.*, **5**, 167–81 (1966)

111. Krieger, D. T., Krieger, H. P. Circadian patterns of urinary electrolyte excretion in central nervous system disease. *Metabolism*, **16**, 815–23 (1967)

112. Reinberg, A., Ghata, J., Sidi, E. Nocturnal asthma attacks: their relationship to the circadian adrenal cycle. *J. Allergy*, **34**, 323–30 (1963)

113. Sakai, M. Diurnal rhythm of 17-ketosteroid and diurnal fluctuation of depressive affect. *Yokohama Med. Bull.*, **11**, 352–67 (1960)

114. Vestergaard, P., Leverett, R. Excretion of combined neutral urinary 17-ketosteroids in short term collection periods. A study of spontaneous variability. *Acta Endocrinol.*, **25**, 45–53 (1957)

115. Vestergaard, P., Leverett, R., Douglas, W. R. Spontaneous variability in the excretion of combined neutral 17-ketosteroids in the urine of chronic schizophrenic patients. *Psychiat. Res. Rept.* **6**, 74–89 (1956)

116. Migeon, C. J., French, A. B., Samuels, L. T., Bowers, J. Z. Plasma 17-hydroxycorticosteroid levels and leucocyte values in the Rhesus monkey, including normal variation and the effect of ACTH. *Am. J. Physiol.*, **182**, 462–68 (1955)

117. Mason, J. W., Harwood, C. T., Rosenthal, N. R. Influence of some environmental factors on plasma and urinary 17-hydroxycorticosteroid levels in the Rhesus monkey. *Am. J. Physiol.*, **190**, 429–33 (1957)

118. Winget, C. M., Card, D. H., Hetherington, N. W. Circadian oscillations of deep-body temperature and heart rate in a primate (Cebus albafrons). *Aerospace Med.*, **39**, 350–53 (1968)

119. Stroebel, C. Behavioral aspects of circadian rhythms. In *Comparative Psychopathology*, 158–72 (Zubin, J., Hunt, H., Eds., Grune & Stratton, New York, 1967)

120. Honjo, S., Fujiwara, T., Takasaka, M, Suzuki, Y., Imaizumi, K. Observations on the diurnal temperature variation of Cynomolgus monkeys (Macaca irus) and on the effect of changes in the routine lighting upon this variation. *Japan. J. Med. Sci. Biol.*, **16**, 189–98 (1963)

121. Simpson, S., Galbraith, J. J. Observations on the normal temperature of the monkey and its diurnal variation, and on the effect of changes in the daily routine on this variation. *Trans. Roy. Soc. Edinburgh*, **45**, 65–104 (1905–06)

122. Halberg, F. Rhythms and the adrenal cortex. *Proc. 4th Panam. Symp. Pharmacol. Therapy, Mexico City* (Excerpta Med. Found., Amsterdam, 1968)

123. Halberg, F. Organisms as circadian systems; temporal analysis of their physiologic and pathologic responses, including injury and death. In *Medical Aspects of Stress in the Military Climate*, 1–36 (Walter Reed Army Inst. Res., Washington, D. C., 1964)

124. Ungar, F., Halberg, F. Circadian rhythm in the in vitro response of mouse adrenal to adrenocorticotropic hormone. *Science*, **137**, 1058–60 (1962)

125. Ungar, F., Halberg, F. In vitro demonstration of circadian rhythm in adrenocorticotropic activity of C mouse hypophysis. *Experientia*, **19**, 158–59 (1963)

126. Haus, E., Halberg, F. Der circadiane

Adrenalzyklus und seine Bedeutung für die Reaktionsbereitschaft der Nebennierenrinde. *Wien. Z. Inn. Med.*, **8**, 361–70 (1962)

127. Andrews, R. V., Folk, G. E. Circadian metabolic patterns in cultured hamster adrenal glands. *Comp. Biochem. Physiol.*, **11**, 393–409 (1964)

128. Andrews, R. V., Folk, G. E., Hedge, R. Metabolic periodicity in adrenal glands cultured from Arctic rodents. *Fed. Proc.*, **24**, 508 (1965)

129. Gibson, R. B. The effects of transposition of the daily routine on the rhythm of temperature variation. *Am. J. Med. Sci.*, **129**, 1048–59 (1905)

130. Ogata, K., Sasaki, T. On the causes of diurnal body temperature rhythm in man, with reference to observations during voyage. *Japan. J. Physiol.*, **13**, 84–96 (1963)

131. Ogata, K., Sasaki, T. Diurnal variation in body temperature with special reference to observation made during a sea-voyage. *Intern. J. Biometeorol.*, **7**, 75–80 (1963)

132. Bugard, P., Henry, M. Quelques aspects de la fatigue dans l'aviation de transport. *Presse Med.*, **69**, 1903–6 (1961)

133. Burton, A. C. The clinical importance of the physiology of temperature regulation. *Can. Med. Assoc. J.*, **75**, 715–20 (1956)

134. Flink, E. B., Doe, R. P. Effect of sudden time displacement by air travel on synchronization of adrenal function. *Proc. Soc. Exptl. Biol. Med.*, **100**, 498–501 (1959)

135. Gerritzen, F. The diurnal rhythm in water, chloride, sodium and potassium excretion during a rapid displacement from east to west and vice versa. *J. Aerospace Med.*, **33**, 697–701 (1962)

136. Gullett, C. C. Jet planes and the circadian cycle. *J. Am. Med. Assoc.*, **197**, 935 (1966)

137. Hauty, G. T., Adams, T. Phase shifts of the human circadian system and performance deficit during the periods of transition: I. East-West flight. *Aerospace Med.*, **37**, 668–74 (1966)

138. Hauty, G. T., Adams, T. Phase shifting of the human circadian system. In *Circadian Clocks* (See Ref. 4), 413–25

139. Sasaki, T. Effect of rapid transposition around the earth on diurnal variation in body temperature. *Proc. Soc. Exptl. Biol. Med.*, **115**, 1129–31 (1964)

140. Strughold, H. Physiological day-night cycle in global flights. *Aviation Med.*, **23**, 464–73 (1952)

141. Strughold, H. Day-night cycling in atmospheric flight, space flight and on other celestial bodies. *Ann. N. Y. Acad. Sci.*, **98**, 1109–15 (1962)

142. Strughold, H. Temporal coordination of day-night cycle after intercontinental flight. *Symp. Circadian Systems, Univ. Minnesota, June 4–7, 1961*

143. Thomas, Lowell. Keep an eye on your inner clock. *Reader's Digest*, 61–64 (August 1966)

144. Report. "Aspects nouveaux du sommeil normal et pathologique (1).— Rappel de la physiologie du sommeil. Les rythmes nycthemeraux. Electroencephalogramme et phases du sommeil." *Actualité de la vie médicale, Suppl. bi-mensuel Vie Med.* [presumably 1966]

145. Juin, G. Les décalages horaires (leurs aspects et leurs conséquences dans l'aviation commerciale). *Arch. Mal. Prof.*, **24**, 113–17 (1963)

146. Lavernhe, J. Rythme de vie et changements rapides de fuseaux horaires au cours des voyages aeriens. *Presse Med.*, **72**, 2623–26 (1964)

147. Juin, G. Une enquête sur la fatigue à bord des "jets". *Presse Med.*, **69**, 1104 (1961)

148. Klein, K. E., Brüner, H., Ruff, S. Untersuchungen zur Belastung des Bordpersonals auf Fernflügen mit Düsenmaschinen. *Z. Flugwiss.*, **14**, 109–21 (1966)

149. Chemin, P. *Les rythmes biologiques chez l'homme application à l'aviation et à la cosmonautique* (Thèse Doctorat Med., Univ. Bordeaux, 1967)

150. LaFontaine, E., Lavernhe, J., Courillon, J., Medvedeff, M., Ghata, J. Influence of air travel east-west and vice-versa on circadian rhythms of urinary elimination of potassium and 17-hydroxycorticosteroids. *Aerospace Med.*, **38**, 944–47 (1967)

151. Hauty, G. T., Adams, T. Phase shifts of the human circadian system and performance deficit during the periods of transition: II. West-East flight. *Aerospace Med.*, **37**, 1027–33 (1966)

152. Hauty, G. T., Adams, T. Phase shifts of the human circadian system and performance deficit during the periods of transition: III. North-South flight. *Ibid.*, 1257–62

153. Perkoff, G. T., Eik-Nes, K., Nugent, C. A., Fred, H. L., Nimer, R. A., Rush, L. Samuels, L. T., Tyler, F. H. Studies of the diurnal variation of plasma 17-hydroxycorticosteroids in man. *J. Clin. Endocrinol.*, **19**, 432 (1959)

154. Sharp, G. W. G. Reversal of diurnal leucocyte variations in man. *J. Endocrinol.*, **21**, 107 (1960)

155. Sharp, G. W. G., Slorach, S. A., Vipond, J. Diurnal rhythms of keto- and ketogenic steroid excretion and the adaptation of changes of the activity-sleep routine. *J. Endocrinol.*, **22**, 377–85 (1961)

156. Sharp, G. W. G. Reversal of diurnal rhythms of water and electrolyte excretion in man. *J. Endocrinol.*, **21**, 97 (1960)

157. Yokobori, S., Miyasaka, T., Shiraishi, A., Tanase, N., Nakagi, S., Tanaka, M., Inoue, S., Naoi, F., Sakio, H., Okazaki, K. Fatigue and the adrenal cortex. *J. Ind. Med. (Tokyo)*, **2**, 15–23 (1960)

158. Yurugi, R., Totsuka, T., Naba, K., Iizuka, M., Akiyama, T., Kimura, K. *Experimental studies on the effects of reverse day-night life cycle upon the twenty-four-hour rhythm of living functions* (Aero-Med. Lab., March 1961)

159. Saito, H., Takamatsu, M. Experimentelle Studien über die Beeinflussung von Inversion der Zeitphasen von täglichen Arbeit, mit besonderen Berücksichtigung von rhythmischen Veränderungen der Blut and Harnbeschaffenheiten während Tag und Nacht. *Rept. Inst. Sci. of Labour No. 477* (1953)

160. Saito, H. *Hours of work, pauses for rest, shift system* (Inst. for Sci. of Labour, Tokyo, 285 pp., 1966)

161. Simpson, H. W., Lobban, M. C. Effect of a 21-hour day on the human circadian excretory rhythms of 17-hydroxycorticosteroids and electrolytes. *Aerospace Med.*, **38**, 1205–13 (1967)

162. Lobban, M. C. Daily rhythms of renal excretion in arctic-dwelling Indians and Eskimos. *Quart. J. Exptl. Physiol.*, **52**, 401–10 (1967)

163. Siffre, M. *Beyond Time* (McGraw-Hill, New York, 228 pp., 1964)

164. Pittendrigh, C. S., Bruce, V. G., Kaus, P. On the significance of transients in daily rhythms. *Proc. Natl. Acad. Sci.*, **44**, 965–73 (1958)

165. Aschoff, J., Wever, R. Resynchronisation der Tagesperiodik von Vögeln nach Phasensprung des Zeitgebers. *Z. Vergleich. Physiol.*, **46**, 321–35 (1963)

166. Halberg, F., Nelson, W., Runge, W., Schmitt, O. H. Delay of circadian rhythm in rat temperature by phase-shift of lighting regimen is faster than advance. *Fed. Proc.*, **26**, 599 (1967)

167. Haus, E., Halberg, F., Nelson, W., Hillman, D. Shifts and drifts in phase of human circadian system following intercontinental flights and in isolation. *Fed. Proc.*, **27**, 224 (1968)

168. Halberg, F. Summarizing discussion. In *Symposium on Circadian Rhythms in Non-Human Primates* (Rholes, F. H., Ed., Karger, Basel, 1969)

169. Holmquest, D. L., Retiene, K., Lipscomb, H. S. Circadian rhythms in rats: effects of random lighting. *Science*, **152**, 662–64 (1966)

170. Dietlein, L. F., Vallbona, C. *Experiment M-4, inflight phonocardiogram—measurements of the duration of the cardiac cycle and its phases during the orbital flight of Gemini V*, 397–402 (Gemini Midprogram Conf., including Expt. Results, NASA, Washington, D. C., 1966)

171. Mills, J. N. Circadian rhythms during and after three months in solitude underground. *J. Physiol.*, **174**, 217–31 (1964)

172. Mills, J. N. Sleeping habits during four months in solitude. *Ibid.*, **189**, 30–31 (1966)

173. Mills, J. N. Keeping in step—away from it all. *New Scientist*, **9**, 350–51 (1967)

174. Clark, C. S., Kripke, D. F., Merritt, J. A., Physiological data processor. *IEEE Conference Record, 5th Ann. Rocky Mountain Bioeng. Symp.*, *May 6–8, 1967*, 88–92

175. Cartwright, N., Kripke, D. F., Cook, P. Statistical reduction of hand-staged sleep analysis. *6571st Aeromed. Res. Lab. Rept. ARL-TR-68-5*, 44 pp. (June 1968)

176. Reimann, H, *Periodic Diseases* (F. A. Davis, Philadelphia, 1963)

177. Bryson, R. W., Martin, D. F. 17-ketosteroid excretion in a case of manic-depressive psychosis. *Lancet*, **2**, 365–67 (1954)

178. Rizzo, N. E., Fox, H. M., Laidlaw, J. C., Thorn, G. W. Concurrent

observations of behavior changes and of adrenocortical variations in a cyclothymic patient during a period of 12 months. *Ann. Internal Med.*, **41**, 798–815 (1954)

179. Jenner, F. A., Gjessing, L. R., Cox, J. R., Davies-Jones, A., Hullin, R. P., Hanna, S. M. A manic-depressive psychotic with a persistent forty-eight hour cycle. *Brit. J. Psychiat.*, **113**, 895–910 (1967)

180. Harding, G., Jeavons, P. M., Jenner, F. A., Drummond, P., Sheridan, M., Howells, G. W. The electroencephalogram in three cases of periodic psychosis. *Electroenceph. Clin. Neurophysiol.*, **21**, 59–66 (1966)

181. Rey, J. H., Willcox, D. R. C., Gibbons, J. L., Tait, H., Lewis, D. J. Serial biochemical and endocrine investigations in recurrent mental illness. *J. Psychosomat. Res.*, **5**, 155–69 (1961)

182. Crammer, J. L. Water and sodium in two psychotics. *Lancet*, 1122–26 (30 May 1959)

183. Crammer, J. L. Rapid weight-changes in mental patients. *Lancet*, 259–62 (10 Aug. 1957)

184. Gjessing, R., Gjessing, L. Some main trends in the clinical aspects of periodic catatonia. *Acta Psychol. Scand.*, **37**, 1–13 (1961)

185. Goodwin, J. C., Jenner, F. A., Lobban, M. C., Sheridan, M. Renal rhythms in a patient with a 48-hour cycle of psychosis during a period of life on an abnormal time routine. *J. Physiol.*, **176**, 16–17 (1965)

186. Scarpelli, P. T., Fantini, F., Boccuni, M., Cagnoni, M. Le Malattie Periodiche. Problematica nosologica ed etiopatogenetica. *Rass. Neurol. Veg.*, **22**, 5–23 (1968)

187. Reiss, Max. Neuroendocrinology and Psychiatry (A critical assessment of the present status). *Intern. J. Neuropsychiat.*, **3**, 441–63 (1967)

188. Benoit, J., Assenmacher, I., Brard, E. Etude de l'évolution testiculaire du canard domestique soumis très jeune à une éclairement permanent pendant deux ans. *Compt. Rend. Acad. Sci.*, **242**, 3113–15 (1956)

189. Farner, D. S. The annual stimulus for migration. *Condor*, **52**, 104–22 (1950)

190. Farner, D. S. Northward transequatorial migration of birds. *Sci. Rev.*, **12**, 29–30 (1954)

191. Farner, D. S. The photoperiodic control of reproductive cycles in birds. *Am. Scientist*, **52**, 137–56 (1964)

192. Gwinner, E. Wirkung des Mondlichtes auf die Nachtaktivität von Zugvögeln. Lotsenversuch an Rotkehlchen (Erithacus rubecula) und Gartenrotschwänzen (Phoenicurus phoenicurus). *Experientia*, **23**, 227 (1967)

193. Gwinner, E. Circannuale Periodik der Mauser und der Zugunruhe bei einem Vogel. *Naturwissenschaften*, **54**, 447 (1967)

194. Gwinner, E. Circannuale Periodik als Grundlage des jahreszeitlichen Funktionswandels bei Zugvögeln. *J. Ornithol.*, **109**, 70–95 (1968)

195. Pengelley, E. T., Fischer, K. C. The effect of temperature and photoperiod on the yearly hibernating behavior of captive golden-mantled ground squirrels (*Citellus lateralis tescorum*). *Can. J. Zool.*, **41**, 1103–20 (1963)

196. Pengelley, E. T., Kelly, K. H. A "circannian" rhythm in hibernating species of the genus *Citellus* with observations on their physiological evolution. *Comp. Biochem. Physiol.*, **19**, 603–17 (1966)

197. Lofts, B. Evidence of an autonomous reproductive rhythm in an equatorial bird (*Quelea quelea*). *Nature*, **201**, 523–24 (1964)

198. Merkel, F. W. Untersuchungen über tages- und jahreszeitliche Aktivitätsänderungen bei gekäfigten Zugvögeln. *Z. Tierpsychol.*, **13**, 278–301 (1956)

199. Merkel, F. W. Long-term effects of constant photoperiods on European Robins and Whitethroats. *Proc. XIII Intern. Ornithol. Congr. Ithaca*, 950–59 (1963)

200. Wolfson, A. Role of light and darkness in the regulation of the annual stimulus for spring migration and reproductive cycles. *Proc. XII Intern. Ornithol. Congr. Helsinki*, 758–89 (1960)

201. Wolfson, A. Regulation of annual periodicity in the migration and reproduction of birds. *Cold Spring Harbor Symp. Quant. Biol.*, **25**, 507–14 (1960)

202. Wolfson, A. Environmental and neuroendocrine regulation of annual gonadal cycles and migratory behavior in birds. *Recent Progr. Hormone Res.*, **22**, 177–244 (1966)

203. Zimmerman, J. L. Effects of extended tropical photoperiod and temperature on the Dickcissel. *Condor*, **68**, 377–87 (1966)

204. Orth, D. N., Island, D. P., Liddle, G. W. Experimental alteration of the circadian rhythm in plasma cortisol (17-OHCS) concentration in man. *J. Clin. Endocrinol. Metab.*, **27**, 549–55 (1967)

205. Eränkö, O. 25-hour day: one solution to the shift-work problem. *Intern. Congr. Occup. Health*, **3**, 134 (1957)

206. Simpson, H. W., Lobban, M. C., Halberg, F. Near-24-hour rhythms in subjects living on a 21-hour routine in the arctic summer at 78°N—revealed by circadian amplitude ratios. *Rass. Neurol. Veg.*

207. Lamar, D. L., Merifield, P. M. Cambrian fossils and origin of Earth-Moon system. *Geol. Soc. Am. Bull.* **78**, 1359–68 (1967)

208. Wells, John W. Coral growth and geochronometry. *Nature*, **197**, 948–50 (1963)

209. Goreau, T. F. The physiology of skeleton formation in corals. I. A method for measuring the rate of calcium deposition by corals under different conditions. *Biol. Bull.*, **116**, 59–75 (1959)

210. Goreau, T. F., Goreau, N. I. The physiology of skeleton formation in corals. II. Calcium deposition by hermatypic corals under various conditions in the reef. *Biol. Bull.*, **117**, 239–50 (1959)

211. Runcorn, S. K. Changes in the Earth's moment of inertia. *Nature*, **204**, 823–25 (1964)

212. Scrutton, C. T. Periodicity in Devonian coral growth. *Palaeontology*, **7**, 552–58 (1964)

213. Gebelein, C. D. Origin and growth rate of subtidal algal stromatolites, Bermuda. *The Geological Society of America Annual Meeting*, 75 (1967)

214. McGugan, A. Possible use of algal stromatolite rhythms on geochronology. *The Geological Society of America Annual Meeting*, 145 (1967)

215. Pannella, G., MacClintock, C. Biological and environmental rhythms reflected in molluscan shell growth. *J. Paleontol.*, **42**, 64–80 (1967)

216. Lamar, D. L., Mc-Gann-Lamar, J. V., Merifield, P. M. Age and origin of Earth-Moon system. In *Paleogeophysics* (Runcorn, S. K., Ed., in press)

217. Munk, W. H., MacDonald, G. J. F. *The Rotation of the Earth* (Cambridge Univ. Press, London, 323 pp., 1960)

218. Marsden, B. G., Cameron, A. G. W. *The Earth-Moon System* (Plenum Press, New York, 288 pp., 1966)

219. Halberg, F., Halberg, E., Barnum, C. P., Bittner, J. J. Physiologic 24-hour periodicity in human beings and mice, the lighting regimen and daily routine. In *Photoperiodism and Related Phenomena in Plants and Animals* (See Ref. 16), 803–78

220. Pittendrigh, C. S., Bruce, V. G. An oscillator model for biological clocks. In *Rhythmic and Synthetic Processes in Growth*, 75–109 (Princeton Univ. Press, 1957)

221. Korein, J., Tick, L. J., Zeitlin, R. A., Randt, C. T. Linear and nonlinear spectral analytic techniques applied to the human electroencephalogram. *Bull. N. Y. Acad. Med.*, **44**, 1126–28 (1968)

222. Pittendrigh, C. S., Bruce, V. G. Daily rhythms as coupled oscillator systems and their relation to thermoperiodism and photoperiodism. In *Photoperiodism and Related Phenomena in Plants and Animals* (See Ref. 16), 475–505

223. Pittendrigh, C. S., Minis, D. H. The entrainment of circadian oscillations by light and their role as photoperiodic clocks. *Am. Naturalist*, **98**, 261–94 (1964)

224. Pittendrigh, C. S. The circadian oscillation in *Drosophila pseudoobscura* pupae: a model for the photoperiodic clock. *Z. Pflanzenphysiol.*, **54**, 275–307 (1966)

225. Strumwasser, F. The demonstration and manipulation of a circadian rhythm in a single neuron. In *Circadian Clocks* (See Ref. 4), 442–62

226. Wever, R. A mathematical model for circadian rhythms. In *Circadian Clocks* (See Ref. 4), 47–63; Pendulum versus relaxation oscillation, 74–83

227. Wever, R. Possibilities of phase control, demonstrated by an electronic model. *Cold Spring Harbor Symp. Quant. Biol.*, **25**, 197–206 (1960)

228. Wever, R. Zum Mechanismus der biologischen 24-Stunden-Periodik. *Kybernetik*, **1**, 139–94 (1962), 213–31 (1963); **2**, 127–44 (1964)

229. Schmitt, O. H. Biophysical and mathematical models of circadian rhythms. *Cold Spring Harbor Symp. Quant. Biol.*, **25**, 207–10 (1960)

230. Wachholder, K. Die allgemeinen physiologischen Grundlagen der Entstehung von Lebensrhythmen. *Acta Med. Scand. Suppl. 307*, 21–31 (1955)

231. Chance, B., Pye, K., Higgins, J. Waveform generation by enzymatic oscillators. *IEEE Spectrum*, **4**, 79–86 (1967)

232. Ehret, C. F., Barlow, J. S. Toward a realistic model of a biological period-measuring mechanism. *Cold Spring Harbor Symp. Quant. Biol.*, **25**, 217–20 (1960)

233. Goodwin, B. C. An entrainment model for timed enzyme synthesis in bacteria. *Nature*, **209**, 479–81 (1966)

234. Ehret, C. F., Trucco, E. Molecular models for the circadian clock. I. The chronon concept. *J. Theoret. Biol.*, **15**, 240–62 (1967)

235. Kalmus, H., Wigglesworth, L. A. Shock excited systems as models for biological rhythms. *Cold Spring Harbor Symp. Quant. Biol.*, **25**, 211–16 (1960)

236. Chance, B., Higgins, J. J., Garfinkel, D. Analogue and digital computer representations of biochemical processes. *Fed. Proc.*, **21**, 75–86 (1962)

237. Higgins, J. A chemical mechanism for oscillation of glycolytic intermediates in yeast cells. *Biochemistry*, **51**, 989–94 (1964)

238. Bünning, E., Zimmer, R. Zur Deutung der Phasenverschiebungen und "Transients" nach exogener Störung endogener Rhythmen. *Planta*, **59**, 1–14 (1962)

239. Winfree, A. T. Biological rhythms and the behavior of populations of coupled oscillators. *J. Theoret. Biol.*, **16**, 15–42 (1967)

240. Spangler, R. A., Snell, F. M. Sustained oscillations in a catalytic chemical system. *Nature*, **191**, 457–58 (1961)

241. Higgins, J. Theory of oscillating reactions. *Ind. Eng. Chem.*, **59**, 18–62 (1967)

242. Frenkel, R. Reduced diphosphopyridine nucleotide oscillations in cell-free extracts from beef heart. *Arch. Biochem. Biophys.*, **115**, 112–21 (1966)

243. Vanden Driessche, T. The nuclear control of the chloroplasts' circadian rhythms. *Sci. Progr. Oxford*, **55**, 293–303 (1967)

244. Vanden Driessche, T., Bonotto, S. Le rythme circadien de la teneur en inuline chloroplastique de *Acetabularia mediterranea*. *Arch. Intern. Physiol. Biochim.*, **76**, 205–6 (1968)

245. Hurwicz, L. Basic mathematical and statistical considerations in the study of rhythms and nearrhythms. *Ann. N. Y. Acad. Sci.*, **98**, 851–57 (1962)

246. Prigogine, I., Balescu, R. Phénomènes cycliques dans la thermodynamique des processus irréversibles. *Bull. Class. Sci. Acad. Roy. Belg.*, **42**, 256–65 (1956)

247. Volterra, V. *Théorie Mathematique de la Lutte de la Vie* (Gautiers-Villars, Paris, 1931)

248. van der Pol, B. On "Relaxation-Oscillations". *Phil. Mag.*, **2**, 978–92 (1926)

249. van der Pol, B., van der Mark, J. The heartbeat considered as a relaxation oscillation, and an electrical model of the heart. *Phil. Mag.*, **6**, 763–75 (1928)

250. Lotka, A. J. Théorie analytique des associations biologiques. In *Exposés de Biometrie et de Statistique Biologique*, **IV** (Hermann et Cie., Paris, 1934)

251. Lotka, A. J. Analytical note on certain rhythmic relations in organic systems. *Proc. Natl. Acad. Sci.*, **6**, 410–15 (1920)

252. Lotka, A. J. Undamped oscillations derived from the law of mass action. *J. Am. Chem. Soc.*, **42**, 1595–99 (1920)

253. Winget, C. M., Card, D. H., Pope, J. M. Circadian oscillations of three parameters at defined light intensities and color. *J. Appl. Physiol.*, **24**, 401–6 (1968)

254. Winget, C. M., Card, D. H. Daily rhythm changes associated with variations in light intensity and color. *Life Sci. Space Res.*, **5**, 148–58 (1967)

255. Winget, C. M., Fryer, T. B. Telemetry system for the acquisition of circadian rhythm data. *Aerospace Med.*, **37**, 800–3 (1966)

256. Stroebel, C. F. Biologic rhythm approach to psychiatric treatment. In *Proc. 7th IBM Medical Symp.* (Steinbeck, H., Ed., IBM Corp., Yorktown Heights, N.Y., 1967)

257. Randall, W., Littschwager, J. The relationship between cyclic changes in thyroid function and behavior of cats with brain stem lesions. *J. Psychiat. Res.*, **5**, 39–58 (1967)

258. Randall, W., Lakso, V. Body weight and food intake rhythms and their relationship to the behavior of cats with brain stem lesions. *Psychon. Sci.*, **11**, 33–34 (1968)

259. Rapoport, M. I., Feigin, R. D., Bruton, J., Beisel, W. R. Circadian rhythm for tryptophan pyrrolase activity and its circulating substrate. *Science*, **153**, 1642–44 (1966)

260. Reinberg, A. Rythmes des fonctions

corticosurrenaliennes et systèmes circadiens. In *Symposium International sur la Neuro-Endocrinologie*, 75–89 (Expansion Sci. Franç., Paris, 1966)

261. Axelrod, J., Wurtman, R. J. The pineal gland: a biological clock (See Ref. 260), 201–12

262. Quay, W. B. Photic relations and experimental dissociation of circadian rhythms in pineal composition and running activity in rats. *Photochem. Photobiol.*, **4**, 425–32 (1965)

263. Quay, W. B. Circadian and estrous rhythms in pineal and brain serotonin. *Progr. Brain Res.*, **8**, 61–63 (1964)

264. Quay, W. B. Regional and circadian differences in cerebral cortical serotonin concentration. *Life Sci.*, **4**, 379 (1965)

265. Brown, F. A., Jr., Park, Y. H. Association-formation between photic and subtle geophysical stimulus patterns—a new biological concept. *Biol. Bull.*, **132**, 311–19 (1967)

266. Brown, F. A., Jr., Park, Y. H. Synodic monthly modulation of the diurnal rhythm of hamsters. *Proc. Soc. Exptl. Biol. Med.*, **125**, 712–15 (1967)

267. Sollberger, A. Biological measurements in time, with particular reference to synchronization mechanisms. *Ann. N. Y. Acad. Sci.*, **138**, 561–99 (1967)

268. Sollberger, A., Apple, H. P., Greenway, R. M., Kind, P. H., Lindan, O., Reswick, J. B. Automation in biological rhythms research with special reference to studies on Homo. In *The Cellular Aspects of Biorhythms*, 184–98 (Springer-Verlag, N. Y., 1967)

269. Halberg, F. Some aspects of biologic data analysis; longitudinal and transverse profiles of rhythms. In *Circadian Clocks* (See Ref. 4), 13–22

270. Giese, A. C. Comparative physiology: annual reproductive cycles of marine invertebrates. *Ann. Rev. Physiol.*, **21**, 547–76 (1959)

271. Saito, H. Some considerations on reduction of working hours in Japan from view-point of science of labour. *J. Sci. Labour*, **40**, 469–86 (1964)

272. Saito, H. Biochemical aspect of fatigue, with special reference to physical and mental burden of work. *Ibid.*, **42**, 427–47 (1966)

273. Gaston, S., Menaker, M. Pineal function: The biological clock in the sparrow? *Science*, **160**, 1125–27 (1968)

274. Butler, P. W. P., Besser, G. M. Pituitary adrenal function in severe depressive illness. *Lancet*, **1**, 1234–36 (1968)

275. Lohrenz, F. N., Fullerton, D. T., Fahs, H., Wenzel, F. J. Adrenocortical function in depressive states—study of circadian variation in plasma and urinary steroids. *Intern. J. Neuropsychiat.*, **4**, 21–25 (1968)

276. Rubin, R. T., Young, W. M., Clark, B. R. 17-hydroxycorticosteroid and vanillylmandelic acid excretion in a rapidly cycling manic-depressive. *Psychosomat. Med.*, **30**, 162–71 (1968)

277. Halberg, F., Vestergaard, P., Sakai, M. Rhythmometry on urinary 17-ketosteroid excretion by healthy men and women and patients with chronic schizophrenia; possible chronopathology in depressive illness (In press, memorial volume in honor of Professor Jacques Benoit)

278. Menaker, M. Extraretinal light perception in the sparrow, I. Entrainment of the biological clock. *Proc. Natl. Acad. Sci.*, **59**, 414–21 (1968)

279. Fenyö, E., Hasznos, T. Periodic EEG complexes in subacute panencephalitis: reactivity, response to drugs and respiratory relationships. *Electroenceph. Clin. Neurophysiol.*, **16**, 446–58 (1964)

280. Poole, E. W. Nervous activity in relation to the respiratory cycle. *Nature*, **189**, 579 (1961)

281. Poole, E. W. Periodic EEG complexes in subacute panencephalitis: reactivity, response to drugs and respiratory relationships. *Electroenceph. Clin. Neurophysiol.*, **16**, 446–58 (1964)

282. Hobson, J. A. Respiration and EEG synchronization in the frog. *Nature*, **213**, 988–89 (1967)

283. Hobson, J. A., Goldfrank, F., Snyder, F. Respiration and mental activity in sleep. *J. Psychiat. Res.*, **3**, 79–90 (1965)

284. Bjerner, B., Holm, A., Swensson, A. Diurnal variation in mental performance; a study of three shift-workers. *Brit. J. Ind. Med.*, **12**, 103–10 (1955)

285. Garcia Sainz, M., Halberg, F. Mitotic rhythms in human cancer, reevaluated by electronic computer programs—evidence for temporal pathology. *J. Natl. Cancer Inst.*, **37**, 279–92 (1966)

286. Nichols, C. T., Tyler, F. H. Diurnal variation in adrenal cortical function. *Ann. Rev. Med.*, **18**, 313–24 (1967)

287. Bunney, W. E., Hartmann, E. L. Study of a patient with 48-hour manic depressive cycles. *Arch. Gen. Psychol.*, **12**, 611–25 (1965)

288. Jenner, F. A., Goodwin, J. C., Sheridan, M., Tauber, I. J., Lobban, M. C. The effect of an altered time regime on biological rhythms in a 48-hour periodic psychosis. *Brit. J. Psychiat.*, **114**, 215–24 (1968)

289. Bryson, R. W. *Psychoendocrinology* (M.D. thesis, Glasgow Univ., 1954)

290. Cookson, B. A., Quarrington, B., Huszka, L. Longitudinal study of periodic catatonia. *J. Psychiat. Res.*, **5**, 15–38 (1967)

291. Quay, W. B. Epiphyseal responses to light and darkness in birds and mammals. In *La Photoregulation de la Reproduction chez les Oiseaux et les Mammiféres* (See Ref. 13)

292. *The Cellular Aspects of Biorhythms Symp. Rhythmic Res., VIII Intern. Congr. Anat., Wiesbaden* (von Mayersbach, H. v., Ed., Springer, Berlin, 198 pp., 1967)

293. Alov, I. A. The mechanism of the diurnal periodicity of mitosis. *Bull. Exptl. Biol. Med.*, **48**, 1418–23 (1959)

294. Scheving, L. E., Pauly, J. E. Effect of adrenalectomy, adrenal medullectomy and hypophysectomy on the daily mitotic rhythm in the corneal epithelium of the rat. In *The Cellular Aspects of Biorhythms* (See Ref. 292), 167–74

295. Cherkovich, G. M. The experimental production of a neurosis in monkeys by changing the diurnal rhythm. *Bull. Exptl. Biol. Med.*, **47**, 935–38 (1959)

296. Brady, J. V. Ulcers in "executive monkeys". *Sci. Am.*, **199**, 95–103 (1958)

297. Brady, J. V. Experimental studies of psychophysiological responses to stressful situations. In *Symposium on Medical Aspects of Stress in the Military Climate*, 271–89 (Walter Reed Army Inst. Res., Washington, D. C., 1964)

298. Rice, H. K. Responding-rest ratio in the production of gastric ulcers in the rat. *Psychol. Record*, **13**, 11–14 (1963)

299. Scheving, L. E., Harrison, W. H., Gordon, P., Pauly, J. E. Daily fluctuation (circadian and ultradian) in biogenic amines of the rat brain. *Am. J. Physiol.*, **214**, 166–73 (1968)

300. Scheving, L. E., Pauly, J. E. Circadian phase relationships of thymidine-3H uptake labeled nuclei, grain counts, and cell division rate in rat corneal epithelium. *J. Cell Biol.*, **32**, 677–83 (1967)

301. Scheving, L. E., Pauly, J. E. Daily rhythmic variations in blood coagulation times in rats. *Anat. Record*, **157**, 657–65 (1967)

302. Wurtman, R. J., Rose, C. M., Chou, C., Larin, F. F. The daily rhythms in the concentrations of various amino acids in human plasma. *New Engl. J. Med.*, **279**, 171–75 (1968)

303. Wurtman, R. J., Chou, C., Rose, C. M. Daily rhythm in tyrosine concentration in human plasma: persistence on low-protein diets. *Science*, **158**, 660–62 (1967)

304. Wurtman, R. J., Axelrod, J., Sedvall, G., Moore, R. Y. Photic and neural control of the 24-hour norepinephrine rhythm in the rat pineal gland. *J. Pharmacol. Exptl. Therap.*, **157**, 487–92 (1967)

305. Ader, R. Gastric erosions in the rat: effects of immobilization at different points in the activity cycle. *Science*, **145**, 406–7 (1964)

306. Tarquini, B., Della Corte, M., Orzalesi, R. Circadian studies on plasma cortisol in subjects with peptic ulcer. *J. Endocrinol.*, **38**, 475–76 (1967)

307. DeVries, K., Goei, J. T., Booy-Noord, H., Orie, N. G. M. Changes during 24 hours in the lung function and histamine hyperreactivity of the bronchial tree in asthmatic and bronchitic patients. *Intern. Arch. Allergy*, **20**, 93–101 (1962)

308. Reinberg, A., Sidi, E., Ghata, J. Circadian reactivity rhythms of human skin to histamine or allergen and the adrenal cycle. *J. Allergy*, **36**, 273–83 (1965)

309. Reinberg, A. Hours of changing responsiveness in relation to allergy and the circadian adrenal cycle. In *Circadian Clocks* (See Ref. 4), 214–18

310. Matthews, J. H., Marte, E., Halberg, F. Fluothane toxicity in mice studied by indirect periodicity analysis. In *Toxicity of Anesthetics*, 197–208 (Fink, B. R., Ed., Williams & Wilkins. Baltimore. 1968)

311. McHugh, R. B. Validity and efficiency in the design of transverse

physiologic periodicity experiments. In *The Cellular Aspects of Biorhythms* (See Ref. 292), 61–86

312. McGeer, E. G., McGeer, P. L. Circadian rhythm in pineal tyrosine hydroxylase. *Science*, **143**, 73–74 (1966)

313. Haus, E. Periodicity in response and susceptibility to environmental stimuli. *Ann. N. Y. Acad. Sci.*, **117**, 292–319 (1964)

314. Bliss, C. I., Blevins, D. L. The analysis of seasonal variation in measles. *Am. J. Hyg.*, **70**, 328–34 (1959)

315. Bliss, C. I., Fleischer, D. A. The analysis in angles of a microbial experiment. *Biometrics*, **20**, 883–91 (1964)

316. Minis, D., Pittendrigh, C. Circadian oscillation controlling hatching: ontogeny during embryogenesis of a moth. *Science*, **159**, 534–36 (1968)

317. Hellbrügge, T., Lange, J. E., Rutenfranz, J., Stehr, K. Circadian periodicity of physiological functions in different stages of infancy and childhood. *Ann. N. Y. Acad. Sci.*, **117**, 361–73 (1964)

318. Hellbrügge, T. Zeitliche Strukturen in der kindlichen Entwicklung. *Monatsschr. Kinderheilk.*, **113**, 252–62 (1965)

319. Hellbrügge, T. Über tageszeitliche Veränderungen der physiologischen Leistungsbereitschaft bei Schulkindern. *Fortschr. Med.*, **78**, 41–44 (1960)

320. Hellbrügge, T., Pechstein, J., Ullner, R., Reindl, K. Zum Verständnis der Periodik-Analyse in der Medizin. *Fortschr. Med.*, **7**, 289–95 (1967)

321. Martin-du-Pan, R. L'apparition du rythme circadien des 17-hydroxystéroïdes chez le nourrisson. Sa modification sous l'effet de la consommation de corticosteroïdes. *Praxis*, **56**, 138–44 (1967)

322. Frazier, T. W., Rummel, J. A., Lipscomb, H. S. Circadian variability in vigilance performance. *Aerospace Med.*, **39**, 383–95 (1968)

323. Baillaud, L. Variations d'une periodicité endogène normalement circadienne affectant le dégagement des entre-noeuds de la Bryone, *Bryonia dioica*, en fonction de facteurs agissant sur la vitesse de croissance. *Z. Pflanzenphysiol.*, **57**, 203–5 (1967)

324. Helmchen, H., Künkel, H., Selbach, H. Periodische Einflüsse auf die individuale Häufigkeit cerebraler Anfälle. *Arch. Psychiat. Z. Ges. Neurol.*, **206**, 293–308 (1964)

325. Yoshimura, H. Seasonal changes in human body fluids. *Japan. J. Physiol.*, **8**, 165–79 (1958)

326. Sueda, T. Schwankungen im 24-Stunden Rhythmus bei manisch-depressiven Kranksein—Pathophysiologie des manisch-depressiven Krankseins. *Psychiat. Neurol. Japon.*, **9**, 1449–85 (1962)

327. Tamura, A. Changes of diurnal rhythm of Na-, K- and Ca-excretion in urine with disorders in brain. *Psychiat. Neurol. Japon.*, **5**, 405–23 (1965)

328. Watanabe, G.-I., Huyama, T. Climatic effect on the alkaline phosphatase activity in human serum. *Japan. J. Med. Progr.*, **43**, 480–89 (1956)

329. Rutenfranz, J., Singer, R. Untersuchungen zur Frage einer Abhängigkeit der Alkoholwirkung von der Tageszeit. *Intern. Z. Angew. Physiol.*, **24**, 1–17 (1967)

330. Hayashi, K., Ota, M., Kato, M., Chiba, Y., Narita, A. Seasonal and diurnal activities of biting insect attacking grazing cattle, with special reference to repellent-spraying. *Japan. J. Zootech. Sci.*, **38**, 376–84 (1967)

331. Hildebrandt, G. Rhythmus und Regulation unter besonderer Berücksichtigung der Blutdruckregulation. *Z. Ges. Inn. Med.*, **22**, 206–13 (1967)

332. Kaiser, I. H. Effect of a 28-hour day on ovulation and reproduction in mice. *Am. J. Obstet. Gynecol.*, **99**, 772–84 (1967)

333. Mohler, S. R. Fatigue in aviation activities. *Aerospace Med.*, **37**, 722–32 (1966)

334. Mohler, S. R., Dille, J. R., Gibbons, H. L. The time zone and circadian rhythms in relation to aircraft occupants taking long-distance flights. *Am. J. Public Health*, **50**, 1404–9, (1968)

335. Holmgren, H., Swensson, Å. Der Einfluss des Lichtes auf den 24-Stunden-Rhythmus der Aktivität, des Leberglykogens und der Körpertemperatur. *Acta Med. Scand. Suppl. 278*, 71–76 (1953)

336. Jurkevich, I. Non-linear regression analysis and anlysis of variance of periods defined by irregular observations. *NASA Publ. NASA-CR-465* (1966)

337. Kovarov, F. I., Zakharov, L. V., Lisovskii, V. A. *Sutochnyi Ritm* (Circadian rhythm of man's physiological functions in health and disease) (Leningrad: Meditsina, 200 pp., 1966)

338. *Behavioral Problems in Aerospace Medicine, Conf. Proc. 25 of Advisory Group for Aerospace Research & Development, NATO* (Tech. Editing & Reproduction Ltd., London, 1967)

339. Cumming, B. G., Wagner, E. Rhythmic processes in plants. *Ann. Rev. Plant Physiol.*, **19**, 381–416 (1968)

340. Lungu, Al. *Orologiile biologice* (Editura Ştiinţifică, Bucureşti, 237 pp., 1968)

341. Szczepanska, E., Preibisz, J., Drzewiecki, K., Kozlowski, S. Studies on the circadian rhythm of variations of the blood antidiuretic hormone in humans. *Polish Med. J.*, **7**, 517–23 (1968)

AUTHOR INDEX

SUBJECT INDEX

as vagal inhibitory transmitter, 208-10
see also Serotonin
5-Hydroxytryptophan
on gastrointestinal motility,
213
Hyoscine
intestinal effects of, 204-5,
208, 212
Hypertension
circulatory factors in, 318-
20
baroreceptor reflex, 318-
19
renal hypertension, 319
renin-angiotensin system,
319-20
effects of exercise on, 102-
3
and hormones, 296,
318
neurohumoral mechanisms
of, 296
pulmonary
adaptive factors in, 174
Hyperventilation
on hepatic ion flux, 236-
37
Hypothalamus
deafferentation of, 396
hypophyseotropic area of,
383
neurohumoral agents of
and gonadotropin secretion,
385-88
methods of assay, 387
regulation of secretion of,
388
on renal tubular function,
158
in reproduction, 383-
408
selective destruction of,
388-89
sexual differentiation of,
403-5
sympathetic tone in, 386
Hypothermia
on ADH, 153
Hypoxia
alveolar
and pulmonary circulation,
173-82
circulatory regulating role
of, 305-8
during exercise, 313-
14
and lung inflation-vasodila-
tation reflexes, 307-8
neonatal effects of, 33-34

I

Iguana
neuroendocrine aspects of
reproduction in, 394
Infant

chronobiology of, 695,
711
Infradian rhythm
definition of, 709
Insect
flight muscles of, 69
hearing in, 562-64
neuromuscular studies of,
43, 47-49, 51, 56, 58,
69-70
Insulin
in bile and gallbladder,
366
on carbohydrate metabolism,
367-69
control of secretion of, 357-
65
carbohydrates, amino
acids, and lipids in, 357-
58
by cations, 359
CNS role in, 363-65
by hormones and cyclic
AMP, 359-63
intestinal factors in,
362
synthesis vs. release, 357
exogenous
on pancreatic β-cells,
363
and fatty acid mobilization
during exercise, 98
on hepatic carbohydrate and
protein metabolism, 240-
46
on hepatic fat transport,
255-57
on hepatic ion fluxes, 236
immunogenic, 354-55
kinetics of disappearance of,
365-66
on lipid metabolism,
369
metabolism and distribution
of, 265-67
distribution, 366-67
kidney role in, 366
removal from plasma, 365-
66
permeability of capillaries
to, 345
precursor of, 355-56
on protein synthesis, 369-
70
secretion
in obesity and diabetes,
370-72
structure and synthesis of,
353-57
abnormal insulin, 356-
57
species variations in amino
acid chains, 353-54
structure-activity relationship, 354
structure-function relationships, 353-55

synthesis, 355-56
two components of, 356
Interneurons
auditory, 564
of visual cortex, 523
Intestine
absorption by
effect of exercise on,
99
adrenergic excitation of,
208
chronic denervation of, 214
morphology of
innervation, 204
motility of
chemical control of, 210-
13
electrical control of, 213-
19
inhibition of, 207-8
synthesis of information
on, 219-23
slow waves of
electrophysiology of, 215-
16, 220-22
forward and backward cou-
pling, 221-22
model of, 220-21
van der Pol's equation,
220-21
small
hemodynamics of, 345
Intralaminar nuclei
relation to somatic sensory
system, 437
Invertebrates
comparative audition in,
562-64
Iodine
membrane selectivity of,
595-99, 613
Iodopyracet (Diodrast)
to study renal blood flow,
121
tubular transport of,
141
Ion exchange resins
development and characterization of, 584-86, 595
Ion movement
in gut, 5
Iproniazid
reserpine block by, 386
Isoleucine
hepatic regulation of,
259
Isoproterenol
hemodynamic effects of,
344
hepatic effects of, 231
on insulin secretion,
363
on pulmonary vascular re-
sistance, 179
Isovaleramide
membrane permeability of,
623

vascular morphology of, 338-39
vascular resistance of, 177-78
ventilation to perfusion in
  adaptive response of, 175-76
  regional differences in, 195-98
volume changes
  and circulatory regulation, 321
  volume/resistance studies, 189-90
Luteotropic hormone
  antiadrenergic block of, 386
  release of
    circadian rhythm of, 389
    ionic stimulation of, 388
  releasing factor for, 386
  secretion of
    in different physiological conditions, 389-92
  short-loop feedback by, 398
Lymph
  insulin levels of, 367
  renal, 123
Lyriform organs
  hearing in, 562
Lysine
  on hypothalamic gonadotropin release, 387

M

Macaca mulatta
  circadian rhythms in, 688
  neurophysiology of vision in, 509, 522, 525
α_2-Macroglobulin
  thrombin inactivation of, 283
Magnesium
  on blood clotting, 277
  on cardiac excitation-contraction coupling, 659
  deficiency
    endocrine effects of, 138
  and muscle contraction, 58
  renal tubular transport of, 137-38
  selectivity studies of, 599-602
Magnesium-dependent adenosine triphosphatase
  and renal transport, 129
Maia squinado
  fiber cannulation in, 46, 52
Malnutrition
  developmental effects of, 35
Mammals

aquatic
  hearing in, 545
  CNS growth and differentiation in, 19, 24
  coclear microphonic of, 550
  neuroendocrine aspects of reproduction in, 383-416
  neuromuscular studies of, 49, 70, 72
Manganese
  selectivity sequence involving, 603
Medial geniculate body
  firing and inhibition in, 557
Median eminence
  selective destruction of, 388-89
Medical education
  reform in, 4
Medlars
  literature retrieval system, 173
Megachiroptera
  echolocation by, 570
Melatonin
  circadian changes in, 708
Membranes
  ion selectivity of, 582-614
    alkali-cation, 583-95
    anion, 595-99
    degree of hydration, 608-9
    divalent-cation, 599-603
    effect of site spacing or ion coordination number, 609
    entropy effects, 609
    introduction to, 582-83
    non-Coulomb forces and meaning of transition sequences, 605-7
    nonequilibrium selectivity, 609-12
    other ions, 603-5
    pore radius, 612-14
    summary of, 614
    uncharged membranes, 607-8
  nonelectrolyte selectivity of, 614-43
    acidity factor, 642
    controlling variables in main-pattern selectivity, 641-42
    effect of branching, 622-24
    effect of size, 624-25, 629
    giant algae and rabbit gall-bladders, 615-18
    incremental thermodynamic quantities, 629-35

inductive effects, 640-41
intermolecular forces, 635-40
intramolecular H bonding, 640
introduction to, 614-15
magnitudes of, 641-42
molecular basis of, 629-41
patterns of nonelectrolyte permeability, 618-29
summary of, 642-43
physical basis of ion and nonelectrolyte selectivity, 581-646
transport through, 117
Memory
  neurological
    in RNA, 35
Menstrual cycle
  LH and FSH levels in, 390
  ovarian steroid output during, 392
Mepyramine
  on pulmonary hypoxia, 181
Meralluride
  on potassium concentration, 137
Meriones
  renal physiology of, 118
Metabolism
  during exercise, 91-99
    carbohydrate, 91-95
    lactate, 95-96
    lipid, 96-99
  hepatic, 238-60
Metarhodopsin
  and visual adaptation, 510
Methanol
  membrane permeability of, 625
Methantheline
  on junctional potentials, 63
Methopyrapone
  rhythm in susceptibility to, 689
α-Methyldopa
  pseudopregnancy induction by, 386
α-Methyl-D-glucoside
  renal transport of, 140
2-Methyl-2,4-pentanediol
  membrane permeability of, 623
α-Methyl-p-tyrosine
  induction of pseudopregnancy by, 386
Methyl urea
  membrane permeability of, 627
  renal tubular transport of, 140
Methysergide

CUMULATIVE INDEXES

VOLUMES 27 - 31

INDEX OF CONTRIBUTING AUTHORS

INDEX OF CHAPTER TITLES

VOLUMES 27 - 31

INDEX OF CHAPTER TITLES 787